MATHEMATICS OF PHYSICS
AND MODERN ENGINEERING

MATHEMATICS

OF PHYSICS AND

MODERN ENGINEERING

I. S. Sokolnikoff

Professor of Mathematics
University of California, Los Angeles

R. M. Redheffer

Associate Professor of Mathematics
University of California, Los Angeles

McGRAW-HILL BOOK COMPANY, INC.

New York   Toronto   London   1958

VI
59624

PREFACE

The rapidly decreasing time lag between scientific discoveries and applications imposes ever-increasing demands on the mathematical equipment of scientists and engineers. Although the mathematical preparation of engineering students has been strengthened materially in the past thirty years, the introduction of courses beyond the traditional "terminal course" in calculus has been largely confined to a few leading institutions. The reluctance to broaden significantly the program of instruction in mathematics can be attributed in part to the crowded engineering curricula, in part to the failure to sense the central position of mathematics in sciences and technology, and in part to the scarcity of suitable staffs and instructional media. The broadening, however, is inevitable, for it is now generally recognized that no professional engineer can keep abreast of scientific developments without substantially extending his mathematical horizons.

This book, in common with its predecessor written by the senior author some twenty-five years ago, has as its main aim a sound extension of such horizons. The authors not only have been guided by their subjective appraisal of the live present-day needs of the engineering profession but have also taken into account the views of the leaders of engineering thought as expressed in numerous conferences and symposia on engineering education sponsored by the National Science Foundation, the American Society of Engineering Education, and its predecessor the Society for the Promotion of Engineering Education.

There are many conflicting and often prejudiced currents of thought as to how mathematics should be presented to students of applied sciences. Some believe that mathematics is one whole and indivisible and hence should be presented unto all alike, regardless of the differing creeds. Others are content with a catalogue of useful formulas, rules, and devices for solving problems. The authors think that these two extreme viewpoints are somewhat limited, since they recognize only two of the many facets of mathematics. A preoccupation with the logic of mathematics and the overemphasis of a convention called rigor are among the best known means for stifling interest in mathematics as a crutch to common sense. On the other hand, a presentation which puts applications above the medium making

v

applications possible is sterile, because it gives no inkling of the supreme importance of generalizations and abstractions in applications. The authors have tried to strike a balance which would make this book both a sound and an inspiring introduction to applied mathematics.

The material in this book appears in nine chapters, each of which is complete and virtually independent of the others. Occasional cross references to other chapters are intended to correlate the topics and to enhance the usefulness of the book as a reference volume. Each chapter is subdivided into functional parts, many of which also form an organized whole. The earlier parts of each chapter are less advanced and should serve as an introduction to more difficult topics treated in the later parts. The text material set in small type usually deals with generalizations and develops the less familiar concepts which are sure to grow in importance in applications.

The choice of topics is based on the authors' estimate of the frequency with which the subjects treated occur in applications. The illustrative material, examples, and problems have been chosen more for their value in emphasizing the underlying principles than as a collection of instances of dramatic uses of mathematics in specific situations confronting practicing engineers.

Although the book is written so as to require little, if any, outside help, the reader is cautioned that no amount of exposition can serve as a substitute for concentration in following the course of the argument in a serious discipline. In order to facilitate the understanding of the principles and to cultivate the art of formulating physical problems in the language of mathematics, numerous illustrative examples are worked out in detail. The authors believe with Newton that *exempla non minus docent quam precaepta.*

I. S. Sokolnikoff
R. M. Redheffer

TO THE INSTRUCTOR

In the sense that a working course in calculus is the sole technical prerequisite, this book is suitable for the beginner in applied mathematics. But when viewed in the light of the present-day requirements of the engineering profession, the text includes a large amount of material of direct interest to practicing engineers.

It is certain that within the next twenty years the methods of functional analysis and, in particular, the Hilbert space theory will be in general use in technology. A foundation for the assimilation of the function-space concepts should be laid now, and we did not hesitate to do so in several places in this book.

We have arranged the contents in nine independent chapters which, in turn, are subdivided into parts, most of which can be read independently of the rest. The earlier parts of each chapter are less advanced, and our experience has shown that several introductory courses for students of science and technology can be based on the material contained in the earlier parts. When taken in sequence, this book has ample substance for four consecutive semester courses meeting three hours a week.

This book is also suitable for courses in mathematical analysis bearing such labels as ordinary differential equations, partial differential equations, vector analysis, advanced calculus, complex variable, and so on.

Thus Chap. 1, when supplemented by Secs. 12 to 14 of Chap. 2, has adequate material for a solid semester course in ordinary differential equations. Instructors wishing to include an introduction to numerical methods of solutions of differential equations will find suitable material in Secs. 14 to 18 of Chap. 9. The use of Laplace transforms in solving differential equations is discussed in Appendix B, which includes, among other things, a meaningful introductory presentation of the "Dirac delta function."

Chapter 6, together with Secs. 18 to 25 of Chap. 2, has ample material for a semester course in partial differential equations.

Chapters 4 and 5 have sufficient content for a modern course in vector analysis.

Chapter 7, preceded by the relevant topics on line integrals in Chap. 5, is adequate for an introductory course in complex variable theory.

Chapter 8 can be used in a semester course on probability theory and applications meeting two hours a week. A course entitled "Probability and Numerical Methods" meeting three hours a week can be based on the material in Chaps. 8 and 9.

Although this book was written primarily for students of physical sciences, it is unlikely that a liberal arts student who followed it in an advanced calculus course would be obliged to "unlearn" anything in his subsequent studies.

The contents of this book include what we believe should be the minimum mathematical equipment of a scientific engineer. It may not be out of place to note that the mathematical preparation of physicists and engineers in Russia exceeds the minimum laid down here. While the curricula of only a few leading American engineering colleges provide now for more than one year of mathematics beyond calculus, their number will continue to increase with the realization that the time allotted to mathematics is a sound capital investment, yielding excellent returns both in the time gained in professional studies and in the depth of penetration.

CONTENTS

CONTENTS

CHAPTER 1

ORDINARY DIFFERENTIAL EQUATIONS

Applications of Linear Equations

Systems of Equations

The power and effectiveness of mathematical methods in the study of natural sciences stem, to a large extent, from the unambiguous language of mathematics, with the aid of which the laws governing natural phenomena can be formulated. Many natural laws, especially those concerned with rates of change, can be phrased as equations involving derivatives or differentials. For example, when a verbal statement of Newton's second law of motion is translated into mathematical symbols, there results an equation relating time derivatives of displacements to forces. A study of such equations then provides a complete qualitative and quantitative characterization of the behavior of mechanical systems under the action of forces. Several broad types of equations studied in this book characterize physical situations of great diversity and practical interest.

The first half of this chapter is concerned with preliminaries and special techniques devised for the solution of the first-order equations arising commonly in applications. The second half contains a comprehensive treatment of linear differential equations with constant coefficients and an introduction to linear equations with variable coefficients. Linear equations occupy a prominent place in the study of the response of elastic structures to impressed forces and in the analysis of electrical circuits and servomechanisms. They also appear in numerous boundary-value problems in the theory of diffusion and heat flow, in quantum mechanics and fluid mechanics, and in electromagnetic theory.

PRELIMINARY REMARKS AND ORIENTATION

1. Definition of Terms and Generalities. Any function containing variables and their derivatives (or differentials) is called a *differential expression*, and every equation involving differential expressions is called a *differential equation*. Differential equations are divided into two classes, *ordinary* and *partial*. The former contain only one independent variable

5

and derivatives with respect to it. The latter contain more than one independent variable.

The order of the highest derivative contained in a differential equation is called the *order* of the differential equation. Thus

$$\left(\frac{d^2y}{dx^2}\right)^4 + 3\frac{dy}{dx} + 5y^2 = 0$$

is an ordinary differential equation of order 2, and

$$\left(\frac{\partial^3 y}{\partial t^3}\right)^2 + 3\frac{\partial^2 y}{\partial x\, \partial t} + yxt = 0$$

is a partial differential equation of order 3.

A function $y = \varphi(x)$ is said to be a *solution* of the differential equation

$$F(x,y,y') = 0, \tag{1-1}$$

if, on the substitution of $y = \varphi(x)$ and $y' = \varphi'(x)$ in the left-hand member of (1-1), the latter vanishes identically.[1] Again, $y = \varphi(x)$ is a solution of the second-order equation $F(x,y,y',y'') = 0$ when the substitution $y = \varphi(x)$, $y' = \varphi'(x)$, $y'' = \varphi''(x)$ reduces this to an identity in x. Similarly for equations of order n.

For example, the first-order differential equation

$$y' + 2xy - e^{-x^2} = 0 \tag{1-2}$$

has a solution $y = xe^{-x^2}$, because the substitution of $y = xe^{-x^2}$ and $y' = e^{-x^2} - 2x^2 e^{-x^2}$ in (1-2) reduces it to an identity $0 \equiv 0$. Also, the equation

$$y'' + y = 0$$

has a solution $y = \sin x$, as can be easily verified by substitution.

We begin our study of differential equations with the first-order equation (1-1), which we suppose can be solved for y' to yield the equation

$$y' = f(x,y). \tag{1-3}$$

For reasons which will become clear presently, we shall always assume that $f(x,y)$ is a continuous function throughout some region in the xy plane, and we shall study the solutions of (1-3) [or, equivalently, of (1-1)] in that region.

The geometrical meaning of the term *solution* of (1-3) is suggested at once by the interpretation of the derivative y' as the slope of the tangent line to some curve $y = \varphi(x)$, for if (x,y) is a point on the curve $y = \varphi(x)$,

---

[1] Here, as elsewhere in this book, primes are used to denote differentiation: $y' \equiv dy/dx$, $y'' \equiv d^2y/dx^2, \ldots, y^{(n)} \equiv d^ny/dx^n$.

and if at every point of this curve the slope is equal to $f(x,y)$, then $\varphi(x)$ is a solution of (1-3).

One can get an idea of the shape of the curve $y = \varphi(x)$ in the following way: Let us choose a point (x_0,y_0) and compute

$$y' = f(x_0,y_0). \tag{1-4}$$

The number $f(x_0,y_0)$ determines a direction of the curve at (x_0,y_0). Now, let (x_1,y_1) be a point near (x_0,y_0) in the direction specified by (1-4). Then $y' = f(x_1,y_1)$ determines a new direction at (x_1,y_1) (Fig. 1). Upon proceeding a short distance in this new direction, we select a new point (x_2,y_2) and at this point determine a new slope $y' = f(x_2,y_2)$. As this process is continued, a curve is built up consisting of short line segments.

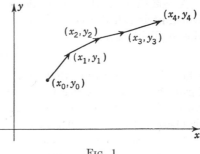

Fig. 1

If the successive points (x_0,y_0), (x_1,y_1), (x_2,y_2), $\ldots$, (x_n,y_n) are chosen near one another, the series of straight-line segments approximates a smooth curve $y = \varphi(x)$ which is a solution of (1-3) associated with the choice of the initial point (x_0,y_0). A different choice of the initial point will, in general, give a different curve, so that the solutions of Eq. (1-3) can be viewed as being given by a whole family of curves. Such curves are called *integral curves*, and each curve in the family represents a *particular solution* or an *integral* of our equation.

Also, we can make a surmise that, unless $f(x,y)$ in the right-hand member of (1-3) is a badly behaving function, for each choice of the initial point there will be just one solution of Eq. (1-3). This surmise is capable of proof, which we do not give here because it requires the use of analytical tools which are not provided in the usual calculus courses. However, the statement of essential facts is easy to grasp, and since it will facilitate the understanding of subsequent developments, we give it here as a basic theorem.

EXISTENCE AND UNIQUENESS THEOREM. *The equation $y' = f(x,y)$ has one and only one integral curve passing through each point of the region in which both $f(x,y)$ and $\partial f/\partial y$ are continuous functions.*[1]

Unless a statement to the contrary is made, we shall suppose that the restrictions imposed on $f(x,y)$ in this theorem are fulfilled, so that Eq.

---

[1] It suffices to suppose that $|\partial f/\partial y|$ is bounded in the region. Proofs of this theorem are contained in many books on differential equations, for example, E. L. Ince, "Ordinary Differential Equations," p. 62. See also Sec. 17 of this chapter.

(1-3) has a unique solution for each choice of (x_0, y_0) in the appropriate region of the xy plane.

Since by changing the initial value $y|_{x=x_0} = y(x_0)$ we get a family of curves depending on the arbitrarily chosen value $y(x_0)$, the equation of this family can be written in the form

$$y = \varphi(x, c) \tag{1-5}$$

involving one arbitrary constant c, corresponding to the arbitrary choices of $y(x_0)$. A particular curve of the family (1-5) passing through (x_0, y_0) is then determined by the value of c such that $y_0 = \varphi(x_0, c)$.

A solution of the first-order equation (1-3) involving one arbitrary constant is called a *general solution*.[1] Such solutions are often written in the implicit form

$$\Phi(x, y, c) = 0, \tag{1-6}$$

where it is understood that (1-6) can be solved for y to yield the explicit form (1-5). In practice it may not be necessary to exhibit the explicit form. The essential feature of the *general solution* [be it given by (1-5) or (1-6)] is that the constant c in it can be determined so that an integral curve passes through a given point (x_0, y_0) of the region under consideration.

We illustrate this by demonstrating that throughout the xy plane the general solution of Eq. (1-2) can be written as

$$y = e^{-x^2}(x + c). \tag{1-7}$$

The fact that (1-7) is, indeed, a solution is easily verified by substituting (1-7) in (1-2). Moreover, it is a general solution, because on setting $x = x_0$ and $y = y_0$ we get

$$y_0 = e^{-x_0^2}(x_0 + c). \tag{1-8}$$

Thus the integral curve passing through (x_0, y_0) corresponds to

$$c = y_0 e^{x_0^2} - x_0.$$

As another example consider the equation

$$\frac{dy}{dx} = f(x), \tag{1-9}$$

where $f(x)$ is any continuous function. A *general* solution of this equation, obtained by direct integration, is

$$y = \int f(x)\, dx + c. \tag{1-10}$$

---

[1] Some first-order equations may have solutions which cannot be determined from the general solution for any value of c. Such solutions, called *singular solutions*, arise only when the conditions imposed on $f(x,y)$ in the basic theorem are not fulfilled.

We show next that (1-10) is a general solution of (1-9). We denote an indefinite integral in (1-10) by $F(x)$, so that $dF/dx = f(x)$. Then (1-10) is the same as

$$y = F(x) + c. \tag{1-11}$$

On setting $x = x_0$, $y = y_0$, we get

$$y_0 = F(x_0) + c,$$

so that

$$c = y_0 - F(x_0),$$

and we can, therefore, write (1-11) as

$$y = F(x) - F(x_0) + y_0$$

$$\equiv F(x)|_{x_0}^{x} + y_0. \tag{1-12}$$

But from the fundamental theorem of integral calculus,

$$\int_{x_0}^{x} f(x)\, dx = F(x)|_{x_0}^{x}$$

and therefore (1-12) yields the desired particular solution

$$y = \int_{x_0}^{x} f(x)\, dx + y_0, \tag{1-13}$$

corresponding to the choice of the initial point (x_0, y_0).

Formula (1-13) illustrates the procedure of deducing particular solutions by integrating the given equation (1-9) between limits. It is frequently simpler than the procedure of determining the desired solution by calculating the constant c in the general solution from the initial data.

The foregoing discussion can be extended to equations of higher order. Thus, *the nth-order equation*

$$F(x, y, y', \ldots, y^{(n)}) = 0, \tag{1-14}$$

which we shall write in the form solved for $y^{(n)}$ as

$$y^{(n)} = f(x, y, y', \ldots, y^{(n-1)}), \tag{1-15}$$

has a unique solution for n arbitrarily assigned initial values,

$$y(x_0),\ y'(x_0), \ldots,\ y^{(n-1)}(x_0), \tag{1-16}$$

whenever the function f in (1-15) *is continuous together with the partial derivatives* $\partial f/\partial y$, $\partial f/\partial y'$, $\ldots$, $\partial f/\partial y^{(n-1)}$.

When the values in (1-16) are varied, we get a family of curves, the so-called *n-parameter family*, corresponding to n independent choices of constants in (1-16). The equation of this family of solutions can be written in the form

$$y = \varphi(x, c_1, c_2, \ldots, c_n) \tag{1-17}$$

involving n arbitrary constants c_i. A solution such as (1-17) is called a *general solution* of the nth-order equation (1-15) [or (1-14)], *provided that the constants c_i in* (1-17) *can be determined for every given set of arbitrarily assigned initial values* (1-16). The general solution (1-17) may also appear in an implicit form as

$$\Phi(x,y,c_1,c_2,\ldots,c_n) = 0, \qquad (1\text{-}18)$$

which on solving for y should give (1-17).

The meaning of the initial conditions (1-16), as they bear on the uniqueness of solution of the second-order equation $F(x,y,y',y'') = 0$, is that *the integral curve of this equation is determined at $x = x_0$ if the ordinate $y_0 = y(x_0)$ and the slope $y'(x_0)$ are specified.*

To determine uniquely the solution of the third-order equation, we must specify the value of the ordinate y_0, the slope y_0', and the value of the second derivative y_0'' at $x = x_0$.

In the following nine sections we shall deal with first-order equations, which we can write in the *differential notation* as

$$P(x,y)\,dx + Q(x,y)\,dy = 0. \qquad (1\text{-}19)$$

If $Q(x,y) \neq 0$, Eq. (1-19) gives

$$\frac{dy}{dx} = -\frac{P(x,y)}{Q(x,y)},$$

which is in the form (1-3) with $f(x,y) = -P(x,y)/Q(x,y)$.

PROBLEMS

Classify the following differential equations as ordinary or partial, and determine their orders:

1. $\dfrac{d^4y}{dx^4} + \left(\dfrac{dy}{dx}\right)^3 = y^2;$

2. $\dfrac{\partial^4 z}{\partial x^4} + 2\,\dfrac{\partial^2 z}{\partial x\,\partial y} = \dfrac{\partial^4 z}{\partial y^4};$

3. $y' + \sin y + x = 0;$

4. $dy = \sqrt{1 - y^2}\,dx;$

5. $y'' + x^2 y' + xy = \sin x;$

6. $\dfrac{\partial z}{\partial t} = a^2\left(\dfrac{\partial^2 z}{\partial x^2} + \dfrac{\partial^2 z}{\partial y^2}\right);$

7. $\sqrt{y} + \sqrt{y''} = y';$

8. $y^{1/2} + y' = y'''.$

Verify that the given expression is a solution of the given differential equation:

9. $y = ce^x,\ y' = y;$
10. $2e^y = e^x + ce^{-x},\ y' = e^{x-y} - 1;$
11. $y = c_1 \sin x + c_2 \cos x,\ y'' + y = 0;$
12. $y = c_1 \sinh x + c_2 \cosh x,\ y'' - y = 0;$
13. $xy = \displaystyle\int f(x)\,dx,\ xy' + y = f(x).$

14. Integrate $y' = 2x$ to show that its general solution is a family of parabolas $y = x^2 + c$. Determine integral curves of this equation through $(0,0)$, $(1,1)$, $(0,1)$, $(1,-1)$.

15. Determine the integral curve for $y'' = 2x$ such that $y(0) = 0$ and $y'(0) = 1$. What is the general solution of this equation?

2. The Slipping of a Belt on a Pulley. To illustrate the prominence of differential equations in the study of various phenomena, this and the following three sections are primarily concerned with the task of setting up differential equations from physical principles.[1] Such solutions as are included are intended merely as a preview of the systematic discussion given in the subsequent sections. If he wishes, the reader may confine his attention to the derivation of the equations only and return to the question of solution after this systematic discussion has been assimilated.

The first example is given by the belt-pulley arrangement of Fig. 2, which is now to be analyzed. Consider an element of the belt, of length Δs, which has end points P and Q and subtends an angle $\Delta\theta$ at the center O. Let T be the tension at P and $T + \Delta T$ at Q, and let ΔF be the normal component of force on Δs due to the pulley. Thus ΔF is the component, along the radius ON, of the total resultant force exclusive of T and $T + \Delta T$.

Assume that the belt is stationary and that the pulley rotates, so that there is slipping. Since the element

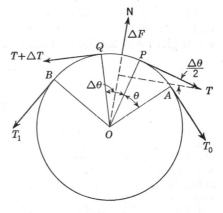

Fig. 2

Δs is in static equilibrium, the components of force along ON must balance. This gives

$$(T + \Delta T) \sin \frac{\Delta\theta}{2} + T \sin \frac{\Delta\theta}{2} = \Delta F, \qquad (2\text{-}1)$$

provided the weight of the belt is negligible or provided the pulley axis is vertical. Equating forces at right angles to ON leads to

$$(T + \Delta T) \cos \frac{\Delta\theta}{2} - T \cos \frac{\Delta\theta}{2} = \mu\, \Delta F, \qquad (2\text{-}2)$$

where μ is the coefficient of sliding friction.[2] From (2-2) we may deduce

$$\Delta T \sim \mu\, \Delta F, \qquad \Delta\theta \to 0, \qquad (2\text{-}3)$$

[1] Further problems of the sort are treated in Secs. 18 to 20.

[2] We define μ by (2-2) and regard it as an experimental fact that μ approaches the coefficient of friction for flat surfaces or, at any rate, some limit independent of θ as $\Delta\theta \to 0$.

where the symbol $\sim$ (read "is asymptotic to") means [1] that the ratio of the quantities on each side tends to 1. Thus, if $a \sim b$, then $\lim a/b = 1$. Equations (2-1) and (2-3) together show that $\Delta T \to 0$ as $\Delta\theta \to 0$. Since $\sin(\Delta\theta/2) \sim \Delta\theta/2$, Eq. (2-1) now gives

$$T \, \Delta\theta \sim \Delta F. \qquad (2\text{-}4)$$

Dividing (2-3) by (2-4) leads to $\Delta T/(T \, \Delta\theta) \sim \mu$, which becomes

$$\frac{dT}{T \, d\theta} = \mu, \qquad (2\text{-}5)$$

since $\lim(\Delta T/\Delta\theta) = dT/d\theta$.

Separating the variables in (2-5) yields $dT/T = \mu \, d\theta$, which, upon integration, becomes $\log T = \mu\theta + c$. The initial condition $T = T_0$ when $\theta = 0$ gives $c = \log T_0$, so that, taking exponentials,

$$T = T_0 e^{\mu\theta}. \qquad (2\text{-}6)$$

PROBLEMS

1. Obtain Eq. (2-3) by equating torques about the point O.

2. If the pulley axis is horizontal, and if the belt weighs w lb per ft, show that Eq. (2-3) becomes $\mu \, \Delta F \sim \Delta T - w \, \Delta s \cos\theta$ and Eq. (2-4) becomes $\Delta F \sim T \, \Delta\theta + w \, \Delta s \sin\theta$, where ΔF is the normal component of the reaction of the pulley on Δs and the line OA in Fig. 2 is horizontal, with P above it. Deduce the differential equation $dT/d\theta - \mu T = wr(\mu \sin\theta + \cos\theta)$, where r is the radius.

3. Show that the equation in Prob. 2 becomes $d(Te^{-\mu\theta}) = wre^{-\mu\theta} (\mu \sin\theta + \cos\theta) \, d\theta$ when multiplied by $e^{-\mu\theta}$, and thus obtain the solution.

3. Growth. Equation (2–5), which was obtained for the tension in a slipping belt, arises in many other connections. For example, radium decomposes at a rate proportional to the amount present. If this amount is A at time t, the foregoing statement means

$$\frac{dA}{dt} = -kA, \qquad k > 0, \qquad (3\text{-}1)$$

the negative sign being chosen because A decreases as t increases. A similar equation is followed by the growth of populations in certain circumstances. Thus, the rate of increase being nearly proportional to the number N present, one can write $dN/dt = kN$. Again, certain organisms

---

[1] The relation symbolized by $\sim$ has many of the properties of strict equality. For example, if $a \sim b$ and $b \sim c$ then $a \sim c$. To see this, observe that $a/b \to 1$, since $a \sim b$; and $b/c \to 1$, since $b \sim c$, and hence, by multiplication, $(a/b)(b/c) \to 1 \cdot 1$. Thus $a/c \to 1$, which is to say, $a \sim c$. The reader may verify similarly that $a \sim b$ and $c \sim d$ together imply $ac \sim bd$ and $a/c \sim b/d$. Finally, if $a \sim b$ and b is constant, we may write $\lim a = b$. These properties are freely used in the text.

grow at a rate proportional to their size S at a given time so that $dS/dt = kS$.

Example 1. In a colony of bacteria each bacterium divides into two after a time interval, on the average, of length τ. If there are n bacteria at time $t = 0$ and m at time $t = 1$, with n large, find the approximate value of τ.

The hypothesis implies that $dN/dt = kN$, approximately, with greater and greater accuracy as the number of bacteria N becomes large. Separating variables gives $dN/N = k\,dt$. Now $t = 0$ corresponds to $N = n$, and $t = 1$ corresponds to $N = m$, by hypothesis. Thus,

$$\int_n^m \frac{dN}{N} = \int_0^1 k\,dt \qquad (3\text{-}2)$$

and similarly

$$\int_n^{2n} \frac{dN}{N} = \int_0^\tau k\,dt, \qquad (3\text{-}3)$$

since N doubles in the interval τ. Equation (3-2) gives $\log m - \log n = k$, and (3-3) gives $\log 2 = k\tau$, so that

$$\tau = \frac{\log 2}{\log m - \log n}.$$

This problem illustrates the useful method of *integration between limits* for the determination of constants. A justification of this procedure is implicit in Sec. 1, Eq. (1-13).

Example 2. A radioactive substance A decomposes into a new substance B, which in turn decomposes into a third substance C. Set up a differential equation for the amount of B at time t.

The rate of increase of B is equal to the rate at which B is formed from A minus the rate at which B decomposes. Thus, denoting the amounts by A and B,

$$\frac{dB}{dt} = -\frac{dA}{dt} - k_1 B. \qquad (3\text{-}4)$$

This equation has two unknowns, A and B. By (3-1), however, $A = ce^{-kt}$, so that (3-4) becomes

$$\frac{dB}{dt} = kce^{-kt} - k_1 B. \qquad (3\text{-}5)$$

A method of solving (3-5) is given in Sec. 10.

PROBLEMS

1. If 3 g of a radioactive substance is present at time $t = 1$ and 1 g at $t = 4$, how much was present initially?

2. In Example 2 of the text set up the differential equation for the amount of substance C present at time t.

3. By actual substitution, determine a and p in such a way that $B = ae^{pt}$ is a solution of Eq. (3-5).

4. The rate of decomposition of a certain chemical substance is proportional to the amount of the substance still unchanged. If the amount of the substance at the end of t hr is x and x_0 is the initial amount, show that $x = x_0 e^{-kt}$, where k is the constant of proportionality. Find k if x changes from 1,000 to 500 g in 2 hr.

5. A torpedo moving in still water is retarded with a force proportional to the velocity. Find the speed at the end of t sec and the distance traveled in t sec if the initial speed is 30 mph.

6. The rate at which a body is cooling is proportional to the difference in the temperatures of the body and the surrounding medium. It is known that the temperature of a body fell from 120 to 70°C in 1 hr when it was placed in air at 20°C. How long will it take the body to cool to 40°C? 30°C? 20°C?

7. The percentage of incident light absorbed in passing through a thin layer of material is proportional to the thickness of the material. If 1 in. of material reduces the light to half its intensity, how much additional material is needed to reduce the intensity to one-eighth of its initial value? Obtain the answer by inspection, and check by solving an appropriate differential equation.

4. Diffusion and Chemical Combination. Problems involving chemical reactions and the formation of mixtures often lead to differential equations; the discussion is similar to that of Sec. 3. For example, suppose that a tank contains g gal of water and that brine containing w lb of salt per gallon flows into the tank and out again at a constant rate r gpm, starting at time $t = 0$. At the same time a piece of rock salt is dropped into the tank, where it dissolves at a constant rate of q lb per min. The mixture being kept uniform by stirring, it is required to find the amount of salt present at any time $t \geq 0$.

This problem may be taken as the typical problem for many questions involving chemical reactions, mixing, and going into solution. The differential equation is obtained by writing down the equation of continuity (increase equals income minus outgo) *for the amount of salt*. Call this amount $x = x(t)$ at time t. In the time interval from t to $t + \Delta t$ the number of gallons entering the tank is $r \, \Delta t$, since the rate of flow is r. Now each gallon contains w lb of salt. Hence the $r \, \Delta t$ gal contains

$$wr \, \Delta t \qquad (4\text{-}1)$$

pounds of salt, and this, then, represents income due to the inflowing brine. The income due to the dissolving salt is

$$q \, \Delta t, \qquad (4\text{-}2)$$

by the definition of q.

It remains to compute the amount of salt lost in the mixture leaving the system. The number of *gallons* leaving is $r \, \Delta t$, the concentration of the mixture in pounds per gallon is x/g at time t, and hence the number of *pounds* leaving is

$$\frac{\bar{x}}{g} r \, \Delta t. \qquad (4\text{-}3)$$

Here $\bar{x}$ denotes the mean value of x over the interval $(t, \, t + \Delta t)$. We assume x to be continuous, so that

$$\lim_{\Delta t \to 0} \bar{x} = x. \tag{4-4}$$

From (4-1), (4-2), and (4-3) we obtain

$$\Delta x = wr\, \Delta t + q\, \Delta t - \frac{\bar{x}}{g}\, r\, \Delta t,$$

which gives

$$\frac{dx}{dt} = wr + q - \frac{rx}{g} \tag{4-5}$$

when we divide by Δt and let $\Delta t \to 0$, using (4-4).

Example: Find the concentration of salt at the end of 4 min when $w = 1$, $g = 2$ $q = 3$, $r = 4$.

The differential equation is $dx/dt = 7 - 2x$ or $dx/(7 - 2x) = dt$. Multiplying by -2 and integrating give $\log (7 - 2x) = -2t + c$. Since $x = 0$ when $t = 0$, it is necessary that $c = \log 7$, so that $-2t = \log (7 - 2x) - \log 7 = \log (1 - 2x/7)$ or, taking exponentials, $1 - 2x/7 = e^{-2t}$. This gives the amount of dissolved salt x at the end of t min. Putting $t = 4$, solving for x, and noting that the concentration is not x but x/g give $\frac{7}{4}(1 - e^{-8})$ as the final answer.

PROBLEMS

1. Solve the example of the text by the method of integration between limits. (See Example 1, Sec. 3. Here $x = 0$ at $t = 0$, $x = x$ at $t = 4$.)

2. How would the discussion in Sec. 4 change if the rock salt had been added at time $t = t_0$ instead of time $t = 0$?

3. How would the discussion in Sec. 4 change if the rock salt dissolved at a rate proportional to the amount undissolved, rather than at the constant rate q? *Hint:* If A is this amount, $dA/dt = -kA$. From this find A at time t, and from that find $q = -dA/dt$.

4. Let A be the amount of a substance at the beginning of a chemical reaction, and let x be the amount of the substance entered in the reaction after t sec. Assuming that the rate of change of the substance is proportional to the amount remaining, deduce that $dx/dt = c(A - x)$, where c is a constant depending on the reaction. Show that $x = A(1 - e^{-ct})$.

5. Let a solution contain two substances whose amounts expressed in gram molecules, at the beginning of a reaction, are A and B. If an equal amount x of both substances has changed at the time t, and if the rate of change is jointly proportional to the amounts of the substances remaining, obtain the equation $dx/dt = k(A - x)(B - x)$. Solve, assuming that $x = 0$ when $t = 0$.

6. Formulate the appropriate differential equation if the rate at which a substance dissolves is jointly proportional to the amount present and to the difference between the actual concentration and the saturate concentration.

5. The Elastic Curve. Consider a horizontal elastic beam under the action of vertical loads. It is assumed that all the forces acting on the beam lie in a plane containing the central axis of the beam. Choose the x axis along the central axis of the beam in undeformed state and the positive y axis down (Fig. 3).   Under the action of external forces F_i the beam is bent and its central axis deformed.   The deformed central axis, shown in the figure by the dashed line, is known as the *elastic curve*, and it is an important problem in the theory of elasticity to determine its shape.

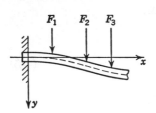

A beam made of elastic material that obeys Hooke's law is known to deform in such a way that the curvature K of the elastic curve is proportional to the bending moment M.   In fact,

$$K = \frac{y''}{[1 + (y')^2]^{3/2}} = \frac{M}{EI}, \qquad (5\text{-}1)$$

FIG. 3

where E is Young's modulus, I is the moment of inertia of the cross section of the beam about a horizontal line passing through the centroid of the section and lying in the plane of the cross section, and y is the ordinate of the elastic curve. The important relation (5-1) bears the name *Bernoulli-Euler law*.   When the deflection of the beam is small, the slope of the elastic curve is also generally small and one can neglect the term $(y')^2$ in (5-1) to obtain an approximate equation

$$y'' = \frac{M}{EI}. \qquad (5\text{-}2)$$

The bending moment M in any cross section of the beam is equal to the algebraic sum of the moments of all the forces F_i acting on one side of the section.   The moments of the forces F_i are taken about a horizontal line lying in the cross section in question.

Example: Consider a cantilever beam of length l, built in at the end $x = 0$ and carrying in addition to a distributed load $w(x)$ lb per ft a concentrated load W lb and a couple L ft-lb applied at the end $x = l$ (Fig. 4).

The resultant moment in a cross section x ft from the end $x = 0$, produced by the loads acting to the right of that section, is

$$M(x) = \int_x^l (\xi - x)w(\xi)\,d\xi + W(l - x) + L. \qquad (5\text{-}3)$$

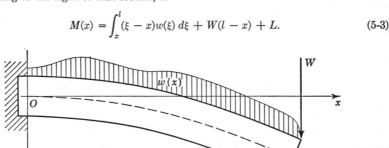

FIG. 4

If $w(x) = 0$ and $L = 0$, this formula yields $M = W(l - x)$, and hence, from (5-2), the differential equation of the central line of a cantilever beam subjected to the end load W is

$$y'' = \frac{W}{EI}(l - x).$$

On integrating this equation we get

$$y = \frac{W}{EI}\left(\frac{x^2}{2} - \frac{x^3}{6}\right) + c_1 x + c_2.$$

The integration constants c_1 and c_2 can be evaluated from the conditions $y(0) = 0$, $y'(0) = 0$, stating that the displacement and the slope of the central line vanish at the built-in end. It is readily checked that these conditions lead to

$$y = \frac{W}{2EI}\left(lx^2 - \frac{x^3}{3}\right),$$

so that the displacement d at the free end is $d = Wl^3/3EI$.

PROBLEMS

1. A beam of length l is freely supported at its ends and is loaded in the center by a concentrated vertical load W, which is large in comparison with the weight of the beam (see Fig. 5). By symmetry, the behavior of this beam is the same as that of a cantilever beam of length $l/2$ loaded by a concentrated load of magnitude $W/2$ at its free end. Verify this equivalence by direct computation of the elastic curve. *Hint:*

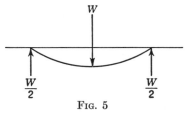

$$M = -\frac{W}{2}x, \qquad 0 < x < \frac{l}{2},$$

$$= -\frac{W}{2}(l - x), \qquad \frac{l}{2} \le x \le l.$$

Fig. 5

2. A uniform unloaded beam of length l weighs w lb per ft. Find the maximum deflection when it is used as a cantilever beam and also when it is freely supported at each end. *Hint:* Since the reaction at the end $x = l$ is $R = W/2$, the moment in the cross section at a distance x from the end $x = 0$ is

$$M = w\int_x^l (\xi - x)\,d\xi - \frac{wl}{2}(l - x).$$

THE SOLUTION OF FIRST-ORDER EQUATIONS

6. Equations with Separable Variables. Generally speaking, the problem of solving differential equations is a very difficult one. Even such a simple equation as $y' = f(x,y)$ cannot be solved in general; that is, no formulas are available for solving the general differential equation of the first order. It is possible, however, to classify some of the first-order differential equations according to several types and to indicate special methods of solution suitable for each of these.

Prominent among these types are the equations with *separable variables*, that is, equations which can be put in the form

$$P(x)\,dx + Q(y)\,dy = 0,$$

where $P(x)$ is a function of x only and $Q(y)$ is a function of y only. This type of equation has already been encountered in the special examples solved above. Its general solution is

$$\int P(x)\,dx + \int Q(y)\,dy = c,$$

where c is an arbitrary constant. In order to obtain an explicit solution all that is necessary is to perform the indicated integrations.

Example: Find a solution of $y' + e^x y = e^x y^2$ which goes through $(0, \frac{1}{2})$.
The equation can be written as $y' + e^x(y - y^2) = 0$ or

$$\frac{dy}{y - y^2} + e^x\,dx = 0.$$

Integration gives

$$\log \frac{y}{1 - y} + e^x = c,$$

which is a general solution. Putting $x = 0$, $y = \frac{1}{2}$ gives $c = \log 1 + e^0 = 1$, so that the required particular solution is

$$\log \frac{y}{1 - y} + e^x = 1.$$

PROBLEMS

Solve the following differential equations. In Probs. 4 to 6 find a solution through the point $(0,1)$.

1. $\sqrt{1 - x^2}\,dy = \sqrt{1 - y^2}\,dx.$ **2.** $y' = xy^2 - x.$

3. $y' = \dfrac{\sin^2 x}{\sin y}.$ **4.** $\sin x \cos^2 y\,dx = \cos^2 x\,dy.$

5. $\sqrt{1 + x}\,dy = (1 + y^2)\,dx.$ **6.** $y' = \dfrac{1 + y}{1 + x}.$

7. Homogeneous Differential Equations. A function $f(x,y)$ of the two variables x and y is said to be *homogeneous of degree n* provided that

$$f(\lambda x, \lambda y) \equiv \lambda^n f(x,y), \qquad \lambda > 0.$$

Thus, $f(x,y) = x^3 + x^2 y + y^3$ is a homogeneous function of degree 3, and $f(x,y) = x^2 \sin (x/y) + xy$ is a homogeneous function of degree 2, as follows at once on replacing x by λx and y by λy.

If the differential equation is of the form

$$P(x,y) \, dx + Q(x,y) \, dy = 0, \qquad (7\text{-}1)$$

where $P(x,y)$ and $Q(x,y)$ are homogeneous functions of the same degree, then (7-1) can be written in the form

$$y' = -\frac{P(x,y)}{Q(x,y)} \equiv \phi(x,y), \qquad (7\text{-}2)$$

where $\phi(x,y)$ is a homogeneous function of degree zero; that is,

$$\phi(\lambda x, \lambda y) \equiv \lambda^0 \phi(x,y) \equiv \phi(x,y).$$

If λ is set equal to $1/x$, then

$$\phi(x,y) \equiv \phi(\lambda x, \lambda y) = \phi\left(1, \frac{y}{x}\right),$$

which shows that a homogeneous function of degree zero can always be expressed as a function of y/x. This suggests making the substitution $y/x = v$. Then, since $y = vx$,

$$\frac{dy}{dx} = \frac{dv}{dx} x + v.$$

Substituting this value of dy/dx in (7-2) gives

$$x \frac{dv}{dx} + v = \phi(1,v).$$

This equation is of the type considered in Sec. 6. Separating the variables leads to

$$\frac{dv}{\phi(1,v) - v} = \frac{dx}{x},$$

which can be integrated at once.

Example: Solve

$$y^2 + x^2 \frac{dy}{dx} = xy \frac{dy}{dx}.$$

This equation can be put in the form

$$\frac{dy}{dx} = \frac{y^2}{xy - x^2} = \frac{(y/x)^2}{y/x - 1}.$$

Letting $y/x = v$ and computing dy/dx from $y = vx$ give

$$v + x \frac{dv}{dx} = \frac{v^2}{v - 1} \qquad \text{or} \qquad x \frac{dv}{dx} = \frac{v}{v - 1}.$$

Separation of the variables leads to

$$\frac{dx}{x} + \frac{1 - v}{v} \, dv = 0,$$

and integration yields $\log x + \log v - v = c$ or $\log vx - v = c$. Since $v = y/x$, the final answer is $\log y - y/x = c$.

PROBLEMS

Solve the following differential equations. In Probs. 4 to 6 find a solution through the point (1,1).

1. $(x^2 + y^2)\, dy + 2xy\, dx = 0$.

2. $xy' - y = \sqrt{x^2 - y^2}$.

3. $x \cos \dfrac{y}{x} \dfrac{dy}{dx} = y \cos \dfrac{y}{x} - x$.

4. $(x + y)y' = x - y$.

5. $x^2 y\, dx = (x^3 - y^3)\, dy$.

6. $\dfrac{dy}{dx} = \dfrac{xy - y^2}{x^2}$.

Some of the following equations are separable; some are homogeneous. Solve them.

7. $\sinh x\, dy + \cosh y\, dx = 0$.

8. $\dfrac{dy}{dx} = \dfrac{y}{x - \sqrt{xy}}$.

9. $x(\sqrt{xy} + y)\, dx = x^2\, dy$.

10. $x^2 y' - y^2 = x^2 y y'$.

11. $xy' = y + xe^{y/x}$.

12. $y' = y' \log y + \tan x \sec^2 x$.

8. Exact Differential Equations. An expression $P(x,y)\, dx + Q(x,y)\, dy$ is said to be *exact* if it coincides with the differential

$$dF = \frac{\partial F}{\partial x}\, dx + \frac{\partial F}{\partial y}\, dy$$

of some function $F(x,y)$, that is, if

$$P(x,y)\, dx + Q(x,y)\, dy = \frac{\partial F}{\partial x}\, dx + \frac{\partial F}{\partial y}\, dy. \tag{8-1}$$

In these circumstances the equation

$$P(x,y)\, dx + Q(x,y)\, dy = 0 \tag{8-2}$$

is simply $dF = 0$, and its general solution, therefore, is

$$F(x,y) = c. \tag{8-3}$$

When a function $F(x,y)$ satisfying the relation (8-1) exists, we conclude that

$$\frac{\partial F}{\partial x} = P(x,y), \qquad \frac{\partial F}{\partial y} = Q(x,y). \tag{8-4}$$

Moreover, if $\partial^2 F/(\partial x\, \partial y) = \partial^2 F/(\partial y\, \partial x)$, we obtain by differentiating (8-4) a necessary condition,

$$\frac{\partial P}{\partial y} = \frac{\partial Q}{\partial x} \tag{8-5}$$

for the existence of $F(x,y)$. This condition also suffices to construct $F(x,y)$ in every rectangular region throughout which P, Q, $\partial P/\partial y$, and $\partial Q/\partial x$ are continuous.[1] Indeed, on integrating the first of Eqs. (8-4) with respect to x, we get

$$F(x,y) = \int P(x,y)\, dx + f(y), \qquad (8\text{-}6)$$

where $f(y)$ is an arbitrary differentiable function of y, since y appearing in the integral of (8-6) is treated as a constant. We next determine $f(y)$ so as to satisfy the second of Eqs. (8-4). Differentiating (8-6) with respect to y and equating the result to $Q(x,y)$ give

$$\frac{\partial F}{\partial y} = \frac{\partial}{\partial y}\int P(x,y)\, dx + f'(y) = Q(x,y),$$

so that $\qquad f'(y) = Q(x,y) - \dfrac{\partial}{\partial y}\int P(x,y)\, dx.$

This determines

$$f(y) = \int [Q(x,y) - \frac{\partial}{\partial y}\int P(x,y)\, dx]\, dy, \qquad (8\text{-}7)$$

provided the expression in the brackets in (8-7) is a function of y only. But that is always the case, since its derivative with respect to x is $\partial Q/\partial x - \partial P/\partial y$, and this vanishes whenever (8-5) holds. Accordingly, the substitution of $f(y)$ from (8-7) in (8-6) gives the function $F(x,y)$ and thus the desired solution $F(x,y) = c$.

Example: Solve the equation

$$(2xy + 1)\, dx + (x^2 + 4y)\, dy = 0.$$

This equation is exact, since $\partial P/\partial y = \partial Q/\partial x = 2x$. Thus there is a function $F(x,y)$ such that

$$\frac{\partial F}{\partial x} = 2xy + 1, \qquad \frac{\partial F}{\partial y} = x^2 + 4y. \qquad (8\text{-}8)$$

From the first of Eqs. (8-8) we conclude that

$$F(x,y) = \int (2xy + 1)\, dx + f(y)$$
$$= x^2 y + x + f(y). \qquad (8\text{-}9)$$

To satisfy the second of Eqs. (8-8), we must have

$$\frac{\partial F}{\partial y} = x^2 + f'(y) = x^2 + 4y$$

so that $\qquad f'(y) = 4y.$

The integration yields

$$f(y) = 2y^2,$$

and the substitution in (8-9) gives $F(x,y) = x^2 y + x + 2y^2$. The desired solution, therefore, is

$$x^2 y + x + 2y^2 = c.$$

---

[1] For details and general discussion see Chap. 5, Sec. 9.

PROBLEMS

Integrate the following equations if they are exact:

1. $(e^x + 1)\, dx + dy = 0;$ **2.** $\left(2x + \dfrac{1}{y}\, e^{x/y}\right) dx = \dfrac{1}{2}\, e^{x/y}\, dy;$

3. $(3x^2y - y^3)\, dx = (3y^2x - x^3)\, dy;$ **4.** $x\, dy + y\, dx = 0;$

5. $\dfrac{y}{x^2} \cos \dfrac{y}{x}\, dx = \dfrac{1}{x} \cos \dfrac{y}{x}\, dy;$ **6.** $x\, dx + y\, dy = 0;$

7. $(3x^2y - y^3)\, dx - (x^3 + 3y^2x)\, dy = 0;$

8. $(y \cos xy + 2x)\, dx + x \cos xy\, dy = 0;$

9. $(y^2 + 2xy + 1)\, dx + (2xy + x^2)\, dy = 0;$

10. $3x^2y\, dx + (x^3 - 3y^2x^2)\, dy = 0.$

9. Integrating Factors.   Suppose that

$$M(x,y)\, dx + N(x,y)\, dy = 0 \tag{9-1}$$

has a solution

$$F(x,y) = c, \tag{9-2}$$

where $F(x,y)$ is a differentiable function.   On differentiating (9-2) with respect to x, we get

$$\frac{\partial F}{\partial x} + \frac{\partial F}{\partial y}\, y' = 0, \tag{9-3}$$

and from (9-1) we find

$$M(x,y) + N(x,y)y' = 0. \tag{9-4}$$

The elimination of y' from (9-3) and (9-4) gives

$$\frac{\partial F/\partial x}{M(x,y)} = \frac{\partial F/\partial y}{N(x,y)} \equiv \mu(x,y), \tag{9-5}$$

where $\mu(x,y)$ is the value of the common ratio.   It follows from (9-5) that

$$\frac{\partial F}{\partial x} = \mu(x,y)M(x,y), \qquad \frac{\partial F}{\partial y} = \mu(x,y)N(x,y)$$

and hence that

$$\mu(x,y)(M\, dx + N\, dy) = 0$$

is an exact equation; namely, it is the equation $dF = 0$.

The function $\mu(x,y)$ is termed an *integrating factor*.   It is clear from the above discussion that every equation (9-1) has an integrating factor and, in fact, an unlimited number of them.[1]   Nevertheless, it must not be concluded that an integrating factor can always be found easily.   In simpler cases, however, it can be found by inspection.

---

[1] Some integrating factors introduce extraneous solutions y which make $\mu(x,y) = 0$ but do not satisfy (9-1).

Thus, in order to solve

$$x \, dy - y \, dx = 0$$

which is not exact as it stands, multiply both sides by $1/xy$. Then the equation becomes

$$\frac{dy}{y} - \frac{dx}{x} = 0,$$

which is exact. Another integrating factor for this same equation is $1/x^2$. Similarly, multiplication by $1/y^2$ makes the equation exact.

Example: Solve the differential equation

$$(y^2 - x^2) \, dy + 2xy \, dx = 0.$$

This is not an exact equation, but on rearrangement it becomes

$$y^2 \, dy + 2xy \, dx - x^2 \, dy = 0,$$

which can be made exact with the aid of the integrating factor $1/y^2$. The resulting equation is

$$dy + \frac{2xy \, dx - x^2 \, dy}{y^2} = 0,$$

which integrates to

$$y + \frac{x^2}{y} = c.$$

PROBLEMS

The following problems give a few of the integrable combinations that commonly occur in practice. Verify the equations by differentiating:

1. $d\left(\tan^{-1}\frac{y}{x}\right) = \dfrac{x \, dy - y \, dx}{x^2 + y^2}$;

2. $d\left(\log\frac{y}{x}\right) = \dfrac{x \, dy - y \, dx}{xy}$;

3. $d\left(\dfrac{x}{y}\right) = -\dfrac{x \, dy - y \, dx}{y^2}$;

4. $d\left(\dfrac{y}{x}\right) = \dfrac{x \, dy - y \, dx}{x^2}$;

5. $\tfrac{1}{2}\,d(x^2 + y^2) = x \, dx + y \, dy$;

6. $d(xy) = x \, dy + y \, dx$.

Solve the following equations by finding a suitable integrating factor:

7. $x \, dy + x^2 \, dx = y \, dx$;

8. $(xy^2 + y) \, dx = (x^2 y - x) \, dy$;

9. $x \, dy + 3y \, dx = xy \, dy$;

10. $(x^2 + y^2 + 2x) \, dy = 2y \, dx$;

11. $x \, dy - y \, dx = xy \, dy$;

12. $(x^2 - y^2) \, dy = 2xy \, dx$.

10. The First-order Linear Equation.

An equation of the form

$$\frac{dy}{dx} + M(x)y = N(x) \qquad (10\text{-}1)$$

is termed *linear* for reasons given in Sec. 21.

If we set $y = uv$, where u and v are functions of x to be determined later, we get on substitution in (10-1)

$$uv' + vu' + Muv = N,$$

or $$v(u' + Mu) + uv' = N. \tag{10-2}$$

If u is suitably chosen, the parenthesis in (10-2) can be made equal to zero, thus reducing (10-2) to a simpler form. To this end, set

$$u' + Mu = 0, \tag{10-3}$$

which is a separable equation for u. We get

$$\frac{du}{u} + M \, dx = 0,$$

so that $$\log u + \int M \, dx = c. \tag{10-4}$$

Since any solution of (10-3) reduces (10-2) to the form

$$uv' = N, \tag{10-5}$$

we choose the simplest one, corresponding to $c = 0$. With this choice, (10-4) yields

$$u = e^{-\int M \, dx}, \tag{10-6}$$

and (10-5) becomes

$$v' = N e^{\int M \, dx}. \tag{10-7}$$

Since the right-hand member in (10-7) depends only on x, we get, on integrating,

$$v = \int N e^{\int M \, dx} \, dx + c.$$

Recalling the assumption that $y = uv$, we get the general solution

$$y = e^{-\int M \, dx} \int N e^{\int M \, dx} \, dx + c e^{-\int M \, dx}. \tag{10-8}$$

Example 1. Solve $y' + y \cos x = \sin 2x$. Here $M(x) = \cos x$ and $N(x) = \sin 2x$. Since $\int M \, dx = \int \cos x \, dx = \sin x$, (10-8) yields

$$y = e^{-\sin x} \int e^{\sin x} \sin 2x \, dx + c e^{-\sin x},$$

which is easily evaluated by replacing $\sin 2x$ by $2 \sin x \cos x$.

Example 2. Solve $(x + 1)y' + 2y = (x + 1)^4$. Dividing by $x + 1$ shows that this equation is linear with $M = 2/(x + 1)$ and $N = (x + 1)^3$. Hence

$$e^{\int M \, dx} = e^{\int \frac{2 \, dx}{x+1}} = e^{2 \log (x+1)} = (x + 1)^2,$$

while $$e^{-\int M \, dx} = (x + 1)^{-2}.$$

Thus (10-8) yields

$$y = (x + 1)^{-2} \int (x + 1)^5 \, dx + c(x + 1)^{-2}$$

$$= \frac{(x + 1)^4}{6} + c(x + 1)^{-2}.$$

PROBLEMS

Solve the following equations. In Probs. 3 to 5 find a solution through the point $(0,-1)$.

1. $(1 + x^2) \, dy = \left(\dfrac{1}{x} - xy \right) dx.$ **2.** $(x^2 + 1)y' + 2xy = x^2.$

3. $y' = e^{-x^2} - 2xy.$ **4.** $y' + xy - x = 0.$

5. $y' + y \cos x = \cos^3 x.$ **6.** $xy' + y = x^2 \sin x.$

7. Show, on writing Eq. (10-1) in the form

$$dy + My \, dx = N \, dx,$$

that $e^{\int M \, dx}$ is an integrating factor of this equation, and thus obtain formula (10-8).

Solve the following equations, each of which is separable, homogeneous, exact, or linear. (It is instructive to use several methods when possible.)

8. $y' = y + \cos x - \sin x.$ **9.** $\dfrac{dy}{dx} = \dfrac{y^2 - x\sqrt{x^2 - y^2}}{xy}.$

10. $\dfrac{dx}{dy} + yx = y.$ **11.** $x^2(1 + 4y^2) \, dx + 3yx^3 \, dy = 0.$

12. $y' + yx = y.$ **13.** $\dfrac{\sin^{-1} x}{y} \, dx + (1 - e^y) \, dy = 0.$

11. Equations Solvable for y or y'.   Certain special types of equations can be solved by writing $p = dy/dx$ and expressing p as a function of x and y.   Another method is to solve for y in terms of x and p and then differentiate with respect to x, using $dy/dx = p$.   These procedures change the given first-order equation into a new one.

Example 1. Solve $2p^2 - (2y^2 + x)p + xy^2 = 0$, where $p = dy/dx$.
   Factoring gives $(p - y^2)(2p - x) = 0$ so that, at each x, we have either $p = y^2$ or $p = x/2$.   The fact that y is to be differentiable ensures that one or other of these relations actually holds throughout an interval.   Hence, with $p = dy/dx$, they can be regarded as differential equations and solved in the ordinary way.   From $dy/dx = y^2$ there results

$$x + \frac{1}{y} = c_1, \tag{11-1}$$

and from $dy/dx = x/2$ is obtained

$$y = \frac{x^2}{4} + c_2. \tag{11-2}$$

These two sets of curves represent the desired solution.   Although there is no advantage in doing so, one may write (11-1) and (11-2) as a single equation with a single parameter,

$$\left(x + \frac{1}{y} + c\right)\left(y - \frac{x^2}{4} + c\right) = 0.$$

Example 2.   Solve $p^5 + py = 1$, where $p = dy/dx$.

Since it is impractical to solve this equation for p to obtain $p = f(y)$ (which would have led to a separable equation), we solve it for y and obtain

$$y = \frac{1}{p} - p^4. \tag{11-3}$$

Differentiating (11-3) with respect to x leads to

$$\frac{dy}{dx} = p = -\frac{1}{p^2}\frac{dp}{dx} - 4p^3\frac{dp}{dx},$$

which can be written as

$$dx = -\frac{1}{p^3}\,dp - 4p^2\,dp.$$

After integration we get

$$x = \frac{1}{2p^2} - \frac{4p^3}{3} + c, \tag{11-4}$$

which, together with (11-3), gives the desired solution in parametric form.   There is no advantage in eliminating the parameter p in Eqs. (11-3) and (11-4), even when it is possible to do so.   Plotting the curves representing the solution as p varies, one obtains not only the locus (x,y) but also the slope p at each point.

The method used to solve the equation in the preceding example can be applied to solve the *Lagrange equation*

$$y = xf(y') + g(y'), \tag{11-5}$$

where f and g are differentiable functions of $y' = p$.   On setting $y' = p$ in (11-5) one obtains

$$y = xf(p) + g(p). \tag{11-6}$$

Differentiating with respect to x yields

$$p = xf'(p)\,\frac{dp}{dx} + f(p) + g'(p)\,\frac{dp}{dx},$$

which can be written as

$$\frac{dx}{dp} - \frac{f'(p)}{p - f(p)}\,x = \frac{g'(p)}{p - f(p)}. \tag{11-7}$$

This equation is linear in x; that is, it is of the form $dx/dp + M(p)x = N(p)$, and it can be solved by the method of Sec. 10.   Its solution for x as a function of p, together with (11-6), yields the solution of the original equation in parametric form, with p as parameter.

The reader will find it instructive to apply this method to solve $y = xy' + (y')^2$ and show that $y = cx + c^2$.

PROBLEMS

Problems 1 and 2 are to be solved by the method of Example 1; Probs. 3 and 4 by that of Example 2.

1. $p^2 - 2yp = 3y^2$.   **2.** $p^2 + 1 = 2p$.
3. $p^4 = p^2 y + 2$.   **4.** $p^3 + 2p = e^y$.
5. $p^2 x - py + 1 = 0$.   **6.** $p^2 + y^2 = 1$.
7. $p^2 + (2x - y)p = 2xy$.   **8.** $p^2 + (x - e^x)p = xe^x$.
9. $x = 2y - p^3$.

10. Show that Clairaut's equation $y = xp + f(p)$ is a special case of Lagrange's equation (11-5), and thus obtain the solution.

12. The Method of Substitution. Many first-order equations can be solved by a suitable change of variable. This has already been demonstrated in the substitution $y = vx$ for the homogeneous equation (Sec. 7), in the substitution $y = uw$ of Sec. 10, and in the use of $p = dy/dx$ as independent variable in Sec. 11. Further examples of the substitution method are given in this section.

Thus, the *Bernoulli equation*

$$y' + P(x)y = Q(x)y^n \tag{12-1}$$

can be reduced to a linear equation by setting $z = y^{1-n}$.

On dividing (12-1) by y^n, we get

$$y^{-n}y' + P(x)y^{-n+1} = Q(x).$$

But since $(y^{1-n})' = (1 - n)y^{-n}y'$, we can write this as

$$\frac{1}{1 - n}(y^{1-n})' + P(x)y^{1-n} = Q(x).$$

On making the substitution $z = y^{1-n}$, we get the linear equation

$$z' + (1 - n)P(x)z = (1 - n)Q(x), \tag{12-2}$$

which is solvable by the method of Sec. 10.

The equation

$$\frac{dy}{dx} = f\left(\frac{a_1 x + a_2 y + a_3}{b_1 x + b_2 y + b_3}\right) \tag{12-3}$$

can be solved by the substitution $x = u - h$, $y = v - k$ if the constants h, k are chosen so as to make the resulting equation homogeneous. This procedure, which is simply a translation of axes, is illustrated in Example 2.

Because of the habitual use of the notation dy/dx, which implies that y is a dependent variable, one may fail to recognize that an equation is solvable if the roles of x and y are interchanged. For example, an equation which is nonlinear in y may become linear if x is regarded as the unknown and y is regarded as the independent variable. If an equation seems intractable as it stands, it is often helpful to interchange x and y, simplify, and attempt to solve the new equation. Then interchange x and y in the solution of this to obtain the solution to the original equation. The procedure, which is illustrated in Example 3, amounts simply to the change of variable $x = y$, $y = x$.

Example 1. Solve the equation $y' + y = xy^3$.

This is a special case of Bernoulli's equation. Set $z = y^{-2}$ to obtain $z' - 2z = -2x$ by direct calculation or by (12-2). The general solution is $z = ce^{2x} + x + \frac{1}{2}$, so that $y^{-2} = ce^{2x} + x + \frac{1}{2}$ is the solution of the original equation.

Example 2. Solve

$$\frac{dy}{dx} = \frac{x - y - 2}{x + y + 6}$$

by means of the substitution $x = u - h$, $y = v - k$, where h, k are suitably chosen constants.

Substituting gives

$$\frac{dv}{du} = \frac{u - v - (h - k + 2)}{u + v - (h + k - 6)}. \tag{12-4}$$

If h and k are so determined that

$$h - k + 2 = 0,$$
$$h + k - 6 = 0, \tag{12-5}$$

then (12-4) becomes the homogeneous equation

$$\frac{dv}{du} = \frac{u - v}{u + v},$$

whose solution is

$$u^2 - 2uv - v^2 = c_1 \tag{12-6}$$

by Sec. 7. Equations (12-5) give $h = 2$, $k = 4$, so that $u = x + h = x + 2$, $v = y + k = y + 4$. Substitution in (12-6) leads to the final answer

$$x^2 - 2xy - y^2 - 4x - 12y = c$$

after simplification.

Example 3. Solve $(x - y^3)\, dy = y\, dx$.

Interchanging x and y gives $(y - x^3)\, dx = x\, dy$ or $y' - y/x = -x^2$. This equation is linear in y and gives $2y = cx - x^3$ by the method of Sec. 10. Hence the solution of the original equation is $2x = cy - y^3$.

Example 4. Show how to solve the equation $y' = P(ax + by + c)$, where a, b, c are constant.

Let $z = ax + by + c$, so that $z' = a + by'$. Combining this with the original equation gives $z' - a = by' = bP(ax + by + c) = bP(z)$, or $z' = a + bP(z)$. This equation is separable. The procedure fails if $b = 0$, but then the original equation is separable.

PROBLEMS

Solve the following special cases of Bernoulli's equation:

1. $y^3 \dfrac{dy}{dx} + \dfrac{y^4}{x} = \sin x;$ 2. $y' + y = xy^3;$

3. $\dfrac{1}{y^6}\dfrac{dy}{dx} + \dfrac{1}{xy^5} = x^2;$

4. $y' - x^{-1}y + x^{-2}y^2 = 0;$

5. $xy' + y = y^2 \log x;$

6. $y' + xy = x^3y^3.$

Reduce the following equations to a form which is homogeneous or has separable variables, but do not solve:

7. $y' = \dfrac{x + y - 1}{2x + y + 2};$

8. $y' = \dfrac{3x + y + 6}{3x + y + 7};$

9. $y' = \sin\dfrac{x - y + 2}{x + y + 3};$

10. $y' = \cos(x + y).$

Solve by interchanging x and y and using an appropriate method on the result:

11. $\dfrac{dx}{dy} = yx^3 - x;$

12. $y\,dx = (x + y^3)\,dy;$

13. $y + xy' = e^y y';$

14. $1 + xy' \tan y = y'.$

Solve the following review problems by any method:

15. $y(1 + x^2)^{-1}\,dx + \tan^{-1}x\,dy = 0;$

16. $(1 + x^2)\,dy = (1 + y^2)\,dx;$

17. $\dfrac{dx}{dy} + \dfrac{x}{y} + y^2 = 0;$

18. $\sin 2y\,dx + 2x\cos 2y\,dy = 0;$

19. $e^x y' = e^x + e^y;$

20. $dx = (yx^3 - x)\,dy;$

21. $dx + 2x\,dy = y\,dy;$

22. $(x^2 + y^2)\,dx = xy\,dy;$

23. $dy = (2y + e^{3x})\,dx;$

24. $y^2 = (xy - x^3 e^y)y';$

25. $(x - y + 1)\,dx + (x + y - 1)\,dy = 0.$

13. Reduction of Order.

With $y' = p$, the transformations

$$y'' = \frac{d}{dx}y' = \frac{dp}{dx}, \tag{13-1}$$

$$y'' = \frac{dp}{dx} = \frac{dp}{dy}\frac{dy}{dx} = \frac{dp}{dy}p \tag{13-2}$$

often enable us to reduce an equation of second order in y to one of first order in p. For example, the equations

$$F(x,y',y'') = 0, \tag{13-3}$$

$$F(y,y',y'') = 0 \tag{13-4}$$

become by (13-1) and (13-2), respectively,

$$F\left(x,p,\frac{dp}{dx}\right) = 0, \tag{13-5}$$

$$F\left(y,p,p\frac{dp}{dy}\right) = 0. \tag{13-6}$$

These are first-order equations in p, and when p has been found, the substitution $p = y'$ yields a first-order equation for y.

Example 1.   Find the solution of $y'' \sin y' = \sin x$ which satisfies the conditions $y(1) = 2$ and $y'(1) = 1$.

Being free of y the equation has the form (13-3), and it becomes

$$\frac{dp}{dx} \sin p = \sin x$$

by (13-1). Solving this separable equation yields

$$- \cos p = - \cos x + c,$$

which is reduced to $p = x$ by the condition $p = 1$ at $x = 1$. Writing dy/dx for p in the equation $p = x$ gives on integration the final answer

$$y = \tfrac{1}{2}(x^2 - 1) + 2$$

in view of the condition $y(1) = 2$.

Example 2.   Solve $yy'' - 2(y')^2 + y^2 = 0$.

This equation has the form (13-4), since it does not contain x. The transformation (13-2) gives

$$yp\frac{dp}{dy} - 2p^2 + y^2 = 0,$$

which is a homogeneous equation with y as *independent* variable. Setting $p = vy$ and proceeding as in Sec. **7** give, after calculation,

$$p = \pm y\sqrt{1 + c^2 y^2}. \tag{13-7}$$

With $p = dy/dx$ in (13-7) we separate variables to obtain the final answers,

$$x + c_1 = \mp \sinh^{-1}\frac{1}{cy}.$$

PROBLEMS

Problems 1 and 2 are to be solved by the method of Example 1, Probs. 3 and 4 by that of Example 2, and Probs. 5 to **7** by whichever method is more suitable.

1. $(1 - x^2)y'' = xy'$.

2. $x(y'' + y'^2) = y'$.

3. $y'' + e^y = 0$.

4. $y'' = yy'$.

5. $x^2 y'' = 1 - x$.

6. $yy'' = y'^2$.

7. $xy'' = 4x - 2y'$.

8. Solve $y'' = 1 + y'^2$ by both methods of this section, and verify the agreement of the results.

GEOMETRY AND THE FIRST-ORDER EQUATION

14. Orthogonal Trajectories. In a variety of practical investigations, it is desirable to determine the equation of a family of curves that intersect the curves of a given family at right angles. For example, it is known that the lines of equal potential, due to a distribution of steady current flowing in a homogeneous conducting medium, intersect the lines of current flow at right angles. Again, the streamlines of a steady flow of liquid intersect the lines of equal velocity potential (see Chap. 7, Sec. 19) at right angles.

Let the equation of the given family of curves be

$$f(x,y,c) = 0, \qquad (14\text{-}1)$$

where c is an arbitrary parameter. By specifying the values of the parameter c, one obtains a family of curves (see solid curves in Fig. 6). Let it be required to determine the equation of a family of curves orthogonal to the family defined by (14-1).

The differential equation of the family of curves (14-1) can be obtained by eliminating the parameter c from (14-1) and its derivative,

$$\frac{\partial f}{\partial x} + \frac{\partial f}{\partial y}\frac{dy}{dx} = 0. \qquad (14\text{-}2)$$

Let the resulting differential equation be

$$F\left(x,y,\frac{dy}{dx}\right) = 0.$$

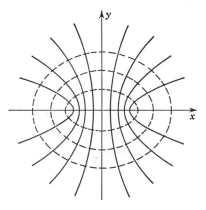

Fig. 6

Now, by definition, the orthogonal family of curves cuts the curves of the given family (14-1) at right angles. Hence, the slope at any point of a curve of the orthogonal family is the negative reciprocal of the slope of the curves of the given family. Thus, the differential equation of the desired family of curves is

$$F\left(x,y,-\frac{dx}{dy}\right) = 0.$$

This is a differential equation of the first order, and its general solution has the form

$$\phi(x,y,c) = 0. \qquad (14\text{-}3)$$

The family of curves defined by (14-3) is the desired family of curves orthogonal to the curves of the given family (14-1). It is called the family of *orthogonal trajectories*.

If the equation of a family of curves is given in polar coordinates as $f(r,\theta,c) = 0$, the tangent of the angle α made by the radius vector and the tangent line at any point (r,θ) of a curve of the family is equal to $r\,d\theta/dr$

(Fig. 7). Hence, by the preceding discussion, the differential equation of the orthogonal trajectories of the given family of curves is obtained by replacing $r \, d\theta/dr$ by $-dr/(r \, d\theta)$ in the differential equation of the given family of curves.

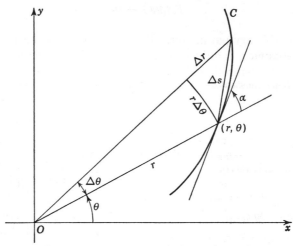

FIG. 7

Example: Let it be required to find the family of curves orthogonal to the family of circles (Fig. 8)

$$x^2 + y^2 - cx = 0. \tag{14-4}$$

The differential equation of the family (14-4) can be obtained by differentiating (14-4) with respect to x and eliminating the parameter c between (14-4) and the equation that results from the differentiation.

The reader will check that the differential equation of the family (14-4) is

$$2xy \frac{dy}{dx} + x^2 - y^2 = 0.$$

Hence, the differential equation of the family of curves orthogonal to (14-4) is

$$2xy \frac{dx}{dy} - x^2 + y^2 = 0.$$

This is a homogeneous differential equation whose solution is found to be

$$x^2 + y^2 - cy = 0.$$

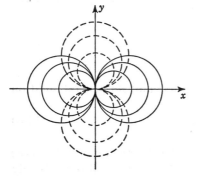

FIG. 8

Thus, the desired family of curves is a family of circles with centers on the y axis (see Fig. 8).

PROBLEMS

Sketch the following families of curves, find the orthogonal trajectories, and add them to your sketch:

1. $x^2 + y^2 = a^2$;

2. $xy = c$;

3. $y = cx^n$;

4. $\dfrac{x^2}{4} + \dfrac{y^2}{9} = c^2$;

5. $r = c$;

6. $r = e^{c\theta}$;

7. $r = c(1 - \cos\theta)$;

8. $r = \dfrac{p}{1 - e\cos\theta}$.

9. If a and b are constant and λ a parameter, show that the family of curves

$$\frac{x^2}{a^2 + \lambda} + \frac{y^2}{b^2 + \lambda} = 1$$

satisfies an equation, free of λ, which is unaltered when y' is replaced by $-1/y'$. What does this indicate concerning the orthogonal trajectories?

10. Find the algebraic equation, the differential equation, and the orthogonal trajectories for the family of circles tangent to the y axis at the origin. Verify your result by plane geometry. (The configuration is a special case of so-called *bipolar coordinates*.)

15. Parabolic Mirror. Pursuit Curves.

Besides the problem of finding orthogonal trajectories, many other questions in geometry lead to first-order differential equations. The following examples show how geometrical conditions of this sort stem from physical conditions. The first is taken from optics, the second from the theory of pursuit.

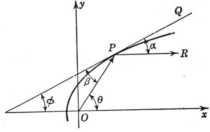

Example 1. Find a mirror such that light from a point source at the origin O is reflected in a beam parallel to the x axis.

Let the ray of light OP strike the mirror at P and be reflected along PR (Fig. 9). If PQ is the tangent at P and α, β, ϕ, and θ are the angles indicated, we have $\alpha = \beta$ by the optical law of reflection and $\alpha = \phi$ by geometry. Hence $\beta = \phi$. The equation

Fig. 9

$$\tan\theta = \tan(\beta + \phi) = \tan 2\phi = \frac{2\tan\phi}{1 - \tan^2\phi}$$

gives

$$\frac{y}{x} = \frac{2y'}{1 - (y')^2},$$

since $y' = \tan\phi$. Solution of this quadratic equation for y' gives

$$y' = \frac{-x \pm \sqrt{x^2 + y^2}}{y},$$

whence

$$\frac{x\,dx + y\,dy}{\pm\sqrt{x^2 + y^2}} = dx.$$

The left-hand member of this is an exact differential, and we get, on integrating,

$$\pm\sqrt{x^2 + y^2} = x + c,$$

which, on squaring, yields $y^2 = 2cx + c^2$. The curves form a family of parabolas with focus at the origin.

Example 2. A boat A moves along the y axis with constant speed a. Find the path of a second boat B which moves in the left-hand half of the xy plane with constant speed b and always points directly at A.

At a time t min after A is at $(0,0)$, we shall have A at $(0,at)$ and B at (x,y), say. Since the line AB is tangent to the path of B, the slope of this line equals the slope of the path, so that

$$\frac{y - at}{x - 0} = \frac{dy}{dx}$$

or
$$xy' - y = -at. \tag{15-1}$$

To eliminate t, we first differentiate (15-1) and obtain

$$(xy' - y)' = xy'' = -a\frac{dt}{dx}. \tag{15-2}$$

Since $ds/dt = b$, where s is an arc on the trajectory, we have

$$\frac{dt}{dx} = \frac{dt}{ds}\frac{ds}{dx} = \frac{1}{b}\sqrt{1 + y'^2}. \tag{15-3}$$

With r defined as a/b, substituting (15-3) in (15-2) yields

$$xy'' = -r\sqrt{1 + y'^2}, \qquad r = \frac{a}{b}, \tag{15-4}$$

which is reduced to a separable equation of first order by letting $p = y'$ as in Sec. 13. The solution is

$$y' = p = \sinh\left(r\log\frac{c}{x}\right) = \frac{1}{2}\left[\left(\frac{c}{x}\right)^r - \left(\frac{x}{c}\right)^r\right] \tag{15-5}$$

and from this, y is found by integration.

PROBLEMS

Find the curves in the xy plane which satisfy the following conditions:

1. (*a*) The tangents pass through the origin; (*b*) the normals pass through the origin.

2. (*a*) The segment of tangent between a point on the curve and the x axis has unit length; (*b*) the projection on the x axis of this segment has unit length.

3. (*a*) The area bounded by the curve, the x axis, and the ordinate equals the ordinate; (*b*) the area equals the length of the curve from $(0,1)$ to (x,y).

4. Find the path of a small boat in a wide river with uniform current if the boat has constant speed relative to the water and always heads toward a fixed point on the bank.

5. Solve Example 2 completely under the assumption that A is at $(0,0)$ and B is at $(x_0,0)$, at time $t = 0$. Distinguish the cases $r = 1$ and $r \neq 1$. If $r < 1$, at what point and when does B overtake A? If $r = 1$, how close can B get to A?

16. Singular Solutions. It was remarked in Sec. 1 that a differential equation may possess singular solutions, that is, solutions which cannot be obtained from the general solution by specifying the arbitrary constants. For investigation of this phenomenon let the family of integral curves defined by

$$\phi(x,y,c) = 0 \tag{16-1}$$

be the general solution of the first-order equation

$$F(x,y,y') = 0. \tag{16-2}$$

Assume that the family of curves (16-1) possesses an *envelope*, that is, a fixed curve C such that every member of the family is tangent to C and such that C is tangent, at each of its points, to some member of the family. At a point (x,y) on the envelope, the values x, y, y' for the envelope are the same as for the integral curve, and hence these values x, y, y' satisfy (16-2). Thus *an envelope of a family of solutions is again a solution.*

In general, the envelope is not a curve belonging to the family of curves defined by (16-1), and hence its equation cannot be obtained from (16-1) by specifying the value of the arbitrary constant c. It is known from calculus that the equation of the envelope is obtained by eliminating the parameter c between the equations

$$\phi(x,y,c) = 0 \quad \text{and} \quad \phi_c(x,y,c) = 0,$$

where $\phi_c \equiv \partial\phi/\partial c$.

Example: The family of integral curves associated with the equation

$$y^2(y')^2 + y^2 = a^2 \tag{16-3}$$

is the family of circles

$$(x - c)^2 + y^2 = a^2. \tag{16-4}$$

The equation of the envelope of the family (16-4) is obtained by eliminating c between (16-4) and $\phi_c = -2(x - c) = 0$. There results

$$y = \pm a, \tag{16-5}$$

which represents the equation of a pair of lines tangent to the family of circles (16-4) (Fig. 10). Obviously, (16-5) is a singular solution of (16-3), for it is a solution, and it cannot be obtained from (16-4) by any choice of the constant c. On referring to Sec. 1, it is easy to check that the conditions of the theorem ensuring uniqueness of the solution are violated in this example.

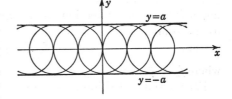

FIG. 10

PROBLEMS

1. (a) Show that $y - c = (x - c)^2$ represents a family of congruent parabolas with vertex on the line $y = x$, and sketch. (b) By differentiating with respect to c obtain the envelope $y = x - \frac{1}{4}$. (c) By direct computation, verify that the parabolas and the envelope have the same slope at corresponding points. (*d*) Obtain a first-order differential equation for the family, and (*e*) verify that $y = x - \frac{1}{4}$ is a singular solution of this equation.

2. A particle on the x axis has velocity $v = \sqrt[3]{s}$, where s is the distance to the origin. Show that the motion is uniquely determined if the particle is at any point other than the origin but that infinitely many different behaviors can occur if the particle ever reaches the origin.

3. (*a*) Obtain the equation $yy' + y'^2 + x = 0$ for the orthogonal trajectories of the family $y = cx + 1/c$. (*b*) Show that $y = 2\sqrt{x}$ is the envelope of the family. (*c*) At points of the curve $y = 2\sqrt{x}$ find the slope of the solutions of $yy' + (y')^2 + x = 0$ in terms of x. Then find the slope of the curve $y = 2\sqrt{x}$ in terms of x. How are these two slopes related? Why? (*d*) Sketch the family, the envelope, and the orthogonal trajectories in a single diagram.

17. The General Behavior of Solutions. The foregoing paragraphs indicate that from suitable geometric conditions on a curve, one can obtain a differential equation for the curve. Now, in this section the point of view is to be reversed. Starting from the differential equation we obtain certain geometric conditions, which enable us to describe the solution qualitatively even when the equation itself cannot be solved.

The function $f(x,y)$ in the general first-order equation

$$\frac{dy}{dx} = f(x,y) \tag{17-1}$$

gives the slope of the solution curve at each point (x,y). Hence the solution curves are increasing functions of x in regions of the xy plane in which $f(x,y)$ is positive and decreasing in regions where $f(x,y)$ is negative. For continuous $f(x,y)$ the boundary between these regions is part or all of the curve

$$f(x,y) = 0. \tag{17-2}$$

Equation (17-2) gives the locus of the critical points, and their character (maximum, minimum, neither) is shown by the sign of $f(x,y)$ at neighboring points. The inflection points and sense of concavity are similarly found from

$$y'' = f_x + f_y y' = f_x + f_y f, \tag{17-3}$$

where $f_x \equiv \partial f/\partial x$ and $f_y \equiv \partial f/\partial y$.

For more detailed information one can plot the curves

$$f(x,y) = c, \tag{17-4}$$

called *isoclines*. At any point (x,y) where (17-4) holds, the solution curve approximates a straight-line segment of slope c, a fact which can be used as a check on the qualitative information obtained from (17-2) and (17-3). From this viewpoint (17-1) is equivalent to a direction field in the xy plane as discussed in Sec. 1. Any curve whose tangent at each point has the direction of the field is a solution, and conversely. The isoclines (17-4) and the direction field discussed in Sec. 1 lie at the basis of some methods for numerical solution of differential equations.

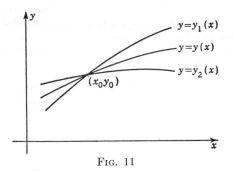

FIG. 11

A technique of obtaining approximate solutions, based on a comparison idea, was developed by S. A. Chaplygin for equations of first and higher orders (see Fig. 11). Let $y_1(x)$, $y(x)$, and $y_2(x)$ be solutions of

$$\frac{dy_1}{dx} = f_1(x,y_1), \qquad \frac{dy}{dx} = f(x,y), \qquad \frac{dy_2}{dx} = f_2(x,y_2). \qquad (17\text{-}5)$$

By subtraction, the difference $y - y_1$ satisfies

$$\frac{d}{dx}(y - y_1) = f(x,y) - f_1(x,y_1), \qquad y = y(x), \qquad y_1 = y_1(x). \quad (17\text{-}6)$$

Now, if $f(x,y) > f_1(x,y_1)$ in a range of x, then $y - y_1$ is an *increasing* function of x in that range. In this case the condition $y - y_1 = 0$ at some point x_0 ensures that $y - y_1 > 0$ for $x > x_0$ and $y - y_1 < 0$ for $x < x_0$. Similar remarks apply to $y_2 - y$. Hence the conditions

$$f_1(x,y) \geq f(x,y) \geq f_2(x,y),$$
$$y_1(x_0) = y(x_0) = y_2(x_0), \qquad\qquad (17\text{-}7)$$

in (17-5) enable us to conclude that

$$y_1(x) \geq y(x) \geq y_2(x), \qquad x > x_0,$$
$$y_1(x) \leq y(x) \leq y_2(x), \qquad x < x_0. \qquad (17\text{-}8)$$

One chooses $f_1(x,y)$ and $f_2(x,y)$ in such a way that the solutions y_1, y_2 are obtainable by elementary methods. Equation (17-8) then gives an explicit estimate for $y(x)$.

A refinement of these ideas leads to an explicit and important inequality for estimating the error in certain approximations. Let $y(x)$ be an exact solution of $y' = f(x,y)$

through the point (x_0,y_0), and let $y_1(x)$ be an approximate solution through this point. Substituting $y_1(x)$ into the equation gives

$$\frac{dy_1}{dx} = f[x,y_1(x)] + e(x), \tag{17-9}$$

where the error term $e(x)$ arises because y_1 is not an exact solution. Now, what can be said about the *solution error* $|y_1 - y|$ in terms of the *substitution error* $e(x)$?

To answer this question we suppose that $f(x,y)$ is continuous in a region containing (x_0,y_0) and satisfies a so-called *Lipschitz condition* there; that is,

$$|f(x,y_1) - f(x,y)| < k|y_1 - y|, \qquad k \text{ const}, \tag{17-10}$$

for some k and all x, y, and y_1 in the region. The condition (17-10) stipulates that $f(x,y)$ shall not change too rapidly when y changes. In case f_y exists, the mean-value theorem gives

$$f(x,y) - f(x,y_1) = f_y(x,\xi)(y - y_1), \qquad y < \xi < y_1, \tag{17-11}$$

and hence (17-10) *holds in any region throughout which*

$$|f_y(x,y)| < k. \tag{17-12}$$

Returning to the original question, in (17-9) let $E(x)$ be the error in y_1,

$$E(x) = y_1(x) - y(x). \tag{17-13}$$

Since $y(x)$ is an exact solution, we have $y' = f(x,y)$, and hence, subtracting from (17-9),

$$\frac{dy_1}{dx} - \frac{dy}{dx} = \frac{dE}{dx} = f(x,y_1) - f(x,y) + e(x). \tag{17-14}$$

If (17-10) holds, and if $|e(x)| < m$, then (17-14) leads to

$$\left|\frac{dE}{dx}\right| \le |f(x,y_1) - f(x,y)| + |e(x)|$$

$$\le k|y_1 - y| + m = k|E(x)| + m. \tag{17-15}$$

If we could drop the absolute values in (17-15) and replace the $\le$ by $=$, we should obtain the linear equation

$$\frac{dE}{dx} = kE(x) + m. \tag{17-16}$$

The solution with $E(x_0) = 0$ is

$$E(x) = \frac{m}{k}(e^{k(x-x_0)} - 1). \tag{17-17}$$

Now, it is plausible and can be proved rigorously that $E(x)$ in (17-17) is the maximum possible $E(x)$ subject to (17-15), with $x \ge x_0$. Hence the solution error $E = y_1 - y$ satisfies

$$|y_1(x) - y(x)| \le \frac{m}{k}(e^{k|x-x_0|} - 1), \qquad \begin{cases} m = \max|e(x)|, \\ k = \text{Lipschitz constant}, \end{cases} \tag{17-18}$$

where $|x - x_0|$ is used rather than $(x - x_0)$ to account for the case $x < x_0$.

Equation (17-18) leads at once to a uniqueness theorem, for if $y_1(x)$ is an exact solution, then $e(x) \equiv 0$ in (17-9), hence $m = 0$ in (17-18), and therefore $y_1(x) = y(x)$.

Example 1. Discuss the integral curves for the equation $y' = xy - 1$ without solving the equation.

The hyperbola $xy = 1$ is the locus where $y' = 0$. If $xy > 1$, then $y' > 0$ and the solution curves are increasing, but if $xy < 1$, they are decreasing. Hence, $xy = 1$ gives a locus of minima in the first quadrant, maxima in the third quadrant. Since $y' = -1$ when $x = 0$ or $y = 0$, all integral curves intersect the axes at an angle of 135°. From

$$y'' = xy' + y = x(xy - 1) + y = y(x^2 + 1) - x,$$

the curve is concave up if $y > x/(x^2 + 1)$ and concave down when this inequality is reversed. The curves have the appearance shown in Fig. 12.

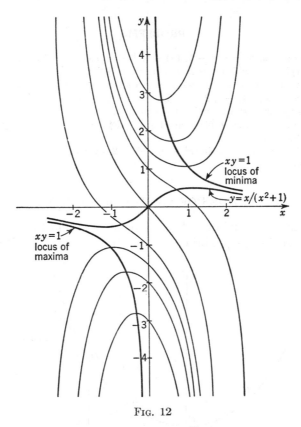

FIG. 12

Example 2. If $y' = \sin xy$, $y(0) = 1$, show that

$$e^{x^2/\pi} \leq y < e^{x^2/2},$$

at least for $0 \leq x \leq 0.8$.

A glance at the graph of $\sin u$ shows that

$$\frac{2}{\pi} u < \sin u < u$$

for $0 < u < \pi/2$, and hence

$$\frac{2}{\pi} xy < \sin xy < xy.$$

The solution of the given equation therefore lies between the solutions to

$$y' = \frac{2}{\pi} xy, \qquad y' = xy.$$

This gives the desired inequality for the range $0 < xy < \pi/2$. Since $y < e^{x^2/2}$, it suffices to have

$$0 < xe^{x^2/2} < \pi/2,$$

and this is true for $0 < x < 0.8$.

PROBLEMS

1. For the equation $y' = y/x - 1$, (a) sketch the locus $y' = 0$ in the xy plane. (b) Indicate the regions in which y is increasing; decreasing. (c) When is y concave up? Down? (d) At what slope do the solutions cross the axes? (e) Sketch the locus where the solutions have slope 1, -1, 2, -2, 5, -5. (f) Sketch the solutions as well as you can. (g) Verify your work by solving the equation.

2. In what regions of the xy plane are the solutions of $y' = \sin(x^2 + y^2)$ increasing? Decreasing? Sketch.

3. Discuss the equation $y' = \sin(x^2 + y)$, $y(0) = 2$, by comparing with suitably chosen simpler equations.

APPLICATIONS OF FIRST-ORDER EQUATIONS

18. The Hanging Chain. Let it be required to find the curve assumed by a flexible chain in equilibrium under gravity (Fig. 13). With s as arc

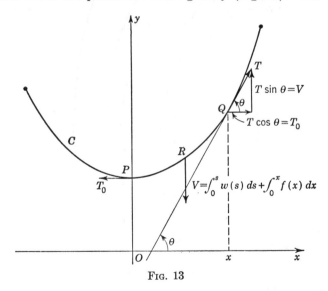

Fig. 13

from the point $x = 0$, let the weight density of the chain be $w(s)$ lb per ft and let the loading function be $f(x)$ lb per ft. The equation of the curve

$y = y(x)$ will be obtained from the fact that the portion of chain between 0 and x is in static equilibrium.

Equating horizontal forces gives

$$T_0 = T \cos \theta, \tag{18-1}$$

where T_0 is the tension at the lowest point and θ the angle which the tangent to the curve makes with the horizontal. Similarly, equating vertical forces gives

$$\int_0^s w(s)\, ds + \int_0^x f(x)\, dx = T \sin \theta \tag{18-2}$$

since the weight of the chain-plus-load must be balanced by the vertical component of T. Both (18-1) and (18-2) require that the function $y(x)$ be differentiable (so that θ is well defined) and they use the fact that the tension is tangential, for a flexible chain.

From (18-1) we have $T = T_0/\cos \theta$, so that

$$T \sin \theta = T_0 \tan \theta = T_0 y', \tag{18-3}$$

the latter equation resulting from the definition of y' as slope. Substitution in (18-2) gives

$$\int_0^s w(s)\, ds + \int_0^x f(x)\, dx = T_0 y'. \tag{18-4}$$

When w and f are continuous, (18-4) may be differentiated with respect to x, a procedure which leads to the differential equation for the curve

$$w(s) \frac{ds}{dx} + f(x) = T_0 y'' \tag{18-5}$$

in view of the fact that

$$\frac{d}{dx} \int_0^s w(s)\, ds = \left[\frac{d}{ds} \int_0^s w(s)\, ds \right] \frac{ds}{dx}.$$

Example: Show that a uniform flexible chain acted upon by gravitational forces alone assumes the shape of a catenary, and find the tension in terms of the height y.

Here $f(x) = 0$, $w(s) = w_0$, a constant. Since $ds/dx = \sqrt{1 + y'^2}$, Eq. (18-5) gives

$$w_0 \sqrt{1 + y'^2} = T_0 y''. \tag{18-6}$$

This is a second-order equation, which can be reduced to one of first order by the method of Sec. 13. With $p = dy/dx$ we have

$$y'' = \frac{dp}{dx} = \frac{dp}{dy} \frac{dy}{dx} = \frac{dp}{dy} p \tag{18-7}$$

and hence (18-6) becomes

$$c\sqrt{1 + p^2} = p \frac{dp}{dy}, \qquad c = \frac{w_0}{T_0}.$$

This equation is separable, the solution being

$$cy = \sqrt{1 + p^2} \tag{18-8}$$

when the axis is so chosen that $cy = 1$ when $p = 0$. Equations (18-1) and (18-8) now give $T = T_0 \sec \theta = T_0\sqrt{1 + \tan^2 \theta} = T_0\sqrt{1 + p^2} = T_0 cy = w_0 y$, which gives the tension. Writing $p = dy/dx$ in (18-8) and separating variables yield

$$y = \frac{T_0}{w_0} \cosh \frac{w_0 x}{T_0},$$

as the reader will verify.

PROBLEMS

1. A flexible weightless cable supports a uniform roadway weighing w_0 lb per ft. The tensions at the highest and lowest points are T and T_0, the roadway is $2a$ ft long, the sag is b, and the length of the cable is $2s$. If the cable is symmetric about the y axis and has its lowest point at the origin, show that the equation of the curve is

$$y = \frac{w_0 x^2}{2T_0},$$

and thus obtain the relations $T_0 = w_0 a^2/2b$, $T = w_0(a/b)\sqrt{a^2/4 + b^2}$,

$$s = \int_0^a \sqrt{1 + (2bx/a^2)^2}\,dx, \qquad s - a \sim 2b^2/3a$$

as $b \to 0$. *Hint:* $\sqrt{1 + u} - 1 \sim u/2$ as $u \to 0$.

2. One end of a flexible uniform telephone wire is b ft above the lowest point, at a distance a ft from it measured horizontally and at a distance s ft from it along the wire. If $u = aw_0/T_0$, in the notation of Sec. 18, show that u satisfies the transcendental equations $(\cosh u - 1)/u = b/a$, $(\sinh u)/u = s/a$ and hence by division the nontranscendental equation $\tanh (u/2) = b/s$. Also find the relations $T_0 = w_0 a/u = w_0 s \operatorname{csch} u$, $T = w_0 a (\cosh u)/u = w_0 s \coth u$ for T_0 and for T, the tension at the highest point. The student familiar with infinite series will obtain simplified expressions by expansion of the hyperbolic functions when u is small, that is, when the tension is large.

19. Newton's Law of Motion. Newton's second law of motion states that the time rate of change of momentum is equal to the impressed force. In symbols,

$$\frac{d}{dt}(mv) = F, \tag{19-1}$$

where F = component of force in the direction of motion

m = mass of the moving particle

$v = ds/dt$ = velocity of the moving particle

It is supposed that the particle moves in a straight line, its distance from some fixed point on that line being s.

The differential equation (19-1) is quite general, since the force may depend on the time t, on the displacement s, and, in the case of damped motion, on the velocity v. Also the mass may be variable in some problems, for example, those concerned with rocket flight or with high-speed electrons.

Since

$$\frac{d(mv)}{dt} = \frac{d(mv)}{ds}\frac{ds}{dt} = \frac{d(mv)}{ds}v, \tag{19-2}$$

Eq. (19-1) may be put in the form

$$v\frac{d(mv)}{ds} = F, \tag{19-3}$$

which gives an alternative statement of Newton's law. Multiplying (19-3) by m leads to $(mv)d(mv)/ds = Fm$, which may be written

$$\frac{d}{ds}\frac{1}{2}(mv)^2 = Fm. \tag{19-4}$$

This gives still another formulation.

In case m and F are known in terms of s only, $m = m(s)$, $F = F(s)$, then (19-4) may be solved completely:

$$\tfrac{1}{2}(mv)^2 - \tfrac{1}{2}(m_0v_0)^2 = \int_{s_0}^{s}F(s)m(s)\,ds. \tag{19-5}$$

If the mass is constant, (19-5) becomes

$$\tfrac{1}{2}mv^2 - \tfrac{1}{2}mv_0^2 = \int_{s_0}^{s}F(s)\,ds, \tag{19-6}$$

since $m(s)$ may be factored out of the integral. Then (19-6) is the *law of conservation of energy*, for the left side of (19-6) is the change in kinetic energy while the right side represents the work done when the particle moves from s_0 to s. Thus the right side is the change in potential energy. The steps leading to (19-6) are evidently reversible if $F(s)$ is continuous, and hence *Newton's law is equivalent to the principle of conservation of energy, when the mass is constant and the force is a continuous function of position only.*

When F and m are known functions of s, it has been seen that one can obtain a so-called *first integral* of the equations. If F is a known function of t, the same is true; we have

$$mv - m_0v_0 = \int_{t_0}^{t}F(t)\,dt, \tag{19-7}$$

by inspection of (19-1). And similarly, when F and m are known functions of v, one can write $d(mv) = m(v)\,dv + vm'(v)\,dv$. Substitution in (19-1) and separation of variables now give

$$t - t_0 = \int_{v_0}^{v}\frac{m(v) + vm'(v)}{F(v)}\,dv. \tag{19-8}$$

The same process in (19-3) yields

$$s - s_0 = \int_{v_0}^{v} \frac{m(v) + vm'(v)}{F(v)} v \, dv. \tag{19-9}$$

For several particles addition gives

$$\frac{d}{dt} \Sigma m_i v_i = \Sigma F_i \tag{19-10}$$

With M as the total mass $M = \Sigma m_i$ and with V as the mean velocity, $MV = \Sigma m_i v_i$, this may be written $(d/dt)(MV) = F$. Here $F = \Sigma F_i$ is the total force; but since the internal forces cancel in pairs, by Newton's law of equal and opposite reaction, F is also the total *external* force acting on the system. The extension to continuous mass distributions is made by analogy, the equations being defined as the limiting form of those for a set of approximating discrete distributions. Thus any point moving with the mean velocity V satisfies Newton's law in the form (19-1). It can be shown that this point actually remains "inside" the body if the v_i are suitably restricted, but some restriction is necessary. Of course, if the masses are constant, then $V = dS/dt$, where S is the position of the center of mass, $MS = \Sigma m_i s_i$. In that case the center of mass itself follows (19-1).

Example 1. The force on a particle of mass m is proportional to its distance from the origin and is directed toward the origin. Find a differential equation for its motion.

The force is ks if s is the distance from the origin at time t. Since the force is directed toward the origin, it has at all times a sign opposite to that of s. Thus k is negative, and one may write $k = -m\omega^2$ for some constant ω. Equation (19-1) will now give $d(mv)/dt = -m\omega^2 s$ or, dividing by m and putting $v = ds/dt$,

$$\frac{d^2 s}{dt^2} + \omega^2 s = 0. \tag{19-11}$$

This is the equation for simple harmonic motion, an important type of periodic motion that arises in many mechanical and electrical systems. The general solution of (19-11) is

$$s = A \cos(\omega t + B) \tag{19-12}$$

as shown in Probs. 2 and 3 and in the Example of Sec. 21. Hence the motion is periodic, with period $2\pi/\omega$ independent of the amplitude A and phase B.

Example 2. A gun containing a bullet moves with nonnegative velocity v on a straight, horizontal, frictionless track and points in a direction exactly opposite to that of the motion. The mass of bullet-plus-gun is m, and that of the bullet is $-\Delta m$, where Δm is negative. If the bullet is fired with velocity c relative to the gun, show that $(v - c) \Delta m$ equals the momentum of the gun after firing minus the momentum of the bullet-plus-gun before firing.

By (19-1) the momentum of the bullet-plus-gun is constant, since there is (we assume) no external force on this system as a whole. Hence

$$mv = (m + \Delta m)(v + \Delta v) + (-\Delta m)v_b, \tag{19-13}$$

where $v + \Delta v$ is the new velocity of the gun and v_b of the bullet:

$$v_b = v - c. \tag{19-14}$$

Computing $(m + \Delta m)(v + \Delta v) - mv$ from (19-13) and (19-14) gives the result.

Two remarks are in order. First, the "equation of continuity for momentum," Eq. (19-13), has been seen to follow from Newton's law; it is not a new assumption. Second, if one replaces (19-14) by

$$v_b = v + \Delta v - c \qquad (19\text{-}15)$$

(which is a justifiable alternative), the result is altered only by the second-order term $\Delta v\, \Delta m$. Hence there is no change at all when the increments are replaced by differentials as in the following example.

Example 3. A rocket fires some of its mass backward at a constant rate r kg per sec and at a constant speed c m per sec relative to the rocket. Show that the thrust developed is $r(c - v)$ when the velocity of the rocket is v. If the rocket starts with velocity v_0 and there is no other force acting, $v = v_0 + c \log 2$ when half the mass is used up.

With m and v the mass and velocity of the rocket at time t, the differential in momentum $d(mv)$ due to external forces is $F\, dt$ by (19-1). That due to loss of a mass $-dm$ at speed $c - v$ in the backward direction is $d(mv) = (c - v)(-dm)$ by Example 2; for differentials, not increments, the result is exact. Thus is obtained a fundamental relation for rocket problems:

$$d(mv) = F\, dt - (c - v)\, dm. \qquad (19\text{-}16)$$

In the present case $dm = -r\, dt$, so that (19-16) gives

$$\frac{d(mv)}{dt} = F + r(c - v) \qquad (19\text{-}17)$$

after division by dt. Hence *the effect of the rocket motor is to add* $r(c - v)$ *to the force* F, and that is what was to be shown.

Substituting

$$m = m_0 - rt \qquad (19\text{-}18)$$

for m in (19-17) gives $(m_0 - rt)(dv/dt) = rc + F$ after slight simplification. Hence, by separating variables,

$$v - v_0 = \left(c + \frac{F}{r}\right) \log \frac{m_0}{m}, \qquad \text{for constant } F. \qquad (19\text{-}19)$$

Putting $F = 0$, $m = m_0/2$ gives the second result.

Example 4. Starting with velocity v_0 an electron is accelerated for a distance s by a constant electric field of magnitude E. What is the terminal velocity?

Let c be the velocity of light, so that the mass m of the electron is given in terms of its rest mass m_0 and its velocity v by

$$m = \frac{m_0}{\sqrt{1 - v^2/c^2}}. \qquad (19\text{-}20)$$

If we write

$$\frac{v}{c} = \sin \theta, \qquad \sqrt{1 - \frac{v^2}{c^2}} = \cos \theta \qquad (19\text{-}21)$$

as we may for $v < c$, then (19-20) gives $m = m_0 \sec \theta$ and $mv = cm_0 \tan \theta$. Substituting in (19-3) with $F = Ee$, where e is the charge on the electron, gives

$$\frac{d}{ds} (cm_0 \tan \theta) = \frac{F}{v} = \frac{eE}{c} \csc \theta.$$

Hence $\sec^2 \theta (d\theta/ds) = (eE/m_0 c^2) \csc \theta$, and by integration

$$\sec \theta = \sec \theta_0 + \frac{seE}{m_0 c^2} \qquad (19\text{-}22)$$

where θ_0 refers to the initial value. For numerical calculation it is more efficient to use the form (19-22) with trigonometric tables than to obtain v explicitly by (19-21).

PROBLEMS

1. A brick is set moving in a straight line over ice with an initial velocity of 20 fps. If the coefficient of friction between the brick and the ice is 0.2, how long will it be before the brick stops?

2. Find a value of a for which $s = c_1 \sin (at + c_2)$ is a solution of (19-11). Does this expression have enough independent constants to be a general solution? Determine c_1 and c_2 in such a way that the displacement s is maximum at $t = 0$ and has then the value A. Determine c_1 and c_2 in such a way that the maximum displacement is A and the maximum velocity occurs at $t = 0$.

3. Apply the transformations used in the derivation of (19-6) to obtain the appropriate form of (19-6) from (19-11). Check by direct comparison with (19-6). Solve the resulting equation by separating variables, and thus show that the solution obtained in Prob. 2 includes *every* solution.

4. Suppose the rocket in Example 3 is subject to a retarding force of magnitude $mg + kv$, where g and k are constant. From (19-17) and (19-18) obtain a linear equation for v as a function of t. Show that $(m_0 - rt)^{-k/r}$ is an integrating factor, solve for v, and obtain the position s at time t from $s = \int v \, dt$.

5. The equation of a cycloid is $x = \theta + \sin \theta$, $y = 1 - \cos \theta$. Show that the arc s from the lowest point satisfies $s^2 = 8y$, and deduce the equation $4v^2 = g(s_0^2 - s^2)$ for a particle sliding down the curve. By differentiation obtain the equation $4d^2s/dt^2 = -gs$, which shows that the motion is simple harmonic. What is the period?

6. In a microwave electron accelerator the field is $E \sin \omega t$. If an electron starts with velocity v_0, find the maximum possible terminal velocity. *Hint:* The maximum occurs when the time for passage is exactly π/ω, for an electron starting at time $t = 0$. Use (19-8).

20. Newton's Law of Gravitation.

Another law of Newton is the law of gravitation, to which he was led in his attempt to explain the motion of the planets. This law states that two bodies attract each other with a force proportional to the product of their masses and inversely proportional to the square of the distance between them, the distance being large compared with the dimensions of the bodies. If the force of attraction is denoted by F, the masses of the two bodies by m_1 and m_2, and the distance between them by r, then

$$F = \frac{\gamma m_1 m_2}{r^2}, \qquad (20\text{-}1)$$

where γ is a proportionality constant, called the *gravitational constant*. In the cgs system the value of γ is 6.664×10^{-8}.

It can be established that a uniform spherical shell attracts a particle at an external point as if the whole mass of the shell were collected at the center (see Chap. 5, Sec. 14). Hence, by integration, the same is true for a solid sphere provided the density is a function of the radius only. If the sphere is the earth, one can therefore write

$$F = mg \left(\frac{r_e}{r}\right)^2 \qquad \text{toward the earth,} \qquad (20\text{-}2)$$

where r_e = earth's mean radius

r = distance from particle to center of earth

g = new constant called acceleration of gravity

Its value in the cgs system is approximately 980 cm per sec per sec and in the fps system 32.2 ft per sec per sec. Since the earth is not a perfect sphere, and since the density varies from place to place, the value of g depends slightly on location. One uses a plus or a minus sign in (20-2) according as the positive direction is taken toward or away from the earth's center.

It can be shown that a uniform spherical shell exerts no force on a particle which is in the hollow space enclosed by the shell (Chap. 5, Sec. 14). Hence the force on a particle of mass m at distance r from the center of a sphere is

$$\frac{\gamma m}{r^2} \int_0^r 4\pi u^2 \rho(u)\, du \qquad (20\text{-}3)$$

when the density of the material forming the sphere is a continuous function $\rho(u)$ of the distance u to the center. The special case $\rho(u) = 0$ for $u > r_0$ gives the result for a particle outside the sphere, as discussed previously.

Equation (20-3) gives

$$F = mg \frac{r}{r_e} \qquad (20\text{-}4)$$

for a particle inside the earth if ρ is taken as constant. In case the particle is close to the surface, we have $r \cong r_e$, so that either (20-2) or (20-4) takes the simple form

$$F = mg. \qquad (20\text{-}5)$$

The error in (20-5) is less than 1 per cent for heights up to about 20 miles.

Example 1. Neglecting air resistance, discuss the velocity of a particle falling toward the earth.

The principle of conservation of energy combines with (20-2) to give

$$\frac{1}{2}mv^2 - \frac{1}{2}mv_0^2 = -\int_{r_0}^r mg \left(\frac{r_e}{r}\right)^2 dr$$

or, after carrying out the integration,

$$\frac{1}{2}v^2 - \frac{1}{2}v_0^2 = gr_e^2 \left(\frac{1}{r} - \frac{1}{r_0}\right). \qquad (20\text{-}6)$$

If the particle starts from rest at a very great distance, the velocity with which it strikes the earth is

$$v_e = \sqrt{2gr_e} \qquad (20\text{-}7)$$

as we see by setting $v_0 = 0$, $r_0 = \infty$, $r = r_e$ in (20-6). This terminal velocity is also the minimum velocity of escape for a particle which leaves the earth never to return. Since r_e is approximately 4,000 miles, we find from (20-7) that v_e is nearly 7 miles per sec.

Example 2. Obtain a differential equation relating the density and pressure in the interior of a spherical star if each is a function of the distance to the center only: $\rho = \rho(r)$, $p = p(r)$. Assume $\rho(r)$ continuous.

Consider a column of material of unit cross section extending along a radius from r to r_s, the radius of the star. The pressure at the base of this column equals the total downward force on the column due to gravitation. The differential force on an element of the column from $r = q$ to $r = q + dq$ is given by

$$dF = \gamma \frac{\rho(q)\,dq}{q^2}\left[\int_0^q 4\pi u^2 \rho(u)\,du\right] \equiv \phi(q)\,dq,$$

in accordance with (20-3), and the total force is given by integration:

$$p(r) = F = \int_r^{r_s} \phi(q)\,dq = -\int_{r_s}^r \phi(q)\,dq. \tag{20-8}$$

Since the right side of Eq. (20-8) has a continuous derivative, so does $p(r)$:

$$\frac{dp}{dr} = -\phi(r) = -\gamma \frac{\rho(r)}{r^2}\int_0^r 4\pi u^2 \rho(u)\,du.$$

Multiplying by $r^2/\rho(r)$ and differentiating again lead to

$$\frac{d}{dr}\left(\frac{r^2}{\rho}\frac{dp}{dr}\right) + 4\pi\gamma r^2\rho = 0.$$

Example 3. Assuming conservation of energy for motion in a curved path, obtain an expression giving the period of a simple pendulum.

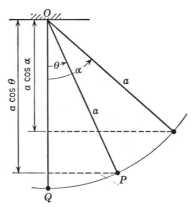

Fig. 14

Let P denote the position of a pendulum bob suspended from O, and let θ be the angle made by OP with the position of equilibrium OQ, as shown in Fig. 14. The work required to change θ to any other value α is the work required to raise the bob through a vertical distance $a\cos\theta - a\cos\alpha$, if a is the pendulum length. With α chosen as the angle for maximum displacement, so that $v = 0$ at $\theta = \alpha$, conservation of energy gives

$$\frac{1}{2}mv^2 = \frac{1}{2}m\left(\frac{ds}{dt}\right)^2 = \frac{1}{2}ma^2\left(\frac{d\theta}{dt}\right)^2 = mga(\cos\theta - \cos\alpha),$$

where m is the mass of the bob. Separating variables gives t in terms of θ and hence, implicitly, θ in terms of t. In particular the time required for θ to increase from 0 to α is

$$\frac{T}{4} = \sqrt{\frac{a}{2g}} \int_0^\alpha \frac{d\theta}{\sqrt{\cos\theta - \cos\alpha}}, \tag{20-9}$$

so that the period T depends on the amplitude α. This dependence leads to the so-called *circular error* in pendulum clocks.

The identities $\cos\theta = 1 - 2\sin^2(\theta/2)$, $\cos\alpha = 1 - 2\sin^2(\alpha/2)$ give

$$T = 2\sqrt{\frac{a}{g}} \int_0^\alpha \frac{d\theta}{\sqrt{k^2 - \sin^2(\theta/2)}}, \qquad k = \sin\frac{\alpha}{2}. \tag{20-10}$$

If a new variable of integration ϕ is defined by

$$\sin\frac{\theta}{2} = k\sin\phi, \tag{20-11}$$

then ϕ ranges from 0 to $\pi/2$ when θ ranges from 0 to α. Also by (20-11)

$$d\theta = \frac{2k\cos\phi\,d\phi}{\cos\theta/2} = \frac{2\sqrt{k^2 - \sin^2(\theta/2)}}{\sqrt{1 - k^2\sin^2\phi}}\,d\phi.$$

Substitution into (20-10) yields a so-called *elliptic integral*

$$T = 4\sqrt{\frac{a}{g}} \int_0^{\pi/2} \frac{d\phi}{\sqrt{1 - k^2\sin^2\phi}}, \qquad k = \sin\frac{\alpha}{2}. \tag{20-12}$$

The advantage of (20-12) over (20-9) is that (20-12) has been extensively studied and is available in tables. A series expansion is easily obtained, by expanding the radical for small α. The result is

$$T = 2\pi\sqrt{\frac{a}{g}} \left[1 + \left(\frac{1}{2}\right)^2 k^2 + \left(\frac{1\cdot 3}{2\cdot 4}\right)^2 k^4 + \left(\frac{1\cdot 3\cdot 5}{2\cdot 4\cdot 6}\right)^2 k^6 + \cdots \right].$$

The function

$$F(k,x) \equiv \int_0^x \frac{d\phi}{\sqrt{1 - k^2\sin^2\phi}}$$

is called the *elliptic integral of the first kind*. See Chap. 2, Sec. 10.

PROBLEMS

1. A stone is thrown vertically upward with velocity 8 fps at time $t = 0$. Using (20-5), write an expression for the position and velocity at time t and also for the velocity as a function of distance s. Find the time at which the velocity is zero, and show that the height is then maximum. Show that the maximum height agrees with that obtained by equating kinetic and potential energy, that is, with $mgh = mv_0^2/2$.

2. A particle slides down an inclined plane, making an angle θ with the horizontal. If the initial velocity is zero and friction may be neglected, the component of force in the direction of motion is $F = mg\sin\theta$. What are the velocity of the particle and the distance traveled during the time t? Find the speed as a function of the vertical distance fallen, and verify that the same result would be given by equating energies as in Prob. 1.

At any given instant, show that the locus of the particles obtained for various θs is a circle (Fig. 15).

3. Suppose the pressure in the atmosphere is a known function of the density, $p = f(\rho)$. Show that the height h at which the density has first dropped to zero from the sea-level value ρ_0 satisfies $gh/(1 + h/r_e) = \int_0^{\rho_0} [f'(\rho)/\rho]\, d\rho$, when (20-2) is used. Hence the dependence of gravitation on distance introduces an effect which depends on h only, not on $f(\rho)$, and the effect is less than $0.02h$ when h is less than 80 miles. Obtain an explicit expression for h in the case of adiabatic expansion, $p = k\rho^a$. For what values of a does this give a finite height? (For air $a = 1.5$; the height thus obtained turns out to be about 18 miles.)

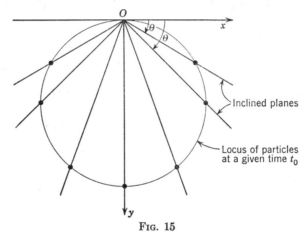

Inclined planes

Locus of particles at a given time t_0

Fig. 15

4. A man and a parachute weighing w lb fall from rest under the force of gravity. If the air resistance is proportional to the square of the speed v, and if the limiting speed is v_0, find the speed as a function of the time t and as a function of the distance fallen s. *Hint:* $(w/g)(dv/dt) = w - kv^2$.

5. A projectile is fired, with an initial velocity v_0, at an angle α with the horizontal. Find the equation of the path under the assumption that the force of gravity is the only force acting on the projectile. For what α is the range maximum? Describe the region which is within the range of the gun. *Hint:* Find the envelope of the trajectories when v_0 is fixed but α varies.

6. A cylindrical tumbler containing liquid is rotated with a constant angular velocity about the axis of the tumbler. Show that the surface of the liquid assumes the shape of a paraboloid of revolution. *Hint:* The resultant force acting on a particle of the liquid is directed normally to the surface. This resultant is compounded of the force of gravity and the centrifugal force, since pressure at the free boundary is zero.

7. Water is flowing out through a circular hole in the side of a cylindrical tank 2 ft in diameter. The velocity of the water in the jet has the value which it would attain by a free fall through a distance equal to the head. How long will it take the water to fall from a height of 25 ft to a height of 9 ft above the orifice if the stream of water is 1 in. in diameter?

8. Water is flowing out from a 2-in. horizontal pipe running full. Find the discharge in cubic feet per second if the jet of water strikes the ground 4 ft beyond the end of the pipe when the pipe is 2 ft above the ground.

LINEAR DIFFERENTIAL EQUATIONS

21. Linear Homogeneous Second-order Equations. An equation of the form

$$y'' + p_1(x)y' + p_2(x)y = 0, \tag{21-1}$$

in which $p_1(x)$ and $p_2(x)$ are specified continuous functions of x in a given interval (a,b), is called a *linear homogeneous equation of second order.* From the existence and uniqueness theorem of Sec. 1 it follows that this equation has a unique solution for every $x = x_0$ in (a,b), satisfying the initial conditions $y(x_0) = y_0$, $y'(x_0) = y_0'$. Thus, the integral curve for Eq. (21-1) is determined uniquely when the ordinate and the slope of the curve are specified at a given point of the interval.

Equation (21-1) is called linear because its solutions satisfy the following *linearity properties:*

1. If $y = y_1(x)$ is a solution of (21-1), then $y = cy_1(x)$, where c is a constant, is also a solution.

2. If $y = y_1(x)$ and $y = y_2(x)$ are two solutions of (21-1), then their sum $y = y_1(x) + y_2(x)$ is also a solution.

It follows from these properties that the sum of any number of solutions of (21-1) each multiplied by a constant is also a solution.

The proof that properties 1 and 2 hold is simple.

Thus, suppose that $y = y_1(x)$ is a solution of (21-1); then the substitution in (21-1) gives an identity

$$y_1'' + p_1 y_1' + p_2 y_1 \equiv 0. \tag{21-2}$$

We must show that

$$(cy_1)'' + p_1(cy)' + p_2(cy_1) \tag{21-3}$$

vanishes identically for every constant c. But since c can be taken outside the differentiation sign, we can write (21-3) as

$$c(y_1'' + p_1 y_1' + p_2 y_1),$$

and this vanishes because (21-2) does.

This establishes property 1.

To establish property 2, suppose that $y = y_1(x)$ and $y = y_2(x)$ are two solutions of (21-1). Then

$$y_1'' + p_1 y_1' + p_2 y_1 \equiv 0,$$
$$y_2'' + p_1 y_2' + p_2 y_2 \equiv 0. \tag{21-4}$$

We must show that

$$(y_1 + y_2)'' + p_1(y_1 + y_2)' + p_2(y_1 + y_2) \equiv 0. \tag{21-5}$$

Inasmuch as the derivative of the sum of two functions is the sum of the derivatives, we can rewrite the left-hand member in (21-5) as

$$(y_1'' + p_1 y_1' + p_2 y_1) + (y_2'' + p_1 y_2' + p_2 y_2),$$

and this vanishes by (21-4).

Let us suppose now that by some means we have obtained two solutions $y_1(x)$ and $y_2(x)$ of (21-1). Then by the foregoing

$$y(x) = c_1 y_1(x) + c_2 y_2(x) \tag{21-6}$$

is a solution for every choice of the constants c_i. We say that (21-6) is a *general solution* of (21-1) provided that for a suitable choice of the constants c_i the solution satisfies *arbitrarily* specified initial conditions,

$$y(x_0) = y_0, \qquad y'(x_0) = y_0'. \tag{21-7}$$

To determine the restrictions on $y_1(x)$ and $y_2(x)$ ensuring that the solution (21-6) is, indeed, general, we insert (21-6) in (21-7) and obtain two linear algebraic equations,

$$
\begin{aligned}
c_1 y_1(x_0) + c_2 y_2(x_0) &= y_0, \\
c_1 y_1'(x_0) + c_2 y_2'(x_0) &= y_0',
\end{aligned}
\tag{21-8}
$$

for c_1 and c_2. The system (21-8) can be solved for c_1 and c_2 (for arbitrarily specified x_0, y_0, and y_0') if, and only if, the determinant

$$W(y_1, y_2) \equiv \begin{vmatrix} y_1(x) & y_2(x) \\ y_1'(x) & y_2'(x) \end{vmatrix} \neq 0 \tag{21-9}$$

for every $x = x_0$ in the interval. If $W(y_1, y_2) = 0$ for some value of x, the constants c_i cannot be determined for every choice of y_0 and y_0' and the solution (21-6) is not general. The determinant $W(y_1, y_2)$ is called the *Wronskian* after the Polish mathematician G. Wronski, who deduced the criterion (21-9) for the generality of solution (21-6).

The condition (21-9) is equivalent to the statement that the solutions $y_1(x)$ and $y_2(x)$ are linearly independent. We say that $y_1(x)$ and $y_2(x)$ are *linearly independent* if the identity

$$c_1 y_1(x) + c_2 y_2(x) \equiv 0 \tag{21-10}$$

can be satisfied only by choosing $c_1 = c_2 = 0$. When nonzero constants c_1 and c_2 can be found such that $c_1 y_1(x) + c_2 y_2(x) \equiv 0$, we say that $y_1(x)$ and $y_2(x)$ are *linearly dependent*. In other words, linear independence of $y_1(x)$ and $y_2(x)$ means that the *ratio* $y_2(x)/y_1(x)$ *is not a constant*. But if this ratio is not a constant, its derivative

$$\frac{y_2' y_1 - y_1' y_2}{y_1^2} \tag{21-11}$$

is not identically zero. We note that the numerator in (21-11) is precisely $W(y_1, y_2) = y_2' y_1 - y_1' y_2$. We have shown that if the solutions y_1 and y_2 are linearly independent, then $W(y_1, y_2) \neq 0$ for some value of x. Conversely, if $W(y_1, y_2) = 0$ for some $x = x_0$, so that

$$\begin{vmatrix} y_1(x_0) & y_2(x_0) \\ y_1'(x_0) & y_2'(x_0) \end{vmatrix} = 0,$$

we can show that the solutions $y_1(x)$ and $y_2(x)$ are *linearly dependent*, for we can choose *nonzero* constants c_1 and c_2 in (21-6) so that at the given point $x = x_0$ our solution satisfies the initial conditions

$$y(x_0) = 0, \qquad y'(x_0) = 0. \tag{21-12}$$

But if $y(x)$ in (21-6) satisfies these conditions, then $y(x) \equiv 0$ because there exists *only one* solution of Eq. (21-1) satisfying initial conditions (21-12) and a solution $y(x) = 0$ obviously satisfies these conditions. We have thus shown that the nonzero constants c_1 and c_2 can be found such that $c_1 y_1(x) + c_2 y_2(x) = 0$ for all values of x, and hence the solutions $y_1(x)$ and $y_2(x)$ are linearly dependent.[1]

It follows from this that the problem of finding the general solution of (21-1) reduces to the search for some pair of linearly independent solutions $y_1(x)$, $y_2(x)$. It should be remarked that no formula is available for the determination of solutions of the general second-order linear equation. In the special instance when the coefficients p_1 and p_2 in (21-1) are constants, the general solution, as we shall see in the following section, is deduced easily.

Example: Verify that

$$y = c_1 \sin x + c_2 \cos x \tag{21-13}$$

is the general solution of

$$y'' + y = 0 \tag{21-14}$$

and determine the particular solution such that

$$y(0) = 1, \qquad y'(0) = \tfrac{1}{2}. \tag{21-15}$$

The fact that $y_1 = \sin x$ and $y_2 = \cos x$ are, indeed, solutions of (21-14) is easily verified by substituting $y = \sin x$ and $y = \cos x$ in (21-14). Hence their linear combination (21-13) is a general solution provided that the determinant (21-9) does not vanish. In our case,

$$W(y_1, y_2) = \begin{vmatrix} \sin x & \cos x \\ \cos x & -\sin x \end{vmatrix} = -1,$$

and thus (21-13) is the general solution. To determine the constants c_i such that the solution satisfies conditions (21-15), we form the set of Eqs. (21-8),

$$c_1 \sin 0 + c_2 \cos 0 = 1,$$

$$c_1 \cos 0 - c_2 \sin 0 = \tfrac{1}{2},$$

[1] See in this connection Prob. 6, Sec. 21.

from which it follows that $c_1 = \frac{1}{2}$, $c_2 = 1$. Thus the desired solution is $y = \frac{1}{2} \sin x + \cos x$.

PROBLEMS

1. Verify that $y = e^x$ and $y = e^{-x}$ are linearly independent solutions of $y'' - y = 0$. Also show that $y_1 = \sinh x$ and $y_2 = \cosh x$ are a pair of linearly independent solutions of this equation.

2. Show that $y = c_1 e^x + c_2 e^{2x}$ is the general solution of $y'' - 3y' + 2y = 0$, and find the solution satisfying the conditions $y(0) = 0$, $y'(0) = 1$. What is the solution satisfying $y(0) = y'(0) = 0$?

3. Show that $y_1 = 1/x$ and $y_2 = x^5$ are linearly independent solutions of $x^2 y'' - 3xy' - 5y = 0$ if $x \neq 0$.

4. Verify that $y = c_1 x^2 + c_2 x$ is the general solution of $x^2 y'' - 2xy' + 2y = 0$ if $x \neq 0$, and find the solution such that $y(1) = 2$ and $y'(1) = 0$.

5. Show that $y = c_1 e^{2x} + c_2 x e^{2x}$ is the general solution of $y'' - 4y' + 4y = 0$, and find the solution for which $y(0) = 1$, $y'(0) = 4$. Also find the solution such that $y(0) = y'(0) = 0$.

6. Compute the derivative of $W(y_1, y_2) = y_1 y_2' - y_2 y_1'$, where $y_1(x)$ and $y_2(x)$ are two solutions of (21-1). Show that $y_1 y_2'' - y_2 y_1'' + p_1(x)(y_1 y_2' - y_2 y_1') = 0$ and $dW/dx + p_1(x) W = 0$. Thus $W(y_1, y_2) = W_0 e^{-\int_{x_0}^{x} p_1(x)dx}$, where W_0 is the value of $W(y_1, y_2)$ at $x = x_0$. Conclude from this that if $W(y_1, y_2)$ does not vanish at $x = x_0$, it does not vanish for any value of x. This result is known as *Abel's theorem*.

22. Homogeneous Second-order Linear Equations with Constant Coefficients.

Consider the equation

$$y'' + p_1 y' + p_2 y = 0 \tag{22-1}$$

with constant coefficients p_1, p_2. If we substitute

$$y = e^{mx} \tag{22-2}$$

in (22-1) and note that $y' = me^{mx}$, $y'' = m^2 e^{mx}$, we obtain the equation

$$(m^2 + p_1 m + p_2)e^{mx} = 0,$$

or

$$m^2 + p_1 m + p_2 = 0, \tag{22-3}$$

since $e^{mx} \neq 0$. Thus, if m in (22-2) is chosen as a root of the *characteristic equation* (22-3), then (22-2) will be a solution of the given equation. The roots of the quadratic equation (22-3) are

$$m = \frac{-p_1 \pm \sqrt{p_1^2 - 4p_2}}{2}. \tag{22-4}$$

If $p_1^2 - 4p_2 > 0$, there will be two distinct real roots, $m = m_1$ and $m = m_2$. In this event,

$$y = e^{m_1 x}, \qquad y = e^{m_2 x}$$

are a pair of linearly independent solutions of Eq. (22-1), since

$$\frac{y_1}{y_2} = e^{(m_1 - m_2)x}$$

is not a constant when $m_1 \neq m_2$. Hence if $m_1 \neq m_2$, the general solution of (22-1) is

$$y = c_1 e^{m_1 x} + c_2 e^{m_2 x}. \qquad (22\text{-}5)$$

If $p_1^2 - 4p_2 < 0$, the roots (22-4) are *conjugate complex numbers*,

$$m_1 = a + bi, \qquad m_2 = a - bi,$$

and the complex functions

$$y_1 = e^{(a+bi)x}, \qquad y_2 = e^{(a-bi)x} \qquad (22\text{-}6)$$

are linearly independent solutions of (22-1). We can write (22-6) in a trigonometric form with the aid of Euler's formula [cf. Eq. (17-3), Chap. 2]

$$e^{(a \pm bi)x} = e^{ax}(\cos bx \pm i \sin bx),$$

so that
$$y_1 = e^{ax}(\cos bx + i \sin bx),$$
$$y_2 = e^{ax}(\cos bx - i \sin bx), \qquad (22\text{-}7)$$

are the complex solutions of (22-1).

We show next that when Eq. (22-1) with real coefficients p_1 and p_2 has a complex solution of the form $y = u + iv$, then the real functions u and v are solutions of this equation. Indeed, the substitution of $y = u + iv$ in (22-1) yields on rearrangement

$$(u'' + p_1 u' + p_2 u) + i(v'' + p_1 v' + p_2 v) = 0,$$

and this can vanish if, and only if,

$$u'' + p_1 u' + p_2 u = 0,$$
$$v'' + p_1 v' + p_2 v = 0.$$

Thus $y = u$ and $y = v$ satisfy (22-1).

Referring to (22-7) we see that corresponding to a pair of complex roots $m = a \pm bi$ of the characteristic equation, we have a pair of linearly independent real solutions

$$y_1 = e^{ax} \cos bx, \qquad y_2 = e^{ax} \sin bx. \qquad (22\text{-}8)$$

It remains to consider the case when $p_1^2 - 4p_2 = 0$. In this event the characteristic equation (22-3) has a double root

$$m_1 = m_2 = \frac{-p_1}{2},$$

and the foregoing method yields just one distinct solution $y_1 = e^{mx}$, with $m = -p_1/2$. We can verify by direct substitution that another solution is $y_2 = xe^{mx}$, which is obviously linearly independent, since $y_2/y_1 =$

$x \neq$ const. Thus, when the characteristic equation has a double root $m = -p_1/2$, the general solution of (22-1) is

$$y = (c_1 + c_2x)e^{mx}. \tag{22-9}$$

In the following section we deduce this solution with the aid of the useful notion of differential operators, which will be of help in resolving the corresponding situation involving multiple roots of linear equations with constant coefficients of order higher than 2.

We illustrate the foregoing discussion by examples.

Example 1. Find two linearly independent solutions of $y'' + 3y' + 2y = 0$, and thus obtain the general solution. Referring to (22-3), we see that the characteristic equation in this case is

$$m^2 + 3m + 2 = 0, \tag{22-10}$$

which, on factoring, yields

$$(m + 1)(m + 2) = 0.$$

Thus, the roots of (22-10) are $m_1 = -1$, $m_2 = -2$, and hence the general solution is $y = c_1e^{-x} + c_2e^{-2x}$.

Example 2. Solve $y'' + 2y' + 5y = 0$.   The characteristic equation is

$$m^2 + 2m + 5 = 0,$$

and hence

$$m = \frac{-2 \pm \sqrt{4 - 20}}{2} = -1 \pm 2i.$$

Accordingly, the complex solutions are

$$y_1 = e^{(-1+2i)x}, \qquad y_2 = e^{(-1-2i)x}, \tag{22-11}$$

and by (22-8) the linearly independent real solutions are

$$y_1 = e^{-x} \cos 2x, \qquad y_2 = e^{-x} \sin 2x. \tag{22-12}$$

It should be remarked that for many purposes the complex form of solutions (22-11) is just as useful as the real form (22-12).

Example 3. Solve $y'' + 2y' + y = 0$.   The characteristic equation

$$m^2 + 2m + 1 = 0$$

has a double root $m = -1$. Accordingly, a pair of linearly independent solutions of the given equation is $y_1 = e^{-x}$, $y_2 = xe^{-x}$. By (22-9) the general solution is

$$y = (c_1 + c_2x)e^{-x}.$$

PROBLEMS

Find the general solutions of:

1. $y'' + 3y' - 54y = 0$;
2. $y'' - 5y' + 6y = 0$;
3. $y'' - 2y' + y = 0$;
4. $y'' - 4y = 0$;
5. $y'' + 4y = 0$;
6. $y'' - 4y' + 4y = 0$;
7. $y'' - 4y' + 5y = 0$.

23. Differential Operators. We introduce a new notation for the derivative symbol and write $D \equiv d/dx$ and, more generally, $D^n \equiv d^n/dx^n$. Thus, $D \sin x$ means $(d \sin x)/dx = \cos x$, and $D^2 \sin x = (d^2 \sin x)/dx^2 = d/dx \, (d \sin x)/dx = -\sin x$. Since

$$\frac{dcu(x)}{dx} = c\frac{du}{dx} \quad \text{and} \quad \frac{d(u+v)}{dx} = \frac{du}{dx} + \frac{dv}{dx},$$

we see that

$$Dcu(x) = cDu \quad \text{and} \quad D(u+v) = Du + Dv. \qquad (23\text{-}1)$$

Moreover, since

$$\frac{d^n}{dx^n}\frac{dy}{dx} = \frac{d^{n+1}y}{dx^{n+1}},$$

we can write

$$D^n(Dy) = D^{n+1}y. \qquad (23\text{-}2)$$

We agree also that

$$(D+m)y \equiv Dy + my.$$

If the symbol $(D + m_1)(D + m_2)y$, where m_1 and m_2 are constants, is interpreted to mean that $(D + m_1)$ operates on $(D + m_2)y \equiv (dy/dx) + m_2 y$, we find that

$$(D + m_1)(D + m_2)y = [D^2 + (m_1 + m_2)D + m_1 m_2]y. \qquad (23\text{-}3)$$

From the structure of the right-hand member of (23-3) it follows that

$$(D + m_1)(D + m_2)y = (D + m_2)(D + m_1)y. \qquad (23\text{-}4)$$

Making use of these properties, we can write Eq. (22-1), namely,

$$\frac{d^2y}{dx^2} + p_1\frac{dy}{dx} + p_2 y = 0, \qquad (23\text{-}5)$$

as

$$(D^2 + p_1 D + p_2)y = 0, \qquad (23\text{-}6)$$

in which the *differential operator*

$$D^2 + p_1 D + p_2$$

behaves as though it were an algebraic polynomial.

We observe that this polynomial is identical with the polynomial in the characteristic equation (22-3). On noting (23-3), we see that (23-6) can be written in factored form as

$$(D - m_1)(D - m_2)y = 0, \qquad (23\text{-}7)$$

where m_1 and m_2 are the roots of (22-3). Now, if $m_1 \neq m_2$, the general solution of (23-7), as shown in the preceding section, is

$$y = c_1 e^{m_1 x} + c_2 e^{m_2 x}.$$

To obtain the general solution of (23-7) when $m_1 = m_2 \equiv m$, we proceed as follows: We set in (23-7)

$$(D - m)y = v \tag{23-8}$$

and obtain a first-order equation for v,

$$(D - m)v = 0, \tag{23-9}$$

or

$$\frac{dv}{dx} - mv = 0.$$

Its general solution is $v = c_1 e^{mx}$. The substitution of this in the right-hand member of (23-8) yields the first-order linear equation for y

$$\frac{dy}{dx} - my = c_1 e^{mx},$$

whose general solution is easily found from (10-8). We thus get the solution

$$y = c_1 e^{mx} + c_2 x e^{mx}, \tag{23-10}$$

which agrees with (22-9).

Example 1. Find the general solution of $y'' + 5y' + 6y = 0$. This equation can be written as
$$(D^2 + 5D + 6)y = 0.$$

On factoring the operator we get
$$(D + 2)(D + 3)y = 0,$$

and thus the general solution is
$$y = c_1 e^{-2x} + c_2 e^{-3x}.$$

Example 2. Solve $y'' - 4y' + 4y = 0$. We write this equation as
$$(D^2 - 4D + 4)y = 0$$

or
$$(D - 2)(D - 2)y = 0.$$

Since the roots of the characteristic equation are equal, the general solution is
$$y = c_1 e^{2x} + c_2 x e^{2x}.$$

PROBLEMS

Solve:

1. $(D^2 - \frac{1}{2}D - \frac{1}{2})y = 0$;
2. $(D^2 - 1)y = 0$;
3. $(D^2 + D - 2)y = 0$;
4. $(D - 3)^2 y = 0$;
5. $(D^2 + 2D + 1)y = 0$.

24. Nonhomogeneous Second-order Linear Equations. The equation

$$y'' + p_1(x)y' + p_2(x)y = f(x), \tag{24-1}$$

in which the right-hand member $f(x)$ is a known continuous function, is called *nonhomogeneous*. The existence and uniqueness theorem of Sec. 1 guarantees that this equation has one, and only one, solution satisfying the conditions

$$y(x_0) = y_0, \qquad y'(x_0) = y_0',$$

whenever the coefficients $p_i(x)$ are continuous functions. If $y = u(x)$ is any solution of (24-1) and $y_1(x)$ and $y_2(x)$ are linearly independent solutions of the associated homogeneous equation

$$y'' + p_1(x)y' + p_2(x)y = 0, \tag{24-2}$$

the general solution of (24-1) is

$$y = c_1 y_1(x) + c_2 y_2(x) + u(x). \tag{24-3}$$

The fact that (24-3) is, indeed, a solution of (24-1) follows upon substituting (24-3) in (24-1) and noting that

$$u''(x) + p_1(x)u'(x) + p_2(x)u(x) = f(x)$$

and that $y = c_1 y_1(x) + c_2 y_2(x)$ satisfies the homogeneous equation (24-2). The proof that (24-3) is the general solution is virtually identical with the proof in Sec. 21 for the homogeneous equation.[1]

We shall see in Sec. 28 that a particular integral $u(x)$ of (24-1) can always be determined whenever the *general solution*[2] *of the associated homogeneous equation* (24-2) *is known*. In special instances, however, particular integrals of nonhomogeneous equations can be deduced without the knowledge of the general solution of the homogeneous equation. This simpler technique, based on judicious guesses of the probable forms of particular integrals, is known as the method of *undetermined coefficients*. It is applicable to linear equations with constant coefficients only when the right-hand member $f(x)$ has certain special simple forms.

We illustrate the essence of this method by several examples and develop it in greater detail in the following section.

Example 1. The right-hand member of

$$y'' + 3y' + 2y = 2e^x \tag{24-4}$$

suggests that it probably has a solution of the form $y = ae^x$, for the differentiation of

---

[1] The only difference is that the terms $y_0 - u(x_0)$ and $y_0' - u_0'(x_0)$ instead of y_0 and y_0' now appear in the right-hand members of Eqs. (21-8).

[2] This general solution is often called the *complementary function*.

exponentials yields exponentials. Accordingly, we take $y = ae^x$ as our trial solution, substitute it in (24-4), and obtain

$$ae^x + 3ae^x + 2ae^x = 2e^x.$$

On dividing by e^x we get

$$6a = 2 \quad \text{or} \quad a = \tfrac{1}{3}.$$

Thus, $y = \tfrac{1}{3}e^x$ is a solution of (24-4). The characteristic equation of the associated homogeneous equation

$$y'' + 3y' + 2y = 0 \tag{24-5}$$

is

$$m^2 + 3m + 2 = 0$$

or

$$(m + 1)(m + 2) = 0.$$

Hence a pair of linearly independent solutions of (24-5) is $y = e^{-x}$, $y = e^{-2x}$, and the general solution of the given equation (24-4) is $y = c_1 e^{-x} + c_2 e^{-2x} + \tfrac{1}{3}e^x$.

If the solution of (24-4) satisfying the given initial conditions is required, the constants c_i must be determined from these conditions. For example, if we seek the solution such that $y(0) = -\tfrac{2}{3}$ and $y'(0) = 0$, we obtain, on setting $x = 0$ in the general solution,

$$-\tfrac{2}{3} = c_1 + c_2 + \tfrac{1}{3},$$

or

$$c_1 + c_2 = -1.$$

Also,

$$y' = -c_1 e^{-x} - 2c_2 e^{-2x} + \tfrac{1}{3}e^x,$$

and since $y'(0) = 0$, we have

$$0 = -c_1 - 2c_2 + \tfrac{1}{3},$$

or

$$c_1 + 2c_2 = \tfrac{1}{3}.$$

We easily verify that $c_1 = -\tfrac{7}{3}$, $c_2 = +\tfrac{4}{3}$, and the desired solution therefore is

$$y = -\tfrac{7}{3}e^{-x} + \tfrac{4}{3}e^{-2x} + \tfrac{1}{3}e^x.$$

Example 2. If we attempt to obtain a solution of

$$y'' + 3y' + 2y = 2e^{-x} \tag{24-6}$$

by taking a trial solution $y = ae^{-x}$, we get

$$ae^{-x} - 3ae^{-x} + 2ae^{-x} = 2e^{-x}.$$

This gives a nonsensical result, $0 = 2e^{-x}$. The reason that the trial solution of the form $y = ae^{-x}$ is not suitable in this case is the following: The homogeneous equation associated with (24-6), as we saw in the preceding example, has a solution $y = ae^{-x}$, and the substitution of it in (24-6) naturally makes its left-hand member vanish. In this case we take the trial solution in the form $y = axe^{-x}$. Then, $y' = ae^{-x} - axe^{-x}$, $y'' = -ae^{-x} - ae^{-x} + axe^{-x}$, and the substitution in (24-6) now yields

$$-2ae^{-x} + axe^{-x} + 3ae^{-x} - 3axe^{-x} + 2axe^{-x} = 2e^{-x},$$

or

$$ae^{-x} = 2e^{-x}.$$

Thus $a = 2$, and a solution of (24-6) is $y = 2xe^{-x}$. The general solution of (24-6), therefore, is

$$y = c_1 e^{-x} + c_2 e^{-2x} + 2xe^{-x}.$$

Example 3. Find the general solution of

$$y'' + 2y' + y = e^{-x}.$$ (24-7)

We recall (Example 3, Sec. 22) that a pair of linearly independent solutions of the associated homogeneous equation is $y = e^{-x}$, $y = xe^{-x}$. Accordingly, neither $y = ae^{-x}$ nor $y = axe^{-x}$ is suitable as a trial solution of (24-7). In this case we take the trial solution

$$y = ax^2e^{-x}.$$ (24-8)

We compute

$$y' = 2axe^{-x} - ax^2e^{-x},$$

$$y'' = 2ae^{-x} - 2axe^{-x} - 2axe^{-x} + ax^2e^{-x}$$

and on making substitutions in (24-7) find

$$2ae^{-x} - 4axe^{-x} + ax^2e^{-x} + 4axe^{-x} - 2ax^2e^{-x} + ax^2e^{-x} = e^{-x}$$

or

$$2ae^{-x} = e^{-x}.$$

Thus, $a = \frac{1}{2}$, and from (24-8) $y = \frac{1}{2}x^2e^{-x}$ is a solution of (24-7). Its general solution is

$$y = c_1e^{-x} + c_2xe^{-x} + \frac{1}{2}x^2e^{-x}.$$

These examples suggest a procedure to be followed in obtaining particular integrals of equations with constant coefficients of the type

$$y'' + p_1y' + p_2y = Ae^{kx}.$$ (24-9)

The characteristic equation associated with (24-9) is

$$m^2 + p_1m + p_2 = 0.$$ (24-10)

If this equation has two distinct roots $m = m_1$ and $m = m_2$, then the linearly independent solutions of the homogeneous equation

$$y'' + p_1y' + p_2y = 0$$ (24-11)

are $y = e^{m_1x}$ and $y = e^{m_2x}$. When Eq. (24-10) has a double root $m_2 = m_1$, the linearly independent solutions of (24-11) are $y = e^{m_1x}$ and $y = xe^{m_1x}$. Now, if k in the right-hand member of (24-9) is not equal to either m_1 or m_2, Eq. (24-9) has a solution of the form $y = ae^{kx}$. If k is a simple root of (24-10), then (24-9) has a solution of the form $y = axe^{kx}$. When k is a double root of (24-10), the particular integral can be taken in the form $y = ax^2e^{kx}$.

Similar considerations apply to equations of the form

$$y'' + p_1y' + p_2y = A_0 + A_1x + \cdots + A_nx^n.$$ (24-12)

If [1] $p_2 \neq 0$, we can take the trial solution

$$y = a_0 + a_1x + \cdots + a_nx^n.$$ (24-13)

[1] This means that $m = 0$ is not a root of the characteristic equation (24-10) and hence (24-11) has no solution $y = $ const.

The substitution of (24-13) in (24-12) then yields on comparison of like powers of x on both sides of the resulting equation the values of the unknown constants a_i. If $p_2 = 0$, the characteristic equation (24-10) has $m = 0$ as one of its roots. In this event the trial solution can be taken in the form

$$y = x(a_0 + a_1 x + \cdots + a_n x^n). \tag{24-14}$$

We illustrate the use of these rules by two examples.

Example 4.   Find a solution of

$$y'' + 3y' + 2y = 1 + 2x. \tag{24-15}$$

Since $p_2 = 2 \neq 0$, we take the trial solution

$$y = a_0 + a_1 x, \tag{24-16}$$

substitute it in (24-15), and find

$$3a_1 + 2(a_0 + a_1 x) = 1 + 2x.$$

On comparing like powers of x, we get

$$3a_1 + 2a_0 = 1, \qquad 2a_1 = 2,$$

whence

$$a_1 = 1, \qquad a_0 = -1.$$

The substitution of these values in (24-16) gives the desired solution $y = -1 + x$.

Example 5.   Find the solution of

$$y'' + 3y' = 1 - 9x^2 \tag{24-17}$$

satisfying the conditions $y(0) = 0$, $y'(0) = 1$.

Since $p_2 = 0$ in (24-17), we seek a solution in the form

$$y = x(a_0 + a_1 x + a_2 x^2). \tag{24-18}$$

We compute

$$y' = a_0 + 2a_1 x + 3a_2 x^2,$$

$$y'' = 2a_1 + 6a_2 x$$

and insert in (24-17). The result is

$$2a_1 + 6a_2 x + 3(a_0 + 2a_1 x + 3a_2 x^2) = 1 - 9x^2$$

or

$$2a_1 + 3a_0 + (6a_2 + 6a_1)x + 9a_2 x^2 = 1 - 9x^2.$$

Hence

$$2a_1 + 3a_0 = 1,$$

$$6a_2 + 6a_1 = 0,$$

$$9a_2 = -9.$$

Solving these equations, we get

$$a_2 = -1, \qquad a_1 = 1, \qquad a_0 = -\tfrac{1}{3},$$

and the substitution of these values in (24-18) gives

$$y = x(-\tfrac{1}{3} + x - x^2).$$

The characteristic equation for (24-17) is

$$m^2 + 3m = 0.$$

Since its roots are $m = 0$, $m = -3$, the general solution of (24-17) is

$$y = c_1 + c_2 e^{-3x} + x(-\tfrac{1}{3} + x - x^2). \tag{24-19}$$

To determine the constants so that the solution (24-19) satisfies the given conditions, we compute

$$y'(x) = -3c_2 e^{-3x} - (\tfrac{1}{3} - 2x + 3x^2).$$

The conditions $y(0) = 0$ and $y'(0) = 1$ then demand that

$$c_1 + c_2 = 0,$$

$$-3c_2 - \tfrac{1}{3} = 1.$$

Thus, $c_2 = -\tfrac{4}{9}$, $c_1 = \tfrac{4}{9}$, and hence the desired solution is

$$y = \tfrac{4}{9} - \tfrac{4}{9} e^{-3x} + x(-\tfrac{1}{3} + x - x^3).$$

We state in conclusion that the trial solution for the more general equation

$$y'' + p_1 y' + p_2 y = e^{kx}(A_0 + A_1 x + \cdots + A_n x^n) \tag{24-20}$$

can be sought in the form

$$y = e^{kx}(a_0 + a_1 x + \cdots + a_n x^n) \tag{24-21}$$

if k is not a root of (24-10). If k is a simple root of (24-10), the trial solution (24-21) must be multiplied by x and, if the root is double, by x^2.

PROBLEMS

Obtain the general solution:

1. $y'' - 5y' + 6y = e^{4x}$;
2. $y'' + 2y' + y = x$;
3. $y'' + 5y' + 6y = e^x$;
4. $y'' - 2y' + y = x$;
5. $(D^2 - 1)y = 5x - 2$;
6. $(D^2 - 1)y = e^{2x}(x - 1)$;
7. $(D - 1)^2 y = xe^x$;
8. $(D^2 - 6D + 9)y = e^{3x}$;
9. $D(D + 9)y = 3$;
10. $y'' + 9y = x^2 - 2x + 1$;
11. $y'' - y = e^x$;
12. $y'' + y = x^3 + x$;
13. $y'' - 5y' + 6y = x^3 e^{2x}$;
14. $(D - 1)^2 y = e^x(x - 1)$;
15. $(D^2 - 5D + 6)y = 3x^2 + 4x - 2$;
16. $(D^2 - 5D)y = 3x^2 + 4x - 2$.

Obtain the solution for each of the following equations satisfying the given conditions:

17. $y'' + 5y' + 4y = 20e^x$, $y(0) = 0$, $y'(0) = -2$;
18. $y'' + y' = 1 + 2x$, $y(0) = 0$, $y'(0) = 0$;
19. $y'' + y' = 0$, $y(0) = 0$, $y'(0) = 0$;
20. $y'' + 4y' + 3y = x$, $y(0) = -\tfrac{4}{9}$, $y'(0) = \tfrac{3}{9}$;
21. $y'' + 4y' + 3y = 0$, $y(0) = 0$, $y'(0) = 0$;
22. $y'' + 4y' + 3y = x$, $y(0) = 1$, $y'(0) = 0$.

25. The Use of Complex Forms of Solutions in Evaluating Particular Integrals. The method of determining particular integrals of Eq. (24-9), described in the preceding section, can be extended to equations of the form

$$y'' + p_1 y' + p_2 y = Ae^{kx} \cos nx, \qquad (25\text{-}1)$$

$$y'' + p_1 y' + p_2 y = Ae^{kx} \sin nx, \qquad (25\text{-}2)$$

in which k may be equal to zero. If we recall the formula

$$e^{inx} = \cos nx + i \sin nx,$$

it becomes clear that $Ae^{kx} \cos nx$ and $Ae^{kx} \sin nx$ are, respectively, the real and imaginary parts of the function $Ae^{(k+in)x}$. Now, if instead of Eqs. (25-1) and (25-2) we consider the equation

$$y'' + p_1 y' + p_2 y = Ae^{(k+in)x} \qquad (25\text{-}3)$$

and obtain its solution $y = u + iv$, the real part u of such a solution will satisfy Eq. (25-1) and the imaginary part v will be a solution of (25-2). We illustrate this method of deducing solutions of equations in the forms (25-1) and (25-2) by examples.

Example 1. Find a solution of

$$y'' + y = 3 \sin 2x. \qquad (25\text{-}4)$$

Since $e^{i2x} = \cos 2x + i \sin 2x$, we consider, instead of (25-4), the equation

$$y'' + y = 3(\cos 2x + i \sin 2x) = 3e^{2ix}. \qquad (25\text{-}5)$$

The imaginary part of a solution of (25-5) is clearly a solution of (25-4). Equation (25-5) has the form (24-9) with $k = 2i$, and since neither of the roots of the characteristic equation $m^2 + 1 = 0$ is equal to $2i$, we take the trial solution

$$y = ae^{2ix}.$$

Now
$$y' = 2iae^{2ix},$$

$$y'' = (2i)^2 ae^{2ix} = -4ae^{2ix},$$

and the substitution in (25-5) yields

$$-4ae^{2ix} + ae^{2ix} = 3e^{2ix}.$$

Thus, $a = -1$, and consequently $y = -e^{2ix}$ is an integral of (25-5). The imaginary part of $-e^{2ix}$ is $-\sin 2x$, and hence a solution of (25-4) is $y = -\sin 2x$.

Example 2. Find one integral of

$$y'' + y = 3 \cos x. \qquad (25\text{-}6)$$

Since $e^{ix} = \cos x + i \sin x$, we consider

$$y'' + y = 3(\cos x + i \sin x) \equiv 3e^{ix}, \qquad (25\text{-}7)$$

the real part of the solution of which satisfies (25-6). This time k in (24-9) is $+i$, and since the roots of the characteristic equation are $\pm i$, we take the trial solution

$$y = axe^{ix}. \tag{25-8}$$

From (25-8),

$$y' = ae^{ix} + aixe^{ix},$$

$$y'' = 2aie^{ix} - axe^{ix},$$

and the substitution in (25-7) gives

$$2aie^{ix} - axe^{ix} + axe^{ix} = 3e^{ix}.$$

Thus, $a = 3/2i = -\frac{3}{2}i$, and therefore

$$y = -\tfrac{3}{2}ixe^{ix} = -\tfrac{3}{2}ix(\cos x + i \sin x)$$

is a solution of (25-7). The real part of this solution is $\frac{3}{2}x \sin x$, and we conclude that $y = \frac{3}{2}x \sin x$ is a solution of (25-6).

Example 3. Find a solution of

$$y'' + 2y' + 2y = e^{-x} \cos x. \tag{25-9}$$

Since $e^{-x} \cos x$ is the real part of

$$e^{-x}(\cos x + i \sin x) = e^{-x}e^{ix} = e^{x(-1+i)},$$

we consider the equation

$$y'' + 2y' + 2y = e^{x(-1+i)}. \tag{25-10}$$

The roots of the characteristic equation

$$m^2 + 2m + 2 = 0$$

are $m = -1 \pm i$, and since one of these roots appears in the exponent in (25-10), we take the trial solution

$$y = axe^{x(-1+i)}.$$

Then,

$$y' = ae^{x(-1+i)} + ax(-1+i)e^{x(-1+i)},$$

$$y'' = 2a(-1+i)e^{x(-1+i)} + ax(-1+i)^2e^{x(-1+i)},$$

and on making substitutions in (25-10), we find

$$2aie^{x(-1+i)} = e^{x(-1+i)},$$

so that

$$a = \frac{1}{2i}.$$

Thus an integral of (25-10) is

$$y = \frac{1}{2i}xe^{x(-1+i)} = \frac{1}{2i}xe^{-x}(\cos x + i \sin x).$$

The real part of this, $\frac{1}{2}xe^{-x} \sin x$, is a solution of (25-9).

The methods of this and the preceding section can be extended to equations

$$y'' + p_1y' + p_2y = f(x) \tag{25-11}$$

in which the right-hand member is a sum of several functions of the types considered in these sections, for suppose that $f(x) = f_1(x) + f_2(x)$, so that (25-11) reads

$$y'' + p_1 y' + p_2 y = f_1(x) + f_2(x). \tag{25-12}$$

If we consider a pair of equations

$$y'' + p_1 y' + p_2 y = f_1(x),$$
$$y'' + p_1 y' + p_2 y = f_2(x), \tag{25-13}$$

and denote the solution of the first of these by $y = u_1(x)$ and that of the second by $y = u_2(x)$, then $y = u_1(x) + u_2(x)$ will be a solution of (25-12). The proof follows at once on inserting $y = u_1(x) + u_2(x)$ in (25-12). As an illustration of the use of this theorem we consider a simple example.

Example 4. Find one solution of

$$y'' + y = 3 \cos x + 1 + 2e^x.$$

We consider three equations:

$$y'' + y = 3 \cos x,$$
$$y'' + y = 1,$$
$$y'' + y = 2e^x.$$

A particular integral of the first of these, as shown in Example 2, is $y = \frac{3}{2}x \sin x$, and solutions of the second and third equations are, respectively, $y = 1$ and $y = e^x$, as is clear by inspection. Hence an integral of the given equation is $y = \frac{3}{2}x \sin x + 1 + e^x$.

PROBLEMS

Solve:

1. $(D^2 - 3D + 2)y = \cos 2x;$
2. $(D^2 + 4)y = \cos 3x;$
3. $(D^2 - \frac{1}{2}D - \frac{1}{2})y = -\cos x - 3 \sin x;$
4. $y'' + 5y' + 6y = 3e^{-2x} + e^{3x};$
5. $y'' + 2y' + 5y = e^x \sin 2x;$
6. $y'' - y' - 6y = e^{3x} \cos 3x;$
7. $(D^2 - 25)y = e^{5x} + x^2 - 4x;$
8. $(D^2 + 1)y = 3 \sin 2x - 9 \cos 3x.$

Obtain the solution satisfying the conditions $y(0) = 0$, $y'(0) = 0$ for each of the following:

9. $y'' - y = \sin x;$
10. $y'' + 2y' + 5y = 0;$
11. $y'' - 2y' = e^{-x} \cos x;$
12. $y'' + y = \cos x + 1.$

26. Linear nth-order Equations with Constant Coefficients.

The results of Secs. 22 to 25 are easily extended to nth-order linear equations

$$y^{(n)} + p_1 y^{(n-1)} + \cdots + p_n y = f(x) \tag{26-1}$$

with constant coefficients. In dealing with such equations it is convenient to make a systematic use of the operator notation introduced in Sec. 23 and write (26-1) in the form

$$(D^n + p_1 D^{n-1} + \cdots + p_{n-1} D + p_n)y = f(x). \qquad (26\text{-}2)$$

The homogeneous equation associated with (26-2) is

$$(D^n + p_1 D^{n-1} + \cdots + p_{n-1} D + p_n)y = 0, \qquad (26\text{-}3)$$

and if one substitutes in it $y = e^{mx}$, there results

$$(m^n + p_1 m^{n-1} + \cdots + p_{n-1} m + p_n)e^{mx} = 0.$$

It follows that $y = e^{mx}$ is a solution of (26-3) whenever m is a root of the *characteristic equation*

$$m^n + p_1 m^{n-1} + \cdots + p_{n-1} m + p_n = 0. \qquad (26\text{-}4)$$

If this equation has n distinct roots

$$m = m_1, \qquad m = m_2, \qquad \ldots, \qquad m = m_n,$$

then
$$y = e^{m_1 x}, \qquad y = e^{m_2 x}, \qquad \ldots, \qquad y = e^{m_n x}$$

are distinct solutions, and we can conclude (see Sec. 27) that

$$y = c_1 e^{m_1 x} + c_2 e^{m_2 x} + \cdots + c_n e^{m_n x} \qquad (26\text{-}5)$$

is a general solution in the sense that the arbitrary constants c_i in (26-5) can be determined to satisfy the prescribed initial conditions

$$y(x_0) = y_0, \qquad y'(x_0) = y_0', \qquad \ldots, \qquad y^{(n-1)}(x_0) = y_0^{(n-1)}. \qquad (26\text{-}6)$$

Since the coefficients in (26-4) are real, the complex roots of (26-4) must necessarily occur in conjugate pairs. Thus, if $m_1 = a + bi$ and $m_2 = a - bi$ are a pair of such roots, the solutions corresponding to them are

$$y_1 = e^{(a+bi)x} = e^{ax}(\cos bx + i \sin bx),$$

$$y_2 = e^{(a-bi)x} = e^{ax}(\cos bx - i \sin bx).$$

As in Sec. 22, we prove that the real and imaginary parts of these solutions yield a pair of linearly independent real solutions

$$y = e^{ax} \cos bx, \qquad y = e^{ax} \sin bx.$$

When the roots of characteristic equation (26-4) are not simple, and if, for example, the root m_1 has the multiplicity k, then corresponding to it there will be a set of k distinct solutions,[1]

$$y_1 = e^{m_1 x}, \qquad y_2 = xe^{m_1 x}, \qquad \ldots, \qquad y_k = x^{k-1}e^{m_1 x}. \qquad (26\text{-}7)$$

The proof of this assertion follows upon making obvious modifications in the argument presented in Sec. 23.

We illustrate these statements by two examples.

Example 1. Find the general solution of the fourth-order equation

$$y^{\text{IV}} - 2y''' + 2y'' - 2y' + y = 0, \qquad (26\text{-}8)$$

or

$$(D^4 - 2D^3 + 2D^2 - 2D + 1)y = 0. \qquad (26\text{-}9)$$

The characteristic equation for (26-8) has the structure determined by the operator in (26-9). It is

$$m^4 - 2m^3 + 2m^2 - 2m + 1 = 0.$$

On factoring this we get

$$(m^2 + 1)(m - 1)^2 = 0.$$

Thus, there are two simple roots $m_1 = i$, $m_2 = -i$ and the double root $m_3 = m_4 = 1$. Solutions corresponding to these roots are

$$y_1 = e^{ix}, \qquad y_2 = e^{-ix}, \qquad y_3 = e^x, \qquad y_4 = xe^x,$$

and the general solution is

$$y = c_1 e^{ix} + c_2 e^{-ix} + c_3 e^x + c_4 x e^x.$$

This can be written in real form as

$$y = C_1 \cos x + C_2 \sin x + (C_3 + C_4 x)e^x.$$

Example 2. The equation

$$(D^4 + 3D^3 + 3D^2 + D)y = 0$$

or

$$D(D + 1)^3 y = 0$$

has the characteristic equation

$$m(m + 1)^3 = 0.$$

Accordingly, the general solution is

$$y = c_1 e^{0x} + c_2 e^{-x} + c_3 x e^{-x} + c_4 x^2 e^{-x}.$$

An argument in every respect similar to that given in Sec. 24 yields the result that when $y = u(x)$ is any solution of Eq. (26-1) and $y = c_1 y_1(x) + c_2 y_2(x) + \cdots + c_n y_n(x)$ is the general solution of the homogeneous equation (26-3), then the general solution of (26-1) is

$$y = c_1 y_1(x) + c_2 y_2(x) + \cdots + c_n y_n(x) + u(x). \qquad (26\text{-}10)$$

---

[1] If the complex root $m_1 = a + bi$ is of multiplicity k, then corresponding to this root and to its conjugate $m_2 = a - bi$, there will be a set of $2k$ real solutions:

$$e^{ax} \cos bx, \ xe^{ax} \cos bx, \ \ldots, \ x^{k-1}e^{ax} \cos bx,$$

$$e^{ax} \sin bx, \ xe^{ax} \sin bx, \ \ldots, \ x^{k-1}e^{ax} \sin bx.$$

The calculation of particular solutions $u(x)$ by the method of undetermined coefficients for functions $f(x)$ of the type considered in Secs. 24 and 25 follows, with obvious minor modifications, the pattern of those sections. Without further ado we illustrate the procedure by examples.[1]

Example 3.   Find a solution of

$$y''' + y'' + 2y' = x^2 + 3x + 1. \tag{26-11}$$

The left-hand member of this equation contains no y (that is, $p_3 = 0$). On recalling the statement made for Eq. (24-12), we take the trial solution

$$y = x(a_0 + a_1 x + a_2 x^2).$$

On computing the first three derivatives we obtain

$$y' = a_0 + 2a_1 x + 3a_2 x^2,$$

$$y'' = 2a_1 + 6a_2 x,$$

$$y''' = 6a_2.$$

Substitution in (26-11) then yields

$$(2a_0 + 2a_1 + 6a_2) + (6a_2 + 4a_1)x + 6a_2 x^2 = x^2 + 3x + 1.$$

Hence
$$6a_2 = 1,$$

$$6a_2 + 4a_1 = 3,$$

$$2a_0 + 2a_1 + 6a_2 = 1$$

and we conclude that
$$a_2 = \tfrac{1}{6}, \qquad a_1 = \tfrac{1}{2}, \qquad a_0 = -\tfrac{1}{2}.$$

Accordingly, $y = x(-\tfrac{1}{2} + \tfrac{1}{2}x + \tfrac{1}{6}x^2)$ is a solution of (26-11).

Example 4.   Obtain the general solution of

$$(D^3 - 3D^2 + 2D)y = 4 + 60e^{5x}. \tag{26-12}$$

The characteristic equation for (26-12) is

$$m^3 - 3m^2 + 2m = m(m - 1)(m - 2) = 0.$$

Thus, the general solution is

$$y = c_1 + c_2 e^x + c_3 e^{2x} + u(x),$$

where $u(x)$ is some integral of (26-12). To obtain $u(x)$ it is simpler to add the particular integrals of

$$(D^3 - 3D^2 + 2D)y = 4, \tag{26-13}$$

$$(D^3 - 3D^2 + 2D)y = 60e^{5x}. \tag{26-14}$$

For the first of these we take a trial solution $y = ax$. We find on inserting it in (26-13) that $a = 2$, so that $y = 2x$ is an integral of (26-13). The substitution of $y = ae^{5x}$ in (26-14) yields, after simple calculation, $a = 1$; hence $y = e^{5x}$ is a solution of (26-14). Accordingly, an integral of (26-12) is $y = 2x + e^{5x}$, and the desired general solution is

$$y = c_1 + c_2 e^x + c_3 e^{2x} + 2x + e^{5x}.$$

[1] A general method is presented in Sec. 28.

Example 5. Obtain one solution of $(D^3 + 2D + 7)y = -24e^x \cos 2x$. The right-hand side is the real part of $-24e^x e^{2ix}$. To solve

$$(D^3 + 2D + 7)y = -24e^x e^{2ix} = -24e^{(1+2i)x}, \qquad (26\text{-}15)$$

try $y = ae^{(1+2i)x}$. Substitution gives

$$(D^3 + 2D + 7)ae^{(1+2i)x} = [(1 + 2i)^3 + 2(1 + 2i) + 7]ae^{(1+2i)x}$$

$$= (-2 + 2i)ae^{(1+2i)x} = -24e^{(1+2i)x},$$

where the last equality is stated because we want to obtain a solution of (26-15). It follows that

$$a = \frac{-24}{-2 + 2i} = \frac{12}{1 - i} = \frac{12}{1 - i}\frac{1 + i}{1 + i} = 6(1 + i),$$

and hence a solution of (26-15) is

$$y = 6(1 + i)e^{(1+2i)x} = 6e^x(1 + i)(\cos 2x + i \sin 2x). \qquad (26\text{-}16)$$

Since $-24e^x \cos 2x$ is the real part of $-24e^{(1+2i)x}$, a solution of the original problem is found by taking the real part of y in (26-16). Thus,

$$y = 6e^x \cos 2x - 6e^x \sin 2x.$$

PROBLEMS

Find the general solutions:

1. $(D - 5)(2D + 3)Dy = 0;$
2. $(D^2 + 1)(D^2 + 2D + 5)y = 0;$
3. $(D^3 + 3D^2 + 3D + 1)y = 0;$
4. $(D^3 + 8)y = 0;$
5. $(D^3 - 2D^2 + D)y = 0;$
6. $(D^4 + 3D^3 + 3D^2 + D)y = 0;$
7. $(D^4 - k^4)y = 0;$
8. $(D^3 - 3D^2 + 4)y = 0;$
9. $(D^3 - D^2 + 4D)y = 4x + e^x;$
10. $(D^4 + 1)y = 2 \cos x;$
11. $(D - 1)(D - 2)^2 y = x^2;$
12. $(D + 1)(D - 1)(D - 2)y = 1 - e^x.$

13. Find the solution of $y''' + 2y'' - y' - 2y = 2e^{-3x} + 4x^2$ which satisfies $y(0) = y'(0) = 0$, $y''(0) = -25/2$.

27. General Linear Differential Equations of nth Order. It is not difficult to extend the considerations of Sec. 21 to a homogeneous nth-order linear equation

$$y^{(n)} + p_1(x)y^{(n-1)} + p_2(x)y^{(n-2)} + \cdots + p_{n-1}(x)y' + p_n(x)y = 0 \qquad (27\text{-}1)$$

with variable coefficients $p_i(x)$. Word-for-word repetition of the argument used to establish properties 1 and 2 of Sec. 21 leads to the conclusion that

$$y = c_1 y_1(x) + c_2 y_2(x) + \cdots + c_k y_k(x) \qquad (27\text{-}2)$$

is a solution of (27-1), for an arbitrary choice of the constants c_i, whenever $y_1(x)$, $y_2(x)$, ..., $y_k(x)$ is a set of solutions of (27-1).

A set of k such solutions is said to be *linearly independent* if the relation

$$c_1 y_1(x) + c_2 y_2(x) + \cdots + c_k y_k(x) \equiv 0 \qquad (27\text{-}3)$$

holds only when $c_1 = c_2 = \cdots = c_k = 0$. When a set of constants c_i, not all of which are zero, can be found such that Eq. (27-3) is true, the solutions $y_i(x)$ are *linearly dependent*.

It follows from the existence and uniqueness theorem of Sec. 1 that Eq. (27-1) has exactly n linearly independent solutions $y_1(x)$, $\ldots$, $y_n(x)$, so that

$$y = c_1 y_1(x) + c_2 y_2(x) + \cdots + c_n y_n(x) \qquad (27\text{-}4)$$

is a general solution of (27-1). This solution is general in the sense that the constants c_i in (27-4) can always be found, so that there is a unique solution of (27-1) for the arbitrarily specified initial values

$$y(x_0) = y_0, \qquad y'(x_0) = y_0', \qquad \ldots, \qquad y^{(n-1)}(x_0) = y_0^{(n-1)}. \qquad (27\text{-}5)$$

An argument analogous to that used to establish the condition (21-9) for linear independence of two solutions leads to the result that the set of n solutions $\{y_i(x)\}$, $i = 1$, $\ldots$, n, is linearly independent if, and only if, the Wronskian determinant

$$W(y_1, y_2, \ldots, y_n) = \begin{vmatrix} y_1 & y_2 & \cdots & y_n \\ y_1' & y_2' & \cdots & y_n' \\ \cdot & \cdot & \cdots & \cdot \\ y_1^{(n-1)} & y_2^{(n-1)} & \cdots & y_n^{(n-1)} \end{vmatrix} \qquad (27\text{-}6)$$

does not vanish for any x in the interval where solutions are sought.

In contradistinction to the case of linear equations with constant co-efficients, no formulas are available for solving general linear equations with variable coefficients of order 2 or higher. Certain special types of such equations, however, have been studied extensively, and as shown in Chap. 2, Sec. 12, their solutions may be obtained as power series.

Just as in Sec. 24, we can show that if $y = u(x)$ is any solution of the nonhomogeneous equation

$$y^{(n)} + p_1(x)y^{(n-1)} + \cdots + p_{n-1}(x)y' + p_n(x)y = f(x), \qquad (27\text{-}7)$$

then $\qquad y = c_1 y_1(x) + c_2 y_2(x) + \cdots + c_n y_n(x) + u(x) \qquad (27\text{-}8)$

is the general solution of (27-7) whenever the $y_i(x)$ are linearly independent solutions of the homogeneous equation (27-1). The determination of particular integrals of (27-7), as we shall see in the next section, is a straight-forward process provided that the general solution of the associated homogeneous equation is known.

Example 1. Show that the set of functions $y_1 = x$, $y_2 = x^2$, $y_3 = x^3$ is linearly inde-pendent if $x \neq 0$. The Wronskian (27-6) for this set of functions is

$$W(y_1, y_2, y_3) = \begin{vmatrix} x & x^2 & x^3 \\ 1 & 2x & 3x^2 \\ 0 & 2 & 6x \end{vmatrix} = 2x^3.$$

Since $W(y_1, y_2, y_3)$ does not vanish as long as $x \neq 0$, this set is linearly independent in any interval that does not include $x = 0$.

Example 2. Test for linear independence $y_1 = x^2 + 2x$, $y_2 = x^3 + x$, $y_3 = 2x^3 - x^2$. We compute the Wronskian for this set of functions:

$$W(y_1, y_2, y_3) = \begin{vmatrix} x^2 + 2x & x^3 + x & 2x^3 - x^2 \\ 2x + 2 & 3x^2 + 1 & 6x^2 - 2x \\ 2 & 6x & 12x - 2 \end{vmatrix} = 0.$$

Since $W(y_1, y_2, y_3) = 0$, the given set is linearly dependent. This implies that a set of constants c_1, c_2, c_3, not all zero, can be found such that

$$c_1 y_1 + c_2 y_2 + c_3 y_3 = 0.$$

This, in turn, means that at least one of these functions can be expressed linearly in terms of the remaining ones. In fact, it is easy to check that $y_3 = 2y_2 - y_1$.

PROBLEMS

Test for linear dependence the following sets of functions:

1. e^{-x}, 1, e^x, $\sinh x$;
2. 1, $\sin x$, $\cos x$;
3. $x^2 - 2x + 5$, $3x - 1$, $\sin x$;
4. $(x + 1)^2$, $(x - 1)^2$, $3x$;
5. e^{ax}, e^{bx}, e^{cx}, $a \neq b \neq c \neq a$;
6. e^{ix}, $\sin x$, $\cos x$;
7. e^x, xe^x, $x^2 e^x$.

28. Variation of Parameters. We proceed to show that a particular integral $y = u(x)$ of every nth-order linear equation (27-7) can be calculated by the so-called method of *variation of parameters* whenever the general solution of the related homogeneous equation (27-1) is known.

To make the procedure clear, we first develop it for the second-order equation

$$y'' + p_1(x)y' + p_2(x)y = f(x) \tag{28-1}$$

and then extend it to the general case of Eq. (27-7). Let us suppose that

$$y = c_1 y_1(x) + c_2 y_2(x) \tag{28-2}$$

is the general solution of the homogeneous equation

$$y'' + p_1(x)y' + p_2(x)y = 0. \tag{28-3}$$

We shall attempt to find an integral of (28-1) in the form

$$y = v_1(x)y_1(x) + v_2(x)y_2(x), \tag{28-4}$$

obtained from (28-2) by replacing the constants c_i by some unknown functions $v_i(x)$.

If we substitute (28-4) in (28-1), we shall obtain one equation which imposes a condition to be satisfied by two unknown functions $v_1(x)$ and $v_2(x)$. Since one such condition does not determine the unknown functions, we need another equation relating v_1 and v_2. We shall impose this second condition in a way that would tend to simplify the calculation of v_1 and v_2.

If we differentiate (28-4), we get

$$y' = (v_1 y_1' + v_2 y_2') + (v_1' y_1 + v_2' y_2). \qquad (28\text{-}5)$$

Now, the calculation of y'' will be materially simplified if v_1 and v_2 are chosen so that the expression in the second parentheses in (28-5) vanishes. Accordingly, we set

$$v_1' y_1 + v_2' y_2 = 0 \qquad (28\text{-}6)$$

and take

$$y' = v_1 y_1' + v_2 y_2'. \qquad (28\text{-}7)$$

Then

$$y'' = v_1 y_1'' + v_2 y_2'' + v_1' y_1' + v_2' y_2'. \qquad (28\text{-}8)$$

The substitution from (28-4), (28-7), and (28-8) in the original equation (28-1) yields, on rearrangement,

$$v_1(y_1'' + p_1 y_1' + p_2 y_1) + v_2(y_2'' + p_1 y_2' + p_2 y_2) + v_1' y_1' + v_2' y_2' = f(x). \qquad (28\text{-}9)$$

But since y_1 and y_2 are known to satisfy (28-3), the expressions in the parentheses in (28-9) vanish. We thus get

$$v_1' y_1' + v_2' y_2' = f(x). \qquad (28\text{-}10)$$

The pair of equations (28-6) and (28-10) can be solved for v_1' and v_2' to yield

$$v_1' = \frac{\begin{vmatrix} 0 & y_2 \\ f & y_2' \end{vmatrix}}{\begin{vmatrix} y_1 & y_2 \\ y_1' & y_2' \end{vmatrix}}, \qquad v_2' = \frac{\begin{vmatrix} y_1 & 0 \\ y_1' & f \end{vmatrix}}{\begin{vmatrix} y_1 & y_2 \\ y_1' & y_2' \end{vmatrix}}, \qquad (28\text{-}11)$$

since the determinant

$$W(y_1, y_2) = \begin{vmatrix} y_1 & y_2 \\ y_1' & y_2' \end{vmatrix}$$

never vanishes inasmuch as y_1 and y_2 are *linearly independent* solutions of Eq. (28-3).

The right-hand members of Eqs. (28-11) are known functions of x, and on integrating them we obtain $v_1(x)$ and $v_2(x)$. We can thus write an integral of (28-1) in the form

$$y = y_1(x) \int \frac{-f y_2}{W(y_1, y_2)}\, dx + y_2(x) \int \frac{f y_1}{W(y_1, y_2)}\, dx, \qquad (28\text{-}12)$$

obtained by inserting $v_1(x)$ and $v_2(x)$ in (28-4).

Example 1. Find an integral of

$$x^2 y'' - 2xy' + 2y = x \log x, \qquad \text{if } x > 0. \qquad (28\text{-}13)$$

It is easily checked that a pair of linearly independent solutions of the homogeneous equation associated with (28-13) is $y_1 = x$, $y_2 = x^2$. Thus its general solution is $y = c_1 x + c_2 x^2$. Accordingly, we seek an integral of (28-13) in the form

$$y = v_1 x + v_2 x^2. \qquad (28\text{-}14)$$

On dividing (28-13) through by x^2 to reduce it to the standard form (28-1), we see that $f(x) = (\log x)/x$. Thus, Eqs. (28-6) and (28-10) yield

$$v_1' x + v_2' x^2 = 0,$$

$$v_1' 1 + v_2' 2x = \frac{\log x}{x}.$$

Solving these for v_1' and v_2' we obtain

$$v_1' = -\frac{\log x}{x}, \qquad v_2' = \frac{\log x}{x^2},$$

and thus

$$v_1 = -\int \frac{\log x}{x}\, dx, \qquad v_2 = \int \frac{\log x}{x^2}\, dx.$$

Integrating these and dropping integration constants (for any integral will do), we find

$$v_1 = -\tfrac{1}{2}(\log x)^2, \qquad v_2 = -\frac{1}{x}(1 + \log x). \qquad (28\text{-}15)$$

The substitution from (28-15) in (28-14) yields the desired integral of (28-13) in the form

$$y = -x[1 + \log x + \tfrac{1}{2}(\log x)^2].$$

Of course, we could have obtained this result directly from formula (28-12).

The foregoing procedure can be generalized to compute an integral of

$$y^{(n)} + p_1(x)y^{(n-1)} + \cdots + p_{n-1}(x)y' + p(x)y = f(x). \qquad (28\text{-}16)$$

If $y_1(x), \ldots, y_n(x)$ is a known set of linearly independent solutions of the corresponding homogeneous equation, we seek an integral of (28-16) in the form

$$y = v_1(x)y_1(x) + v_2(x)y_2(x) + \cdots + v_n(x)y_n(x), \qquad (28\text{-}17)$$

where the $v_i(x)$ are unknown functions. To determine them we form the set of $n - 1$ equations by equating to zero the terms involving the $v_i'(x)$ in the expressions resulting from differentiating (28-17) successively $n - 1$ times. The nth equation is got by inserting the corresponding values of derivatives in (28-16). We illustrate the procedure by an example.[1]

---

[1] See also Prob. 5 at the end of this section.

Example 2. Find an integral of

$$y''' + \frac{1}{x^2} y' - \frac{1}{x^3} y = \frac{1}{x^2} \log x, \qquad x \neq 0. \tag{28-18}$$

A set of linearly independent solutions of the corresponding homogeneous equation is known to be [1]

$$y_1 = x, \qquad y_2 = x \log x, \qquad y_3 = x(\log x)^2. \tag{28-19}$$

Accordingly, we take the integral of (28-18) in the form

$$y = v_1 x + v_2 x \log x + v_3 x (\log x)^2. \tag{28-20}$$

For the third-order equation the procedure just sketched yields the system of three equations:

$$v_1' y_1 + v_2' y_2 + v_3' y_3 = 0,$$
$$v_1' y_1' + v_2' y_2' + v_3' y_3' = 0, \tag{28-21}$$
$$v_1' y_1'' + v_2' y_2'' + v_3' y_3'' = f(x).$$

The reader will verify that, on setting $f(x) = (1/x^2) \log x$ and noting (28-19), the system (28-21) yields

$$v_1' = \frac{1}{2x} (\log x)^3, \qquad v_2' = -\frac{1}{x} (\log x)^2, \qquad v_3' = \frac{1}{2x} \log x,$$

and we can take

$$v_1 = \tfrac{1}{8}(\log x)^4, \qquad v_2 = -\tfrac{1}{3}(\log x)^3, \qquad v_3 = \tfrac{1}{4}(\log x)^2.$$

Substitution in (28-20) gives finally $y = (x/24)(\log x)^4$.

PROBLEMS

1. Use the method of variation of parameters to find integrals of the following equations with constant coefficients:

(a) $y' + 3y = x^3$;

(b) $y'' + 5y' + 6y = e^x$;

(c) $y'' - 2y' + y = x$;

(d) $y''' - 3y' + 2y = 2(\sin x - 2 \cos x)$.

2. Find the solution of

$$\frac{dy}{dx} + f_1(x)y = f_2(x)$$

by the method of variation of parameters, and compare your result with that of Sec. 10. The solution of the related homogeneous equation is obtained easily by separation of the variables.

3. By the method of variation of parameters, find a particular integral of

$$\frac{d^2y}{dx^2} - \frac{3}{x} \frac{dy}{dx} - \frac{5}{x^2} y = \log x,$$

where the general solution of the related homogeneous equation is

$$y = \frac{c_1}{x} + c_2 x^5.$$

[1] See Example 1, Sec. 30.

4. Find the general solution of

$$\frac{d^2y}{dx^2} + \frac{x}{1-x}\frac{dy}{dx} - \frac{1}{1-x}y = 1 - x,$$

where the general solution of the related homogeneous equation is $c_1e^x + c_2x$.

5. Show that the formula corresponding to (28-12) for an integral of (28-16) is

$$y(x) = \sum_{i=1}^{n} y_i(x) \int \frac{W_i(y_1,y_2,\ldots,y_n)}{W(y_1,y_2,\ldots,y_n)} f(x)\,dx,$$

where $W(y_1,y_2,\ldots,y_n)$ is the Wronskian and W_i is the determinant obtained from W by replacing the ith column by $(0,0,0,\ldots,1)$.

29. Reduction of the Order of Linear Equations. The method of variation of parameters can be used to reduce the solution of every nth-order linear homogeneous equation to the solution of a linear equation of order $n - 1$ when one solution of the nth-order equation is known. This matter is of some importance in deducing general solutions of second-order linear equations, because one integral of such equations can often be determined by inspection.

Let $y_1(x)$ be a solution of

$$y'' + p_1(x)y' + p_2(x)y = 0, \tag{29-1}$$

so that $y = cy_1(x)$ is a solution for any constant c. If we replace c by an unknown function $v(x)$ and seek a solution of (29-1) in the form

$$y = v(x)y_1(x), \tag{29-2}$$

we get, on differentiating (29-2),

$$y' = vy_1' + v'y_1, \tag{29-3}$$

$$y'' = vy_1'' + 2v'y_1' + v''y_1.$$

Substituting from (29-2) and (29-3) in (29-1) and noting that $y_1(x)$ is a solution of (29-1), we get a separable equation

$$v''y_1 + v'(2y_1' + p_1y_1) = 0 \tag{29-4}$$

for $v(x)$.

Separation of variables in (29-4) gives

$$\frac{v''}{v'} = -2\frac{y_1'}{y_1} - p_1,$$

so that

$$\log v' = -2 \log y_1 - \int p_1\,dx.$$

Hence

$$v' = \frac{1}{y_1^2}e^{-\int p_1\,dx}. \tag{29-5}$$

We see that $v'(x) \neq 0$, so that $v \neq$ const.

Integrating (29-5) we obtain

$$v = \int y_1^{-2} e^{-\int p_1 \, dx} \, dx, \tag{29-6}$$

so that the second linearly independent solution of (29-1), by (29-2), is

$$y_2 = y_1(x) \int y_1^{-2}(x) e^{-\int p_1(x) \, dx} \, dx. \tag{29-7}$$

We dispense with quite analogous calculations showing that the solution of an nth-order linear equation can be reduced to that of a linear equation of order $n - 1$ when one integral of the nth-order equation is known.

Example: The equation

$$y'' - \frac{4x}{2x - 1} y' + \frac{4}{2x - 1} y = 0,$$

with $x \neq \frac{1}{2}$, has an obvious solution $y_1 = x$. To determine another solution we set $y = vx$. The function v, determined by formula (29-6), is

$$v = \int x^{-2} e^{\int \frac{4x}{2x-1} \, dx} \, dx$$

$$= \int x^{-2} e^{\int \left(2 + \frac{2}{2x-1}\right) \, dx} \, dx$$

$$= \int x^{-2} e^{2x + \log(2x-1)} \, dx$$

$$= \int \frac{(2x - 1)e^{2x}}{x^2} \, dx = 2 \int \frac{e^{2x}}{x} \, dx - \int \frac{e^{2x}}{x^2} \, dx$$

$$= \frac{e^{2x}}{x} + \int \frac{e^{2x}}{x^2} \, dx - \int \frac{e^{2x}}{x^2} \, dx$$

$$= \frac{e^{2x}}{x}.$$

Thus the second solution is $y = vx = e^{2x}$.

PROBLEMS

1. The equation $x^2 y'' + 2xy' = 0$ has an obvious solution $y = 1$. Show that $y = 1/x$ is another solution, and thus find the general solution.

2. One solution of

$$y'' + \frac{x^2 - 2x - 2}{x^2 + x} y' - \frac{2x^2 - 2x - 2}{x^3 + x^2} y = 0$$

obviously is $y = x^2$. Show that a second solution is $y = xe^{-x}$.

3. A special case of Legendre's equation

$$(1 - x^2)y'' - 2xy' + 2y = 0$$

has an obvious solution $y = x$. Obtain a first-order equation for a second linearly independent solution of this equation, and solve.

30. The Euler-Cauchy Equation.

An equation of the form

$$x^n y^{(n)} + a_1 x^{n-1} y^{(n-1)} + \cdots + a_{n-1} x y' + a_n y = f(x), \qquad (30\text{-}1)$$

where the a_i are constants, is usually called Cauchy's equation, although it was examined earlier by Euler. We show that by a change of the independent variable x, it can be transformed into an equation with constant coefficients which can be solved by familiar methods.

If we set

$$x = e^z, \qquad (30\text{-}2)$$

then

$$\frac{dx}{dz} = e^z \quad \text{and} \quad \frac{dz}{dx} = e^{-z}.$$

On writing $D \equiv d/dz$, we get

$$y' = \frac{dy}{dx} = \frac{dy}{dz}\frac{dz}{dx} = e^{-z}\, Dy.$$

Also

$$y'' = \frac{dy'}{dx} = \frac{dy'}{dz}\frac{dz}{dx} = (Dy')e^{-z}$$

$$= e^{-2z}(D^2 - D)y$$

$$= e^{-2z}D(D - 1)y.$$

In a similar way we find

$$y^{(n)} = e^{-nz}D(D - 1)(D - 2) \cdots (D - n + 1)y. \qquad (30\text{-}3)$$

From (30-2), $x^n = e^{nz}$, and the substitution from (30-3) in (30-1) therefore yields the equation with constant coefficients

$$[D(D - 1)(D - 2) \cdots (D - n + 1)$$

$$+ a_1 D(D - 1) \cdots (D - n + 2) + \cdots + a_{n-1}D + a_n]y = f(e^z). \quad (30\text{-}4)$$

If a solution of (30-4) is denoted by $y = F(z)$, then the solution of the original equation, as follows from (30-2), is $y = F(\log x)$.

Example 1. Find the general solution of

$$x^3 y''' + x y' - y = x \log x. \qquad (30\text{-}5)$$

Upon setting $x = e^z$, this equation becomes

$$[D(D - 1)(D - 2) + D - 1]y = ze^z$$

or

$$(D^3 - 3D^2 + 3D - 1)y = ze^z. \qquad (30\text{-}6)$$

The roots of the characteristic equation obviously are $m_1 = m_2 = m_3 = 1$. Hence the solution of the homogeneous equation is $(c_1 + c_2 z + c_3 z^2)e^z$.

Inasmuch as the characteristic equation has a triple root and the right-hand member of (30-6) is a solution of the homogeneous equation, we take the trial integral in the form (see Sec. 27)

$$y = az^4 e^z.$$

The substitution of the trial integral in (30-6) shows that $a = \frac{1}{24}$, so that the general solution of (30-6) is

$$y = (c_1 + c_2 z + c_3 z^2)e^z + \frac{1}{24} z^4 e^z.$$

Finally, the substitution of $z = \log x$ gives

$$y = [c_1 + c_2 \log x + c_3(\log x)^2]x + \frac{1}{24} x(\log x)^4,$$

which is the desired solution of (30-5).

The general solution of the homogeneous equation

$$x^n y^{(n)} + a_1 x^{n-1} y^{(n-1)} + \cdots + a_{n-1} xy' + a_n y = 0,$$

associated with (30-1), can often be found by taking a trial solution $y = x^m$. This is illustrated in the following example.

Example 2. Solve $x^2 y'' + 2xy' = 0$. The substitution of $y = x^m$ yields the equation

$$m(m - 1)x^m + 2mx^m = 0,$$

or

$$m(m - 1) + 2m = 0.$$

Since $m = 0$ and $m = -1$ satisfy this equation, $y = x^0 = 1$ and $y = x^{-1}$ are linearly independent solutions of the given equation. The general solution, therefore, is

$$y = c_1 + c_2 x^{-1}.$$

PROBLEMS

Find the general solutions of:

1. $x^2 y'' + 4xy' + 2y = \log x$;   2. $x^3 y''' - 4x^2 y'' + 5xy' - 2y = 1$;
3. $x^2 y'' + y = x^2$;   4. $x^2 y'' - 2xy' + 2y = x \log x$.

By assuming a solution of the form $y = x^m$ solve:

5. $x^2 y'' - 4xy' + 6y = 0$;   6. $x^2 y'' + 2xy' - n(n + 1)y = 0$.

APPLICATIONS OF LINEAR EQUATIONS

31. Free Vibrations of Electrical and Mechanical Systems. We saw in Sec. 19 that the equation

$$\frac{d(mv)}{dt} = F(s,v,t), \tag{31-1}$$

stating Newton's second law of motion, is readily integrable when the external force F is a function of the displacement s alone, when it is a function of the velocity v alone, or when it depends only on the time t.

In this section we examine other types of this equation which are of cardinal importance in the analysis of oscillating electrical and mechanical systems.

Throughout this discussion we shall assume that the mass m is constant, so that Eq. (31-1) can be written as

$$m \frac{d^2s}{dt^2} = F(s,v,t),$$

where $v \equiv ds/dt$.

We begin our study with a simple mechanical system which is a proto-type of more general systems that appear in the analysis of vibrations of elastic structures.

Let it be required to determine the position of the end of an elastic spring set oscillating in a vacuum. If a mass M is applied to one end of the spring whose other end is fixed, it will produce the elongation s, which,

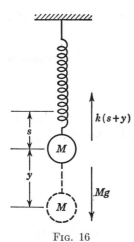

FIG. 16

according to Hooke's law, is proportional to the applied force $F = Mg$, g being the gravitational acceleration. Thus,

$$F = ks = Mg,$$

where k is the stiffness of the spring.

If at any later time t an additional force is applied to produce an extension y, after which this additional force is removed, the spring will start oscillating. The problem is to determine the position of the end point of the spring at any subsequent time.

The forces acting on the mass M are the force of gravity Mg downward, which will be taken as the positive direction for the displacement y, and the tension T in the spring, which acts in the direction opposite to that of the force of gravity (Fig. 16). Hence, from Newton's second law of motion,

$$M \frac{d^2y}{dt^2} = Mg - T.$$

Since T is the tension in the spring when its elongation is $s + y$, Hooke's law states that $T = k(s + y)$, so that

$$M \frac{d^2y}{dt^2} = Mg - k(s + y).$$

But $Mg = ks$, and therefore the foregoing equation becomes

$$M \frac{d^2y}{dt^2} + ky = 0.$$

Setting $k/M = a^2$ reduces this to

$$\frac{d^2y}{dt^2} + a^2 y = 0 \qquad \text{or} \qquad (D^2 + a^2)y = 0. \qquad (31\text{-}2)$$

Factoring gives $(D - ai)(D + ai)y = 0$, from which it is clear that the general solution is

$$y = c_1 e^{-ait} + c_2 e^{ait},$$

or, in real form,

$$y = A \cos at + B \sin at.$$

The arbitrary constants A and B can be determined from the initial conditions. The solution reveals the fact that the spring vibrates with a simple harmonic motion whose period is

$$T = \frac{2\pi}{a} = 2\pi \sqrt{\frac{M}{k}}.$$

The period depends on the stiffness of the spring as would be expected—the stiffer the spring, the greater the frequency of vibration.

It is instructive to compare the solution just obtained with that of the corresponding electrical problem. It will be seen that a striking analogy exists between the mechanical and electrical systems. This analogy permits one to replace a study of complicated mechanical systems by the analysis of performance of mathematically equivalent simple electrical circuits.

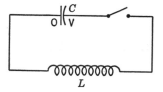

FIG. 17

Let a condenser (Fig. 17) be discharged through an inductive coil of negligible resistance. It is known that the charge Q on a condenser plate is proportional to the potential difference of the plates; that is,

$$Q = CV,$$

where C is the capacity of the condenser. Moreover, the current I flowing through the coil is

$$I = -\frac{dQ}{dt},$$

and, if the inductance be denoted by L, the emf opposing V is $L \, dI/dt$, since the IR drop is assumed to be negligible. Thus,

$$V - L\frac{dI}{dt} = 0$$

or

$$\frac{Q}{C} - L\left[\frac{d}{dt}\left(-\frac{dQ}{dt}\right)\right] = 0.$$

Simplifying gives

$$\frac{d^2Q}{dt^2} + \frac{1}{CL}Q = 0,$$

which is of precisely the same form as (31-2), where $a^2 = 1/CL$, and the general solution is then

$$Q = A\cos\frac{t}{\sqrt{CL}} + B\sin\frac{t}{\sqrt{CL}}.$$

The period of oscillation is

$$T = 2\pi\sqrt{CL}.$$

Note that we can make the inductance L correspond to the mass M of the mechanical example and $1/C$ correspond to the stiffness k of the spring.

32. Viscous Damping. Let the spring of the mechanical example of Sec. 31 be placed in a resisting medium in which the damping force is proportional to the velocity. This kind of damping is termed *viscous damping*.

Since the resisting medium opposes the displacement, the damping force $r(dy/dt)$ acts in the direction opposite to that of the displacement of the mass M. The force equation, in this case, becomes

$$M\frac{d^2y}{dt^2} = Mg - k(y + s) - r\frac{dy}{dt}$$

or, since $Mg = ks$,

$$\frac{d^2y}{dt^2} + \frac{r}{M}\frac{dy}{dt} + \frac{k}{M}y = 0.$$

To solve this equation we write it in the more convenient form

$$\frac{d^2y}{dt^2} + 2b\frac{dy}{dt} + a^2y = 0, \tag{32-1}$$

where $2b = r/M$ and $a^2 = k/M$. In this case the characteristic equation is

$$m^2 + 2bm + a^2 = 0$$

and its roots are

$$m = -b \pm \sqrt{b^2 - a^2},$$

so that the general solution is

$$y = c_1 e^{(-b+\sqrt{b^2-a^2}\,)t} + c_2 e^{(-b-\sqrt{b^2-a^2}\,)t}. \tag{32-2}$$

It will be instructive to interpret the physical significance of the solution (32-2) corresponding to the three distinct cases that arise when $b^2 - a^2 > 0$,

$b^2 - a^2 = 0$, and $b^2 - a^2 < 0$. If $b^2 - a^2$ is positive, the roots m are real and distinct. Denote them by m_1 and m_2, so that (32-2) is

$$y = c_1 e^{m_1 t} + c_2 e^{m_2 t}. \qquad (32\text{-}3)$$

The arbitrary constants c_1 and c_2 are determined from the initial conditions. Thus, let the spring be stretched so that $y = d$ and then released without giving the mass M an initial velocity. The conditions are then

$$y = d$$

when $t = 0$ and

$$\frac{dy}{dt} = 0$$

when $t = 0$.

Substituting these values into (32-3) and the derivative of (32-3) gives the two equations

$$d = c_1 + c_2 \qquad \text{and} \qquad 0 = m_1 c_1 + m_2 c_2.$$

These determine

$$c_1 = -\frac{m_2 d}{m_1 - m_2} \qquad \text{and} \qquad c_2 = \frac{m_1 d}{m_1 - m_2}.$$

Hence, the solution (32-3) is

$$y = \frac{d}{m_1 - m_2} (m_1 e^{m_2 t} - m_2 e^{m_1 t}).$$

The graph of the displacement represented as a function of t is of the type shown in Fig. 18. Theoretically, y never becomes zero, although it comes arbitrarily close to it. This is the so-called overdamped case. The retarding force is so great in this case that no vibration can occur.

If $b^2 - a^2 = 0$, the two roots of the characteristic equation are equal and the general solution of (32-1) becomes

$$y = e^{-bt}(c_1 + c_2 t).$$

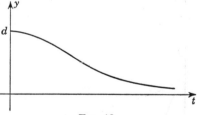

FIG. 18

If the initial conditions are $y = d$, $dy/dt = 0$ when $t = 0$, the solution is

$$y = de^{-bt}(1 + bt).$$

This type of motion of the spring is called *deadbeat*. If the retarding force is decreased by an arbitrarily small amount, the motion will become oscillatory.

The most interesting case occurs when $b^2 < a^2$, so that the roots of the characteristic equation are imaginary. Denote $b^2 - a^2$ by $-\alpha^2$, so that

$$m = -b \pm i\alpha$$

and

$$y = c_1 e^{(-b+i\alpha)t} + c_2 e^{(-b-i\alpha)t}$$

$$= e^{-bt}(A \cos \alpha t + B \sin \alpha t).$$

If the initial conditions are chosen as before,

$$y = d$$

when $t = 0$ and

$$\frac{dy}{dt} = 0$$

when $t = 0$, the arbitrary constants A and B can be evaluated. The result is

$$y = de^{-bt}\left(\cos \alpha t + \frac{b}{\alpha} \sin \alpha t\right),$$

which can be put in a more convenient form by the use of the identity

$$A \cos \theta + B \sin \theta \equiv \sqrt{A^2 + B^2} \cos\left(\theta - \tan^{-1} \frac{B}{A}\right).$$

The solution then appears as

$$y = \frac{d}{\alpha} \sqrt{\alpha^2 + b^2}\, e^{-bt} \cos\left(\alpha t - \tan^{-1} \frac{b}{\alpha}\right). \tag{32-4}$$

The nature of the motion as described by (32-4) is seen from Fig. 19. It is an oscillatory motion with the amplitude decreasing exponentially. The period of the motion is $T = 2\pi/\alpha$. In the undamped case the period is $T = 2\pi/a$, and since

$$\alpha = \sqrt{a^2 - b^2} < a,$$

it follows that

$$\frac{2\pi}{\alpha} > \frac{2\pi}{a}.$$

Thus the period of oscillation is increased by the damping.

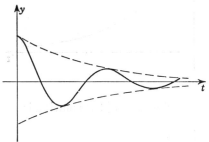

Fig. 19

An electrical problem corresponding to the example of the viscous damping of a spring is the following: A condenser (Fig. 20) of capacity C is discharged through an inductive coil whose resistance is not negligible.

Referring to Sec. 31 and remembering that the IR drop is not negligible, we find the voltage equation to be

$$V - L\frac{dI}{dt} - IR = 0$$

or

$$\frac{Q}{C} + L\frac{d^2Q}{dt^2} + R\frac{dQ}{dt} = 0.$$

Simplifying gives

$$\frac{d^2Q}{dt^2} + \frac{R}{L}\frac{dQ}{dt} + \frac{Q}{CL} = 0,$$

and this equation is of the same form as that in the mechanical example. The mass M corresponds to the inductance L, r corresponds to the electrical resistance R, and the stiffness k corresponds to $1/C$. Its solution is the same as that of the corresponding mechanical example and is obtained by setting $2b = R/L$ and $a^2 = 1/CL$.

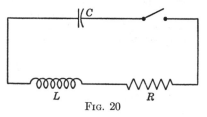

Fig. 20

PROBLEMS

1. The force of 1,000 dynes will stretch a spring 1 cm. A mass of 100 g is suspended at the end of the spring and set vibrating. Find the equation of motion and the frequency of vibration if the mass is pulled down 2 cm and then released. What will be the solution if the mass is projected down from rest with a velocity of 10 cm per sec?

2. Two equal masses are suspended at the end of an elastic spring of stiffness k. One mass falls off. Describe the motion of the remaining mass.

3. The force of 98,000 dynes extends a spring 2 cm. A mass of 200 g is suspended at the end, and the spring is pulled down 10 cm and released. Find the position of the mass at any instant t if the resistance of the medium is neglected.

4. Solve Prob. 3 under the assumption that the spring is viscously damped. It is given that the resistance is 2,000 dynes for a velocity of 1 cm per sec. What must the resistance be in order that the motion be a deadbeat?

5. A condenser of capacity 4 μf is charged so that the potential difference of the plates is 100 volts. The condenser is then discharged through a coil of resistance 500 ohms and inductance 0.5 henry. Find the potential difference at any later time t. How large must the resistance be in order that the discharge just fails to be oscillatory? Determine the potential difference for this case. Note that the equation in this case is

$$L\frac{d^2V}{dt^2} + R\frac{dV}{dt} + \frac{V}{C} = 0.$$

6. Solve Prob. 5 if $R = 100$ ohms, $C = 0.5$ μf, and $L = 0.001$ henry.

7. A simple pendulum of length l is oscillating through a small angle θ in a medium in which the resistance is proportional to the velocity. Show that the differential equation of the motion is

$$\frac{d^2\theta}{dt^2} + 2k\frac{d\theta}{dt} + \frac{g}{l}\theta = 0.$$

Discuss the motion, and show that the period is $2\pi/\sqrt{\omega^2 - k^2}$ where $\omega^2 = g/l$.

8. An iceboat weighing 500 lb is driven by a wind that exerts a force of 25 lb. Five pounds of this force is expended in overcoming frictional resistance. What speed will this boat acquire at the end of 30 sec if it starts from rest? *Hint:* The force producing the motion is $F = 25 - 5 = 20$. Hence, $500 \, dv/dt = 20g$.

9. A body is set sliding down an inclined plane with an initial velocity of v_0 fps. If the angle made by the plane with the horizontal is θ and the coefficient of friction is μ, show that the distance traveled in t sec is

$$s = \tfrac{1}{2}g(\sin \theta - \mu \cos \theta)t^2 + v_0 t.$$

Hint: $m \, d^2s/dt^2 = mg \sin \theta - \mu mg \cos \theta$.

10. One end of an elastic rubber band is fastened at a point P, and the other end supports a mass of 10 lb. When the mass is suspended freely, its weight doubles the length of the band. If the original length of the band is 1 ft and the weight is dropped from the point P, how far will the band extend? What is the equation of motion?

11. It is shown in books on strength of materials and elasticity that the deflection of a long beam lying on an elastic base, the reaction of which is proportional to the deflection y, satisfies the differential equation

$$EI \frac{d^4y}{dx^4} = -ky.$$

Set $a^4 = k/4EI$, and show that the characteristic equation corresponding to the resulting differential equation is $m^4 + 4a^4 = 0$, whose roots are $m = \pm a \pm ai$. Thus show that the general solution is

$$y = c_1 e^{ax} \cos ax + c_2 e^{ax} \sin ax + c_3 e^{-ax} \cos ax + c_4 e^{-ax} \sin ax.$$

12. If a long column is subjected to an axial load P and the assumption that the curvature is small is not made, the Bernoulli-Euler law gives (see Sec. 5)

$$\frac{d^2y/dx^2}{[1 + (dy/dx)^2]^{3/2}} = \frac{M}{EI}.$$

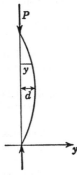

Since the moment M is equal to $-Py$ (Fig. 21), it follows upon setting $dy/dx = p$ that the differential equation of the deformed central axis is

$$\frac{p(dp/dy)}{(1 + p^2)^{3/2}} = -\frac{Py}{EI}.$$

Solve this differential equation for p, and show that the length of the central line is given by the formula

FIG. 21

$$s = 2\sqrt{\frac{EI}{P}} \, F\left(k, \frac{\pi}{2}\right),$$

where $k^2 = d^2P/4EI$, d is the maximum deflection, and $F(k,\pi/2)$ is the elliptic integral of the first kind [see Eq. (20-12)]. The equation of the elastic curve, in this case, cannot be expressed in terms of elementary functions, for the formula for y leads to an elliptic integral. See, however, Chap. 2, Sec. 10.

33. Forced Vibrations. Resonance.

In the discussion of Sec. 32, it was supposed that the vibrations were free. Thus, in the case of the mechanical example, it was assumed that the point of support of the spring was stationary and, in the electrical example, that there was no source of emf placed in series with the coil.

Now, suppose that the point of support of the spring is vibrating in accordance with some law which gives the displacement of the top of the spring as a function of the time t, say $x = f(t)$, where x is measured positively downward. Just as before, the spring is supposed to be supporting a mass M, which produces an elongation s of the spring. If the displacement of the mass M from its position of rest is y, it is clear that when the top of the spring is displaced through a distance x, the actual extension of the spring is $y - x$. If the resistance of the medium is neglected, the force equation is

$$M \frac{d^2y}{dt^2} = Mg - k(s + y - x) = -k(y - x),$$

whereas if the spring is viscously damped, it is

$$M \frac{d^2y}{dt^2} = Mg - k(s + y - x) - r \frac{dy}{dt}.$$

Upon simplification this last equation becomes

$$M \frac{d^2y}{dt^2} + r \frac{dy}{dt} + ky = kx, \qquad (33\text{-}1)$$

where x is supposed to be a known function of t.

The corresponding electrical example is that of a condenser (Fig. 22)

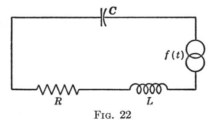

Fig. 22

which is placed in series with the source of emf and discharges through a coil containing inductance and resistance. The voltage equation is

$$-RI - L \frac{dI}{dt} + V = f(t),$$

where $f(t)$ is the impressed emf given as a function of t. Since

$$-I = \frac{dQ}{dt} = C \frac{dV}{dt},$$

the equation becomes

$$CL\frac{d^2V}{dt^2} + CR\frac{dV}{dt} + V = f(t). \tag{33-2}$$

An interesting case arises when the impressed emf is sinusoidal; for example,

$$f(t) = E_0 \sin \omega t.$$

Then the equation takes the form

$$\frac{d^2V}{dt^2} + \frac{R}{L}\frac{dV}{dt} + \frac{1}{CL}V = \frac{1}{CL}E_0 \sin \omega t.$$

Both (33-1) and (33-2) are nonhomogeneous linear equations with constant coefficients of the type

$$\frac{d^2y}{dt^2} + 2b\frac{dy}{dt} + a^2y = a^2f(t). \tag{33-3}$$

The solution of this equation is the sum of the complementary function and a particular integral. The complementary function has the form (32-2), namely,

$$c_1e^{m_1t} + c_2e^{m_2t},$$

where

$$m_1 = -b + \sqrt{b^2 - a^2} \quad \text{and} \quad m_2 = -b - \sqrt{b^2 - a^2}.$$

A particular integral $y = u(t)$ can be deduced for Eq. (33-3) for an arbitrary continuous function $f(t)$ by the method of variation of parameters.[1] If the impressed force $f(t)$ in (33-3) is simple harmonic of period $2\pi/\omega$ and amplitude a_0, then

$$f(t) = a_0 \sin \omega t$$

and an integral $y = u(t)$ can be obtained by the method of Sec. 25. The result is

$$y(t) = \frac{a^2a_0}{\sqrt{(a^2 - \omega^2)^2 + 4b^2\omega^2}} \sin(\omega t - \epsilon), \tag{33-4}$$

where

$$\epsilon = \tan^{-1}\frac{2b\omega}{a^2 - \omega^2}.$$

From discussion in Sec. 32, it is clear that the part of the general solution of (33-3) which is due to free vibrations is a decreasing function of t, becoming negligibly small after a sufficient lapse of time. Thus, the "steady-state solution" is given by the particular integral (33-4).

[1] See the corresponding computation at the end of this section for the case when $b = 0$.

It must be observed that when the impressed frequency ω is very high, the amplitude of the sinusoid in (33-4) is small. When ω is nearly equal to the natural frequency a, the amplitude is nearly $a_0a/2b$. This may be dangerously large if the resistance parameter b is small. For a and b fixed, the maximum amplitude occurs when

$$\frac{d}{d\omega}[(a^2 - \omega^2)^2 + 4b^2\omega^2] = 0,$$

that is, when

$$\omega^2 = a^2 - 2b^2. \tag{33-5}$$

Stated in terms of the physical quantities of electrical and mechanical examples, a large amplitude in (33-4) means a large maximum emf, or a large maximum displacement of the spring. These, as we have already noted, may become excessively large when the resistance r of the medium is small and the impressed frequency ω is close to the natural frequency a. This phenomenon, known as *resonance*, is of profound importance in numerous engineering and physical situations.[1]

If $b = 0$, Eq. (33-3) reduces to

$$\frac{d^2y}{dt^2} + a^2y = a^2f(t). \tag{33-6}$$

We can easily deduce a formula for an integral $y(t)$ of (33-6) for an arbitrary forcing function $f(t)$. Since $\sin at$ and $\cos at$ are linearly independent solutions of Eq. (33-6) with $f(t) = 0$, the method of variation of parameters of Sec. 28 suggests taking a solution in the form

$$y(t) = v_1(t) \cos at + v_2(t) \sin at. \tag{33-7}$$

For the determination of $v_1(t)$ and $v_2(t)$ we have a pair of equations [see Eqs. (28-6) and (28-10)]

$$v_1' \cos at + v_2' \sin at = 0,$$

$$-av_1' \sin at + av_2' \cos at = a^2f(t).$$

Solving these for v_1' and v_2' we get

$$v_1' = -af(t) \sin at, \qquad v_2' = af(t) \cos at,$$

which on integration between the limits 0 and t yield

$$v_1(t) = -a\int_0^t f(t) \sin at \, dt, \qquad v_2(t) = a\int_0^t f(t) \cos at \, dt.$$

---

[1] The failure of the Tacoma bridge was explained by some authorities on the basis of resonant forced vibrations, and there are instances of the collapse of buildings induced by the rhythmic swaying of dancing couples. The failure of propeller shafts is often attributed to forced torsional vibrations. See also Joshua 6:5.

Formula (33-7) then yields

$$y(t) = -a \cos at \int_0^t f(\lambda) \sin a\lambda \, d\lambda + a \sin at \int_0^t f(\lambda) \cos a\lambda \, d\lambda, \quad (33\text{-}8)$$

in which we have replaced the integration variable t by λ so as not to confuse it with the variable t in the limits. It follows directly from (33-8) that the integral $y(t)$ corresponds to the initial conditions $y(0) = y'(0) = 0$.

If we combine integrals in (33-8), we get the desired formula

$$y(t) = a \int_0^t f(\lambda) \sin a(t - \lambda) \, d\lambda. \quad (33\text{-}9)$$

When the forcing function $f(t)$ is taken in the form $f(t) = a_0 \sin at$ (so that the impressed frequency is equal to the natural frequency), this formula yields

$$y(t) = a a_0 \int_0^t \sin a\lambda \sin a(t - \lambda) \, d\lambda.$$

After simple integration we obtain

$$y = \frac{a_0}{2} (\sin at - at \cos at),$$

representing a vibration whose amplitude increases with time, for the amplitude $a_0/2$ in the first term is constant and the amplitude of the second term, $a_0 at/2$, grows with t. In any physical situation, some resistance is present, and a reference to (33-4) shows that b prevents oscillations from becoming arbitrarily large. Nevertheless, they may be dangerously large if b is small and a is near ω.

PROBLEM

Obtain a formula for a particular integral of Eq. (33-3) analogous to (33-9), and deduce from it the result (33-4). The integration will be simplified if $\sin \omega t$ is replaced by $(e^{i\omega t} - e^{-i\omega t})/2i$.

34. The Euler Column. Rotating Shaft. It is known from experiments that a long rectilinear rod subjected to the action of axial compressive forces is compressed and retains its initial shape as long as the compressive forces do not exceed a certain critical value. Upon gradual increase of the compressive load P, a value of $P = P_1$ is reached when the rod buckles suddenly and becomes curved. The deflections of rods so compressed become extremely sensitive to minute changes of the load and increase rapidly with the increase in P. A detailed analysis of this *instability* or *buckling* phenomenon depends on rather delicate considerations in nonlinear theory of elasticity. However, if the argument of Euler is followed, it is possible to deduce the magnitude of the critical load P_1 from linear differential equations governing small deflections of loaded rods.

Thus, consider a rod of uniform cross section and length l, compressed by the forces P applied to its ends (Fig. 23). Initially this rod is straight,

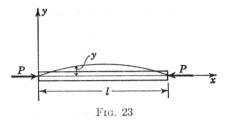

FIG. 23

but after the critical load P_1 is reached, it becomes curved, and we denote the deflections of its central line by y.

It is known from the Bernoulli-Euler law (5-2) that for small deflections

$$\frac{d^2y}{dx^2} = \frac{M}{EI},$$

where, in our case, the bending moment $M = -Py$. Thus

$$\frac{d^2y}{dx^2} = -\frac{Py}{EI},$$

or

$$y'' + k^2y = 0, \tag{34-1}$$

where

$$k^2 \equiv \frac{P}{EI}. \tag{34-2}$$

Equation (34-1) must be solved subject to the end conditions

$$y(0) = 0, \quad y(l) = 0, \tag{34-3}$$

since the ends of the rod remain on the x axis.

The *boundary-value problem* characterized by Eqs. (34-1) and (34-2) is quite different from the initial-value problems considered heretofore. In the initial-value problems we seek solutions of differential equations satisfying specified conditions at *one* point only, while in the boundary-value problem stated above the solution y must satisfy conditions (34-3) assigned at *two* points $x = 0$ and $x = l$. It is not obvious that a solution of a differential equation satisfying specified conditions at two points exists in general. We shall see, however, that for suitable choices of the parameter k Eq. (34-1) does have solutions vanishing at the end points $x = 0, x = l$.

Now the general solution of (34-1) is

$$y = c_1 \cos kx + c_2 \sin kx \tag{34-4}$$

and, on imposing the conditions (34-3), we get two equations

$$0 = c_1 \cos k0 + c_2 \sin k0$$

$$0 = c_1 \cos kl + c_2 \sin kl.$$

These demand that

$$c_1 = 0, \qquad c_2 \sin kl = 0. \tag{34-5}$$

The choice $c_1 = c_2 = 0$ gives $y = 0$, corresponding to the rectilinear shape of the rod. If the rod does not remain straight, $c_2 \neq 0$, and we conclude from (34-5) that $\sin kl = 0$, so that

$$k = \frac{n\pi}{l}, \qquad n = 0, 1, 2, \ldots. \tag{34-6}$$

The choice of $n = 0$ again gives $y = 0$. If $n = 1$, $k = \pi/l$, and on recalling the definition (34-2), we see that the corresponding value of P is

$$P_1 = EI \frac{\pi^2}{l^2}. \tag{34-7}$$

This is the *critical*, or the *Euler*, *load*.

The shape of the central line of the rod, in this case, is

$$y = c_2 \sin \frac{\pi x}{l}.$$

The choice of $n = 2, 3, \ldots$ in (34-6) gives other "critical loads" P_2, P_3, $\ldots$ and the corresponding solutions

$$y = c_2 \sin \frac{n\pi x}{l}.$$

The maximum deflection c_2 is not determined in this analysis, and, indeed, no far-reaching conclusions should be made from such calculations inasmuch as they are based on the assumption of small deflections implicit in our use of the Bernoulli-Euler law.

Another interesting problem, essentially of the same sort, arises in the study of rotating shafts. It has been noted that when a long shaft supported by bearings at $x = 0$ and $x = l$ is allowed to rotate, its initially rectilinear shape is preserved only if the speed of rotation ω does not exceed a certain critical value ω_1. On approaching the speed ω_1 the shaft starts pulsating and its shape changes. On further increase of the speed another critical value ω_2 is reached when the shaft starts beating and its shape changes again, and so on. This phenomenon can, in part, be explained by calculations similar to those used in determining the Euler load.

Let us suppose that the shaft is rotating with the angular speed ω. An element of length dx of the shaft experiences the centrifugal force

$$F \, dx = \rho \, dx \, \omega^2 y,$$

where ρ is the density per unit length of the shaft and y is the deflection at the point x. Thus,

$$F = \rho \omega^2 y \tag{34-8}$$

is the force per unit length of the shaft distributed along its length. It is shown in books on strength of materials that when the forces F acting on a rod are normal to its axis, then

$$F = \frac{d^2 M}{dx^2},$$

where the bending moment M is given by the Bernoulli-Euler law

$$M = EI \frac{d^2 y}{dx^2}. \tag{34-9}$$

Thus,
$$F = \frac{d^2}{dx^2} \left(EI \frac{d^2 y}{dx^2} \right), \tag{34-10}$$

and if the *flexural rigidity* EI is constant, Eq. (34-10) reads

$$\frac{d^4 y}{dx^4} = \frac{F}{EI}. \tag{34-11}$$

The substitution for F from (34-8) gives the desired equation for the rotating shaft:

$$\frac{d^4 y}{dx^4} - k^4 y = 0 \tag{34-12}$$

with
$$k^4 \equiv \frac{\rho \omega^2}{EI}. \tag{34-13}$$

Since the roots of the characteristic equation $m^4 - k^4 = 0$ are $m = \pm k$, $m = \pm ki$, the general solution of (34-12) is

$$y = c_1 e^{kx} + c_2 e^{-kx} + c_3 \cos kx + c_4 \sin kx. \tag{34-14}$$

If at the points of support $x = 0$, $x = l$ the deflection y and the moment M are zero, then [see (34-9)]

$$y(0) = 0, \qquad y''(0) = 0,$$
$$y(l) = 0, \qquad y''(l) = 0. \tag{34-15}$$

The substitution from (34-14) into the boundary conditions (34-15) yields four equations:

$$c_1 + c_2 + c_3 = 0,$$
$$c_1 + c_2 - c_3 = 0,$$
$$c_1 e^{kl} + c_2 e^{-kl} + c_3 \cos kl + c_4 \sin kl = 0,$$
$$c_1 e^{kl} + c_2 e^{-kl} - c_3 \cos kl - c_4 \sin kl = 0.$$

$$(34\text{-}16)$$

The solution $c_1 = c_2 = c_3 = c_4 = 0$, yielding $y = 0$, corresponds to the straight shaft. The system (34-16) also has nonzero solutions for certain values of k. From the first two equations (34-16) we find

$$c_1 = -c_2, \qquad c_3 = 0,$$

and the substitution of these values in the two remaining equations gives

$$c_1 = c_2 = c_3 = 0, \qquad c_4 \sin kl = 0.$$

Thus, $\sin kl = 0$ unless $c_4 = 0$, and hence

$$k = \frac{n\pi}{l}, \qquad n = 1, 2, \ldots.$$

Using the value of k for $n = 1$ in (34-13) gives the first critical speed

$$\omega_1 = \frac{\pi^2}{l^2} \sqrt{\frac{EI}{\rho}}.$$

The critical speeds $\omega_2, \omega_3, \ldots$ are determined by taking k with $n = 2, 3, \ldots$.

PROBLEMS

1. When a beam lies on an elastic foundation, then in addition to the transverse external load $F(x)$, there is a restoring force $R = -a^2 y$ proportional to the deflection y. The equation of the axis of the beam then has the form

$$EI y^{IV} + a^2 y = F(x).$$

Solve this equation for $F(x) = p$, a constant, by assuming that the ends of the beam are hinged so that

$$y(0) = y''(0) = y(l) = y''(l) = 0.$$

2. The differential equation of the deflection y of the truss of a suspension bridge has the form

$$EI \frac{d^4 y}{dx^4} - (H + h) \frac{d^2 y}{dx^2} = p - q \frac{h}{H},$$

where H = horizontal tension in cable under dead load q
h = tension due to live load p
E = Young's modulus

I = moment of inertia of cross section of truss about horizontal axis of truss through center of gravity of section and perpendicular to direction of length of truss

Solve this equation under the assumption that $p - qh/H$ is a constant.

3. The differential equation of the buckling of an elastically supported beam under an axial load P has the form

$$\frac{d^4y}{dx^4} + \frac{P}{EI}\frac{d^2y}{dx^2} + \frac{k}{EI}y = 0,$$

where EI is the flexural rigidity and k is the modulus of the foundation. Solve this equation.

SYSTEMS OF EQUATIONS

35. Reduction of Systems to a Single Equation. We saw in Sec. 13 that it may prove advantageous to reduce the solution of a second-order equation to the solution of a system of two equations of first order. Thus the dynamical equation considered in Sec. 31,

$$\frac{d^2s}{dt^2} = F(s,s',t)$$

with $s' \equiv ds/dt$, can be reduced to a system of two equations,

$$\frac{dv}{dt} = F(s,v,t),$$

$$\frac{ds}{dt} = v,$$

by setting $s' = v$.

In the same manner, the third-order equation

$$\frac{d^3y}{dt^3} = F(y,y',y'',t), \tag{35-1}$$

in which $y' \equiv dy/dt$ and $y'' \equiv d^2y/dt^2$, is reducible to a system of three first-order equations in x_1, x_2, x_3 defined by

$$y = x_1, \qquad y' = x_2, \qquad y'' = x_3.$$

With these definitions, Eq. (35-1) can be replaced by a system of three equations:

$$\frac{dx_1}{dt} = x_2, \qquad \frac{dx_2}{dt} = x_3, \qquad \frac{dx_3}{dt} = F(x_1,x_2,x_3,t). \tag{35-2}$$

This procedure can be extended to nth-order equations.

A reduction of the nth-order equation to a system of n first-order equations is of some practical importance in numerical integration of equations on differential analyzers and electronic calculators. Such computing devices are usually so designed that it is simpler to calculate n first derivatives than one derivative of order n.   The reduction has also numerous advantages in theoretical considerations.

Systems of differential equations appear naturally in problems involving dynamical systems with several degrees of freedom.   Thus, the motion of a particle constrained to move on a surface can be described by two positional coordinates [1] (x,y).   These coordinates satisfy equations of the form

$$\frac{d^2x}{dt^2} = F\left(x,y,\frac{dx}{dt},\frac{dy}{dt},t\right),$$

$$\frac{d^2y}{dt^2} = G\left(x,y,\frac{dx}{dt},\frac{dy}{dt},t\right).$$

This pair of second-order equations can be reduced to a system of four first-order equations.

Alternatively, a system of n first-order equations can usually be reduced to a single nth-order equation.   A general discussion of this problem is involved, and we confine our remarks to systems of linear equations, because such systems commonly occur in applications.

A system of n first-order equations

$$\frac{dy_1}{dt} = a_{11}y_1 + a_{12}y_2 + \cdots + a_{1n}y_n + f_1(t),$$

$$\frac{dy_2}{dt} = a_{21}y_1 + a_{22}y_2 + \cdots + a_{2n}y_n + f_2(t),$$

$$\cdots \cdots \cdots \cdots \cdots \cdots \cdots \cdots \cdots \cdots$$

$$\frac{dy_n}{dt} = a_{n1}y_1 + a_{n2}y_2 + \cdots + a_{nn}y_n + f_n(t),$$

(35-3)

in which the a_{ij} and the $f_i(t)$ are continuous functions of t, is called *linear*. If the $f_i(t)$ are all zero, the system is called *homogeneous*.

The system (35-3) is linear because the solutions of the associated homogeneous system satisfy the linearity properties stated in Sec. 21.   Thus if

$$y_1^{(1)}(t), y_2^{(1)}(t), \ldots, y_n^{(1)}(t)$$

and
$$y_1^{(2)}(t), y_2^{(2)}(t), \ldots, y_n^{(2)}(t)$$

are any two solutions of the homogeneous system, then the set of functions

$$c_1y_1^{(1)} + c_2y_1^{(2)}, c_1y_2^{(1)} + c_2y_2^{(2)}, \ldots, c_1y_n^{(1)} + c_2y_n^{(2)}$$

is a solution of the homogeneous system for any choice of the constants c.

[1] If a particle moves on a sphere, for example, x and y may be taken as the latitude and longitude, respectively.

Furthermore, it can be shown that the homogeneous system associated with (35-3) has a set of n solutions

$$y_1^{(1)}, y_2^{(1)}, \ldots, y_n^{(1)} \qquad \text{first solution}$$

$$y_1^{(2)}, y_2^{(2)}, \ldots, y_n^{(2)} \qquad \text{second solution}$$

$$\cdot\ \cdot\ \cdot\ \cdot\ \cdot\ \cdot\ \cdot$$

$$y_1^{(n)}, y_2^{(n)}, \ldots, y_n^{(n)}, \qquad n\text{th solution}$$

such that the determinant

$$\begin{vmatrix} y_1^{(1)} & y_2^{(1)} & \cdots & y_n^{(1)} \\ y_1^{(2)} & y_2^{(2)} & \cdots & y_n^{(2)} \\ \cdot & \cdot & \cdot & \cdot \\ y_1^{(n)} & y_2^{(n)} & \cdots & y_n^{(n)} \end{vmatrix} \neq 0.$$

The general solution of the system (35-3) is then given by the set of n functions

$$y_i = c_1 y_i^{(1)} + c_2 y_i^{(2)} + \cdots + c_n y_i^{(n)} + u_i(t), \qquad i = 1, 2, \ldots, n, \qquad (35\text{-}4)$$

where $y_1 = u_1(t)$, $y_2 = u_2(t)$, $\ldots$, $y_n = u_n(t)$ is any solution of the nonhomogeneous system and the c_i are arbitrary constants. The solution (35-4) is general in the sense that the cs can be always chosen so that there is a unique solution of the system (35-3) satisfying the arbitrarily prescribed initial conditions:

$$y_1(t_0) = y_{10}, \qquad y_2(t_0) = y_{20}, \qquad \ldots, \qquad y_n(t_0) = y_{n0}.$$

We indicate next how a system of first-order linear equations with *constant coefficients* can ordinarily be reduced to an equivalent single linear equation with constant coefficients whose order is equal to the number of equations in the system.

Consider the system of two equations

$$\frac{dx}{dt} + a_1 x + a_2 y = f_1(t),$$

$$\frac{dy}{dt} + b_1 x + b_2 y = f_2(t). \qquad (35\text{-}5)$$

We introduce the operator $D \equiv d/dt$ and write (35-5) as

$$(D + a_1)x + a_2 y = f_1(t),$$

$$b_1 x + (D + b_2)y = f_2(t). \qquad (35\text{-}6)$$

Operating on the second equation in (35-6) with $(1/b_1)(D + a_1)$, we get

$$(D + a_1)x + \frac{1}{b_1}(D + a_1)(D + b_2)y = \frac{1}{b_1}(D + a_1)f_2(t). \qquad (35\text{-}7)$$

If we subtract the first equation in (35-6) from (35-7), we get, on multiplying through by b_1,

$$(D + a_1)(D + b_2)y - b_1 a_2 y = (D + a_1)f_2(t) - b_1 f_1(t). \qquad (35\text{-}8)$$

This is a second-order linear differential equation with constant coefficients whose right-hand member is a known function. Hence its general solution $y = y(t)$ can readily be obtained.

The characteristic equation for (35-8) is

$$(m + a_1)(m + b_2) - b_1 a_2 = 0, \tag{35-9}$$

and if its roots $m = m_1$, $m = m_2$ are distinct, the general solution of (35-8) is

$$y = c_1 e^{m_1 t} + c_2 e^{m_2 t} + u(t),$$

where $u(t)$ is a particular integral of (35-8). If (35-8) has a double root $m_1 = m_2$, the corresponding solution is

$$y = c_1 e^{m_1 t} + c_2 t e^{m_1 t} + u(t).$$

Having obtained y, we can compute the solution for x, without further integration, by substituting $y(t)$ in the second equation in (35-5). Thus

$$x(t) = \frac{1}{b_1} \left[f_2(t) - b_2 y(t) - \frac{dy}{dt} \right].$$

The procedure for reduction of larger systems or for systems of equations of order higher than 1 is similar.[1]

Example 1.   Consider

$$\frac{dx}{dt} + 2x - 2y = t,$$

$$\frac{dy}{dt} - 3x + y = e^t,$$

or

$$(D + 2)x - 2y = t,$$

$$-3x + (D + 1)y = e^t.$$

Operate on the second of these equations with $\tfrac{1}{3}(D + 2)$ to obtain

$$-(D + 2)x + \tfrac{1}{3}(D + 2)(D + 1)y = \tfrac{1}{3}(D + 2)e^t,$$

and add this result to the first equation. The result is

$$\tfrac{1}{3}(D + 2)(D + 1)y - 2y = \tfrac{1}{3}(D + 2)e^t + t,$$

which simplifies to

$$(D^2 + 3D - 4)y = 3e^t + 3t.$$

This equation can be solved for y as a function of t, and the result can be substituted in the second of the given equations to obtain x.

[1] See Example 2, p. 99.

Example 2. Let the two masses M_1 and M_2 be suspended from two springs, as indicated in Fig. 24, and assume that the coefficients of stiffness of the springs are k_1 and k_2, respectively. Denote the displacements of the masses from their positions of equilibrium by x and y. Then it can be established that the following equations must hold:

$$M_2 \frac{d^2y}{dt^2} = -k_2(y - x),$$

$$M_1 \frac{d^2x}{dt^2} = k_2(y - x) - k_1 x.$$

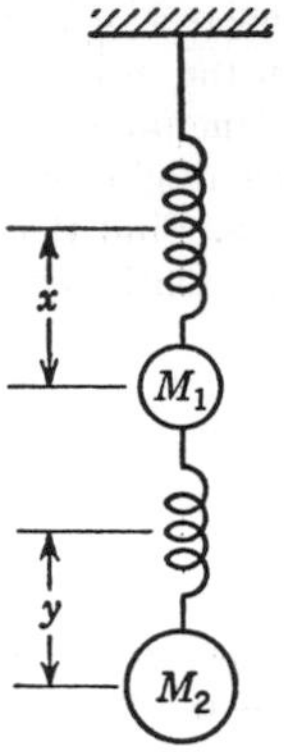

These equations can be simplified to read

$$\frac{d^2y}{dt^2} + \frac{k_2}{M_2} y - \frac{k_2}{M_2} x = 0,$$

$$\frac{d^2x}{dt^2} - \frac{k_2}{M_1} y + \frac{k_1 + k_2}{M_1} x = 0.$$

By setting

$$\frac{k_1}{M_1} = a^2, \qquad \frac{k_2}{M_2} = b^2, \qquad \frac{M_2}{M_1} = m,$$

FIG. 24

the equations reduce to

$$(D^2 + b^2)y - b^2 x = 0,$$

$$-b^2 m y + (D^2 + a^2 + b^2 m)x = 0.$$

Operating on the second of these reduced equations with $(1/b^2 m)(D^2 + b^2)$ and adding the result to the first of the equations give

$$(D^2 + b^2)(D^2 + a^2 + b^2 m)x - b^4 m x = 0$$

or

$$[D^4 + (a^2 + b^2 + b^2 m)D^2 + a^2 b^2]x = 0.$$

This is a fourth-order differential equation which can be solved for x as a function of t. It is readily checked that

$$x = A \sin (\omega t - \epsilon)$$

is a solution, provided that ω is suitably chosen. There will be two positive values of ω which will satisfy the conditions. The motion of the spring is a combination of two simple harmonic motions of different frequencies.

PROBLEMS

Solve the systems:

1. $\dfrac{dx}{dt} = y, \dfrac{dy}{dt} = -x;$

2. $\dfrac{dx}{dt} = y, \dfrac{dy}{dt} = x;$

3. $\dfrac{dx}{dt} = 3x - 2y, \dfrac{dy}{dt} = 2x - y;$

4. $\dfrac{d^2x}{dt^2} = y, \dfrac{d^2y}{dt^2} = x;$

5. $\dfrac{dy}{dt} + \dfrac{dx}{dt} = 2y, \dfrac{dy}{dt} - \dfrac{dx}{dt} = 2x \cdot$

6. $(D + 1)x + (2D + 1)y = e^t, (D - 1)x + (D + 1)y = 1.$

7. Determine the solution in Example 1 satisfying $y(0) = 0$, $x(0) = 0$.

8. The equations of motion of a particle of mass m are

$$m\frac{d^2x}{dt^2} = X, \qquad m\frac{d^2y}{dt^2} = Y, \qquad m\frac{d^2z}{dt^2} = Z,$$

where x, y, z are the coordinates of the particle and X, Y, Z are the components of force in the directions of the x, y, and z axes, respectively. If the particle moves in the xy plane under a central attractive force, proportional to the distance of the particle from the origin, find the differential equations of motion of the particle.

9. Find the equation of the path of a particle whose coordinates x and y satisfy the differential equations

$$m\frac{d^2x}{dt^2} + He\frac{dy}{dt} = Ee,$$

$$m\frac{d^2y}{dt^2} - He\frac{dx}{dt} = 0,$$

where H, E, e, and m are constants. Assume that $x = y = dx/dt = dy/dt = 0$ when $t = 0$. This system of differential equations occurs in the determination of the ratio of the charge to the mass of an electron.

10. The currents I_1 and I_2 in the two coupled circuits shown in Fig. 25 satisfy the following differential equations:

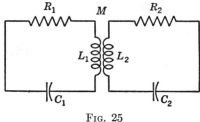

$$M\frac{d^2I_1}{dt^2} + L_2\frac{d^2I_2}{dt^2} + R_2\frac{dI_2}{dt} + \frac{I_2}{C_2} = 0,$$

$$M\frac{d^2I_2}{dt^2} + L_1\frac{d^2I_1}{dt^2} + R_1\frac{dI_1}{dt} + \frac{I_1}{C_1} = 0.$$

Fig. 25

Reduce the solution of this system to that of a single fourth-order differential equation. Solve the resulting equation under the assumption that the resistances R_1 and R_2 are negligible.

36. Systems of Linear Equations with Constant Coefficients.

We have indicated in the preceding section how a system of linear equations with constant coefficients can be solved by reducing the problem to the solution of one equation of higher order. In this section we sketch another mode of attack on the problem of solving the homogeneous system

$$\frac{dy_1}{dt} = a_{11}y_1 + a_{12}y_2 + \cdots + a_{1n}y_n,$$

$$\frac{dy_2}{dt} = a_{21}y_1 + a_{22}y_2 + \cdots + a_{2n}y_n,$$

$$\cdots \cdots \cdots \cdots \cdots \cdots \cdots$$ (36-1)

$$\frac{dy_n}{dt} = a_{n1}y_1 + a_{n2}y_2 + \cdots + a_{nn}y_n,$$

with constant coefficients. A third method, based on Laplace transform, is given in Appendix B.

Let us seek our solution in the form

$$y_1(t) = k_1 e^{\lambda t}, \qquad y_2(t) = k_2 e^{\lambda t}, \qquad \ldots, \qquad y_n(t) = k_n e^{\lambda t}, \quad (36\text{-}2)$$

where the constants k_i and λ are to be determined so that Eqs. (36-1) are satisfied identically.

The substitution from (36-2) in (36-1) yields

$$\lambda k_1 e^{\lambda t} = (a_{11}k_1 + a_{12}k_2 + \cdots + a_{1n}k_n)e^{\lambda t},$$
$$\lambda k_2 e^{\lambda t} = (a_{21}k_1 + a_{22}k_2 + \cdots + a_{2n}k_n)e^{\lambda t},$$
$$\cdots \cdots \cdots \cdots \cdots \cdots \cdots \cdots \cdots$$
$$\lambda k_n e^{\lambda t} = (a_{n1}k_1 + a_{n2}k_2 + \cdots + a_{nn}k_n)e^{\lambda t}.$$

On dividing each equation by $e^{\lambda t}$ and transposing all terms to one side, we get the system

$$(a_{11} - \lambda)k_1 + \qquad a_{12}k_2 + \cdots + \qquad a_{1n}k_n = 0,$$
$$a_{21}k_1 + (a_{22} - \lambda)k_2 + \cdots + \qquad a_{2n}k_n = 0,$$
$$\cdots \cdots \cdots \cdots \cdots \cdots \cdots \cdots \cdots \qquad (36\text{-}3)$$
$$a_{n1}k_1 + \qquad a_{n2}k_2 + \cdots + (a_{nn} - \lambda)k_n = 0.$$

This system is a system of linear homogeneous algebraic equations for the unknown ks. It has an obvious solution

$$k_1 = k_2 = \cdots = k_n = 0$$

corresponding to the trivial solution

$$y_1 = y_2 = \cdots = y_n = 0.$$

Since we are interested in solutions (36-2) which are not all zero, we must seek values of the ks which are not all zero. Now, a system of Eqs. (36-3) will have such solutions for the k_i if, and only if, its determinant [1]

$$D = \begin{vmatrix} a_{11} - \lambda & a_{12} & \cdots & a_{1n} \\ a_{21} & a_{22} - \lambda & \cdots & a_{2n} \\ \cdots & \cdots & \cdots & \cdots \\ a_{n1} & a_{n2} & \cdots & a_{nn} - \lambda \end{vmatrix} = 0. \quad (36\text{-}4)$$

The equation $D = 0$ is called the *characteristic equation* for the system (36-1). On expanding the determinant, we see that (36-4) is an algebraic equation of degree n in λ, and thus it has n real or complex roots:

$$\lambda = \lambda_1, \qquad \lambda = \lambda_2, \qquad \ldots, \qquad \lambda = \lambda_n.$$

[1] See Appendix A.

If all these roots are distinct, then corresponding to each root $\lambda = \lambda_i$ there will be a solution of the form (36-2), namely,

$$y_1(t) = k_1 e^{\lambda_i t}, \qquad y_2(t) = k_2 e^{\lambda_i t}, \qquad \ldots, \qquad y_n(t) = k_n e^{\lambda_i t}. \qquad (36\text{-}5)$$

The constants k_i in (36-5) must satisfy Eqs. (36-3) with λ replaced by λ_i.

When Eq. (36-4) has multiple roots, the forms of solutions corresponding to multiple roots are more complicated. One solution corresponding to a multiple root $\lambda = \lambda_i$ surely has the form (36-5), but there will also be solutions in the form of polynomials in t multiplied [1] by $e^{\lambda_i t}$.

To clarify this discussion we consider a simple example.

Example: Solve the system

$$\frac{dy_1}{dt} = 2y_1 + 3y_2,$$

$$\frac{dy_2}{dt} = 2y_1 + y_2. \qquad (36\text{-}6)$$

We take a solution in the form

$$y_1 = k_1 e^{\lambda t}, \qquad y_2 = k_2 e^{\lambda t}. \qquad (36\text{-}7)$$

The characteristic equation (36-4) now reads

$$\begin{vmatrix} 2 - \lambda & 3 \\ 2 & 1 - \lambda \end{vmatrix} = 0.$$

On expanding it we get

$$\lambda^2 - 3\lambda - 4 = 0,$$

the roots of which are $\lambda_1 = -1$, $\lambda_2 = 4$. Thus, corresponding to the root $\lambda_1 = -1$, we have a solution

$$y_1 = k_1 e^{-t}, \qquad y_2 = k_2 e^{-t}. \qquad (36\text{-}8)$$

To determine k_1 and k_2 we form the system (36-3),

$$(2 - \lambda)k_1 + 3k_2 = 0,$$

$$2k_1 + (1 - \lambda)k_2 = 0, \qquad (36\text{-}9)$$

set $\lambda = -1$, and solve it for the ks. The result is

$$k_1 = -k_2.$$

Thus, one of the ks can be chosen at will. If we take $k_1 = a$, we see from (36-8) that one solution of (36-6) is

$$y_1 = ae^{-t}, \qquad y_2 = -ae^{-t}, \qquad (36\text{-}10)$$

the constant a being arbitrary.

Another solution is obtained by taking $\lambda = 4$. It has the form

$$y_1 = k_1 e^{4t}, \qquad y_2 = k_2 e^{4t} \qquad (36\text{-}11)$$

---

[1] Recall the corresponding situation in Sec. 26.

with ks determined by Eqs. (36-9) with $\lambda = 4$. We find this time

$$k_2 = \tfrac{2}{3}k_1,$$

so that, again, one of the ks can be chosen at will. If we take $k_1 = b$, we obtain a solution

$$y_1 = be^{4t}, \qquad y_2 = \tfrac{2}{3}be^{4t}. \tag{36-12}$$

From (35-4) it follows that the general solution of the system (36-6) is obtained by forming a linear combination of solutions (36-12) and (36-10). We thus get the general solution

$$y_1 = ae^{-t} + be^{4t}, \qquad y_2 = -ae^{-t} + \tfrac{2}{3}be^{4t}.$$

This solution could have been obtained more easily by the method of Sec. 35. Thus, on writing the given system in the form

$$(D - 2)y_1 - 3y_2 = 0,$$
$$-2y_1 + (D - 1)y_2 = 0, \tag{36-13}$$

we operate on the first equation with $\tfrac{1}{3}(D - 1)$, add the result to the second, and get

$$\tfrac{1}{3}(D - 1)(D - 2)y_1 - 2y_1 = 0. \tag{36-14}$$

The corresponding characteristic equation is

$$\tfrac{1}{3}(m - 1)(m - 2) - 2 = 0,$$

or

$$m^2 - 3m - 4 = 0.$$

Since its roots are $m_1 = -1$, $m_2 = 4$, the general solution of Eq. (36-14) is

$$y_1 = c_1e^{-t} + c_2e^{4t}.$$

From the first of Eqs. (36-13) we have

$$y_2 = \tfrac{1}{3}(D - 2)y_1 = \tfrac{1}{3}(D - 2)(c_1e^{-t} + c_2e^{4t}) = -c_1e^{-t} + \tfrac{2}{3}c_2e^{4t}.$$

This checks the result found previously.

The main object of this section is not so much to provide a new method for solving systems of linear equations but to introduce a few ideas on which the important study of stability of solutions of differential equations is based. There are several notions of stability of solutions, and we illustrate only two such by considering some simple examples.

The system

$$\frac{dy}{dt} = x,$$
$$\frac{dx}{dt} = -2bx - a^2y, \tag{36-15}$$

is, obviously, equivalent to one second-order equation

$$\frac{d^2y}{dt^2} + 2b\frac{dy}{dt} + a^2y = 0. \tag{36-16}$$

As we saw in Sec. 32, its general solution when $b^2 - a^2 > 0$ is

$$y = c_1 e^{(-b+\sqrt{b^2-a^2})t} + c_2 e^{(-b-\sqrt{b^2-a^2})t}. \tag{36-17}$$

If $b^2 - a^2 < 0$, we can write (36-17) as

$$y = e^{-bt}(A \cos \sqrt{a^2 - b^2}\, t + B \sin \sqrt{a^2 - b^2}\, t). \tag{36-18}$$

If $b = a$, we have the solution

$$y = e^{-bt}(c_1 + c_2 t). \tag{36-19}$$

For $b = 0$, we have the equation

$$\frac{d^2 y}{dt^2} + a^2 y = 0, \tag{36-20}$$

whose general solution is

$$y = A \cos at + B \sin at. \tag{36-21}$$

We observe that if $b > 0$, the solutions (36-17) and (36-19) are damped. That is, $|y(t)| \to 0$ as $t \to \infty$. If $b < 0$, these solutions are not damped because $|y(t)| \to \infty$ for a sequence of values $t \to \infty$. As regards the case $b = 0$, we see from (36-21) that $y(t)$ oscillates between $+\sqrt{A^2 + B^2}$ and $-\sqrt{A^2 + B^2}$ [see the formula just above (32-4)].

If we write Eq. (36-16) in the form

$$\frac{d^2 y}{dt^2} + a^2 y = -2by', \qquad y' \equiv \frac{dy}{dt} \tag{36-22}$$

and compare it with (36-20), we are tempted to say that the solutions of (36-22), for small values of b, can differ only slightly from solutions of (36-20), because the right-hand members of these equations are nearly equal if b is sufficiently small. The fact that this is not so is obvious from the foregoing remarks concerning the different behaviors of solutions of (36-16) for positive and negative values of b.

Thus, in general, small changes (or perturbations) in the coefficients of a differential equation may completely alter the nature of its solutions. This remark has an important bearing on the problem of constructing differential equations that purport to represent the behavior of physical systems. In physical problems, the coefficients in a differential equation are usually related to physical quantities. Such quantities are determined from measurements which are subject to experimental errors. For this reason, it is exceedingly important to know just what effect small variations in the coefficients of a given equation have on the character of its solutions. When small changes in the coefficients result in small changes in the solutions, the solutions are termed *stable*.

Another type of the stability problem occurs in the study of the dependence of solutions on small changes in the initial values. In practice one ordinarily seeks particular solutions that satisfy specified initial data. The initial data are generally determined either experimentally or from a specific assumption that certain physical conditions hold. (For example, one may assume that the deflection of a beam at a given point is zero.) If the initial conditions are altered slightly, is it true that the solution of a given equation will not be affected by a great deal? The fact that solutions of differential equations need not be continuous functions of initial conditions is clear from the following examples.

Consider the solution of

$$\frac{dy}{dt} = -a^2 y, \qquad a \neq 0, \tag{36-23}$$

subject to the initial condition $y(0) = y_0$. The desired solution obviously is

$$y(t) = y_0 e^{-a^2 t}.$$

Now, if y_0 is changed by a small amount Δy_0, the corresponding solution is

$$\bar{y}(t) = (y_0 + \Delta y_0) e^{-a^2 t}.$$

Because of the factor $e^{-a^2 t}$,

$$|\bar{y}(t) - y(t)| \to 0 \qquad \text{as } t \to \infty,$$

and hence for any $\epsilon > 0$ we can choose a t_0 such that

$$|\bar{y}(t) - y(t)| < \epsilon \qquad \text{if } t \geq t_0.$$

Having chosen t_0, we let Δy be so small that

$$|\bar{y}(t) - y(t)| < \epsilon \qquad \text{if } 0 \leq t \leq t_0.$$

Then it follows that $|\bar{y} - y| < \epsilon$ on the whole interval $0 \leq t < \infty$, and hence the solutions are *stable*. By (36-5) similar arguments apply to systems of equations with constant coefficients, and it is found that the system (36-1) has stable solutions when *all* roots of the characteristic equation (36-4) have negative real parts.

On the other hand, if we solve

$$\frac{dy}{dt} = a^2 y, \qquad a \neq 0, \tag{36-24}$$

subject to the same initial condition $y(0) = y_0$, we get

$$y(t) = y_0 e^{a^2 t}.$$

On replacing y_0 by $y_0 + \Delta y_0$ we get

$$\bar{y}(t) = (y_0 + \Delta y_0)e^{a^2 t},$$

and this time $|\bar{y}(t) - y(t)| = e^{a^2 t}|\Delta y_0|$. This becomes infinite as $t \to \infty$, no matter how small Δy_0 is, so that the solutions of (36-24) are *unstable*.

PROBLEMS

1. Use the method of this section to obtain the general solution of the system

$$\frac{dy_1}{dt} = y_1 + y_2, \qquad \frac{dy_2}{dt} = 4y_1 + y_2.$$

2. A system of linear second-order equations

$$\frac{d^2 y_1}{dt^2} = a_{11}y_1 + a_{12}y_2 + \cdots + a_{1n}y_n,$$

$$\frac{d^2 y_2}{dt^2} = a_{21}y_1 + a_{22}y_2 + \cdots + a_{2n}y_n,$$

$$\cdot \; \cdot \; \cdot \; \cdot \; \cdot \; \cdot \; \cdot \; \cdot \; \cdot \; \cdot \; \cdot \; \cdot \; \cdot \; \cdot$$

$$\frac{d^2 y_n}{dt^2} = a_{n1}y_1 + a_{n2}y_2 + \cdots + a_{nn}y_n,$$

where the a_{ij} are constants, is encountered frequently in dynamics. Show by assuming solutions in the form

$$y_i = k_i \cos (\lambda t + \alpha), \qquad i = 1, 2, \ldots, n,$$

that one is led to the following characteristic equation for λ:

$$\begin{vmatrix} a_{11} + \lambda^2 & a_{12} & \cdots & a_{1n} \\ a_{21} & a_{22} + \lambda^2 & \cdots & a_{2n} \\ \cdot \; \cdot & \cdot \; \cdot \; \cdot \; \cdot \; \cdot & \cdot & \cdot \; \cdot \\ a_{n1} & a_{n2} & \cdots & a_{nn} + \lambda^2 \end{vmatrix} = 0.$$

The constants k_i are determined from the system of linear equations analogous to (36-3), and the constant α remains arbitrary.

3. Reduce the system of n second-order linear equations with constant coefficients,

$$\frac{d^2 y_i}{dt^2} = \sum_{j=1}^{n} a_{ij}y_j + \sum_{j=1}^{n} b_{ij}\frac{dy_j}{dt}, \qquad i = 1, 2, \ldots, n$$

to a system of $2n$ first-order equations.

CHAPTER 2

INFINITE SERIES

The General Theory

Power Series and Taylor's Formula

Power Series and Differential Equations

Series with Complex Terms

Fourier Series

Additional Topics in Fourier Series

Although many functions encountered in applications are not elementary, virtually every such function may be represented as an infinite series. Nonelementary integrals like $\int (\sin x^2)\, dx$ may be written down by inspection as a so-called power series, and such series also give a simple, systematic method of solving differential equations. Another use of power series is in the study of functions of a complex variable $z = x + iy$; thus, from the series for $\sin x$ one can ascertain the appropriate definition and the important properties of $\sin z$. A type of series known as *Fourier series* arises when one studies the response of a linear system to a periodic input, for example, in circuit analysis, in transmission-line problems, and in the theory of mechanical systems. Fourier series and their generalizations are also useful for solving the boundary-value problems of mathematical physics. Inasmuch as an indiscriminate use of series may lead to incorrect results, the applications presented in this chapter are accompanied by discussion of the circumstances in which those applications are valid.

THE GENERAL THEORY

1. Convergence and Divergence. A *series* is a sum of terms. Thus, $1 + 3 + 5$ is a series consisting of three terms, and $a_1 + a_2 + \cdots + a_n$ is a series consisting of n terms. An *infinite series* is a series

$$a_1 + a_2 + a_3 + \cdots + a_n + \cdots \qquad (1\text{-}1)$$

which has infinitely many terms. We shall frequently use the symbol Σa_n to denote the series (1-1).

To get a numerical value for the expression (1-1) we consider the following sequence of so-called *partial sums* of the series,

$$s_1 = a_1$$

$$s_2 = a_1 + a_2$$

$$s_3 = a_1 + a_2 + a_3 \qquad (1\text{-}2)$$

$$\cdot \ \cdot \ \cdot \ \cdot \ \cdot \ \cdot \ \cdot \ \cdot \ \cdot \ \cdot \ \cdot \ \cdot$$

$$s_n = a_1 + a_2 + a_3 + \cdots + a_n$$

and examine the limit of the nth partial sum s_n as $n \to \infty$. If

$$\lim_{n \to \infty} s_n = s, \tag{1-3}$$

we say that the series *converges* to the *sum s* and write

$$s = a_1 + a_2 + a_3 + \cdots + a_n + \cdots.$$

If the limit of s_n does not exist, the series (1-1) is said to *diverge*, and no numerical value is assigned to the series. The precise meaning of the statement (1-3) is that *for any preassigned positive number ϵ, however small, one can find a number N such that*

$$|s - s_n| < \epsilon \qquad \text{for all } n > N. \tag{1-4}$$

To illustrate the definition (1-4) consider the series

$$\frac{1}{1 \cdot 2} + \frac{1}{2 \cdot 3} + \frac{1}{3 \cdot 4} + \cdots + \frac{1}{n(n+1)} + \cdots \tag{1-5}$$

The first three partial sums of (1-5) are

$$s_1 = a_1 = \frac{1}{2 \cdot 1} = \frac{1}{2},$$

$$s_2 = s_1 + a_2 = \frac{1}{2} + \frac{1}{2 \cdot 3} = \frac{2}{3},$$

$$s_3 = s_2 + a_3 = \frac{2}{3} + \frac{1}{3 \cdot 4} = \frac{3}{4},$$

and the nth partial sum is $s_n = n/(n+1)$ (cf. Prob. 1). It is obvious that the limit of s_n as $n \to \infty$ is 1. If, however, we want to *prove* this fact, we must demonstrate that for any preassigned number $\epsilon > 0$ we can find a number N such that the condition (1-4) is satisfied for all partial sums s_n with $n > N$. In our problem

$$|s - s_n| = \left| 1 - \frac{n}{n+1} \right| = \frac{1}{n+1}.$$

Given $\epsilon > 0$, we require, then, that

$$\frac{1}{n+1} < \epsilon \qquad \text{for } n > N$$

and this is equivalent to

$$n + 1 > \frac{1}{\epsilon} \qquad \text{for } n > N.$$

Hence the choice $N = (1/\epsilon) - 1$ fulfills the requirement of the definition. If $\epsilon = \frac{1}{10}$, then $N = 9$; if $\epsilon = \frac{1}{100}$, then $N = 99$, and so on. To attain higher accuracy in approximating the sum of the series (1-5) by its nth partial sum s_n we must, clearly, increase n.

The number ϵ in (1-4) can be thought of as a measure of error made in approximating the sum s by the sum of its first n terms. The actual error in the approximation is

$$r_n \equiv s - s_n \tag{1-6}$$

and the condition (1-4) demands that $|r_n| < \epsilon$ for all sufficiently large values of n. We shall call r_n the *remainder of the series* (1-1) *after n terms.*

The limit (1-3) may fail to exist either when s_n increases indefinitely with n or when the partial sums s_n oscillate without approaching a limit as $n \to \infty$. Thus, the series

$$1 + 1 + 1 + 1 + \cdots$$

diverges because its nth partial sum $s_n = n$ increases with n without limit, while the series

$$1 - 1 + 1 - 1 + \cdots$$

diverges because its partial sums $s_1 = 1$, $s_2 = 0$, $s_3 = 1$, ... oscillate.

As another example, consider the so-called *harmonic series*

$$1 + \tfrac{1}{2} + \tfrac{1}{3} + \tfrac{1}{4} + \tfrac{1}{5} + \tfrac{1}{6} + \tfrac{1}{7} + \tfrac{1}{8} + \cdots + 1/n + \cdots. \quad (1\text{-}7)$$

The terms of the series (1-7) may be grouped as follows:

$$1 + \tfrac{1}{2} + (\tfrac{1}{3} + \tfrac{1}{4}) + (\tfrac{1}{5} + \tfrac{1}{6} + \tfrac{1}{7} + \tfrac{1}{8}) + (\tfrac{1}{9} + \cdots + \tfrac{1}{16}) + \cdots.$$
$$(1\text{-}8)$$

Now, each term of the foregoing series is at least as large as the corresponding term of

$$\tfrac{1}{2} + \tfrac{1}{2} + (\tfrac{1}{4} + \tfrac{1}{4}) + (\tfrac{1}{8} + \tfrac{1}{8} + \tfrac{1}{8} + \tfrac{1}{8}) + (\tfrac{1}{16} + \cdots + \tfrac{1}{16}) + \cdots.$$
$$(1\text{-}9)$$

The latter series, however, reduces to

$$\tfrac{1}{2} + \tfrac{1}{2} + \tfrac{1}{2} + \tfrac{1}{2} + \tfrac{1}{2} + \cdots,$$

which is divergent. Hence (1-8) is divergent.

This example illustrates the idea of *comparison*, which is fundamental in the study of series. The divergence of (1-8) was established by comparing (1-8) with a simpler series, (1-9), whose divergence is obvious. The full chain of reasoning is as follows: "Each term of (1-8) is at least as great as the corresponding term of (1-9). Hence the partial sums of (1-8) are at least as great as the corresponding partial sums of (1-9). But the partial sums of (1-9) become arbitrarily large if we take enough terms. Hence the partial sums of (1-8) also become arbitrarily large, and the series diverges." The student who understands this example will have no difficulty with the more detailed applications which follow.

The use of the criterion (1-4) for convergence of the series (1-1) requires knowledge of its sum s. Frequently it is possible to infer the existence of a limit s without knowing its value. For example, consider the series

$$0.1 + 0.01 + 0.001 + \cdots$$

whose partial sums are $s_1 = 0.1$, $s_2 = 0.1 + 0.01 = 0.11$, $s_3 = 0.1 + 0.01 + 0.001 = 0.111$, and so on. Each partial sum, being a decimal, is less than 1. On the other hand the s_n increase with n. If the successive values of s_n are plotted as points on a straight line (Fig. 1), the points move to the right but never progress as far as the point 1. It is intuitively clear that there must be some point s, at the left of 1, which the numbers s_n approach as limit. In this case the numerical value of the limit was not ascertained, but its existence has been established with the aid of a FUNDAMENTAL

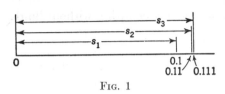

FIG. 1

PRINCIPLE: *If an infinite sequence of numbers s_n satisfies the condition $s_{n+1} \geq s_n$ for each n, and if $s_n \leq M$, where M is some fixed number, then s_n has a limit that is not greater than M.* In other words: *Every bounded increasing sequence has a limit.* Considering $-s_n$ instead of s_n gives a corresponding statement for decreasing sequences.

From the geometrical interpretation of the fundamental principle it appears that when an increasing sequence of partial sums s_n has a limit, the difference between the successive values of s_n must tend to zero as $n \to \infty$. Since $s_n - s_{n-1} = a_n$, the foregoing statement is equivalent to the assertion that $\lim\limits_{n \to \infty} a_n = 0$. This can be established from the definition (1-3) without appeal to the fundamental principle and without the assumption that s_n is increasing.

Indeed, since

$$a_n = s_n - s_{n-1} \qquad (1\text{-}10)$$

and since the series converges by hypothesis, we have $\lim s_n = \lim s_{n-1} = s$ as $n \to \infty$. Hence (1-10) shows that

$$\lim_{n \to \infty} a_n = \lim_{n \to \infty} s_n - \lim_{n \to \infty} s_{n-1} = 0. \qquad (1\text{-}11)$$

We state the result (1-11) as a theorem:

THEOREM I. *If a series converges, then the general term must approach zero, and hence if the general term does not approach zero, the series diverges.*

The reader is cautioned that the converse of this theorem is *not* true. For instance, the harmonic series (1-7) was found to diverge even though the general term $1/n$ approaches zero.

There is a more elaborate version of Theorem I which does have a converse. By writing out the sums in full we find a relation analogous to (1-10):

$$a_m + a_{m+1} + \cdots + a_n = s_n - s_{m-1}, \qquad n \geq m > 1. \qquad (1\text{-}12)$$

If the infinite series converges, so that $\lim s_n = s$, then both the sums on the right of (1-12) become arbitrarily close to s, provided m and n are chosen large enough. Hence the right-hand side becomes arbitrarily small in magnitude, and we are led to the following: *If Σa_k converges, then for any $\epsilon > 0$ there is an N such that*

$$|a_m + a_{m+1} + \cdots + a_n| < \epsilon \qquad (1\text{-}13)$$

whenever $n \geq m \geq N$. Now this statement admits a converse.[1] *If, for each* $\epsilon > 0$, *there is an* N *such that* (1-13) *holds whenever* $n \geq m \geq N$, *then* Σa_k *converges.* The theorem, together with its converse, constitutes the so-called *Cauchy convergence criterion.*

Example 1. A certain series has partial sums $s_n = r^n$, where r is a constant such that $0 \leq r < 1$. By use of the fundamental principle, show that the series converges to zero. We have to show that $\lim s_n = 0$ as $n \to \infty$, or in other words

$$\lim_{n \to \infty} r^n = 0 \qquad \text{for } 0 \leq r < 1. \tag{1-14}$$

Since $r \geq 0$, it is evident that $s_n \geq 0$, and hence the sequence s_n is *bounded from below.* Also $r^{n+1} = rr^n$, or in other words

$$s_{n+1} = rs_n. \tag{1-15}$$

Since $r < 1$, this shows that $s_{n+1} < s_n$, so that the sequence s_n is *decreasing.* Hence the limit of s_n exists by the fundamental principle. If we write $s = \lim s_n$ and take the limit as $n \to \infty$ in (1-15), there results

$$s = \lim s_{n+1} = \lim (rs_n) = r \lim s_n = rs.$$

From $s = rs$ it follows that $s = 0$, since $r \neq 1$, and this gives (1-14).

Example 2. The *geometric series* is defined by

$$1 + x + x^2 + x^3 + \cdots + x^n + \cdots.$$

Show that this series converges to $1/(1 - x)$ when $|x| < 1$ but diverges when $|x| \geq 1$.

The geometric series is an example of a series

$$u_1(x) + u_2(x) + u_3(x) + \cdots + u_n(x) + \cdots$$

in which the terms are functions of x. For each choice of x the function $u_n(x)$ is simply a number, the series becomes a series of constants, and hence it can be tested for convergence just as any other series of constants is tested.

We have to decide whether the partial sums

$$s_n = 1 + x + x^2 + \cdots + x^{n-2} + x^{n-1} \tag{1-16}$$

tend to a limit. If the foregoing equation is multiplied by x, there results

$$xs_n = x + x^2 + \cdots + x^{n-1} + x^n \tag{1-17}$$

and subtracting (1-17) from (1-16) yields $s_n - xs_n = 1 - x^n$. Solving for s_n we get

$$s_n = \frac{1 - x^n}{1 - x}. \tag{1-18}$$

---

[1] Since we shall not require the converse, the proof is not presented here. The interested reader is referred to I. S. Sokolnikoff, "Advanced Calculus," pp. 11–13, McGraw-Hill Book Company, Inc., New York, 1939.

If $|x| < 1$, then $\lim\limits_{n \to \infty} |x|^n = 0$ by (1-14) and hence (1-18) gives

$$\lim_{n \to \infty} s_n = \frac{1-0}{1-x} = \frac{1}{1-x}.$$

This establishes the required convergence when $|x| < 1$. On the other hand if $|x| \geq 1$, the general term does not approach zero and the series diverges by Theorem I. The value x is called the *ratio* for the series, since x equals the ratio of two successive terms. We have shown that the geometric series converges if, and only if, the ratio is less than 1 in magnitude.

PROBLEMS

1. Show that the nth partial sum of the series (1-5) is $n/(n+1)$. *Hint:* Since $1/[n(n+1)] = 1/n - 1/(n+1)$, the sum of the first n terms is

$$s_n = (\tfrac{1}{1} - \tfrac{1}{2}) + (\tfrac{1}{2} - \tfrac{1}{3}) + (\tfrac{1}{3} - \tfrac{1}{4}) + \cdots + [1/n - 1/(n+1)].$$

A series such as this is called a *telescoping series*.

2. Show that the following series converges to zero if $|r| < 1$ but to 1 if $r = 1$. Sketch the graph of the sum as a function of r:

$$r + (r^2 - r) + (r^3 - r^2) + \cdots + (r^n - r^{n-1}) + \cdots.$$

2. Some Basic Properties of Series. We shall write infinite series in the condensed notation

$$\sum_{n=1}^{\infty} a_n \equiv a_1 + a_2 + a_3 + \cdots + a_n + \cdots. \tag{2-1}$$

Finite sums are expressed similarly, with the limits of summation $(1,\infty)$ replaced by the appropriate values. The limits of summation are frequently omitted if they need not be emphasized or are clear from the context. Whenever the limits are omitted in Secs. 2 to 7 of this chapter, the reader may assume that the summation range is from 1 to ∞.

In many respects convergent series behave like finite sums. For example, if the sum of the series (2-1) is s and if each term of the series (2-1) is multiplied by a constant p, then

$$\Sigma p a_n = p \Sigma a_n = ps. \tag{2-2}$$

That is, *a convergent series may be multiplied termwise by any constant.*

The proof of (2-2) follows at once from the observation that the partial sums S_n of the series $\Sigma p a_n$ are related to the partial sums s_n of (2-1) by

$$S_n = p s_n$$

and therefore

$$\lim_{n \to \infty} S_n = p \lim_{n \to \infty} s_n = ps.$$

If we are given two convergent series Σa_k and Σb_k, then

$$\Sigma(a_k \pm b_k) = \Sigma a_k \pm \Sigma b_k. \tag{2-3}$$

That is, *two convergent series may be added or subtracted term by term*. Again the proof is simple. We denote the sum of the series Σa_n by A, that of Σb_n by B, and the corresponding partial sums by A_n and B_n. Then the nth partial sum of $\Sigma(a_k \pm b_k)$ is

$$\sum_{k=1}^{n} (a_k \pm b_k) = A_n \pm B_n$$

and the result (2-3) follows on letting $n \to \infty$.

As an illustration, consider the geometric series

$$s = 1 + x + x^2 + \cdots + x^n + \cdots.$$

By (2-2)

$$xs = x + x^2 + \cdots + x^n + \cdots$$

and hence, by (2-3), we have $s - xs = 1$. This shows that *if the series converges*, it must converge to $1/(1 - x)$. The question of convergence was discussed in Example 2 of Sec. 1.

Another obvious but important property is used so often that we state it as a theorem:

THEOREM I. *If finitely many terms of an infinite series are altered the convergence is not affected (though, of course, the value of the sum may be affected).*

To prove this we denote the original terms by a_k and the new terms by $a_k + b_k$, where all but a finite number [1] of b_ks are zero. The result is then a consequence of (2-3). It should be noticed that this argument not only establishes convergence but shows that the new value of the sum can be found by the obvious arithmetical calculation. For instance, if the seventh term of a convergent series is increased by 2.4 the sum is also increased by 2.4, and similarly in other cases.

Example: Establish the divergence of

$$\tfrac{1}{12} + \tfrac{1}{16} + \tfrac{1}{20} + \tfrac{1}{24} + \cdots. \tag{2-4}$$

Multiplying by 4 we get the series

$$\tfrac{1}{3} + \tfrac{1}{4} + \tfrac{1}{5} + \tfrac{1}{6} + \cdots$$

which is obviously divergent, since it differs from the harmonic series $\Sigma 1/n$ only in that it lacks the first two terms. Hence (2-4) is divergent.

[1] Any finite series $b_1 + \cdots + b_n$ may be regarded as an infinite series with all terms beyond the nth equal to zero. If we do so regard it, the definition of convergence given in Sec. 1 makes the finite series converge to its ordinary sum.

This use of (2-2) to establish divergence is readily justified, even though (2-2) applies to convergent series only. Thus, assume that (2-4) converges. The foregoing analysis shows, then, that $\Sigma 1/n$ would have to converge, and that is a contradiction.

PROBLEMS

1. Write the following series in full, without using Σ notation:

$$\sum_{k=1}^{\infty} \frac{1}{2k}, \quad \sum_{i=2}^{\infty} \left(-\frac{43}{44}\right)^i, \quad \sum_{n=1}^{\infty} \frac{n^2+1}{2n+3}, \quad \sum_{j=7}^{\infty} \frac{3}{j}, \quad \sum_{m=1}^{\infty} (\cos x)^{2m}.$$

2. Write the following series in condensed form, using Σ notation:

$$(\tfrac{2}{3})^2 + (\tfrac{2}{3})^3 + (\tfrac{2}{3})^4 + (\tfrac{2}{3})^5 + \cdots, \qquad \tfrac{1}{6} + \tfrac{1}{9} + \tfrac{1}{12} + \tfrac{1}{15} + \cdots,$$

$$\frac{1}{1,000} + \frac{1}{1,002} + \frac{1}{1,004} + \frac{1}{1,006} + \cdots, \qquad 0.2 - 0.02 + 0.002 - \cdots,$$

$$\frac{1}{1} + \frac{1}{1\cdot2} + \frac{1}{1\cdot2\cdot3} + \frac{1}{1\cdot2\cdot3\cdot4} + \cdots, \qquad \tfrac{1}{20} + \tfrac{1}{30} + \tfrac{1}{40} + \tfrac{1}{50} + \cdots.$$

3. Some of the series in Probs. 1 and 2 are divergent because the general term does not approach zero. Which ones are they?

4. Some of the series in Probs. 1 and 2 are convergent because they are geometric series with ratio less than 1 in magnitude (or multiples of such a series). Which ones are they?

5. Some of the series in Probs. 1 and 2 are divergent because $\Sigma 1/n$ is divergent. Which ones are they?

6. Show that $(1-1) + (1-1) + (1-1) + \cdots$ converges but would diverge if the parentheses were dropped.

7. (a) Does the series $\Sigma \left[\dfrac{4}{n(n+1)} + \left(\dfrac{2}{3}\right)^n \right]$ converge? Explain. (b) Does the

series $\Sigma \left[\dfrac{1}{n} - \left(\dfrac{2}{3}\right)^n \right]$ converge? Explain. *Hint:* In (a) see (1-5). In (b) note that

$\dfrac{1}{n} = \left[\dfrac{1}{n} - \left(\dfrac{2}{3}\right)^n \right] + \left(\dfrac{2}{3}\right)^n$. If the given series converges, what could you deduce about

$\Sigma \dfrac{1}{n}$?

3. Improper Integrals and the Integral Test.

In the development of the calculus a definite integral such as $\int_a^b f(x)\,dx$ is defined, at first, only for a finite interval $[a,b]$. The extension to an infinite interval is then made by a simple passage to the limit; thus

$$\int_a^{\infty} f(x)\,dx = \lim_{b \to \infty} \int_a^b f(x)\,dx. \tag{3-1}$$

The integral at the left of (3-1) is called an *improper integral*. If the limit at the right exists, we say that the improper integral *converges* (to the value of the limit) and it *diverges* if the limit does not exist. The definition is quite analogous to the corresponding definition

$$\sum_{k=1}^{\infty} a_k = \lim_{n \to \infty} \sum_{k=1}^{n} a_k$$

for infinite series.

An example of a divergent improper integral is

$$\int_1^{\infty} \frac{1}{x}\, dx = \lim \int_1^{b} \frac{dx}{x} = \lim \left(\log x \,\big|_1^b \right) = \lim \log b = \infty. \tag{3-2}$$

On the other hand if p is constant and $p \neq 1$, then

$$\int_1^{\infty} \frac{1}{x^p}\, dx = \lim \int_1^{b} x^{-p}\, dx = \lim \left(\frac{x^{1-p}}{1-p} \bigg|_1^b \right) = \lim \frac{b^{1-p} - 1}{1 - p}. \tag{3-3}$$

The question of convergence now depends on the behavior of b^{1-p} as $b \to \infty$. If the exponent $1 - p$ is positive, then $b^{1-p} \to \infty$ and the integral (3-3), like (3-2), is divergent. But if $1 - p$ is negative, then $p - 1 > 0$ and hence

$$b^{1-p} = \frac{1}{b^{p-1}} \to 0, \qquad \text{as } b \to \infty.$$

In this case the integral (3-3) converges to the value $1/(p - 1)$.

The result of this discussion may be summarized as follows:

THEOREM I. *The improper integral $\displaystyle\int_1^{\infty} \frac{1}{x^p}\, dx$ converges if, and only if, the constant $p > 1$.*

Theorem I suggests the following analogous result for infinite series:

THEOREM II. *The infinite series $\displaystyle\sum_{k=1}^{\infty} \frac{1}{k^p}$ converges if, and only if, the constant $p > 1$.*

It will be seen that Theorem II is valid; in fact, there is a close connection between infinite series and improper integrals which will now be discussed.

Suppose the terms of an infinite series Σa_k are positive and decreasing; that is, $a_n > a_{n+1} > 0$ for each positive integer n. In this case there is a continuous decreasing function $f(x)$ such that [1]

$$a_n = f(n), \qquad n = 1, 2, 3, \ldots. \tag{3-4}$$

Each term a_n of the series may be thought of as representing the area of a rectangle of base unity and height $f(n)$ (see Fig. 2). The sum of the areas

---

[1] For instance, let the graph of $y = f(x)$ consist of straight-line segments joining the points (n, a_n) and $(n + 1, a_{n+1})$.

of the first n circumscribed rectangles is greater than the area under the curve from 1 to $n + 1$, so that

$$a_1 + a_2 + \cdots + a_n > \int_1^{n+1} f(x)\, dx. \qquad (3\text{-}5)$$

This shows that *if the integral* $\int_1^\infty f(x)\, dx$ *diverges, then the sum* Σa_k *also diverges.*

On the other hand, the sum of the areas of the inscribed rectangles is less than the area under the curve, so that

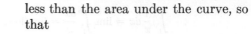

$$a_2 + a_3 + \cdots + a_n < \int_1^n f(x)\, dx. \qquad (3\text{-}6)$$

If the integral converges, we have [since $f(x) > 0$]

$$\int_1^n f(x)\, dx < \int_1^\infty f(x)\, dx \equiv M,$$

so that the partial sums are bounded independently of n:

$$s_n = a_1 + a_2 + \cdots + a_n < M + a_1.$$

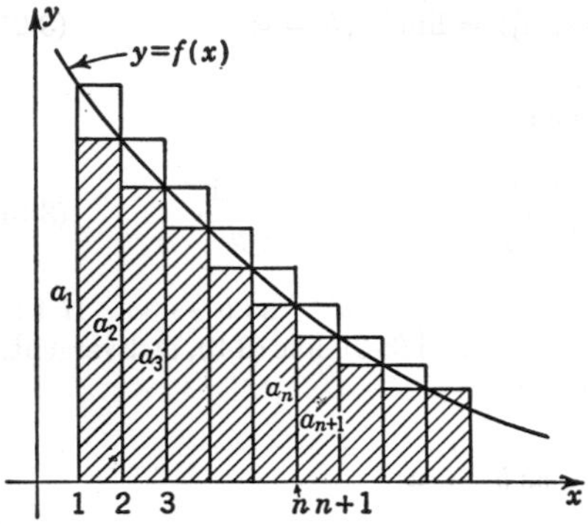

Fig. 2

Since each a_k is positive, these partial sums form an increasing sequence. Hence, the fundamental principle stated in Sec. 1 ensures that Σa_k is convergent.

The result of this discussion may be summarized as follows:

THEOREM III.   *For* $x \geq 1$ *let* $f(x)$ *be positive, continuous, and decreasing. Then the series* $\sum_{n=1}^\infty f(n)$ *and the integral* $\int_1^\infty f(x)\, dx$ *both converge or both diverge.   In either case the partial sums are bounded as follows:*

$$\int_1^{n+1} f(x)\, dx < \sum_{k=1}^n f(k) < \int_1^n f(x)\, dx + f(1). \qquad (3\text{-}7)$$

Choosing $f(x) = x^{-p}$ in Theorem III, we see that Theorem II is a consequence of Theorem I.   The test for convergence contained in Theorem III is commonly called *the Cauchy integral test,* though it was first discovered by Maclaurin.   The result (3-7) is especially useful because it enables us to estimate the value of the sum.

Example 1.   Show that the series

$$\frac{1}{1 + 1^2} + \frac{1}{1 + 2^2} + \frac{1}{1 + 3^2} + \frac{1}{1 + 4^2} + \cdots + \frac{1}{1 + n^2} + \cdots$$

converges to a value which is between 0.7 and 1.3.

Here we choose $f(x) = 1/(1 + x^2)$. Since

$$\int_1^b \frac{1}{1 + x^2}\, dx = \tan^{-1} x \,\big|_1^b \to \frac{\pi}{2} - \frac{\pi}{4} = \frac{\pi}{4}, \qquad \text{as } b \to \infty,$$

the integral is convergent, and hence the series is convergent. Moreover

$$0.79 \doteq \frac{\pi}{4} < \sum_{k=1}^{\infty} \frac{1}{1 + k^2} < \frac{\pi}{4} + \frac{1}{2} \doteq 1.29$$

by letting $n \to \infty$ in (3-7) and noting that $f(1) = \frac{1}{2}$. The next example shows how the accuracy in such an estimate may be improved to any extent desired.

Example 2. Compute the sum of the following series within ± 0.01:

$$s = 1 + \frac{1}{4} + \frac{1}{9} + \frac{1}{16} + \frac{1}{25} + \frac{1}{36} + \cdots + \frac{1}{n^2} + \cdots.$$

It is easily verified that the first six terms give the sum 1.491. To estimate the remainder we have, from (3-7) on taking $f(x) = 1/(x + 6)^2$,

$$\int_1^{\infty} \frac{1}{(x + 6)^2}\, dx < \sum_1^{\infty} \frac{1}{(n + 6)^2} < \int_1^{\infty} \frac{1}{(x + 6)^2}\, dx + \frac{1}{49}. \qquad (3\text{-}8)$$

The two limits in (3-8) are 0.143 and 0.163, as the reader can verify. Hence

$$1.634 = 1.491 + 0.143 < s < 1.491 + 0.163 = 1.654. \qquad (3\text{-}9)$$

It is interesting to see how many terms are needed to get the same accuracy by direct computation. The remainder after n terms is given by (3-7) as

$$\sum_{k=n+1}^{\infty} \frac{1}{k^2} \doteq \int_{n+1}^{\infty} \frac{1}{x^2}\, dx = \frac{1}{n + 1}.$$

To make this as small as the uncertainty interval $1.654 - 1.634$ obtained in (3-9), we must have $1/(n + 1) \le 0.02$, or $n \ge 49$. Thus, direct summation of the series requires almost 50 terms for the accuracy which we obtained by adding 6 terms only.

PROBLEMS

1. Test the following integrals for convergence, and evaluate if convergent:

$$\int_1^{\infty} \frac{dx}{1 + x}, \quad \int_1^{\infty} e^{-x}\, dx, \quad \int_1^{\infty} x^{-4}\, dx, \quad \int_2^{\infty} \frac{dx}{x(\log x)^2}, \quad \int_2^{\infty} \frac{dx}{x \log x}.$$

2. Test the following series for convergence:

$$\Sigma \frac{1}{(n + 1)^{3/2}}, \quad \Sigma n^{-1.01}, \quad \sum_{n=2}^{\infty} \frac{1}{n(\log n)}, \quad \sum_{n=2}^{\infty} \frac{1}{n(\log n)^{1.01}}, \quad \Sigma \frac{2n}{1 + n^2}.$$

3. (*a*) For what values of the constant c does $\int_1^{\infty} e^{cx}\, dx$ converge? (*b*) Using the result (*a*), discuss the convergence of Σe^{cn}. (*c*) Show that the series (*b*) is a geometric series, and also show that your results are consistent with those of Sec. 1.

4. How many terms of the harmonic series Σn^{-1} are needed to make the sum of those terms larger than 1,000?

5. Estimate the value of $\sum_{n=1}^{\infty} n^{-4}$ by direct use of Theorem III and also by adding the first five terms and using Theorem III to estimate the remainder. In both cases find approximately how many terms of the series you would have to add up to get comparable accuracy.

Problem for Review

6. (a) By (1-18), show that the partial sums of the series

$$1 + \frac{1}{2} + \frac{1}{2^2} + \frac{1}{2^3} + \cdots + \frac{1}{2^n} + \cdots$$

are all less than 2.

(b) Show that the partial sums of the series

$$1 + \frac{1}{2!} + \frac{1}{3!} + \frac{1}{4!} + \cdots + \frac{1}{n!} + \cdots$$

are also less than 2. *Hint:* Compare the partial sums with those of the series (a).

(c) Deduce, by the fundamental principle, that the series (b) converges.

4. Comparison Term by Term. One way to test a series of positive terms for convergence is to compare that series with another whose convergence is known. Let Σa_n and Σb_n be two series with positive terms such that $a_n \leq b_n$ and Σb_n converges. The inequality

$$s_n \equiv \sum_{1}^{n} a_n \leq \sum_{1}^{n} b_n \leq \sum_{1}^{\infty} b_n$$

shows that the partial sums s_n are bounded, and since s_n is increasing, the limit exists by the fundamental principle. It is left for the student to verify also that if $a_n \geq b_n \geq 0$ and Σb_n diverges, then Σa_n diverges.

This discussion establishes the following result, known as the *comparison test*:

THEOREM I. *If $0 \leq a_n \leq b_n$, then the convergence of Σa_n follows from the convergence of Σb_n. And if $a_n \geq b_n \geq 0$, then the divergence of Σa_n follows from the divergence of Σb_n.*

Since the first few terms of a series do not affect the convergence, we need the hypothesis not for all n but only for n sufficiently large (see Sec. 2, Theorem I). Similar remarks apply to every convergence test, and we shall make constant use of this fact in the sequel.

For example, suppose we want to establish the convergence of $\Sigma 9/n^n$. Although the inequality

$$\frac{9}{n^n} < \frac{1}{2^n} \tag{4-1}$$

is not valid for all n, it is valid when n is sufficiently large. Hence the series converges by comparison with the geometric series. Another example is given by the series

$$\sum_{n=2}^{\infty} \frac{1}{100 \log n}. \tag{4-2}$$

Although it is not true that

$$\frac{1}{100 \log n} > \frac{1}{n}$$

for all n, this is true for all sufficiently large n, and hence the series (4-2) diverges by comparison with the harmonic series.

It is customary to write $a_n \sim b_n$ (read "a_n is asymptotic to b_n") if

$$\lim_{n \to \infty} \frac{a_n}{b_n} = 1$$

(compare Chap. 1, Sec. 2). For example, $n + 1 \sim n$ and also $5n^2 + 3n + 4 \sim 5n^2$, but it is not the case that $2/n \sim 1/n$ even though the difference between these quantities tends to zero. In this notation we can state the following theorem, which is very useful for determining convergence:

THEOREM II.   *If $a_n \sim b_n$ and $b_n > 0$, then the series Σa_n and Σb_n are both convergent or both divergent.*

The proof is simple. Since $\lim (a_n/b_n) = 1$, we shall have

$$\frac{1}{2} < \frac{a_n}{b_n} < 2 \tag{4-3}$$

whenever n is sufficiently large. Equation (4-3) yields

$$\tfrac{1}{2}b_n < a_n < 2b_n$$

and hence the conclusion follows from Theorem I together with (2-2).

Example 1.   Does $\Sigma n^{-\log n}$ converge?
For all large n we have $\log n > 2$ (since $\log n \to \infty$). Hence

$$\frac{1}{n^{\log n}} < \frac{1}{n^2}$$

for all large n, and the series converges by comparison with the convergent series $\Sigma 1/n^2$ (Theorem II, Sec. 3).

Example 2.   Does $\Sigma(n^2 + 5n + 3)^{-\frac{1}{2}}$ converge?
Inasmuch as $n^2 + 5n + 3 = n^2(1 + 5/n + 3/n^2) \sim n^2$, we have

$$(n^2 + 5n + 3)^{-\frac{1}{2}} \sim (n^2)^{-\frac{1}{2}} = n^{-1} = \frac{1}{n}.$$

Since $\Sigma 1/n$ diverges, the given series diverges.

Example 3.   Consider the series

$$\Sigma \left(\frac{n^4 + 4n^3 + 1}{7n^7 + 5n^4 + 8n} \right)^{\frac{2}{5}}.$$

Since $n^4 + 4n^3 + 1 \sim n^4$, and since $7n^7 + 5n^4 + 8n \sim 7n^7$, the general term is asymptotic to

$$\left(\frac{n^4}{7n^7} \right)^{\frac{2}{5}} = \frac{1}{7^{\frac{2}{5}}} \frac{1}{n^{\frac{6}{5}}}.$$

The series with general term $1/n^{\frac{6}{5}}$ converges by Theorem II, Sec. 3, and hence the **given** series also converges.

Examples 2 and 3 illustrate two properties of the relation "$\sim$", which are now set forth explicitly. First, we show that *any polynomial is asymptotic to its leading term.* Indeed, if $a \neq 0$ and $m \geq 1$, then as $n \to \infty$,

$$\frac{an^m + bn^{m-1} + \cdots + rn + s}{an^m} = 1 + \frac{b}{an} + \cdots + \frac{r}{an^{m-1}} + \frac{s}{an^m} \to 1.$$

This shows that $an^m + bn^{m-1} + \cdots + rn + s \sim an^m$, as stated.

Second, *if $a_n \sim b_n$ and $c_n \sim d_n$, then it follows that*

$$a_n^{\alpha} c_n^{\beta} \sim b_n^{\alpha} d_n^{\beta}$$

for any constants α and β. To establish this consider the ratio

$$\frac{a_n^{\alpha} c_n^{\beta}}{b_n^{\alpha} d_n^{\beta}} = \left(\frac{a_n}{b_n}\right)^{\alpha} \left(\frac{c_n}{d_n}\right)^{\beta} \to 1^{\alpha} 1^{\beta} = 1.$$

PROBLEMS

1. Test the following series for convergence by comparing with the series $\Sigma 1/n^p$:

$$\Sigma \frac{4}{\sqrt{n}}, \ \Sigma \frac{1}{2n\sqrt{n} + 1}, \ \Sigma \frac{\cos^2 nx}{(2n + 1)^2}, \ \Sigma \frac{n}{(2n + 1)^2}.$$

2. Test the following series for convergence by using Theorem II:

$$\Sigma \frac{n^2 + 1}{n^3 + 1}, \ \Sigma \frac{n^4 + n^2}{3n^6 + n}, \ \Sigma \left(\frac{1}{n} + \frac{1}{n^2}\right), \ \Sigma \frac{3^n + 4^n}{4^n + 5^n}, \ \Sigma \frac{n + 1}{n^4 + 4}.$$

3. Test the following series for convergence by any method:

$$\Sigma e^{-n^2}, \ \Sigma \frac{1}{n \log (n + 1)}, \ \Sigma \frac{1}{n^{\sqrt{n}}}, \ \Sigma \frac{n^4}{n^6 + 3}.$$

4. (a) If $a_n \sim b_n$ and $b_n \sim c_n$, show that $a_n \sim c_n$. (b) If $a_n \sim b_n$ and $c_n \sim d_n$, is it necessary that $a_n + c_n \sim b_n + d_n$? Prove your answer by an example. (c) Find a_n and b_n such that $a_n \sim b_n$ but $a_n - b_n \to \infty$. (d) Find a_n and b_n such that $a_n/b_n \to \infty$ but $a_n - b_n \to 0$.

Problem for Review

5. (a) By direct use of the definition of limit show that $0.111111\ldots = \frac{1}{9}$. *Hint:* If $s_1 = 0.1$, $s_2 = 0.11$, $s_3 = 0.111$, $\ldots$, then $|s_1 - \frac{1}{9}| = \frac{1}{90}$, $|s_2 - \frac{1}{9}| = \frac{1}{900}$, and so on. (b) With s_n as in (a), and with $\epsilon > 0$, how large must you choose N to make

$$|s_n - \tfrac{1}{9}| < \epsilon \qquad \text{for all } n > N?$$

(c) If $s = 0.111111\ldots$, evaluate s by considering $10s - s$. (d) Evaluate s in (c) by the formula for sum of a geometric series.

5. Comparison of Ratios. It often happens that the general term of an infinite series is complicated whereas the ratio of two successive terms is simple. For example, in the series

$$\Sigma \frac{x^{2n}}{n!} \tag{5-1}$$

we have

$$\frac{a_{n+1}}{a_n} = \frac{x^{2n+2}}{(n+1)!} \frac{n!}{x^{2n}} = \frac{x^2}{n+1}. \tag{5-2}$$

The following theorem enables us to deduce convergence by considering this ratio rather than the general term itself:

THEOREM I. *Let Σa_n and Σb_n be two series with positive terms. If*

$$\frac{a_{n+1}}{a_n} \leq \frac{b_{n+1}}{b_n}, \qquad n = 1, 2, 3, \ldots, \tag{5-3}$$

then the convergence of Σa_n follows from the convergence of Σb_n. And if

$$\frac{a_{n+1}}{a_n} \geq \frac{b_{n+1}}{b_n}, \qquad n = 1, 2, 3, \ldots, \tag{5-3a}$$

then the divergence of Σa_n follows from the divergence of Σb_n.

The proof is simple. In the first case we have

$$a_n = a_1 \frac{a_2}{a_1} \frac{a_3}{a_2} \cdots \frac{a_n}{a_{n-1}} \leq a_1 \frac{b_2}{b_1} \frac{b_3}{b_2} \cdots \frac{b_n}{b_{n-1}} = \frac{a_1}{b_1} b_n.$$

Hence the convergence of Σb_n implies that of Σa_n by the comparison test (Theorem I, Sec. 4). The discussion of (5-3a) is similar.

If we take $b_n = r^n$ in Theorem I, then Σb_n converges whenever $r < 1$. Also

$$\frac{b_{n+1}}{b_n} = \frac{r^{n+1}}{r^n} = r.$$

Hence the theorem shows that Σa_n converges if there is a fixed number $r < 1$ such that

$$\frac{a_{n+1}}{a_n} < r, \qquad n = 1, 2, 3, \ldots. \tag{5-4}$$

Since the condition (5-4) is needed only for large n, the series Σa_n also converges whenever

$$\lim_{n \to \infty} \frac{a_{n+1}}{a_n} = r < 1. \tag{5-5}$$

The test based on (5-4) and (5-5) is termed the *ratio test*. To illustrate the ratio test consider the series (5-1). By (5-2) we have

$$\lim \frac{a_{n+1}}{a_n} = \lim \frac{x^2}{n+1} = 0$$

and hence (5-5) holds for all x. Thus the series (5-1) converges for all x.

The ratio test is useful but very crude. It cannot even establish the convergence of a series such as Σn^{-100}, which is rapidly convergent. To obtain a better test one may use the series $\Sigma 1/n^p$ for Σb_n rather than the geometric series. In this case

$$\frac{b_{n+1}}{b_n} = \frac{1}{(n+1)^p} n^p = \left(\frac{n}{n+1}\right)^p = \left(1 + \frac{1}{n}\right)^{-p}.$$

By the binomial theorem [1]

$$\left(1 + \frac{1}{n}\right)^{-p} = 1 - \frac{p}{n} + \frac{p(p+1)}{2n^2} - \cdots$$

and hence

$$\frac{b_{n+1}}{b_n} - 1 \sim - \frac{p}{n}.$$

Since Σb_n converges if $p > 1$ and diverges if $p \leq 1$, we are led to the result stated in part (*b*) of Theorem II. The result (5-5) is stated in part (*a*).

Theorem II. *Let Σa_n be a series of positive terms, and let r and p be constant. (a) If $a_{n+1}/a_n \sim r$, then Σa_n converges when $r < 1$ and diverges when $r > 1$. (b) If $a_{n+1}/a_n - 1 \sim -p/n$, then Σa_n converges when $p > 1$ and diverges when $p < 1$.*

Example 1.   Does $\Sigma n^2/2^n$ converge?
With $a_n = n^2/2^n$ we have

$$\frac{a_{n+1}}{a_n} = \frac{(n+1)^2}{2^{n+1}} \frac{2^n}{n^2} = \left(\frac{n+1}{n}\right)^2 \frac{1}{2} \sim \frac{1}{2} < 1$$

Hence the series converges by the ratio test, Theorem II*a*.
Example 2.   Apply the ratio test to the harmonic series.
With $a_n = 1/n$ we have

$$\frac{a_{n+1}}{a_n} = \frac{n}{n+1} \sim 1.$$

Since this is the case $r = 1$, the test gives no information. Moreover,

$$\frac{a_{n+1}}{a_n} - 1 = \frac{n}{n+1} - 1 = - \frac{1}{n+1} \sim - \frac{1}{n}.$$

Since this is the case $p = 1$, the more refined test of Theorem II*b* also gives no information.[2]

---

[1] The binomial theorem for arbitrary exponents is established in Sec. 12.
[2] More general tests may be found in I. S. Sokolnikoff, "Advanced Calculus," chap. 7, McGraw-Hill Book Company, Inc., New York, 1939.

Example 3. For what values of the constant c does the following converge?

$$\frac{c}{1!} + \frac{c(c+1)}{2!} + \frac{c(c+1)(c+2)}{3!} + \cdots.$$

For sufficiently large n the terms are of constant sign, and hence Theorem II is applicable. We have

$$\frac{a_{n+1}}{a_n} = \frac{c(c+1)(c+2)\ldots(c+n)}{(n+1)!} \frac{n!}{c(c+1)\ldots(c+n-1)} = \frac{c+n}{n+1}.$$

Since

$$\frac{c+n}{n+1} - 1 = \frac{c-1}{n+1} \sim \frac{c-1}{n} = -\frac{1-c}{n},$$

the series is convergent if $1 - c > 1$ and divergent if $1 - c < 1$. Hence, it is convergent when $c < 0$ and divergent when $c > 0$. In this example Theorem IIa gives no information but Theorem IIb solves the problem completely.

PROBLEMS

1. Determine the convergence by using the ratio test, Theorem IIa:

$$\Sigma \frac{n}{2^n}, \ \Sigma \frac{n!}{n^2}, \ \Sigma \frac{n^2}{n!}, \ \Sigma \frac{x^{2n}}{2^n}, \ \Sigma \frac{(x^2+1)^n}{n!}.$$

2. Show that Theorem IIa gives no information, and test for convergence by Theorem IIb:

$$\Sigma \frac{1}{n^2}, \ \Sigma \frac{n!}{c(c+1)(c+2)\ldots(c+n)}, \ \Sigma \frac{(2n)!}{4^n(n!)^2}.$$

3. Test for convergence by any method:

$$\Sigma \frac{n!}{1 \cdot 3 \cdot 5 \ldots (2n+1)}, \ \Sigma \frac{\log n}{n^2}, \ \Sigma \frac{2^n+3^n}{3^n+4^n}, \ \Sigma \frac{2n-1}{2n+1}.$$

4. Give an example of a divergent series Σa_n such that all the terms satisfy $a_n > 0$ and $a_{n+1}/a_n < 1$. Does this contradict the remarks made in connection with (5-4)?

5. If x is constant prove that $\lim_{n \to \infty} x^n/n! = 0$. *Hint:* The series $\Sigma |x|^n/n!$ converges by the ratio test.

6. Absolute Convergence.

The preceding tests for convergence apply to series with positive terms. We shall now see how these tests can be used to establish convergence even when the signs of the terms change infinitely often.[1]

DEFINITION. *A series Σa_n is said to be* **absolutely convergent** *if the series of absolute values $\Sigma |a_n|$ is convergent.*

---

[1] If all but a finite number of terms have the same sign, then we may consider those terms only (Sec. 2, Theorem I). Multiplication by -1, if necessary, yields a series with positive terms, so that the foregoing methods apply. This fact was used in Example 3 of the preceding section.

For example, the series $\Sigma(-1)^n/n^2$ is absolutely convergent, since

$$\Sigma|a_n| = \Sigma\left|\frac{(-1)^n}{n^2}\right| = \Sigma\frac{1}{n^2}$$

converges. On the other hand the series $\Sigma(-1)^n/n$ is not absolutely convergent, as the reader can verify. The importance of absolute convergence stems partly from the following theorem:

THEOREM I. *If $\Sigma|a_n|$ converges, then Σa_n converges.*

In other words, *an absolutely convergent series is convergent.* The definition of absolute value yields

$$0 \le \frac{a_n + |a_n|}{2} \le |a_n|.$$

Hence, by the comparison test, the series

$$\Sigma\frac{a_n + |a_n|}{2}$$

converges when $\Sigma|a_n|$ converges. And then the series with general term

$$a_n = 2\left(\frac{a_n + |a_n|}{2}\right) - |a_n|$$

converges by (2-2) and (2-3).

To illustrate the use of Theorem I consider the series

$$\Sigma\frac{\cos nx}{2^n}. \tag{6-1}$$

Since the signs change infinitely often,[1] none of the preceding methods is applicable. We may, however, apply those methods to the series of *absolute values.* In view of the fact that

$$\left|\frac{\cos nx}{2^n}\right| = \frac{|\cos nx|}{2^n} \le \frac{1}{2^n},$$

the series
$$\Sigma\left|\frac{\cos nx}{2^n}\right|$$

is convergent. Hence the original series (6-1) is convergent.

A series whose terms are alternately positive and negative is called an *alternating series.* There is a simple test due to Leibniz that establishes the convergence of many such series even when the series does not converge absolutely.

---

[1] Except when x is an integral multiple of 2π.

THEOREM II.   *Suppose the alternating series* $\sum_{n=1}^{\infty} (-1)^{n+1} a_n$ *is such that*
$a_n > a_{n+1} > 0$ *and* $\lim a_n = 0$. *Then the series converges, and the remainder after* n *terms has a value which is between zero and the first term not taken.*

For example, if the sum of the series is approximated by the first five terms

$$s \doteq s_5 = a_1 - a_2 + a_3 - a_4 + a_5,$$

then the error in that approximation is between zero and $-a_6$:

$$0 > s - s_5 > -a_6.$$

The value given by s_5 is *too large*, because s_5 ends with a *positive* term, $+a_5$. The value s_6 is too small, since s_6 ends with a negative term, and so on.

To prove the theorem, we have

$$s_{2n} = (a_1 - a_2) + (a_3 - a_4) + \cdots + (a_{2n-1} - a_{2n})$$

$$= a_1 - (a_2 - a_3) - \cdots - (a_{2n-2} - a_{2n-1}) - a_{2n}$$

and hence s_{2n} is positive but less than a_1 for all n.   Also

$$s_2 < s_4 < s_6 \ldots$$

so that these sums tend to a limit by the fundamental principle (Sec. 1). Since $s_{2n+1} = s_{2n} + a_{2n+1}$ and $\lim a_{2n+1} = 0$, it follows that the partial sums of odd order tend to this same limit, and hence the series converges.   The proof of the second statement is left as an exercise for the reader. Actually Theorem II becomes rather obvious when we plot the partial sums s_n on the x axis.

Since the choice $a_n = 1/n$ satisfies the requirements of Theorem II, the alternating harmonic series

$$s = 1 - \frac{1}{2} + \frac{1}{3} - \frac{1}{4} + \frac{1}{5} - \frac{1}{6} + \cdots + \frac{(-1)^{n+1}}{n} + \cdots \qquad (6\text{-}2)$$

is convergent. If the sum is approximated by the first two terms, then Theorem II says that the error is between 0 and $\frac{1}{3}$; that is, $0 < s - \frac{1}{2} < \frac{1}{3}$, or

$$\tfrac{1}{2} < s < \tfrac{5}{6}. \qquad (6\text{-}3)$$

Inasmuch as the series of absolute values diverges, we could not establish the convergence by use of Theorem I. A series such as this, which converges but not absolutely, is said to be *conditionally convergent*.

By rearranging the order of terms in a conditionally convergent series, one can make the resulting series converge to any desired value. In illustration of this fact we shall rearrange the series (6-2) in such a way that the new sum is π, though (6-3) shows that the original sum is not π.

The terms of (6-2) are obtained by choosing alternately from the series

$$1 + \tfrac{1}{3} + \tfrac{1}{5} + \tfrac{1}{7} + \cdots \qquad (6\text{-}4)$$

and from the series

$$-\tfrac{1}{2} - \tfrac{1}{4} - \tfrac{1}{6} - \tfrac{1}{8} - \cdots \qquad (6\text{-}5)$$

both of which are *divergent*. To form a series that converges to π, first pick out, in order, as many positive terms (6-4) as are needed to make the sum just greater than π. Then pick out, in order, enough negative terms (6-5) so that the sum of all terms so far chosen will be just less than π. Then choose more positive terms until the total sum is just greater than π, and so on. The process is possible because the series (6-4) and (6-5) are divergent; the resulting series converges to π because the error is less than the last term taken.

To get a physical interpretation of this result, suppose we place unit positive charges P at the points

$$x = 1,\ -\sqrt{2},\ \sqrt{3},\ -\sqrt{4},\ \sqrt{5},\ -\sqrt{6},\ \ldots$$

and attempt to find the force on a unit negative charge N located at the origin (see Fig. 3). By Coulomb's law two opposite unit charges a distance $\sqrt{n}$ apart experience an

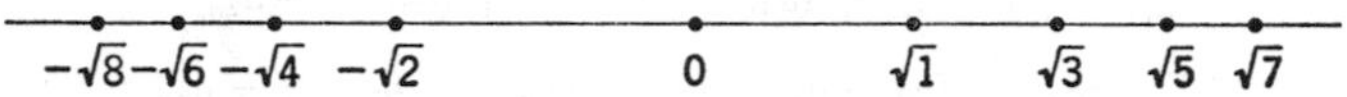

$$-\sqrt{8} \ -\sqrt{6} \ -\sqrt{4} \ \ -\sqrt{2} \qquad\qquad 0 \qquad\qquad \sqrt{1} \quad\ \sqrt{3} \ \ \sqrt{5} \ \sqrt{7}$$

Fig. 3

attraction of magnitude $1/n$. Since the attraction of charges at the left of N exerts a force toward the left whereas attraction of the other charges exerts a force toward the right, the total force on N is given formally by the series (6-2). Now, the fact that this series is conditionally convergent makes the force depend not only on the final configuration of charges but also on the manner in which the charges were introduced. If we obtained the final configuration by putting 10 charges at the left, then 1 at the right, then 100 more at the left, and 1 again at the right, and so on, the net force will be directed toward the left. But if we had a preponderance of charges at the right while setting up the final configuration, then the final force would be directed toward the right.

The foregoing behavior is perhaps not very surprising. What is surprising is that a rearrangement such as this will always give the *same* value provided the series in question is *absolutely convergent*. For example, let the configuration consist of unit positive charges P at the points $x = 1,\ -2,\ 3,\ -4,\ 5,\ -6,\ \ldots$, so that the force is given by the absolutely convergent series

$$1 - \frac{1}{2^2} + \frac{1}{3^2} - \frac{1}{4^2} + \cdots + \frac{(-1)^{n+1}}{n^2} + \cdots.$$

In this case, as we shall show, the force does not depend on the way in which the final configuration was reached.[1]

The preceding examples may assist the reader to appreciate the following theorem, which describes what is perhaps the most important property of absolute convergence.

THEOREM III. *The terms of an absolutely convergent series may be rearranged in any manner without altering the value of the sum.*

[1] One may say that the "charges at infinity" now have no influence, whereas in the former case (6-2) they were important.

We establish this result first for series of positive terms. Let Σp_k be such a series and $\Sigma p_k'$ a rearrangement. For every n we have

$$\sum_{k=1}^{n} p_k' \leq \sum_{k=1}^{\infty} p_k$$

inasmuch as each term p_k' is to be found among the terms of Σp_k. Hence $\Sigma p_k'$ converges (by the fundamental principle), and also

$$\Sigma p_k' \leq \Sigma p_k.$$

In just the same way we find $\Sigma p_k \leq \Sigma p_k'$, and hence $\Sigma p_k' = \Sigma p_k$.

To obtain the result for an arbitrary but absolutely convergent series Σa_k, denote the rearrangement by $\Sigma a_k'$ and observe that

$$
\begin{aligned}
a_k &= (a_k + |a_k|) - |a_k| \\
a_k' &= (a_k' + |a_k'|) - |a_k'|.
\end{aligned}
\tag{6-6}
$$

By the result for positive series we have

$$\Sigma |a_k'| = \Sigma |a_k|$$

$$\Sigma (a_k' + |a_k'|) = \Sigma (a_k + |a_k|).$$

Hence (6-6) gives $\Sigma a_k' = \Sigma a_k$ when we recall (2-3).

By methods quite similar to the foregoing [1] one can establish the following, which expresses a third fundamental property of absolutely convergent series:

THEOREM IV. *If $\Sigma a_k = a$ and $\Sigma b_k = b$ are absolutely convergent, then these series can be multiplied like finite sums and the product series will converge to ab. Moreover, the product series is absolutely convergent, hence may be rearranged in any manner.* For example,

$$ab = a_1 b_1 + (a_2 b_1 + a_1 b_2) + (a_3 b_1 + a_2 b_2 + a_1 b_3) + \cdots.$$

Example: Consider the series $\Sigma x^n / \sqrt{n}$.
With $a_n = x^n / \sqrt{n}$ we have

$$\frac{|a_{n+1}|}{|a_n|} = \left| \frac{x^{n+1}}{\sqrt{n+1}} \frac{\sqrt{n}}{x^n} \right| = |x| \sqrt{\frac{n}{n+1}} \sim |x|.$$

Hence the series converges absolutely if $|x| < 1$ and diverges if $|x| > 1$. To see what happens when $x = \pm 1$, we substitute these values into the original series, obtaining

$$\Sigma \frac{(-1)^n}{\sqrt{n}} \quad \text{and} \quad \Sigma \frac{1}{\sqrt{n}}$$

for $x = -1$ and $x = +1$, respectively. The first series is conditionally convergent, and the second is divergent. Hence the series converges absolutely when $|x| < 1$, it converges conditionally when $x = -1$, and it diverges for all other values of x.

---

[1] The proof is given in full in Sokolnikoff, *op. cit.,* pp. 242–244.

PROBLEMS

1. Classify the following series as absolutely convergent, conditionally convergent, or divergent:

$$\Sigma \frac{(-1)^n}{\sqrt{n}}, \ \Sigma(-1)^n \frac{2n+3}{2n}, \ \Sigma \frac{(-1)^n}{n^2}, \ \Sigma \frac{n}{2^n}, \ \frac{1}{3} - \frac{1\cdot3}{3\cdot6} + \frac{1\cdot3\cdot5}{3\cdot6\cdot9} - \frac{1\cdot3\cdot5\cdot7}{3\cdot6\cdot9\cdot12} + \cdots.$$

2. Determine the values of x for which the following series are absolutely convergent, conditionally convergent, or divergent:

$$\Sigma(-1)^n \frac{x^n}{n}, \ \Sigma(-1)^n \frac{x^{2n}}{(2n)!}, \ \Sigma(-1)^n x^n, \ \Sigma \frac{1}{nx^n}, \ \Sigma \frac{1}{n}\left(\frac{2x}{x+4}\right)^n, \ \Sigma n! x^n, \ \Sigma \frac{(x-2)^n}{\log(n+1)}.$$

3. Approximately how many terms of the series $\sum_{1}^{\infty} (-1)^n/n^4$ are needed to give the sum within 10^{-8}? Evaluate the sum to two places of decimals.

7. Uniform Convergence. If a finite number of functions that are all continuous in an interval [1] $[a,b]$ are added together, the sum is also a continuous function in $[a,b]$. The question arises as to whether or not this property will be retained in the case of an infinite series of continuous functions. Moreover, it is frequently desirable to obtain the derivative (or integral) of a function $f(x)$ by means of term-by-term differentiation (or integration) of an infinite series that defines $f(x)$. Unfortunately such operations are not always valid, and many important investigations have led to erroneous results solely because of the improper handling of infinite series. The analysis of these questions is based on a property known as *uniform convergence*, which is now to be described.

If a series of functions $\sum_{n=1}^{\infty} u_n(x)$ converges for each value of x in an interval $[a,b]$, then the sum defines a function of x,

$$s(x) = \Sigma u_n(x).$$

We denote the nth partial sum by $s_n(x)$,

$$s_n(x) = u_1(x) + u_2(x) + u_3(x) + \cdots + u_n(x),$$

and the remainder after n terms by $r_n(x)$:

$$r_n(x) = s(x) - s_n(x) = u_{n+1}(x) + u_{n+2}(x) + \cdots. \tag{7-1}$$

Since the series converges to $s(x)$, $\lim s_n(x) = s(x)$ as $n \to \infty$, and hence

$$\lim r_n(x) = 0. \tag{7-2}$$

The statement embodied in (7-2) means that for any preassigned positive number ϵ, however small, one can find a number N such that

$$|r_n(x)| < \epsilon \qquad \text{for all } n > N.$$

[1] We use $[a,b]$ to indicate the closed interval $a \le x \le b$.

It is important to note that, in general, the magnitude of N depends not only on the choice of ϵ but also on the value of x.

This last remark may be clarified by considering the series

$$x + (x - 1)x + (x - 1)x^2 + \cdots + (x - 1)x^{n-1} + \cdots.$$

Since

$$s_n(x) = x + (x - 1)x + (x - 1)x^2 + \cdots + (x - 1)x^{n-1} = x^n,$$

it is evident that

$$\lim_{n \to \infty} s_n(x) \equiv \lim_{n \to \infty} x^n = 0, \qquad \text{if } 0 \leq x < 1.$$

Thus, $s(x) = 0$ for all values of x in the interval $0 \leq x < 1$, and therefore

$$|r_n(x)| = |s_n(x) - s(x)| = |x^n - 0| = x^n.$$

Hence, the requirement that $|r_n(x)| < \epsilon$, for an arbitrary ϵ, will be satisfied only if $x^n < \epsilon$. This inequality leads to the condition

$$n \log x < \log \epsilon.$$

Since $\log x$ is negative for x between 0 and 1, it follows that it is necessary to have

$$n > \frac{\log \epsilon}{\log x}$$

which clearly shows the dependence of N on both ϵ and x. In fact, if $\epsilon = 0.01$ and $x = 0.1$, n must be greater than $\log 0.01 / \log 0.1 = -2/(-1) = 2$, so that N can be chosen as any number greater than 2. If $\epsilon = 0.01$ and $x = 0.5$, N must be chosen larger than $\log 0.01 / \log 0.5$, which is greater than 6. Since the values of $\log x$ approach zero as x approaches 1, the ratio $\log \epsilon / \log x$ will increase indefinitely and it will be impossible to find a single value of N which will serve for $\epsilon = 0.01$ and for all values of x in $0 \leq x < 1$.

This is the situation which is to be expected in general. In many important cases, however, it is possible to find a single, fixed N, for any preassigned positive ϵ, which will serve for all values of x in the interval. The series is then said to be *uniformly convergent*.

DEFINITION. *The series $\Sigma u_n(x)$ is uniformly convergent in the interval $[a,b]$ if for each $\epsilon > 0$ there is a number N, **independent of x**, such that the remainder $r_n(x)$ satisfies $|r_n(x)| < \epsilon$ for all $n > N$.*

It is the words in boldface type that give the whole distinction between ordinary convergence and uniform convergence.

To illustrate this distinction in a specific case, we shall discuss the geometric series $\sum_{n=0}^{\infty} x^n$ on the interval $-\tfrac{1}{2} \leq x \leq \tfrac{1}{2}$.

According to the result of Sec. 1, Example 2, the sum, partial sum, and remainder are, respectively,

$$s(x) = \frac{1}{1-x}, \qquad s_n(x) = \frac{1-x^n}{1-x}, \qquad r_n(x) = \frac{x^n}{1-x}. \tag{7-3}$$

The condition $|r_n(x)| < \epsilon$ gives $|x^n| < \epsilon(1 - x)$ or, upon taking the logarithm and solving for n,

$$n > \frac{\log \epsilon(1 - x)}{\log |x|}. \tag{7-4}$$

Again it appears that the choice of N depends on both x and ϵ, but in this case it is possible to choose an N that will serve for all values of x in $[-\frac{1}{2}, \frac{1}{2}]$. Given a small ϵ, the ratio $\log \epsilon(1 - x)/\log |x|$ assumes its maximum value when $x = +\frac{1}{2}$. Hence if N is chosen so that

$$N > \frac{\log \epsilon/2}{\log \frac{1}{2}} = 1 - \frac{\log \epsilon}{\log 2}$$

then the inequality (7-4) will be satisfied for all $n \geq N$.

Upon recalling the conditions for uniform convergence, we see that the series Σx^n converges uniformly for $-\frac{1}{2} \leq x \leq \frac{1}{2}$. However, the series does not converge uniformly in the interval $(-1,1)$, for, in this interval, the ratio appearing in (7-4) will increase indefinitely as x approaches the values ± 1.

Generally speaking, any test for convergence becomes a test for uniform convergence provided its conditions are satisfied uniformly, that is, independently of x. For instance, the ratio test takes the form: If there is a number r *independent of* x such that for all large n

$$\left| \frac{u_{n+1}(x)}{u_n(x)} \right| \leq r < 1,$$

then $\Sigma u_n(x)$ converges uniformly. Similarly, the comparison test takes the form: If $\Sigma v_n(x)$ is a *uniformly convergent* series such that $|u_n(x)| \leq v_n(x)$, then $\Sigma u_n(x)$ converges uniformly. The simplest example of a uniformly convergent series $\Sigma v_n(x)$ is a series of constants. Choosing such a series in the comparison test, we are led to the so-called *Weierstrass M test*:

THEOREM I. *If there is a convergent series of constants, ΣM_n, such that $|u_n(x)| \leq M_n$ for all values of x on $[a,b]$, then the series $\Sigma u_n(x)$ is uniformly (and absolutely) convergent on $[a,b]$.*

The proof is simple. Since ΣM_n is convergent, for any prescribed $\epsilon > 0$ there is an N such that

$$M_{n+1} + M_{n+2} + M_{n+3} + \cdots < \epsilon \qquad \text{for all } n > N.$$

By the ordinary comparison test $\Sigma u_n(x)$ converges for each x, so that $r_n(x)$ is well defined. We have, moreover,

$$|r_n(x)| = |u_{n+1}(x) + u_{n+2}(x) + \cdots| \leq |u_{n+1}(x)| + |u_{n+2}(x)| + \cdots$$

$$\leq M_{n+1} + M_{n+2} + \cdots < \epsilon$$

for all $n > N$. Since N does not depend on x, this establishes the theorem. The other tests for uniform convergence mentioned above are established similarly.

The fact that the Weierstrass test establishes the absolute convergence, as well as the uniform convergence, of a series means that it is applicable only to series which converge absolutely. There are other tests that are not so restricted, but these tests are more complex. It should be emphasized that a series may converge uniformly but not absolutely, and vice versa.

To illustrate the use of the M test consider the series $\sum_{n=1}^{\infty} \dfrac{\sin nx}{n^2}$. Since $|\sin nx| \leq 1$ for all values of x, the convergent series $\Sigma 1/n^2$ will serve as an M series. It follows that $\Sigma (\sin nx)/n^2$ is uniformly and absolutely convergent on every interval, no matter how large.

For another example consider the geometric series Σx^n. In any interval $[-a,a]$ with $0 < a < 1$ the series of positive constants Σa^n could be used as an M series, since $|x^n| \leq a^n$ on the given interval and since Σa^n converges.

The importance of uniform convergence rests upon the following theorems:

THEOREM II.   *Let $\Sigma u_k(x)$ be a series such that each $u_k(x)$ is a continuous function of x in the interval $[a,b]$. If the series is uniformly convergent in $[a,b]$, then the sum of the series is also a continuous function of x in $[a,b]$.*

THEOREM III.   *If a series of continuous functions $\Sigma u_n(x)$ converges uniformly to $s(x)$ in $[a,b]$, then*

$$\int_{\alpha}^{\beta} s(x) \; dx = \int_{\alpha}^{\beta} u_1(x) \; dx + \int_{\alpha}^{\beta} u_2(x) \; dx + \cdots + \int_{\alpha}^{\beta} u_n(x) \; dx + \cdots,$$

where $a \leq \alpha \leq b$ and $a \leq \beta \leq b$. Moreover, the convergence is uniform with respect to α and β.

THEOREM IV.   *Let $\Sigma u_k(x)$ be a series of differentiable functions that converges to $s(x)$ in $[a,b]$. If the series $\Sigma u_k'(x)$ converges uniformly in $[a,b]$, then it converges to $s'(x)$.*

The proof is not difficult, and serves well to illustrate the idea of uniform convergence (see words in boldface). In Theorem II, if x and $x + h$ are on $[a,b]$, we have

$$s(x) = s_n(x) + r_n(x),$$

$$s(x + h) = s_n(x + h) + r_n(x + h),$$

and hence

$$s(x + h) - s(x) = s_n(x + h) - s_n(x) + r_n(x + h) - r_n(x). \tag{7-5}$$

Given $\epsilon > 0$, pick n so that $|r_n(t)| <$ **ϵ for all t** on $[a,b]$. Now, $s_n(x)$ is a finite sum of continuous functions, hence continuous. Therefore

$$|s_n(x + h) - s_n(x)| < \epsilon$$

whenever $|h|$ is sufficiently small. From (7-5) it follows that

$$\begin{aligned} |s(x + h) - s(x)| &\leq |s_n(x + h) - s_n(x)| + |r_n(x + h)| + |r_n(x)| \\ &< \qquad\qquad \epsilon \qquad\qquad + \qquad \epsilon \qquad + \quad \epsilon \quad . \end{aligned}$$

This shows that $|s(x + h) - s(x)|$ becomes arbitrarily small provided $|h|$ is sufficiently small, and hence $s(x)$ is continuous.

For Theorem III, note that $s(x)$ and $r_n(x)$ are continuous by Theorem II. Hence

$$\int_\alpha^\beta s(x)\,dx = \int_\alpha^\beta s_n(x)\,dx + \int_\alpha^\beta r_n(x)\,dx.$$

If we choose n so large that $|r_n(x)| < \epsilon$ for all x on $[a,b]$, then

$$\left| \int_\alpha^\beta s(x)\,dx - \int_\alpha^\beta s_n(x)\,dx \right| \leq \left| \int_\alpha^\beta \epsilon\,dx \right| = |\beta - \alpha|\,\epsilon \leq (b - a)\epsilon.$$

Since the finite sum $s_n(x)$ can be integrated term by term and since $(b - a)\epsilon$ is arbitrarily small independently of α and β, the desired result follows. Theorem IV follows from Theorem III when $u_k'(x)$ is continuous; [1] we simply write down the differentiated series and integrate term by term.

A geometric interpretation of uniform convergence may be obtained by considering the graphs of $y = s(x)$ and of the nth approximating curves $y = s_n(x)$. The condition $|r_n(x)| < \epsilon$ is equivalent to

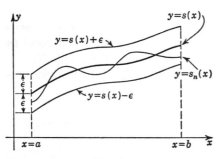

FIG. 4

$$s(x) - \epsilon < s_n(x) < s(x) + \epsilon \qquad (7\text{-}6)$$

which means that the graph of $y = s_n(x)$ lies in a strip of width 2ϵ centered on the graph of $y = s(x)$ (see Fig. 4). No matter how narrow the strip may be, this condition must hold for all sufficiently large n; otherwise the convergence is not uniform.

With such an interpretation, many facts about uniform convergence become rather obvious. For example, the conclusion of Theorem III is

$$\int_\alpha^\beta s(x)\,dx = \lim_{n \to \infty} \int_\alpha^\beta s_n(x)\,dx \qquad (7\text{-}7)$$

and the truth of (7-7) is strongly suggested by considering appropriate areas in Fig. 4.

A graphical illustration of *nonuniform* convergence is given in Fig. 5. Here, the partial sums

$$s_n(x) = \frac{n^2 x}{1 + n^3 x^2} \qquad (7\text{-}8)$$

are plotted for $n = 3$, 5, and 10. By inspection of (7-8)

$$s(x) = \lim_{n \to \infty} s_n(x) = 0, \qquad -\infty < x < \infty.$$

---

[1] A proof free of this restriction is given in K. Knopp, "Theory and Application of Infinite Series," p. 343, Blackie & Son, Ltd., Glasgow.

Nevertheless the approximating curves (7-8) have peaks near $x = 0$ which grow higher with increasing n. Since $y = s_n(x)$ does not lie in a strip $-\epsilon < y < \epsilon$ for arbitrarily small [1] ϵ and all large n, the convergence is not uniform in any interval containing the point $x = 0$.

By looking at Fig. 5 one cannot easily see whether the areas under the curves $y = s_n(x)$ tend to 0 or not; that is, one cannot tell whether (7-7)

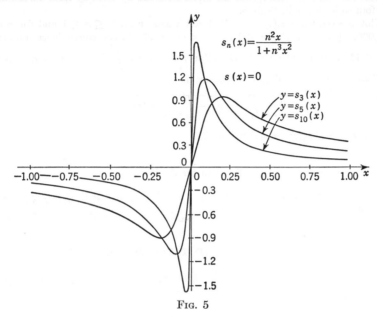

FIG. 5

holds or not. A short calculation based on (7-8) shows that, in fact, (7-7) does hold. Thus, the conclusion of Theorem III may be true even when the convergence is not uniform. It is left for the student to verify that (7-7) does not hold when $\alpha = 0$, $\beta = 1$, and, instead of (7-8),

$$s_n(x) = \frac{n^2 x}{1 + n^2 x^2 \log n}. \tag{7-9}$$

The graphs of $y = s_n(x)$ in (7-9) give a figure quite similar to Fig. 5.

PROBLEMS

1. The partial sums of a series are $s_n(x) = x^n$. Show that the series is uniformly convergent in the interval $[0, \frac{1}{2}]$.

2. By using the definition of uniform convergence, show that

$$\frac{1}{x+1} - \frac{1}{(x+1)(x+2)} - \cdots - \frac{1}{(x+n-1)(x+n)} - \cdots$$

[1] In this case the condition does not even hold for large values of ϵ.

is uniformly convergent in the interval $0 \leq x \leq 1$. *Hint:* Rewrite the series to show that $s_n(x) = 1/(x + n)$ and therefore $s_n(x) - s(x) = 1/(x + n)$. See Prob. 1, Sec. 1.

3. Test the following series for uniform convergence:

$$\Sigma \frac{\cos nx}{n^3}, \ \Sigma(10x)^n, \ \Sigma n(\sin x)^n, \ \Sigma \frac{1}{1 + x^{2n}}.$$

4. Test for uniform convergence the series obtained by term-by-term differentiation of the four series given in Prob. 3.

5. Plot the sequence $s_n(x) = nx/(1 + nx)$ versus x for $0 \leq x \leq 1$ and for $n = 10$, 100, 1,000. Does $\lim s_n(x) = s(x)$ exist for every x? Is the convergence uniform on $0 \leq x \leq 1$? Is $s(x)$ continuous? Does $\lim \int_\alpha^\beta s_n(x) \, dx = \int_\alpha^\beta s(x) \, dx$ for all α, β on $[0,1]$?

6. If $s_n(x) = 2nxe^{-nx^2}$, $0 \leq x \leq 1$, show that

$$\lim_{n \to \infty} \int_0^1 s_n(x) \, dx - \int_0^1 \lim_{n \to \infty} s_n(x) \, dx = 1.$$

Is the convergence $s_n(x) \to s(x)$ uniform?

Problem for Review

7. Show that Σa_n converges absolutely if $\lim \sqrt[n]{|a_n|} = r < 1$. *Hint:* Choose r' so that $r < r' < 1$. Then $\sqrt[n]{|a_n|} < r'$ for sufficiently large n, and hence $|a_n| < (r')^n$.

POWER SERIES AND TAYLOR'S FORMULA

8. Properties of Power Series. One of the most important types of infinite series is the power series [1]

$$\sum_{n=0}^{\infty} a_n x^n = a_0 + a_1 x + a_2 x^2 + \cdots + a_n x^n + \cdots \tag{8-1}$$

so called because it is arranged in ascending powers of the variable. Typical examples are given by the three series [2]

$$\Sigma x^n n!, \ \frac{\Sigma x^n}{n!}, \ \Sigma x^n, \tag{8-2}$$

which were already encountered in the foregoing sections.

For many power series the region of convergence is easily determined by means of the ratio test. In the first series (8-2), for instance, the ratio of two successive terms leads to

$$\left| \frac{x^n n!}{x^{n-1}(n - 1)!} \right| = |xn| = |x|n \to \infty \qquad \text{for } x \neq 0$$

[1] Throughout Secs. 8 to 14, Σ means $\sum_0^\infty$ rather than $\sum_1^\infty$.

[2] It is customary to take $0! = 1$, so that the relation $n! = n(n - 1)!$ will hold for $n = 1$ as well as for $n = 2, 3, 4, \ldots$.

and hence the series converges only for $x = 0$. In just the same way it is found that the second series gives a ratio $|x|/n$, which approaches zero. Hence the second series converges for all x. The third series is the geometric series, which, as we know, converges for $|x| < 1$.

It is a remarkable fact that every power series, without exception, behaves like one of these three examples. The series converges for $x = 0$ only, or it converges for all x, or there is a number r such that [1] the series converges whenever $|x| < r$ but diverges whenever $|x| > r$. The number r is called the *radius of convergence*, and the interval $|x| < r$ is called the *interval of convergence*. The fact that every power series has an interval of convergence may be deduced [2] from the following theorem:

THEOREM I.   *If $\Sigma a_n x^n$ converges for a particular value $x = x_0$, then the series converges absolutely whenever $|x| < |x_0|$ and uniformly in the interval $|x| \leq |x_1|$ for each fixed x_1 such that $|x_1| < |x_0|$. And if it diverges for $x = x_0$, then it diverges for all x such that $|x| > |x_0|$.*

To establish Theorem I, observe that $\lim a_n x_0^n = 0$, since $\Sigma a_n x_0^n$ converges (Sec. 1, Theorem I). Hence $|a_n x_0^n| < 1$ for all sufficiently large n, or

$$|a_n| < \frac{1}{|x_0|^n} \qquad \text{for all } n > N, \text{ say.} \qquad (8\text{-}3)$$

This shows that $\Sigma |a_n| |x|^n$ converges by comparison with the geometric series

$$\Sigma \frac{1}{|x_0|^n} |x|^n = \Sigma \left(\frac{|x|}{|x_0|} \right)^n$$

provided $|x| < |x_0|$. The statement concerning uniform convergence is established by the same calculation, since $\Sigma (|x_1|/|x_0|)^n$ serves as an M series for the Weierstrass M test. Finally, the statement concerning divergence follows from the result on convergence. That is, if the series converged for x, it would have to converge for x_0, since $|x_0| < |x|$, and this is contrary to the hypothesis.

The uniform convergence mentioned in Theorem I shows that a power series represents a continuous function for all values of x interior to its interval of convergence (see Theorem II, Sec. 7). For instance, $\Sigma x^n = 1/(1 - x)$ is continuous for $|x| < 1$, though not at $x = 1$. We shall soon see that such functions not only are continuous but have derivatives of all orders and the derivatives can be found by termwise differentiation of the series.

---

[1] For simplicity of nomenclature one may incorporate the first two cases into the third by allowing $r = 0$ and $r = \infty$. The case $r = 0$ arises when the series converges for $x = 0$ only, whereas $r = \infty$ if the series converges for all x.

[2] A complete discussion is given in Sec. 16.

As an illustration of this fact consider the geometric series Σx^n mentioned above. Term-by-term differentiation yields the series $\Sigma n x^{n-1}$. Because of the coefficient n, which tends to infinity, one might expect the latter series to have a smaller interval of convergence than the former. Actually, however, the intervals are the same. Since

$$\left| \frac{nx^{n-1}}{(n-1)x^{n-2}} \right| = \left| \frac{n}{n-1} x \right| = \frac{n}{n-1} |x| \to |x|, \qquad \text{as } n \to \infty,$$

the ratio test shows that the differentiated series, like the original series, has the interval of convergence $|x| < 1$. A similar result is found if we differentiate repeatedly. Each differentiation multiplies the ratio by $n/(n-1)$. Inasmuch as $n/(n-1) \to 1$, this factor does not change the *limit* of the ratio, hence does not change the interval of convergence.

For many power series the ratio $|a_{n+1}/a_n|$ has no limit as $n \to \infty$, and the foregoing analysis does not apply. However, suppose the series (8-1) converges for some value $x = x_0 \neq 0$, so that, as before, we have the estimate (8-3). If $|x| < |x_0|$, the differentiated series $\Sigma n a_n x^{n-1}$ converges by comparison with

$$\Sigma n \frac{1}{|x_0|^n} |x|^n = \Sigma n \left(\frac{|x|}{|x_0|} \right)^n.$$

(Note that the latter series was shown to be convergent in the previous paragraph.) The same calculation establishes *uniform* convergence of the derivative series if $|x| \leq |x_1| < |x_0|$, since

$$\Sigma n \left(\frac{|x_1|}{|x_0|} \right)^n$$

serves as an M series for the Weierstrass M test. Hence, the result of the differentiation is actually the derivative of the original series $\Sigma a_n x^n$ (see Theorem IV, Sec. 7).

The foregoing argument is practically identical with that used to prove Theorem I. A third use of the same method establishes the corresponding result for the integrated series $\Sigma a_n x^{n+1}/(n+1)$. In this case the comparison series are, respectively,

$$\Sigma \frac{1}{n+1} \left(\frac{|x|}{|x_0|} \right)^n \qquad \text{and} \qquad \Sigma \frac{1}{n+1} \left(\frac{|x_1|}{|x_0|} \right)^n.$$

Summarizing this discussion we can state the following, which is perhaps the most important and useful result in the whole theory of power series:

THEOREM II. *A power series may be differentiated (or integrated) term by term in any interval interior to its interval of convergence. The resulting series has the same interval of convergence as the original series and represents the derivative (or integral) of the function to which the original series converges.*

Consider, for example, the geometric series

$$(1-x)^{-1} = 1 + x + x^2 + \cdots + x^n + \cdots, \qquad |x| < 1. \qquad (8\text{-}4)$$

Differentiating termwise we obtain

$$(1-x)^{-2} = 1 + 2x + 3x^2 + \cdots + nx^{n-1} + \cdots, \qquad |x| < 1. \qquad (8\text{-}5)$$

Differentiating again gives an expansion for $(1-x)^{-3}$, and so on. Since the series (8-4) converges for $|x| < 1$, Theorem II shows *without further discussion* that all these other expansions are also valid for $|x| < 1$.

On the other hand, if the series (8-4) is integrated termwise from zero to x, there results an expansion

$$-\log(1-x) = x + \frac{x^2}{2} + \frac{x^3}{3} + \cdots + \frac{x^n}{n} + \cdots, \qquad |x| < 1, \qquad (8\text{-}6)$$

which can be used for numerical computation of the logarithm.

Equations (8-4) to (8-6) give power-series representations for the functions on the left. It will now be established that such representations are always unique.

THEOREM III. *If two power series converge to the same sum throughout an interval, then corresponding coefficients are equal.*

For proof, assume that $\Sigma a_n x^n = \Sigma b_n x^n$ so that, by (2-3),

$$0 = (a_0 - b_0) + (a_1 - b_1)x + (a_2 - b_2)x^2 + \cdots + (a_n - b_n)x^n + \cdots.$$

The choice $x = 0$ yields $a_0 = b_0$. Differentiating with respect to x yields

$$0 = (a_1 - b_1) + 2(a_2 - b_2)x + \cdots + n(a_n - b_n)x^{n-1} + \cdots$$

and if we now set $x = 0$, we get $a_1 = b_1$. Upon differentiating again and setting $x = 0$, we get $a_2 = b_2$, and so on.

This process not only shows that the coefficients are uniquely determined but yields a simple formula for their values. Let

$$f(x) = a_0 + a_1 x + a_2 x^2 + \cdots + a_n x^n + \cdots, \qquad \text{for } |x| < x_0.$$

Upon differentiating n times we get

$$f^{(n)}(x) = 0 + 0 + 0 + \cdots + 0 + n!a_n + \cdots$$

where the second group of terms "$+ \cdots$" involves x, x^2, or higher powers. These terms disappear when we set $x = 0$, and hence $f^{(n)}(0) = n!a_n$, or

$$a_n = \frac{f^{(n)}(0)}{n!}. \qquad (8\text{-}7)$$

In the following section we shall be led to the same formula (8-7), though by an entirely different method.

The algebraic properties described in Sec. 2 for series in general give corresponding properties for power series: Two power series may be added term by term, a power series may be multiplied by a constant, and so on.

Since power series converge absolutely in the interval of convergence, Theorem IV, Sec. 6, yields the following additional property:

THEOREM IV. *Two power series may be multiplied like polynomials for values x which are interior to both intervals of convergence.* Thus,

$$(\Sigma a_n x^n)(\Sigma b_n x^n) = \Sigma c_n x^n,$$

where $c_n = a_0 b_n + a_1 b_{n-1} + a_2 b_{n-2} + \cdots + a_n b_0$.

So far, nothing has been said about the behavior of power series at the ends of the interval of convergence. As a matter of fact all behaviors are possible. For example, each of the series

$$\sum_1^\infty \frac{x^n}{n^2}, \ \sum_1^\infty x^n, \ \sum_1^\infty \frac{x^n}{n}, \ \sum_1^\infty \frac{(-1)^n x^n}{n}$$

has $|x| < 1$ as interval of convergence. However, the first series converges at $x = 1$ and -1, the second diverges at $x = 1$ and -1, the third converges at $x = -1$ but diverges at $x = 1$, and the fourth diverges at $x = -1$ but converges at $x = 1$.

For applications, the most important theorem concerning the behavior at the ends of the convergence interval is Abel's theorem [1] on continuity of power series, which reads as follows:

ABEL'S THEOREM. *Suppose the power series $\Sigma a_n x^n$ converges for $x = x_0$, where x_0 may be an end point of the interval of convergence.* Then

$$\lim_{x \to x_0} \Sigma a_n x^n = \Sigma a_n x_0^n$$

provided $x \to x_0$ through values interior to the interval of convergence.

To illustrate the theorem, let $x \to -1$ through values greater than -1 in the series (8-6). The limit of the left side is $-\log 2$, since the logarithm is continuous, and the limit of the right side is $\sum_1^\infty \frac{(-1)^n}{n}$ by virtue of Abel's theorem. Hence,

$$\log 2 = 1 - \frac{1}{2} + \frac{1}{3} - \frac{1}{4} + \cdots + \frac{(-1)^{n+1}}{n} + \cdots.$$

As another example of Abel's theorem, let $x \to 1$ in Theorem IV to obtain the following: *If*

$$c_n = a_0 b_n + a_1 b_{n-1} + \cdots + a_n b_0,$$

then $(\Sigma a_n)(\Sigma b_n) = \Sigma c_n$ provided each series is convergent. Hence, with the particular arrangement of the product series which is given by Σc_n, we do not need *absolute* convergence as in Theorem IV of Sec. 6.

PROBLEMS

1. Find the interval of convergence, and determine the behavior at the end points of the interval:

$$\Sigma(-1)^n n x^{n-1}, \ \Sigma \frac{x^{2n}}{2^n(n+1)}, \ \Sigma \frac{x^{2n+1}}{(2n+1)!}, \ \Sigma \frac{n^3 x^{2n}}{9^n}, \ \Sigma \frac{x^{4n}}{3^n}.$$

[1] A proof is given in I. S. Sokolnikoff, "Advanced Calculus," pp. 278–279, McGraw-Hill Book Company, Inc., New York, 1939.

2. Show that the radius of convergence of $\Sigma a_n x^n$ is given by $r = \lim\limits_{n \to \infty} |a_n/a_{n+1}|$ whenever this limit exists.

3. (a) By letting $x = -t^2$ in (8-4), obtain the expansion

$$\frac{1}{1+t^2} = 1 - t^2 + t^4 - t^6 + \cdots + (-1)^n t^{2n} + \cdots.$$

(b) By integrating from zero to x, obtain an expansion for $\tan^{-1} x$. (c) Using your result (b), show that

$$\frac{\pi}{4} = 1 - \frac{1}{3} + \frac{1}{5} - \frac{1}{7} + \cdots.$$

4. (a) Show that the series $y = \Sigma x^n/n!$ satisfies $y' = y$. (b) Deduce an expansion for e^x. For what values of x is this expansion valid? (c) Obtain series expansions for e and $1/e$ by taking $x = \pm 1$ in (b). (d) Using your series, compute e and $1/e$ to three significant figures, and check your work by finding the product $e(1/e)$.

5. Using results given in the text, express the following integrals as power series:

$$\int_0^x \frac{dt}{1+t^4}, \quad \int_0^x \log(1+t^5)\,dt, \quad \int_0^x \frac{t^6\,dt}{(1-t^3)^2}.$$

Hint: In the third case, for example, let $x = t^3$ in (8-5), multiply through by t^6, and finally integrate term by term.

6. By multiplication of series obtain the expansion of $(1 + x + x^2 + \cdots + x^n + \cdots)^2$. In particular, compute the coefficients of 1, x, x^2, x^3, and x^n in the product series.

9. Taylor's Formula.

The usefulness of power series is greatly increased by the so-called *Taylor formula*, which yields the power-series expansion for an arbitrary function $f(x)$ together with an expression for the remainder after n terms. Let $f(x)$ be a function with a continuous nth derivative throughout the interval $[a,b]$. Taylor's formula is obtained by integrating this nth derivative n times in succession between the limits a and x, where x is any point on $[a,b]$. Thus,

$$\int_a^x f^{(n)}(x)\,dx = f^{(n-1)}(x)\Big|_a^x = f^{(n-1)}(x) - f^{(n-1)}(a)$$

$$\int_a^x \int_a^x f^{(n)}(x)\,(dx)^2 = \int_a^x f^{(n-1)}(x)\,dx - \int_a^x f^{(n-1)}(a)\,dx$$

$$= f^{(n-2)}(x) - f^{(n-2)}(a) - (x-a)f^{(n-1)}(a)$$

$$\int_a^x \int_a^x \int_a^x f^{(n)}(x)\,(dx)^3 = f^{(n-3)}(x) - f^{(n-3)}(a) - (x-a)f^{(n-2)}(a)$$

$$- \frac{(x-a)^2}{2!} f^{(n-1)}(a)$$

$$\cdots \cdots \cdots \cdots \cdots \cdots \cdots$$

$$\int_a^x \cdots \int_a^x f^{(n)}(x)\,(dx)^n = f(x) - f(a) - (x-a)f'(a) - \frac{(x-a)^2}{2!}f''(a)$$

$$- \cdots - \frac{(x-a)^{n-1}}{(n-1)!} f^{(n-1)}(a).$$

Solving for $f(x)$ gives

$$f(x) = f(a) + (x - a)f'(a) + \frac{(x - a)^2}{2!}f''(a)$$

$$+ \cdots + \frac{(x - a)^{n-1}}{(n - 1)!}f^{(n-1)}(a) + R_n, \quad (9\text{-}1)$$

where
$$R_n = \int_a^x \cdots \int_a^x f^{(n)}(x)\,(dx)^n. \quad (9\text{-}2)$$

The formula given by (9-1) is known as Taylor's formula, and the particular form of R_n given in (9-2) is called the *integral form* of the remainder after n terms. The *Lagrangian form* of the remainder, which is often more useful, is

$$R_n = \frac{(x - a)^n}{n!}f^{(n)}(\xi), \qquad a \le \xi \le x. \quad (9\text{-}3)$$

To derive this from the form (9-2), let M be the maximum and m the minimum of $f^{(n)}(t)$ for $a \le t \le x$. Then the integral (9-2) clearly lies between

$$\int_a^x \cdots \int_a^x M\,(dx)^n \quad \text{and} \quad \int_a^x \cdots \int_a^x m\,(dx)^n.$$

Upon carrying out the integration we find that these bounds are

$$\frac{(x - a)^n}{n!}\,M \quad \text{and} \quad \frac{(x - a)^n}{n!}\,m,$$

respectively. Since the continuous function $f^{(n)}(t)$ assumes all values between its maximum M and minimum m, there must be a number $t = \xi$ such that (9-3) holds. We have written our inequalities for the case $a < x$; in any case, ξ is between a and x.

In general the remainder R_n depends on x, as is obvious from the representation (9-2). It may happen, however, that $f(x)$ has derivatives of all orders and that the remainder R_n approaches zero as $n \to \infty$ for each value x on $[a,b]$. In this case we obtain a representation for $f(x)$ as an infinite series

$$f(x) = \sum_{n=0}^{\infty} \frac{f^{(n)}(a)(x - a)^n}{n!} \quad (9\text{-}4)$$

and R_n now gives the error which arises when the series is approximated by its nth partial sum. The series in (9-4) is called *the Taylor series for $f(x)$* about the point $x = a$. The special case

$$f(x) = \sum_{n=0}^{\infty} \frac{f^{(n)}(0)x^n}{n!} \quad (9\text{-}5)$$

is often called *Maclaurin's series*, though Taylor's work preceded Maclaurin's.

To illustrate the use of Taylor's formula, let $f(x) = e^x$. Then $f'(x) = e^x$, $f''(x) = e^x$, ..., and hence $f^{(n)}(0) = 1$. Equation (9-5) suggests that

$$e^x = 1 + x + \frac{x^2}{2!} + \frac{x^3}{3!} + \cdots + \frac{x^n}{n!} + \cdots \tag{9-6}$$

and indeed, by the ratio test this series converges for all x. However, to show that it converges to e^x we must consider the remainder, which takes the form

$$R_n = \frac{x^n}{n!} e^\xi, \qquad 0 \le \xi \le x, \tag{9-7}$$

when we use (9-3). Since this approaches zero [1] as $n \to \infty$, the series does converge to e^x.

As another example we find the expansion of $\cos x$ in powers of $x - (\pi/2)$. The values of f, f', f'', f''' are, respectively,

$$\cos x, \ -\sin x, \ -\cos x, \ \sin x. \tag{9-8}$$

Since the next term is $f^{iv} = \cos x$, the next four derivatives repeat the sequence (9-8), the next four repeat again, and so on. Evaluating at $x = \pi/2$ we get, respectively,

$$0, \ -1, \ 0, \ 1; \ 0, \ -1, \ 0, \ 1; \ 0, \ -1, \ 0, \ 1; \ \cdots$$

and hence Eq. (9-4) suggests the expansion

$$\cos x = -\left(x - \frac{\pi}{2}\right) + \frac{1}{3!}\left(x - \frac{\pi}{2}\right)^3 - \frac{1}{5!}\left(x - \frac{\pi}{2}\right)^5 + \cdots. \tag{9-9}$$

To determine if the series converges to the function on the left, we consider the remainder after n terms. Now, (9-8) gives $f^{(n)}(x) = \pm \sin x$ or $\pm \cos x$, so that (9-3) implies $|R_n| \le |x - \pi/2|^n/n!$. Since $\lim R_n = 0$, the expansion (9-9) is valid.

Upon setting $x = \pi/2 - t$ and noting that $\cos(\pi/2 - t) = \sin t$, we get an expansion for $\sin t$

$$\sin t = t - \frac{t^3}{3!} + \frac{t^5}{5!} - \frac{t^7}{7!} + \cdots + \frac{(-1)^n t^{2n+1}}{(2n+1)!} + \cdots \tag{9-10}$$

which is consistent with (9-5). It is left as an exercise for the reader to obtain a similar expansion for the cosine by use of (9-5) and (9-3):

$$\cos x = 1 - \frac{x^2}{2!} + \frac{x^4}{4!} - \frac{x^6}{6!} + \cdots + \frac{(-1)^n x^{2n}}{(2n)!} + \cdots. \tag{9-11}$$

In these examples the fact that the series converges *to the function* was established by direct examination of R_n. Such examination is necessary even when the series is found to be convergent by other means. For example, if we define

$$f(x) = e^{-1/x^2}, \qquad f(0) = 0,$$

it can be shown that the Taylor series about $x = 0$ converges for all x but converges to $f(x)$ only when $x = 0$. The trouble with this function is that it does not admit *any* power-series expansion valid over an interval containing $x = 0$, and we have the following:

---

[1] The fact that (9-6) converges shows that $x^n/n! \to 0$. (Cf. Prob. 5, Sec. 5.)

THEOREM I. *Suppose a function $f(x)$ admits a series representation in powers of $x - a$, so that $f(x) = \Sigma a_n(x - a)^n$ for some interval $|x - a| < \epsilon$. Then the Taylor series generated by $f(x)$ coincides with the given expansion [and hence the Taylor series converges to $f(x)$].*

For proof, differentiate [1] n times and set $x = a$, just as in the discussion of (8-7). It will be found that $a_n = f^{(n)}(a)/n!$, and hence the given series is identical with the Taylor series.

Theorem I shows that a valid power-series expansion obtained by any method whatever must coincide with the Taylor series. For instance, to find the Taylor series for $\sin x^2$ about $x = 0$, we set $t = x^2$ in (9-10). This is far simpler than direct use of Taylor's formula, as the reader can verify.

Example: Obtain the expansion of

$$f(x) = \frac{1}{(x - 2)(x - 3)}$$

in powers of $x - 1$.

With $t = x - 1$, the given function becomes

$$\frac{1}{(t - 1)(t - 2)} = \frac{-1}{t - 1} + \frac{1}{t - 2} = \frac{1}{1 - t} - \frac{1}{2}\frac{1}{1 - \frac{1}{2}t}$$

$$= \Sigma t^n - \frac{1}{2}\Sigma\left(\frac{1}{2}t\right)^n = \Sigma\left(1 - \frac{1}{2}\frac{1}{2^n}\right)t^n \qquad (9\text{-}12)$$

when we use partial fractions and the known formula for sum of a geometric series. Upon recalling that $t = x - 1$, we get the required result

$$\frac{1}{(x - 2)(x - 3)} = \sum_{n=0}^{\infty}\left(1 - \frac{1}{2^{n+1}}\right)(x - 1)^n. \qquad (9\text{-}13)$$

Since the two geometric series (9-12) converge for $|t| < 1$ and $|t| < 2$, respectively, the expansion (9-13) is valid for $|x - 1| < 1$. By Theorem I, this expansion coincides with the Taylor series.

PROBLEMS

1. For the following functions find the Taylor series about the point $x = 0$ and also about the point $x = 1$:

$$e^{2x},\ \sin \pi x,\ \cos (x - 1),\ 2 + x^2,\ (x + 2)^{-1}.$$

2. (a) Expand e^x about the point $x = a$ by writing $e^x = e^a e^{x-a}$ and using (9-6). (b) Expand $\log x$ about $x = 1$ by writing $\log x = \log [1 - (1 - x)]$ and using (8-6). (c) Obtain the general Taylor series from Maclaurin's. *Hint:* If $g(t) = f(a + t)$, then

$$f(a + t) = g(t) = \Sigma g^{(n)}(0)t^n/n! = \Sigma f^{(n)}(a)t^n/n!.$$

Now let $t = x - a$.

---

[1] The fact that the series now considered are in powers of $x - a$ rather than x causes no trouble. By a simple translation of axes, $\bar{x} = x - a$, these series become power series of the type considered in the preceding section, hence are subject to the theorems of **the** preceding section.

3. Expand the following fractions about the point $x = 1$:

$$\frac{1}{x}, \quad \frac{1}{x^2 - 4}, \quad \frac{1}{x(x^2 - 4)}.$$

4. Show that the Taylor series for $\sin x$ in powers of $x - a$ converges to $\sin x$ for every value of x and a, and find the expansion of $\sin x$ in powers of $x - \pi/6$.

5. Obtain the Maclaurin series for $\cos x$ by differentiating the series for $\sin x$.

6. By means of the known series for e^u, $\sin u$, and $\log (1 - u)$, find Taylor's expansions for

$$e^{-x^2}, \ \sin x^2, \ e^x + e^{-x}, \ e^x - e^{-x}, \ x^{-2} \log (1 + x^4).$$

7. What is the Taylor series for $(1 + x)^p$ if p is constant? Find the interval of convergence, and discuss the absolute convergence at the end points of the interval. *Hint:* Use Theorem IIb, Sec. 5. Analysis of the remainder R_n is difficult and may be omitted. A proof that the series converges to $(1 + x)^p$ will be found in Sec. 12.

10. The Expression of Integrals as Infinite Series. Many difficult integrals can be represented as power series. For example, if we let $x = t^2$ in the series (9-11) for $\cos x$, we get

$$\cos t^2 = 1 - \frac{t^4}{2!} + \frac{t^8}{4!} + \cdots + \frac{(-1)^n t^{4n}}{(2n)!} + \cdots$$

and hence, integrating term by term,

$$\int_0^x \cos t^2 \, dt = x - \frac{x^5}{5 \cdot 2!} + \cdots + \frac{(-1)^n x^{4n+1}}{(4n + 1)(2n)!} + \cdots . \quad (10\text{-}1)$$

This integral is called the *Fresnel cosine integral;* it is important in the theory of diffraction. Although the Fresnel integral is not expressible in terms of elementary functions in closed form, the expansion (10-1) is valid for all x and gives a representation which is entirely adequate for many purposes.

Sometimes one may obtain a power series involving a parameter rather than the variable of integration as in the last example. To illustrate this possibility we shall express the arc length of an ellipse as a power series in the eccentricity k. If the equation of the ellipse is given in parametric form as

$$x = a \sin \theta, \qquad y = b \cos \theta, \qquad a \geq b,$$

then the arc s satisfies

$$ds^2 = dx^2 + dy^2 = (a^2 \cos^2 \theta + b^2 \sin^2 \theta) \, d\theta^2.$$

Upon noting that $\cos^2 \theta = 1 - \sin^2 \theta$, we obtain

$$ds = a \sqrt{1 - k^2 \sin^2 \theta} \, d\theta,$$

where $k = (a^2 - b^2)^{1/2}/a$ is the eccentricity. Hence, the arc from $\theta = 0$ to $\theta = \phi$ is

$$s = a \int_0^\phi \sqrt{1 - k^2 \sin^2 \theta} \, d\theta \equiv aE(k,\phi).$$

The integral $E(k,\phi)$ defined by this equation is called the *elliptic integral of the second kind*. Although $E(k,\phi)$ is not elementary, it may be expressed as a power series.

By the binomial theorem (Sec. 12)

$$(1 - k^2 \sin^2 \theta)^{\frac{1}{2}} = 1 - \tfrac{1}{2}k^2 \sin^2 \theta - \tfrac{1}{8}k^4 \sin^4 \theta - \cdots \tag{10-2}$$

for $k^2 < 1$, which is the case when $b \neq 0$. Since

$$1 + \tfrac{1}{2}k^2 + \tfrac{1}{8}k^4 + \cdots$$

serves as an M series, (10-2) is uniformly convergent and term-by-term integration is permissible. Hence we obtain the desired expression

$$E(k,\phi) = \phi - \frac{1}{2}k^2 \int_0^\phi \sin^2 \theta \, d\theta - \frac{k^4}{2\cdot 4} \int_0^\phi \sin^4 \theta \, d\theta - \cdots$$

$$- \frac{1\cdot 3\cdot 5 \, \ldots \, (2n - 3)}{2\cdot 4\cdot 6 \, \ldots \, 2n} k^{2n} \int_0^\phi \sin^{2n} \theta \, d\theta - \cdots .$$

In a similar manner it can be shown that the *elliptic integral of the first kind* (cf. Example 3, Sec. 20, Chap. 1),

$$F(k,\phi) \equiv \int_0^\phi \frac{d\theta}{\sqrt{1 - k^2 \sin^2 \theta}}, \qquad k^2 < 1,$$

has the expansion

$$F(k,\phi) = \phi + \frac{1}{2}k^2 \int_0^\phi \sin^2 \theta \, d\theta + \frac{1\cdot 3}{2\cdot 4} k^4 \int_0^\phi \sin^4 \theta \, d\theta + \cdots$$

$$+ \frac{1\cdot 3\cdot 5 \, \ldots \, (2n - 1)}{2\cdot 4\cdot 6 \, \ldots \, 2n} k^{2n} \int_0^\phi \sin^{2n} \theta \, d\theta + \cdots .$$

The *elliptic integral of the third kind* is

$$\Pi(n,k,\phi) = \int_0^\phi \frac{d\theta}{(1 + n \sin^2 \theta)\sqrt{1 - k^2 \sin^2 \theta}}$$

and this, too, can be expressed as a series by expanding the radical.

Any integral of the form

$$\int (a \sin x + b \cos x + c)^{\pm \frac{1}{2}} \, dx$$

or of the form

$$\int R(x, \sqrt{ax^4 + bx^3 + cx^2 + dx + e}) \, dx, \qquad R(x,y) = \text{rational function},$$

is expressible in terms of the elliptic integrals [1] together with elementary functions. For this reason elliptic integrals have great practical importance and have been extensively tabulated.

---

[1] See, for example, P. Franklin, "Methods of Advanced Calculus," chap. 7, McGraw-Hill Book Company, Inc., New York, 1944.

PROBLEMS

1. Expand the following integrals as power series:

$$\int_0^x e^{-t^2}\, dt, \quad \int_0^x \frac{e^t - e^{-t}}{t}\, dt, \quad \int_0^x \sin(t^2)\, dt, \quad \int_0^x \frac{\sin t}{t}\, dt.$$

2. Express $\int_0^\pi e^{x\,\sin t}\, dt$ as a power series in x.   *Hint:* By Wallis' formula,

$$\int_0^\pi \sin^n t\, dt = \frac{(n-1)(n-3) \ldots 2 \text{ or } 1}{n(n-2) \ldots 2 \text{ or } 1}\, \alpha,$$

where $\alpha = 2$ if n is odd and $\alpha = \pi$ if n is even.

3. Express the *incomplete gamma function*

$$\int_0^x t^{p-1} e^{-t}\, dt$$

as a series in powers of x.   For what values of x and p is your expansion valid?

4. The *beta function* is defined by

$$B(p,q) = \int_0^1 x^{p-1}(1-x)^{q-1}\, dx.$$

Express this as a series by using the binomial theorem for $(1-x)^{q-1}$ and integrating term by term.   For what values of p and q is the resulting series absolutely convergent? (See Theorem II*b*, Sec. 5.   Although the range of integration includes the value $x = 1$, which is an *end point* of the convergence interval, the integration is easily justified.   Thus, one might consider $\int_0^x$ and let $x \to 1$ through values less than 1.   The desired result then follows from Abel's theorem, Sec. 8.)

11. Approximation by Means of Taylor's Formula.   If a function $f(x)$ has a convergent Taylor series, then the partial sums of that series can be used to approximate the function.   In this way, calculations of great intrinsic complexity are reduced to calculations involving polynomials.   The method is especially important because Taylor's formula not only gives a polynomial approximation but gives a means of estimating the error.   Thus, the remainder R_n in (9-2) and (9-3) is precisely the difference between $f(x)$ and the nth partial sum of its Taylor series.

To illustrate the use of Taylor's series for numerical computation, let us find $\sin 10°$ within $\pm 10^{-7}$.   The value $10° = \pi/18$ radian is closer to zero than to any other value of x for which $\sin x$ and its derivatives are easily found, and hence the expansion is taken about the point $x = 0$.   To estimate the number of terms required, (9-3) gives

$$|R_n| = \left| \frac{f^{(n)}(\xi)}{n!}\, x^n \right| \leq \frac{x^n}{n!} = \left(\frac{\pi}{18}\right)^n \frac{1}{n!} = \frac{(0.175)^n}{n!} \tag{11-1}$$

when $a = 0$, and when we set $x = \pi/18 = 0.175$ and recall that $\sin x$ together with its derivatives is less than 1 in magnitude.   The successive bounds for R_n as given by (11-1) may be computed recursively; indeed, the nth value is obtained by applying a factor $(0.175/n)$ to the preceding one. For $n = 1$ the bound (11-1) is 0.175 and the next few are as follows:

Value of n..........	2	3	4	5	6
Bound for $\|R_n\|$	1.5×10^{-2}	8.8×10^{-4}	3.9×10^{-5}	1.4×10^{-6}	4.0×10^{-8}

From a list such as this the n sufficient for any prescribed accuracy can be determined at once. In particular, an accuracy of $\pm 10^{-7}$ is found if we take $n = 6$. Thus

$$\sin 10° = \frac{\pi}{18} - \left(\frac{\pi}{18}\right)^3 \frac{1}{3!} + \left(\frac{\pi}{18}\right)^5 \frac{1}{5!} + R_6,$$

where $|R_6| \leq 4.0 \times 10^{-8}$; more explicitly, $0 \geq R_6 \geq -4.0 \times 10^{-8}$, since $f^{(6)}(\xi) = - \sin \xi \leq 0$. Inasmuch as the next term of the series is zero, *the first six terms are the same as the first seven terms.* Hence the error is also equal to R_7, where

$$0 \geq R_7 \geq -1.0 \times 10^{-9}. \tag{11-2}$$

An improvement of accuracy such as this is to be expected whenever the series is terminated just before one or more terms with zero coefficients.

In modern computing practice an automatic computing machine is so programmed that it keeps track of the remainder, which can often be estimated recursively as in this example. The machine is then instructed to take as many terms as are needed to make the remainder less than some preassigned amount. This process was illustrated in the foregoing calculation, where the value $n = 6$ was chosen, not at random, but by consideration of the desired accuracy.

The reader may have noticed that the series for $\sin (\pi/18)$ is an alternating series with terms decreasing in magnitude. Hence, the estimate for the error (11-2) could have been found by Theorem II of Sec. 6. Taylor's formula, however, has the merit of applying to general power series, whether alternating or not.

Many important approximations are obtained by using the first few terms of the Taylor-series expansion instead of the function itself. For example, the formula

$$k = y''[1 + (y')^2]^{-\frac{3}{2}}$$

for curvature of the curve whose equation is $y = f(x)$ yields

$$k = y'' \left[1 - \frac{3}{2} (y')^2 + \frac{1}{2!} \frac{3}{2} \cdot \frac{5}{2} (y')^4 - \cdots \right]$$

when we use the binomial theorem. The first-term approximation $k \cong y''$ is sufficient for most applications.

As another example, in railroad surveying it is frequently useful to know the difference between the length of a circular arc and the length of the corresponding chord. Let r be the radius of curvature of the arc AB (Fig. 6), and let α be the angle intercepted by the arc. Then, if s is the length of the arc AB and c is the length of the chord AB, $s = r\alpha$ and $c = 2r \sin \frac{1}{2}\alpha$. Since

$$\sin x = x - \frac{x^3}{3!} + \frac{x^5}{5!} \cos \xi,$$

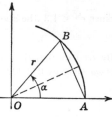

where $0 \leq \xi \leq x$, the error in using only the first two terms of the expansion is certainly less than $x^5/5!$. Then,

$$c = 2r \sin \frac{\alpha}{2} = 2r \left(\frac{\alpha}{2} - \frac{\alpha^3}{8 \cdot 6} \right)$$

Fig. 6

with an error less than

$$2r \left(\frac{\alpha^5}{32 \cdot 120} \right) = \frac{r\alpha^5}{1,920}.$$

Therefore, $s - c = \alpha^3 r/24$ with an error that is less than $r\alpha^5/1,920$.

Example 1. For the nonelementary integral $\int_0^t e^{u^2}\, du$ obtain a polynomial approximation valid within ± 0.00001 when $0 \leq x \leq \frac{1}{2}$.

According to (9-6) and (9-7),

$$e^x = 1 + x + \frac{x^2}{2!} + \cdots + \frac{x^{n-1}}{(n-1)!} + \frac{x^n}{n!} e^\xi, \qquad 0 \leq \xi \leq x.$$

If we set $x = u^2$, this becomes

$$e^{u^2} = 1 + u^2 + \frac{u^4}{2!} + \cdots + \frac{u^{2n-2}}{(n-1)!} + \frac{u^{2n}}{n!} e^\xi, \qquad 0 \leq \xi \leq u^2,$$

and integrating from 0 to x yields

$$\int_0^x e^{u^2}\, du = x + \frac{x^3}{3} + \frac{x^5}{5 \cdot 2!} + \cdots + \frac{x^{2n-1}}{(2n-1)(n-1)!} + \int_0^x \frac{u^{2n}}{n!} e^\xi\, du.$$

To estimate the integral on the right we note that

$$e^\xi \leq e^{u^2} \leq e^{x^2},$$

since $\xi \leq u^2$ and $u \leq x$. Hence

$$\int_0^x u^{2n} e^\xi\, du \leq e^{x^2} \int_0^x u^{2n}\, du = e^{x^2} \frac{x^{2n+1}}{2n+1}.$$

It follows that if we write

$$\int_0^x e^{u^2}\, du = \sum_{n=1}^\infty \frac{x^{2n-1}}{(2n-1)(n-1)!},$$

then the error R_{2n} after the term x^{2n-1} satisfies

$$0 \leq R_{2n} \leq \frac{e^{x^2} x^{2n+1}}{n!(2n+1)}.$$

For an approximation valid within ± 0.00001 when $0 \leq x \leq \frac{1}{2}$, we choose n large enough to make

$$\frac{e^{\frac{1}{4}}(\frac{1}{2})^{2n+1}}{n!(2n+1)} \leq 0.00002.$$

Since $e^{\frac{1}{4}} < 1.3$, the above condition is satisfied when

$$n!(2n+1)2^{2n+1} \geq 65,000.$$

By trial we find that $n = 4$ suffices. This choice of n yields an approximation which is *too small* by 0.00002 at most. If 0.00001 is added to the approximation, we get

$$\int_0^x e^{u^2} \, du = x + \frac{x^3}{3} + \frac{x^5}{10} + \frac{x^7}{42} + 0.00001 \tag{11-3}$$

within ± 0.00001 when $0 \leq x \leq \frac{1}{2}$.

Example 2. Obtain a polynomial approximation for $\int_0^x e^{\sin x} \, dx$ valid near $x = 0$.

Keeping terms as far as x^3 and no terms beyond x^3, we have

$$e^{\sin x} = 1 + (\sin x) + \frac{(\sin x)^2}{2!} + \frac{(\sin x)^3}{3!} + \cdots$$

$$= 1 + \left(x - \frac{x^3}{6}\right) + \frac{1}{2}\left(x - \frac{x^3}{6}\right)^2 + \frac{1}{6}\left(x - \frac{x^3}{6}\right)^3 + \cdots$$

$$= 1 + x + \frac{1}{2}x^2 + 0 \cdot x^3 + \cdots.$$

Hence

$$\int_0^x e^{\sin x} \, dx = x + \frac{x^2}{2} + \frac{x^3}{6} + \cdots;$$

where the terms omitted involve x^5 or higher powers.

This calculation of the series for $e^{\sin x}$ illustrates a principle which is often useful. Let $f(y) = \Sigma b_n y^n$ and $y = \Sigma a_n x^n$ be power series with nonzero radii of convergence. If $y = 0$ when $x = 0$, then *the power series for $f(y)$ as a function of x also has a nonzero radius of convergence. This series may be found by substituting the series for y into the series for $f(y)$ and collecting terms.*[1] By uniqueness, the series so obtained is the Taylor series.

PROBLEMS

1. It is desired to approximate a function $f(x)$ by a polynomial $p(x)$,

$$p(x) = a_0 + a_1 x + \cdots + a_n x^n,$$

in such a way that at the origin $p(x)$ has the same value and the same first n derivatives as $f(x)$. (a) How should the coefficients be determined? *Hint:* $a_0 = p(0) = f(0)$, $a_1 = p'(0) = f'(0)$, $2a_2 = p''(0) = f''(0)$, …. (b) If the coefficients are determined as in (a), what relation does $p(x)$ have to the Maclaurin series for $f(x)$?

2. For the following functions obtain a polynomial approximation valid near $x = 0$ by finding the first three nonzero terms of the Maclaurin series:

$$\tan x, \; e^{\tan x}, \; \sec x, \; \frac{e^x}{1 + e^x}, \; \frac{\sin x}{e^x - 1}, \; \sqrt{\cos x}.$$

[1] For proof, see K. Knopp, "Theory and Application of Infinite Series," p. 180, Blackie & Son, Ltd., Glasgow, 1928.

3. (*a*) By means of series compute $x - 10 \sin (x/10)$ to three significant figures when $x = 1.000$. (*b*) Attempt the same calculation by using a table of $\sin x$ (note that x is in radians). How many significant figures for $\sin x$ are needed?

4. If $y = 10 (\tan x - x)/x^3$, (*a*) use series to evaluate y near $x = 0$. In particular, what is the limit of y as $x \to 0$? (*b*) Plot y versus x for $0 < x \leq 0.2$. (*c*) Discuss the construction of such a graph by use of a table of $\tan x$, without series.

5. By use of series compute to three places of decimals:

(*a*) $e^{1.1} = ee^{0.1} = 2.7183e^{0.1}$;   (*b*) $\cos 10° = \cos (\pi/18)$;

(*c*) $\sin 33° = \sin (30° + 3°)$;   (*d*) $\sqrt[5]{35} = 2(1 + \tfrac{3}{32})^{\frac{1}{5}}$.

6. Evaluate by series the first three integrals to three places of decimals and the last to two places:

$$\int_0^1 \sin (x^2)\, dx, \quad \int_0^{\frac{1}{2}} \frac{\sin x\, dx}{\sqrt{1 - x^2}}, \quad \int_0^{0.1} \frac{\log (1 - z)}{z}\, dz,$$

$$\int_0^1 (2 - \cos x)^{-\frac{1}{2}}\, dx = \int_0^1 \left(1 + 2 \sin^2 \frac{x}{2}\right)^{-\frac{1}{2}} dx.$$

7. Determine the magnitude of α if the error in the approximation $\sin \alpha \cong \alpha$ is not to exceed 1 per cent. *Hint:* $(\alpha - \sin \alpha)/\alpha = 0.01$ and $\sin \alpha = \alpha - (\alpha^3/3!) + (\alpha^5/5!) - \cdots$.

8. Discuss the percentage error in the approximation (11-3) as $x \to 0$. How would the percentage error behave if the term 0.00001 had not been added? (This shows that it may be better not to alter the Taylor series even when such alteration reduces the absolute error.)

9. As in Example 1 of the text, obtain a polynomial approximation for the *Fresnel sine integral* $\int_0^x \sin (t^2)\, dt$ which is valid within ± 0.00001 for $0 \leq x \leq \tfrac{1}{2}$.

POWER SERIES AND DIFFERENTIAL EQUATIONS

12. First-order Equations. One of the most important uses of power series is in the solution of differential equations. For example, to solve the equation $y' = y$ assume that

$$y = a_0 + a_1 x + a_2 x^2 + a_3 x^3 + \cdots + a_n x^n + \cdots.$$

Then, according to Theorem II, Sec. 8,

$$y' = a_1 + 2a_2 x + 3a_3 x^2 + 4a_4 x^3 + \cdots + (n + 1)a_{n+1} x^n + \cdots.$$

Since $y' = y$, Theorem III of Sec. 8 shows that the series for y' and the series for y must have the same coefficients. Thus,

$$a_1 = a_0, \quad 2a_2 = a_1, \quad 3a_3 = a_2, \quad \ldots, \quad (n + 1)a_{n+1} = a_n, \quad \ldots.$$

Starting with $a_0 = c$, a constant, we solve for $a_1, a_2, \ldots$ in succession to obtain

$$a_1 = c, \quad a_2 = \frac{c}{2}, \quad a_3 = \frac{c}{2 \cdot 3}, \quad \ldots, \quad a_n = \frac{c}{n!}, \quad \ldots$$

and hence

$$y = c + cx + \frac{cx^2}{2!} + \frac{cx^3}{3!} + \cdots + \frac{cx^n}{n!} + \cdots.$$

This discussion is tentative only, since at first we had no assurance that the equation $y' = y$ possesses a solution expressible as a power series. However, the ratio test shows that the series obtained converges for all x. Hence by Theorem II of Sec. 8 the term-by-term differentiation is justified and the equation $y' = y$ has actually been solved.

As another illustration, we obtain a power-series solution for the differential equation

$$(1 + x)y' = py, \qquad p = \text{const}, \tag{12-1}$$

such that $y = 1$ when $x = 0$. If $y = \Sigma a_n x^n$, then [1]

$$y' = a_1 + 2a_2 x + 3a_3 x^2 + \cdots + (n + 1)a_{n+1} x^n + \cdots$$
$$xy' = \qquad a_1 x + 2a_2 x^2 + \cdots + \qquad na_n x^n + \cdots$$
$$py = pa_0 + pa_1 x + pa_2 x^2 + \cdots + \qquad pa_n x^n + \cdots$$

and the substitution in (12-1) yields

$$a_1 + (2a_2 + a_1)x + (3a_3 + 2a_2)x^2 + \cdots + [(n + 1)a_{n+1} + na_n]x^n + \cdots$$
$$= pa_0 + pa_1 x + pa_2 x^2 + \cdots + pa_n x^n + \cdots.$$

Equating coefficients of like powers of x gives the set of equations

$$a_1 = pa_0$$
$$2a_2 + a_1 = pa_1$$
$$3a_3 + 2a_2 = pa_2$$
$$\cdot \ \cdot \ \cdot \ \cdot \ \cdot \ \cdot \ \cdot \ \cdot \ \cdot$$
$$(n + 1)a_{n+1} + na_n = pa_n$$

which must be solved for the as.

Since $y = 1$ at $x = 0$, we must have $a_0 = 1$. Then we get, in succession,

$$a_1 = p, \qquad a_2 = \frac{p(p - 1)}{2!}, \qquad a_3 = \frac{p(p - 1)(p - 2)}{3!}, \qquad \cdots$$

so that the solution is

$$y = 1 + px + \frac{p(p - 1)}{2!} x^2 + \cdots$$
$$+ \frac{p(p - 1)(p - 2) \cdots (p - n + 1)}{n!} x^n + \cdots. \tag{12-2}$$

Throughout Secs. 12 to 14 Σ means $\sum\limits_{0}^{\infty}$. A brief review of this *sigma notation* is given in Sec. 2.

Hence, if the differential equation (12-1) has a series solution, that solution must be (12-2). However, the ratio test shows that the series (12-2) converges for $|x| < 1$. Hence for $|x| < 1$ the term-by-term differentiation was justified, and this shows *without further discussion* that (12-2) is a solution for $|x| < 1$.

Equation (12-1) can be solved by elementary methods as follows. Separating variables, we get

$$\frac{dy}{y} = p \frac{dx}{1 + x},$$

so that $\log y = p \log (1 + x) = \log (1 + x)^p$ when we recall that $y = 1$ at $x = 0$. Hence

$$y = (1 + x)^p.$$

Comparing this solution with that found formerly [1] gives

$$(1 + x)^p = 1 + \sum_{n=1}^{\infty} \frac{p(p - 1)(p - 2) \ldots (p - n + 1)}{n!} x^n, \quad (12\text{-}3)$$

which the reader will recognize is the binomial theorem. *Since no assumption was made about p the result is valid for all p provided $|x| < 1$.*

PROBLEMS

1. Obtain power-series solutions of the following differential equations, which satisfy $y = 1$ at $x = 0$:

$$y' = 2y, \qquad y' = y + x, \qquad y' + y = 1.$$

2. Obtain the first three terms of a series solution $y = \Sigma a_n x^n$ for the problem $y' = 2xy$, $y = 1$ when $x = 0$. From these three terms compute the curvature $k = y''[1 + (y')^2]^{-\frac{3}{2}}$ at $x = 0$. Is your value for curvature exact or only approximate?

3. By considering the equation $y' = (1 - x^2)^{-\frac{1}{2}}$ obtain a series expansion for $\sin^{-1} x$. In particular, show that

$$\frac{\pi}{6} = \frac{1}{2} + \frac{1}{2} \frac{1}{3 \cdot 2^3} + \frac{1 \cdot 3}{2 \cdot 4} \frac{1}{5 \cdot 2^5} + \frac{1 \cdot 3 \cdot 5}{2 \cdot 4 \cdot 6} \frac{1}{7 \cdot 2^7} + \cdots.$$

13. Second-order Equations. Legendre Functions.

To illustrate the use of series for solving second-order differential equations consider the equation

$$y'' - xy' + y = 0. \tag{13-1}$$

If $y = \Sigma a_n x^n$, then $y' = \Sigma n a_n x^{n-1}$ and $y'' = \Sigma n(n - 1)a_n x^{n-2}$ and, hence,

$$y'' = 2a_2 + 3 \cdot 2a_3 x + \cdots + (n + 2)(n + 1)a_{n+2} x^n + \cdots$$

$$-xy' = \quad - \quad a_1 x - \cdots - \quad \quad n a_n x^n - \cdots$$

$$y = a_0 + \quad a_1 x + \cdots + \quad \quad a_n x^n + \cdots.$$

[1] By Chap. 1, Sec. 17, the problem has only one solution.

According to (13-1) the sum of these three power series is zero, and therefore, by Theorem III of Sec. 8, the coefficient of x^n in this sum is zero for
each n:

$$2a_2 + a_0 = 0, \qquad \text{coefficient of } x^0,$$

$$3 \cdot 2a_3 - a_1 + a_1 = 0, \qquad \text{coefficient of } x^1,$$

$$\cdot \ \cdot \ \cdot \ \cdot \ \cdot \ \cdot \ \cdot \ \cdot \ \cdot \ \cdot \ \cdot \ \cdot \ \cdot \ \cdot$$

$$(n + 2)(n + 1)a_{n+2} - na_n + a_n = 0, \qquad \text{coefficient of } x^n.$$

Hence,

$$a_{n+2} = \frac{n - 1}{(n + 1)(n + 2)} a_n. \tag{13-2}$$

This recursion formula gives, in succession,

$$a_2 = -\frac{1}{2} a_0 = -\frac{1}{2!} a_0,$$

$$a_4 = \frac{1}{3 \cdot 4} a_2 = -\frac{1}{4!} a_0,$$

$$a_6 = \frac{3}{5 \cdot 6} a_4 = -\frac{3}{6!} a_0,$$

$$\cdot \ \cdot \ \cdot \ \cdot \ \cdot \ \cdot \ \cdot \ \cdot \ \cdot \ \cdot \ \cdot \ \cdot$$

$$a_{2n} = -\frac{1 \cdot 3 \cdot 5 \ldots (2n - 3)}{(2n)!} a_0, \qquad n > 1.$$

Similarly, $a_3 = 0 \cdot a_1 = 0$, $a_5 = 0$, $a_7 = 0$, and so on. Hence the solution is

$$y = a_0 \left(1 - \frac{1}{2!} x^2 - \frac{1}{4!} x^4 - \frac{1 \cdot 3}{6!} x^6 - \frac{1 \cdot 3 \cdot 5}{8!} x^8 - \cdots \right) + a_1 x$$

with the two arbitrary constants a_0 and a_1. There should be two constants
in the general solution because the equation is of the second order (Chap. 1,
Sec. 21).

The ratio of two successive nonzero terms of the infinite series satisfies

$$\left| \frac{a_{2n+2} x^{2n+2}}{a_{2n} x^{2n}} \right| = \frac{2n - 1}{(2n + 1)(2n + 2)} |x^2| \sim \frac{1}{2n} |x^2|, \tag{13-3}$$

as is seen by using (13-2) with $2n$ written in place of n. Since the limit of (13-3) is zero,
the series converges for all x. Hence the term-by-term differentiation is justified, and
we really do get a solution.

Upon choosing $a_0 = 0$, $a_1 = 1$ we see that a particular solution is

$$y_1 = x \tag{13-4}$$

and the choice $a_0 = 1$, $a_1 = 0$ shows that another particular solution is

$$y_2 = 1 - \frac{1}{2!}x^2 - \frac{1}{4!}x^4 - \frac{1 \cdot 3}{6!}x^6 - \frac{1 \cdot 3 \cdot 5}{8!}x^8 - \cdots. \tag{13-5}$$

According to Chap. 1, Sec. 21, two solutions y_1 and y_2 such as this are *linearly independent* if the equation $c_1 y_1 + c_2 y_2 \equiv 0$ can hold for constants c_1 and c_2 only when $c_1 = c_2 = 0$. The solutions (13-4) and (13-5) are independent, since one is an odd function and the other is even.[1] Hence the expression $a_0 y_1 + a_1 y_2$ is the general solution of (13-1) (Chap. 1, Sec. 21). The independence of y_1 and y_2 can also be deduced from the following theorem:

THEOREM I.   *Let $y_1 = \Sigma a_n x^n$ and $y_2 = \Sigma b_n x^n$ be power series with nonzero radii of convergence, and suppose that $y_1 \not\equiv 0$. If y_1 and y_2 are linearly dependent, then there is a constant c such that $b_n = c a_n$ for all values of n.*

From $c_1 \Sigma a_n x^n + c_2 \Sigma b_n x^n = 0$, it follows that

$$c_1 a_n + c_2 b_n = 0, \qquad n = 0, 1, 2, \ldots. \tag{13-6}$$

If $c_2 = 0$, then (13-6) gives $a_n = 0$ for all n, contrary to hypothesis. Hence $c_2 \neq 0$, and (13-6) gives $b_n = (-c_1/c_2) a_n$. This is the required result.

Obviously not every differential equation has solutions that can be represented by the power series.[2] The following theorem due to Fuchs, which we state without proof,[3] gives sufficient conditions for the existence of power-series solutions of second-order linear equations.

THEOREM II.   *Let $y'' + f_1(x)y' + f_2(x)y = 0$ have coefficients $f_1(x)$ and $f_2(x)$ which can be expanded in convergent power series for $|x| < r$. Then every solution y can be expanded in a convergent power series for $|x| < r$.*

The solution series converges at least for $|x| < r$ but may converge in a larger interval. For example, consider the equation

$$(2 - x)y'' + (x - 1)y' - y = 0. \tag{13-7}$$

Writing (13-7) in the form

$$y'' + \frac{x - 1}{2 - x}y' - \frac{1}{2 - x}y = 0$$

(so that the coefficient of y'' is 1 as in Theorem II) we get

$$f_1(x) = \frac{x - 1}{2 - x} = \frac{1}{2}\frac{x - 1}{1 - \frac{1}{2}x},$$

$$f_2(x) = -\frac{1}{2 - x} = -\frac{1}{2}\frac{1}{1 - \frac{1}{2}x}.$$

---

[1] A function $f(x)$ is *odd* if $f(-x) \equiv -f(x)$, *even* if $f(-x) \equiv f(x)$.

[2] Thus, $xy' = 1$ has a solution $y = \log x$ which cannot be expanded in Maclaurin's series.

[3] A simple proof is given in H. T. H. Piaggio, "An Elementary Treatise on Differential Equations and Their Applications," 2d ed., George Bell & Sons, Ltd., London, 1928.

Since $f_1(x)$ and $f_2(x)$ have power-series expansions for $|x| < 2$, Theorem II asserts that the solution y also has a power-series expansion valid for $|x| < 2$. Actually, the solution of (13-7) is

$$y = c_1 e^x + c_2(1 - x) = c_1 \Sigma \frac{x^n}{n!} + c_2(1 - x),$$

which converges for all x.

As another example we shall find the complete solution of *Legendre's equation*

$$(1 - x^2)y'' - 2xy' + p(p + 1)y = 0, \tag{13-8}$$

where p is a constant.

By Theorem II this equation has a power-series solution valid at least for $|x| < 1$. Assuming $y = \Sigma a_n x^n$, we get

$$y'' = \Sigma a_{n+2}(n + 2)(n + 1)x^n$$

$$-x^2 y'' = \Sigma - a_n n(n - 1)x^n$$

$$-2xy' = \Sigma - 2n a_n x^n$$

$$p(p + 1)y = \Sigma a_n p(p + 1)x^n.$$

By (13-8) the sum of these series is zero. Considering the coefficient of x^n yields

$$a_{n+2}(n + 2)(n + 1) = a_n[n(n + 1) - p(p + 1)] \tag{13-9}$$

after slight simplification. For all $n \geq 0$ we have

$$a_{n+2} = -a_n \frac{(p - n)(p + n + 1)}{(n + 1)(n + 2)}, \tag{13-10}$$

after factoring the bracket in (13-9) and dividing by $(n + 2)(n + 1)$. The coefficients for even n are determined from a_0, and those for odd n from a_1. Computing the coefficients successively, we get the final result

$$y = a_0 \left[1 - \frac{p(p + 1)}{2!} x^2 + \frac{p(p - 2)(p + 1)(p + 3)}{4!} x^4 - \cdots \right]$$

$$+ a_1 \left[x - \frac{(p - 1)(p + 2)}{3!} x^3 + \frac{(p - 1)(p - 3)(p + 2)(p + 4)}{5!} x^5 - \cdots \right].$$

Theorem II guarantees that the general solution can be obtained in this fashion, and indeed, by Theorem I, the coefficients of a_0 and a_1 in the foregoing expressions are independent. Equation (13-9) shows that the series converge for $|x| < 1$ when we apply the ratio test to the ratio of successive nonzero terms. When p is a positive even integer, however, the expression involving a_0 reduces to a polynomial, hence converges for all x. If a_0 is so chosen that the polynomial has the value unity when $x = 1$, we get the sequence

$$P_0(x) = 1,$$

$$P_2(x) = \frac{3}{2} x^2 - \frac{1}{2},$$

$$P_4(x) = \frac{7 \cdot 5}{4 \cdot 2} x^4 - 2 \frac{5 \cdot 3}{4 \cdot 2} x^2 + \frac{3 \cdot 1}{4 \cdot 2},$$

and so on. Similarly, when p is a positive odd integer, the coefficient of a_1 terminates and we get a sequence of which the first three terms are

$$P_1(x) = x,$$

$$P_3(x) = \frac{5}{2}x^3 - \frac{3}{2}x,$$

$$P_5(x) = \frac{9 \cdot 7}{4 \cdot 2}x^5 - 2\frac{7 \cdot 5}{4 \cdot 2}x^3 + \frac{5 \cdot 3}{4 \cdot 2}x.$$

These polynomials are known as *Legendre polynomials;* they arise in several branches of applied mathematics.

PROBLEMS

1. Solve by means of power series:

$$y'' + y = 0, \qquad y'' + y = 1, \qquad y'' - xy = 1.$$

2. For Eq. (13-7), show that $y = \Sigma a_n x^n$ leads to

$$2(n + 2)(n + 1)a_{n+2} - (n + 1)^2 a_{n+1} + (n - 1)a_n = 0.$$

(a) By taking $a_0 = a_1 = 1$, find a solution satisfying $y = y' = 1$ at $x = 0$. (b) By another choice of a_0 and a_1 find a solution satisfying $y = -1$, $y' = 1$ at $x = 0$.

3. Solve by means of power series if $y(0) = y'(0)$:

$$(x^2 - 3x + 2)y'' + (x^2 - 2x - 1)y' + (x - 3)y = 0.$$

4. Solve $y'' - (x - 2)y = 0$ by assuming $y = \Sigma a_n(x - 2)^n$. Also obtain the first three terms of the solution in the form $y = \Sigma a_n x^n$.

5. It can be shown [1] that

$$(1 - 2xh + h^2)^{-\frac{1}{2}} = P_0(x) + P_1(x)h + P_2(x)h^2 + \cdots + P_n(x)h^n + \cdots.$$

Verify this equality through the terms in h^5. *Hint:* Expand $[1 - (2hx - h^2)]^{-\frac{1}{2}}$ by the binomial theorem, and collect powers of h. The function $(1 - 2xh + h^2)^{-\frac{1}{2}}$ is called the *generating function* of the sequence $P_n(x)$.

6. Verify *Rodrigues' formula* [2]

$$P_n(x) = \frac{1}{2^n n!} \frac{d^n}{dx^n}(x^2 - 1)^n$$

for $n = 0, 1, 2, 3$.

14. Generalized Power Series. Bessel's Equation.

An important differential equation was encountered by the German astronomer and mathematician F. W. Bessel in a study of planetary motion. The so-called *Bessel functions* which arise from the solution of this equation are indispensable in the study of vibration of chains, propagation of electric currents in cylindrical conductors, heat flow in cylinders, vibration of circular membranes, and many other problems of applied mathematics.

Bessel's equation is

$$x^2 y'' + xy' + (x^2 - p^2)y = 0, \tag{14-1}$$

[1] E. J. Whittaker and G. N. Watson, "Modern Analysis," pp. 302–303. Cambridge University Press, London, 1952.

[2] *Ibid.*

where p is a constant. Theorem II of Sec. 13 does not apply to this equation, since

$$f_1(x) = \frac{1}{x}, \qquad f_2(x) = 1 - \frac{p^2}{x^2}$$

and these functions cannot be expanded in power series near $x = 0$. For this reason we do not expect a power-series solution $y = \Sigma a_n x^n$. It was shown by Fuchs, however, that a wide class of equations, including (14-1), have solutions of the form [1]

$$y = x^\rho \Sigma a_n x^n = \sum_{n=0}^{\infty} a_n x^{n+\rho}, \qquad a_0 \neq 0 \tag{14-2}$$

where ρ is constant. The theorem of Fuchs reads as follows:

THEOREM I.   *Let $xf_1(x)$ and $x^2 f_2(x)$ have power-series expansions valid for $|x| < r$. Then the equation*

$$y'' + f_1(x)y' + f_2(x)y = 0$$

has a solution of form (14-2), also valid for $|x| < r$.

Since Bessel's equation gives

$$xf_1(x) = 1, \qquad x^2 f_2(x) = x^2 - p^2,$$

Theorem I asserts that the series (14-2), when found, will be valid for all x. To obtain this series, note that

$$x^2 \sum_{n=0}^{\infty} a_n x^{n+\rho} = \sum_{n=0}^{\infty} a_n x^{n+\rho+2} = \sum_{n=2}^{\infty} a_{n-2} x^{n+\rho}, \tag{14-3}$$

as is seen by writing out in full. The limits $(2,\infty)$ on the latter summation may be changed to $(0,\infty)$ if we agree to define

$$a_n = 0 \qquad \text{for all negative } n. \tag{14-4}$$

Hence,

$$x^2 y'' = \Sigma a_n (n + \rho)(n + \rho - 1)x^{n+\rho}$$
$$xy' = \Sigma a_n (n + \rho)x^{n+\rho}$$
$$x^2 y = \Sigma a_{n-2} x^{n+\rho}$$
$$-p^2 y = \Sigma - p^2 a_n x^{n+\rho}.$$

According to Eq. (14-1), which we wish to solve, the sum of the four terms on the left of the above equations is zero. Hence, the same is true for the series on the right. Equating to zero the coefficient of $x^{n+\rho}$ in the sum of these series gives

$$a_n(n + \rho)(n + \rho - 1) + a_n(n + \rho) + a_{n-2} - p^2 a_n = 0$$

[1] The novelty is that we allow ρ to be any number, whereas if (14-2) is an ordinary power series, ρ must be an integer. Since ρ may be increased at will, the assumption $a_0 \neq 0$ involves no loss of generality.

or, after simplification,

$$a_n[(n + \rho)^2 - p^2] + a_{n-2} = 0. \tag{14-5}$$

Equation (14-5) is valid for all n. For negative n Eq. (14-5) holds automatically by virtue of (14-4). The first nontrivial case of (14-5) is called the *indicial equation;* it is obtained in the present example by putting $n = 0$ and takes the form

$$a_0(\rho^2 - p^2) + 0 = 0, \qquad \text{indicial equation.} \tag{14-6}$$

This shows that $\rho = p$ or $\rho = -p$, since $a_0 \neq 0$. The other values of a_n are determined from (14-5) in the form

$$a_n = -\frac{1}{(n + \rho)^2 - p^2} a_{n-2}. \tag{14-7}$$

The choice $n = 1$ gives [1] $a_1 = 0$, and hence $a_n = 0$ for all odd n. Also

$$a_2 = -\frac{a_0}{(2 + \rho)^2 - p^2},$$

$$a_4 = -\frac{a_2}{(4 + \rho)^2 - p^2} = \frac{a_0}{[(4 + \rho)^2 - p^2][(2 + \rho)^2 - p^2]},$$

and so on. In this way it is easily verified that the series corresponding to $\rho = p$ is

$$y = a_0 x^p \left[1 - \frac{x^2}{2(2p + 2)} + \frac{x^4}{2 \cdot 4(2p + 2)(2p + 4)} - \cdots \right]$$

and that the series for $\rho = -p$ is the same, with $-p$ in place of p.

When p is a nonnegative integer, the expression may be simplified by use of factorials, as follows. We take a factor 2 from each term of the denominator and place it with the x in the numerator, obtaining

$$y = a_0 x^p \left[1 - \frac{(x/2)^2}{1(p + 1)} + \frac{(x/2)^4}{1 \cdot 2(p + 1)(p + 2)} - \cdots \right]. \tag{14-8}$$

If the denominators are now multiplied by $p!$, there results

$$y = a_0 p! x^p \left[\frac{1}{p!} - \frac{(x/2)^2}{1 \cdot (p + 1)!} + \frac{(x/2)^4}{2!(p + 2)!} - \cdots \right],$$

and since $x^p = 2^p(x/2)^p$, this yields $y = a_0 p! 2^p J_p(x)$, where

$$J_p(x) = \sum_{n=0}^{\infty} \frac{(-1)^n (x/2)^{2n+p}}{n!(p + n)!}. \tag{14-9}$$

[1] Provided the denominator in (14-7) does not vanish. See Prob. 7.

The function $J_p(x)$ is called *the Bessel function of order* p. The graphs of $J_0(x)$ and $J_1(x)$ are shown in Fig. 7.

Now, the differential equation (14-1) is meaningful even when p is not a positive integer, and the series solution (before introduction of factorials) is also well defined for general p. It is natural to inquire if we can define $p!$ in such a way that (14-9) is meaningful and satisfies (14-1) for p unrestricted. A glance at (14-8) shows that such an extension may not be possible when p is a negative integer, but there appears to be no difficulty otherwise.

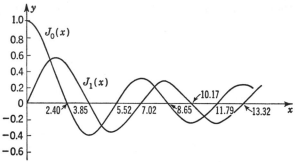

FIG. 7

To obtain an appropriate definition of $p!$ for arbitrary p, we introduce the so-called *gamma function* $\Gamma(p)$ defined by

$$\Gamma(p+1) = \int_0^\infty t^p e^{-t}\, dt, \qquad p \geq 0. \tag{14-10}$$

This function was discovered by the celebrated Swiss mathematician L. Euler. Because of its connection with $p!$ the function $\Gamma(p+1)$ is often called the *factorial function* and is written $p!$ or $\Pi(p)$. We shall use the notation $p!$ as soon as we have established that (14-10) gives the appropriate value when p is an integer. For comparison with other notations,

$$p! \equiv \Pi(p) \equiv \Gamma(p+1).$$

If $p \geq 1$, integration by parts [1] in (14-10) gives

$$\int_0^\infty t^p e^{-t}\, dt = \left. -t^p e^{-t}\right|_0^\infty + p \int_0^\infty t^{p-1} e^{-t}\, dt.$$

Since the integrated term drops out, the foregoing relation simplifies to

$$\Gamma(p+1) = p\Gamma(p) \tag{14-11}$$

when we use (14-10).

Writing (14-11) in the form

$$\Gamma(p) = p^{-1}\Gamma(p+1) \tag{14-12}$$

---

[1] Since the improper integrals (Sec. 3) are convergent, the process is justified by writing b in place of ∞, carrying out the partial integration, and then letting $b \to \infty$. Actually (14-10) holds for $p > -1$, and the partial integration is valid for $p > 0$.

enables us to define $\Gamma(p)$ for negative values [1] of p. Thus, if any number p between 0 and 1 is used on the left side of (14-12) then the right side gives the value of $\Gamma(p)$, for when $p \geq 0$, $\Gamma(p + 1)$ is determined by (14-10). If the recursion formula (14-12) is used again, the values for $-1 < p < 0$ can be found from those for $0 < p < 1$. That is, $p + 1$ in (14-12) ranges over the interval $(0,1)$ if p ranges over the interval $(-1,0)$. Similarly, when we know $\Gamma(p)$ for $-1 < p < 0$, we can find $\Gamma(p)$ for $-2 < p < -1$, and so on.

Inasmuch as (14-10) gives

$$\Gamma(1) = \int_0^\infty t^0 e^{-t} \, dt = -e^{-t} \Big|_0^\infty = 1, \qquad (14\text{-}13)$$

the method fails for $p = 0$. Thus

$$\lim_{p \to 0} \Gamma(p) = \lim_{p \to 0} p^{-1}\Gamma(p + 1) = +\infty \text{ or } -\infty$$

according as $p \to 0$ through positive values or through negative values. Similar behavior is found for all negative integers, and hence the graph of $\Gamma(p)$ has the appearance shown in Fig. 8. However, by use of (14-10) and (14-11) it is easily verified that $\Gamma(p)$ never vanishes, and hence, if we agree that $1/\Gamma(p) = 0$ for p a negative integer, it will follow that the function $1/\Gamma(p)$ is well behaved for every value of p without exception.[2]

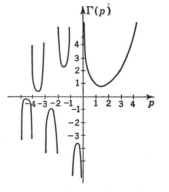

Equations (14-11) and (14-13) give $\Gamma(2) = \Gamma(1) = 1$ and, in succession,

$$\Gamma(3) = 2\Gamma(2) = 2 \cdot 1$$

$$\Gamma(4) = 3\Gamma(3) = 3 \cdot 2 \cdot 1$$

. . . .

$$\Gamma(n + 1) = n\Gamma(n) = n(n - 1) \ldots 3 \cdot 2 \cdot 1.$$

Hence, the definition

Fig. 8

$$p! = \Gamma(p + 1) \qquad (14\text{-}14)$$

furnishes the desired generalization; it gives a meaning to $p!$ for all p except $p = -1$, $-2, -3, \ldots$, and it gives the familiar value when p is a positive integer. The properties

$$p! = p(p - 1)! \quad \text{ or } \quad p\frac{1}{p!} = \frac{1}{(p - 1)!} \qquad (14\text{-}15)$$

are ensured by (14-11). The former fails when p is zero or a negative integer, but the latter holds for all p, without exception.

The result of this discussion is that $1/p!$ is well defined everywhere, and $p!$ is well defined except for $p = -1, -2, -3, \ldots$, at which values $1/p!$ vanishes. Moreover, we have the fundamental formula (14-15). When a series containing factorials is obtained by solving a differential equation, it is almost always this relation (14-15) that makes the series a valid solution,

[1] Equation (14-10) does not serve this purpose, because the behavior of t^p at $t = 0$ makes the integral diverge when $p \leq -1$.

[2] The relation of $\Gamma(p)$ and $1/\Gamma(p)$ is quite analogous to the relation of csc p and sin p, respectively.

and hence the extended definition of $p!$ may be used without hesitation. In particular, $J_p(x)$ and $J_{-p}(x)$ are solutions of (14-1) no matter what value p may have.

For most values of p the functions $J_p(x)$ and $J_{-p}(x)$ are independent, by Theorem I, Sec. 13, and the general solution of Bessel's equation is

$$y = c_1 J_p(x) + c_2 J_{-p}(x), \qquad c_1 \text{ and } c_2 \text{ const.}$$

If $p = 0$, however, then the two roots of the indicial equation are both $\rho = 0$, so that we obtain only the single function $J_0(x)$. Another exceptional case arises when $p = \pm 1, \pm 2, \ldots.$ Although the series (14-8) is meaningless when p is a negative integer, the series (14-9) is well defined and satisfies

$$J_{-m}(x) = (-1)^m J_m(x), \qquad m = 0, 1, 2, 3, \ldots. \tag{14-16}$$

To see this, we observe that

$$J_{-m}(x) = \sum_{n=0}^{\infty} \frac{(-1)^n (x/2)^{2n-m}}{n!(n-m)!} = \sum_{n=m}^{\infty} \frac{(-1)^n (x/2)^{2n-m}}{n!(n-m)!}, \tag{14-17}$$

since the factor $1/(n-m)!$ is zero when $n < m$. If the sums (14-9) and (14-17) are written in full, then (14-16) follows at once.[1] Because of (14-16) the functions $J_{-m}(x)$ and $J_m(x)$ are dependent, so that we obtain only one solution rather than two.

This failure of the method to provide both solutions is not a serious shortcoming, since the second solution can always be found from the first by the method of Chap. 1, Sec. 29. Carrying out the calculation in the general case yields the following theorem:[2]

THEOREM II. *When the roots ρ_1 and ρ_2 of the indicial equation are distinct and do not differ by an integer, the method of Theorem I yields two linearly independent solutions. If the roots do differ by an integer a second solution can be found by assuming that*

$$y_2 = c y_1(x) \log x + \sum_{n=0}^{\infty} a_n x^{n+\rho_2} \tag{14-18}$$

where $y_1(x)$ is the solution given by Theorem I for the root $\rho = \rho_1$.

By setting $y_1(x) = J_0(x)$, for example, one can show that a second solution of Bessel's equation for $p = 0$ is

$$K_0(x) = J_0(x) \log x - \sum_{k=1}^{\infty} \frac{(-1)^k (x/2)^{2k}}{(k!)^2} \left(1 + \frac{1}{2} + \cdots + \frac{1}{k} \right).$$

[1] It is suggested that the reader verify this statement by actually writing the sums in full.

[2] It was shown by Frobenius that the second solution can also be obtained by differentiating the first solution with respect to the exponent ρ; cf. Piaggio's book cited in Sec. 13.

This function is called the Bessel function of the zeroth order and second kind. Thus, the general solution of

$$xy'' + y' + xy = 0$$

is $y = c_1 J_0(x) + c_2 K_0(x)$. Other functions $K_m(x)$ of the second kind are obtained similarly. By considering linear combinations of $J_m(x)$ and $K_m(x)$ we get the *modified Bessel functions* of the first and second kinds, denoted in the literature by $I_m(x)$, $Y_m(x)$, $N_m(x)$, and $H_m(x)$.

PROBLEMS

1. Show that $J_0'(x) = -J_1(x)$ and also that

$$\frac{d}{dx} x^n J_n(x) = x^n J_{n-1}(x), \qquad \frac{d}{dx} x^{-n} J_n(x) = -x^{-n} J_{n+1}(x).$$

Deduce that

$$J_{n-1}(x) - J_{n+1}(x) = 2J_n'(x),$$

$$J_{n-1}(x) + J_{n+1}(x) = \frac{2n}{x} J_n(x).$$

2. The *confluent hypergeometric equation* is

$$xy'' + py' = xy' + qy,$$

where p and q are constant.

(a) According to Theorem I, what range of validity do you expect for a solution of the form $\Sigma a_n x^{n+\rho}$?

(b) Assuming that $y = \Sigma a_n x^{n+\rho}$, verify that $xy'' = \Sigma a_{n+1}(n + \rho + 1)(n + \rho)x^{n+\rho}$ and find similar expressions for py', xy', and qy.

(c) By considering the coefficient of $x^{n+\rho}$, deduce

$$a_{n+1}(n + \rho + 1)(n + \rho + p) = a_n(n + \rho + q)$$

for all values of n.

3. In Prob. 2, (a) show that the roots of the indicial equation are $\rho = 0$ and $\rho = 1 - p$. *Hint:* The first nontrivial case arises when $n = -1$.

(b) When $\rho = 0$, show that

$$a_{n+1} = a_n \frac{n + q}{(n + 1)(n + p)}$$

if p is not zero or a negative integer. Thus get the solution

$$y_1 = a_0 \left[1 + \frac{q}{p} \frac{x}{1!} + \frac{q(q + 1)}{p(p + 1)} \frac{x^2}{2!} + \frac{q(q + 1)(q + 2)}{p(p + 1)(p + 2)} \frac{x^3}{3!} + \cdots \right].$$

(c) Similarly, obtain the solution corresponding to $\rho = 1 - p$ when p is not a positive integer.

4. For the *hypergeometric equation* of Gauss,

$$x(1 - x)y'' + [c - (a + b + 1)x]y' - aby = 0,$$

obtain one solution in the form

$$y = \sum_{n=0}^{\infty} \frac{\Gamma(a + n)}{\Gamma(1 + n)} \frac{\Gamma(b + n)}{\Gamma(c + n)} x^n$$

when a and b are not negative integers.

5. For the equation

$$xy'' + (1 - 2p)y' + xy = 0$$

obtain a recursion formula for the coefficients of a series solution, and show that one solution is $y = x^p J_p(x)$.

6. As in Prob. 5, show that $y = x^{\frac{1}{2}} J_p(\lambda x)$ satisfies

$$4x^2 y'' + (4\lambda^2 x^2 - 4p^2 + 1)y = 0.$$

7. (a) Given that $\Gamma(\frac{1}{2}) = \sqrt{\pi}$, obtain the formulas

$$J_{\frac{1}{2}}(x) = \sqrt{\frac{2}{\pi x}} \sin x, \qquad J_{-\frac{1}{2}}(x) = \sqrt{\frac{2}{\pi x}} \cos x.$$

(b) What is the general solution of Bessel's equation with $p = \frac{1}{2}$? (This shows that Theorem I may yield the general solution even if $\rho_2 - \rho_1$ is an integer.)

8. The generating function of the sequence $J_n(x)$ is

$$e^{\frac{x}{2}\left(h - \frac{1}{h}\right)} = \sum_{n=-\infty}^{\infty} J_n(x) h^n.$$

Verify that the coefficient of h^0 in the expansion of the exponential is, in fact, $J_0(x)$. *Hint:* By the series for e^u the exponential is

$$\sum \left(\frac{x}{2}\right)^n \left(h - \frac{1}{h}\right)^n \frac{1}{n!}.$$

Pick out the term independent of h in the binomial expansion of $[h - (1/h)]^n$ when n is even, and note that there is no such term when n is odd.

SERIES WITH COMPLEX TERMS

15. Complex Numbers. The equation $x^2 + 1 = 0$ cannot be solved by means of real numbers because the rule of signs does not allow the square of a real number to be negative. But if one adjoins a symbol i to the real numbers, which satisfies the equation

$$i^2 = -1 \qquad\qquad (15\text{-}1)$$

by definition, then one can construct the so-called *complex numbers* $a + bi$. The latter satisfy the algebraic laws obeyed by real numbers, and they include the real numbers as a special case. Moreover, complex numbers enable us to solve not only the equation $x^2 + 1 = 0$ but *every* polynomial equation.

Since we want to keep the familiar laws of algebra, it is easy to see how addition and multiplication of complex numbers ought to be defined. Indeed,[1] if a, b, and i in $a + ib$ are to be treated like any other numbers of elementary algebra, then

$$(a + ib) + (c + id) = (a + c) + i(b + d). \qquad (15\text{-}2)$$

---

[1] See also Chap. 7, which contains a discussion of complex numbers and functions from a somewhat different point of view.

This equation is now taken as the definition of addition. In the same way we are led to define multiplication by

$$(a + ib)(c + id) = (ac - bd) + i(bc + ad), \qquad (15\text{-}3)$$

since elementary algebra would give the product

$$ac + ibc + iad + i^2bd = ac + i^2bd + i(bc + ad),$$

and (15-1) asserts that $i^2 = -1$. Finally, we agree that $a + ib = a + bi$.

It is easy to verify that these definitions (15-2) and (15-3) do preserve the familiar rules of algebra (including those rules that were not considered in framing the definitions). For example, complex numbers z_k satisfy

$$z_1 + z_2 = z_2 + z_1, \qquad (z_1 + z_2) + z_3 = z_1 + (z_2 + z_3),$$

$$z_1 z_2 = z_2 z_1, \qquad\qquad (z_1 z_2)z_3 = z_1(z_2 z_3),$$

$$z_1(z_2 + z_3) = z_1 z_2 + z_1 z_3.$$

Also there is a zero, and there is a unit:

$$z + (0 + 0i) = z, \qquad z(1 + 0i) = z \qquad \text{for all } z.$$

Moreover, the complex number $a + 0i$ is found to be equivalent in every respect, except notation, to the real number a. Hence in this sense the complex numbers contain the reals as a special case, and we have a right to consider that

$$a + 0i = a. \qquad (15\text{-}4)$$

The convention (15-4) also agrees with our purpose of keeping the rules of algebra intact. Using (15-4) we write 0 and 1 for the zero and unit element of our algebra. Subtraction is defined by considering the equation $(a + ib) + z = 0$; it will be found that

$$-(a + bi) = (-a) + (-b)i = (-1)(a + ib).$$

Although we made no attempt to preserve the cancellation law, it is nevertheless valid; that is,

$$z_1 z_2 = 0 \text{ only if } z_1 = 0 \text{ or } z_2 = 0.$$

And finally, the possibility of division is suggested by

$$z = \frac{a + ib}{c + id} = \frac{(a + ib)(c - id)}{(c + id)(c - id)}$$

$$= \frac{ac + bd}{c^2 + d^2} + i\frac{bc - ad}{c^2 + d^2}.$$

Now, the latter expression can be shown by (15-3) to satisfy the equation

$$(c + id)z = a + ib.$$

Hence, the result of this heuristic calculation is, in fact, the quotient. The process breaks down if $c + id = 0$, but only then.

The general tenor of this discussion is that the algebra of complex numbers agrees with the algebra of real numbers and we need not hesitate to apply the familiar rules to the new symbols. There is one new feature, however. When we say that $a + ib$ is a symbol for a complex number, we assume, naturally, that different symbols represent different numbers. In other words, if

$$a + ib = a' + ib' \text{ for } a, a', b, b' \text{ real}, \qquad \text{then } a = a' \text{ and } b = b'. \quad (15\text{-}5)$$

This important relation may be taken as the definition of *equality*. Unlike the algebraic properties described hitherto, (15-5) is true for complex numbers only; it does not hold if i is replaced by a real number.

The following alternative analysis of (15-5) shows the role of the equation $i^2 = -1$ and also shows why a, a', b, b' must be assumed real. If $a + ib = a' + ib'$, then

$$a - a' = i(b' - b).$$

Squaring gives $(a - a')^2 = -(b - b')^2$ because $i^2 = -1$, and hence

$$(a - a')^2 + (b - b')^2 = 0.$$

Since the square of a real number is positive unless the number is zero, the latter equation implies $a - a' = 0$ and $b - b' = 0$.

Complex numbers $z = x + iy$ may be represented graphically in the so-called *z plane* by introducing two perpendicular axes, one for x and one for y (Fig. 9). The x axis is called the *real axis*, and x is the *real part* of $x + iy$; the iy axis is the imaginary axis, and iy is the imaginary part of $x + iy$. The *absolute value* of z is the distance from the representative point to the origin; it is denoted by $|z|$, as in the case of real numbers. Evidently, the points satisfying $|z| = r$ lie on a circle of radius r centered at the origin. The interior of this circle consists of the points $|z| < r$. When $z = x + iy$, then

$$|z| = \sqrt{x^2 + y^2}. \qquad (15\text{-}6)$$

A short calculation based on (15-6) gives

$$|z_1 z_2| = |z_1|\,|z_2|, \qquad \left|\frac{z_1}{z_2}\right| = \frac{|z_1|}{|z_2|} \qquad \text{if } z_2 \neq 0,$$

so that the absolute value of a product is the product of the absolute values, and similarly for quotients.

Since real and imaginary parts are added separately, computation of $z_1 + z_2$ can be effected as shown [1] in Fig. 9. Inasmuch as the sum of two sides of any triangle is greater than the third, the figure gives the important inequality

$$|z_1 + z_2| \leq |z_1| + |z_2|. \qquad (15\text{-}7)$$

---

[1] One may think of $z = x + iy$ as a vector with components x and y. The method of adding vectors by adding components agrees with the definition (15-2), and hence the construction of Fig. 9 is simply the parallelogram rule familiar from mechanics.

A similar result may be obtained from this one for any number of complex numbers.

If $s_n = u_n + iv_n$ and $s = u + iv$, we define $\lim s_n = s$ to mean that simultaneously

$$\lim u_n = u, \qquad \lim v_n = v. \tag{15-8}$$

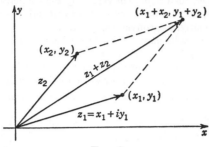

FIG. 9

This shows that the theory of limits for complex numbers can be based on the corresponding theory for real numbers.

PROBLEMS

1. Show that $|z_1 z_2| = |z_1|\,|z_2|$.

2. Show that $\lim s_n = s$ if, and only if, $\lim |s_n - s| = 0$.

3. Sketch the set of points z in the complex plane described by (a) $|z| = 1$, (b) $|z| < 2$, (c) $|z| \geq 1$, (d) $|z - 2| < 1$. *Hint:* $|z - a|$ is the distance from the representative point for z to that for a.

16. Complex Series. Convergence of infinite series of complex numbers is defined by considering the limit of partial sums, just as for real series. By (15-8) the complex series converges if, and only if, the two real series obtained by considering real and imaginary parts are both convergent. In other words,

$$\Sigma(p_n + iq_n) = p + iq$$

if, and only if, $\Sigma p_n = p$ and $\Sigma q_n = q$. Because of this correspondence of real and complex series, most of the results presented hitherto in this chapter apply with little change to the complex case, and the proof also involves nothing new.

As an illustration let us show that *the general term of a convergent series approaches zero.* If a_n is complex, we have

$$a_n = \sum_{k=1}^{n} a_k - \sum_{k=1}^{n-1} a_k,$$

and taking the limit as $n \to \infty$ yields $\lim a_n = 0$, exactly as in the proof for real series. Alternatively, one may use the *result* for real series. Namely, if $a_k = p_k + iq_k$, then the convergence of Σa_k implies the convergence of Σp_k and of Σq_k. Hence, by the theorem for real series, $\lim p_n = 0$ and $\lim q_n = 0$. Consequently, $\lim a_n = 0$.

As a second illustration, we show that *an absolutely convergent series is convergent.* With $a_k = p_k + iq_k$, we have

$$|p_k| = \sqrt{p_k^2} \leq \sqrt{p_k^2 + q_k^2} = |a_k|.$$

Hence, if $\Sigma|a_k|$ converges, then $\Sigma|p_k|$ converges by the comparison test for real series, and then Σp_k converges, because we know that for *real* series absolute convergence implies convergence. Similarly, Σq_k converges, and hence $\Sigma(p_k + iq_k)$ converges.

As a third example, the reader may obtain the analogue of Theorem I, Sec. 8, for complex series. That is, if $\Sigma a_n z^n$ converges for $z = z_0$, then the series converges absolutely for all z such that $|z| < |z_0|$ and uniformly for all z such that $|z| \leq |z_1| < |z_0|$. It will be found that the proof is the same, word for word, as the proof in the case of real series. The symbol for absolute value, however, has the meaning assigned in (15-6).

For many series $\Sigma u_n(z)$, the set of points z at which the series converges gives a complicated region in the z plane. It is a remarkable fact that for a power series the region of convergence is always a circle centered at the origin. The circle is called the *circle of convergence*, and the radius of the circle is the *radius of convergence*. We agree to take the radius as zero if the series converges for $z = 0$ only and as infinity if the series converges for all z. At points on the boundary of the circle the series may either converge or diverge, just as in the case of the interval of convergence for real series.

For proof that the region is a circle, let $\Sigma a_n z^n$ be a power series which converges for some value $z = z_0 \neq 0$ but diverges for some other value $z = z_1$. As we have already noted, the fact that the series converges for $z = z_0$ makes the series converge throughout the circle $|z| < |z_0|$. On the other hand, the series obviously does not converge throughout any circle containing the point z_1 (see Fig. 10). We let C be *the largest circle* $|z| = r$ such that the series converges at every interior point of C. The radius r of C is at least equal to $|z_0|$ but does not exceed $|z_1|$.

To show that C is the circle of convergence, all we have to do is establish that the series diverges at every point exterior to C. Let z_2 be an exterior point, so that $|z_2| > r$. If the series converges at z_2, then it would have to converge throughout the circle $|z| < |z_2|$. But this contradicts the fact that C is the *largest* circle throughout which the series converges, and hence the proof is complete.[1]

To illustrate the concept of circle of convergence consider the series

$$\frac{1}{1 + x^2} = 1 - x^2 + x^4 + \cdots + (-1)^n x^{2n} + \cdots$$

---

[1] The fact that a *largest circle* exists is quite clear from the geometry. An analytical proof may be given, if desired, by constructing circles with successively larger radii and using the fundamental principle (Sec. 1).

which converges for $|x| < 1$ but diverges at $x = \pm 1$. If $1/(1 + x^2)$ is regarded as a function of the *real* variable x, there appears to be no reason why the series should diverge when $|x| \geq 1$, for $1/(1 + x^2)$ has derivatives of all orders at every value of x. But when we regard x as a *complex* variable, the divergence is explained by the fact that the denominator $1 + x^2$ vanishes at $x = \pm i$. Clearly, if the circle of convergence cannot contain the points $\pm i$, then the radius of convergence cannot exceed 1.

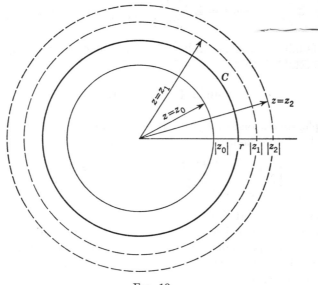

FIG. 10

PROBLEMS

1. Verify that the series $\sum\limits_{1}^{\infty} z^n/n^2$ converges absolutely at every boundary point of its circle of convergence whereas $\sum\limits_{1}^{\infty} n^2 z^n$ converges at no boundary point of its circle of convergence.

2. If $f(z) = e^{-1/z^2}$ and $f(0) = 0$,

   (a) How does $f(z)$ behave when $z = x$ and $x \to 0$ through real values?

   (b) How does $f(z)$ behave when $z = iy$ and $y \to 0$ through real values?

   (c) Could this function have a power-series expansion valid in some circle containing the origin? Explain.

17. Applications. By means of power series the functions $\sin x$, e^x, $\log x$, $\tan^{-1} x$, $J_p(x)$, and so on, may be extended to a complex variable z. For example, since the series

$$- \log (1 - x) = x + \frac{x^2}{2} + \frac{x^3}{3} + \cdots + \frac{x^n}{n} + \cdots$$

converges for $|x| < 1$, we know *without further discussion* that

$$z + \frac{z^2}{2} + \frac{z^3}{3} + \cdots + \frac{z^n}{n} + \cdots$$

converges for $|z| < 1$. The latter series is the definition of $-\log(1-z)$. Similarly e^z, $\sin z$, and $\cos z$ are defined by

$$e^z = \Sigma \frac{z^n}{n!}, \qquad \sin z = \Sigma \frac{(-1)^n z^{2n+1}}{(2n+1)!}, \qquad \cos z = \Sigma \frac{(-1)^n z^{2n}}{(2n)!}.$$

Many familiar formulas can be extended at once to the complex-variable case. To establish that

$$\sin^2 z + \cos^2 z = 1, \tag{17-1}$$

for example, we reason as follows. It is known that (17-1) holds when z is a real variable x, and hence

$$\left[\Sigma \frac{(-1)^n x^{2n+1}}{(2n+1)!}\right]^2 + \left[\Sigma \frac{(-1)^n x^{2n}}{(2n)!}\right]^2 - 1 = 0 \tag{17-2}$$

when x is real. The left side of (17-2) is a power series, as we see by imagining that the terms are collected. Since the power series is zero for an interval of x values, every coefficient must be zero (Sec. 8, Theorem III). Hence the power series is also zero when x is replaced by a complex variable z, and this establishes (17-1).

The same method may be used to prove formulas involving two variables; for example, from

$$e^{x_1 + x_2} = e^{x_1} e^{x_2} \qquad \text{for } x_1 \text{ and } x_2 \text{ real,}$$

it follows *without detailed calculation* that

$$e^{z_1 + z_2} = e^{z_1} e^{z_2} \qquad \text{for } z_1 \text{ and } z_2 \text{ complex.}$$

The systematic development of this idea leads to a branch of analysis known as the theory of *analytic continuation*.

Upon letting $z = ix$ in the series for e^z, we get

$$e^{ix} = \Sigma \frac{(ix)^n}{n!} = 1 - \frac{x^2}{2!} + \frac{x^4}{4!} - \frac{x^6}{6!} + \cdots + i\left(x - \frac{x^3}{3!} + \frac{x^5}{5!} - \frac{x^7}{7!} + \cdots\right)$$

when we write out the sum in full, noting that

$$i^2 = -1, \qquad i^3 = -i, \qquad i^4 = 1, \qquad i^5 = ii^4 = i, \qquad \cdots.$$

The series representations for $\cos x$ and $\sin x$ now give *Euler's formula,*

$$e^{ix} = \cos x + i \sin x, \tag{17-3}$$

which expresses the exponential function in terms of the trigonometric functions. On the other hand (17-3) also leads to

$$\cos x = \frac{e^{ix} + e^{-ix}}{2}, \qquad \sin x = \frac{e^{ix} - e^{-ix}}{2i}, \tag{17-4}$$

as the reader can verify. These equations are constantly used in the study of periodic phenomena, for example, in network analysis and synthesis, in physical optics, and in electromagnetic theory. The calculations are ordinarily carried out by complex exponentials, and then the appropriate trigonometric form is obtained by taking real or imaginary parts [cf. (17-3)].

Example 1.   Obtain the trigonometric identity

$$\cos u + \cos 2u + \cdots + \cos nu = \frac{\sin (n + \frac{1}{2})u}{2 \sin \frac{1}{2}u} - \frac{1}{2} \tag{17-5}$$

for $u \neq 0, \pm 2\pi, \pm 4\pi, \ldots,$ by considering the exponential sum

$$s = e^{iu} + e^{2iu} + \cdots + e^{niu}.$$

The series s is a geometric series with ratio $r = e^{iu}$, and hence

$$s = e^{iu} \frac{e^{inu} - 1}{e^{iu} - 1} \tag{17-6}$$

by (1-18). If the numerator and denominator in (17-6) are multiplied by $e^{-i\frac{1}{2}u}$, we get

$$s = e^{i\frac{1}{2}u} \frac{e^{inu} - 1}{e^{i\frac{1}{2}u} - e^{-i\frac{1}{2}u}} = \frac{e^{i(n+\frac{1}{2})u} - e^{i\frac{1}{2}u}}{2i \sin \frac{1}{2}u}$$

upon using (17-4). By (17-3) this yields another expression for the exponential sum s,

$$s = \frac{\cos (n + \frac{1}{2})u + i \sin (n + \frac{1}{2})u - \cos \frac{1}{2}u - i \sin \frac{1}{2}u}{2i \sin \frac{1}{2}u},$$

which leads to (17-5) when we equate real parts.

Example 2.   Show that $\int_0^{2\pi} e^{ikx} \, dx = 0$ if k is a nonzero integer, and deduce

$$\int_0^{2\pi} \cos nx \cos mx \, dx = \begin{cases} 0, & \text{if } m \neq n, \\ \pi, & \text{if } m = n, \end{cases}$$

$$\int_0^{2\pi} \cos nx \sin mx \, dx = 0 \tag{17-7}$$

$$\int_0^{2\pi} \sin nx \sin mx \, dx = \begin{cases} 0, & \text{if } m \neq n, \\ \pi, & \text{if } m = n, \end{cases}$$

whenever m and n are positive integers.

If k is a nonzero integer, (17-3) gives

$$\int_0^{2\pi} e^{ikx}\, dx = \int_0^{2\pi} (\cos kx + i \sin kx)\, dx = 0, \tag{17-8}$$

which is the first result.   By (17-4),

$$4\int_0^{2\pi} \cos nx \cos mx\, dx = \int_0^{2\pi} (e^{inx} + e^{-inx})(e^{imx} + e^{-imx})\, dx$$

$$= \int_0^{2\pi} [e^{i(m+n)x} + e^{i(m-n)x} + e^{i(n-m)x} + e^{-i(m+n)x}]\, dx.$$

Each term is of the form e^{ikx} with k an integer, and hence we get zero unless $m = n$. If $m = n$, the two middle terms give 2, so that the integral is 4π.   The other relations (17-7) are established similarly.

PROBLEMS

1. By using the series definition for e^z, show that $(d/dx)e^{cx} = ce^{cx}$ when c is a complex constant.   (Since we have not defined the derivative with respect to a complex variable, assume that x is real.)

2. Sum the series $\sin x + \sin 2x + \cdots + \sin nx$.

3. Evaluate $\int e^{ax} \cos bx\, dx$ and $\int e^{ax} \sin bx\, dx$ by considering $\int e^{(a+ib)x}\, dx$ and equating real and imaginary parts.   *Hint:* $\dfrac{e^{(a+ib)x}}{a+ib} = \dfrac{e^{ax}e^{ibx}(a-ib)}{a^2+b^2}.$

4. Evaluate $\int_0^{2\pi} (2 \cos x)^4\, dx$ by using the formula

$$2 \cos x = e^{ix} + e^{-ix}$$

together with (17-8).

5. Show that every complex number z may be written in the form $z = re^{i\theta}$, where $r \geq 0$ and $0 \leq \theta < 2\pi$.   *Hint:* If $z = x + iy$, introduce polar coordinates (r, θ), so that $x = r \cos \theta$ and $y = r \sin \theta$.

6. (a) For $0 \leq r < 1$ obtain the expansion

$$\frac{1}{1 - re^{i\theta}} = \Sigma r^n (\cos n\theta + i \sin n\theta)$$

by letting $z = re^{i\theta}$ in the series for $1/(1 - z)$.

(b) Separate $1/(1 - re^{i\theta})$ into real and imaginary parts, by noting that

$$\frac{1 - re^{-i\theta}}{1 - re^{-i\theta}} \frac{1}{1 - re^{i\theta}} = \frac{1 - r \cos \theta + ir \sin \theta}{1 - 2r \cos \theta + r^2}.$$

(c) From (a) and (b) deduce that

$$\frac{1 - r \cos \theta}{1 - 2r \cos \theta + r^2} = \sum_{n=0}^{\infty} r^n \cos n\theta, \qquad 0 \leq r < 1,$$

$$\frac{r \sin \theta}{1 - 2r \cos \theta + r^2} = \sum_{n=0}^{\infty} r^n \sin n\theta, \qquad 0 \leq r < 1.$$

[The first series of (c) is an example of a *Fourier cosine series*, and the second is a *Fourier sine series*.   The study of such series by real-variable methods forms the topic of the next eight sections.]

Math 92 Begins

FOURIER SERIES

18. The Euler-Fourier Formulas. Trigonometric series of the form

$$f(x) = \tfrac{1}{2}a_0 + \sum_{n=1}^{\infty} (a_n \cos nx + b_n \sin nx) \qquad (18\text{-}1)$$

this is $n = 0$ term

are required in the treatment of many physical problems, for example, in the theory of sound, heat conduction, electromagnetic waves, electric circuits, and mechanical vibrations. An important advantage of the series (18-1) is that it can represent discontinuous functions, whereas a Taylor series represents only functions that have derivatives of all orders.

We take the point of view that $f(x)$ in (18-1) is known on $(-\pi, \pi)$ and that the coefficients a_n and b_n are to be found. In order to determine a_0, we integrate (18-1) term by term from $-\pi$ to π. Since

$$\int_{-\pi}^{\pi} \cos nx \, dx = \int_{-\pi}^{\pi} \sin nx \, dx = 0 \qquad \text{for } n = 1, 2, \ldots,$$

the calculation yields

$$\boxed{\int_{-\pi}^{\pi} f(x) \, dx = a_0 \pi.} \qquad \qquad a\,\frac{1}{\pi}\int_{-\pi}^{\pi} f(x)\, dx = a_0 \qquad (18\text{-}2)$$

The coefficient a_n is determined similarly. Thus, if we multiply (18-1) by $\cos nx$, there results

$$f(x) \cos nx = \tfrac{1}{2}a_0 \cos nx + \cdots + a_n \cos^2 nx + \cdots, \qquad (18\text{-}3)$$

where the terms not written involve products of the form $\sin mx \cos nx$ or of the form $\cos mx \cos nx$ with $m \neq n$. It is easily verified [1] that for integral values of m and n,

$$\int_{-\pi}^{\pi} \sin mx \cos nx \, dx = 0, \qquad \text{in general,}$$

$$\int_{-\pi}^{\pi} \cos mx \cos nx \, dx = 0, \qquad \text{when } m \neq \pm n,$$

and hence integration of (18-3) yields

$$\int_{-\pi}^{\pi} f(x) \cos nx \, dx = a_n \int_{-\pi}^{\pi} \cos^2 nx \, dx = a_n \pi.$$

Therefore,

$$a_n = \frac{1}{\pi} \int_{-\pi}^{\pi} f(x) \cos nx \, dx. \qquad (18\text{-}4)$$

By (18-2), this result is also valid [2] for $n = 0$.

---

[1] See Example 2 of Sec. 17.
[2] That is the reason for writing the constant term as $\tfrac{1}{2}a_0$ rather than a_0.

Similarly, multiplying (18-1) by $\sin nx$ and integrating yield

$$b_n = \frac{1}{\pi} \int_{-\pi}^{\pi} f(x) \sin nx \, dx. \tag{18-4a}$$

The formulas (18-4) are called the *Euler-Fourier formulas*, and the series (18-1) which results when a_n and b_n are determined by the Euler-Fourier formulas is called the *Fourier series* of $f(x)$. More specifically, a Fourier series is a trigonometric series in which the coefficients are given, for some absolutely integrable function [1] $f(x)$, by (18-4).

The distinction between a *convergent trigonometric series* and a *Fourier series* is important in the modern development of the subject and is a genuine distinction. For instance, it is known that the trigonometric series

$$\sum_{n=1}^{\infty} \frac{\sin nx}{\log(1+n)}$$

is convergent for every value of x without exception, and yet this series is not a Fourier series. In other words, there is no absolutely integrable function $f(x)$ such that

$$\int_{-\pi}^{\pi} f(x) \cos nx \, dx = 0, \qquad \int_{-\pi}^{\pi} f(x) \sin nx \, dx = \frac{\pi}{\log(1+n)}.$$

On the other hand a series may be a Fourier series for some function $f(x)$ and yet diverge. Although such functions are not considered in this book, they often arise in practice, for example, in the theory of Brownian motion, in problems of filtering and noise, or in analyzing the ground return to a radar system. Even when divergent, the Fourier series represents the main features of $f(x)$, and for this reason Fourier series are an indispensable aid in problems of the sort just mentioned.

Treatises devoted to Fourier series commonly replace the sign of equality in (18-1) by $\sim$, $\cong$, or some similar symbol to indicate that the series on the right is the Fourier series of the function on the left. We shall continue to use the equality sign because the series obtained in this book do, in fact, converge to the function from which the coefficients were derived.

To illustrate the calculation of a Fourier series, let $f(x) = x$. By Eqs. (18-4)

$$a_n = \frac{1}{\pi} \int_{-\pi}^{\pi} x \cos nx \, dx = 0,$$

$$b_n = \frac{1}{\pi} \int_{-\pi}^{\pi} x \sin nx \, dx = -\frac{2}{n} \cos n\pi = \frac{2}{n}(-1)^{n+1},$$

so that, upon substituting in (18-1),

$$x = 2\left(\sin x - \frac{\sin 2x}{2} + \frac{\sin 3x}{3} - \cdots \right). \tag{18-5}$$

In Sec. 24 it is shown that the series (18-5) does converge to x for $-\pi < x < \pi$. To discuss the convergence outside this interval, we introduce the notion of periodicity. A function $f(x)$ is said to be *periodic* if $f(x + p)$

[1] This means that $|f(x)|$, as well as $f(x)$, is integrable.

$= f(x)$ for all values of x, where p is a nonzero constant. Any number p with this property is a *period* of $f(x)$; for instance, $\sin x$ has the periods 2π, -2π, 4π, ...

Now, each term of the series (18-5) has period 2π, and hence the sum also has period 2π. The graph of the sum therefore has the appearance shown in Fig. 11. Evidently, the sum is equal to x only on the interval $-\pi < x < \pi$, and not on the whole interval $-\infty < x < \infty$.

It remains to describe what happens at the points $x = \pm\pi, \pm3\pi, \ldots$, where the sum of the series exhibits an abrupt jump from $-\pi$ to $+\pi$.

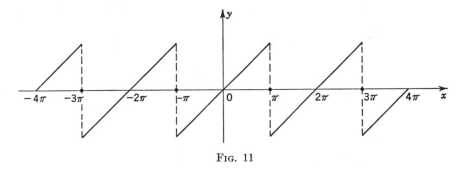

FIG. 11

Upon setting $x = \pm\pi, \pm3\pi, \ldots$ in (18-5), we see that every term is zero. Hence the sum is zero, and this fact is indicated in the figure by placing a dot at the points in question.

The term $a_n \cos nx + b_n \sin nx$ in (18-1) is sometimes called the nth *harmonic* (from analogy with the theory of musical instruments). The first four harmonics of the series (18-5) are

$$2 \sin x, \ - \sin 2x, \ \tfrac{2}{3} \sin 3x, \ -\tfrac{1}{2} \sin 4x.$$

These and the next two harmonics are plotted as the numbered curves in Fig. 12. The sum of the first four harmonics is

$$y = 2 \sin x - \sin 2x + \tfrac{2}{3} \sin 3x - \tfrac{1}{2} \sin 4x.$$

Since this is a partial sum of the Fourier series, it may be expected to approximate the function x. The closeness of the approximation is indicated by the upper curves in Fig. 12, which show this partial sum of four terms together with the sums of six and ten terms. As the number of terms increases, the approximating curves approach $y = x$ for each fixed x on $-\pi < x < \pi$ but not for $x = \pm\pi$.

The foregoing example illustrates certain features which are characteristic of Fourier series in general and which will now be discussed from a general standpoint. Each term of the series (18-1) has period 2π, and hence if $f(x)$ is to be represented by the sum, then $f(x)$ must also have period 2π. Whenever we consider a series such as (18-1), we shall suppose that $f(x)$ is given for $-\pi \leq x < \pi$ and that outside this interval $f(x)$ is determined by

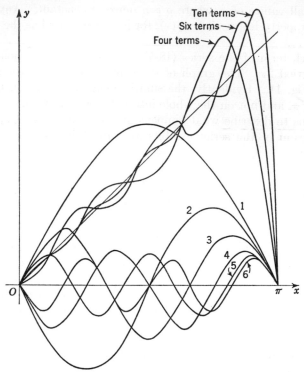

Ten terms →
Six terms →
Four terms →

Fɪɢ. 12

the periodicity condition

$$f(x + 2\pi) = f(x).$$

Of course, any interval $a \le x < a + 2\pi$ would do equally well.

The term *simple discontinuity* [1] is used to describe the situation that arises when the function $f(x)$ suffers a finite jump at a point $x = x_0$ (see Fig. 13). Analytically, this means that the two limiting values of $f(x)$, as x approaches x_0 from the right-hand and the left-hand sides, exist but are unequal; that is,

$$\lim_{\epsilon \to 0} f(x_0 + \epsilon) \ne \lim_{\epsilon \to 0} f(x_0 - \epsilon), \qquad \epsilon > 0.$$

In order to economize on space, these right-hand and left-hand limits are written as $f(x_0+)$ and $f(x_0-)$, respectively, so that the foregoing inequality can be written as

$$f(x_0+) \ne f(x_0-).$$

A function $f(x)$ is said to be *bounded* if the inequality

$$|f(x)| \le M$$

[1] For an example of a discontinuity which is not simple, consider $\sin (1/x)$ near $x = 0$.

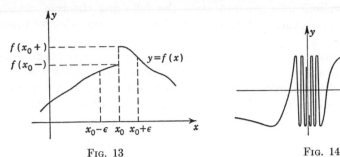

FIG. 13

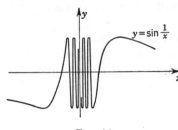

FIG. 14

holds for some constant M and for all x under consideration. For example, $\sin x$ is bounded, but the function

$$f(x) = \frac{1}{x}, \qquad \text{for } x \neq 0,$$

$$f(0) = 0,$$

is not, even though the latter is well defined for every value of x. It can be shown that if a bounded function has only a finite number of maxima and minima and only a finite number of discontinuities, then all its discontinuities are simple. That is, $f(x+)$ and $f(x-)$ exist at every value of x.

The functions illustrated in Figs. 11 and 13 satisfy these conditions in every finite interval. On the other hand, the function $\sin (1/x)$ has infinitely many maxima near $x = 0$, and as we have noted, the discontinuity at $x = 0$ is not simple. The function defined by

$$f(x) = x^2 \sin \frac{1}{x}, \qquad x \neq 0,$$

$$f(0) = 0$$

also has infinitely many maxima near $x = 0$, although it is continuous and differentiable for every value of x. The behavior of these two functions is illustrated graphically in Figs. 14 and 15.

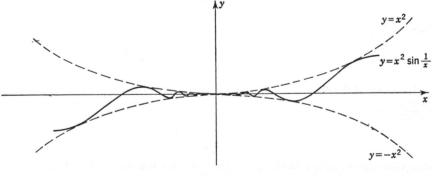

FIG. 15

With these preliminaries, we can state the following theorem, which establishes the convergence of Fourier series for a very large class of functions:

DIRICHLET'S THEOREM. *For* $-\pi \leq x < \pi$ *suppose* $f(x)$ *is well defined, is bounded, has only a finite number of maxima and minima, and has only a finite number of discontinuities. Let* $f(x)$ *be defined for other values of* x *by the periodicity condition* $f(x + 2\pi) = f(x)$. *Then the Fourier series for* $f(x)$ *converges to*

$$\tfrac{1}{2}[f(x+) + f(x-)]$$

at every value of x *[and hence it converges to* $f(x)$ *at points where* $f(x)$ *is continuous].*

The conditions imposed on $f(x)$ are called *Dirichlet conditions*, after the mathematician Dirichlet who discovered the theorem. In Sec. 24 we establish the conclusion under slightly more restrictive conditions which are sufficient, however, for almost all applications.

Example 1. Find the Fourier series of the periodic function defined by

$$f(x) = 0, \qquad \text{if } -\pi \leq x \leq 0,$$

$$f(x) = \pi, \qquad \text{if } 0 \leq x < \pi.$$

By (18-4) we have

$$a_0 = \frac{1}{\pi}\left(\int_{-\pi}^{0} 0 \, dx + \int_{0}^{\pi} \pi \, dx\right) = \pi,$$

$$a_n = \frac{1}{\pi}\int_{0}^{\pi} \pi \cos nx \, dx = 0, \qquad n \geq 1,$$

$$b_n = \frac{1}{\pi}\int_{0}^{\pi} \pi \sin nx \, dx = \frac{1}{n}(1 - \cos n\pi).$$

The factor $(1 - \cos n\pi)$ assumes the following values as n increases:

$n =$	1	2	3	4	5	...
$(1 - \cos n\pi) =$	2	0	2	0	2	...

Determining b_n by use of this table, we obtain the required Fourier series

$$\frac{\pi}{2} + 2\left(\frac{\sin x}{1} + \frac{\sin 3x}{3} + \frac{\sin 5x}{5} + \cdots\right).$$

The graph of $f(x)$ consists of the x axis from $-\pi$ to 0 and of the line AB from 0 to π (Fig. 16). There is a simple discontinuity at $x = 0$, at which point the series reduces to $\pi/2$. Since

$$\frac{\pi}{2} = \frac{f(0-) + f(0+)}{2},$$

this value agrees with Dirichlet's theorem. Similar behavior is found at $x = \pm\pi$, $\pm2\pi$, ...

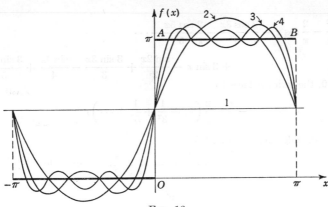

FIG. 16

The figure shows the first four partial sums, whose equations are

$$y = \frac{\pi}{2}, \qquad y = \frac{\pi}{2} + 2 \sin x, \qquad y = \frac{\pi}{2} + 2\left(\sin x + \frac{\sin 3x}{3}\right),$$

$$y = \frac{\pi}{2} + 2\left(\sin x + \frac{\sin 3x}{3} + \frac{\sin 5x}{5}\right).$$

For most functions it is only the *infinite* series that reduces to $\frac{1}{2}[f(x-) + f(x+)]$ at points of discontinuity. In the present example, however, this condition is satisfied by the partial sums, as the reader can verify. That is, the graph of each partial sum contains the points $(0, \pi/2)$, $(\pm \pi, \pi/2)$, ...

Example 2. Find the Fourier series for the periodic function $f(x)$ defined by

$$f(x) = -\pi, \qquad \text{if } -\pi < x < 0,$$

$$f(x) = x, \qquad \text{if } 0 < x < \pi.$$

The integral (18-4) may be expressed as an integration from $-\pi$ to 0, followed by integration from 0 to π. If the appropriate formula for $f(x)$ is used in these two intervals, we get

$$a_n = \frac{1}{\pi}\left(\int_{-\pi}^{0} -\pi \cos nx \, dx + \int_{0}^{\pi} x \cos nx \, dx\right)$$

$$= \frac{1}{\pi}\left(0 + \frac{\cos n\pi}{n^2} - \frac{1}{n^2}\right) = \frac{1}{\pi}\left(\frac{\cos n\pi - 1}{n^2}\right).$$

The integration assumes that $n \neq 0$; if $n = 0$, we get $a_0 = -\pi/2$, as the reader can verify. Similarly,

$$b_n = \frac{1}{\pi}\left(\int_{-\pi}^{0} -\pi \sin nx \, dx + \int_{0}^{\pi} x \sin nx \, dx\right)$$

$$= \frac{1}{\pi}\left(\frac{\pi}{n} - \frac{\pi}{n}\cos n\pi - \frac{\pi}{n}\cos n\pi\right) = \frac{1}{n}(1 - 2\cos n\pi)$$

Therefore

$$f(x) = -\frac{\pi}{4} - \frac{2}{\pi}\cos x - \frac{2}{\pi}\frac{\cos 3x}{3^2} - \frac{2}{\pi}\frac{\cos 5x}{5^2} - \cdots$$

$$+ 3\sin x - \frac{\sin 2x}{2} + \frac{3\sin 3x}{3} - \frac{\sin 4x}{4} + \frac{3\sin 5x}{5} - \cdots.$$

When $x = 0$, the series reduces to

$$-\frac{\pi}{4} - \frac{2}{\pi}\left(\frac{1}{1^2} + \frac{1}{3^2} + \frac{1}{5^2} + \cdots\right),$$

since sin n0 = 0
+ cos n0 = 1

which must coincide with (see Fig. 17)

$$\frac{f(0+) + f(0-)}{2} = -\frac{\pi}{2}.$$ ← *Dirichlets Th.*

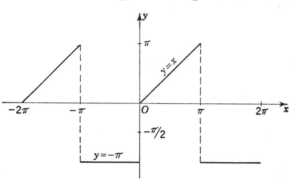

FIG. 17

Thus

$$-\frac{\pi}{4} - \frac{2}{\pi}\left(\frac{1}{1^2} + \frac{1}{3^2} + \frac{1}{5^2} + \cdots\right) = -\frac{\pi}{2}.$$ *sum of series*

Hence

$$\frac{1}{1^2} + \frac{1}{3^2} + \frac{1}{5^2} + \cdots = \frac{\pi^2}{8}.$$ *Troughf obeys Th.*

This example suggests the use of Fourier series in evaluating sums of series of constants.

PROBLEMS

1. Evaluate $\displaystyle\int_{-\pi}^{\pi} \cos mx \cos nx \, dx$ for integral m and n by use of the identity

$$2\cos A \cos B = \cos(A + B) + \cos(A - B).$$

✓ 2. Find the Fourier-series expansion for $f(x)$, if

$$f(x) = \frac{\pi}{2}, \qquad \text{for } -\pi < x < \frac{\pi}{2},$$

$$f(x) = 0, \qquad \text{for } \frac{\pi}{2} < x < \pi.$$

3. If

$$f(x) = -x, \qquad \text{for } -\pi < x < 0,$$

$$f(x) = 0, \qquad \text{for } 0 < x < \pi,$$

then $\qquad$ $f(x) = \dfrac{\pi}{4} - \dfrac{2}{\pi} \displaystyle\sum_{n=1}^{\infty} \dfrac{\cos(2n-1)x}{(2n-1)^2} + \displaystyle\sum_{n=1}^{\infty} \dfrac{(-1)^n \sin nx}{n}.$

4. If

$$f(x) = 0, \qquad \text{for } -\pi \leq x \leq 0,$$

$$f(x) = \sin x, \qquad \text{for } 0 \leq x < \pi,$$

then $\qquad$ $f(x) = \dfrac{1}{\pi} - \dfrac{2}{\pi} \displaystyle\sum_{n=1}^{\infty} \dfrac{\cos 2nx}{4n^2 - 1} + \dfrac{1}{2}\sin x.$

5. Deduce from the expansion of $f(x) = x + x^2$ in Fourier series in the interval $(-\pi,\pi)$ that

$$\sum_{n=1}^{\infty} \frac{1}{n^2} = \frac{\pi^2}{6}.$$

6. In Probs. 2 to 5, sketch the graph of the function to which the Fourier series converges in the range $-4\pi \leq x \leq 4\pi$.

19. Even and Odd Functions. For many functions the Fourier sine or cosine coefficients can be determined by inspection, and this possibility is now to be investigated. A function $f(x)$ is said to be *even* if

$$f(-x) \equiv f(x), \tag{19-1}$$

and the function $f(x)$ is *odd* if

$$f(-x) \equiv -f(x). \tag{19-2}$$

For example, x^2 and $\cos x$ are even, whereas x and $\sin x$ are odd. The graph of an even function is symmetric about the y axis, as shown in Fig. 18, and the graph of an odd function is skew symmetric (Fig. 19). By inspection of the figures it is evident that

$$\int_{-a}^{a} f(x)\, dx = 2\int_{0}^{a} f(x)\, dx \qquad \text{if } f(x) \text{ is even,} \tag{19-3}$$

$$\int_{-a}^{a} f(x)\, dx = 0 \qquad \text{if } f(x) \text{ is odd,} \tag{19-4}$$

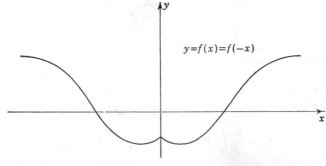

$$y = f(x) = f(-x)$$

FIG. 18

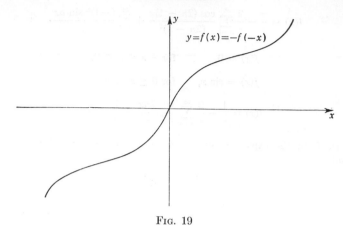

$$y = f(x) = -f(-x)$$

FIG. 19

FIG. 19

since the integrals represent the signed areas under the curves.[1] For example,

$$\int_{-a}^{a} \sin nx \, dx = 0,$$

since $\sin nx$ is an odd function.

Products of even and odd functions obey the rules

$$(\text{even})(\text{even}) = \text{even}, \qquad (\text{even})(\text{odd}) = \text{odd}, \qquad (\text{odd})(\text{odd}) = \text{even},$$

which correspond to the familiar rules

$$(+1)(+1) = +1, \qquad (+1)(-1) = -1, \qquad (-1)(-1) = +1.$$

For proof, let $F(x) = f(x)g(x)$, where $f(x)$ and $g(x)$ are even. Then

$$F(-x) = f(-x)g(-x) = f(x)g(x) = F(x),$$

which shows that the product $f(x)g(x)$ is even. The other two relations are verified similarly. As an example, the product $\cos nx \sin mx$ is odd because $\cos nx$ is even and $\sin mx$ is odd. Hence, (19-4) gives

$$\int_{-a}^{a} \cos mx \sin nx \, dx = 0$$

without detailed calculation.

The application of these results is facilitated by the following theorem:

Theorem. *If $f(x)$ defined in the interval $-\pi < x < \pi$ is even, the Fourier series has cosine terms only and the coefficients are given by*

$$a_n = \frac{2}{\pi} \int_0^{\pi} f(x) \cos nx \, dx, \qquad b_n = 0. \tag{19-5}$$

[1] An analytic proof of (19-3) and (19-4) may be based on (19-1) and (19-2).

If $f(x)$ is odd, the series has sine terms only and the coefficients are given by

$$b_n = \frac{2}{\pi} \int_0^\pi f(x) \sin nx \, dx, \qquad a_n = 0. \tag{19-6}$$

To see this, let $f(x)$ be even. Then $f(x) \cos nx$ is the product of an even function times an even function, hence is even. Therefore,

$$a_n = \frac{1}{\pi} \int_{-\pi}^\pi f(x) \cos nx \, dx = \frac{2}{\pi} \int_0^\pi f(x) \cos nx \, dx,$$

by (19-3). On the other hand $f(x) \sin nx$ is an even function times an odd function, hence is odd. By (19-4),

$$b_n = \int_{-\pi}^\pi f(x) \sin nx \, dx = 0.$$

The result (19-6) is established similarly.

For example, let $f(x) = x$ for $-\pi < x < \pi$ (Fig. 20). Since this function is odd, the Fourier series reduces to a sine series, and we need not bother to write down or calculate the cosine terms. It was found in the preceding section that

$$x = 2 \left(\sin x - \frac{\sin 2x}{2} + \frac{\sin 3x}{3} - \cdots \right). \tag{19-7}$$

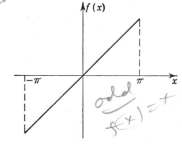

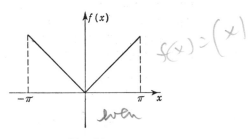

FIG. 20   FIG. 21

As another example, let $f(x) = |x|$ for $-\pi < x < \pi$ (Fig. 21). In this case $f(x)$ is even, so that $b_n = 0$ and

$$a_n = \frac{1}{\pi} \int_{-\pi}^\pi |x| \cos nx \, dx = \frac{2}{\pi} \int_0^\pi x \cos nx \, dx,$$

by use of (19-5). The integration gives $a_0 = \pi$ and

$$a_n = \frac{2}{n^2 \pi} [(-1)^n - 1].$$

Hence, for $-\pi < x < \pi$,

$$|x| = \frac{\pi}{2} - \frac{4}{\pi} \left(\frac{\cos x}{1} + \frac{\cos 3x}{3^2} + \frac{\cos 5x}{5^2} + \cdots \right). \tag{19-8}$$

The function to which this series converges is illustrated in Fig. 22, and the sum of the series (19-7) is presented graphically in Fig. 11.

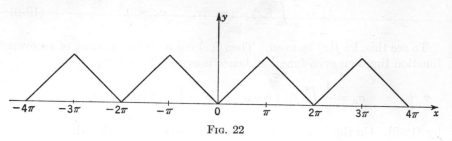

FIG. 22

Since $|x| = x$ for $x \geq 0$, the two series (19-7) and (19-8) converge to the same function x when $0 \leq x < \pi$. The first expression (19-7) is called the *Fourier sine series* for x, and (19-8) is the *Fourier cosine series*. Any function $f(x)$ defined in $(0,\pi)$ which satisfies the Dirichlet conditions can be expanded in a sine series and in a cosine series on $0 < x < \pi$. To obtain a sine series, we extend $f(x)$ over the interval $-\pi < x < 0$ in such a way that the extended function is odd. That is, we define

$$F(x) = f(x) \qquad \text{on } 0 < x < \pi,$$

$$F(x) = -f(|x|) \qquad \text{on } -\pi < x < 0.$$

The Fourier series for $F(x)$ consists of sine terms only, since $F(x)$ is odd. And the coefficients are given by (19-6) because $F(x) = f(x)$ on the interval $0 < x < \pi$. Similarly, if it is desired to obtain a cosine series for $f(x)$ on $0 < x < \pi$, the coefficients are given by (19-5).

Example: Obtain a cosine series and also a sine series for $\sin x$.
For the cosine series (19-5) gives $b_n = 0$ and, after a short calculation,

$$a_n = \frac{2}{\pi} \int_0^\pi \sin x \cos nx \, dx = \frac{2(1 + \cos n\pi)}{\pi(1 - n^2)}, \qquad n \neq 1.$$

For $n = 1$ the result of the integration is zero, and hence

$$\sin x = \frac{2}{\pi} - \frac{4}{\pi} \left(\frac{\cos 2x}{2^2 - 1} + \frac{\cos 4x}{4^2 - 1} + \frac{\cos 6x}{6^2 - 1} + \cdots \right)$$

when $0 < x < \pi$. Since the sum of the series is an even function, it converges to $|\sin x|$ rather than $\sin x$ when $-\pi \leq x \leq 0$. This shows, by periodicity, that the series converges to $|\sin x|$ for all values of x.

To obtain a sine series, (19-6) gives $a_n = 0$ and

$$b_n = \frac{2}{\pi} \int_0^\pi \sin x \sin nx \, dx = \begin{cases} 0, & \text{for } n \geq 2, \\ 1, & \text{for } n = 1. \end{cases}$$

Hence the Fourier sine series for $\sin x$ is $\sin x$, just as one would expect. That this is not a coincidence is shown by a UNIQUENESS THEOREM: *If two trigonometric series of the form* (18-1) *converge to the same sum for all values of* x, *then corresponding coefficients are equal.*[1]

PROBLEMS

1. Classify the following functions as even, odd, or neither:

$$x^2,\ x \sin x,\ x^3 \cos nx,\ x^4,\ \log \frac{1+x}{1-x},\ e^x,\ g(x^2).$$

2. Prove that any function can be represented as the sum of an even function and an odd function. *Hint:* $f(x) = \frac{1}{2}[f(x) + f(-x)] + \frac{1}{2}[f(x) - f(-x)]$.

3. For $0 < x < \pi$ show that

$$\frac{\pi}{4} = \sin x + \frac{\sin 3x}{3} + \frac{\sin 5x}{5} + \cdots.$$

Hint: Take $f(x) = \pi/4$ in (19-6).

4. A function is defined by $f(x) = \pi$ for $0 < x < \pi/2$ and $f(x) = 0$ elsewhere in $(-\pi,\pi)$. Find the Fourier series, the Fourier sine series, and the Fourier cosine series. In each case sketch the graph of the sum of the series for $-4\pi \le x < 4\pi$.

5. By taking $f(x) = x^2$ in (19-5) show that

$$x^2 = \frac{\pi^2}{3} + 4 \sum_{n=1}^{\infty} (-1)^n \frac{\cos nx}{n^2}$$

for $-\pi < x < \pi$, and deduce that

$$\frac{\pi^2}{12} = \frac{1}{1^2} - \frac{1}{2^2} + \frac{1}{3^2} - \frac{1}{4^2} + \cdots.$$

6. Show that if $f(x) = x$ for $0 < x < \pi/2$ and $f(x) = \pi - x$ for $\pi/2 < x < \pi$, then

$$f(x) = \frac{\pi}{4} - \frac{2}{\pi} \left(\frac{\cos 2x}{1^2} + \frac{\cos 6x}{3^2} + \frac{\cos 10x}{5^2} + \cdots \right).$$

7. Show that for $-\pi \le x \le \pi$,

$$\cos \alpha x = \frac{\sin \pi\alpha}{\pi\alpha} + \sum_{n=1}^{\infty} (-1)^n \frac{2\alpha \sin \pi\alpha}{\pi(\alpha^2 - n^2)} \cos nx,$$

when α is not an integer. Deduce

$$\cot \pi\alpha = \frac{1}{\pi} \left(\frac{1}{\alpha} - \sum_{n=1}^{\infty} \frac{2\alpha}{n^2 - \alpha^2} \right).$$

20. Extension of the Interval.

The methods developed up to this point restrict the interval of expansion to $(-\pi,\pi)$. In many problems it is desired to develop $f(x)$ in a Fourier series that will be valid over a wider interval. By letting the length of the interval increase indefinitely one may expect to get an expansion valid for all x.

---

[1] This theorem is due chiefly to Riemann. It is much deeper than the analogous statement for power series, and the proof would be quite out of place in the present book. See E. C. Titchmarsh, "The Theory of Functions," pp. 427–432, Oxford University Press, London, 1950.

To obtain an expansion valid on the interval $(-l,l)$, change the variable from x to lz/π. If $f(x)$ satisfies the Dirichlet conditions on $(-l,l)$, then the function $f(lz/\pi)$ can be developed in a Fourier series in z,

$$f\left(\frac{lz}{\pi}\right) = \frac{a_0}{2} + \sum_{n=1}^{\infty} a_n \cos nz + \sum_{n=1}^{\infty} b_n \sin nz \tag{20-1}$$

for $-\pi \le z < \pi$. Since $z = \pi x/l$, the series (20-1) becomes

$$f(x) = \frac{a_0}{2} + \sum_{n=1}^{\infty} a_n \cos \frac{n\pi x}{l} + \sum_{n=1}^{\infty} b_n \sin \frac{n\pi x}{l}. \tag{20-2}$$

By applying (18-4) to the series (20-1), we see that

$$a_n = \frac{1}{\pi} \int_{-\pi}^{\pi} f\left(\frac{lz}{\pi}\right) \cos nz \, dz = \frac{1}{l} \int_{-l}^{l} f(x) \cos \frac{n\pi x}{l} \, dx$$

and

$$b_n = \frac{1}{\pi} \int_{-\pi}^{\pi} f\left(\frac{lz}{\pi}\right) \sin nz \, dz = \frac{1}{l} \int_{-l}^{l} f(x) \sin \frac{n\pi x}{l} \, dx.$$

As an illustration we develop $f(x)$ in Fourier series in the interval $(-2,2)$ if $f(x) = 0$ for $-2 < x < 0$ and $f(x) = 1$ for $0 < x < 2$. Here

$$a_0 = \frac{1}{2}\left(\int_{-2}^{0} 0 \cdot dx + \int_{0}^{2} 1 \cdot dx\right) = 1,$$

$$a_n = \frac{1}{2}\left(\int_{-2}^{0} 0 \cdot \cos \frac{n\pi x}{2} \, dx + \int_{0}^{2} 1 \cdot \cos \frac{n\pi x}{2} \, dx\right) = \frac{1}{n\pi} \sin \frac{n\pi x}{2} \Big|_{0}^{2} = 0,$$

$$b_n = \frac{1}{2}\left(\int_{-2}^{0} 0 \cdot \sin \frac{n\pi x}{2} \, dx + \int_{0}^{2} 1 \cdot \sin \frac{n\pi x}{2} \, dx\right) = \frac{1}{n\pi}(1 - \cos n\pi).$$

Therefore,

$$f(x) = \frac{1}{2} + \frac{2}{\pi}\left(\sin \frac{\pi x}{2} + \frac{1}{3} \sin \frac{3\pi x}{2} + \frac{1}{5} \sin \frac{5\pi x}{2} + \cdots\right).$$

If n is any integer, then

$$\cos \frac{n\pi(x + 2l)}{l} = \cos\left(\frac{n\pi x}{l} + 2n\pi\right) = \cos\left(\frac{n\pi x}{l}\right),$$

and similarly for sines. Hence, each term of the series (20-2) has period $2l$, and therefore the sum also has period $2l$. For this reason the sum cannot represent an arbitrary function on $(-\infty,\infty)$; it represents periodic functions only.

Subject to the Dirichlet conditions, however, the function may be chosen arbitrarily on the interval $(-l,l)$, and it is natural to inquire if a representation for arbitrary functions on $(-\infty,\infty)$ might be obtained by letting $l \to \infty$. We shall see that such a representation is possible. The process leads to the so-called *Fourier integral theorem*, which has many practical applications.[1]

Assume that $f(x)$ satisfies the Dirichlet conditions in every interval $(-l,l)$ (no matter how large) and that the integral

$$M = \int_{-\infty}^{\infty} |f(x)| \, dx$$

converges. As we have just seen, $f(x)$ is given by (20-2), where [2]

$$a_n = \frac{1}{l} \int_{-l}^{l} f(t) \cos \frac{n\pi t}{l} \, dt, \qquad b_n = \frac{1}{l} \int_{-l}^{l} f(t) \sin \frac{n\pi t}{l} \, dt.$$

Substituting these values of the coefficients into (20-2) gives

$$f(x) = \frac{1}{2l} \int_{-l}^{l} f(t) \, dt + \frac{1}{l} \sum_{n=1}^{\infty} \int_{-l}^{l} f(t) \cos \frac{n\pi(t-x)}{l} \, dt \qquad (20\text{-}3)$$

when we recall that

$$\cos \frac{n\pi t}{l} \cos \frac{n\pi x}{l} + \sin \frac{n\pi t}{l} \sin \frac{n\pi x}{l} = \cos \frac{n\pi(t-x)}{l}.$$

Since $\int_{-\infty}^{\infty} |f(x)| \, dx$ is assumed to be convergent,

$$\left| \frac{1}{2l} \int_{-l}^{l} f(t) \, dt \right| \leq \frac{1}{2l} \int_{-l}^{l} |f(t)| \, dt \leq \frac{M}{2l},$$

which obviously tends to zero as l is allowed to increase indefinitely. Also, if the interval $(-l,l)$ is made large enough, the quantity π/l, which appears in the integrands of the sum, can be made as small as desired. Therefore, the sum in (20-3) can be written as

$$\frac{1}{\pi} \left[\Delta\alpha \int_{-l}^{l} f(t) \cos \Delta\alpha(t-x) \, dt \right.$$

$$+ \Delta\alpha \int_{-l}^{l} f(t) \cos 2 \, \Delta\alpha(t-x) \, dt$$

$$+ \cdots \cdots \cdots \cdots \cdots$$

$$+ \Delta\alpha \int_{-l}^{l} f(t) \cos n \, \Delta\alpha(t-x) \, dt$$

$$\left. + \cdots \cdots \cdots \cdots \cdots \cdots \right], \qquad (20\text{-}4)$$

where $\Delta\alpha = \pi/l$.

---

[1] Some of these applications are presented in Chap. 6.

[2] We use t as variable of integration to avoid confusion with the x in (20-2). If $f(x)$ is discontinuous at $x = x_0$, the left side of (20-2) means $\frac{1}{2}[f(x_0+) + f(x_0-)]$.

This sum suggests the definition of the definite integral of the function

$$F(\alpha) = \int_{-l}^{l} f(t) \cos \alpha(t - x) \, dt$$

in which the values of the function $F(\alpha)$ are calculated at the points

$$\frac{\pi}{l}, \frac{2\pi}{l}, \frac{3\pi}{l}, \ \ldots$$

Now, for large values of l

$$\int_{-l}^{l} f(t) \cos \alpha(t - x) \, dt$$

differs little from

$$\int_{-\infty}^{\infty} f(t) \cos \alpha(t - x) \, dt$$

and it appears plausible that as l increases indefinitely, the sum (20-4) will approach the limit

$$\frac{1}{\pi} \int_{0}^{\infty} d\alpha \int_{-\infty}^{\infty} f(t) \cos \alpha(t - x) \, dt.$$

If such is the case, then (20-3) can be written as

$$f(x) = \frac{1}{\pi} \int_{0}^{\infty} d\alpha \int_{-\infty}^{\infty} f(t) \cos \alpha(t - x) \, dt. \tag{20-5}$$

The foregoing discussion is heuristic and cannot be regarded as a rigorous proof. However, the validity of formula (20-5) can be established rigorously [1] if the function $f(x)$ satisfies the conditions enunciated above. The integral (20-5) bears the name of the *Fourier integral*.

Formula (20-5) assumes a simpler form if $f(x)$ is an even or an odd function. Expanding the integrand of (20-5) gives

$$\frac{1}{\pi} \int_{0}^{\infty} d\alpha \left[\int_{-\infty}^{\infty} f(t) \cos \alpha t \cos \alpha x \, dt + \int_{-\infty}^{\infty} f(t) \sin \alpha t \sin \alpha x \, dt \right]$$

for the right-hand member. If $f(t)$ is odd, then $f(t) \cos \alpha t$ is an odd function times an even function, hence is odd. Similarly, $f(t) \sin \alpha t$ is even when $f(t)$ is odd. Upon applying (19-4) to the first integral in the foregoing expression and (19-3) to the second integral, we see that

$$f(x) = \frac{2}{\pi} \int_{0}^{\infty} d\alpha \int_{0}^{\infty} f(t) \sin \alpha t \sin \alpha x \, dt \tag{20-6}$$

[1] See H. S. Carslaw, "Fourier's Series and Integrals," pp. 283–294, The Macmillan Company, New York, 1921, or E. C. Titchmarsh, "The Theory of Functions," p. 433, Oxford University Press, London, 1950.

when $f(x)$ is odd. A similar argument shows that if $f(x)$ is even, then

$$f(x) = \frac{2}{\pi} \int_0^\infty d\alpha \int_0^\infty f(t) \cos \alpha t \cos \alpha x \, dt. \qquad (20\text{-}7)$$

If $f(x)$ is defined only in the interval $(0,\infty)$, then both (20-6) and (20-7) may be used, since $f(x)$ may be thought to be defined in $(-\infty,0)$ so as to make it either odd or even. This corresponds to the fact that a function given on $(0,\pi)$ may be expanded in either a sine series or a cosine series.

Since the Fourier series converges to $\frac{1}{2}[f(x+) + f(x-)]$ at points of discontinuity, the Fourier integral does also. In particular for an odd function [1] the integral converges to zero at $x = 0$, and this fact is verified by setting $x = 0$ in (20-6).

Example: By (20-7) obtain the formula

$$\int_0^\infty \frac{\sin \alpha \cos \alpha x}{\alpha} \, d\alpha = \begin{cases} \pi/2, & \text{if } 0 \leq x < 1, \\ \pi/4, & \text{if } x = 1, \\ 0, & \text{if } x > 1. \end{cases}$$

We choose $f(x) = 1$ for $0 \leq x < 1$ and $f(x) = 0$ for $x > 1$. Then

$$\int_0^\infty f(t) \cos \alpha t \, dt = \int_0^1 \cos \alpha t \, dt = \frac{\sin \alpha}{\alpha}, \qquad \alpha \neq 0.$$

Substitution into (20-7) gives

$$\int_0^\infty \frac{\sin \alpha}{\alpha} \cos \alpha x \, d\alpha = \frac{\pi}{2} f(x)$$

after multiplying by $\pi/2$. Upon recalling the definition of $f(x)$, we see that the desired result is obtained for $0 \leq x < 1$ and for $x > 1$. The fact that the integral is $\pi/4$ when $x = 1$ follows from

$$\frac{1}{2} = \frac{f(1-) + f(1+)}{2}.$$

PROBLEMS

1. If $f(x)$ is an odd function on $(-l,l)$, show that the Fourier series takes the form

$$f(x) = \sum_{n=1}^\infty b_n \sin \frac{n\pi x}{l}, \qquad b_n = \frac{2}{l} \int_0^l f(x) \sin \frac{n\pi x}{l} \, dx.$$

Similarly, if $f(x)$ is even, then

$$f(x) = \frac{a_0}{2} + \sum_{n=1}^\infty a_n \cos \frac{n\pi x}{l}, \qquad a_n = \frac{2}{l} \int_0^l f(x) \cos \frac{n\pi x}{l} \, dx.$$

[1] It should be noted that every odd function, if defined at $x = 0$, satisfies $f(0) = 0$ [although for an even function $f(0)$ is arbitrary]. Hence a function defined for $x = 0$ must sometimes be redefined at $x = 0$ before it can be made into an odd function.

2. Expand the function defined by $f(x) = 1$ on $(0,2)$ and $f(x) = -1$ on $(-2,0)$.

3. Expand $f(x) = |x|$ in the interval $(-1,1)$.

4. Expand $f(x) = \cos \pi x$ in the interval $(-1,1)$.

5. Find the expansion in the series of cosines, if

$$f(x) = 1, \qquad \text{when } 0 < x < \pi,$$

$$f(x) = 0, \qquad \text{when } \pi < x < 2\pi.$$

Hint: Regard $f(x)$ as being an even function.

6. Expand

$$f(x) = \tfrac{1}{4} - x, \qquad \text{if } 0 < x < \tfrac{1}{2},$$

$$f(x) = x - \tfrac{3}{4}, \qquad \text{if } \tfrac{1}{2} < x < 1.$$

7. Show that the series

$$\frac{l}{\pi} \sum_{n=1}^{\infty} \frac{1}{n} \sin \frac{2n\pi x}{l}$$

represents $\tfrac{1}{2}l - x$ when $0 < x < l$.

8. Show, with the aid of (20-6) and (20-7), that

$$\int_0^\infty \frac{\alpha \sin \alpha x}{\alpha^2 + \beta^2} \, d\alpha = \frac{\pi}{2} e^{-\beta x}, \qquad \text{if } \beta > 0,$$

$$\int_0^\infty \frac{\cos \alpha x}{\alpha^2 + \beta^2} \, d\alpha = \frac{\pi}{2\beta} e^{-\beta x}, \qquad \text{if } \beta > 0.$$

Hint: Take $f(x) = e^{-\beta x}$.

9. An *integral equation* is an equation in which an unknown function appears under an integral sign. If $F(t)$ is known and $f(x)$ is to be found, the *integral equation of Fourier* is

$$\int_0^\infty f(x) \cos xt \, dx = F(t).$$

(a) Using (20-7) show that a solution is given by

$$f(x) = \frac{2}{\pi} \int_0^\infty F(t) \cos xt \, dt.$$

(b) State a similar integral equation which can be solved by use of (20-6), and solve it.

21. Complex Form of Fourier Series.   The Fourier series

$$f(x) = \frac{a_0}{2} + \sum_{n=1}^{\infty} (a_n \cos nx + b_n \sin nx) \tag{21-1}$$

with $\qquad a_n = \frac{1}{\pi} \int_{-\pi}^{\pi} f(t) \cos nt \, dt, \qquad b_n = \frac{1}{\pi} \int_{-\pi}^{\pi} f(t) \sin nt \, dt$

can be written, with the aid of the Euler formula [1]

$$e^{iu} = \cos u + i \sin u \tag{21-2}$$

[1] See Sec. 17.

in an equivalent form, namely,

$$f(x) = \sum_{n=-\infty}^{+\infty} c_n e^{inx},$$ (21-3)

where the coefficients c_n are defined by the equation

$$c_n = \frac{1}{2\pi} \int_{-\pi}^{\pi} f(t) e^{-int}\, dt.$$ (21-4)

The index of summation n in (21-3) runs through the set of all positive and negative integral values including zero.

The equivalence of (21-3) and (21-1) can be established in the following manner: Substituting from (21-2) in (21-4) gives, for $n > 0$,

$$c_n = \frac{1}{2\pi} \int_{-\pi}^{\pi} f(t)(\cos nt - i \sin nt)\, dt$$

$$= \frac{1}{2\pi} \int_{-\pi}^{\pi} f(t) \cos nt\, dt - \frac{i}{2\pi} \int_{-\pi}^{\pi} f(t) \sin nt\, dt$$

$$= \frac{a_n}{2} - i \frac{b_n}{2}.$$

A similar calculation gives

$$c_{-n} = \frac{a_n}{2} + i \frac{b_n}{2},$$

while

$$c_0 = \frac{a_0}{2}.$$

Now (21-3) can be written in the form

$$f(x) = c_0 + \sum_{n=1}^{\infty} c_n e^{inx} + \sum_{n=1}^{\infty} c_{-n} e^{-inx}.$$

Making use of the expressions for the c_n just found gives

$$f(x) = \frac{a_0}{2} + \sum_{n=1}^{\infty} \frac{a_n - ib_n}{2} e^{inx} + \sum_{n=1}^{\infty} \frac{a_n + ib_n}{2} e^{-inx}$$

$$= \frac{a_0}{2} + \sum_{n=1}^{\infty} a_n \frac{e^{inx} + e^{-inx}}{2} - i \sum_{n=1}^{\infty} b_n \frac{e^{inx} - e^{-inx}}{2}.$$

By (21-2),

$$e^{iu} + e^{-iu} = 2 \cos u \qquad \text{and} \qquad e^{iu} - e^{-iu} = 2i \sin u$$

and hence the latter series is identical with (21-1).

To illustrate the use of (21-4), consider the function $f(x) = e^{\alpha x}$ on $(-\pi, \pi)$. Here,

$$2\pi c_n = \int_{-\pi}^{\pi} e^{\alpha t} e^{-int}\, dt = \int_{-\pi}^{\pi} e^{(\alpha - in)t}\, dt = \frac{e^{(\alpha - in)t}}{\alpha - in}\Big|_{-\pi}^{\pi} = \frac{e^{\alpha\pi}e^{-in\pi} - e^{-\alpha\pi}e^{in\pi}}{\alpha - in}.$$

Since (21-2) gives $e^{\pm in\pi} = \cos(\pm n\pi) = (-1)^n$, we obtain

$$c_n = \frac{e^{\alpha\pi} - e^{-\alpha\pi}}{2\pi}\frac{(-1)^n}{\alpha - in} = \frac{\sinh \pi\alpha}{\pi}\frac{(-1)^n}{\alpha^2 + n^2}(\alpha + in),$$

and hence by (21-3),

$$e^{\alpha x} = \frac{\sinh \pi\alpha}{\pi}\sum_{n=-\infty}^{\infty}\frac{(-1)^n}{\alpha^2 + n^2}(\alpha + in)e^{inx}. \tag{21-5}$$

The methods of the last section yield

$$f(x) = \sum_{n=-\infty}^{\infty} c_n e^{in\pi x/l}, \quad \text{with } c_n = \frac{1}{2l}\int_{-l}^{l} f(t)e^{-in\pi t/l}\, dt, \tag{21-6}$$

for the expansion on an arbitrary interval $(-l, l)$. Upon letting $l \to \infty$, we obtain the Fourier integral theorem in the form

$$f(x) = \lim_{A \to \infty}\frac{1}{2\pi}\int_{-A}^{A} d\alpha \int_{-\infty}^{\infty} f(t)e^{i\alpha(x-t)}\, dt \tag{21-7}$$

when $f(x)$ satisfies the conditions postulated for (20-5).
   If

$$g(u) = \frac{1}{\sqrt{2\pi}}\int_{-\infty}^{\infty} e^{-iux}f(x)\, dx, \tag{21-8}$$

then (21-7) gives, after renaming some of the variables,

$$f(x) = \lim_{A \to \infty}\frac{1}{\sqrt{2\pi}}\int_{-A}^{A} e^{iux}g(u)\, du. \tag{21-9}$$

The transform **T** defined by

$$\mathbf{T}(f) = \frac{1}{\sqrt{2\pi}}\int_{-\infty}^{\infty} e^{-iux}f(x)\, dx$$

is called the *Fourier transform*; it is one of the most powerful tools in the whole repertoire of modern analysis. Although **T** is related to the Laplace transform **L** introduced in Appendix B, **T** is much easier to invert; that is, one can readily find $f(x)$ by (21-9) when $\mathbf{T}(f)$ is known.

PROBLEMS

1. Derive (21-6) from (21-3) and (21-4).

2. (a) Show that

$$a_0 = 2c_0, \qquad a_n = c_n + c_{-n}, \qquad b_n = i(c_n - c_{-n})$$

[and hence the real form (21-1) can be deduced from the complex form (21-3)].

(b) By applying your result (a) to (21-5) obtain the real Fourier series (21-1) for $e^{\alpha x}$.

$$\int \sin^2 u \, du = \frac{u}{2} - \frac{\sin 2u}{4} \qquad \int \cos^2 u \, du = \frac{u}{2} + \frac{\sin 2u}{4}$$

3. By setting $x = 0$ in (21-5) obtain the expansion

$$\frac{\pi}{\alpha \sinh \pi\alpha} = \sum_{n=-\infty}^{\infty} \frac{(-1)^n}{\alpha^2 + n^2}.$$

get $\sin A \sin B$
etc.

ADDITIONAL TOPICS IN FOURIER SERIES

22. Orthogonal Functions. A sequence of functions $\theta_n(x)$ is said to be *orthogonal* on the interval (a,b) if

$$\int_a^b \theta_m(x)\theta_n(x)\, dx \begin{cases} = 0 & \text{for } m \neq n, \\ \neq 0 & \text{for } m = n. \end{cases} \qquad (22\text{-}1)$$

conditions.

For example, the sequence

$$\theta_1(x) = \sin x, \qquad \theta_2(x) = \sin 2x, \qquad \ldots, \qquad \theta_n(x) = \sin nx, \qquad \ldots$$

is orthogonal on $(0,\pi)$ because

$$\int_0^\pi \theta_m(x)\theta_n(x)\, dx = \int_0^\pi \sin mx \sin nx \, dx = \begin{cases} 0 & \text{for } m \neq n, \\ \pi/2 & \text{for } m = n. \end{cases}$$

The sequence

In general $1, \sin mx, \cos mx$

$$1, \sin x, \cos x, \sin 2x, \cos 2x, \ldots \qquad (22\text{-}2)$$

do's odd's Even walk

is orthogonal on $(0,2\pi)$, though not on $(0,\pi)$.

In the foregoing sections the functions (22-2) were used to form Fourier series. Actually, one may form series analogous to Fourier series by means of any orthogonal set. These generalized Fourier series are an indispensable aid in electromagnetic theory, acoustics, heat flow, and many other branches of mathematical physics.[1]

The formula for Fourier coefficients is especially simple if the integral (22-1) has the value 1 for $m = n$. The functions $\theta_n(x)$ are then said to be *normalized*, and $\{\theta_n(x)\}$ is called an *orthonormal* set. If

$$\int_a^b [\theta_n(x)]^2 \, dx = A_n$$

in (22-1), it is easily seen that the functions

$$\phi_n(x) = (A_n)^{-\frac{1}{2}}\theta_n(x)$$

are orthonormal; in other words,

orthonormal functions

$$\int_a^b \phi_m(x)\phi_n(x)\, dx \begin{cases} = 0 & \text{for } m \neq n, \\ = 1 & \text{for } m = n. \end{cases} \qquad (22\text{-}3)$$

For example, since

$$\int_0^{2\pi} 1\, dx = 2\pi, \qquad \int_0^{2\pi} \sin^2 nx \, dx = \pi, \qquad \int_0^{2\pi} \cos^2 nx \, dx = \pi$$

[1] See Chap. 6.

$$\sinh x = \frac{e^x - e^{-x}}{2}, \qquad \cosh x = \frac{e^x + e^{-x}}{2}$$

etc.

for $n \geq 1$, the orthonormal set corresponding to the orthogonal set (22-2) is

$$(2\pi)^{-\frac{1}{2}}, \ \pi^{-\frac{1}{2}} \sin x, \ \pi^{-\frac{1}{2}} \cos x, \ \ldots, \ \pi^{-\frac{1}{2}} \sin nx, \ \pi^{-\frac{1}{2}} \cos nx, \ \ldots$$

The product of two different functions in this set gives zero but the square of each function gives 1, when integrated from zero to 2π.

Let $\{\phi_n(x)\}$ be an orthonormal set of functions on (a,b), and suppose that another function $f(x)$ is to be expanded in the form

$$f(x) = c_1\phi_1(x) + c_2\phi_2(x) + \cdots + c_n\phi_n(x) + \cdots. \qquad (22\text{-}4)$$

To determine the coefficients c_n we multiply by $\phi_n(x)$, getting

$$f(x)\phi_n(x) = c_1\phi_1(x)\phi_n(x) + \cdots + c_n[\phi_n(x)]^2 + \cdots.$$

Here, the terms not written involve products $\phi_n(x)\phi_m(x)$ with $m \neq n$. If we integrate from a to b, these terms disappear, and hence

$$\int_a^b f(x)\phi_n(x)\ dx = \int_a^b c_n[\phi_n(x)]^2\ dx = c_n. \qquad (22\text{-}5)$$

According to Theorem III, Sec. 7, the term-by-term integration is justified when the series is uniformly convergent and the functions are continuous. The foregoing procedure shows that if $f(x)$ has an expansion of the desired type, then the coefficients c_n must be given by (22-5). In the following section (22-5) is obtained in a different manner, which does not assume uniform convergence.

The formula (22-5) is called the *Euler-Fourier formula*, the coefficients c_n are called the *Fourier coefficients* of $f(x)$ with respect to $\{\phi_n(x)\}$, and the resulting series (22-4) is called the *Fourier series* of $f(x)$ with respect to $\{\phi_n(x)\}$. The reader can verify that the foregoing results applied to the sequence (22-2) yield the ordinary Fourier series, as described in the foregoing sections.

Orthogonal sets of functions are obtained in practice by solving differential equations, and this possibility will be discussed next. On a given interval $a \leq x \leq b$ consider the equation

$$\frac{d}{dx}\left[p(x)\frac{dy}{dx} \right] + q(x)y = \lambda r(x)y, \qquad \lambda = \text{const}, \qquad (22\text{-}6)$$

or, in abbreviated form,

$$(py')' + qy = \lambda ry, \qquad ' = \frac{d}{dx}.$$

It will be convenient to require the additional condition

$$\int_a^b ry^2\ dx \neq 0$$

which, in particular, rules out the trivial solution $y \equiv 0$.

Let y_m be a solution when λ has the value λ_m, and let y_n be a solution when λ has a different value, λ_n. Thus,

$$(py_m')' + qy_m = \lambda_m r y_m, \tag{22-7}$$

$$(py_n')' + qy_n = \lambda_n r y_n. \tag{22-8}$$

If (22-7) is multiplied by y_n and (22-8) by y_m, we get

$$y_n(py_m')' - y_m(py_n')' = \lambda_m r y_m y_n - \lambda_n r y_m y_n \tag{22-9}$$

after subtracting the resulting expressions. Since

$$[y_n(py_m') - y_m(py_n')]' = y_n(py_m')' + y_n'(py_m') - y_m(py_n')' - y_m'(py_n')$$
$$= \text{left side of (22-9)},$$

the foregoing result (22-9) may be written

$$\frac{d}{dx}[p(y_n y_m' - y_m y_n')] = (\lambda_m - \lambda_n) r y_m y_n.$$

Integrating from a to b yields the fundamental formula

$$p(y_n y_m' - y_m y_n') \Big|_a^b = (\lambda_m - \lambda_n) \int_a^b r y_m y_n \, dx, \tag{22-10}$$

when r is continuous.

If the conditions at a and b are such that the left side of (22-10) is zero, we can deduce

$$\int_a^b r y_m y_n \, dx = 0, \qquad m \neq n, \tag{22-11}$$

since $\lambda_m \neq \lambda_n$. The relation (22-11) may be written

$$\int_a^b (\sqrt{r}\, y_m)(\sqrt{r}\, y_n) \, dx = 0, \qquad m \neq n,$$

and hence the sequence $\theta_n(x)$ defined by

$$\theta_n(x) = \sqrt{r}\, y_n = \sqrt{r(x)}\, y_n(x) \tag{22-12}$$

satisfies the orthogonality criterion (22-1). An orthonormal set $\{\phi_n\}$ may be obtained from $\{\theta_n\}$ as described previously.

When $r(x)$ is negative, the foregoing process does not yield a real sequence $\{\theta_n(x)\}$, and it is better to work directly with (22-11). Functions y_n satisfying (22-11) are said to be orthogonal *with respect to the weighting function* $r(x)$; the definition (22-1) corresponds to the case $r \equiv 1$. Fourier series based on the more general concept of orthogonality (22-11) are quite analogous to those based on (22-1) (cf. Prob. 2).

Example 1. Show that the sequence (22-2) is orthogonal on the interval $(-\pi, \pi)$.

Since $\sin nx$ and $\cos nx$ satisfy $y'' = -n^2 y$, we may use the formula (22-10) with $p = r = 1$. The result is

$$(y_n y_m' - y_m y_n') \Big|_{-\pi}^{\pi} = (-m^2 + n^2) \int_{-\pi}^{\pi} y_m y_n \, dx, \tag{22-13}$$

where $y_n = \sin nx$ or $\cos nx$ and $y_m = \sin mx$ or $\cos mx$. Since $y_n y_m' - y_m y_n'$ has period 2π, the value at π is the same as the value at $-\pi$, and hence the left side of (22-13) is zero. This yields the desired orthogonality except in the case $m = n$. If $m = n$, however, the relevant integral may be evaluated by inspection:

$$\int_{-\pi}^{\pi} \cos nx \sin nx \, dx = \int_{-\pi}^{\pi} \tfrac{1}{2} \sin 2nx \, dx = 0.$$

Example 2. Show that the Legendre functions $P_n(x)$ are orthogonal on the interval $(-1,1)$.

Legendre's equation (13-8) may be written

$$[(1 - x^2)y']' = \lambda y,$$

where λ is constant; $\lambda = -n(n+1)$ when $y = P_n(x)$. The special case $p = (1 - x^2)$, $q = 0$, $r = 1$ in (22-6) and (22-10) yields

$$(1 - x^2)(P_n P_m' - P_m P_n') \Big|_{-1}^{1} = [-m(m+1) + n(n+1)]\int_{-1}^{1} P_m(x)P_n(x) \, dx.$$

Since $(1 - x^2)$ vanishes at ± 1, the left side is zero and the orthogonality follows. It can be shown [1] also that

$$\int_{-1}^{1} [P_n(x)]^2 \, dx = \frac{2}{2n+1},$$

and hence the corresponding orthonormal set is

$$\varphi_n(x) = (n + \tfrac{1}{2})^{1/2} P_n(x).$$

Example 3. Let the sequence $\rho_1, \rho_2, \ldots$ be the distinct positive roots of the equation $J_\mu(x) = 0$, so that $J_\mu(\rho_n) = 0$. If $\mu \geq 0$ the functions

$$\phi_n(x) = \sqrt{2x}\, \frac{J_\mu(\rho_n x)}{J_\mu'(\rho_n)} \tag{22-14}$$

are orthonormal on the interval $(0,1)$.

By (14-1) it is found that $y = J_\mu(\rho x)$ satisfies

$$(xy')' - \frac{\mu^2 y}{x} = \lambda xy, \qquad \lambda = -\rho^2$$

and hence (22-10) holds with $p = r = x$. If we choose $y_n = J_\mu(\rho x)$ and $y_m = J_\mu(\rho_m x)$, the left side of (22-10) is

$$x\left[J_\mu(\rho x) \frac{d}{dx} J_\mu(\rho_m x) - J_\mu(\rho_m x) \frac{d}{dx} J_\mu(\rho x) \right] \Big|_0^1,$$

which reduces to $J_\mu(\rho)\rho_m J_\mu'(\rho_m)$, since $J_\mu(\rho_m) = 0$. It follows that

$$(-\rho_m^2 + \rho^2)\int_0^1 xJ_\mu(\rho_m x)J_\mu(\rho x) \, dx = \rho_m J_\mu(\rho)J_\mu'(\rho_m). \tag{22-15}$$

[1] See E. J. Whittaker and G. N. Watson, "Modern Analysis," p. 305, Cambridge University Press, London, 1952; J. M. MacRobert, "Spherical Harmonics," p. 92, Dover Publications, New York, 1948; W. E. Byerly, "Fourier Series and Spherical Harmonics," p. 170, Ginn & Company, Boston, 1893.

Since $J_\mu(\rho_n) = 0$, the choice $\rho = \rho_n$ in (22-15) yields

$$\int_0^1 x J_\mu(\rho_m x) J_\mu(\rho_n x)\, dx = 0, \qquad m \ne n. \tag{22-16}$$

Moreover, differentiating (22-15) with respect to ρ we get

$$2\rho \int_0^1 x J_\mu(\rho_m x) J_\mu(\rho x)\, dx + (\rho^2 - \rho_m^2)\int_0^1 x^2 J_\mu(\rho_m x) J_\mu'(\rho x)\, dx = \rho_m J_\mu'(\rho) J_\mu'(\rho_m),$$

which reduces to

$$2\int_0^1 x[J_\mu(\rho_m x)]^2\, dx = [J_\mu'(\rho_m)]^2 \tag{22-17}$$

when $\rho = \rho_m$. Equations (22-16) and (22-17) show that the sequence (22-14) is ortho-normal on (0,1), as desired.

The fact that the equation $J_\mu(x) = 0$ has infinitely many roots ρ_n is established in treatises on Bessel functions; analysis of such questions for general differential equations constitutes the so-called *Sturm-Liouville theory*. It can be shown that Fourier series of Bessel or Legendre functions actually converge; that is, an analogue of Dirichlet's theorem holds in such cases.[1] These questions are treated, from a very general point of view, in a branch of analysis known as *spectral theory*.

PROBLEMS

1. By considering the equation $y'' = \lambda y$ show that the sequence $\sin n\pi x/l$ is orthogonal on the interval (0,l), and construct the corresponding orthonormal set.

2. Suppose an arbitrary function $f(x)$ is expanded in a uniformly convergent series $f(x) = \Sigma c_n y_n(x)$, where y_n are the functions in (22-11). Show that

$$c_n = \left(\int_a^b r(x)f(x)y_n(x)\, dx\right)\left(\int_a^b r(x)[y_n(x)]^2\, dx\right)^{-1}.$$

Hint: Multiply the given series by $r(x)y_n(x)$, and integrate term by term.

3. If $m + n$ is positive, show that

$$(m^2 - n^2)\int_0^l x^{-1}J_m(x)J_n(x)\, dx = l[J_n(l)J_m'(l) - J_m(l)J_n'(l)].$$

Hint: Bessel's equation (14-1) may be written

$$(xy')' + xy = \frac{\lambda}{x}y,$$

where $\lambda = n^2$ when $y = J_n(x)$. To avoid difficulty at $x = 0$ one may consider $\int_\epsilon^l$ and let $\epsilon \to 0$. The convergence follows from (14-9), since (14-9) gives

$$J_m(x)J_n(x) \sim (\text{const})\, x^{m+n}, \qquad \text{as } x \to 0.$$

4. It can be shown that as $|x| \to \infty$,

$$J_n(x) \sim \sqrt{\frac{2}{\pi x}}\cos\left(x - \frac{\pi}{4} - \frac{n\pi}{2}\right), \qquad J_n'(x) \sim -\sqrt{\frac{2}{\pi x}}\sin\left(x - \frac{\pi}{4} - \frac{n\pi}{2}\right).$$

[1] E. A. Coddington and N. Levinson, "Theory of Ordinary Differential Equations," chap. **7**, McGraw-Hill Book Company, Inc., New York, 1955.

By letting $l \to \infty$ in Prob. 3, deduce

$$(m^2 - n^2) \int_0^\infty x^{-1} J_m(x) J_n(x) \, dx = \frac{2}{\pi} \sin (m - n) \frac{\pi}{2}, \qquad m + n > 0.$$

5. If $\phi_n(x)$ are orthonormal on the interval $(0,1)$, show that

$$\psi_n(x) = a^{-\frac{1}{2}} \phi_n(x/a)$$

are orthonormal on the interval $(0,a)$.

23. The Mean Convergence of Fourier Series. If we try to approximate a function $f(x)$ by another function $p_n(x)$, the quantity

$$|f(x) - p_n(x)| \qquad \text{or} \qquad [f(x) - p_n(x)]^2 \qquad (23\text{-}1)$$

gives a measure of the error in the approximation. The sequence $p_n(x)$ converges to $f(x)$ whenever the expressions (23-1) approach zero as $n \to \infty$.

These measures of the error are appropriate for discussing convergence at any fixed point x. But it is often useful to have a measure of error which applies simultaneously to a whole interval of x values, $a \le x \le b$. Such a measure is easily found if we integrate (23-1) from a to b:

$$\int_a^b |f(x) - p_n(x)| \, dx \qquad \text{or} \qquad \int_a^b [f(x) - p_n(x)]^2 \, dx. \qquad (23\text{-}2)$$

These expressions are called the *mean* [1] *error* and *mean-square error*, respectively. If either expression (23-2) approaches zero as $n \to \infty$, we say that the sequence $p_n(x)$ converges *in mean* to $f(x)$ and we speak of *mean convergence*.

Even though (23-2) involves an integration which is not present in (23-1), for Fourier series it is much easier to discuss the mean-square error and the corresponding mean convergence than the ordinary convergence. Such a discussion is presented now.

Let $\phi_n(x)$ be a set of functions normal and orthogonal on $a \le x \le b$, so that, as in the last section,

$$\int_a^b \phi_n(x) \phi_m(x) \, dx = \begin{cases} 0 & \text{for } m \ne n, \\ 1 & \text{for } m = n. \end{cases} \qquad (23\text{-}3)$$

We seek to approximate $f(x)$ by a linear combination of $\phi_n(x)$,

$$p_n(x) = a_1 \phi_1(x) + a_2 \phi_2(x) + \cdots + a_n \phi_n(x),$$

in such a way that the mean-square error (23-2) is minimum: [2]

---

[1] Note that if the expressions (23-2) are multiplied by $1/(b - a)$, we get precisely the mean values of the corresponding expressions (23-1).

[2] We use f and ϕ_n as abbreviations for $f(x)$ and $\phi_n(x)$, respectively. It is assumed that f and ϕ_n are integrable on $a \le x \le b$. If the integrals are improper, the convergence of $\int_a^b f^2 \, dx$ and $\int_a^b \phi_n^2 \, dx$ is required.

$$E \equiv \int_a^b [f - (a_1\phi_1 + \cdots + a_n\phi_n)]^2 \, dx = \min. \qquad (23\text{-}4)$$

Upon expanding the bracket we see that (23-4) yields

$$\int_a^b f^2 \, dx - 2\int_a^b f(a_1\phi_1 + \cdots + a_n\phi_n) \, dx + \int_a^b (a_1\phi_1 + \cdots + a_n\phi_n)^2 \, dx.$$
$$(23\text{-}5)$$

If the Fourier coefficients of f relative to ϕ_k are denoted by

$$c_k = \int_a^b f\phi_k \, dx,$$

then the second integral (23-5) is

$$\int_a^b f(a_1\phi_1 + \cdots + a_n\phi_n) \, dx = a_1c_1 + a_2c_2 + \cdots + a_nc_n.$$

The third integral (23-5) may be written

$$\int_a^b (a_1\phi_1 + \cdots + a_n\phi_n)(a_1\phi_1 + \cdots + a_n\phi_n) \, dx$$
$$= \int_a^b (a_1^2\phi_1^2 + a_2^2\phi_2^2 + \cdots + a_n^2\phi_n^2 + \cdots) \, dx$$
$$= a_1^2 + \cdots + a_n^2,$$

where the second group of terms "$+ \cdots$" involves cross products $\phi_i\phi_j$ with $i \neq j$. By (23-3) these terms integrate to zero, and the expression reduces to the value indicated.

Hence, (23-5) yields

$$E \equiv \int_a^b f^2 \, dx - 2\sum_{k=1}^n a_kc_k + \sum_{k=1}^n a_k^2 \qquad (23\text{-}6)$$

for the mean-square error in the approximation. Inasmuch as

$$-2a_kc_k + a_k^2 \equiv -c_k^2 + (a_k - c_k)^2,$$

the error E in (23-6) is also equal to

$$E = \int_a^b f^2 \, dx - \sum_{k=1}^n c_k^2 + \sum_{k=1}^n (a_k - c_k)^2, \qquad (23\text{-}7)$$

and we have established a theorem of central importance:

THEOREM I.   *If ϕ_n is a set of normal and orthogonal functions, the mean-square error (23-4) may be written in the form (23-7), where c_k are the Fourier coefficients of f relative to ϕ_k.*

By going back and forth between the two expressions (23-4) and (23-7), one obtains a number of interesting and significant theorems with the greatest ease. In the first place, the terms $(a_k - c_k)^2$ in (23-7) are positive unless $a_k = c_k$, in which case they are zero. Hence the choice of a_k that makes E minimum is obviously $a_k = c_k$, and we have the following:

Corollary 1. The partial sums of the Fourier series

$$c_1\phi_1 + \cdots + c_n\phi_n, \qquad c_k = \int_a^b f\phi_k \, dx$$

give a smaller mean-square error $\int_a^b (f - p_n)^2 \, dx$ *than is given by any other linear combination*

$$p_n = a_1\phi_1 + \cdots + a_n\phi_n.$$

Upon setting $a_k = c_k$ in (23-7), we see that the minimum value of the error is

$$\min E = \int_a^b f^2 \, dx - \sum_{k=1}^n c_k^2. \tag{23-8}$$

Now, the expression (23-4) shows that $E \geq 0$, because the integrand in (23-4), being a square, is not negative. Since $E \geq 0$ for all choices of a_k, it is clear that the minimum of E (which arises when $a_k = c_k$) is also ≥ 0. The expression (23-8) yields, then,

$$\int_a^b f^2 \, dx - \sum_{k=1}^n c_k^2 \geq 0 \qquad \text{or} \qquad \sum_{k=1}^n c_k^2 \leq \int_a^b f^2 \, dx.$$

Upon letting $n \to \infty$ we obtain [1]

Corollary 2. If $c_k = \int_a^b f\phi_k \, dx$ *are the Fourier coefficients of f relative to the orthonormal set* ϕ_n *then the series* Σc_k^2 *converges and satisfies the so-called Bessel inequality*

$$\sum_{k=1}^\infty c_k^2 \leq \int_a^b [f(x)]^2 \, dx. \tag{23-9}$$

Because the general term of a convergent series must approach zero (Sec. 1, Theorem I) we deduce the following from Corollary 2:

Corollary 3. The Fourier coefficients $c_n = \int_a^b f\phi_n \, dx$ *tend to zero as* $n \to \infty$.

For applications it is important to know whether or not the mean square error approaches zero as $n \to \infty$. Evidently the error approaches zero, for some choice of the a_ks, only if the *minimum* error (23-8) does so. Letting $n \to \infty$ in (23-8) we get the so-called *Parseval equality*

$$\int_a^b f^2 \, dx - \sum_{k=1}^\infty c_k^2 = 0$$

as the condition for zero error:

[1] Since $c_k^2 \geq 0$, the sequence $\sum_{k=1}^n c_k^2$ is nondecreasing. We have just seen that it is bounded, and hence the limit exists by the fundamental principle (Sec. 1).

Corollary 4. If f is approximated by the partial sums of its Fourier series, the mean-square error approaches zero as $n \rightarrow \infty$ if, and only if, Bessel's inequality (23-9) becomes Parseval's equality

$$\sum_{n=1}^{\infty} c_n^2 = \int_a^b [f(x)]^2 \, dx. \tag{23-10}$$

In other words, the Fourier series converges to f in the mean-square sense if, and only if, (23-10) holds. If this happens for every choice of f, the set $\phi_n(x)$ is said to be *closed*. A closed set, then, is a set that can be used for mean-square approximation of arbitrary functions. It can be shown that the trigonometrical functions $\cos nx$ and $\sin nx$ are closed on $0 \leq x \leq 2\pi$, though the proof is too long for inclusion here.[1]

A set $\phi_n(x)$ is said to be *complete* if there is no nontrivial function [2] $f(x)$ which is orthogonal to all of the ϕ_ns. That is, the set is complete if

$$c_k = \int_a^b f(x)\phi_k(x) \, dx = 0 \qquad \text{for } k = 1, 2, 3, \ldots, \tag{23-11}$$

implies that

$$\int_a^b [f(x)]^2 \, dx = 0. \tag{23-12}$$

Now, whenever (23-10) holds, (23-11) yields (23-12) at once. Hence we have:

Corollary 5. Every closed set $\phi_n(x)$ is complete.

The converse is also true: *Every complete set is closed*. This converse, however, requires a more general integral than that of Riemann. The generalized integral is known as the *Lebesgue* integral; it was first constructed to deal with this very problem. A brief description of the Lebesgue integral is given in Appendix C.

The notions of *closure* and *completeness* have simple analogues in the elementary theory of vectors. Thus, a set of vectors V_1, V_2, V_3 is said to be *closed* if every vector V can be written in the form

$$V = c_1 V_1 + c_2 V_2 + c_3 V_3$$

for some choice of the constants c_k. The set of vectors V_1, V_2, V_3 is said to be *complete* if there is no nontrivial vector orthogonal to all of them. That is, the set is complete if the condition

$$V \cdot V_k = 0 \qquad \text{for } k = 1, 2, 3$$

implies $V \cdot V = 0$.

In this setting, it is obvious that closure and completeness are equivalent, for both conditions simply state that the three vectors V_1, V_2, V_3 are not coplanar. These matters are taken up more fully in Chap. 4.

---

[1] See E. C. Titchmarsh, "The Theory of Functions," p. 414, Oxford University Press, London, 1950.

[2] In the theory of mean convergence $f(x)$ is regarded as *trivial* if $f(x) = 0$ for so many values of x that $\int_a^b [f(x)]^2 \, dx = 0$.

PROBLEMS

1. (*a*) Show that Parseval's equality takes the form

$$\frac{1}{\pi} \int_0^{2\pi} [f(x)]^2 \, dx = \frac{1}{2} a_0^2 + \sum_{n=1}^{\infty} (a_n^2 + b_n^2)$$

when $\phi_n(x)$ are the trigonometric functions on $(0, 2\pi)$. (*b*) Specialize to sine and cosine series on $(0, \pi)$.

2. It is desired to approximate 1 by

$$p(x) = a_1 \sin x + a_2 \sin 2x + a_3 \sin 3x$$

in such a way that $\int_0^\pi [1 - p(x)]^2 \, dx$ is minimum. How should the coefficients a_i be determined?

3. Give a direct proof that as $n \to \infty$,

$$\int_0^{2\pi} f(x) \sin nx \, dx \to 0, \qquad \int_0^{2\pi} f(x) \cos nx \, dx \to 0,$$

if $f(x)$ is periodic of period 2π and has a continuous derivative $f'(x)$. *Hint:* Integrate by parts.

4. Obtain the formula $a_k = c_k$ from (23-4) by using the fact that $\partial E / \partial a_k = 0$ at the minimum value of E.

24. The Pointwise Convergence of Fourier Series.

We shall now obtain an explicit formula for the difference between a function and the nth partial sum of its (trigonometric) Fourier series. The formula will enable us to establish the convergence for a class of functions which includes all the examples given in this book.

If $f(x)$ is a bounded integrable function of period 2π, the nth partial sum of its Fourier series is

$$s_n(x) = \frac{1}{2} a_0 + \sum_{k=1}^{n} (a_k \cos kx + b_k \sin kx), \qquad (24\text{-}1)$$

where the coefficients are given by

$$a_k = \frac{1}{\pi} \int_{-\pi}^{\pi} f(t) \cos kt \, dt, \qquad b_k = \frac{1}{\pi} \int_{-\pi}^{\pi} f(t) \sin kt \, dt. \qquad (24\text{-}2)$$

Substituting (24-2) into the series (24-1) we get

$$s_n(x) = \frac{1}{\pi} \int_{-\pi}^{\pi} f(t) \left[\frac{1}{2} + \sum_{k=1}^{n} (\cos kt \cos kx + \sin kt \sin kx) \right] dt$$

$$= \frac{1}{\pi} \int_{-\pi}^{\pi} f(t) \left[\frac{1}{2} + \sum_{k=1}^{n} \cos k(t - x) \right] dt.$$

If we define the so-called *Dirichlet kernel* by

$$D_n(u) = \frac{1}{2} + \sum_{k=1}^{n} \cos ku, \tag{24-3}$$

the foregoing result takes the simpler form

$$s_n(x) = \frac{1}{\pi} \int_{-\pi}^{\pi} f(t) D_n(t - x) \, dt. \tag{24-4}$$

Setting $t - x = u$ in (24-4) yields

$$s_n(x) = \frac{1}{\pi} \int_{-\pi-x}^{\pi-x} f(x + u) D_n(u) \, du. \tag{24-5}$$

Now, $D_n(u)$ has period 2π by inspection of (24-3), and $f(x)$ also has period 2π. Hence, the integral of $f(u + x)D_n(u)$ over any interval of length 2π is the same as the integral over any other interval of length 2π, and (24-5) may be replaced by

$$s_n(x) = \frac{1}{\pi} \int_{-\pi}^{\pi} f(x + u) D_n(u) \, du. \tag{24-6}$$

Since $D_n(-u) = D_n(u)$ by (24-3), we may replace u by $-u$ in (24-6) to obtain the alternative form

$$s_n(x) = \frac{1}{\pi} \int_{-\pi}^{\pi} f(x - u) D_n(u) \, du. \tag{24-7}$$

The sum of (24-6) and (24-7) yields

$$2s_n(x) = \frac{1}{\pi} \int_{-\pi}^{\pi} [f(x + u) + f(x - u)] D_n(u) \, du.$$

Since the integrand is an even function of u, the integral from 0 to π is half the integral from $-\pi$ to π, and we have thus established that

$$s_n(x) = \frac{1}{\pi} \int_{0}^{\pi} [f(x + u) + f(x - u)] D_n(u) \, du. \tag{24-8}$$

To introduce $f(x)$ into our considerations, we observe that

$$\frac{1}{2} = \frac{1}{\pi} \int_{0}^{\pi} D_n(u) \, du, \tag{24-9}$$

since the terms involving $\cos ku$ in (24-3) integrate to zero. If (24-9) is multiplied by $2f(x)$ (which is constant with respect to the integration variable u), we get

$$f(x) = \frac{1}{\pi} \int_{0}^{\pi} 2f(x) D_n(u) \, du. \tag{24-10}$$

Subtracting (24-10) from (24-8) gives the fundamental formula

$$s_n(x) - f(x) = \frac{1}{\pi} \int_0^\pi [f(x+u) - 2f(x) + f(x-u)]D_n(u)\, du, \quad (24\text{-}11)$$

which will now be used to study the convergence of $s_n(x)$ to $f(x)$.

We shall say that $f(x)$ is *piecewise smooth* if the graph of $f(x)$ consists of a finite number of curves on each of which $f'(x)$ exists. We suppose also that the derivative exists at the end points of these curves, in the sense

$$\lim_{u \to 0+} \frac{f(x+u) - f(x+)}{u} \qquad \text{or} \qquad \lim_{u \to 0+} \frac{f(x-u) - f(x-)}{-u}, \quad (24\text{-}12)$$

where "$u \to 0+$" means $u \to 0$ through positive values. Such a function may have finitely many discontinuities. However, since the Fourier coefficients of $f(x)$ are not altered if $f(x)$ is redefined at a finite number of points, we can assume that

$$f(x) = \frac{f(x+) + f(x-)}{2} \qquad\qquad (24\text{-}13)$$

at every point x, whether $f(x)$ is continuous at x or not.

These preliminaries lead to the following theorem:

THEOREM. *If $f(x)$ is periodic of period 2π, is piecewise smooth, and is defined at points of discontinuity by* (24-13), *then the Fourier series for $f(x)$ converges to $f(x)$ at every value of x.*

To establish this theorem we recall that the series (24-3) was summed in Sec. 17, Example 1. The result (17-5) yields

$$D_n(u) = \frac{\sin\,(n + \tfrac{1}{2})u}{2 \sin \tfrac{1}{2}u}. \qquad\qquad (24\text{-}14)$$

If we substitute this into (24-11) and replace $2f(x)$ by $f(x+) + f(x-)$ in accordance with (24-13), we get

$$s_n(x) - f(x)$$

$$= \frac{1}{\pi} \int_0^\pi \frac{f(x+u) - f(x+) + f(x-u) - f(x-)}{2 \sin \tfrac{1}{2}u} \sin\left(n + \frac{1}{2}\right)u\, du.$$

Now, the expression

$$\frac{f(x+u) - f(x+)}{2 \sin \tfrac{1}{2}u} = \frac{f(x+u) - f(x+)}{u}\,\frac{(u/2)}{\sin\,(u/2)} \qquad (24\text{-}15)$$

has a limit as $u \to 0+$, since

$$\lim \frac{u/2}{\sin\,(u/2)} = 1, \qquad \text{as } u \to 0$$

and since the limits (24-12) exist by hypothesis. If we define the value of (24-15) at $u = 0$ to be this limit, then the expression is continuous for $u \geq 0$ as long as the points

$$[x, f(x+)] \quad \text{and} \quad [x + u, f(x + u)]$$

are on the same smooth curve belonging to the graph of $f(x)$.

On the other hand, for $u \neq 0$ the function (24-15) is just as well behaved as the numerator $f(x + u) - f(x+)$, since $\sin \frac{1}{2}u$ does not vanish. This shows that the graph of (24-15) consists of a finite number of continuous curves, which have finite limits as one approaches their end points and hence are bounded.

It follows from Corollary 3 of the preceding section [1] that

$$\lim_{n \to \infty} \int_0^\pi \frac{f(x + u) - f(x+)}{2 \sin \frac{1}{2}u} \sin\left(n + \frac{1}{2}\right) u \, du = 0.$$

In just the same way it is found that

$$\lim_{n \to \infty} \int_0^\pi \frac{f(x - u) - f(x-)}{2 \sin \frac{1}{2}u} \sin\left(n + \frac{1}{2}\right) u \, du = 0$$

and hence the integral representing $s_n(x) - f(x)$ tends to zero as $n \to \infty$. This shows that

$$\lim_{n \to \infty} s_n(x) = f(x)$$

and completes the proof of the theorem.

25. The Integration and Differentiation of Fourier Series. If $f(x)$ is piecewise continuous [2] on $[-\pi, \pi]$, then the function

$$F(x) = \int_{-\pi}^x f(t) \, dt \tag{25-1}$$

is continuous and piecewise smooth (Sec. 24). Moreover, $F(x)$ remains continuous when defined to have period 2π, provided $F(-\pi) = F(\pi)$. Since $F(-\pi) = 0$, the latter condition reduces to

$$F(\pi) = \int_{-\pi}^\pi f(t) \, dt = \pi a_0 = 0 \tag{25-2}$$

where $\frac{1}{2}a_0$ is the first Fourier coefficient of $f(x)$. Applying the theorem of

---

[1] The presence of the $\frac{1}{2}$ in $\sin (n + \frac{1}{2})u$ causes no trouble, since

$$\sin (n + \frac{1}{2})u = \sin nu \cos \frac{1}{2}u + \cos nu \sin \frac{1}{2}u$$

and Corollary 3 applies to each term.

[2] This means that the interval $[-\pi, \pi]$ can be divided by points $x_1, x_2, \ldots, x_n$ into a finite number of intervals on each of which $f(x)$ is continuous. Also $f(x)$ must have a limit as $x \to x_k+$ and as $x \to x_k-$.

the preceding section, we can now deduce that the Fourier series for the periodic function $F(x)$ converges to $F(x)$ at every value of x.

This result can be obtained when $f(x)$ and $|f(x)|$ are only assumed integrable, without being piecewise continuous. Indeed, we can always write $f(x) = P(x) - N(x)$ where $P(x)$ is positive and $-N(x)$ is negative. The equation

$$F(x) = \int_{-\pi}^{x} P(t)\, dt - \int_{-\pi}^{x} N(t)\, dt$$

expresses $F(x)$ as the difference of two increasing continuous functions. Since such functions satisfy the Dirichlet conditions, the desired result can be deduced from Dirichlet's theorem as quoted in Sec. 18.

We shall show next that the Fourier series for $F(x)$ is obtained by integrating the series for $f(x)$. If $n \geq 1$, the Fourier cosine coefficient A_n of $F(x)$ satisfies

$$\pi A_n = \int_{-\pi}^{\pi} F(x) \cos nx\, dx = F(x) \left. \frac{\sin nx}{n} \right|_{-\pi}^{\pi} - \int_{-\pi}^{\pi} \frac{\sin nx}{n} F'(x)\, dx$$

when we integrate by parts. Since $F(-\pi) = F(\pi) = 0$, the integrated part drops out, and since $F'(x) = f(x)$, the expression becomes

$$\pi A_n = -\frac{1}{n} \int_{-\pi}^{\pi} \sin nx\, f(x)\, dx = -\pi \frac{b_n}{n}.$$

In the same way $B_n = a_n/n$, and also

$$A_0 = -\frac{1}{\pi} \int_{-\pi}^{\pi} xf(x)\, dx. \tag{25-3}$$

These considerations establish the following remarkable theorem:

THEOREM I.   *Let $f(x)$ be a function of period 2π which has a Fourier series*

$$\Sigma(a_n \cos nx + b_n \sin nx). \tag{25-4}$$

Then, with A_0 given by (25-3),

$$\int_{-\pi}^{x} f(t)\, dt = \frac{1}{2} A_0 + \Sigma \left(\frac{a_n}{n} \sin nx - \frac{b_n}{n} \cos nx \right), \tag{25-5}$$

and this equation holds for all x, even if the Fourier series (25-4) does not converge. Moreover, the series (25-5) is actually the Fourier series of the function on the left.

In case $a_0 \neq 0$, so that the Fourier series for $f(x)$ is

$$\tfrac{1}{2}a_0 + \Sigma(a_n \cos nx + b_n \sin nx),$$

we apply Theorem I to $f(x) - \tfrac{1}{2}a_0$. Inasmuch as

$$\int_{\alpha}^{\beta} f(x)\, dx = \int_{-\pi}^{\beta} f(x)\, dx - \int_{-\pi}^{\alpha} f(x)\, dx = F(\beta) - F(\alpha)$$

for all α and β, the reader may deduce, by Theorem I, that

$$\int_\alpha^\beta f(x)\, dx = \int_\alpha^\beta (\tfrac{1}{2}a_0)\, dx + \Sigma \int_\alpha^\beta (a_n \cos nx + b_n \sin nx)\, dx. \quad (25\text{-}6)$$

This result may be summarized as follows:

THEOREM II.   *Any Fourier series (whether convergent or not) can be integrated term by term between any limits.   The integrated series converges to the integral of the periodic function corresponding to the original series.*

For example, according to (18-5) the Fourier series for $\tfrac{1}{2}x$ is

$$\frac{1}{2}x = \sin x - \frac{\sin 2x}{2} + \frac{\sin 3x}{3} + \cdots + (-1)^{n-1}\frac{\sin nx}{n} + \cdots. \quad (25\text{-}7)$$

If we integrate from α to x by Theorem II, we get

$$\frac{1}{4}(x^2 - \alpha^2) = \sum_{n=1}^{\infty} (-1)^n \frac{\cos nx - \cos n\alpha}{n^2}.$$

Treating α as constant, we see that

$$\frac{1}{4}x^2 = C + \sum_{n=1}^{\infty}(-1)^n \frac{\cos nx}{n^2} \quad (25\text{-}8)$$

where C is constant.   Since C is the first Fourier coefficient of $\tfrac{1}{4}x^2$,

$$C = \frac{1}{2\pi} \int_{-\pi}^{\pi} \frac{1}{4}x^2\, dx = \frac{\pi^2}{12}. \quad (25\text{-}9)$$

Alternatively, because $a_0 = 0$ in (25-7), we can use (25-3) to obtain

$$A_0 = -\frac{1}{\pi} \int_{-\pi}^{\pi} \frac{1}{2}x^2\, dx = -\frac{\pi^2}{3}$$

and hence, by (25-5),

$$F(x) = \frac{1}{4}(x^2 - \pi^2) = -\frac{\pi^2}{6} + \sum_{n=1}^{\infty}(-1)^n \frac{\cos nx}{n^2}.$$

The consistency of this result with (25-8) and (25-9) is easily verified.

Although Fourier series can always be integrated, as we have just seen, the differentiation of Fourier series requires caution.   For example, the series (25-7) converges for all x, and yet the series

$$\cos x - \cos 2x + \cos 3x - \cos 4x + \cdots$$

obtained by differentiating (25-7) diverges for all x.   The trouble is that the function $\tfrac{1}{2}x$ (when made periodic) has no derivative at the points $\pm\pi$, $\pm3\pi$, $\pm5\pi$, $\ldots$.

This example is quite typical of the general situation, which can be described as follows: *There is not much hope of being able to differentiate a Fourier series, unless the* **periodic** *function generating the series has a derivative at* **every** *value of x.*   On the other hand, when this condition is fulfilled, we usually can differentiate, as is shown by the following theorem:

THEOREM III. *Let $f(x)$ have period 2π, and suppose $f'(x)$ exists for every value of x, without exception. If $f'(x)$ is continuous,[1] the Fourier series for $f'(x)$ can be obtained by differentiating the Fourier series for $f(x)$. If $f'(x)$ is continuous and has only a finite number of maxima and minima on $[-\pi,\pi]$, the differentiated series actually converges to $f'(x)$ for every x.*

Repeated application of the theorem gives the corresponding result for higher derivatives. For instance, the series for $f''(x)$ can be found by differentiating the series for $f(x)$ twice, provided $f''(x)$ satisfies the conditions of the theorem.

We shall establish Theorem III by applying Theorem I to the function $f'(x)$. Being continuous, $f'(x)$ has a Fourier series, and the constant term a_0 can be found from

$$\pi a_0 = \int_{-\pi}^{\pi} f'(x)\, dx = f(\pi) - f(-\pi) = 0.$$

Thus, the series for $f'(x)$ has the form (25-4), namely,

$$\Sigma(a_n \cos nx + b_n \sin nx). \qquad (25\text{-}10)$$

It follows from Theorem I that the Fourier series for the function

$$\int_{-\pi}^{x} f'(t)\, dt = f(x) - f(-\pi)$$

has the form (25-5), and hence the series for $f(x)$ is

$$f(-\pi) + \frac{1}{2} A_0 + \Sigma \left(\frac{a_n}{n} \sin nx - \frac{b_n}{n} \cos nx \right). \qquad (25\text{-}11)$$

By inspection, we see that differentiating (25-11) gives (25-10). In other words, the Fourier series for $f'(x)$ can be found by differentiating the series for $f(x)$, and this is the main assertion in Theorem III.

Since the differentiated series is a Fourier series, its convergence can be tested by the usual methods. In particular, if $f'(x)$ satisfies the Dirichlet conditions and is continuous, then the Fourier series for $f'(x)$ converges to $f'(x)$. Thus, Theorem III is established.

The foregoing methods lead to some important inequalities for the Fourier coefficients. When a function $f(x)$ satisfies the Dirichlet conditions, it can be shown [2] that the Fourier coefficients have the order of magnitude $1/n$. That is, there is a constant M depending on $f(x)$ but not on n

---

[1] It can be shown that if $f'(x)$ satisfies the conditions of Dirichlet, then $f'(x)$ is necessarily continuous. This follows from Darboux's theorem. See, for example, L. Brand, "Advanced Calculus," p. 112, John Wiley & Sons, Inc., New York, 1955.

[2] See I. S. Sokolnikoff, "Advanced Calculus," p. 406, McGraw-Hill Book Company, Inc., New York, 1939. Cf. also Prob. 4.

such that

$$|a_n| \leq \frac{M}{n}, \qquad |b_n| \leq \frac{M}{n}. \tag{25-12}$$

Now, if the Fourier coefficients of $f'(x)$ in (25-10) satisfy these conditions, then (25-11) shows that the coefficients of $f(x)$ are bounded by M/n^2. More generally, we can start with $f^{(k)}(x)$ and integrate k times. The constants of integration drop out as in the derivation of (25-10), and we obtain:

THEOREM IV. *Let $f(x)$ have period 2π and suppose the kth derivative of $f(x)$ satisfies the conditions of Dirichlet on $[-\pi,\pi]$. Then the Fourier coefficients of $f(x)$ satisfy the inequalities*

$$|a_n| \leq \frac{M}{n^{k+1}}, \qquad |b_n| \leq \frac{M}{n^{k+1}},$$

where the constant M depends on $f(x)$ but not on n.

PROBLEMS

1. By integrating the series (25-8) from 0 to x deduce that

$$x(x^2 - \pi^2) = 12 \sum_{n=1}^{\infty} (-1)^n \frac{\sin nx}{n^3}.$$

2. By integrating the series in Prob. 1 from $-\pi$ to x deduce that

$$\frac{1}{48}(x^2 - \pi^2)^2 = \frac{\pi^4}{90} - \sum_{n=1}^{\infty} (-1)^n \frac{\cos nx}{n^4}.$$

3. Show that the following is not a Fourier series:

$$\sum_{n=1}^{\infty} \frac{\sin nx}{\log(1+n)}.$$

Hint: If it is a Fourier series, the integrated series must converge for all x.

4. Deduce (25-12) when $f(x)$ is piecewise smooth on $[-\pi,\pi]$. *Hint:* Let the points x_k divide $[-\pi,\pi]$ into a finite number of intervals on each of which $f'(x)$ is continuous. The Fourier coefficients are obtained by adding integrals of the type

$$\int_{x_k}^{x_{k+1}} f(x) \cos nx \, dx \qquad \text{or} \qquad \int_{x_k}^{x_{k+1}} f(x) \sin nx \, dx,$$

and these can be integrated by parts.

CHAPTER 3

FUNCTIONS OF SEVERAL VARIABLES

The Technique of Differentiation

Applications of Differentiation

Integrals with Several Variables

The considerations of the preceding chapters were confined primarily to functions $y = f(x)$ of a single independent variable x. One does not have to go far to encounter functional relationships depending on two or more independent variables. In courses in analytic geometry and calculus the reader has learned that a functional relationship of the form $z = f(x,y)$ may be represented as a surface, and he has made use of partial derivatives to study some properties of surfaces. In this chapter the familiar concepts underlying the study of real functions of two variables are sharpened and extended to functions of many variables. The bearing of such extensions on the calculation of rates of change and maximum and minimum values of functions of several variables is indicated in numerous problems of practical interest.

The concluding sections of the chapter deal with integrals of functions of several variables. They contain an introduction to the calculus of variations—a subject of great importance in physics and technology. Many situations can be characterized by statements to the effect that certain integrals attain extreme values. The determination of such extremes is in the province of calculus of variations.

THE TECHNIQUE OF DIFFERENTIATION

1. Basic Notions. Let $z = f(x,y)$ be a *real-valued* function of two independent variables (x,y). We can think of (x,y) as the coordinates of a point in the xy plane and interpret z as the height of the surface defined by $z = f(x,y)$. The function $f(x,y)$ may be determined for every point (x,y) in the xy plane, or the points for which it is determined may occupy a certain region R in that plane.

For example,

$$z = x^2 + y^2 \tag{1-1}$$

represents the paraboloid of revolution for every pair of values (x,y), while

$$z = \sqrt{1 - x^2 - y^2} \tag{1-2}$$

217

represents the surface of the hemisphere only for those values of (x,y)
for which $x^2 + y^2 \leq 1$. In the example (1-1) the region R is the entire
xy plane, while in (1-2) it is the interior and the boundary of the unit
circle $x^2 + y^2 = 1$. The function

$$z = \frac{1}{\sqrt{1 - x^2 - y^2}} \tag{1-3}$$

is defined in the circular region $x^2 + y^2 < 1$, but *not* on the boundary
$x^2 + y^2 = 1$. If the region of definition of the function includes its
boundary C, we shall say that the function is defined in the *closed region* R.
When the boundary of the region R is not included, the region is said to
be *open*.

To define the continuity of $z = f(x,y)$ at a given point we need the
notion of the *neighborhood* of that point. The neighborhood of $P(x_0,y_0)$
is the set of all points $P(x,y)$ interior to a circle with center at (x_0,y_0).
If the radius of this circle is $\delta > 0$, then the neighborhood of (x_0,y_0) is
a circular region $(x - x_0)^2 + (y - y_0)^2 < \delta^2$. The positive number δ
can be chosen arbitrarily small. The extension of this definition to spaces
of more than two dimensions is immediate. The neighborhood of
$P(x_0,y_0z_0)$ is the open spherical region

$$(x - x_0)^2 + (y - y_0)^2 + (z - z_0)^2 < \delta^2.$$

The neighborhood of the point $P_0(x_0,y_0,z_0,t_0)$ in the space of four variables
x, y, z, t is the set of "points" (x,y,z,t) such that

$$(x - x_0)^2 + (y - y_0)^2 + (z - z_0)^2 + (t - t_0)^2 < \delta^2,$$

and so on for spaces of higher dimensionality.

Intuitively the notion of continuity of $z = f(x,y)$ at a given point
$P_0(x_0,y_0)$ means that the value of $f(x,y)$ throughout a neighborhood of
(x_0,y_0) will differ from $f(x_0,y_0)$ by as little as desired if the neighborhood is
chosen sufficiently small. In symbols this means that if one specifies a
positive number ϵ, no matter how small, then for all points in a certain
circular region $(x - x_0)^2 + (y - y_0)^2 < \delta^2$ we have

$$|f(x,y) - f(x_0,y_0)| < \epsilon. \tag{1-4}$$

An alternative notation for (1-4) is

$$\lim_{(x,y) \to (x_0y_0)} f(x,y) = f(x_0,y_0), \tag{1-5}$$

which states that as the point (x,y) is made to approach (x_0,y_0), the value
of the limit is equal to the value of the function at (x_0,y_0).

We extend this definition (1-5) to functions $f(x_1,x_2,\ldots,x_n)$ of n variables
in the obvious way: A function $f(x_1,x_2,\ldots,x_n)$ is continuous at the point

$P_0(x_1^0, x_2^0, \ldots, x_n^0)$ whenever

$$\lim_{P \to P_0} f(x_1, x_2, \ldots, x_n) = f(x_1^0, x_2^0, \ldots, x_n^0).$$

The "point P" here means the set of n real numbers $(x_1, x_2, \ldots, x_n)$. Clearly, $f(x_1, x_2, \ldots, x_n)$ cannot be continuous at $(x_1, x_2, \ldots, x_n)$ if it is not defined at that point.

Whenever $f(x_1, x_2, \ldots, x_n)$ is continuous at every point P of the given region R, it is said to be *continuous in the region R*. Functions with which we shall deal for the most part will be continuous in some region, open or closed.

PROBLEM

Describe the regions of definition and the surfaces defined by the following functions z:

(a) $x - y + z = 1$;   (b) $z = y$;
(c) $y^2 + z^2 = 25$;   (d) $z = 1/(x^2 + y^2)$;
(e) $z = 1/x$;   (f) $z = \sqrt{1 - (x - 1)^2 - y^2}$.

2. Partial Derivatives. Let $u = f(x,y)$ be a function of two independent variables x, y, and let it be defined at a point (x_0, y_0) and for all values of (x,y) in some neighborhood of (x_0, y_0). If y is set equal to y_0, then u becomes a function of one variable x, namely,

$$u = f(x, y_0).$$

If this function has a derivative with respect to x, the derivative is called the *partial derivative of $f(x,y)$ with respect to x for $y = y_0$*. In like manner, if x is assigned a constant value x_0, the derivative with respect to y of the resulting function $f(x_0, y)$ is called the *partial derivative of $f(x,y)$ with respect to y for $x = x_0$*. The customary notations for the partial derivative of $u = f(x,y)$ with respect to x are

$$\frac{\partial u}{\partial x}, \quad u_x, f_x, \text{ and } \frac{\partial f}{\partial x}.$$

The partial derivatives of a function $f(x_1, x_2, \ldots, x_n)$ of n independent variables are obtained by fixing in it the values of $n - 1$ variables and computing the derivative of the resulting function of a single variable. Thus,

$$f(x,y) = yx^2 - 2yx \tag{2-1}$$

has the partial derivatives

$$\frac{\partial f}{\partial x} = 2xy - 2y, \qquad \frac{\partial f}{\partial y} = x^2 - 2x. \tag{2-2}$$

If $u = f(x,y)$ is a function of two independent variables, it is easy to provide a simple geometric interpretation of partial derivatives u_x and u_y. The equation $u = f(x,y)$ is the equation of a surface (see Fig. 1). If x

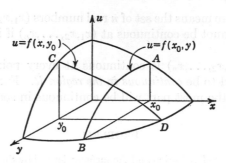

FIG. 1

is given a fixed value x_0, $u = f(x_0,y)$ is the equation of the curve AB on the surface formed by the intersection of the surface and the plane $x = x_0$. Then

$$u_y \equiv \frac{\partial u}{\partial y} = \lim_{\Delta y \to 0} \frac{f(x_0,\, y_0 + \Delta y) - f(x_0,y_0)}{\Delta y}$$

is the slope at any point of AB. Similarly, if y is assigned the constant value y_0, then $u = f(x,y_0)$ is the equation of the curve CD on the surface and

$$u_x \equiv \frac{\partial u}{\partial x} = \lim_{\Delta x \to 0} \frac{f(x_0 + \Delta x,\, y_0) - f(x_0,y_0)}{\Delta x}$$

is the slope at any point of CD.

In Chap. 5 we shall see that the partial derivatives u_x, u_y, u_z of $u = f(x,y,z)$ can be interpreted as rectangular components of a certain vector, called the *gradient* of u. This vector provides a measure of the space rate of change of u.

The partial derivatives $f_{x_1}, f_{x_2}, \ldots, f_{x_n}$ of $f(x_1,x_2,\ldots,x_n)$ are functions of $x_1, x_2, \ldots, x_n$, and they may have partial derivatives with respect to some or all of these variables. These derivatives are called *second partial derivatives* of $f(x_1,x_2,\ldots,x_n)$. If there are only two independent variables, $f(x,y)$ may have the second partial derivatives

$$\frac{\partial}{\partial x}\left(\frac{\partial f}{\partial x}\right) \equiv \frac{\partial^2 f}{\partial x^2} \equiv f_{xx}, \qquad \frac{\partial}{\partial y}\left(\frac{\partial f}{\partial x}\right) \equiv \frac{\partial^2 f}{\partial y\, \partial x} \equiv f_{xy},$$

$$\frac{\partial}{\partial x}\left(\frac{\partial f}{\partial y}\right) \equiv \frac{\partial^2 f}{\partial x\, \partial y} \equiv f_{yx}, \qquad \frac{\partial}{\partial y}\left(\frac{\partial f}{\partial y}\right) \equiv \frac{\partial^2 f}{\partial y^2} \equiv f_{yy}.$$

It should be noted that f_{xy} means that $\partial f/\partial x$ is first found and then $\partial/\partial y(\partial f/\partial x)$ is determined, so that the subscripts indicate the order in which the derivatives are computed. In

$$\frac{\partial^2 f}{\partial y\, \partial x} = \frac{\partial}{\partial y}\left(\frac{\partial f}{\partial x}\right),$$

the order is in keeping with the meaning of the symbol, so that the order appears as the reverse of the order in which the derivatives are taken.

For the function $f(x,y)$ in (2-1) we get, on noting (2-2),

$$f_{xy} = \frac{\partial}{\partial y}\left(\frac{\partial f}{\partial x}\right) = \frac{\partial}{\partial y}\,(2xy - 2y) = 2x - 2,$$

$$f_{yx} = \frac{\partial}{\partial x}\left(\frac{\partial f}{\partial y}\right) = \frac{\partial}{\partial x}\,(x^2 - 2x) = 2x - 2$$

$$f_{yy} = \frac{\partial}{\partial y}\,(x^2 - 2x) = 0,$$

$$f_{xx} = \frac{\partial}{\partial x}\,(2xy - 2y) = 2y.$$

In this example $f_{xy} = f_{yx}$, and indeed, one rarely meets functions for which the so-called *mixed* derivatives are unequal. In fact one can prove [1] that

$$\frac{\partial^2 f}{\partial x\, \partial y} = \frac{\partial^2 f}{\partial y\, \partial x}$$

whenever these derivatives are continuous at the point in question.

The process of defining partial derivatives of higher orders is obvious from the foregoing, and it is possible to establish equalities such as $f_{xyx} = f_{xxy} = f_{yxx}$ and $f_{yxy} = f_{xyy} = f_{yyx}$ whenever these derivatives are continuous at the point in question.

We note in conclusion that although the notation $\partial u/\partial x$ for the partial derivative u_x suggests a quotient of some quantities analogous to the differentials dy and dx in the notation dy/dx for the derivative of $y = f(x)$, no such interpretation is available for partial derivatives. To stress the point that $\partial u/\partial x$ should never be thought of as a fraction, we give an example.

Example: Consider the equation for an ideal gas $pv = RT$, where p is the pressure, v is the volume, T is the absolute temperature, and R is a physical constant. It should be noted first that the concept of partial derivatives hinges on the agreement as to which variables in a given functional relationship are assumed to be independent. Thus, if

[1] See I. S. Sokolnikoff, "Advanced Calculus," sec. 31, McGraw-Hill Book Company, Inc., New York, 1939.

we solve our gas equation for p, we obtain

$$p = \frac{RT}{v}.$$

We can then compute

$$\frac{\partial p}{\partial v} = -\frac{RT}{v^2} \quad \text{and} \quad \frac{\partial p}{\partial T} = \frac{R}{v}. \tag{2-3}$$

On the other hand, if we solve for v, we get

$$v = \frac{RT}{p},$$

in which p and T are now regarded as the independent variables, and we can, therefore, compute

$$\frac{\partial v}{\partial T} = \frac{R}{p}, \quad \frac{\partial v}{\partial p} = -\frac{RT}{p^2}. \tag{2-4}$$

We can also solve for T and get

$$T = \frac{pv}{R},$$

in which p and v are to be considered as the independent variables, so that

$$\frac{\partial T}{\partial p} = \frac{v}{R}, \quad \frac{\partial T}{\partial v} = \frac{p}{R}. \tag{2-5}$$

From Eqs. (2-3) to (2-5) we obtain

$$\frac{\partial p}{\partial v}\frac{\partial v}{\partial T}\frac{\partial T}{\partial p} = -\frac{RT}{v^2}\frac{R}{p}\frac{v}{R} = -1, \tag{2-6}$$

since $pv = RT$. But if it were possible to treat the terms in the left-hand member of (2-6) as fractions, we should have obtained $+1$.

PROBLEMS

1. Find $\partial z/\partial x$ and $\partial z/\partial y$ for each of the following functions:

(a) $z = y/x$; (b) $z = x^3y + \tan^{-1}(y/x)$; (c) $z = \sin xy + x$; (d) $z = e^x \log y$; (e) $z = x^2y + \sin^{-1} x$.

2. Find $\partial u/\partial x$, $\partial u/\partial y$, and $\partial u/\partial z$ for each of the following functions:

(a) $u = x^2y + yz - xz^2$; (b) $u = xyz + \log xy$; (c) $u = z \sin^{-1}(x/y)$; (d) $u = (x^2 + y^2 + z^2)^{\frac{1}{2}}$; (e) $u = (x^2 + y^2 + z^2)^{-\frac{1}{2}}$.

3. Verify that $\partial^2 f/\partial x\,\partial y = \partial^2 f/\partial y\,\partial x$ for

(a) $f = \cos xy^2$, (b) $f = \sin^2 x \cos y$, (c) $f = e^{y/x}$.

4. Prove that if

(a) $f(x,y) = \log(x^2 + y^2) + \tan^{-1}\dfrac{y}{x}$, then $\dfrac{\partial^2 f}{\partial x^2} + \dfrac{\partial^2 f}{\partial y^2} = 0$;

(b) $f(x,y,z) = (x^2 + y^2 + z^2)^{-\frac{1}{2}}$, then $\dfrac{\partial^2 f}{\partial x^2} + \dfrac{\partial^2 f}{\partial y^2} + \dfrac{\partial^2 f}{\partial z^2} = 0$.

3. Total Differentials. The differential dy of a function $y = f(x)$ is defined by the formula

$$dy = f'(x)\, dx, \tag{3-1}$$

where $dx \equiv \Delta x$ is an arbitrary increment of the *independent* variable x. We agree to call an increment of the *independent* variable x the *differential* of x.

Since (Fig. 2)

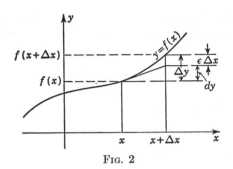

FIG. 2

$$f'(x) = \lim_{\Delta x \to 0} \frac{\Delta y}{\Delta x} = \lim_{\Delta x \to 0} \frac{f(x + \Delta x) - f(x)}{\Delta x}, \tag{3-2}$$

we can write, on recalling the definition of the limit,

$$\frac{\Delta y}{\Delta x} = f'(x) + \epsilon, \tag{3-3}$$

where $\lim_{\Delta x \to 0} \epsilon = 0$. Hence

$$\Delta y = f'(x)\, \Delta x + \epsilon\, \Delta x. \tag{3-4}$$

The substitution from (3-1) in (3-4) then yields

$$\Delta y = dy + \epsilon\, \Delta x,$$
$$\lim \epsilon = 0 \qquad \text{as } \Delta x \to 0. \tag{3-5}$$

Figure 2 illustrates geometrically the relations between Δy, dy, and dx, and formula (3-5) shows that for small values of Δx, the increment Δy is a good approximation to the differential dy in the sense that

$$\frac{\Delta y - dy}{\Delta x} = \epsilon, \tag{3-6}$$

where $\epsilon \to 0$ as $\Delta x \to 0$.

One can construct a similar approximation to the increment Δu for the function $u = f(x,y)$ when x and y are allowed to acquire the respective increments Δx and Δy.

The presentation of the essential ideas in this construction is greatly simplified by the use of the mean-value theorem of the differential calculus. This theorem states that whenever $f(x)$ has the derivative $f'(x)$ at every point of the interval $(x, x + \Delta x)$, then

$$\frac{f(x + \Delta x) - f(x)}{\Delta x} = f'(\xi), \tag{3-7}$$

where ξ is an intermediate point in the interval. The geometric meaning of this theorem is exceedingly simple. Formula (3-7) states that the slope

$$\frac{f(x + \Delta x) - f(x)}{\Delta x}$$

of the secant line AB (Fig. 3) is equal to the slope $f'(\xi)$ of the tangent

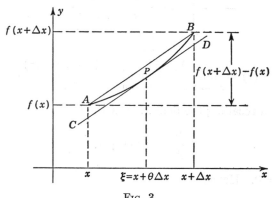

FIG. 3

line CD to the curve $y = f(x)$ at an intermediate point ξ in the interval. Since $\xi = x + \theta \Delta x$, where $\theta \Delta x$ is some fraction of the length Δx, we can write (3-7) as

$$f(x + \Delta x) - f(x) = f'(x + \theta \Delta x) \Delta x, \qquad 0 < \theta < 1. \tag{3-8}$$

Consider now a function $u = f(x,y)$ of two variables. The increment Δu that results from replacing x by $x + \Delta x$ and y by $y + \Delta y$ is

$$\Delta u = f(x + \Delta x, y + \Delta y) - f(x,y). \tag{3-9}$$

If we add and subtract $f(x, y + \Delta y)$ in the right-hand member of (3-9), we obtain

$$\Delta u = [f(x + \Delta x, y + \Delta y) - f(x, y + \Delta y)] + [f(x, y + \Delta y) - f(x,y)].$$
$$\tag{3-10}$$

The expression in the first pair of brackets in (3-10) is the increment in the function $f(x,y)$ when the second variable in it has a fixed value $y + \Delta y$. Accordingly, we can apply formula (3-8) to it and write

$$f(x + \Delta x, y + \Delta y) - f(x, y + \Delta y) = f_x(x + \theta_1 \Delta x, y + \Delta y)\, \Delta x, \quad (3\text{-}11)$$

where $0 < \theta_1 < 1$.

Similarly, the application of (3-8) to the expression in the second set of brackets in (3-10), in which x has a fixed value, yields

$$f(x, y + \Delta y) - f(x,y) = f_y(x, y + \theta_2 \Delta y)\, \Delta y, \qquad (3\text{-}12)$$

where $0 < \theta_2 < 1$.

Now if the partial derivatives $f_x(x,y)$ and $f_y(x,y)$ are continuous functions, then

$$f_x(x + \theta_1 \Delta x, y + \Delta y) = f_x(x,y) + \epsilon_1,$$
$$f_y(x, y + \theta_2 \Delta y) = f_y(x,y) + \epsilon_2, \qquad (3\text{-}13)$$

where $\lim \epsilon_1 = 0$ and $\lim \epsilon_2 = 0$ as Δx and Δy approach zero. Hence we can write (3-11) and (3-12) in the forms

$$f(x + \Delta x, y + \Delta y) - f(x, y + \Delta y) = [f_x(x,y) + \epsilon_1]\, \Delta x,$$
$$f(x, y + \Delta y) - f(x,y) = [f_y(x,y) + \epsilon_2]\, \Delta y,$$

so that (3-10) becomes

$$\Delta u = f_x(x,y)\, \Delta x + f_y(x,y)\, \Delta y + \epsilon_1 \Delta x + \epsilon_2 \Delta y. \qquad (3\text{-}14)$$

If we define the differential du of $u = f(x,y)$ by the formula

$$du = f_x\, \Delta x + f_y\, \Delta y \qquad (3\text{-}15)$$
$$\equiv \frac{\partial f}{\partial x}\, \Delta x + \frac{\partial f}{\partial y}\, \Delta y$$

we can write (3-14) in a form analogous to (3-5):

$$\Delta u = du + \epsilon_1 \Delta x + \epsilon_2 \Delta y,$$
$$\lim \epsilon_1 = 0, \qquad \lim \epsilon_2 = 0 \qquad \text{as } \Delta x \to 0 \text{ and } \Delta y \to 0. \qquad (3\text{-}16)$$

Formula (3-16) shows that when the increments Δx and Δy are small, the differential du is a good approximation to Δu in the sense that

$$\frac{\Delta u - du}{\sqrt{(\Delta x)^2 + (\Delta y)^2}} = \frac{\epsilon_1 \Delta x + \epsilon_2 \Delta y}{\sqrt{(\Delta x)^2 + (\Delta y)^2}} \to 0$$

as Δx and Δy approach zero.

As in the case of functions of one independent variable, we agree to write the increments Δx and Δy in the *independent variables* as dx and dy, respectively.   Then (3-15) reads

$$du = \frac{\partial f}{\partial x}\, dx + \frac{\partial f}{\partial y}\, dy. \qquad (3\text{-}17)$$

Whenever (3-16) holds, the function $u = f(x,y)$ is said to be *differentiable*, and du in (3-17) is called the *total differential*.[1] A function which is differentiable at each point of a region is said to be *differentiable in the region*. The foregoing discussion shows that a function $f(x,y)$ is differentiable whenever the partial derivatives f_x and f_y are continuous.

The foregoing considerations can be extended to functions $u = f(x_1, x_2, \ldots, x_n)$ of n independent variables.   The total differential du is given by the formula

$$du = \frac{\partial f}{\partial x_1}\, dx_1 + \frac{\partial f}{\partial x_2}\, dx_2 + \cdots + \frac{\partial f}{\partial x_n}\, dx_n \qquad (3\text{-}18)$$

whenever the partial derivatives f_{x_i} are continuous functions.

It should be noted that the total differential du is equal to the sum of n terms involving *independent increments* dx_i.   When a number of small changes are taking place simultaneously in a system, each one proceeds as if it were independent of the others, and the total change is the sum of the effects due to the independent changes.   Physically, this corresponds to the principle of superposition of effects.

Example 1.   Find the total differential of $u = e^x y z^2$.   Since u_x, u_y, u_z are obviously continuous functions, formula (3-18) yields

$$du = e^x y z^2\, dx + e^x z^2\, dy + 2e^x y z\, dz.$$

Example 2.   A metal box without a top has inside dimensions 6 by 4 by 2 ft.   If the metal is 0.1 ft thick, find the actual volume of the metal used and compare it with the approximate volume found by using the differential.

The actual volume is ΔV, where

$$\Delta V = 6.2 \times 4.2 \times 2.1 - 6 \times 4 \times 2 = 54.684 - 48 = 6.684 \text{ ft}^3.$$

Since $V = xyz$, where $x = 6$, $y = 4$, $z = 2$,

$$dV = yz\, dx + xz\, dy + xy\, dz$$

$$= 8(0.2) + 12(0.2) + 24(0.1) = 6.4 \text{ ft}^3.$$

[1] In Chap. 5 we shall encounter expressions of the form (3-17) in which f_x and f_y become discontinuous at certain points of the region and u is a multiple-valued function. Such expressions are generally called *exact differentials*, and they are also denoted by the same symbol du.   For technical reasons, explained in Chap. 5, it is usually necessary to assume the continuity of f_x and f_y, in which event the terms *exact* and *total* differentials become synonymous.   A geometric meaning of the differential (3-17) is given in Sec. 10, Chap. 4.

Example 3. Two sides of a triangular piece of land (Fig. 4) are measured as 100 and 125 ft, and the included angle is measured as 60°. If the possible errors are 0.2 ft in measuring the sides and 1° in measuring the angle, what is the approximate error in the area?

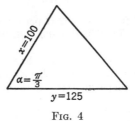

$y=125$

FIG. 4

Since $A = \tfrac{1}{2}xy \sin \alpha$,

$$dA = \tfrac{1}{2}(y \sin \alpha\, dx + x \sin \alpha\, dy + xy \cos \alpha\, d\alpha),$$

and the approximate error is therefore

$$dA = \frac{1}{2}\left[125 \left(\frac{\sqrt{3}}{2}\right)(0.2) + 100 \left(\frac{\sqrt{3}}{2}\right)(0.2) + 100(125)\left(\frac{1}{2}\right)\frac{\pi}{180}\right] = 74.0 \text{ ft}^2.$$

PROBLEMS

1. A closed cylindrical tank is 4 ft high and 2 ft in diameter (inside dimensions). What is the approximate amount of metal in the wall and the ends of the tank if they are 0.2 in. thick?

2. The angle of elevation of the top of a tower is found to be 30°, with a possible error of 0.5°. The distance to the base of the tower is found to be 1,000 ft, with a possible error of 0.1 ft. What is the possible error in the height of the tower as computed from these measurements?

3. What is the possible error in the length of the hypotenuse of a right triangle if the legs are found to be 11.5 and 7.8 ft, with a possible error of 0.1 ft in each measurement?

4. The constant C in Boyle's law $pv = C$ is calculated from the measurements of p and v. If p is found to be 5,000 lb per ft^2 with a possible error of 1 per cent and v is found to be 15 ft^3 with a possible error of 2 per cent, find the approximate possible error in C computed from these measurements.

5. The volume v, pressure p, and absolute temperature T of a perfect gas are connected by the formula $pv = RT$, where R is a constant. If $T = 500°$, $p = 4,000$ lb per ft^2, and $v = 15.2$ ft^3, find the approximate change in p when T changes to 503° and v to 15.25 ft^3.

6. In estimating the cost of a pile of bricks measured as 6 by 50 by 4 ft, the tape is stretched 1 per cent beyond the estimated length. If the count is 12 bricks to 1 ft^3 and bricks cost \$20 per thousand, find the approximate error in cost.

7. In determining specific gravity by the formula $s = A/(A - W)$, where A is the weight in air and W is the weight in water, A can be read within 0.01 lb and W within 0.02 lb. Find approximately the maximum error in s if the readings are $A = 1.1$ lb and $W = 0.6$ lb. Find the maximum relative error $\Delta s/s$.

8. The equation of a perfect gas is $pv = RT$. At a certain instant a given amount of gas has a volume of 16 ft^3 and is under a pressure of 36 psi. Assuming $R = 10.71$, find the temperature T. If the volume is increasing at the rate of $\tfrac{1}{3}$ cfs and the pressure is decreasing at the rate $\tfrac{1}{8}$ psi per sec, find the rate at which the temperature is changing.

9. The period of a simple pendulum with small oscillations is

$$T = 2\pi\sqrt{\frac{l}{g}}.$$

If T is computed using $l = 8$ ft and $g = 32$ ft per sec per sec, find the approximate error in T if the true values are $l = 8.05$ ft and $g = 32.01$ ft per sec per sec. Find also the percentage error.

10. The diameter and altitude of a can in the shape of a right circular cylinder are measured as 4 and 6 in., respectively. The possible error in each measurement is 0.1 in. Find approximately the maximum possible error in the values computed for the volume and the lateral surface.

11. We define an approximate relative error e in the differentiable function f by the formula $e = df/f$. Show that the approximate relative error of the product is equal to the sum of the approximate relative errors of the factors. *Hint:* $e = d \log f$.

4. Chain Rule. Let $u = f(x,y)$ be a function of the variables x and y which, in turn, are functions of some independent variable t. If t is given an increment Δt, the functions x and y will acquire increments Δx and Δy, and consequently u will receive an increment Δu.

Assuming that $u = f(x,y)$ is continuous together with its partial derivatives, one can write [see (3-14)]

$$\Delta u = \frac{\partial u}{\partial x} \Delta x + \frac{\partial u}{\partial y} \Delta y + \epsilon_1 \Delta x + \epsilon_2 \Delta y.$$

Dividing both sides of this expression by Δt gives

$$\frac{\Delta u}{\Delta t} = \frac{\partial u}{\partial x} \frac{\Delta x}{\Delta t} + \frac{\partial u}{\partial y} \frac{\Delta y}{\Delta t} + \epsilon_1 \frac{\Delta x}{\Delta t} + \epsilon_2 \frac{\Delta y}{\Delta t}. \tag{4-1}$$

Now if it is supposed that x and y can be differentiated with respect to t, the expression (4-1) gives, upon passing to the limit as $\Delta t \to 0$,

$$\frac{du}{dt} = \frac{\partial u}{\partial x}\frac{dx}{dt} + \frac{\partial u}{\partial y}\frac{dy}{dt}$$

$$\equiv \frac{\partial f}{\partial x}\frac{dx}{dt} + \frac{\partial f}{\partial y}\frac{dy}{dt}, \tag{4-2}$$

since $\epsilon_1 \to 0$ and $\epsilon_2 \to 0$. The reason for the vanishing of ϵ_1 and ϵ_2 as $\Delta t \to 0$ is as follows: Since x and y are assumed to be differentiable functions of t, the identities

$$\Delta x = \frac{\Delta x}{\Delta t} \Delta t, \qquad \Delta y = \frac{\Delta y}{\Delta t} \Delta t,$$

show that $\Delta x \to 0$ and $\Delta y \to 0$ as $\Delta t \to 0$. But when $\Delta x \to 0$ and $\Delta y \to 0$ we know that ϵ_1 and ϵ_2 approach zero by (3-16).

Formula (4-2) gives the rule for the differentiation of composite functions. It is clear that if u is a function of a set of variables, $x_1, x_2, \ldots, x_n$, where each variable is a differentiable function of an independent variable t, the derivative of u with respect to t is given by the *chain rule:*

$$\frac{du}{dt} = \frac{\partial u}{\partial x_1}\frac{dx_1}{dt} + \frac{\partial u}{\partial x_2}\frac{dx_2}{dt} + \cdots + \frac{\partial u}{\partial x_n}\frac{dx_n}{dt}. \tag{4-3}$$

A special case of formula (4-2) is of interest. If it is assumed that $t = x$, (4-2) becomes

$$\frac{du}{dx} = \frac{\partial u}{\partial x} + \frac{\partial u}{\partial y}\frac{dy}{dx}. \tag{4-4}$$

Formula (4-4) can be used to calculate the derivative of the implicit function given by

$$f(x,y) = 0. \tag{4-5}$$

Let it be assumed that (4-5) can be solved for y to yield a real solution

$$y = \varphi(x); \tag{4-6}$$

then the substitution of (4-6) in the left-hand member of (4-5) gives an identity

$$0 = f(x,y), \qquad \text{where } y = \varphi(x). \tag{4-7}$$

Applying (4-4) to (4-7) gives

$$0 = \frac{\partial f}{\partial x} + \frac{\partial f}{\partial y}\frac{dy}{dx},$$

and solving for dy/dx,

$$\frac{dy}{dx} = -\frac{\partial f/\partial x}{\partial f/\partial y}. \tag{4-8}$$

The formula (4-8) assumes that $\partial f/\partial y$ does not vanish for the point (x_0, y_0) at which the derivative is calculated.

Example 1. Let $f(x,y) = 3x^3y^2 + x \cos y = 0$; then

$$\frac{\partial f}{\partial x} = 9x^2y^2 + \cos y, \qquad \frac{\partial f}{\partial y} = 6x^3y - x \sin y$$

so that

$$\frac{dy}{dx} = -\frac{9x^2y^2 + \cos y}{6x^3y - x \sin y}$$

for all values of x and y that satisfy the equation

$$3x^3y^2 + x \cos y = 0$$

and for which $6x^3y - x \sin y \neq 0$.

Example 2. Let $x^2 + y^2 = 0$; then $\partial f/\partial x = 2x$, $\partial f/\partial y = 2y$. But it does not follow that

$$\frac{dy}{dx} = -\frac{x}{y}.$$

This result is absurd inasmuch as the only real values of x and y that satisfy $x^2 + y^2 = 0$ are $x = 0$ and $y = 0$. Since $\partial f/\partial y$ vanishes at this point, the formal procedure used in obtaining dy/dx is meaningless.

Example 3. Let $f(x,y) = 0$ represent the locus of a curve, and let $P(x_0,y_0)$ be a point on the curve. The equation of the tangent line to the curve at the point P is

$$y - y_0 = \left(\frac{dy}{dx}\right)_{x=x_0} (x - x_0).$$

It follows from (4-8) that this equation can be written in the form

$$f_x(x_0,y_0)(x - x_0) + f_y(x_0,y_0)(y - y_0) = 0.$$

PROBLEMS

1. Find the equation of the tangent line to the ellipse

$$\frac{x^2}{a^2} + \frac{y^2}{b^2} = 1$$

at the point (x_0,y_0).

2. Find the equation of the tangent line to the folium of Descartes

$$x^3 + y^3 - 3axy = 0.$$

Note particularly the behavior of the tangent line to the folium at $(0,0)$.

3. Find du/dt if

$$u = \tan^{-1}\frac{y}{x} \quad \text{and} \quad \begin{cases} x = e^t + e^{-t} \\ y = e^t - e^{-t}. \end{cases}$$

4. Find the equation of the tangent line to the ellipse

$$x = a \cos\theta,$$
$$y = b \sin\theta,$$

at the point where $\theta = \pi/4$.

5. (a) Find du/dt, if $u = e^x \sin yz$ and $x = t^2$, $y = t - 1$, $z = 1/t$;
(b) find $\partial u/\partial r$ and $\partial u/\partial\theta$, if $u = x^2 - 4y^2$, $x = r\sec\theta$, and $y = r\tan\theta$.

6. (a) Find $\partial u/\partial x$ and du/dx, if $u = x^2 + y^2$ and $y = \tan x$;
(b) given $V = f(x,y,z)$, where $x = r\cos\theta$, $y = r\sin\theta$, $z = t$; compute $\partial V/\partial r$, $\partial V/\partial\theta$, $\partial V/\partial t$ in terms of $\partial V/\partial x$, $\partial V/\partial y$, and $\partial V/\partial z$.

5. Differentiation of Composite and Implicit Functions. The reasoning employed in the preceding section can be applied in obtaining the total differential, and hence the derivative, of a function of n variables

$$u = f(x_1,x_2,\ldots,x_n),$$

where

$$x_i = x_i(t), \quad i = 1, 2, \ldots, n$$

are n differentiable functions of a single variable t. The resulting expression for the total differential is

$$du = \frac{\partial f}{\partial x_1} dx_1 + \frac{\partial f}{\partial x_2} dx_2 + \cdots + \frac{\partial f}{\partial x_n} dx_n. \tag{5-1}$$

A question arises concerning the validity of formula (5-1) in the case where the variables x_i are functions of several independent variables $t_1, t_2, \ldots, t_m$. Thus, let

$$u = f(x_1, x_2, \ldots, x_n) \tag{5-2}$$

be a function of the n variables x_i, where the x_i are functions of the variables $t_1, t_2, \ldots, t_m$, say

$$x_i = x_i(t_1, t_2, \ldots, t_m), \qquad i = 1, 2, \ldots, n. \tag{5-3}$$

If all the variables except one, say t_k, are held fast, (5-2) becomes a function of the single variable t_k and one can calculate the derivative $\partial f/\partial t_k$ with the aid of (5-1). The notation $\partial f/\partial t_k$, instead of df/dt_k, is used to signify the fact that all variables except t_k are held fast.

Assuming the continuity of the derivatives involved, one can write

$$\frac{\partial f}{\partial t_1} = \frac{\partial f}{\partial x_1}\frac{\partial x_1}{\partial t_1} + \frac{\partial f}{\partial x_2}\frac{\partial x_2}{\partial t_1} + \cdots + \frac{\partial f}{\partial x_n}\frac{\partial x_n}{\partial t_1},$$

$$\frac{\partial f}{\partial t_2} = \frac{\partial f}{\partial x_1}\frac{\partial x_1}{\partial t_2} + \frac{\partial f}{\partial x_2}\frac{\partial x_2}{\partial t_2} + \cdots + \frac{\partial f}{\partial x_n}\frac{\partial x_n}{\partial t_2},$$

$$\cdots \cdots \cdots \cdots \cdots \cdots$$

$$\frac{\partial f}{\partial t_m} = \frac{\partial f}{\partial x_1}\frac{\partial x_1}{\partial t_m} + \frac{\partial f}{\partial x_2}\frac{\partial x_2}{\partial t_m} + \cdots + \frac{\partial f}{\partial x_n}\frac{\partial x_n}{\partial t_m}.$$

If $\partial f/\partial t_1$, $\partial f/\partial t_2$, $\ldots$, $\partial f/\partial t_m$ are multiplied, respectively, by dt_1, dt_2, $\ldots$, dt_m and the resulting expressions added, one obtains

$$\frac{\partial f}{\partial t_1}\, dt_1 + \frac{\partial f}{\partial t_2}\, dt_2 + \cdots + \frac{\partial f}{\partial t_m}\, dt_m$$

$$= \frac{\partial f}{\partial x_1}\left(\frac{\partial x_1}{\partial t_1}\, dt_1 + \frac{\partial x_1}{\partial t_2}\, dt_2 + \cdots + \frac{\partial x_1}{\partial t_m}\, dt_m\right)$$

$$+ \frac{\partial f}{\partial x_2}\left(\frac{\partial x_2}{\partial t_1}\, dt_1 + \frac{\partial x_2}{\partial t_2}\, dt_2 + \cdots + \frac{\partial x_2}{\partial t_m}\, dt_m\right)$$

$$+ \cdots \cdots \cdots \cdots \cdots \cdots \cdots$$

$$+ \frac{\partial f}{\partial x_n}\left(\frac{\partial x_n}{\partial t_1}\, dt_1 + \frac{\partial x_n}{\partial t_2}\, dt_2 + \cdots + \frac{\partial x_n}{\partial t_m}\, dt_m\right).$$

The left-hand member of this expression is the total differential of $f(x_1, x_2, \ldots, x_n)$, regarded as a function of the independent variables $t_1, t_2, \ldots, t_m$, whereas the terms in the parentheses in the right-hand member are precisely the total differentials of (5-3). Hence, one can write

$$df = \frac{\partial f}{\partial x_1}\, dx_1 + \frac{\partial f}{\partial x_2}\, dx_2 + \cdots + \frac{\partial f}{\partial x_n}\, dx_n,$$

which shows that formula (5-1) is valid whether the x_is are the independent variables or are functions of any set of other independent variables.

The foregoing can be summarized as follows:

THEOREM. *If $u = f(x_1, x_2, \ldots, x_n)$, then*

$$du = \frac{\partial f}{\partial x_1} dx_1 + \frac{\partial f}{\partial x_2} dx_2 + \cdots + \frac{\partial f}{\partial x_n} dx_n,$$

regardless of whether the variables x_i are the independent variables or are functions of other independent variables t_k. It is understood that all the derivatives involved (the $\partial f/\partial x_k$ and $\partial x_i/\partial t_k$) are continuous functions.

The fact that the total differential of a composite function has the same form irrespective of whether the variables involved are independent or not permits one to use the same formulas for calculating differentials as those established for the functions of a single variable. Thus,

$$d(u + v) = du + dv,$$

$$d(uv) = \frac{\partial(uv)}{\partial u} du + \frac{\partial(uv)}{\partial v} dv$$

$$= v\, du + u\, dv,$$

and so forth.

Example 1. If $u = xy + yz + zx$, $x = t$, $y = e^{-t}$, and $z = \cos t$,

$$\frac{du}{dt} = (y + z)\frac{dx}{dt} + (x + z)\frac{dy}{dt} + (x + y)\frac{dz}{dt}$$

$$= (e^{-t} + \cos t)(1) + (t + \cos t)(-e^{-t}) + (t + e^{-t})(-\sin t)$$

$$= e^{-t} + \cos t - te^{-t} - e^{-t}\cos t - t\sin t - e^{-t}\sin t.$$

This example illustrates the fact that this method of computing du/dt is often shorter than the old method in which the values of x, y, and z in terms of t are substituted in the expression for u before the derivative is computed.

Example 2. If $f(x,y) = x^2 + y^2$, where $x = r\cos\varphi$ and $y = r\sin\varphi$, then

$$\frac{\partial f}{\partial r} = \frac{\partial f}{\partial x}\frac{\partial x}{\partial r} + \frac{\partial f}{\partial y}\frac{\partial y}{\partial r} = 2x\cos\varphi + 2y\sin\varphi = 2r\cos^2\varphi + 2r\sin^2\varphi = 2r.$$

$$\frac{\partial f}{\partial\varphi} = \frac{\partial f}{\partial x}\frac{\partial x}{\partial\varphi} + \frac{\partial f}{\partial y}\frac{\partial y}{\partial\varphi} = 2x(-r\sin\varphi) + 2y(r\cos\varphi)$$

$$= -2r^2\cos\varphi\sin\varphi + 2r^2\cos\varphi\sin\varphi = 0.$$

Also, $df = 2r\, dr$ or $df = 2x\, dx + 2y\, dy.$

Since $f(x,y) = x^2 + y^2 = r^2$, these results could have been obtained directly.

Example 3. Let $z = e^{xy}$, where $x = \log(u + v)$ and $y = \tan^{-1}(u/v)$. Then,

$$\frac{\partial z}{\partial x} = ye^{xy}, \qquad \frac{\partial z}{\partial y} = xe^{xy}, \qquad \frac{\partial x}{\partial u} = \frac{1}{u + v}, \qquad \text{and} \qquad \frac{\partial y}{\partial u} = \frac{v}{v^2 + u^2}.$$

Hence,

$$\frac{\partial z}{\partial u} = \frac{\partial z}{\partial x}\frac{\partial x}{\partial u} + \frac{\partial z}{\partial y}\frac{\partial y}{\partial u} = \frac{ye^{xy}}{u + v} + \frac{xe^{xy}v}{v^2 + u^2}.$$

Similarly,

$$\frac{\partial z}{\partial v} = \frac{ye^{xy}}{u + v} - \frac{xe^{xy}u}{v^2 + u^2}.$$

The same results can be obtained by noting that

$$dz = ye^{xy}\,dx + xe^{xy}\,dy.$$

But

$$dx = \frac{\partial x}{\partial u}\,du + \frac{\partial x}{\partial v}\,dv = \frac{1}{u + v}\,du + \frac{1}{u + v}\,dv$$

and

$$dy = \frac{\partial y}{\partial u}\,du + \frac{\partial y}{\partial v}\,dv = \frac{v}{v^2 + u^2}\,du - \frac{u}{v^2 + u^2}\,dv.$$

Hence,

$$dz = ye^{xy}\frac{du + dv}{u + v} + xe^{xy}\frac{v\,du - u\,dv}{v^2 + u^2}$$

$$= \left(\frac{ye^{xy}}{u + v} + \frac{xe^{xy}v}{v^2 + u^2}\right)du + \left(\frac{ye^{xy}}{u + v} - \frac{xe^{xy}u}{v^2 + u^2}\right)dv.$$

But

$$dz = \frac{\partial z}{\partial u}\,du + \frac{\partial z}{\partial v}\,dv;$$

and since du and dv are independent differentials, equating the coefficients of du and dv in the two expressions for dz gives

$$\frac{\partial z}{\partial u} = \frac{ye^{xy}}{u + v} + \frac{xe^{xy}v}{v^2 + u^2}$$

and

$$\frac{\partial z}{\partial v} = \frac{ye^{xy}}{u + v} - \frac{xe^{xy}u}{v^2 + u^2}.$$

Let $f(x,y,z) = 0$ define any one of the variables as an implicit function of the remaining ones. If x and y are thought to be the independent variables and one can obtain a real differentiable solution for z in terms of x and y, it is possible to write

$$dz = \frac{\partial z}{\partial x}\,dx + \frac{\partial z}{\partial y}\,dy.$$

But

$$df = \frac{\partial f}{\partial x}\,dx + \frac{\partial f}{\partial y}\,dy + \frac{\partial f}{\partial z}\,dz = 0.$$

Substituting the value of dz in this equation gives

$$\frac{\partial f}{\partial x}\,dx + \frac{\partial f}{\partial y}\,dy + \frac{\partial f}{\partial z}\left(\frac{\partial z}{\partial x}\,dx + \frac{\partial z}{\partial y}\,dy\right) = 0,$$

or

$$\left(\frac{\partial f}{\partial x} + \frac{\partial f}{\partial z}\frac{\partial z}{\partial x}\right)dx + \left(\frac{\partial f}{\partial y} + \frac{\partial f}{\partial z}\frac{\partial z}{\partial y}\right)dy = 0.$$

Since x and y are independent variables, we get, on setting in turn $dx = 0$ and $dy = 0$,

$$\frac{\partial f}{\partial x} + \frac{\partial f}{\partial z}\frac{\partial z}{\partial x} = 0$$

and

$$\frac{\partial f}{\partial y} + \frac{\partial f}{\partial z}\frac{\partial z}{\partial y} = 0.$$

These equations could have been obtained directly by applying the chain rule to the equation $f(x,y,z) = 0$, in which z is regarded as a function of x and y, but we wished to illustrate another procedure followed in Sec. 10 and elsewhere. If $\partial f/\partial z \neq 0$, these equations give

$$\frac{\partial z}{\partial x} = -\frac{\partial f/\partial x}{\partial f/\partial z}, \qquad \frac{\partial z}{\partial y} = -\frac{\partial f/\partial y}{\partial f/\partial z}. \tag{5-4}$$

The formulas (5-4) permit one to calculate the partial derivatives of the function z defined implicitly by an equation

$$f(x,y,z) = 0.$$

As an illustration, let

$$x^2 + 2y^2 - 3xz + 1 = 0.$$

Then, by (5-4),

$$\frac{\partial z}{\partial x} = -\frac{2x - 3z}{-3x} \quad \text{and} \quad \frac{\partial z}{\partial y} = -\frac{4y}{-3x}.$$

Example 4. A function $f(x_1,x_2,\ldots,x_n)$ of n variables x_1, x_2, $\ldots$, x_n is said to be *homogeneous of degree m* if the function is multiplied by λ^m when the arguments x_1, x_2, $\ldots$, x_n are replaced by λx_1, λx_2, $\ldots$, λx_n, respectively. For example, $f(x,y) = x^2/\sqrt{x^2 + y^2}$ is homogeneous of degree 1, because the substitution of λx for x and λy for y yields $\lambda x^2/\sqrt{x^2 + y^2}$. Again, $f(x,y) = (1/y) + (\log x - \log y)/x$ is homogeneous of degree -1, whereas $f(x,y,z) = z^2/\sqrt[3]{x^2 + y^2}$ is homogeneous of degree $\frac{2}{3}$.

There is an important theorem, due to Euler, concerning homogeneous functions.

EULER'S THEOREM. *If $u = f(x_1,x_2,\ldots,x_n)$ is homogeneous of degree m and has continuous first partial derivatives, then*

$$x_1\frac{\partial f}{\partial x_1} + x_2\frac{\partial f}{\partial x_2} + \cdots + x_n\frac{\partial f}{\partial x_n} = mf(x_1,x_2,\ldots,x_n).$$

The proof of the theorem follows at once upon substituting

$$x_1' = \lambda x_1, \qquad x_2' = \lambda x_2, \qquad \ldots, \qquad x_n' = \lambda x_n.$$

Then, since $f(x_1,x_2,\ldots,x_n)$ is homogeneous of degree m,

$$f(x_1',x_2',\ldots,x_n') = \lambda^m f(x_1,x_2,\ldots,x_n).$$

Differentiating with respect to λ gives

$$\frac{\partial f}{\partial x_1'}\, x_1 + \frac{\partial f}{\partial x_2'}\, x_2 + \cdots + \frac{\partial f}{\partial x_n'}\, x_n = m\lambda^{m-1} f(x_1, x_2, \ldots, x_n).$$

If λ is set equal to 1, then $x_1 = x_1'$, $x_2 = x_2'$, $\ldots$, $x_n = x_n'$ and the theorem follows.

PROBLEMS

1. (a) Find dy/dx if $x \sec y + x^3 y^2 = 1$;
   (b) find $\partial z/\partial x$ and $\partial z/\partial y$ if $x^3 y - \sin z + z^3 = 0$.

2. If f is a function of u and v, where $u = \sqrt{x^2 + y^2}$ and $v = \tan^{-1}(y/x)$, find $\partial f/\partial x$, $\partial f/\partial y$, $\sqrt{(\partial f/\partial x)^2 + (\partial f/\partial y)^2}$.

3. If f is a function of u and v, where $u = r \cos \theta$ and $v = r \sin \theta$, find

$$\frac{\partial f}{\partial r},\ \frac{\partial f}{\partial \theta},\ \sqrt{\left(\frac{\partial f}{\partial r}\right)^2 + \frac{1}{r^2}\left(\frac{\partial f}{\partial \theta}\right)^2}.$$

4. If $x = x' \cos \theta - y' \sin \theta$, $y = x' \sin \theta + y' \cos \theta$, prove that

$$\left(\frac{\partial f}{\partial x}\right)^2 + \left(\frac{\partial f}{\partial y}\right)^2 = \left(\frac{\partial f}{\partial x'}\right)^2 + \left(\frac{\partial f}{\partial y'}\right)^2.$$

5. Find the total differential if $u = x^2 + y^2$, $x = r \cos \theta$, and $y = r \sin \theta$.

6. If $f = e^{xy}$, where $x = \log(u^2 + v^2)^{1/2}$ and $y = \tan^{-1}(u/v)$, find $\partial f/\partial u$ and $\partial f/\partial v$.

7. If $z = (u + v)/(1 - uv)$, $u = y \sin x$, and $v = e^{yx}$, find $\partial z/\partial x$ and $\partial z/\partial y$.

8. Find $\partial z/\partial r$ and $\partial z/\partial s$ if $z = (x - y)/(1 + xy)$, $x = \tan(r - s)$, and $y = e^{rs}$.

9. Verify Euler's theorem for each of the following functions:

(a) $f(x,y,z) = x^2 y + xy^2 + 2xyz$;

(b) $f(x,y) = \sqrt{y^2 - x^2} \sin^{-1}\dfrac{x}{y}$;

(c) $f(x,y) = \dfrac{1}{y^2} + \dfrac{\log x - \log y}{x^2}$;

(d) $f(x,y,z) = \dfrac{z^2}{\sqrt{x^2 - y^2}}$;

(e) $f(x,y,z) = (x^2 + y^2 + z^2)^{-1/2}$;

(f) $f(x,y) = e^{x/y}$;

(g) $f(x,y) = \dfrac{\sqrt{x + y}}{y}$;

(h) $f(x,y) = \dfrac{x^2 + y^2}{x^2 - y^2}$.

6. Higher Derivatives of Implicit Functions.

The problem of calculating the derivative of y with respect to x when y is an implicit function of the independent variable x defined by

$$f(x,y) = 0 \tag{6-1}$$

was discussed in Sec.4.   It was shown there that

$$f_x(x,y) + f_y(x,y)\,\frac{dy}{dx} = 0. \tag{6-2}$$

Differentiating this equation again and assuming that all the derivatives involved are continuous functions of x and y give

$$f_{xx}(x,y) + 2f_{xy}(x,y)\,\frac{dy}{dx} + f_{yy}(x,y)\left(\frac{dy}{dx}\right)^2 + f_y(x,y)\,\frac{d^2 y}{dx^2} = 0. \tag{6-3}$$

If $f_y(x,y) \neq 0$ at the point where the derivative is desired, (6-3) can be solved for d^2y/dx^2 and the value of dy/dx substituted from (6-2). The result is

$$\frac{d^2y}{dx^2} = -\frac{f_{xx}f_y^2 - 2f_{xy}f_xf_y + f_{yy}f_x^2}{f_y^3}.$$

The process can be continued to obtain the derivatives of higher orders.

A similar procedure can be employed to calculate the partial derivatives of a function z of two independent variables x and y defined implicitly by an equation of the form

$$f(x,y,z) = 0. \tag{6-4}$$

Differentiating (6-4) with respect to x and y in turn gives

$$f_x(x,y,z) + f_z(x,y,z)\frac{\partial z}{\partial x} = 0,$$

$$f_y(x,y,z) + f_z(x,y,z)\frac{\partial z}{\partial y} = 0. \tag{6-5}$$

If $f_z(x,y,z)$ does not vanish for those values of x, y, and z that satisfy (6-4), then Eqs. (6-5) can be solved for $\partial z/\partial x$ and $\partial z/\partial y$. Partial derivatives of higher order can then be obtained by differentiating equations (6-5).

Example: Let it be required to find the derivatives of second order of the function z defined implicitly by the equation

$$\frac{x^2}{a^2} + \frac{y^2}{b^2} + \frac{z^2}{c^2} = 1.$$

Differentiating this equation with respect to x and y gives

$$\frac{2x}{a^2} + \frac{2z}{c^2}\frac{\partial z}{\partial x} = 0,$$

$$\frac{2y}{b^2} + \frac{2z}{c^2}\frac{\partial z}{\partial y} = 0. \tag{6-6}$$

Differentiating the first of Eqs. (6-6) with respect to x and y, one obtains

$$\frac{2}{a^2} + \frac{2}{c^2}\left(\frac{\partial z}{\partial x}\right)^2 + \frac{2z}{c^2}\frac{\partial^2 z}{\partial x^2} = 0,$$

$$\frac{2}{c^2}\frac{\partial z}{\partial x}\frac{\partial z}{\partial y} + \frac{2z}{c^2}\frac{\partial^2 z}{\partial x \partial y} = 0.$$

Solving for $\partial^2 z/\partial x^2$ and $\partial^2 z/\partial x\,\partial y$ and making use of (6-6), one obtains

$$\frac{\partial^2 z}{\partial x^2} = -\frac{c^2}{a^4}\frac{a^2z^2 + c^2x^2}{z^3},$$

$$\frac{\partial^2 z}{\partial x \partial y} = -\frac{c^4}{a^2b^2}\frac{xy}{z^3}.$$

In a similar way the differentiation of the second of Eqs. (6-6) with respect to y yields

$$\frac{\partial^2 z}{\partial y^2} = -\frac{c^2}{b^4}\frac{b^2 z^2 + c^2 y^2}{z^3}.$$

PROBLEMS

1. Find y', y'', y''' if $x^3 + y^3 - 3axy = 0$.

2. Find $\partial z/\partial x$, $\partial z/\partial y$, $\partial^2 z/\partial x^2$, $\partial^2 z/\partial x\,\partial y$, and $\partial^2 z/\partial y^2$ at $(1,1,1)$ if $x^2 - y^2 + z^2 = 1$.

3. Find $\partial z/\partial x$, if

(a) $xz^2 - yz^2 + xy^2 z - 5 = 0$;   (b) $xz^3 - yz + 3xy = 0$.

7. Change of Variables. The main purpose of this section is to develop manipulative skill in calculating the derivatives of implicit functions and to indicate the formal modes of attack on the problem. The continuity of the functions and their partial derivatives is assumed throughout this section and will not be referred to again.

Let

$$w = f(u,v) \tag{7-1}$$

denote a function of two independent variables u and v, and suppose that u and v are connected with some other variables x and y by means of the relations

$$x = x(u,v),$$
$$y = y(u,v). \tag{7-2}$$

If Eqs. (7-2) are solved for x and y to yield

$$u = u(x,y),$$
$$v = v(x,y), \tag{7-3}$$

and the expressions (7-3) are substituted for u and v in (7-1), there will result a function of x and y, say

$$w = F(x,y). \tag{7-4}$$

The partial derivatives of w with respect to x and y can be calculated from (7-4) directly, but frequently it is impracticable to obtain the solution (7-3), and we consider an indirect mode of calculation. By the rule for the differentiation of composite functions,

$$\frac{\partial w}{\partial u} = \frac{\partial w}{\partial x}\frac{\partial x}{\partial u} + \frac{\partial w}{\partial y}\frac{\partial y}{\partial u},$$

$$\frac{\partial w}{\partial v} = \frac{\partial w}{\partial x}\frac{\partial x}{\partial v} + \frac{\partial w}{\partial y}\frac{\partial y}{\partial v}. \tag{7-5}$$

The partial derivatives $\partial x/\partial u$, $\partial y/\partial u$, $\partial x/\partial v$, and $\partial y/\partial v$ can be calculated from (7-2), and hence they may be regarded as known functions of u and *v.* The partial derivatives in the left-hand members of (7-5) are also known functions of u and v, since they can be calculated from (7-1).

Hence, equations (7-5) may be regarded as linear equations for the determination of $\partial w/\partial x$ and $\partial w/\partial y$. Assuming that the *Jacobian J(u,v)* defined by

$$J(u,v) \equiv \begin{vmatrix} \dfrac{\partial x}{\partial u} & \dfrac{\partial y}{\partial u} \\[2mm] \dfrac{\partial x}{\partial v} & \dfrac{\partial y}{\partial v} \end{vmatrix}$$

is not zero and solving by Cramer's rule give

$$\frac{\partial w}{\partial x} = \frac{\begin{vmatrix} \dfrac{\partial w}{\partial u} & \dfrac{\partial y}{\partial u} \\[2mm] \dfrac{\partial w}{\partial v} & \dfrac{\partial y}{\partial v} \end{vmatrix}}{J(u,v)}, \qquad \frac{\partial w}{\partial y} = \frac{\begin{vmatrix} \dfrac{\partial x}{\partial u} & \dfrac{\partial w}{\partial u} \\[2mm] \dfrac{\partial x}{\partial v} & \dfrac{\partial w}{\partial v} \end{vmatrix}}{J(u,v)}.$$

The resulting expressions for $\partial w/\partial x$ and $\partial w/\partial y$ are known functions of u and v and thus can be treated exactly like (7-1) if it is desirable to calculate the derivatives of higher orders.

As an example, consider the function $w(r,\theta)$, and let it be required to calculate the partial derivatives of w with respect to x and y, where $x = r\cos\theta$ and $y = r\sin\theta$. Now

$$\frac{\partial w}{\partial r} = \frac{\partial w}{\partial x}\frac{\partial x}{\partial r} + \frac{\partial w}{\partial y}\frac{\partial y}{\partial r} = \frac{\partial w}{\partial x}\cos\theta + \frac{\partial w}{\partial y}\sin\theta,$$

$$\frac{\partial w}{\partial \theta} = \frac{\partial w}{\partial x}\frac{\partial x}{\partial \theta} + \frac{\partial w}{\partial y}\frac{\partial y}{\partial \theta} = -\frac{\partial w}{\partial x}r\sin\theta + \frac{\partial w}{\partial y}r\cos\theta.$$

Solving these equations for $\partial w/\partial x$ and $\partial w/\partial y$ in terms of $\partial w/\partial r$ and $\partial w/\partial \theta$ gives

$$\frac{\partial w}{\partial x} = \cos\theta\frac{\partial w}{\partial r} - \frac{\sin\theta}{r}\frac{\partial w}{\partial \theta},$$

$$\frac{\partial w}{\partial y} = \sin\theta\frac{\partial w}{\partial r} + \frac{\cos\theta}{r}\frac{\partial w}{\partial \theta}.$$

The Jacobian J is, in this case,

$$\begin{vmatrix} \cos\theta & \sin\theta \\ -r\sin\theta & r\cos\theta \end{vmatrix} = r,$$

which does not vanish unless $r = 0$.

As a somewhat more complicated instance of implicit differentiation, consider a pair of equations

$$F(x,y,u,v) = 0,$$
$$G(x,y,u,v) = 0,$$

(7-6)

and let it be supposed that they can be solved for u and v in terms of x and y to yield

$$u = u(x,y),$$
$$v = v(x,y).$$

(7-7)

The partial derivatives of u and v with respect to x and y can be obtained in the following manner. Considering x and y as the independent variables and differentiating Eqs. (7-6) with respect to x and y give

$$\frac{\partial F}{\partial x} + \frac{\partial F}{\partial u}\frac{\partial u}{\partial x} + \frac{\partial F}{\partial v}\frac{\partial v}{\partial x} = 0, \qquad \frac{\partial F}{\partial y} + \frac{\partial F}{\partial u}\frac{\partial u}{\partial y} + \frac{\partial F}{\partial v}\frac{\partial v}{\partial y} = 0,$$

$$\frac{\partial G}{\partial x} + \frac{\partial G}{\partial u}\frac{\partial u}{\partial x} + \frac{\partial G}{\partial v}\frac{\partial v}{\partial x} = 0, \qquad \frac{\partial G}{\partial y} + \frac{\partial G}{\partial u}\frac{\partial u}{\partial y} + \frac{\partial G}{\partial v}\frac{\partial v}{\partial y} = 0.$$

(7-8)

Equations (7-8) are linear in $\partial u/\partial x$, $\partial u/\partial y$, $\partial v/\partial x$, and $\partial v/\partial y$. If

$$J(u,v) \equiv \begin{vmatrix} \dfrac{\partial F}{\partial u} & \dfrac{\partial F}{\partial v} \\[2mm] \dfrac{\partial G}{\partial u} & \dfrac{\partial G}{\partial v} \end{vmatrix} \neq 0,$$

the partial derivatives in question can be determined from (7-8) by Cramer's rule.

A special case of Eqs. (7-6) is useful in applications. Let

$$x = f(u,v),$$
$$y = g(u,v).$$

Differentiating these equations with respect to x and remembering that x and y are independent variables, one obtains

$$1 = \frac{\partial f}{\partial u}\frac{\partial u}{\partial x} + \frac{\partial f}{\partial v}\frac{\partial v}{\partial x},$$

$$0 = \frac{\partial g}{\partial u}\frac{\partial u}{\partial x} + \frac{\partial g}{\partial v}\frac{\partial v}{\partial x}.$$

(7-9)

These equations can be solved for $\partial u/\partial x$ and $\partial v/\partial x$ if

$$J(u,v) \equiv \begin{vmatrix} \dfrac{\partial f}{\partial u} & \dfrac{\partial f}{\partial v} \\[2mm] \dfrac{\partial g}{\partial u} & \dfrac{\partial g}{\partial v} \end{vmatrix} \neq 0.$$

Example 1. Let

$$u^2 - v^2 + 2x = 0,$$
$$uv - y = 0.$$

Differentiating with respect to x,

$$2\left(u\frac{\partial u}{\partial x} - v\frac{\partial v}{\partial x} + 1\right) = 0,$$

$$v\frac{\partial u}{\partial x} + u\frac{\partial v}{\partial x} = 0.$$

Hence

$$\frac{\partial u}{\partial x} = -\frac{u}{u^2 + v^2}, \qquad \frac{\partial v}{\partial x} = \frac{v}{u^2 + v^2}.$$

Differentiating the first of these results with respect to x gives

$$\frac{\partial^2 u}{\partial x^2} = \frac{-\dfrac{\partial u}{\partial x}(u^2 + v^2) + 2\left(u\dfrac{\partial u}{\partial x} + v\dfrac{\partial v}{\partial x}\right)u}{(u^2 + v^2)^2}$$

$$= \frac{u(u^2 + v^2) - 2u(u^2 - v^2)}{(u^2 + v^2)^3} = \frac{u(3v^2 - u^2)}{(u^2 + v^2)^3}.$$

One obtains similarly $\partial^2 v/\partial x^2$, $\partial^2 u/\partial x\,\partial y$, and higher derivatives.

Example 2. Let

(a)
$$x = u + v,$$
$$y = 3u + 2v.$$

Differentiating with respect to x,

$$1 = \frac{\partial u}{\partial x} + \frac{\partial v}{\partial x},$$

$$0 = 3\frac{\partial u}{\partial x} + 2\frac{\partial v}{\partial x},$$

so that

$$\frac{\partial u}{\partial x} = -2, \qquad \frac{\partial v}{\partial x} = 3.$$

It is easily checked that

$$\frac{\partial u}{\partial y} = 1, \qquad \frac{\partial v}{\partial y} = -1.$$

Equations (a) can be solved for u and v in terms of x and y, and the result is

$$u = -2x + y,$$
$$v = 3x - y.$$

Regarding u and v as the independent variables and differentiating these equations with respect to u, one finds

$$1 = -2\frac{\partial x}{\partial u} + \frac{\partial y}{\partial u},$$

$$0 = 3\frac{\partial x}{\partial u} - \frac{\partial y}{\partial u}.$$

Hence,
$$\frac{\partial x}{\partial u} = 1, \qquad \frac{\partial y}{\partial u} = 3.$$

This agrees with the result obtained by direct differentiation of (a), as of course it should. Note that $\partial u/\partial x$ and $\partial x/\partial u$ are not reciprocals.

Example 3. If $w = uv$ and

$$u^2 + v + x = 0,$$
(b)
$$v^2 - u - y = 0,$$

one can obtain $\partial w/\partial x$ as follows: Differentiation of w with respect to x gives

$$\frac{\partial w}{\partial x} = u\frac{\partial v}{\partial x} + v\frac{\partial u}{\partial x}.$$

The values of $\partial u/\partial x$ and $\partial v/\partial x$ can be calculated from (b) as was done in Example 1. The reader will check that

$$\frac{\partial w}{\partial x} = -\frac{u + 2v^2}{1 + 4uv}, \qquad \frac{\partial w}{\partial y} = \frac{2u^2 - v}{1 + 4uv}.$$

PROBLEMS

1. If $u^2 + v^2 + y^2 - 2x = 0$, $u^3 + v^3 - x^3 + 3y = 0$, find $\partial u/\partial x$, $\partial v/\partial x$, $\partial u/\partial y$, and $\partial v/\partial y$.

2. Find $\partial w/\partial x$ and $\partial w/\partial y$ if $w = u/v$,

$$x = u + v,$$
and
$$y = 3u + 2v.$$

3. Show that if $f(x,y,z) = 0$, then $(\partial z/\partial x)(\partial x/\partial z) = 1$ and $(\partial x/\partial y)(\partial y/\partial z)(\partial z/\partial x) = -1$. Note that in general $\partial z/\partial x$ and $\partial x/\partial z$ are not reciprocals.

4. If $x = x(u,v)$, $y = y(u,v)$ with $\partial x/\partial u = \partial y/\partial v$, and $\partial x/\partial v = -\partial y/\partial u$, then

$$\frac{\partial^2 w}{\partial u^2} + \frac{\partial^2 w}{\partial v^2} = \left(\frac{\partial^2 w}{\partial x^2} + \frac{\partial^2 w}{\partial y^2}\right)\left[\left(\frac{\partial x}{\partial u}\right)^2 + \left(\frac{\partial x}{\partial v}\right)^2\right].$$

5. Show that the expressions

$$V_1 = \left(\frac{\partial z}{\partial x}\right)^2 + \left(\frac{\partial z}{\partial y}\right)^2 \quad \text{and} \quad V_2 = \frac{\partial^2 z}{\partial x^2} + \frac{\partial^2 z}{\partial y^2},$$

upon change of variable by means of $x = r\cos\theta$, $y = r\sin\theta$, become

$$V_1 = \left(\frac{\partial z}{\partial r}\right)^2 + \frac{1}{r^2}\left(\frac{\partial z}{\partial \theta}\right)^2$$

and

$$V_2 = \frac{\partial^2 z}{\partial r^2} + \frac{1}{r^2}\frac{\partial^2 z}{\partial \theta^2} + \frac{1}{r}\frac{\partial z}{\partial r}.$$

6. Show that

$$\frac{\partial^2 V}{\partial t^2} = c^2 \frac{\partial^2 V}{\partial x^2}$$

if $V = f(x + ct) + g(x - ct)$, where f and g are any functions possessing continuous second derivatives.

7. Show that

$$\frac{\partial^2 V}{\partial x^2} + \frac{\partial^2 V}{\partial y^2} = e^{-2r}\left(\frac{\partial^2 V}{\partial r^2} + \frac{\partial^2 V}{\partial \theta^2}\right)$$

if $x = e^r \cos\theta$, $y = e^r \sin\theta$.

8. Find $\partial u/\partial x$ if

$$u^2 - v^2 - x^3 + 3y = 0,$$

$$u + v - y^2 - 2x = 0.$$

9. Prove that

$$\frac{\partial u}{\partial x}\frac{\partial y}{\partial u} + \frac{\partial v}{\partial x}\frac{\partial y}{\partial v} = 0$$

if $F(x,y,u,v) = 0$ and $G(x,y,u,v) = 0$.

10. If $V_1(x,y,z)$ and $V_2(x,y,z)$ satisfy the equation

$$\nabla^2 V \equiv \frac{\partial^2 V}{\partial x^2} + \frac{\partial^2 V}{\partial y^2} + \frac{\partial^2 V}{\partial z^2} = 0,$$

then

$$U \equiv V_1(x,y,z) + (x^2 + y^2 + z^2)V_2(x,y,z)$$

satisfies the equation

$$\nabla^2 \nabla^2 U = 0,$$

where

$$\nabla^2 \equiv \frac{\partial^2}{\partial x^2} + \frac{\partial^2}{\partial y^2} + \frac{\partial^2}{\partial z^2}.$$

11. To indicate explicitly the variables entering in the Jacobian

$$J(u,v) = \begin{vmatrix} \dfrac{\partial x}{\partial u} & \dfrac{\partial y}{\partial u} \\[2ex] \dfrac{\partial x}{\partial v} & \dfrac{\partial y}{\partial v} \end{vmatrix}$$

one frequently writes $J(u,v) = J\left(\dfrac{x,y}{u,v}\right)$. The Jacobian

$$J(x,y) = \begin{vmatrix} \dfrac{\partial u}{\partial x} & \dfrac{\partial v}{\partial x} \\[2ex] \dfrac{\partial u}{\partial y} & \dfrac{\partial v}{\partial y} \end{vmatrix}$$

of the transformation (7-3) is written as $J(x,y) = J\left(\dfrac{u,v}{x,y}\right)$. Prove that:

(a) $J\left(\dfrac{u,v}{x,y}\right) J\left(\dfrac{x,y}{u,v}\right) = 1;$

(b) $J\left(\dfrac{u,v}{x,y}\right) J\left(\dfrac{x,y}{\xi,\eta}\right) = J\left(\dfrac{u,v}{\xi,\eta}\right),$

where $u = u(x,y)$, $v = v(x,y)$, $x = x(\xi,\eta)$, and $y = y(\xi,\eta)$. *Hint:* Write out the Jacobians and multiply.

APPLICATIONS OF DIFFERENTIATION

8. Directional Derivatives. Formula (4-2) has a simple geometrical meaning when interpreted as the space rate of change of a given function $u(x,y)$. Thus, let $u(x,y)$ be specified along a smooth curve C with parametric equations

$$x = x(s),$$
$$y = y(s),$$

(8-1)

where s is the arc-parameter measured along C. By virtue of Eqs. (8-1), $u(x,y)$ can be regarded as a function of s and the rate of change of $u(x,y)$ along C is

$$\frac{du}{ds} = \frac{\partial u}{\partial x}\frac{dx}{ds} + \frac{\partial u}{\partial y}\frac{dy}{ds}.$$

(8-2)

At a given point $P_0(x_0,y_0)$ on C, Eq. (8-2) yields

$$\left.\frac{du}{ds}\right|_{P_0} = u_x(x_0,y_0)\cos\alpha + u_y(x_0,y_0)\sin\alpha,$$

(8-3)

since $dx/ds = \cos\alpha$ and $dy/ds = \sin\alpha$, as is clear from Fig. 5. It follows from (8-3) that the rate of change of $u(x,y)$ at a *given point* depends only on the direction of the curve passing through that point. If the direction of C is that of the x axis, the angle $\alpha = 0$ and $du/ds = \partial u/\partial x$; if the direction of C is that of the y axis, $\alpha = \pi/2$ and $du/ds = \partial u/\partial y$. For an arbitrary direction specified by α, Eq. (8-3) defines the *directional derivative* of $u(x,y)$ in that direction. Thus the derivatives u_x and u_y are directional derivatives in the directions of the coordinate axes indicated by the subscripts.

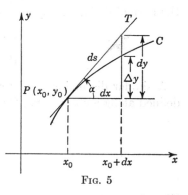

FIG. 5

We now ask the question: What is the angle α for which the directional derivative of $u(x,y)$ at a given point has a maximum value? Since a necessary condition for a maximum is the vanishing of the derivative of (8-3) with respect to α, we get the equation

$$-u_x(x_0,y_0) \sin \alpha + u_y(x_0,y_0) \cos \alpha = 0,$$

from which we conclude that when $u_x(x_0,y_0) \neq 0$,

$$\tan \alpha = \frac{u_y(x_0,y_0)}{u_x(x_0,y_0)}. \tag{8-4}$$

Accordingly, there are two values of α differing by $180°$ which satisfy the condition (8-4). The corresponding values of $\cos \alpha$ and $\sin \alpha$ in (8-3), therefore, are

$$\cos \alpha = \frac{\pm u_x}{\sqrt{u_x^2 + u_y^2}}, \qquad \sin \alpha = \frac{\pm u_y}{\sqrt{u_x^2 + u_y^2}}. \tag{8-5}$$

The substitution in (8-3) of the values from (8-5) with the plus sign yields the desired maximum

$$\left(\frac{du}{ds}\right)_{\max} = \sqrt{u_x^2 + u_y^2}, \tag{8-6}$$

while the other pair of values in (8-5) gives a minimum

$$\left(\frac{du}{ds}\right)_{\min} = -\sqrt{u_x^2 + u_y^2}.$$

The vector pointing in the direction of the greatest rate of increase of $u(x,y)$ at a given point (x,y) and whose length is determined by (8-6) is called the *gradient*, and $\left(\dfrac{du}{ds}\right)_{\max}$ is called the *normal derivative*.[1] We denote the normal derivative by du/dn and write

$$\frac{du}{dn} = \sqrt{u_x^2 + u_y^2}. \tag{8-7}$$

A similar discussion can be applied to a differentiable function $u(x,y,z)$ defined along a space curve C with parametric equations

$$x = x(s),$$
$$y = y(s), \tag{8-8}$$
$$z = z(s).$$

We get

$$\frac{du}{ds} = \frac{\partial u}{\partial x}\frac{dx}{ds} + \frac{\partial u}{\partial y}\frac{dy}{ds} + \frac{\partial u}{\partial z}\frac{dz}{ds}, \tag{8-9}$$

---

[1] The reason for this terminology is given in Chap. 5, Sec. 3.

where (see Fig. 6)

$$\frac{dx}{ds} = \cos(x,s), \qquad \frac{dy}{ds} = \cos(y,s), \qquad \frac{dz}{ds} = \cos(z,s) \qquad (8\text{-}10)$$

are the direction cosines of the tangent line T at a given point P of C.

To determine the particular direction yielding a maximum of (8-9) at a given point $P(x_0,y_0,z_0)$, we must maximize the resulting function of the

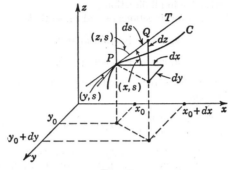

Fig. 6

direction cosines in (8-9). This problem, involving the determination of a maximum of functions of several variables, is discussed in Example 3, Sec. 10, where it is shown that $\left(\dfrac{du}{ds}\right)_{\max}$ for (8-9) is given by the formula

$$\frac{du}{dn} = \sqrt{u_x^2 + u_y^2 + u_z^2}, \qquad (8\text{-}11)$$

analogous to (8-7). The expression (8-11) is called the *normal derivative* of u.

Example 1. Find the directional derivative for $u(x,y) = x^2 + y^2$ at $(1,1)$ in the direction making the angle of $30°$ with the positive x axis.

Formula (8-3) yields

$$\frac{du}{ds}\bigg|_{(1,1)} = 2x\bigg|_{(1,1)} \cos 30° + 2y\bigg|_{(1,1)} \sin 30° = \sqrt{3} + 1.$$

The normal derivative at this point, as found with the aid of formula (8-7), is

$$\frac{du}{dn} = \sqrt{(2x)^2 + (2y)^2}\bigg|_{(1,1)} = 2\sqrt{2}$$

and the corresponding angle α, as follows from (8-4), is $45°$.

Example 2. Find the directional derivative of $u(x,y,z) = xyz$ at $(1,2,3)$ in the direction of the line making equal angles with the coordinate axes. Since the angles are equal and the sum of the squares of the direction cosines is 1, we conclude from

$$\cos^2(x,s) + \cos^2(y,s) + \cos^2(z,s) = 1$$

that $\cos (x,s) = \cos (y,s) = \cos (z,s) = 1/\sqrt{3}$. Also, at the point $(1,2,3)$ we have

$$\frac{\partial u}{\partial x} = yz = 6, \qquad \frac{\partial u}{\partial y} = xz = 3, \qquad \frac{\partial u}{\partial z} = xy = 2.$$

The substitution in (8-9) then yields

$$\frac{du}{ds} = \frac{6}{\sqrt{3}} + \frac{3}{\sqrt{3}} + \frac{2}{\sqrt{3}} = \frac{11}{\sqrt{3}}.$$

Example 3. Show that the directional derivative of $u(x,y)$ in two noncollinear directions determines the derivative in all directions.

Let the derivative be given for directions α_0 and α_1, so that

$$u_x \cos \alpha_0 + u_y \sin \alpha_0 = a,$$

$$u_x \cos \alpha_1 + u_y \sin \alpha_1 = b,$$

where a and b are known. If these are regarded as equations for the unknowns u_x and u_y, the coefficient determinant is

$$\begin{vmatrix} \cos \alpha_0 & \sin \alpha_0 \\ \cos \alpha_1 & \sin \alpha_1 \end{vmatrix} = \cos \alpha_0 \sin \alpha_1 - \cos \alpha_1 \sin \alpha_0.$$

This reduces to $\sin (\alpha_1 - \alpha_0)$, which is zero only if the two directions are collinear. Hence u_x and u_y can be found, and the directional derivative is determined for every direction by (8-3).

PROBLEMS

1. Find the directional derivative of $f(x,y) = x^2y + \sin xy$ at $(1,\pi/2)$, in the direction of the line making an angle of $45°$ with the positive x axis.

2. Find

$$\frac{df}{dn} = \sqrt{\left(\frac{\partial f}{\partial x}\right)^2 + \left(\frac{\partial f}{\partial y}\right)^2}$$

if $x = r \cos \theta$, $y = r \sin \theta$, and f is a function of the variables r and θ.

3. Find the directional derivative of $f(x,y) = x^3y + e^{yx}$ in the direction of the curve which, at the point $(1,1)$, makes an angle of $30°$ with the x axis.

4. Find the normal derivative of $u = x^2 + y^2 + z^2$ at the point $(1,2,3)$ and the directional derivatives at that point along the line joining $(0,0,0)$ and $(1,2,3)$.

9. Maxima and Minima of Functions of Several Variables. A function $f(x,y)$ defined in a region R is said to have a *relative maximum* at a point (a,b) if

$$\Delta f \equiv f(a + h, b + k) - f(a,b) \leq 0 \qquad (9\text{-}1)$$

for all values of h and k in the neighborhood of (a,b). It is said to have a *relative minimum* at (a,b) if

$$\Delta f \equiv f(a + h, b + k) - f(a,b) \geq 0 \qquad (9\text{-}2)$$

for all values (h,k) in the neighborhood of (a,b).

The requirement that the inequalities (9-1) and (9-2) hold for all values of (h,k) in the neighborhood of (a,b) implies that we are concerned here only with the interior and not the boundary points of the region. A function may attain a maximum or a minimum value on the boundary of the region, but the behavior of functions on the boundary requires a separate investigation, the nature of which will be clear from the sequel. The greatest and least values assumed by $f(x,y)$ in the closed region are called, respectively, the *absolute maximum* and the *absolute minimum*. In the following discussion we dispense with the adjective "relative," and we shall refer to relative maxima and minima simply as *maxima* and *minima*.

Let it be assumed that $f(x,y)$ attains a maximum (or minimum) at some interior point (a,b). Then the function $f(x,b)$ of the variable x must attain a maximum (or minimum) at $x = a$. From the study of functions of one variable it follows that the derivative of $f(x,b)$, if it exists, must vanish at $x = a$. The derivative may cease to exist at the critical points when the behavior of the function is like that shown in Fig. 7 in the neigh-

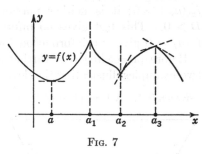

FIG. 7

borhood of $x = a_1$, $x = a_2$, and $x = a_3$. Thus, a *necessary* condition for a maximum (or minimum) of $f(x,b)$ at $x = a$ is that

$$\frac{\partial f}{\partial x} = 0 \qquad (9\text{-}3)$$

if this derivative exists at $x = a$.

A similar consideration of the function $f(a,y)$ leads to the conclusion that

$$\frac{\partial f}{\partial y} = 0 \qquad \text{at } y = b \qquad (9\text{-}4)$$

whenever this derivative exists.

The coordinates (a,b) thus satisfy the pair of equations

$$\frac{\partial f}{\partial x} = 0, \qquad \frac{\partial f}{\partial y} = 0 \qquad (9\text{-}5)$$

at any point (a,b) where $f(x,y)$ attains a maximum or minimum.

This discussion is capable of extension to functions of any number of variables to yield a theorem.

THEOREM. *A function $f(x_1,x_2,\ldots,x_n)$ of n independent variables x_i attains a maximum or a minimum only for those values of the variables x_i for which $f_{x_1}, f_{x_2}, \ldots, f_{x_n}$ either vanish simultaneously or cease to exist.*

We emphasize that the conditions stated in this theorem are necessary but not sufficient for a maximum or a minimum.[1] Although the matter of sufficiency can usually be determined from the nature of the problem and from physical considerations leading to its formulation, we record here a test that may prove useful to settle doubtful cases.[2]

If $f(x,y)$ is a function with continuous second partial derivatives, and if $f_x(a,b) = 0$ and $f_y(a,b) = 0$, then $f(a,b)$ is a *maximum* provided that

$$D \equiv f_{xy}^2(a,b) - f_{xx}(a,b)f_{yy}(a,b) < 0$$

and $f_{xx}(a,b) < 0$, $f_{yy}(a,b) < 0$; it is a *minimum* if $D < 0$ and $f_{xx}(a,b) > 0$, $f_{yy}(a,b) > 0$; it is neither maximum nor minimum (a saddle point) if $D > 0$. This test gives no information if $D = 0$, just as the condition $f''(a) = 0$ gives no information for the function $f(x)$ with $f'(a) = 0$.

Before proceeding to a further study of maxima and minima, we give two examples illustrating the developments of this section.

Example 1.   A long piece of tin 12 in. wide is made into a trough by bending up the sides to form equal angles with the base (Fig. 8). Find the amount to be bent up and the angle of inclination of the sides that will make the carrying capacity a maximum.

The volume will be a maximum if the area of the trapezoidal cross section is a maximum.   The area is

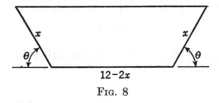

$12-2x$

FIG. 8

$$A = 12x \sin\theta - 2x^2 \sin\theta + x^2 \sin\theta \cos\theta,$$

for $12 - 2x$ is the lower base, $12 - 2x + 2x \cos\theta$ is the upper base, and $x \sin\theta$ is the altitude.   Then,

$$\frac{\partial A}{\partial\theta} = 12x \cos\theta - 2x^2 \cos\theta + x^2 \cos^2\theta - x^2 \sin^2\theta$$

$$= x(12 \cos\theta - 2x \cos\theta + x \cos^2\theta - x \sin^2\theta)$$

and $$\frac{\partial A}{\partial x} = 2 \sin\theta(6 - 2x + x \cos\theta).$$

Now $\partial A/\partial x = 0$ and $\partial A/\partial\theta = 0$ if $\sin\theta = 0$ and $x = 0$, which, from physical considerations, cannot give a maximum.

There remain to be satisfied

$$6 - 2x + x \cos\theta = 0$$

and $$12 \cos\theta - 2x \cos\theta + x \cos^2\theta - x \sin^2\theta = 0.$$

Solving the first equation for x and substituting in the second yield, upon simplification,

$$\cos\theta = \tfrac{1}{2} \quad \text{or} \quad \theta = 60°, \quad \text{and} \quad x = 4.$$

Since physical considerations show that a maximum exists, $x = 4$ and $\theta = 60°$ must give the maximum.

[1] Recall, for example, the situation when $f(x)$ has a point of inflection with a horizontal tangent.

[2] A proof and further discussion are contained in I. S. Sokolnikoff, "Advanced Calculus," sec. 89, McGraw-Hill Book Company, Inc., New York, 1939.

Example 2. Find the maxima and minima of the surface

$$\frac{x^2}{a^2} - \frac{y^2}{b^2} = 2cz.$$

Now,

$$\frac{\partial z}{\partial x} = \frac{1}{c}\frac{x}{a^2}, \qquad \frac{\partial z}{\partial y} = -\frac{1}{c}\frac{y}{b^2},$$

which vanish when $x = y = 0$.   But

$$\frac{\partial^2 z}{\partial x^2} = \frac{1}{a^2 c}, \qquad \frac{\partial^2 z}{\partial y^2} = -\frac{1}{b^2 c}, \qquad \frac{\partial^2 z}{\partial x \, \partial y} = 0.$$

Hence, $D = 1/a^2 b^2 c^2$, and consequently, there is no maximum or minimum at $x = y = 0$. The surface under consideration is a saddle-shaped surface called a *hyperbolic paraboloid*. The points for which the first partial derivatives vanish and $D > 0$ are called *minimax*. The reason for this odd name appears from a consideration of the shape of the hyperbolic paraboloid near the origin of the coordinate system.   The reader will benefit from sketching it in the vicinity of $(0,0,0)$.

PROBLEMS

1. Divide a into three parts such that their product is a maximum.   Test by using the second-derivative criterion.

2. Find the volume of the largest rectangular parallelepiped that can be inscribed in the ellipsoid

$$\frac{x^2}{a^2} + \frac{y^2}{b^2} + \frac{z^2}{c^2} = 1.$$

3. Find the dimensions of the largest rectangular parallelepiped that has three faces in the coordinate planes and one vertex in the plane

$$\frac{x}{a} + \frac{y}{b} + \frac{z}{c} = 1.$$

4. A pentagonal frame is composed of a rectangle surmounted by an isosceles triangle. What are the dimensions for maximum area of the pentagon if the perimeter is given as P?

5. A floating anchorage is designed with a body in the form of a right-circular cylinder with equal ends that are right-circular cones.   If the volume is given, find the dimensions giving the minimum surface area.

6. Given n points P_i whose coordinates are (x_i, y_i, z_i) $(i = 1, 2, \ldots, n)$.   Show that the coordinates of the point $P(x,y,z)$, such that the sum of the squares of the distances from P to the P_i is a minimum, are given by

$$\left(\frac{1}{n} \sum_{i=1}^{n} x_i, \ \frac{1}{n} \sum_{i=1}^{n} y_i, \ \frac{1}{n} \sum_{i=1}^{n} z_i \right).$$

10. Constrained Maxima and Minima. The discussion in the preceding section was confined to the calculation of the maximum and minimum values of functions of several independent variables.   In a large number of investigations, it is required that the maximum and minimum values of a differentiable function $f(x_1, x_2, \ldots, x_n)$ be found when the variables x_i are connected by some functional relationships, so that the x_i are no longer independent. Such problems are called problems in *constrained* maxima to distinguish them from the problems in *free* maxima discussed in Sec. 9.

To avoid circumlocution, we shall speak of the maximum or minimum values as the *extreme* values. Thus, let us consider the problem of finding the extreme values of the function

$$u = f(x,y,z), \tag{10-1}$$

in which the variables x, y, z are constrained by the relation

$$\varphi(x,y,z) = 0. \tag{10-2}$$

This problem can be solved by the procedure of Sec. 9 as follows: Suppose that the constraining relation (10-2) is solved for one of the variables, say z, to yield a differentiable function

$$z = \Phi(x,y). \tag{10-3}$$

If one substitutes z from (10-3) in (10-1), there results the function

$$u = f[x,y,\Phi(x,y)] \equiv F(x,y) \tag{10-4}$$

of two independent variables x, y to which the considerations of Sec. 9 apply.

However, either the solution (10-3) may be difficult to obtain or the function $F(x,y)$ in (10-4) may be so unwieldy that the simultaneous equations $F_x(x,y) = 0$, $F_y(x,y) = 0$ are unpleasant to deal with. In this event an ingenious method devised by the great French analyst Lagrange often leads to a manageable and symmetric system of equations for the determination of extreme values. The central idea of the method hinges on the following observation: In Sec. 9, we saw that a necessary condition for a relative extremum of the differentiable function $f(x_1,x_2,\ldots,x_n)$ of n independent variables is the simultaneous vanishing of all partial derivatives f_{x_i}. Inasmuch as the total differential of f is

$$df = f_{x_1}\,dx_1 + f_{x_2}\,dx_2 + \cdots + f_{x_n}\,dx_n,$$

it is clear that $df = 0$ whenever each $f_{x_i} = 0$. Conversely, if $df = 0$, the partial derivatives f_{x_i} vanish, since the dx_i are independent. But it is also true that the vanishing of the total differential is a necessary condition for an extremum of $f(x_1,x_2,\ldots,x_n)$ even when the variables x_i are dependent because of the invariant character of df stated in the theorem of Sec. 5. We can thus state a theorem:

THEOREM. *A necessary condition for an extremum of a differentiable function $f(x_1,x_2,\ldots,x_n)$ is the vanishing of its total differential at the maximum and minimum points of the function.*

We proceed now to a discussion of the *method of Lagrange multipliers* for determining the extreme values of the function in (10-1) subject to the equation of constraint (10-2).

By the theorem just stated, the differential of (10-1) vanishes at the critical points so that

$$\frac{\partial f}{\partial x}\, dx + \frac{\partial f}{\partial y}\, dy + \frac{\partial f}{\partial z}\, dz = 0. \tag{10-5}$$

Also, since $\varphi(x,y,z) = 0$, its total differential vanishes and we can write

$$\frac{\partial \varphi}{\partial x}\, dx + \frac{\partial \varphi}{\partial y}\, dy + \frac{\partial \varphi}{\partial z}\, dz = 0. \tag{10-6}$$

Let Eq. (10-6) be multiplied by some parameter λ and then added to (10-5). The result is

$$\left(\frac{\partial f}{\partial x} + \lambda \frac{\partial \varphi}{\partial x}\right) dx + \left(\frac{\partial f}{\partial y} + \lambda \frac{\partial \varphi}{\partial y}\right) dy + \left(\frac{\partial f}{\partial z} + \lambda \frac{\partial \varphi}{\partial z}\right) dz = 0. \tag{10-7}$$

If we regard x and y as independent variables, and suppose that $\partial \varphi/\partial z \neq 0$ at the point where the extremum is attained, then we can find a λ such that at this point

$$\frac{\partial f}{\partial z} + \lambda \frac{\partial \varphi}{\partial z} = 0. \tag{10-8}$$

With this choice of λ, Eq. (10-7) reduces to

$$\left(\frac{\partial f}{\partial x} + \lambda \frac{\partial \varphi}{\partial x}\right) dx + \left(\frac{\partial f}{\partial y} + \lambda \frac{\partial \varphi}{\partial y}\right) dy = 0.$$

But since dx and dy are independent increments, we conclude from this equation that

$$\frac{\partial f}{\partial x} + \lambda \frac{\partial \varphi}{\partial x} = 0,$$

$$\frac{\partial f}{\partial y} + \lambda \frac{\partial \varphi}{\partial y} = 0. \tag{10-9}$$

The system of three equations (10-8) and (10-9) contains four unknowns x, y, z, λ, and we must adjoin to it the fourth equation (10-2) to obtain the complete system for the determination of the unknowns.

If $\partial \varphi/\partial z = 0$ at the point where the extremum is attained, but $\partial \varphi/\partial y \neq 0$, the roles of z and y in the foregoing discussion are interchanged. Clearly, the method will fail to yield the desired value of λ when φ_x, φ_y, and φ_z vanish simultaneously at the point where $f(x,y,z)$ has an extremum.

Before proceeding to extend the Lagrange method to the study of extreme values of functions with several constraining conditions, we consider four instructive examples.

Example 1. Find the maximum and the minimum distances from the origin to the curve

$$5x^2 + 6xy + 5y^2 - 8 = 0.$$

The problem here is to determine the extreme values of

$$f(x,y) = x^2 + y^2$$

subject to the condition

$$\varphi(x,y) \equiv 5x^2 + 6xy + 5y^2 - 8 = 0.$$

Equations (10-9) and (10-2) in this case read

$$2x + \lambda(10x + 6y) = 0,$$

$$2y + \lambda(6x + 10y) = 0,$$

$$5x^2 + 6xy + 5y^2 - 8 = 0.$$

Multiplying the first of these equations by y and the second by x and then subtracting give

$$6\lambda(y^2 - x^2) = 0,$$

so that $y = \pm x$. Substituting these values of y in the third equation gives two equations for the determination of x, namely,

$$2x^2 = 1 \quad \text{and} \quad x^2 = 2.$$

The first of these gives $f \equiv x^2 + y^2 = 1$, and the second gives $f \equiv x^2 + y^2 = 4$. Obviously, the first value is a minimum, whereas the second is a maximum. The curve is an ellipse of semiaxes 2 and 1 whose major axis makes an angle of $45°$ with the x axis.

Example 2. Find the dimensions of the rectangular box, without a top, of maximum capacity whose surface is 108 in.^{2}

The function to be maximized is

$$f(x,y,z) \equiv xyz,$$

subject to the condition

$$xy + 2xz + 2yz = 108. \tag{10-10}$$

Equations (10-8) and (10-9) yield

$$yz + \lambda(y + 2z) = 0,$$

$$xz + \lambda(x + 2z) = 0, \tag{10-11}$$

$$xy + \lambda(2x + 2y) = 0.$$

In order to solve these equations, multiply the first by x, the second by y, and the last by z, and add.   There results

$$\lambda(2xy + 4xz + 4yz) + 3xyz = 0,$$

or

$$\lambda(xy + 2xz + 2yz) + \tfrac{3}{2}xyz = 0.$$

Substituting from (10-10) gives

$$108\lambda + \tfrac{3}{2}xyz = 0,$$

or

$$\lambda = -\frac{xyz}{72}.$$

Substituting this value of λ in (10-11) and dividing out common factors give

$$1 - \frac{x}{72}(y + 2z) = 0,$$

$$1 - \frac{y}{72}(x + 2z) = 0,$$

$$1 - \frac{z}{72}(2x + 2y) = 0.$$

From the first two of these equations, it is evident that $x = y$. The substitution of $x = y$ in the third equation gives $z = 18/y$. Substituting for y and z in the first equation yields $x = 6$. Thus, $x = 6$, $y = 6$, and $z = 3$ give the desired dimensions.

Example 3. Show that the maximum value of the directional derivative of $u(x,y,z)$ at any point is given by

$$\frac{du}{dn} = \sqrt{u_x^2 + u_y^2 + u_z^2}.$$

We write the directional derivative [see Eq. (8-9)] in the form

$$f(\alpha,\beta,\gamma) \equiv \frac{du}{ds} = u_x \cos \alpha + u_y \cos \beta + u_z \cos \gamma, \tag{10-12}$$

where $\cos \alpha = \cos(x,s)$, $\cos \beta = \cos(y,s)$, $\cos \gamma = \cos(z,s)$, and maximize $f(\alpha,\beta,\gamma)$ subject to the constraining condition

$$\varphi(\alpha,\beta,\gamma) \equiv \cos^2 \alpha + \cos^2 \beta + \cos^2 \gamma - 1 = 0. \tag{10-13}$$

The system of Eqs. (10-8) and (10-9) then yields

$$-u_x \sin \alpha - 2\lambda \cos \alpha \sin \alpha = 0,$$

$$-u_y \sin \beta - 2\lambda \cos \beta \sin \beta = 0, \tag{10-14}$$

$$-u_z \sin \gamma - 2\lambda \cos \gamma \sin \gamma = 0.$$

The case when either $\sin \alpha$, $\sin \beta$, or $\sin \gamma$ vanishes is trivial because of the constraining condition (10-13). Thus, the system (10-14) reduces to

$$u_x = 2\lambda \cos \alpha, \qquad u_y = 2\lambda \cos \beta, \qquad u_z = 2\lambda \cos \gamma, \tag{10-15}$$

and we conclude that

$$u_x^2 + u_y^2 + u_z^2 = 4\lambda^2.$$

Thus, $\lambda = \frac{1}{2}\sqrt{u_x^2 + u_y^2 + u_z^2}$, and the substitution of this value of λ in (10-15) gives

$$\cos \alpha = \frac{u_x}{\sqrt{u_x^2 + u_y^2 + u_z^2}}, \qquad \cos \beta = \frac{u_y}{\sqrt{u_x^2 + u_y^2 + u_z^2}}, \qquad \cos \gamma = \frac{u_z}{\sqrt{u_x^2 + u_y^2 + u_z^2}}.$$

On inserting these values in (10-12) we get the desired result

$$\left(\frac{du}{ds}\right)_{max} \equiv \frac{du}{dn} = \sqrt{u_x^2 + u_y^2 + u_z^2}.$$

Example 4. Find the shortest distance from the origin to the curve $y = (x - 1)^{3/2}$ in Fig. 9. We apply the procedure employed in Example 1 to minimize

$$f(x,y) = x^2 + y^2 \qquad (10\text{-}16)$$

subject to the constraining condition

$$\varphi(x,y) \equiv y^2 - (x - 1)^3 = 0. \qquad (10\text{-}17)$$

Equations (10-9) now yield

$$2x - 3\lambda(x - 1)^2 = 0,$$
$$2y + 2\lambda y = 0, \qquad (10\text{-}18)$$

which must be solved together with (10-17). The system (10-17) and (10-18) has no solutions for x, y, and λ. This becomes obvious on noting that the minimum is attained at $x = 1$, $y = 0$, and if we insert these values in (10-18), the first of the resulting equations yields a nonsensical result $2 = 0$ while the second is true for all values of λ. The reason that the Lagrange method this time has failed to give the solution is simple. The method depends on the assumption that not *both* φ_x and φ_y vanish at the point where the extremum is attained. In our case $\varphi_x(1,0) = 0$ and $\varphi_y(1,0) = 0$. The moral of this example is that the Lagrange method yields the solution of the problem only when the system of Eqs. (10-8) and (10-9) can be solved for λ.

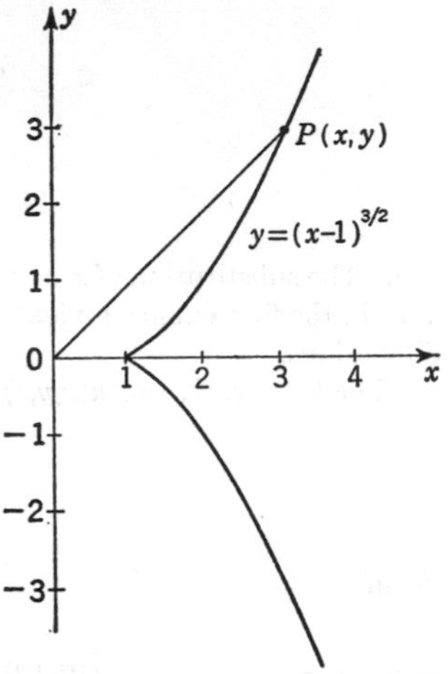

FIG. 9

PROBLEMS

1. Work Probs. 1, 2, and 3, Sec. 9, by using Lagrangian multipliers.

2. Prove that the point of intersection of the medians of a triangle possesses the property that the sum of the squares of its distances from the vertices is a minimum.

3. Find the maximum and the minimum of the sum of the angles made by a line from the origin with (*a*) the coordinate axes of a cartesian system, (*b*) the coordinate planes.

4. Find the maximum distance from the origin to the folium of Descartes $x^3 + y^3 - 3axy = 0$.

5. Find the shortest distance from the origin to the plane

$$ax + by + cz = d.$$

11. Lagrange Multipliers. We now extend the considerations of Sec. 10 to cases where the extremum of the function $f(x_1, x_2, \ldots, x_n)$ is sought under several conditions of constraint.

We consider first the function

$$w = f(x,y,u,v), \qquad (11\text{-}1)$$

in which the variables are constrained by two relations

$$\varphi_1(x,y,u,v) = 0,$$
$$\varphi_2(x,y,u,v) = 0. \qquad (11\text{-}2)$$

If w takes on the extreme values for certain values of (x,y,u,v), then for such values

$$\frac{\partial f}{\partial x}\, dx + \frac{\partial f}{\partial y}\, dy + \frac{\partial f}{\partial u}\, du + \frac{\partial f}{\partial v}\, dv = 0, \tag{11-3}$$

by the theorem in the preceding section. Also, (11-2) yields two equations:

$$\frac{\partial \varphi_1}{\partial x}\, dx + \frac{\partial \varphi_1}{\partial y}\, dy + \frac{\partial \varphi_1}{\partial u}\, du + \frac{\partial \varphi_1}{\partial v}\, dv = 0$$

$$\frac{\partial \varphi_2}{\partial x}\, dx + \frac{\partial \varphi_2}{\partial y}\, dy + \frac{\partial \varphi_2}{\partial u}\, du + \frac{\partial \varphi_2}{\partial v}\, dv = 0. \tag{11-4}$$

We multiply the first of these by λ_1 and the second by λ_2, add the results to (11-3), and obtain

$$\left(\frac{\partial f}{\partial x} + \lambda_1 \frac{\partial \varphi_1}{\partial x} + \lambda_2 \frac{\partial \varphi_2}{\partial x}\right) dx + \left(\frac{\partial f}{\partial y} + \lambda_1 \frac{\partial \varphi_1}{\partial y} + \lambda_2 \frac{\partial \varphi_2}{\partial y}\right) dy$$

$$+ \left(\frac{\partial f}{\partial u} + \lambda_1 \frac{\partial \varphi_1}{\partial u} + \lambda_2 \frac{\partial \varphi_2}{\partial u}\right) du$$

$$+ \left(\frac{\partial f}{\partial v} + \lambda_1 \frac{\partial \varphi_1}{\partial v} + \lambda_2 \frac{\partial \varphi_2}{\partial v}\right) dv = 0. \tag{11-5}$$

Now, if

$$J(u,v) = \begin{vmatrix} \dfrac{\partial \varphi_1}{\partial u} & \dfrac{\partial \varphi_1}{\partial v} \\[2mm] \dfrac{\partial \varphi_2}{\partial u} & \dfrac{\partial \varphi_2}{\partial v} \end{vmatrix} \neq 0,$$

the values of λ_1 and λ_2 can be found such that

$$\frac{\partial f}{\partial u} + \lambda_1 \frac{\partial \varphi_1}{\partial u} + \lambda_2 \frac{\partial \varphi_2}{\partial u} = 0,$$

$$\frac{\partial f}{\partial v} + \lambda_1 \frac{\partial \varphi_1}{\partial v} + \lambda_2 \frac{\partial \varphi_2}{\partial v} = 0, \tag{11-6}$$

and accordingly (11-5) reduces to the sum of two terms involving *arbitrary* differentials dx and dy. The fact that they are arbitrary enables us to conclude that

$$\frac{\partial f}{\partial x} + \lambda_1 \frac{\partial \varphi_1}{\partial x} + \lambda_2 \frac{\partial \varphi_2}{\partial x} = 0,$$

$$\frac{\partial f}{\partial y} + \lambda_1 \frac{\partial \varphi_1}{\partial y} + \lambda_2 \frac{\partial \varphi_2}{\partial y} = 0. \tag{11-7}$$

The system of six equations (11-6), (11-7), and (11-2) serves to determine the parameters λ_1, λ_2 and the point (x,y,u,v) at which the extreme is attained.

The foregoing procedure may be extended to cover the case of more than two constraining conditions and we obtain the following rule:

RULE. *In order to determine the extreme values of a function*

$$f(x_1,x_2,\ldots,x_n) \tag{11-8}$$

whose variables are subjected to m constraining relations

$$\varphi_i(x_1,x_2,\ldots,x_n) = 0, \qquad i = 1, 2, \ldots, m, \tag{11-9}$$

form the function

$$F = f + \sum_{i=1}^{m} \lambda_i \varphi_i$$

and determine the parameters λ_i and the values of x_1, x_2, $\ldots$, x_n from the n equations

$$\frac{\partial F}{\partial x_j} = 0, \qquad j = 1, 2, \ldots, n, \tag{11-10}$$

and the m equations (11-9).

It should be carefully noted that the applicability of this rule to specific problems depends on the possibility of determining the multipliers λ_i. The existence of the λ_i was established above only under the hypothesis that $J \neq 0$.

Example: As an illustration, consider the problem of determining the maximum and the minimum distances from the origin to the curve of intersection of the ellipsoid

$$\frac{x^2}{a^2} + \frac{y^2}{b^2} + \frac{z^2}{c^2} = 1$$

with the plane

$$Ax + By + Cz = 0.$$

The square of the distance from the origin to any point (x,y,z) is

$$f = x^2 + y^2 + z^2,$$

and it is necessary to find the extreme values of this function when the point (x,y,z) is common to the ellipsoid and the plane. The constraining relations are, therefore,

(a)
$$\varphi_1 \equiv \frac{x^2}{a^2} + \frac{y^2}{b^2} + \frac{z^2}{c^2} - 1 = 0$$

and

(b)
$$\varphi_2 \equiv Ax + By + Cz = 0.$$

The function $F = f + \lambda_1 \varphi_1 + \lambda_2 \varphi_2$ is, in this case,

$$F = x^2 + y^2 + z^2 + \lambda_1 \left(\frac{x^2}{a^2} + \frac{y^2}{b^2} + \frac{z^2}{c^2} - 1 \right) + 2\lambda_2(Ax + By + Cz),$$

where the factor of 2 is introduced in the last term for convenience. Equations (11-10) then become

$$x + \lambda_1 \frac{x}{a^2} + \lambda_2 A = 0,$$

(c)
$$y + \lambda_1 \frac{y}{b^2} + \lambda_2 B = 0,$$

$$z + \lambda_1 \frac{z}{c^2} + \lambda_2 C = 0.$$

These equations, together with (a) and (b), give five equations for the determination of the five unknowns x, y, z, λ_1, and λ_2. If the first, second, and third of equations (c) are multiplied by x, y, and z, respectively, and then added, there results

$$x^2 + y^2 + z^2 + \lambda_1 \left(\frac{x^2}{a^2} + \frac{y^2}{b^2} + \frac{z^2}{c^2} \right) + \lambda_2 (Ax + By + Cz) = 0.$$

Making use of (a) and (b), it is evident that

$$\lambda_1 = -(x^2 + y^2 + z^2) = -f.$$

Setting this value of λ_1 in (c) and solving for x, y, and z,

$$x \left(1 - \frac{f}{a^2} \right) + \lambda_2 A = 0, \quad \text{or} \quad x = -\frac{\lambda_2 A a^2}{a^2 - f};$$

$$y \left(1 - \frac{f}{b^2} \right) + \lambda_2 B = 0, \quad \text{or} \quad y = -\frac{\lambda_2 B b^2}{b^2 - f}.$$

$$z \left(1 - \frac{f}{c^2} \right) + \lambda_2 C = 0, \quad \text{or} \quad z = -\frac{\lambda_2 C c^2}{c^2 - f}.$$

When these values of x, y, and z are substituted in (b), one obtains

$$\frac{A^2 a^2}{a^2 - f} + \frac{B^2 b^2}{b^2 - f} + \frac{C^2 c^2}{c^2 - f} = 0,$$

from which f can be readily determined by solving the quadratic equation in f.

PROBLEMS

1. Find the point P, in the plane of the triangle ABC, for which the sum of the distances from the vertices is a minimum.[1]
2. Find the triangle of minimum perimeter which can be inscribed in a given triangle.

12. Taylor's Formula for Functions of Several Variables. Let $f(x,y)$ be a function of two variables x and y that is continuous in the neighborhood of the point (a,b) and that has continuous partial derivatives, up to and including those of order n, in the vicinity of this point.

[1] See E. Goursat's "Mathematical Analysis," English ed., vol. 1, p. 130, for a detailed discussion of this interesting problem.

If a new independent variable t is introduced with the aid of the relations

$$x = a + \alpha t, \qquad y = b + \beta t, \tag{12-1}$$

where α and β are constants, a function of the single variable t will result, namely,

$$F(t) \equiv f(x,y) = f(a + \alpha t, \, b + \beta t). \tag{12-2}$$

Expanding $F(t)$ with the aid of the Maclaurin formula gives

$$F(t) = F(0) + F'(0)t + \frac{F''(0)}{2!} t^2 + \cdots + \frac{F^{(n)}(\theta t)}{n!} t^n, \tag{12-3}$$

where $0 < \theta < 1$.

It follows from (12-1) and (12-2) that [1]

$$F'(t) = f_x(x,y) \frac{dx}{dt} + f_y(x,y) \frac{dy}{dt}$$

$$= f_x(x,y)\alpha + f_y(x,y)\beta.$$

Calculating $F''(t)$ and $F'''(t)$ from this expression gives

$$F''(t) = [f_{xx}(x,y)\alpha + f_{yx}(x,y)\beta] \frac{dx}{dt} + [f_{xy}(x,y)\alpha + f_{yy}(x,y)\beta] \frac{dy}{dt}$$

$$= f_{xx}(x,y)\alpha^2 + 2f_{xy}(x,y)\alpha\beta + f_{yy}(x,y)\beta^2,$$

and

$$F'''(t) = [f_{xxx}(x,y)\alpha^2 + 2f_{xyx}(x,y)\alpha\beta + f_{yyx}(x,y)\beta^2] \frac{dx}{dt}$$

$$+ [f_{xxy}(x,y)\alpha^2 + 2f_{xyy}(x,y)\alpha\beta + f_{yyy}(x,y)\beta^2] \frac{dy}{dt}$$

$$= f_{xxx}(x,y)\alpha^3 + 3f_{xxy}(x,y)\alpha^2\beta + 3f_{xyy}(x,y)\alpha\beta^2 + f_{yyy}(x,y)\beta^3.$$

Higher-order derivatives of $F(t)$ can be obtained by continuing this process, but the form is evident from those already obtained. Symbolically expressed,

$$F'(t) = \left(\alpha \frac{\partial}{\partial x} + \beta \frac{\partial}{\partial y}\right) f(x,y) \equiv \alpha \frac{\partial f}{\partial x} + \beta \frac{\partial f}{\partial y},$$

$$F''(t) = \left(\alpha \frac{\partial}{\partial x} + \beta \frac{\partial}{\partial y}\right)^2 f(x,y) \equiv \alpha^2 \frac{\partial^2 f}{\partial x^2} + 2\alpha\beta \frac{\partial^2 f}{\partial x \, \partial y} + \beta^2 \frac{\partial^2 f}{\partial y^2},$$

$$F'''(t) = \left(\alpha \frac{\partial}{\partial x} + \beta \frac{\partial}{\partial y}\right)^3 f(x,y) \equiv \alpha^3 \frac{\partial^3 f}{\partial x^3} + 3\alpha^2\beta \frac{\partial^3 f}{\partial x^2 \, \partial y}$$

$$+ 3\alpha\beta^2 \frac{\partial^3 f}{\partial x \, \partial y^2} + \beta^3 \frac{\partial^3 f}{\partial y^3}.$$

[1] See Sec. 4.

Then

$$F^{(n)}(t) = \left(\alpha\frac{\partial}{\partial x} + \beta\frac{\partial}{\partial y}\right)^n f(x,y) \equiv \alpha^n\frac{\partial^n f}{\partial x^n} + C_1^n\alpha^{n-1}\beta\frac{\partial^n f}{\partial x^{n-1}\,\partial y}$$

$$+ \cdots + C_{n-1}^n\alpha\beta^{n-1}\frac{\partial^n f}{\partial x\,\partial y^{n-1}} + \beta^n\frac{\partial^n f}{\partial y^n},$$

where
$$C_r^n \equiv \frac{n!}{r!(n-r)!}.$$

Since $t = 0$ gives $x = a$ and $y = b$,

$$F(0) = f(a,b), \qquad F'(0) = \alpha f_x(a,b) + \beta f_y(a,b), \qquad \cdots$$

Substituting these expressions in (12-3) gives

$$F(t) \equiv f(x,y) = f(a,b) + [\alpha f_x(a,b) + \beta f_y(a,b)]t$$

$$+ [\alpha^2 f_{xx}(a,b) + 2\alpha\beta f_{xy}(a,b) + \beta^2 f_{yy}(a,b)]\frac{t^2}{2!} + \cdots + R_n,$$

where $R_n = \dfrac{t^n}{n!}\left(\alpha\dfrac{\partial}{\partial x} + \beta\dfrac{\partial}{\partial y}\right)^n f(a + \theta\alpha t,\, b + \theta\beta t).$

Since $\alpha t = x - a$ and $\beta t = y - b$, the expansion becomes

$$f(x,y) = f(a,b) + f_x(a,b)(x - a) + f_y(a,b)(y - b)$$

$$+ \frac{1}{2!}[f_{xx}(a,b)(x - a)^2 + 2f_{xy}(a,b)(x - a)(y - b) + f_{yy}(a,b)(y - b)^2]$$

$$+ \cdots + R_n. \quad (12\text{-}4)$$

This is Taylor's expansion for a function $f(x,y)$ about the point (a,b). Another useful form of (12-4) is obtained by replacing $x - a$ by h and $y - b$ by k, so that $x = a + h$ and $y = b + k$. Then,

$$f(a + h,\, b + k) = f(a,b) + f_x(a,b)h + f_y(a,b)k$$

$$+ \frac{1}{2!}[f_{xx}(a,b)h^2 + 2f_{xy}(a,b)hk + f_{yy}(a,b)k^2]$$

$$+ \cdots + R_n, \quad (12\text{-}5)$$

where $R_n = \dfrac{1}{n!}\left(h\dfrac{\partial}{\partial x} + k\dfrac{\partial}{\partial y}\right)^n f(a + \theta h,\, b + \theta k).$

This formula is frequently written symbolically as

$$f(a + h,\, b + k) = f(a,b) + \left(h\frac{\partial}{\partial x} + k\frac{\partial}{\partial y}\right)f(a,b)$$

$$+ \frac{1}{2!}\left(h\frac{\partial}{\partial x} + k\frac{\partial}{\partial y}\right)^2 f(a,b) + \cdots + R_n.$$

In particular, if the point (a,b) is $(0,0)$, the formula (12-4) reads

$$f(x,y) = f(0,0) + f_x(0,0)x + f_y(0,0)y$$

$$+ \frac{1}{2!}[f_{xx}(0,0)x^2 + 2f_{xy}(0,0)xy + f_{yy}(0,0)y^2]$$

$$+ \cdots + R_n, \quad (12\text{-}6)$$

where $\quad R_n = \frac{1}{n!}\left(x\frac{\partial}{\partial x} + y\frac{\partial}{\partial y}\right)^n f(\theta x, \theta y), \quad 0 < \theta < 1.$

This development is known as the *Maclaurin formula for functions of two variables*. It is seen from (12-6) that the Maclaurin formula expresses the function $f(x,y)$ in a series each term of which is a homogeneous polynomial in x and y.

The procedure outlined above can be generalized easily to yield similar expansions for functions of more than two variables.

Example: Obtain the expansion of $\tan^{-1}(y/x)$ about $(1,1)$ up to the third-degree terms:

$$f(x,y) = \tan^{-1}\frac{y}{x}, \qquad\qquad f(1,1) = \tan^{-1}1 = \frac{\pi}{4};$$

$$f_x(x,y) = -\frac{y}{x^2+y^2}, \qquad\qquad f_x(1,1) = -\frac{1}{2};$$

$$f_y(x,y) = \frac{x}{x^2+y^2}, \qquad\qquad f_y(1,1) = \frac{1}{2};$$

$$f_{xx}(x,y) = \frac{2xy}{(x^2+y^2)^2}, \qquad\qquad f_{xx}(1,1) = \frac{1}{2};$$

$$f_{xy}(x,y) = \frac{y^2-x^2}{(x^2+y^2)^2}, \qquad\qquad f_{xy}(1,1) = 0;$$

$$f_{yy}(x,y) = \frac{-2xy}{(x^2+y^2)^2}, \qquad\qquad f_{yy}(1,1) = -\frac{1}{2}.$$

Then

$$\tan^{-1}\frac{y}{x} = \frac{\pi}{4} - \frac{1}{2}(x-1) + \frac{1}{2}(y-1) + \frac{1}{2!}\left[\frac{1}{2}(x-1)^2 - \frac{1}{2}(y-1)^2\right] + \cdots.$$

PROBLEMS

1. Obtain the expansion for $xy^2 + \cos xy$ about $(1,\pi/2)$ up to the third-degree terms.
2. Expand $f(x,y) = e^{xy}$ at $(1,1)$, obtaining three terms.
3. Expand $e^x \cos y$ at $(0,0)$ up to the fourth-degree terms.
4. Show that for small values of x and y

$$e^x \sin y = y + xy \text{ (approx)},$$

and $\qquad\qquad e^x \log(1+y) = y + xy - \frac{y^2}{2} \text{ (approx)}.$

5. Expand $f(x,y) = x^3y + x^2y + 1$ about $(0,1)$.
6. Expand $\sqrt{1 - x^2 - y^2}$ about $(0,0)$ up to the third-degree terms.

7. Show that the development obtained in Prob. 6 agrees with the binomial expansion of $[1 - (x^2 + y^2)]^{1/2}$.

INTEGRALS WITH SEVERAL VARIABLES

13. Differentiation under the Integral Sign. The fundamental theorem of integral calculus states that whenever $f(x)$ is a continuous function in the closed interval (a,b) and $F(x)$ is any function such that $F'(x) = f(x)$, then

$$\int_{u_0}^{u_1} f(x)\,dx = F(u_1) - F(u_0) \tag{13-1}$$

for any two points u_0 and u_1 in the interval. If u_0 and u_1 are differentiable functions of another variable α, so that

$$u_0 = u_0(\alpha), \qquad u_1 = u_1(\alpha),$$

the right-hand member in (13-1) is a function of α and the chain rule gives

$$\frac{dF(u_1)}{d\alpha} = F'(u_1)\frac{du_1}{d\alpha} = f(u_1)\frac{du_1}{d\alpha}.$$

Since a similar result holds for $F(u_0)$, differentiation of (13-1) yields the important formula

$$\frac{d}{d\alpha}\int_{u_0(\alpha)}^{u_1(\alpha)} f(x)\,dx = f(u_1)\frac{du_1}{d\alpha} - f(u_0)\frac{du_0}{d\alpha}. \tag{13-2}$$

If the variable α in (13-1) occurs under the integral sign, so that the integral takes the form

$$\varphi(\alpha) = \int_{u_0}^{u_1} f(x,\alpha)\,dx, \tag{13-3}$$

we can compute the derivative of $\varphi(\alpha)$ by calculating the limit of the difference quotient $\Delta\varphi/\Delta\alpha$ as $\Delta\alpha \to 0$. This calculation is simple when the limits u_0, u_1 are constant. Indeed in this case (13-3) gives

$$\Delta\varphi = \varphi(\alpha + \Delta\alpha) - \varphi(\alpha) = \int_{u_0}^{u_1} f(x,\,\alpha + \Delta\alpha)\,dx - \int_{u_0}^{u_1} f(x,\alpha)\,dx$$

$$= \int_{u_0}^{u_1} [f(x,\,\alpha + \Delta\alpha) - f(x,\alpha)]\,dx.$$

Dividing by $\Delta\alpha$ and taking the limit as $\Delta\alpha \to 0$ give

$$\varphi'(\alpha) \equiv \lim_{\Delta\alpha \to 0} \frac{\varphi(\alpha + \Delta\alpha) - \varphi(\alpha)}{\Delta\alpha} = \lim_{\Delta\alpha \to 0} \int_{u_0}^{u_1} \frac{f(x,\,\alpha + \Delta\alpha) - f(x,\alpha)}{\Delta\alpha}\,dx \tag{13-4}$$

provided the limit on the right exists.

If we knew that

$$\lim_{\Delta\alpha \to 0} \int_{u_0}^{u_1} \frac{f(x,\, \alpha + \Delta\alpha) - f(x,\alpha)}{\Delta\alpha}\, dx = \int_{u_0}^{u_1} \lim_{\Delta\alpha \to 0} \frac{f(x,\, \alpha + \Delta\alpha) - f(x)}{\Delta\alpha}\, dx,$$

(13-5)

then the right-hand member of (13-4) would give

$$\int_{u_0}^{u_1} \frac{\partial f}{\partial \alpha}\, dx$$

by the definition of partial derivative. We could then conclude that

$$\frac{d}{d\alpha} \int_{u_0}^{u_1} f(x,\alpha)\, dx = \int_{u_0}^{u_1} f_\alpha(x,\alpha)\, dx, \qquad u_0,\, u_1 \text{ const.} \qquad (13\text{-}6)$$

Interchanging an integral with a limit operation as in (13-5) is not valid in general,[1] but the equality of (13-5) can, in fact, be justified when $f_\alpha(x,\alpha)$ is continuous, and hence (13-6) holds in that case.

Equation (13-2) requires that the integrand be independent of α, while (13-6) assumes that the limits of integration are independent of α.

When the limits and also the integrand depend on α, it can be shown [2] that the correct formula is given by addition of (13-2) and (13-6); namely,

$$\frac{d}{d\alpha} \int_{u_0(\alpha)}^{u_1(\alpha)} f(x,\alpha)\, dx = f(u_1,\alpha) \frac{du_1}{d\alpha} - f(u_0,\alpha) \frac{du_0}{d\alpha} + \int_{u_0(\alpha)}^{u_1(\alpha)} f_\alpha(x,\alpha)\, dx \quad (13\text{-}7)$$

provided that $u_0(\alpha)$ and $u_1(\alpha)$ are differentiable and $f(x,\alpha)$ and $f_\alpha(x,\alpha)$ are continuous. The formula (13-7), known as *Leibniz's formula*, will now be illustrated by several examples.

Example 1. Evaluate $\dfrac{d}{d\alpha} \displaystyle\int_0^1 \log(x^2 + \alpha^2)\, dx$. Inasmuch as the limits are constants, (13-6) yields, when $\alpha \neq 0$,

$$\frac{d}{d\alpha} \int_0^1 \log(x^2 + \alpha^2)\, dx = \int_0^1 \frac{2\alpha}{x^2 + \alpha^2}\, dx.$$

The resulting integral is easily evaluated by the fundamental theorem of integral calculus, since

$$\frac{d}{dx}\left(2\tan^{-1}\frac{x}{\alpha}\right) = \frac{2\alpha}{x^2 + \alpha^2}.$$

We thus obtain

$$\frac{d}{d\alpha} \int_0^1 \log(x^2 + \alpha^2)\, dx = 2\tan^{-1}\frac{x}{\alpha}\Big|_0^1 = 2\tan^{-1}\frac{1}{\alpha}.$$

[1] The reader can verify that

$$\lim_{\alpha \to 0} \int_0^1 \frac{1}{\log\alpha} \frac{2x}{x^2 + \alpha^2}\, dx \neq \int_0^1 \lim_{\alpha \to 0} \frac{1}{\log\alpha} \frac{2x}{x^2 + \alpha^2}\, dx.$$

[2] See I. S. Sokolnikoff, "Advanced Calculus," pp. 121–122, McGraw-Hill Book Company, Inc., New York, 1939.

Example 2. If $\varphi(x) = \int_0^{x^{1/3}} x^2\, dx$, find $\varphi'(x)$ first by evaluating the integral and then differentiating, and also by the Leibniz rule. To avoid confusing the parameter x appearing in the limits of the integral with the variable of integration x, we write

$$\varphi(x) = \int_0^{x^{1/3}} t^2\, dt = \tfrac{1}{3}t^3 \Big|_0^{x^{1/3}} = \tfrac{1}{3}x.$$

Hence $\varphi'(x) = \tfrac{1}{3}$. On the other hand, the application of the rule (13-2) yields

$$\varphi'(x) = \frac{d}{dx}\int_0^{x^{1/3}} t^2\, dt = (x^{1/3})^2 \frac{dx^{1/3}}{dx} = \frac{1}{3},$$

thus checking the result previously obtained.

Example 3. Find $d\varphi/d\alpha$ if $\varphi(\alpha) = \int_{-\alpha^2}^{2\alpha} e^{-x^2/\alpha^2}\, dx$. Since the integrand and the limits in this integral are functions of α, we use formula (13-7). Then

$$\frac{d\varphi}{d\alpha} = \int_{-\alpha^2}^{2\alpha} \frac{2x^2}{\alpha^3} e^{-x^2/\alpha^2}\, dx + e^{-4}(2) - e^{-\alpha^2}(-2\alpha)$$

$$= \int_{-\alpha^2}^{2\alpha} \frac{2x^2}{\alpha^3} e^{-x^2/\alpha^2}\, dx + 2e^{-4} + 2\alpha e^{-\alpha^2}.$$

The integral appearing in this expression cannot be evaluated in a closed form in terms of elementary functions, but it can be readily computed in infinite series (see Chap. 2, Sec. 10).

Example 4. Formula (13-6) can sometimes be used to evaluate definite integrals. Thus consider

$$\varphi(\alpha) = \int_0^1 \frac{x^\alpha - 1}{\log x}\, dx, \qquad \alpha \geq 0. \tag{13-8}$$

Differentiating under the integral sign, we get

$$\varphi'(\alpha) = \int_0^1 \frac{x^\alpha \log x}{\log x}\, dx = \int_0^1 x^\alpha\, dx.$$

The evaluation of the integral is easy, and we find

$$\varphi'(\alpha) = \frac{x^{\alpha+1}}{\alpha + 1}\Big|_0^1 = \frac{1}{\alpha + 1}.$$

Integrating again we get

$$\varphi(\alpha) = \log(\alpha + 1) + c. \tag{13-9}$$

To evaluate the constant c, we note that for $\alpha = 0$, (13-8) gives $\varphi(0) = 0$ while (13-9) for $\alpha = 0$ requires that $\varphi(0) = \log 1 + c$. Hence $c = 0$. We finally have

$$\int_0^1 \frac{x^\alpha - 1}{\log x}\, dx = \log(\alpha + 1).$$

PROBLEMS

1. Find $\dfrac{d\varphi}{d\alpha}$ if $\varphi(\alpha) = \int_0^{\pi/2} \sin \alpha x\, dx$ by using the Leibniz formula, and check your result by direct calculation.

2. Find $\dfrac{d\varphi}{d\alpha}$ if $\varphi(\alpha) = \displaystyle\int_0^\pi (1 - \alpha \cos x)^2 \, dx.$

3. Find $\dfrac{d\varphi}{d\alpha}$ if $\varphi(\alpha) = \displaystyle\int_0^{\alpha^2} \tan^{-1} \dfrac{x}{\alpha^2} \, dx.$

4. Find $\dfrac{d\varphi}{d\alpha}$ if $\varphi(\alpha) = \displaystyle\int_0^\alpha \tan(x - \alpha) \, dx.$

5. Find $\dfrac{d\varphi}{dx}$ if $\varphi(x) = \displaystyle\int_0^{x^2} \sqrt{x} \, dx.$

6. Show in the manner of Example 4 that

$$\varphi(\alpha) = \int_0^\pi \log(1 + \alpha \cos x) \, dx = \pi \log \frac{1 + \sqrt{1 - \alpha^2}}{2} \qquad \text{if } \alpha^2 < 1.$$

7. Differentiate under the sign, and thus evaluate $\displaystyle\int_0^\pi \frac{dx}{(\alpha - \cos x)^2}$ by using

$$\int_0^\pi \frac{dx}{\alpha - \cos x} = \frac{\pi}{(\alpha^2 - 1)^{1/2}} \qquad \text{if } \alpha^2 > 1.$$

8. Show that

$$\int_0^\pi \log(1 - 2\alpha \cos x + \alpha^2) \, dx = 0 \qquad \text{if } \alpha^2 < 1$$

$$= \pi \log \alpha^2 \qquad \text{if } \alpha^2 > 1.$$

9. Verify that

$$y = \frac{1}{k} \int_0^x f(\alpha) \sin k(x - \alpha) \, d\alpha$$

is a solution of the differential equation

$$\frac{d^2 y}{dx^2} + k^2 y = f(x),$$

where k is a constant.

14. The Calculus of Variations. Physical laws can often be deduced from concise mathematical principles to the effect that certain integrals attain extreme values. Thus, the Fermat principle of optics asserts that the actual path traversed by the light particle is such that the integral representing the travel time between two points in every medium is a minimum. Also a considerable part of mechanics can be deduced from the principle of minimum potential energy, stating that the equilibrium configuration of a mechanical system corresponds to the minimum value of a certain integral related to the work done on the system by the forces acting on it. For example, the shape assumed by a flexible chain fixed between two fixed points is such that its center of gravity is as low as possible. To say that the center of gravity is as low as possible is equivalent to saying that the potential energy of the system is as small as possible.

The problems concerned with the determination of extreme values of integrals whose integrands contain unknown functions belong to the *calculus of variations.* The simplest of such problems concerns the determination of an unknown function $y = y(x)$ for which the integral

$$I = \int_{x_0}^{x_1} F(x,y,y') \, dx \tag{14-1}$$

between two fixed points $P_0(x_0,y_0)$ and $P_1(x_1,y_1)$ is a minimum. The function F of the variables x, y, and $y' \equiv dy/dx$ is assumed to be known.

If we imagine that the points P_0 and P_1 in the xy plane are joined by a sufficiently smooth curve $y = f(x)$, then the substitution of $y = f(x)$ and $y' = f'(x)$ in the integrand of (14-1) yields the integral $I(f)$ whose value, ordinarily, depends on the choice of the curve $y = f(x)$. We ask the question: What is the equation of the curve $y = y(x)$ joining P_0 and P_1 which makes the value of the integral (14-1) a minimum? To be certain that this question makes sense, it is necessary to impose some restrictions on the integrand in (14-1) and to specify how the curves that enter in competition for the minimum value of I are to be chosen.

We shall suppose that $F(x,y,y')$, viewed as a function of its arguments x, y, and y', has continuous partial derivatives of the second order, and we assume that there is a curve $y = y(x)$ with continuously turning tangent that minimizes the integral. We then choose the competing family of curves as follows: Let $y = \eta(x)$ be any function with continuous second derivatives which vanishes at the end points of the interval (x_0,x_1). Then

$$\eta(x_0) = 0, \qquad \eta(x_1) = 0. \tag{14-2}$$

If α is a small parameter,

$$\bar{y}(x) = y(x) + \alpha\eta(x) \tag{14-3}$$

represents a family of curves passing through (x_0,y_0) and (x_1,y_1), since the *minimizing curve* $y = y(x)$ passes through these points and $\eta(x_0) = \eta(x_1) = 0$. The situation

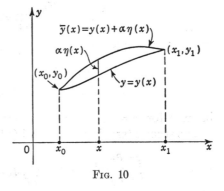

FIG. 10

here is that indicated in Fig. 10. The vertical deviation of a curve in the family (14-3) from the minimizing curve is $\alpha\eta(x)$; it is called the *variation of* $y(x)$.

Now if we substitute $\bar{y}$ and $\bar{y}'$ from (14-3) for y and y' in the integral (14-1), we get a function of α:

$$I(\alpha) = \int_{x_0}^{x_1} F[x, y(x) + \alpha\eta(x), y'(x) + \alpha\eta'(x)] \, dx. \tag{14-4}$$

For $\alpha = 0$, Eq. (14-3) yields $\bar{y}(x) = y(x)$, and since $y = y(x)$ minimizes the integral, we conclude that $I(\alpha)$ must have a minimum for $\alpha = 0$. A necessary condition for this is

$$\frac{dI}{d\alpha}\bigg|_{\alpha=0} = 0. \tag{14-5}$$

We can compute the derivative of $I(\alpha)$ by differentiating (14-4) under the integral sign and get

$$I'(\alpha) = \int_{x_0}^{x_1} \frac{\partial}{\partial \alpha} F(x,Y,Y') \, dx, \tag{14-6}$$

where we have set

$$Y \equiv y(x) + \alpha\eta(x), \qquad Y' \equiv y'(x) + \alpha\eta'(x). \tag{14-7}$$

But by the rule for the differentiation of composite functions,

$$\frac{\partial F(x,Y,Y')}{\partial \alpha} = \frac{\partial F}{\partial Y}\frac{\partial Y}{\partial \alpha} + \frac{\partial F}{\partial Y'}\frac{\partial Y'}{\partial \alpha}$$

$$= \frac{\partial F}{\partial Y}\eta(x) + \frac{\partial F}{\partial Y'}\eta'(x),$$

so that (14-6) can be written as

$$I'(\alpha) = \int_{x_0}^{x_1}\left[\frac{\partial F}{\partial Y}\eta(x) + \frac{\partial F}{\partial Y'}\eta'(x)\right]dx. \tag{14-8}$$

Since $I'(0) = 0$ by (14-5), we get, on setting $\alpha = 0$ in (14-8),

$$\int_{x_0}^{x_1}\left[\frac{\partial F}{\partial y}\eta(x) + \frac{\partial F}{\partial y'}\eta'(x)\right]dx = 0, \tag{14-9}$$

because for $\alpha = 0$, it is evident from (14-7) that $Y = y(x)$, $Y' = y'(x)$. The second term in the integral (14-9) can be integrated by parts to yield

$$\int_{x_0}^{x_1}\frac{\partial F}{\partial y'}\eta'(x)\,dx = \frac{\partial F}{\partial y'}\eta(x)\bigg|_{x_0}^{x_1} - \int_{x_0}^{x_1}\eta(x)\frac{d}{dx}\left(\frac{\partial F}{\partial y'}\right)dx$$

$$= -\int_{x_0}^{x_1}\eta(x)\frac{d}{dx}\left(\frac{\partial F}{\partial y'}\right)dx,$$

since the integrated part drops out because of (14-2). Accordingly, we can write (14-9) as

$$\int_{x_0}^{x_1}\eta(x)\left[\frac{\partial F}{\partial y} - \frac{d}{dx}\left(\frac{\partial F}{\partial y'}\right)\right]dx = 0. \tag{14-10}$$

But $\eta(x)$ is an arbitrary function vanishing at the end points of the interval.

Since the integral (14-10) must vanish for *every* choice of $\eta(x)$, it is easy to conclude that [1]

$$\frac{\partial F}{\partial y} - \frac{d}{dx}\left(\frac{\partial F}{\partial y'}\right) = 0. \tag{14-11}$$

This equation is called the *Euler equation*. On carrying out the differentiation indicated in (14-11), we get the second-order ordinary differential equation

$$\frac{\partial F}{\partial y} - \frac{\partial^2 F}{\partial x\,\partial y'} - \frac{\partial^2 F}{\partial y\,\partial y'}\,y' - \frac{\partial^2 F}{\partial y'^2}\,y'' = 0 \tag{14-12}$$

for the determination of the minimizing function $y(x)$.

The general solution of (14-12) contains two arbitrary constants which must be chosen so that the curve $y = y(x)$ passes through (x_0,y_0) and (x_1,y_1).

It should be noted that the solution of Euler's equation (14-11) may not yield the minimizing curve because the condition (14-5) is necessary but not sufficient for a minimum. Ordinarily one must verify whether or not this solution yields the curve that actually minimizes the integral, but frequently geometrical or physical considerations enable one to tell whether the curve so obtained makes the integral a maximum, a minimum, or neither.

Similar calculations when performed on the integral

$$I(y) = \int_{x_0}^{x_1} F(x,y,y',y'',\ldots,y^{(n)})\,dx \tag{14-13}$$

yield the Euler equation

$$F_y - \frac{d}{dx}F_{y'} + \frac{d^2}{dx^2}F_{y''} - \cdots - (-1)^n \frac{d^n}{dx^n}F_{y^{(n)}} = 0. \tag{14-14}$$

The foregoing discussion can also be generalized to the problem of minimizing the double integral

$$I(u) = \iint_R F(x,y,u,u_x,u_y)\,dx\,dy, \tag{14-15}$$

in which the competing functions $u(x,y)$ assume on the boundary C of the region R preassigned continuous values $u = \varphi(s)$. If it is supposed

---

[1] The proof is by contradiction. Assume that the function in the brackets of (14-10) is not zero at some point $x = \xi$ of the interval (x_0,x_1). Then since it is a continuous function, there will be a subinterval l about $x = \xi$ throughout which $F_y - \frac{d}{dx}F_{y'}$ has the same sign as at $x = \xi$. Choose $\eta(x)$ so that it has the same sign as $F_y - \frac{d}{dx}F_{y'}$ in l and vanishes outside this subinterval. For such a choice of $\eta(x)$, the integrand in (14-10) will be positive, and thus the integral will fail to vanish as demanded by (14-10).

that F, viewed as a function of $x,y,u,u_x \equiv \partial u/\partial x$, $u_y \equiv \partial u/\partial y$, has continuous second partial derivatives with respect to these arguments, the Euler equation corresponding to the integral (14-15) turns out to be

$$F_u - \frac{\partial F_{u_x}}{\partial x} - \frac{\partial F_{u_y}}{\partial y} = 0. \tag{14-16}$$

A special form of the integral (14-15) is of particular interest in the study of the Dirichlet problem, which occurs in numerous applications.[1] It is

$$I(u) = \iint_R [(u_x)^2 + (u_y)^2 + 2f(x,y)u]\, dx\, dy, \tag{14-17}$$

where $f(x,y)$ is a known function. The substitution of $F = (u_x)^2 + (u_y)^2 + 2fu$ in (14-16) yields the *Poisson equation*

$$\nabla^2 u = f(x,y). \tag{14-18}$$

It can be shown that the solution of this equation,[2] assuming specified continuous values $u = \varphi(s)$ on the boundary C of the region, actually minimizes the integral (14-17) on the set of all competing functions which take on C the same boundary values $\varphi(s)$.

Example: What is the equation of the curve $y = y(x)$ for which the area of the surface of revolution got by revolving the curve about the x axis is a minimum?

The integral to be minimized in this problem is

$$I = 2\pi \int_{x_0}^{x_1} y\, ds = 2\pi \int_{x_0}^{x_1} y\sqrt{1 + y'^2}\, dx. \tag{14-19}$$

It has the form (14-1) with

$$F(x,y,y') = 2\pi y\sqrt{1 + y'^2}. \tag{14-20}$$

The substitution from (14-20) in the Euler equation (14-11), after simple calculations, yields

$$\sqrt{1 + y'^2} - \frac{d}{dx}\frac{yy'}{\sqrt{1 + y'^2}} = 0,$$

or

$$yy'' - y'^2 - 1 = 0.$$

This second-order equation is easily solved by setting $y' = p$, $y'' = p\, dp/dy$ (cf. Chap. 1, Sec. 13). The result is

$$y = c_1 \cosh \frac{x - c_2}{c_1}, \tag{14-21}$$

so that the desired curve is a catenary. The integration constants c_1 and c_2 in the general solution (14-21) must be determined so that the curve passes through given points (x_0,y_0), (x_1,y_1).

---

[1] See Chap. 6, Sec. 12, and Chap. 7, Sec. 21.

[2] See, for example, I. S. Sokolnikoff, "Mathematical Theory of Elasticity," 2d ed., sec. 106, McGraw-Hill Book Company, Inc., 1956.

PROBLEMS

1. Show that the curve of minimum length joining a pair of given points in the plane is a straight line.   *Hint:* Minimize

$$\int_{x_0}^{x_1} \sqrt{1 + y'^2}\, dx.$$

2. Solve Prob. 1 by taking

$$\int ds = \int \sqrt{1 + r^2 \left(\frac{d\theta}{dr}\right)^2}\, dr.$$

3. When a bead slides from rest along any smooth curve C from the point P to a point Q on C, the speed v of the bead is $v = \sqrt{2gh}$, where h is the vertical distance from P to Q. Hence the travel time from P to Q is $t = \int_P^Q \frac{ds}{v}$.   Choose P at the origin, and show that the curve for which the travel time is a minimum is a cycloid.

4. Consider the integral $I = \int_{x_0}^{x_1} \dfrac{\sqrt{1 + y'^2}}{y}\, dx$, and show that the general solution of the associated Euler's equation is $y^2 + (x - c_1)^2 = c_2$.   Discuss this solution.

5. Obtain Euler's equation for the integral

$$I(y) = \int_{x}^{x_1} [p(x)(y')^2 + q(x)y^2 + 2f(x)y]\, dx.$$

Special cases of this integral arise in the study of deflection of bars and strings.

15. Variational Problems with Constraints.   Occasionally one seeks a maximum or minimum value of the integral

$$I = \int_{x_0}^{x_1} F(x,y,y')\, dx, \tag{15-1}$$

discussed in the preceding section, subject to the condition that another integral

$$J = \int_{x_0}^{x_1} G(x,y,y')\, dx \tag{15-2}$$

have a known constant value.   A physical problem of this sort has already been mentioned in Sec. 14 where it was required to find the shape of the chain which minimizes the potential energy while the length of the chain is given.   This is one of the so-called *isoperimetric* problems of the calculus of variations.[1]

It is natural to attempt to solve the problem $I = \min$ subject to the condition $J = \text{const}$ by the method of Lagrange multipliers.   We construct the integral

$$I + \lambda J = \int_{x_0}^{x_1} [F(x,y,y') + \lambda G(x,y,y')]\, dx \tag{15-3}$$

---

[1] Isoperimetric because the length (or the perimeter) of the curve is given.

and consider the free extremum of the integral (15-3). The corresponding Euler's equation (14-11) is

$$\frac{\partial(F + \lambda G)}{\partial y} - \frac{d}{dx}\frac{\partial(F + \lambda G)}{\partial y'} = 0 \qquad (15\text{-}4)$$

and on carrying out the indicated differentiation [1] in (15-4), we get the second-order ordinary differential equation containing the parameter λ. The general solution of this equation, in addition to λ, will contain two arbitrary integration constants. The integration constants and the parameter λ must then be determined so that the curve $y = y(x)$ passes through the given end points and satisfies the constraining condition (15-2).

The justification of this procedure is based on an argument similar to that used in Sec. 14, where instead of the one-parameter family of the neighboring curves (14-3) one constructs a suitable two-parameter family.[2]

16. Change of Variables in Multiple Integrals. The reader will recall that the double integral $\iint_R f(x,y)\, dA$ of a continuous function $f(x,y)$ specified in a closed two-dimensional region R of the xy plane is defined as the limit of the sum formed in the following way: The region R is subdivided into n elements of area ΔA_i, and the value of $f(x,y)$ is computed at some point (ξ_i, η_i) of the ΔA_i; the sum $\sum_{i=1}^{n} f(\xi_i, \eta_i)\, \Delta A_i$ is then formed, and its limit is calculated when the number of elements ΔA_i is allowed to increase indefinitely in such a way that the greatest linear dimensions of the elements tend to zero. Thus,

$$\int_R f(x,y)\, dA \equiv \lim_{n \to \infty} \sum_{i=1}^{n} f(\xi_i, \eta_i)\, \Delta A_i. \qquad (16\text{-}1)$$

The calculation of the limit in (16-1) is usually performed by repeated evaluations of two simple integrals, so that

$$\int_R f(x,y)\, dA = \int_{x=a}^{x=b} \int_{y=g_1(x)}^{y=g_2(x)} f(x,y)\, dy\, dx. \qquad (16\text{-}2)$$

The limits in (16-2) are determined from the equations of the boundary of the region (Fig. 11). The triple integral of $f(x,y,z)$ is defined similarly, by subdividing the three-dimensional region R into volume elements $\Delta \tau_i$ and by forming the corresponding sum. Thus

$$\int_R f(x,y,z)\, d\tau \equiv \lim_{n \to \infty} \sum_{i=1}^{n} f(\xi_i, \eta_i, \zeta_i)\, \Delta \tau_i. \qquad (16\text{-}3)$$

---

[1] Compare Eq. (14-12).

[2] See G. A. Bliss, "Calculus of Variations," Carus Monograph, The Open Court Publishing Co., LaSalle. Ill.. 1925.

The limit of the sum in (16-3) is usually evaluated by repeated single integrations. One can write, for example,

$$\int_R f(x,y,z)\,d\tau = \int_{x=a}^{x=b}\int_{y=h_1(x)}^{y=h_2(x)}\int_{z=g_1(x,y)}^{z=g_2(x,y)} f(x,y,z)\,dz\,dy\,dx, \qquad (16\text{-}4)$$

in which the integration limits are determined from equations of the bounding surfaces.

The evaluation of multiple integrals can frequently be simplified by making appropriate changes of the independent variables. Thus in dealing with double integrals, it may prove advantageous to replace x and y by new variables u and v related to x and y by the transformation

$$\begin{aligned} u &= f_1(x,y) \\ v &= f_2(x,y) \end{aligned} \qquad (16\text{-}5)$$

with suitable properties.

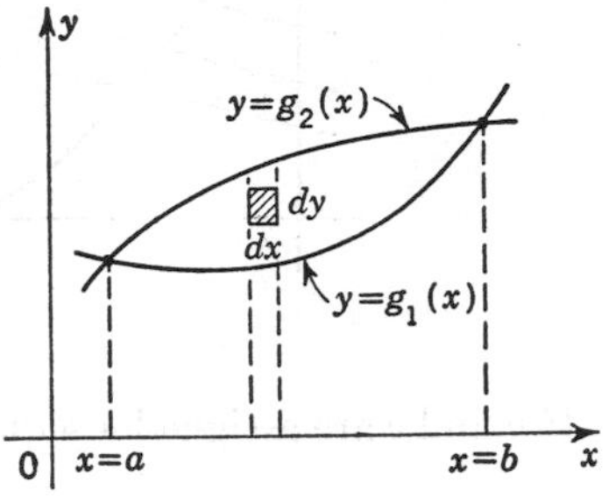

FIG. 11

We shall suppose that the functions f_i in (16-5) have continuous first partial derivatives in the region R and that the *Jacobian* of (16-5)

$$J(x,y) = \begin{vmatrix} \dfrac{\partial u}{\partial x} & \dfrac{\partial v}{\partial x} \\ \dfrac{\partial u}{\partial y} & \dfrac{\partial v}{\partial y} \end{vmatrix} \qquad (16\text{-}6)$$

does not vanish in the region R. In this event, Eqs. (16-5) can be solved for x and y to yield the differentiable solution [1]

$$\begin{aligned} x &= \varphi_1(u,v), \\ y &= \varphi_2(u,v). \end{aligned} \qquad (16\text{-}7)$$

If u and v are assigned some fixed values, say u_0 and v_0, the equations

$$\begin{aligned} u_0 &= f_1(x,y), \\ v_0 &= f_2(x,y), \end{aligned}$$

determine two curves which will intersect in a point (x_0,y_0), such that

$$\begin{aligned} x_0 &= \varphi_1(u_0,v_0), \\ y_0 &= \varphi_2(u_0,v_0). \end{aligned}$$

[1] See, for example, I. S. Sokolnikoff, "Advanced Calculus," chap. 12, McGraw-Hill Book Company, Inc., New York, 1939.

Thus the pair of numbers (u_0, v_0) determines the point (x_0, y_0), in the xy plane (Fig. 12).

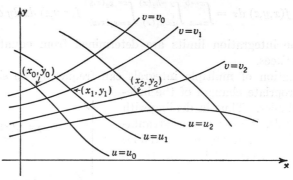

Fig. 12

If u and v are assigned a sequence of constant values

$$(u_1, v_1), (u_2, v_2), (u_3, v_3), \ldots, (u_n, v_n), \ldots,$$

a network of curves will be determined that will intersect in the points

$$(x_1, y_1), (x_2, y_2), (x_3, y_3), \ldots, (x_n, y_n), \ldots.$$

Corresponding to any point whose rectangular coordinates are (x, y) there will be a pair of curves $u = $ const and $v = $ const, which pass through this point. The totality of numbers (u, v) defines a curvilinear coordinate system, and the curves themselves are called the *coordinate lines*.

Thus, if

$$u = \sqrt{x^2 + y^2},$$

$$v = \tan^{-1} \frac{y}{x},$$

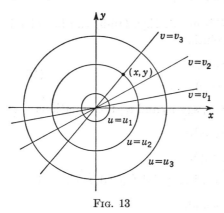

Fig. 13

the family of curves $u = $ const is a family of circles whereas $v = $ const defines a family of radial lines. The curvilinear coordinate system, in this case, is the ordinary polar coordinate system (Fig. 13).

In the cartesian xy coordinates the element of area $dA = dx\, dy$ is the area of a rectangle formed by the intersection of the coordinate lines $x = x_0$, $x = x_0 + dx$, $y = y_0$, $y = y_0 + dy$, as shown in Fig. 14. In the curvilinear uv coordinates the element of area dA can be visualized as the area of the quadrilateral $P_1P_2P_3P_4$ formed by the intersection of the co-ordinate lines $u = u_0$, $u = u_0 + du$, $v = v_0$, $v = v_0 + dv$, shown in Fig. 15.

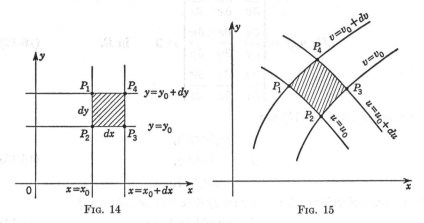

FIG. 14   FIG. 15

The expression for the element of area dA in curvilinear coordinates (u,v) can be calculated with the aid of Eqs. (16-7), but it is somewhat simpler to follow the method of Sec. 2, Chap. 5 (see, in particular, Eq. (2-17) of that section) to show that

$$dA = |J(u,v)| \, du \, dv, \tag{16-8}$$

where

$$J(u,v) = \begin{vmatrix} \dfrac{\partial x}{\partial u} & \dfrac{\partial y}{\partial u} \\[2mm] \dfrac{\partial x}{\partial v} & \dfrac{\partial y}{\partial v} \end{vmatrix} \tag{16-9}$$

is the Jacobian of the transformation (16-7).

The double integral in (16-2) can then be evaluated in the uv coordinates by substituting in $f(x,y)$ from (16-7) to obtain $f[\varphi_1(u,v), \varphi_2(u,v)] \equiv F(u,v)$ and writing dA in the form (16-8). Thus,

$$\int f(x,y) \, dA = \int_{v=\alpha}^{v=\beta} \int_{u=\psi_1(v)}^{u=\psi_2(v)} F(u,v) |J(u,v)| \, du \, dv. \tag{16-10}$$

The limits of integration in (16-10) are determined from the equations of the boundary of R referred to the uv coordinates.

Similar considerations apply to a change of variables (x,y,z) in the triple integral (16-4) by the transformation

$$u = f_1(x,y,z),$$

$$v = f_2(x,y,z), \tag{16-11}$$

$$w = f_3(x,y,z),$$

with the Jacobian

$$J(x,y,z) = \begin{vmatrix} \dfrac{\partial u}{\partial x} & \dfrac{\partial v}{\partial x} & \dfrac{\partial w}{\partial x} \\[2mm] \dfrac{\partial u}{\partial y} & \dfrac{\partial v}{\partial y} & \dfrac{\partial w}{\partial y} \\[2mm] \dfrac{\partial u}{\partial z} & \dfrac{\partial v}{\partial z} & \dfrac{\partial w}{\partial z} \end{vmatrix} \neq 0 \quad \text{in } R. \qquad (16\text{-}12)$$

If the solutions of (16-11) are

$$\begin{aligned} x &= \varphi_1(u,v,w), \\ y &= \varphi_2(u,v,w), \\ z &= \varphi_3(u,v,w), \end{aligned} \qquad (16\text{-}13)$$

the element of volume $d\tau$ in the uvw system can be taken as [1]

$$d\tau = |J(u,v,w)|\, du\, dv\, dw, \qquad (16\text{-}14)$$

where $J(u,v,w)$ is the Jacobian of the transformation (16-13), so that

$$J(u,v,w) = \begin{vmatrix} \dfrac{\partial x}{\partial u} & \dfrac{\partial y}{\partial u} & \dfrac{\partial z}{\partial u} \\[2mm] \dfrac{\partial x}{\partial v} & \dfrac{\partial y}{\partial v} & \dfrac{\partial z}{\partial v} \\[2mm] \dfrac{\partial x}{\partial w} & \dfrac{\partial y}{\partial w} & \dfrac{\partial z}{\partial w} \end{vmatrix}. \qquad (16\text{-}15)$$

Example 1. Let it be required to find the moment of inertia of the area of the circle (Fig. 16)

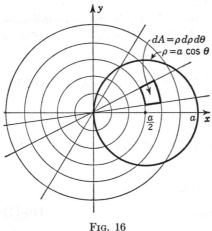

Fig. 16

$$x^2 + y^2 - ax = 0$$

about a diameter of the circle. It is convenient to introduce the polar coordinates

$$x = \rho \cos \theta,$$
$$y = \rho \sin \theta,$$

so that the equation of the circle becomes

$$\rho = a \cos \theta.$$

Calculating the determinant J gives

$$J = \begin{vmatrix} \cos \theta & \sin \theta \\ -\rho \sin \theta & \rho \cos \theta \end{vmatrix} = \rho,$$

so that $\qquad dA = \rho \, d\rho \, d\theta.$

[1] Cf. Chap. 5, Sec. 2.

Therefore,

$$I = \int_R y^2 \, dA = \int_0^\pi \int_0^{a\cos\theta} \rho^2 \sin^2\theta \, \rho \, d\rho \, d\theta = \int_0^\pi \frac{a^4 \cos^4\theta \sin^2\theta}{4} \, d\theta = \frac{\pi a^4}{64}.$$

Example 2. Find the x coordinate of the center of gravity of the part of the solid sphere $x^2 + y^2 + z^2 = a^2$ in the first octant.   We recall that the x coordinate of the center of gravity of the uniform solid is

$$\bar{x} = \frac{\displaystyle\int_R x \, d\tau}{\displaystyle\int_R d\tau}.$$

The value of the denominator in this expression can be written down at once, since the solid under consideration is one octant of a sphere of radius a.   Thus

$$\int_R d\tau = \frac{1}{8} \cdot \frac{4}{3} \pi a^3 = \frac{\pi a^3}{6}.$$

In cartesian coordinates, the numerator can be expressed as (Fig. 17)

$$\int_R x \, d\tau = \int_{z=0}^{z=a} \int_{y=0}^{y=\sqrt{a^2-z^2}} \int_{x=0}^{x=\sqrt{a^2-y^2-z^2}} x \, dx \, dy \, dz.$$

Although the evaluation of this integral is not too difficult, it is simpler to use the spherical coordinates obtained by setting [1]

$$x = \rho \sin\theta \cos\phi,$$
$$y = \rho \sin\theta \sin\phi, \qquad\qquad (16\text{-}16)$$
$$z = \rho \cos\theta.$$

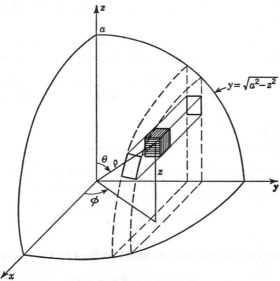

FIG. 17

<hr />

[1] See Chap. 5, Sec. 1.

These equations are in the form (16-13) with $\rho = u$, $\theta = v$, $\phi = w$, and it is easy to verify that (16-14) yields

$$d\tau = \rho^2 \sin\theta \, d\rho \, d\theta \, d\phi.$$

Consequently, the substitution from (16-16) gives

$$\int_R x \, d\tau = \int_{\phi=0}^{\phi=\pi/2} \int_{\theta=0}^{\theta=\pi/2} \int_{\rho=0}^{\rho=a} \rho \sin\theta \cos\phi \rho^2 \sin\theta \, d\rho \, d\theta \, d\phi = \frac{\pi a^4}{16}.$$

Thus,

$$\bar{x} = \frac{\pi a^4/16}{\pi a^3/6} = \frac{3a}{8}.$$

PROBLEMS

1. Use cylindrical coordinates (r,θ,z) defined by

$$x = r\cos\theta, \qquad y = r\sin\theta, \qquad z = z,$$

to compute the moment of inertia of the volume of a right-circular cylinder of height h and radius a about its axis. Also evaluate the integral in cartesian coordinates.

2. Compute the expression for dA in terms of u and v if

$$x = u(1 - v), \qquad y = uv.$$

3. Compute the expression for $d\tau$ in terms of u, v, and w if

$$x = u(1 - v), \qquad y = uv, \qquad z = uvw.$$

4. Show that in the cylindrical coordinates of Prob. 1, the element of volume $d\tau = r \, dr \, d\theta \, dz$.

5. Use the cylindrical coordinates of Prob. 1 to find the volume enclosed by the circular cylinder $r = 2a\cos\theta$, the cone $z = r$, and the plane $z = 0$.

6. Evaluate $\int_R e^{-(x^2+y^2)} \, dy \, dx$, where R is the region bounded by the circle $x^2 + y^2 = a^2$. Use polar coordinates.

7. Find the area outside $\rho = a(1 + \cos\theta)$ and inside $\rho = 3a\cos\theta$.

8. Find the coordinates of the center of gravity of the area between $\rho = 2\sin\theta$ and $\rho = 4\sin\theta$.

9. Calculate the elements of area in the uv coordinate systems which are related to the cartesian coordinate system xy by means of the following equations of transformation:

(a) $x = u + a$, $y = v + b$;
(b) $x = au$, $y = bv$;
(c) $x = u\cos\alpha - v\sin\alpha$, $y = u\sin\alpha + v\cos\alpha$;

where a, b, and α are constants. Interpret your results geometrically.

10. What are the regions of integration in the uv coordinate systems of Prob. 9 if the region R in the xy plane is the interior of the ellipse

$$\frac{x^2}{a^2} + \frac{y^2}{b^2} = 1?$$

11. Discuss the curvilinear coordinate system defined by the relations

$$x = u + v, \qquad y = u - v;$$

and describe the region in the uv plane corresponding to the square $x = 1$, $x = 2$, $y = 1$, $y = 2$.

12. Discuss the curvilinear coordinate system defined by the relations

$$u = x^2 - y^2, \qquad v = 2xy.$$

Sketch the curves $u = $ const and $v = $ const.

13. Show that the attraction of a homogeneous sphere at a point exterior to the sphere is the same as though all of the mass of the sphere were concentrated at the center of the sphere. Assume the inverse-square law of force.

14. The Newtonian potential V, due to a body T, at a point P is defined by the equation $V(P) = \int_T \dfrac{dm}{r}$, where dm is the element of mass of the body and r is the distance from the point P to the element of mass dm. Show that the potential of a homogeneous spherical shell of inner radius b and outer radius a is

$$V = 2\pi\sigma(a^2 - b^2), \qquad \text{if } r < b,$$

and

$$V = \frac{4}{3}\pi\sigma\frac{a^3 - b^3}{r}, \qquad \text{if } r > a,$$

where σ is the density.

15. Find the Newtonian potential on the axis of a homogeneous circular cylinder of radius a.

16. Show that the force of attraction of a right-circular cone upon a point at its vertex is $2\pi\sigma h(1 - \cos \alpha)$, where h is the altitude of the cone and 2α is the angle at the vertex.

17. Show that the force of attraction of a homogeneous right-circular cylinder upon a point on its axis is

$$2\pi\sigma[h + \sqrt{R^2 + a^2} - \sqrt{(R + h)^2 + a^2}],$$

where h is altitude, a is radius, and R is the distance from the point to one base of the cylinder.

17. Surface Integrals. A surface is usually defined as a locus of points determined by the equation

$$z = f(x,y), \tag{17-1}$$

where $f(x,y)$ is a continuous function specified in some region of the xy plane. This definition, however, is too broad to permit one to formulate a meaningful concept of the surface area. Since most surfaces encountered in applications are two-sided and piecewise smooth, we confine our considerations to such surfaces only.

The surface defined by (17-1) is called *smooth* if it has continuous partial derivatives $\partial z/\partial x$ and $\partial z/\partial y$ at each of its points. This implies that a smooth surface has a continuously turning tangent plane and hence a well-defined *normal* at each of its points.[1]

[1] We recall that the equation of the tangent plane to (17-1) at a point $P(x_0,y_0,z_0)$ is

$$z - z_0 = \left(\frac{\partial z}{\partial x}\right)_P (x - x_0) + \left(\frac{\partial z}{\partial y}\right)_P (y - y_0),$$

so that the direction of the normal at P is determined by the ratios $\left(\dfrac{\partial z}{\partial x}\right)_P : \left(\dfrac{\partial z}{\partial y}\right)_P : -1$ (cf. Sec. 10, Chap. 4).

The surface is said to be *piecewise smooth* if it can be subdivided by smooth curves into a finite number of pieces, each of which is smooth. Thus, the surface of a cube is piecewise smooth.

The surface is two-sided when it is possible to paint it with two different colors to distinguish the sides.[1] If two oppositely directed normals PN and PN' (Fig. 18) are drawn at a point P of a smooth two-sided surface and P is allowed to move along any path that does not cross the edge of the surface, the direction of PN can never be brought into coincidence with PN'.

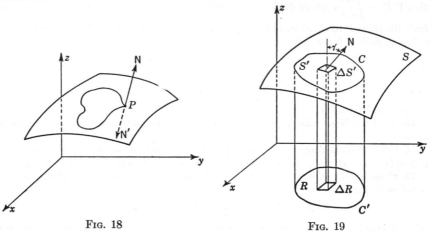

FIG. 18   FIG. 19

It is intuitively clear that a small element of a smooth surface is nearly flat, so that a neighborhood of any point on it is well approximated by a portion of the tangent plane. This observation suggests a procedure for constructing a meaningful definition of the area of a smooth surface.

Thus, let S' be a smooth portion of the surface S bounded by a closed curve C (Fig. 19). We shall suppose that S' is such that every line parallel to some coordinate axis (say the z axis) cuts S' in just one point. If the projection C' of C on the xy plane encloses the region R, we can subdivide R into n small subregions ΔR_i by the families of straight lines parallel to the x and y axes. The planes through these lines, normal to the region R, cut from S' small regions $\Delta S_i'$ of areas $\Delta\sigma_i$. Let ΔA_i be the area of ΔR_i. The projection of $\Delta\sigma_i$ on the xy plane is, approximately,

$$\Delta A_i = \cos\gamma_i\,\Delta\sigma_i,$$

where $\cos\alpha_i$, $\cos\beta_i$, and $\cos\gamma_i$ are the direction cosines of the normal

---

[1] At first glance, it may appear that all surfaces are two-sided, but this is not the case. A simple example of one-sided surface, whose boundary is a closed curve, is given in Sec. 6, Chap. 5.

N to S at a point (x_i, y_i, z_i) of $\Delta S_i'$. Since [1]

$$\cos \alpha_i : \cos \beta_i : \cos \gamma_i = \left(\frac{\partial z}{\partial x}\right)_i : \left(\frac{\partial z}{\partial y}\right)_i : -1$$

and

$$\cos^2 \alpha_i + \cos^2 \beta_i + \cos^2 \gamma_i = 1$$

we have

$$\cos \gamma_i = \frac{-1}{\pm \sqrt{(\partial z/\partial x)_i^2 + (\partial z/\partial y)_i^2 + 1}}.$$

Using the positive value for $\cos \gamma_i$, which amounts to the choice of the positive direction of N, we can write

$$\Delta \sigma_i \doteq \sec \gamma_i \, \Delta A_i = \sqrt{\left(\frac{\partial z}{\partial x}\right)_i^2 + \left(\frac{\partial z}{\partial y}\right)_i^2 + 1} \, \Delta A_i.$$

The surface area of S' can then be approximated by the sum

$$\sum_{i=1}^n \Delta \sigma_i = \sum_{i=1}^n \sqrt{\left(\frac{\partial z}{\partial x}\right)_i^2 + \left(\frac{\partial z}{\partial y}\right)_i^2 + 1} \, \Delta A_i,$$

and we define the area σ of S' by the integral

$$\sigma = \int_R \sqrt{\left(\frac{\partial z}{\partial x}\right)^2 + \left(\frac{\partial z}{\partial y}\right)^2 + 1} \, dA$$

$$\equiv \int_R \sec \gamma \, dA. \tag{17-2}$$

The integral (17-2) can be evaluated by repeated integrations to yield, for example,

$$\sigma = \iint_R \sqrt{\left(\frac{\partial z}{\partial x}\right)^2 + \left(\frac{\partial z}{\partial y}\right)^2 + 1} \, dy \, dx.$$

By considering the projections R' and R'' of S' on the other coordinate planes, we deduce similar formulas:

$$\sigma = \int_{R'} \sec \alpha \, dA, \qquad \sigma = \int_{R''} \sec \beta \, dA.$$

To obtain the surface area of a piecewise smooth surface we need merely to add the areas of its smooth pieces.

The surface integral of a continuous function $\varphi(x,y,z)$ specified on the surface S' is defined as follows: Let S' be subdivided into subregions $\Delta S_i'$

---

[1] See the first footnote in this section.

of areas $\Delta\sigma_i$ and form the sum

$$\sum_{i=1}^{n} \varphi(x_i,y_i,z_i)\, \Delta\sigma_i, \tag{17-3}$$

where (x_i,y_i,z_i) is some point in $\Delta S_i'$. The limit of the sum (17-3) as $n \to \infty$ in such a way that the greatest linear dimensions of the $\Delta S_i'$ tend to zero is the surface integral of $\varphi(x,y,z)$ over S'. It is denoted by the symbol

$$\int_{S'} \varphi(x,y,z)\, d\sigma. \tag{17-4}$$

The integral (17-4) can be evaluated by repeated integrations. Thus, if

$$d\sigma = \sec\gamma\, dA = \sqrt{\left(\frac{\partial z}{\partial x}\right)^2 + \left(\frac{\partial z}{\partial y}\right)^2 + 1}\; dx\, dy,$$

then $$\int_{S'} \varphi(x,y,z)\, d\sigma = \iint_R \varphi[x,y,f(x,y)]\sqrt{\left(\frac{\partial z}{\partial x}\right)^2 + \left(\frac{\partial z}{\partial y}\right)^2 + 1}\; dx\, dy$$

where $z = f(x,y)$ is the equation of S' and R is the projection of S' on the xy plane.

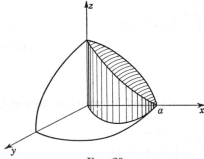

FIG. 20

We shall consider surface integrals in somewhat greater detail in Chap. 5.

Example 1. Find the surface of the sphere $x^2 + y^2 + z^2 = a^2$ cut off by the cylinder $x^2 - ax + y^2 = 0$ (Fig. 20).

From symmetry it is clear that it will suffice to determine the surface in the first octant and multiply the result by 4. Now,

$$\sigma = \int_R \sqrt{\left(\frac{\partial z}{\partial x}\right)^2 + \left(\frac{\partial z}{\partial y}\right)^2 + 1}\; dy\, dx,$$

and since $z = \sqrt{a^2 - x^2 - y^2}$,

$$\frac{\partial z}{\partial x} = \frac{-x}{\sqrt{a^2 - x^2 - y^2}}, \qquad \frac{\partial z}{\partial y} = \frac{-y}{\sqrt{a^2 - x^2 - y^2}}.$$

Thus, the integral becomes

$$\sigma = 4\int_0^a \int_0^{\sqrt{ax-x^2}} \sqrt{\frac{x^2 + y^2}{a^2 - x^2 - y^2} + 1}\; dy\, dx$$

$$= 4\int_0^a \int_0^{\sqrt{ax-x^2}} \frac{a\, dy\, dx}{\sqrt{a^2 - x^2 - y^2}}.$$

It is simpler to evaluate this integral by transforming to cylindrical coordinates. The equation of the cylinder becomes $r = a \cos \theta$, and that of the sphere

$$z = \sqrt{a^2 - x^2 - y^2} = \sqrt{a^2 - r^2}.$$

Thus,

$$\sigma = 4 \int_0^{\frac{\pi}{2}} \int_0^{a\cos\theta} \frac{ar \, dr \, d\theta}{\sqrt{a^2 - r^2}} = 4a^2 \left(\frac{\pi}{2} - 1 \right).$$

Example 2. Find the z coordinate of the center of gravity of one octant of the surface of the sphere $x^2 + y^2 + z^2 = a^2$. Now,

$$\bar{z} = \frac{\int_{S'} z \, d\sigma}{\int_{S'} d\sigma} = \frac{\int_0^a \int_0^{\sqrt{a^2-y^2}} z \sqrt{\left(\frac{\partial z}{\partial x} \right)^2 + \left(\frac{\partial z}{\partial y} \right)^2 + 1} \, dx \, dy}{\dfrac{4\pi a^2}{8}}$$

$$= \frac{2 \int_0^a \int_0^{\sqrt{a^2-y^2}} a \, dx \, dy}{\pi a^2} = \frac{a}{2}.$$

PROBLEMS

1. Find, by the method of Sec. 17, the area of the surface of the sphere $x^2 + y^2 + z^2 = a^2$ that lies in the first octant.

2. Find the surface of the sphere $x^2 + y^2 + z^2 = a^2$ cut off by the cylinder $x^2 - ax + y^2 = 0$.

3. Find the volume bounded by the cylinder and the sphere of Prob. 2.

4. Find the surface of the cylinder $x^2 + y^2 = a^2$ cut off by the cylinder $y^2 + z^2 = a^2$.

5. Find the coordinates of the center of gravity of the portion of the surface of the sphere cut off by the right-circular cone whose vertex is at the center of the sphere.

6. If a sphere is inscribed in a right-circular cylinder, then the surfaces of the sphere and the cylinder intercepted by a pair of planes perpendicular to the axis of the cylinder are equal in area.   Prove it.

CHAPTER 4

ALGEBRA AND GEOMETRY OF VECTORS. MATRICES

Fundamental Operations

Applications

Linear Vector Spaces and Matrices

It is desirable to treat directed quantities like *force* or *velocity* (which are independent of coordinate systems) without reference to a set of coordinate axes. Such a coordinate-free treatment is made possible by the analytical shorthand known as vector analysis. The trajectory of a particle, the dynamics of rigid bodies, and the theory of fluid flow are readily studied by vector methods, as are also such topics as the geometry of curves and surfaces. Introduction of coordinates yields a correspondence between vectors and sets of numbers, and this correspondence permits the use of vector methods in the study of linear equations. Such a study leads to the concept of *matrix*, which has proved fruitful in a variety of fields, ranging from circuit analysis to quantum theory.

FUNDAMENTAL OPERATIONS

1. Scalars, Vectors, and Equality. Some quantities appearing in the study of physical phenomena can be completely specified by their magnitude alone. Thus, the mass of a body can be described by the number of grams, the temperature by degrees on some scale, the volume by the number of cubic units, and so on. A quantity that (after a suitable choice of units) can be completely characterized by a single number is called a *scalar*. There are also quantities, called *vectors*, that require for their complete characterization the specification of direction as well as magnitude. An example of a vector quantity is the displacement of translation of a particle. If a particle is displaced from a position P to a new position P' (Fig. 1), then the change in position can be represented graphically by the directed line segment PP' whose

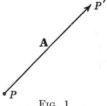

Fig. 1

length equals the amount of the displacement and whose direction is from P to P'. Similarly, a force of magnitude K dynes can be represented by a line segment whose length is K units and whose direction coincides with that of the force.

The initial point P of a directed line segment representing a vector is called the *origin,* and the representation as an arrow suggests that the terminal point be called the *head* of the vector. In many problems the location of the origin for any given vector is immaterial, and in such problems two vectors are regarded as equal if they have the same length and the same direction. Such vectors, which need not coincide to be equal, are termed *free vectors.* In mechanics, it is sometimes convenient to specify vectors by giving the line of action as well as the length and direction. Equality of these so-called *sliding vectors* means that the lengths, directions, and lines of action coincide. Again, in the treatment of space curves and trajectories one is led to specify the origin of the vector as well as its length and direction. Such vectors are termed *bound vectors.*

To distinguish vectors from scalars, boldface type is used for vectors in this book. The length (or *magnitude*) of the vector $\mathbf{A}$ is denoted by $|\mathbf{A}|$:

$$|\mathbf{A}| = \text{length of } \mathbf{A}. \tag{1-1}$$

Equality is denoted by the usual symbol: $\mathbf{A} = \mathbf{B}$. For the most part this chapter deals with free vectors, and hence "$\mathbf{A} = \mathbf{B}$" means that $\mathbf{A}$ and $\mathbf{B}$ have the same length and direction.

2. Addition, Subtraction, and Multiplication by Scalars. If a particle is displaced from its initial position P to P', so that $\overrightarrow{PP'} = \mathbf{A}$, and subsequently it is displaced to a position P'', so that $\overrightarrow{P'P''} = \mathbf{B}$, then the displacement from the original position P to the final position P'' can be accomplished by the single displacement $\overrightarrow{PP''} = \mathbf{C}$. Thus, it is logical to write

$$\mathbf{A} + \mathbf{B} = \mathbf{C}$$

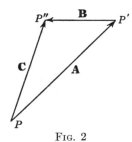

Fig. 2

as the definition of vector addition (Fig. 2). In words, if the initial point of the vector $\mathbf{B}$ is placed in coincidence with the terminal point of the vector $\mathbf{A}$, then the vector $\mathbf{C}$, which joins the initial point of $\mathbf{A}$ with the terminal point of $\mathbf{B}$, is called the *sum* of $\mathbf{A}$ and $\mathbf{B}$ and is denoted by $\mathbf{A} + \mathbf{B} = \mathbf{C}$. This is the familiar *parallelogram law of addition* used in physics, and its extension to three or more vectors is obvious. The symbol $+$ behaves like the $+$ of elementary algebra, in that

$$\mathbf{A} + \mathbf{B} = \mathbf{B} + \mathbf{A}, \qquad \text{commutative law}$$

$$\mathbf{A} + (\mathbf{B} + \mathbf{C}) = (\mathbf{A} + \mathbf{B}) + \mathbf{C}, \qquad \text{associative law.} \tag{2-1}$$

A proof is implicit in Figs. 3 and 4. The associative law enables us to omit parentheses, writing $\mathbf{A} + \mathbf{B} + \mathbf{C}$ for $\mathbf{A} + (\mathbf{B} + \mathbf{C})$.

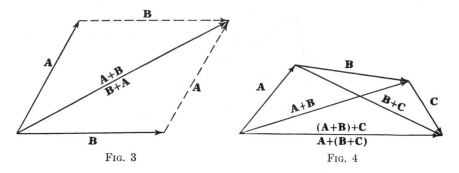

FIG. 3   FIG. 4

It is desirable to give meaning to expressions like 5A, the product of a scalar and a vector. In agreement with the meaning of multiplication familiar from arithmetic, one defines

$$5\mathbf{A} = \mathbf{A} + \mathbf{A} + \mathbf{A} + \mathbf{A} + \mathbf{A} \tag{2-2}$$

(Fig. 5) and similarly in other cases. By a natural extension of this reasoning, $t\mathbf{A}$ *is defined as a vector whose length is* $|t||\mathbf{A}|$ *and whose direction is that*

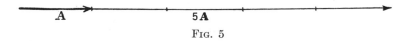

FIG. 5

of $\mathbf{A}$ *if t is positive but opposite to that of* $\mathbf{A}$ *if t is negative.* One defines $\mathbf{A}t$ by the equation

$$\mathbf{A}t = t\mathbf{A}. \tag{2-3}$$

It follows that $1\mathbf{A} = \mathbf{A}$ and also

$$s(t\mathbf{A}) = (st)\mathbf{A}, \qquad \text{associative law,}$$
$$(s + t)\mathbf{A} = s\mathbf{A} + t\mathbf{A}, \qquad \text{distributive law,} \tag{2-4}$$
$$t(\mathbf{A} + \mathbf{B}) = t\mathbf{A} + t\mathbf{B}, \qquad \text{distributive law.}$$

A vector of zero length is denoted by $\mathbf{0}$ and termed the *zero vector*. To introduce the idea of subtraction, one defines $-\mathbf{A}$ as the solution of the equation $\mathbf{A} + \mathbf{X} = \mathbf{0}$. Evidently, $-\mathbf{A}$ is a vector equal in length to $\mathbf{A}$ but of opposite direction, so that $-\mathbf{A} = (-1)\mathbf{A}$. As in elementary algebra, $\mathbf{B} - \mathbf{A}$ is used as an abbreviation for $\mathbf{B} + (-\mathbf{A})$.

Since the laws governing the addition of vectors and multiplication of vectors by scalars are identical with those met in ordinary algebra, one is justified in using the familiar rules of algebra to solve linear equations involving vectors.

Example 1.   The point P in Fig. 6 divides the segment AB in the ratio $m:n$.   Express **R** in terms of the vectors **A**, **B** and the scalars m, n.

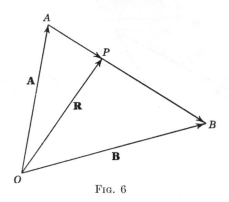

FIG. 6

The vector $\mathbf{X} = \overrightarrow{AB}$ satisfies $\mathbf{A} + \mathbf{X} = \mathbf{B}$ by the definition of vector addition, and hence, solving for **X**,

$$\mathbf{X} = \mathbf{B} - \mathbf{A}. \qquad (2\text{-}5)$$

(This exemplifies the so-called "head-minus-tail" rule for vector subtraction.)   The vector $\overrightarrow{AP}$ is $m/(m+n)$ times **X**, by the hypothesis and by the definition of multiplication by scalars.   Since $\mathbf{R} = \mathbf{A} + \overrightarrow{AP}$ we have, finally,

$$\mathbf{R} = \mathbf{A} + \frac{m}{m+n}(\mathbf{B} - \mathbf{A}) = \frac{n\mathbf{A} + m\mathbf{B}}{m+n}.$$

Example 2.   Prove that the medians of every triangle intersect at a point two-thirds of the way from each vertex to the opposite side.

Let two sides of the triangle be specified by vectors **A** and **B**, as in Fig. 7, so that the third side is $\mathbf{B} - \mathbf{A}$ (cf. Example 1).   The vector median to the side $\mathbf{B} - \mathbf{A}$ is $\frac{1}{2}$ the diag-

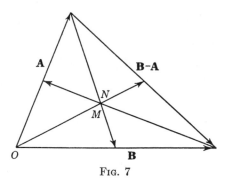

FIG. 7

onal of the parallelogram on **A**, **B**; hence this median is $(\mathbf{A} + \mathbf{B})/2$ (compare the special case $m = n$ of Example 1).   If the point M in Fig. 7 is two-thirds of the way from the vertex O to the side $\mathbf{B} - \mathbf{A}$, along this median, then

$$OM = \frac{2}{3}\frac{A+B}{2} = \frac{A+B}{3}.$$ (2-6)

The vector median to the side A is $A/2 - B$, again by the head-minus-tail rule.   If N is at a point two-thirds of the way toward the side A on this median, then

$$ON = B + \frac{2}{3}\left(\frac{A}{2} - B\right) = \frac{A+B}{3}.$$

Comparison with (2-6) shows that the two points M, N coincide.   That the third median also has the required behavior follows by interchanging the roles of A and B.

PROBLEMS

1. Sketch a vector A of length 1.5 in., parallel to the lower edge of your paper and having an arrow on its right-hand end.   Sketch a second vector B of length 1 in., making an angle of 30° with A.   Now sketch $2A$, $3B$, $A + B$, $A - B$, $2A - 3B$, $(A + B)/2$.

2. Give a condition on three vectors A, B, C which ensures that they can form a triangle.   Generalize to n vectors A, B, C, ..., L.

3. Graphically and algebraically, show how to find two vectors A and B if their sum S and difference D are known.

4. Sketch three vectors A, B, C issuing from a common point.   On your figure show the vectors $A - C$, $B - A$, $C - B$, and thus illustrate the algebraic identity $(A - C) + (B - A) + (C - B) = 0$.

5. (a) Write down a vector of unit length which has the same direction as a given nonzero vector A. (b) Using the result (a), write down a vector bisecting the angle formed by two nonzero vectors A, B issuing from a common point.

6. Show that a line from a vertex of a parallelogram to the mid-point of a nonadjacent side trisects a diagonal.

3. Base Vectors.   Any vector A lying in the plane of two noncollinear vectors a and b can be resolved into so-called *components* directed along a and b. This resolution is accomplished by constructing the parallelogram whose sides are parallel to a and b (Fig. 8).   Then one can write

$$A = xa + yb,$$

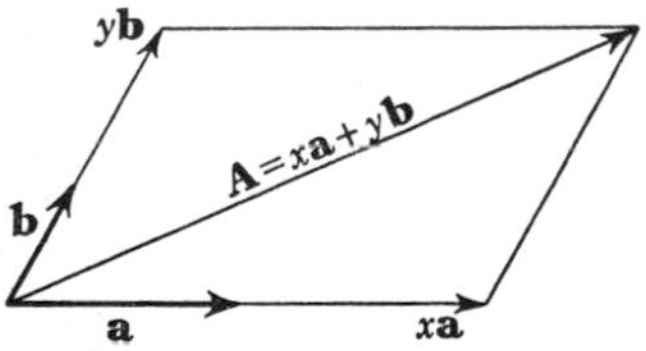

FIG. 8

where x and y are the appropriate scalars.

If three noncoplanar vectors a, b, and c are given, then any vector V can be expressed uniquely as

$$V = xa + yb + zc,$$ (3-1)

where V is the diagonal of the parallelepiped whose edges are xa, yb, and zc (Fig. 9).   The vectors a, b, and c are called the *base vectors*, and the scalars x, y, and z the *measure numbers*.

An important set of base vectors, denoted by i, j, and k, consists of unit vectors directed along the positive directions of the x, y, and z axes, respectively (Fig. 10).   It is assumed that the system of axes is a right-handed system; that is, a right-hand screw directed along the positive z axis advances in the positive direction when it is rotated from the positive

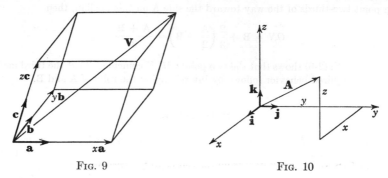

FIG. 9   FIG. 10

x axis toward the positive y axis through the smaller (90°) angle.   Because **i, j, k** are mutually orthogonal, the representation

$$\mathbf{A} = x\mathbf{i} + y\mathbf{j} + z\mathbf{k}$$

yields the important formula

$$|\mathbf{A}|^2 = x^2 + y^2 + z^2 \tag{3-2}$$

by use of Pythagoras's theorem (Fig. 11).

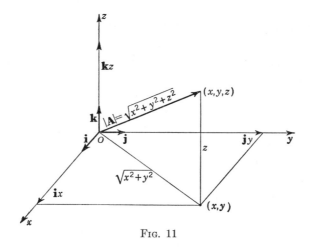

FIG. 11

Example: If $\mathbf{A} = \mathbf{i} + 2\mathbf{j} + 3\mathbf{k}$ and $\mathbf{B} = -\mathbf{j} + 4\mathbf{k}$, compute the length of $2\mathbf{A} - \mathbf{B}$. Since $2\mathbf{A} - \mathbf{B} = 2\mathbf{i} + 5\mathbf{j} + 2\mathbf{k}$, we have

$$|2\mathbf{A} - \mathbf{B}| = (2^2 + 5^2 + 2^2)^{\frac{1}{2}} = \sqrt{33}.$$

PROBLEMS

1. (*a*) In the form $a\mathbf{i} + b\mathbf{j} + c\mathbf{k}$ write down two vectors of length 5 parallel to the y axis. (*b*) If $\mathbf{A} = \mathbf{i} + 2\mathbf{j} + 3\mathbf{k}$, $\mathbf{B} = \mathbf{i} + \mathbf{j} + \mathbf{k}$, $\mathbf{C} = \mathbf{i} - \mathbf{k}$, compute $\mathbf{A} + \mathbf{B}$, $(\mathbf{A} + \mathbf{B}) + \mathbf{C}$, $\mathbf{B} + \mathbf{C}$, and $\mathbf{A} + (\mathbf{B} + \mathbf{C})$. What law does this illustrate? (*c*) In (*b*), find $5\mathbf{A}$, $-2\mathbf{A}$, the sum of these vectors, and the vector $3\mathbf{A}$. What law does this illustrate? (*d*) Also find $3\mathbf{A}$, $3\mathbf{B}$, the sum of these vectors, and the vector $3(\mathbf{A} + \mathbf{B})$. (*e*) In (*b*), a certain vector $\mathbf{D}$ is such that $\mathbf{A}, \mathbf{B}, \mathbf{D}$ can be placed head against tail to form a triangle. What is the z component of $\mathbf{D}$?

2. Sketch the triangle with vertices at the heads of $\mathbf{i} + \mathbf{j} + \mathbf{k}$, $2\mathbf{j} + \mathbf{k}$, and $2\mathbf{i} + \mathbf{j}$, and make the sides into vectors with head against tail. Find the vectors forming the sides of the triangle, and verify that the sum of these vectors is zero.

3. Draw a figure illustrating the inequality $|\mathbf{A} + \mathbf{B}| \leq |\mathbf{A}| + |\mathbf{B}|$, and by combining this with (3-2), deduce an algebraic inequality. Can you give a purely algebraic proof?

4. (*a*) Let $\mathbf{A}, \mathbf{B}, \mathbf{C}, \ldots$ be vectors from the center to the vertices of a regular decagon (ten-sided polygon). By choosing a suitable basis $\mathbf{i}, \mathbf{j}$ and using symmetry, show that the sum $\mathbf{A} + \mathbf{B} + \mathbf{C} + \cdots$ is zero. (*b*) By picking another basis $\mathbf{i}', \mathbf{j}'$, with $\mathbf{i}'$ making an angle θ with $\mathbf{A}$, deduce the identity $\cos \theta + \cos (\theta + \pi/5) + \cos (\theta + 2\pi/5) + \cdots + \cos (\theta + 9\pi/5) = 0$.

4. The Dot Product.

The *dot product*[1] of two vectors is defined to be the product of their lengths by the cosine of the angle between them. In symbols,

$$\mathbf{A} \cdot \mathbf{B} = |\mathbf{A}| \, |\mathbf{B}| \, \cos (\mathbf{A}, \mathbf{B}), \tag{4-1}$$

where $(\mathbf{A}, \mathbf{B})$ is the angle from $\mathbf{A}$ to $\mathbf{B}$. Thus $\mathbf{A} \cdot \mathbf{B}$ is a *scalar*, not a vector. Geometrically,

$$\mathbf{A} \cdot \mathbf{B} = |\mathbf{A}| \times (\text{projection of } \mathbf{B} \text{ on } \mathbf{A})$$

$$= |\mathbf{B}| \times (\text{projection of } \mathbf{A} \text{ on } \mathbf{B}). \tag{4-2}$$

Evidently $(\mathbf{A}, \mathbf{B})$ can be measured in several ways. However, since $\cos \theta = \cos (-\theta) = \cos (2\pi - \theta)$, these different measures all yield the same value for $\mathbf{A} \cdot \mathbf{B}$. The fact that $\cos \theta = \cos (-\theta)$ also yields

$$\mathbf{A} \cdot \mathbf{B} = \mathbf{B} \cdot \mathbf{A}, \qquad \text{commutative law}, \tag{4-3}$$

and one easily verifies the additional properties

$$(t\mathbf{A}) \cdot \mathbf{B} = t(\mathbf{A} \cdot \mathbf{B}), \qquad \text{associative law}, \tag{4-4}$$

$$\mathbf{A} \cdot (\mathbf{B} + \mathbf{C}) = \mathbf{A} \cdot \mathbf{B} + \mathbf{A} \cdot \mathbf{C}, \qquad \text{distributive law}. \tag{4-5}$$

For proof of (4-5) use (4-1) to transform (4-5) into

$$|\mathbf{A}| \, |\mathbf{B} + \mathbf{C}| \cos \psi = |\mathbf{A}| \, |\mathbf{B}| \cos \phi + |\mathbf{A}| \, |\mathbf{C}| \cos \theta, \tag{4-6}$$

where the angles are defined in Fig. 12. Now (4-6) follows from

$$|\mathbf{B} + \mathbf{C}| \cos \psi = |\mathbf{B}| \cos \phi + |\mathbf{C}| \cos \theta \tag{4-7}$$

[1] The terms *scalar product* and *inner product* are often used.

and (4-7) is evident from Fig. 12, when the vectors are coplanar and the angles are in the first quadrant. In view of (4-2) the property amounts merely to the assertion that projections are additive, and the extension to arbitrary angles is not difficult.

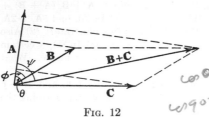

FIG. 12

For the mutually orthogonal unit vectors **i**, **j**, **k** introduced in Sec. 3 we have, by inspection of (4-1),

$$\mathbf{i}\cdot\mathbf{i} = \mathbf{j}\cdot\mathbf{j} = \mathbf{k}\cdot\mathbf{k} = 1,$$
$$\mathbf{i}\cdot\mathbf{j} = \mathbf{j}\cdot\mathbf{k} = \mathbf{i}\cdot\mathbf{k} = 0. \tag{4-8}$$

Hence, expanding the product by (4-4) and (4-5), we get

$$(x\mathbf{i} + y\mathbf{j} + z\mathbf{k})\cdot(x_1\mathbf{i} + y_1\mathbf{j} + z_1\mathbf{k}) = xx_1 + yy_1 + zz_1. \tag{4-9}$$

By (4-1) and (4-9) the dot product gives a simple way to find the angle between two vectors and, in particular, to decide when two vectors are perpendicular. Indeed, if we agree to regard the zero vector as perpendicular to every vector, then from (4-1)

$$\mathbf{A}\cdot\mathbf{B} = 0 \text{ if, and only if, } \mathbf{A} \perp \mathbf{B}. \tag{4-10}$$

The case in which **B** is parallel to **A** is also worthy of note. In particular when **B** = **A** we have

$$\mathbf{A}\cdot\mathbf{A} = |\mathbf{A}|^2. \tag{4-11}$$

Example: Compute the cosine of the angle between **A** and **B** if $\mathbf{A} = \mathbf{i} + \mathbf{j} + 2\mathbf{k}$, $\mathbf{B} = -\mathbf{i} + z\mathbf{k}$, and find a value of z for which $\mathbf{A} \perp \mathbf{B}$.
We have $\mathbf{A}\cdot\mathbf{B} = -1 + 0 + 2z = 2z - 1$ and hence, by (4-1),

$$\cos(\mathbf{A},\mathbf{B}) = \frac{2z - 1}{|\mathbf{A}|\,|\mathbf{B}|} = \frac{2z - 1}{\sqrt{6 + 6z^2}}.$$

The result is zero, and hence the vectors are perpendicular, when $z = \frac{1}{2}$.

PROBLEMS

1. Given $\mathbf{A} = \mathbf{i} + 2\mathbf{j} + 3\mathbf{k}$, $\mathbf{B} = -\mathbf{i} + 2\mathbf{j} + \mathbf{k}$, $\mathbf{C} = 2\mathbf{i} + \mathbf{j}$. (*a*) Find the dot product of $3\mathbf{i} + 2\mathbf{j} + \mathbf{k}$ with each of these vectors. (*b*) Find $\mathbf{A}\cdot\mathbf{B}$, $\mathbf{A}\cdot\mathbf{C}$, $\mathbf{B} + \mathbf{C}$, $\mathbf{A}\cdot(\mathbf{B} + \mathbf{C})$. What law is illustrated? (*c*) Find $2\mathbf{A}$ and $(2\mathbf{A})\cdot\mathbf{B}$. Compare $\mathbf{A}\cdot\mathbf{B}$ as found in (*b*). (*d*) Find the angle between **A** and **B**. (*e*) Find the projection of **A** on **C**. (*f*) Find a scalar s such that $\mathbf{A} + s\mathbf{B}$ is perpendicular to **A**. (*g*) Find a vector of form $\mathbf{i}x + \mathbf{j}y + \mathbf{k}$ which is perpendicular both to **A** and to **B**.

2. (*a*) Show that $\mathbf{i} + \mathbf{j} + \mathbf{k}$, $\mathbf{i} - \mathbf{k}$, and $\mathbf{i} - 2\mathbf{j} + \mathbf{k}$ are mutually orthogonal. (*b*) Choose x, y, and z so that $\mathbf{i} + \mathbf{j} + 2\mathbf{k}$, $-\mathbf{i} + z\mathbf{k}$, and $2\mathbf{i} + x\mathbf{j} + y\mathbf{k}$ are mutually orthogonal.

3. (*a*) If $\mathbf{A}\cdot\mathbf{B} = \mathbf{A}\cdot\mathbf{C}$ for some $\mathbf{A} \neq \mathbf{0}$, is it necessary that $\mathbf{B} = \mathbf{C}$? Illustrate your answer by an example. (*b*) If $\mathbf{A}\cdot\mathbf{B} = \mathbf{A}\cdot\mathbf{C}$ for every **A**, is it necessary that $\mathbf{B} = \mathbf{C}$?

5. The Cross Product. Besides the multiplication just considered there is a second kind of multiplication, which yields a product known as the *vector product* or *cross product*. The cross product of **A** and **B**, denoted by **A** × **B**, is a vector **C** which is normal to the plane of **A** and **B** and is so directed that the vectors **A**, **B**, **C** form a right-handed system. The length of **C** is the product of the length of **A** by the length of **B** by the sine of the smaller angle between them:

$$|\mathbf{A} \times \mathbf{B}| = |\mathbf{A}|\,|\mathbf{B}|\,\sin(\mathbf{A},\mathbf{B}). \tag{5-1}$$

The expression (5-1) represents the area of the parallelogram having **A**, **B** as adjacent edges (Fig. 13). The student is warned, incidentally, that

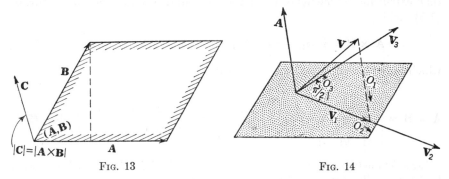

FIG. 13   FIG. 14

(5-1) does not give **A** × **B**; it gives the length $|\mathbf{A} \times \mathbf{B}|$ only.

Since rotation from **B** to **A** is opposite to that from **A** to **B**, we have

$$\mathbf{A} \times \mathbf{B} = -\mathbf{B} \times \mathbf{A}, \tag{5-2}$$

so that the commutative law does not hold for vector products. On the other hand it is the case that

$$(t\mathbf{A}) \times \mathbf{B} = t(\mathbf{A} \times \mathbf{B}), \qquad \text{associative law}, \tag{5-3}$$

$$\mathbf{A} \times (\mathbf{B} + \mathbf{C}) = \mathbf{A} \times \mathbf{B} + \mathbf{A} \times \mathbf{C}, \qquad \text{distributive law}. \tag{5-4}$$

The proof of equation (5-3) is trivial, and (5-4) is readily established if we note that **A** × **V** is obtained from the arbitrary vector **V** by performing the following three operations O_i illustrated in Fig. 14.

O_1: Project **V** on the plane perpendicular to **A** to obtain a vector $\mathbf{V}_1 \perp \mathbf{A}$ of magnitude $|\mathbf{V}|\sin(\mathbf{A},\mathbf{V})$.

O_2: Multiply $\mathbf{V}_1$ by $|\mathbf{A}|$ to obtain $\mathbf{V}_2 \perp \mathbf{A}$ of magnitude $|\mathbf{A}|\,|\mathbf{V}|\sin(\mathbf{A},\mathbf{V})$.

O_3: Rotate $\mathbf{V}_2$ about **A** through $90°$ to obtain $\mathbf{V}_3 = \mathbf{A} \times \mathbf{V}$.

It is easily checked that each of these operators is distributive; that is, $O_i(\mathbf{B} + \mathbf{C}) = O_i\mathbf{B} + O_i\mathbf{C}$ for all vectors **B** and **C**. Hence the composite operator $O_3O_2O_1$ is distributive; namely,

$$O_3O_2O_1(\mathbf{B} + \mathbf{C}) = O_3O_2(O_1\mathbf{B} + O_1\mathbf{C}), \qquad \text{since } O_1 \text{ is distributive},$$

$$= O_3(O_2O_1\mathbf{B} + O_2O_1\mathbf{C}), \qquad \text{since } O_2 \text{ is distributive},$$

$$= O_3O_2O_1\mathbf{B} + O_3O_2O_1\mathbf{C}, \qquad \text{since } O_3 \text{ is distributive}.$$

Because $O_3O_2O_1\mathbf{V} = \mathbf{A} \times \mathbf{V}$ for every vector **V**, the latter equation yields (5-4).

The definitions of vector product and of $\mathbf{i}$, $\mathbf{j}$, $\mathbf{k}$ lead to

$$\mathbf{i} \times \mathbf{i} = \mathbf{j} \times \mathbf{j} = \mathbf{k} \times \mathbf{k} = 0, \qquad \mathbf{i} \times \mathbf{j} = -\mathbf{j} \times \mathbf{i} = \mathbf{k},$$

$$\mathbf{j} \times \mathbf{k} = -\mathbf{k} \times \mathbf{j} = \mathbf{i}, \qquad \mathbf{k} \times \mathbf{i} = -\mathbf{i} \times \mathbf{k} = \mathbf{j}. \qquad (5\text{-}5)$$

If $\mathbf{A}$ and $\mathbf{B}$ are given by their components as

$$\mathbf{A} = x\mathbf{i} + y\mathbf{j} + z\mathbf{k}, \qquad \mathbf{B} = x_1\mathbf{i} + y_1\mathbf{j} + z_1\mathbf{k}$$

then expansion by means of (5-3) and (5-4) and simplification by means of (5-5) yield

$$\mathbf{A} \times \mathbf{B} = \mathbf{i}(yz_1 - zy_1) + \mathbf{j}(x_1z - xz_1) + \mathbf{k}(xy_1 - yx_1)$$

which may be written as a determinant [1]

$$\mathbf{A} \times \mathbf{B} = \begin{vmatrix} \mathbf{i} & \mathbf{j} & \mathbf{k} \\ x & y & z \\ x_1 & y_1 & z_1 \end{vmatrix} \equiv \mathbf{i} \begin{vmatrix} y & z \\ y_1 & z_1 \end{vmatrix} - \mathbf{j} \begin{vmatrix} x & z \\ x_1 & z_1 \end{vmatrix} + \mathbf{k} \begin{vmatrix} x & y \\ x_1 & y_1 \end{vmatrix}. \qquad (5\text{-}6)$$

Example: Find a vector perpendicular to $\mathbf{i} + 2\mathbf{k}$ and $\mathbf{i} + \mathbf{j} - \mathbf{k}$, and find the area of the triangle with these two vectors as adjacent sides.

Both questions are settled by calculating the cross product. We have, from (5-6),

$$(\mathbf{i} + 2\mathbf{k}) \times (\mathbf{i} + \mathbf{j} - \mathbf{k}) = \begin{vmatrix} \mathbf{i} & \mathbf{j} & \mathbf{k} \\ 1 & 0 & 2 \\ 1 & 1 & -1 \end{vmatrix}$$

$$= \mathbf{i} \begin{vmatrix} 0 & 2 \\ 1 & -1 \end{vmatrix} - \mathbf{j} \begin{vmatrix} 1 & 2 \\ 1 & -1 \end{vmatrix} + \mathbf{k} \begin{vmatrix} 1 & 0 \\ 1 & 1 \end{vmatrix}$$

$$= -2\mathbf{i} + 3\mathbf{j} + \mathbf{k}.$$

This vector is perpendicular to the given vectors. The area of the triangle is half the area of the parallelogram:

$$\text{Area } \Delta = \tfrac{1}{2} |-2\mathbf{i} + 3\mathbf{j} + \mathbf{k}| = \tfrac{1}{2}\sqrt{14}.$$

PROBLEMS

1. Given $\mathbf{A} = \mathbf{i} + 2\mathbf{j} + \mathbf{k}$, $\mathbf{B} = 3\mathbf{i} + 2\mathbf{j}$, $\mathbf{C} = -\mathbf{i} + \mathbf{j} + 3\mathbf{k}$. (*a*) Find $\mathbf{A} \times \mathbf{B}$, $\mathbf{A} \times \mathbf{C}$, $\mathbf{A} \times \mathbf{B} + \mathbf{A} \times \mathbf{C}$, $\mathbf{B} + \mathbf{C}$, and $\mathbf{A} \times (\mathbf{B} + \mathbf{C})$. What law is illustrated? (*b*) Find a vector perpendicular to $\mathbf{B}$ and $\mathbf{C}$, and verify your answer by use of the dot product. (*c*) If $\mathbf{A}$, $\mathbf{B}$, $\mathbf{C}$ have their origins at a common point, find a vector perpendicular to the plane in which their heads lie. (*d*) Find the area of the triangle formed by the heads in (*c*).

2. Show that the cross product for each two of the following vectors is parallel to the third: $\mathbf{i} + \mathbf{j} + \mathbf{k}$, $\mathbf{i} - \mathbf{k}$, $\mathbf{i} - 2\mathbf{j} + \mathbf{k}$. What does this indicate about the vectors?

---

[1] The reader unfamiliar with second- or third-order determinants is referred to Appendix A.

3. Give an example of three unequal vectors such that the cross product of any two is perpendicular to the third.

4. If $\mathbf{A} \times \mathbf{B} = 0$ and $\mathbf{A} \cdot \mathbf{B} = 0$, is it necessary that $\mathbf{A} = 0$ or $\mathbf{B} = 0$?

5. In refraction at the plane interface of two homogeneous media let $\mathbf{A}$, $\mathbf{B}$, $\mathbf{C}$ be unit vectors, respectively along the incident, reflected, and refracted rays, and let $\mathbf{N}$ be the unit normal to the interface. (*a*) Show that the law of reflection is equivalent to $\mathbf{A} \times \mathbf{N} = \mathbf{B} \times \mathbf{N}$. (*b*) Show that the law of refraction is equivalent to $n_1\mathbf{A} \times \mathbf{N} = n_2\mathbf{C} \times \mathbf{N}$, where n_1 and n_2 are the indices of refraction.

6. Continued Products. With the two multiplications previously defined, we can form the products $(\mathbf{A} \cdot \mathbf{B})\mathbf{C}$, $\mathbf{A} \cdot (\mathbf{B} \times \mathbf{C})$ and $\mathbf{A} \times (\mathbf{B} \times \mathbf{C})$; some of the other possible combinations, however, have no meaning. For example, $(\mathbf{A} \cdot \mathbf{B}) \times \mathbf{C}$ is meaningless because the two factors in a cross product must both be vectors.

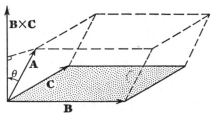

FIG. 15

The first product, $(\mathbf{A} \cdot \mathbf{B})\mathbf{C}$, denotes simply the product of the scalar $\mathbf{A} \cdot \mathbf{B}$ with the vector $\mathbf{C}$ and may be dismissed without further comment. By definition of dot product, the second expression, $\mathbf{A} \cdot (\mathbf{B} \times \mathbf{C})$, called the *scalar triple product*, has the value

$$\mathbf{A} \cdot (\mathbf{B} \times \mathbf{C}) = |\mathbf{A}| \cos \theta |\mathbf{B} \times \mathbf{C}|, \qquad (6\text{-}1)$$

where θ is the angle between $\mathbf{A}$ and $\mathbf{B} \times \mathbf{C}$. Since $\mathbf{B} \times \mathbf{C}$ is perpendicular to the face of the parallelepiped containing $\mathbf{B}$ and $\mathbf{C}$ (Fig. 15), and since $|\mathbf{B} \times \mathbf{C}|$ is the area of this face, (6-1) shows that $\mathbf{A} \cdot (\mathbf{B} \times \mathbf{C})$ *represents the signed volume of the parallelepiped having* $\mathbf{A}$, $\mathbf{B}$, $\mathbf{C}$ *as adjacent edges.* Moreover, we have the formula

$$\mathbf{A} \cdot (\mathbf{B} \times \mathbf{C}) = \begin{vmatrix} A_x & A_y & A_z \\ B_x & B_y & B_z \\ C_x & C_y & C_z \end{vmatrix}, \qquad \begin{cases} \mathbf{A} = \mathbf{i}A_x + \mathbf{j}A_y + \mathbf{k}A_z, \\ \mathbf{B} = \mathbf{i}B_x + \mathbf{j}B_y + \mathbf{k}B_z, \\ \mathbf{C} = \mathbf{i}C_x + \mathbf{j}C_y + \mathbf{k}C_z, \end{cases} \quad (6\text{-}2)$$

as will now be seen. The expression (5-6) yields

$$\mathbf{B} \times \mathbf{C} = \begin{vmatrix} \mathbf{i} & \mathbf{j} & \mathbf{k} \\ B_x & B_y & B_z \\ C_x & C_y & C_z \end{vmatrix} = \mathbf{i}P + \mathbf{j}Q + \mathbf{k}R, \qquad (6\text{-}3)$$

say, where P, Q, R are certain second-order determinants. Taking the dot product of $\mathbf{i}A_x + \mathbf{j}A_y + \mathbf{k}A_z$ with (6-3) leads to

$$\mathbf{A} \cdot (\mathbf{B} \times \mathbf{C}) = A_x P + A_y Q + A_z R,$$

which is the expansion of the determinant (6-2) on elements of the first row.

Since interchanging two rows of a determinant merely changes its sign, (6-2) yields the useful relations

$$\mathbf{A} \cdot (\mathbf{B} \times \mathbf{C}) = \mathbf{B} \cdot (\mathbf{C} \times \mathbf{A}) = \mathbf{C} \cdot (\mathbf{A} \times \mathbf{B})$$

$$= -\mathbf{B} \cdot (\mathbf{A} \times \mathbf{C}) = -\mathbf{A} \cdot (\mathbf{C} \times \mathbf{B}) = -\mathbf{C} \cdot (\mathbf{B} \times \mathbf{A}). \qquad (6\text{-}4)$$

These results as to magnitude are evident from the volume interpretation, though further discussion is needed to establish the algebraic sign in this way.   Because of (6-4) it is customary to write

$$\mathbf{A} \cdot (\mathbf{B} \times \mathbf{C}) = \mathbf{A} \cdot \mathbf{B} \times \mathbf{C} = (\mathbf{ABC}). \qquad (6\text{-}5)$$

To evaluate the *vector triple product* $\mathbf{A} \times (\mathbf{B} \times \mathbf{C})$, let $\mathbf{i}$ be a unit vector parallel to $\mathbf{B}$ and $\mathbf{j}$ a unit vector perpendicular to $\mathbf{i}$ in the plane of $\mathbf{B}$ and $\mathbf{C}$. Thus

$$\mathbf{B} = B_x \mathbf{i}, \qquad \mathbf{C} = C_x \mathbf{i} + C_y \mathbf{j}, \qquad \mathbf{A} = A_x \mathbf{i} + A_y \mathbf{j} + A_z \mathbf{k}, \qquad (6\text{-}6)$$

where $\mathbf{k}$ is a unit vector perpendicular to $\mathbf{i}$ and $\mathbf{j}$, so oriented that the three form a right-handed system.   Since $\mathbf{B} \times \mathbf{C} = B_x C_y \mathbf{k}$ by (6-6) and (5-6), we have

$$\mathbf{A} \times (\mathbf{B} \times \mathbf{C}) = -A_x B_x C_y \mathbf{j} + A_y B_x C_y \mathbf{i}$$

$$= (A_x C_x + A_y C_y) B_x \mathbf{i} - A_x B_x (C_x \mathbf{i} + C_y \mathbf{j})$$

$$= \mathbf{B}(\mathbf{A} \cdot \mathbf{C}) - \mathbf{C}(\mathbf{A} \cdot \mathbf{B}). \qquad (6\text{-}7)$$

Example: Establish the identity

$$(\mathbf{A} \times \mathbf{B}) \cdot (\mathbf{C} \times \mathbf{D}) = \begin{vmatrix} \mathbf{A} \cdot \mathbf{C} & \mathbf{B} \cdot \mathbf{C} \\ \mathbf{A} \cdot \mathbf{D} & \mathbf{B} \cdot \mathbf{D} \end{vmatrix}. \qquad (6\text{-}8)$$

The expression is the scalar triple product of $\mathbf{A} \times \mathbf{B}$, $\mathbf{C}$, and $\mathbf{D}$.   Interchanging the dot and cross, as we may by (6-4), we obtain

$$(\mathbf{A} \times \mathbf{B}) \cdot \mathbf{C} \times \mathbf{D} = (\mathbf{A} \times \mathbf{B}) \times \mathbf{C} \cdot \mathbf{D} = [(\mathbf{A} \cdot \mathbf{C})\mathbf{B} - (\mathbf{B} \cdot \mathbf{C})\mathbf{A}] \cdot \mathbf{D}$$

$$= (\mathbf{A} \cdot \mathbf{C})(\mathbf{B} \cdot \mathbf{D}) - (\mathbf{B} \cdot \mathbf{C})(\mathbf{A} \cdot \mathbf{D}), \qquad (6\text{-}9)$$

since $(\mathbf{A} \times \mathbf{B}) \times \mathbf{C} = -\mathbf{C} \times (\mathbf{A} \times \mathbf{B}) = (\mathbf{A} \cdot \mathbf{C})\,\mathbf{B} - (\mathbf{B} \cdot \mathbf{C})\,\mathbf{A}$ by (6-7).

PROBLEMS

1. Verify (6-2), (6-7), and (6-8) by direct calculation for the special case $\mathbf{A} = \mathbf{i} + \mathbf{j}$, $\mathbf{B} = -\mathbf{i} + 2\mathbf{k}$, $\mathbf{C} = \mathbf{j} + 2\mathbf{k}$, $\mathbf{D} = \mathbf{i} + \mathbf{j} + \mathbf{k}$.

2. (*a*) In Prob. 1 find the volume of the parallelepiped having $\mathbf{A}$, $\mathbf{B}$, and $\mathbf{C}$ as adjacent edges.   (*b*) Find x such that the vectors $2\mathbf{i} + \mathbf{j} - 2\mathbf{k}$, $\mathbf{i} + \mathbf{j} + 3\mathbf{k}$, and $x\mathbf{i} + \mathbf{j}$ are coplanar. *Hint:* A certain parallelepiped must have zero volume.   (*c*) State a simple necessary and sufficient condition that three arbitrary vectors $\mathbf{A}$, $\mathbf{B}$, $\mathbf{C}$ be coplanar.   (*d*) Evaluate $(\mathbf{AAB})$ and $(\mathbf{ABA})$, where $\mathbf{A}$, $\mathbf{B}$ are arbitrary.

3. By (6-7) show that $\mathbf{A} \times (\mathbf{B} \times \mathbf{C}) + \mathbf{B} \times (\mathbf{C} \times \mathbf{A}) + \mathbf{C} \times (\mathbf{A} \times \mathbf{B}) = 0$.

4. Show that $(\mathbf{B} \times \mathbf{C}) \times (\mathbf{C} \times \mathbf{A}) = \mathbf{C}(\mathbf{ABC})$, and deduce

$$(\mathbf{A} \times \mathbf{B}) \cdot (\mathbf{B} \times \mathbf{C}) \times (\mathbf{C} \times \mathbf{A}) = (\mathbf{ABC})^2.$$

5. The vectors **A**, **B**, **C** issue from a common point and have their heads in a plane. Show that $(\mathbf{A} \times \mathbf{B}) + (\mathbf{B} \times \mathbf{C}) + (\mathbf{C} \times \mathbf{A})$ is perpendicular to this plane.

7. Differentiation. If for each value of a scalar t a vector $\mathbf{R}(t)$ is defined, we say that $\mathbf{R}$ is a vector function of t. In a particular problem t may denote the time and $\mathbf{R}$ the position vector of a moving point relative to some origin O. As in the calculus of scalars, we say that $\mathbf{R}(t)$ is a *continuous vector function* of t at $t = t_0$ provided that

$$\lim_{t \to t_0} \mathbf{R}(t) = \mathbf{R}(t_0). \tag{7-1}$$

The precise meaning of (7-1) is that $|\mathbf{R}(t) - \mathbf{R}(t_0)|$ becomes as small as desired whenever t is sufficiently near t_0.

The cartesian components of the vector $\mathbf{R}(t)$ are functions of t, so that one may write

$$\mathbf{R}(t) = \mathbf{i}x(t) + \mathbf{j}y(t) + \mathbf{k}z(t). \tag{7-2}$$

It follows from (7-1) that the functions $x(t)$, $y(t)$, $z(t)$ are continuous if, and only if, $\mathbf{R}(t)$ is continuous.

We define the derivative of $\mathbf{R}(t)$ with respect to t by the formula

$$\frac{d\mathbf{R}}{dt} = \lim_{\Delta t \to 0} \frac{\mathbf{R}(t + \Delta t) - \mathbf{R}(t)}{\Delta t}. \tag{7-3}$$

The substitution of (7-2) in the definition (7-3) leads immediately to the result that $\mathbf{R}$ is differentiable if, and only if, x, y, z are, and in that case

$$\frac{d\mathbf{R}}{dt} = \mathbf{i}\frac{dx}{dt} + \mathbf{j}\frac{dy}{dt} + \mathbf{k}\frac{dz}{dt}. \tag{7-4}$$

As in scalar calculus we shall write $\mathbf{R}'(t)$ for $d\mathbf{R}/dt$, $\mathbf{R}''(t)$ for $d^2\mathbf{R}/dt^2$, and so on.

Products involving vectors are differentiated by the familiar rules of elementary calculus, and the proof of these rules also involves only familiar ideas. For example, the formula

$$\frac{d}{dt}(\mathbf{A} \times \mathbf{B}) = \mathbf{A} \times \frac{d\mathbf{B}}{dt} + \frac{d\mathbf{A}}{dt} \times \mathbf{B} \tag{7-5}$$

follows from

$$\Delta(\mathbf{A} \times \mathbf{B}) = (\mathbf{A} + \Delta\mathbf{A}) \times (\mathbf{B} + \Delta\mathbf{B}) - \mathbf{A} \times \mathbf{B}$$

$$= \mathbf{A} \times \Delta\mathbf{B} + \Delta\mathbf{A} \times \mathbf{B} + \Delta\mathbf{A} \times \Delta\mathbf{B}$$

when we divide by Δt and let $\Delta t \to 0$. Of course, the order of the factors in (7-5) must be preserved, since the cross product is not commutative.

A geometric interpretation of the derivative may be obtained as follows: Let the vector $\mathbf{R}(t)$ be regarded as a *bound* vector with its origin at the origin of coordinates. The head of $\mathbf{R}$ then traces out a space curve as t varies (see Fig. 16). The vector

$$\Delta\mathbf{R} = \mathbf{R}(t + \Delta t) - \mathbf{R}(t) \tag{7-6}$$

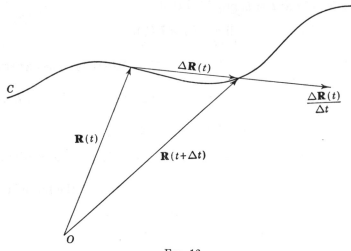

Fig. 16

is directed along a secant of the curve, $\Delta\mathbf{R}/\Delta t$ is parallel to this secant, and hence $\lim (\Delta\mathbf{R}/\Delta t)$ is tangent. *Thus, the vector $\mathbf{R}'(t)$ is tangent to the space curve $\mathbf{R} = \mathbf{R}(t)$ whenever $\mathbf{R}'(t)$ exists and $\mathbf{R}'(t) \neq \mathbf{0}$.*

To interpret the magnitude $|\mathbf{R}'(t)|$, let s be the length of the curve from the fixed point given by $t = t_0$ to the variable point given by t. Assuming $\mathbf{R}'(t) \neq 0$, we have $\Delta\mathbf{R} \neq \mathbf{0}$ for small $\Delta t > 0$, and hence

$$\frac{\Delta s}{\Delta t} = \frac{\Delta s}{|\Delta\mathbf{R}|} \frac{|\Delta\mathbf{R}|}{\Delta t} = \frac{\Delta s}{|\Delta\mathbf{R}|} \left| \frac{\Delta\mathbf{R}}{\Delta t} \right|. \tag{7-7}$$

Since $|\Delta\mathbf{R}|$ is the length of the chord, and since the ratio $\Delta s/|\Delta\mathbf{R}|$ of arc to chord [1] tends to 1, Eq. (7-7) gives

$$\frac{ds}{dt} = \left| \frac{d\mathbf{R}}{dt} \right| \tag{7-8}$$

when $\Delta t \to 0$. Thus, *the vector $\mathbf{R}'(t)$ has magnitude $|\mathbf{R}'| = ds/dt$ where s*

---

[1] We assume that s increases with t; otherwise a minus sign is needed. The fact that (arc)/(chord) $\to$ 1 follows from the familiar interpretation of arc as limit of lengths of inscribed polygons. It is also possible to take (arc)/(chord) $\to$ 1 as one of the defining properties of arc and proceed, as in the text, to obtain the formula (7-9).

is the arc length along the curve. If $\mathbf{R}'(t)$ is continuous, the arc is given explicitly by

$$s = \int_{t_0}^{t} |\mathbf{R}'(t)| \, dt = \int_{t_0}^{t} \sqrt{(x')^2 + (y')^2 + (z')^2} \, dt. \qquad (7\text{-}9)$$

Introduction of s as parameter instead of t facilitates the study of space curves (see Sec. 10).

In two dimensions the interpretation of $\mathbf{R}'(t)$ given here agrees with the results of elementary calculus. Let a smooth curve C be represented parametrically by $x = x(t)$, $y = y(t)$, so that the slope is given by

$$\text{Slope} = \frac{dy}{dx} = \frac{dy/dt}{dx/dt} \equiv \frac{y'}{x'} \qquad (7\text{-}10)$$

for $x' \neq 0$. If the same curve is described in the form $\mathbf{R} = \mathbf{i}x + \mathbf{j}y$, we have $\mathbf{R}' = \mathbf{i}x' + \mathbf{j}y'$, and hence the slope of the vector $\mathbf{R}'$ is y'/x'. In view of (7-10), *the fact that $\mathbf{R}'$ is tangent to the curve agrees with the fact that dy/dx is the slope of the curve.* The formula $ds/dt = |\mathbf{R}'|$ is also familiar; it states that

$$\frac{ds}{dt} = \sqrt{(x')^2 + (y')^2} = \sqrt{\left(\frac{dx}{dt}\right)^2 + \left(\frac{dy}{dt}\right)^2},$$

which becomes $ds^2 = dx^2 + dy^2$ when squared and multiplied by $(dt)^2$.

Physically, one may regard t as time, so that the head of the bound vector $\mathbf{R}(t)$ gives the position of a moving particle at time t. Since the velocity is defined to be $\mathbf{V} = \mathbf{R}'(t)$, the foregoing result means that *the velocity vector is tangent to the trajectory and has magnitude equal to the speed ds/dt with which the particle is moving.*

Example 1. The position of a particle at time t is determined by the bound vector

$$\mathbf{R}(t) = \mathbf{i}t + \mathbf{j}t^3 + \mathbf{k}\sin t.$$

Find a vector tangent to the orbit at time t, and find the speed of the particle at time $t = 0$.

We have $\mathbf{R}'(t) = \mathbf{i} + 3\mathbf{j}t^2 + \mathbf{k}\cos t$, which is the required tangent vector. At $t = 0$ the velocity is $\mathbf{R}'(0) = \mathbf{i} + \mathbf{k}$, and hence the speed is $ds/dt = |\mathbf{R}'(0)| = \sqrt{2}$.

Example 2. If a differentiable vector $\mathbf{R}(t)$ has constant length, show that $\mathbf{R}'$ is perpendicular to $\mathbf{R}$, and interpret geometrically.

From $\mathbf{R} \cdot \mathbf{R} = \text{const}$, differentiation yields $\mathbf{R} \cdot \mathbf{R}' + \mathbf{R}' \cdot \mathbf{R} = 0$, whence $\mathbf{R}' \cdot \mathbf{R} = 0$. Geometrically, if $\mathbf{R}$ is a bound vector of constant length, its head traces out a curve lying on a sphere. The tangent to the curve is tangent to the sphere, hence perpendicular to the radius vector. Thus, $\mathbf{R}' \perp \mathbf{R}$.

PROBLEMS

1. If $\mathbf{R}(t) = \mathbf{i}2t + \mathbf{j}3t^2 + \mathbf{k}t^3$, (*a*) find the derivative $\mathbf{R}'(t)$. (*b*) At the point $(2,3,1)$ find a tangent to the space curve which is traced out by the head of $\mathbf{R}$ when $\mathbf{R}$ is regarded as a bound vector. *Hint:* The point $(2,3,1)$ corresponds to $t = 1$. (*c*) If $\mathbf{R}(t)$ is a bound vector giving the position of a moving particle at time t, find the velocity and speed of this particle at time $t = 1$.

2. (*a*) Differentiate the vector $\mathbf{R}(t) = \mathbf{i}t + \mathbf{j}\sin t + \mathbf{k}\cos t$, compute $|\mathbf{R}'(t)|$, and simplify. (*b*) If $\mathbf{R}(t)$ is a bound vector, find the length of the curve traced out by the head of $\mathbf{R}$ as t varies from $t = 0$ to $t = 2$.

3. By writing $\mathbf{A}\cdot\mathbf{B}$ in component form and differentiating, deduce $(\mathbf{A}\cdot\mathbf{B})' = \mathbf{A}'\cdot\mathbf{B} + \mathbf{A}\cdot\mathbf{B}'$.

4. If $\mathbf{R}_0$ and $\mathbf{A}$ are constant, find a vector tangent to the curve described by the bound vector $\mathbf{R} = \mathbf{R}_0 + \mathbf{A}t$.

5. If $\mathbf{R}(t)$ is a bound vector giving the position of a moving particle at time t, the acceleration is defined to be $\mathbf{A} = \mathbf{R}''(t)$. Show that $\mathbf{A}$ is constant if $\mathbf{R}(t) = \mathbf{R}_0 + \mathbf{R}_1 t + \mathbf{R}_2 t^2$, where $\mathbf{R}_0$, $\mathbf{R}_1$, and $\mathbf{R}_2$ are constant vectors. Is the converse true?

6. Show that $(\mathbf{ABC})' = (\mathbf{A}'\mathbf{BC}) + (\mathbf{AB}'\mathbf{C}) + (\mathbf{ABC}')$, when $\mathbf{A}$, $\mathbf{B}$, $\mathbf{C}$ are differentiable, and write out in determinant form.

7. If $\mathbf{R} = \mathbf{A} + f(t)\mathbf{B}$, where $\mathbf{A}$ and $\mathbf{B}$ are constant and f is twice differentiable, then $\mathbf{R}' \times \mathbf{R}'' = 0$.

APPLICATIONS

8. Mechanics and Dynamics. The work W done by a constant force $\mathbf{F}$ producing a displacement $\mathbf{S}$ in the direction of $\mathbf{F}$ is $|\mathbf{F}|\,|\mathbf{S}|$. More generally, if $\mathbf{F}$ makes an angle θ with $\mathbf{S}$, the work is $|\mathbf{F}|\,|\mathbf{S}|\,\cos\theta$, and hence

$$W = \mathbf{F}\cdot\mathbf{S}. \qquad (8\text{-}1)$$

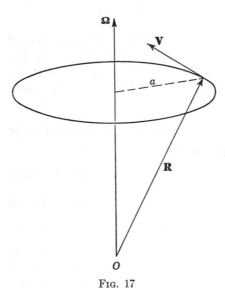

FIG. 17

Because of this equation the dot product plays a central role in certain branches of mechanics.

To illustrate the application of cross products, let the vector $\mathbf{\Omega}$ represent the angular velocity of a rotating body; that is, let $\mathbf{\Omega}$ be a vector whose magnitude is the angular speed in radians per second and whose direction is parallel to the axis of rotation. The positive sense of $\mathbf{\Omega}$ is chosen as that in which a right-handed screw would advance if the screw were rotated in the same direction as the body. Let $\mathbf{R}$ be a vector locating any point P of the body relative to some point O on the axis of rotation. It is required to find the instantaneous velocity $\mathbf{V}$ of the point P. If the distance of P from the axis of rotation is a, then by Fig. 17

$$|\mathbf{V}| = |\mathbf{\Omega}|a = |\mathbf{\Omega}|\,|\mathbf{R}|\sin(\mathbf{R},\mathbf{\Omega}).$$

Moreover, $\mathbf{V}$ is normal to the plane of $\mathbf{R}$ and $\mathbf{\Omega}$ and is so directed that

Ω, $\mathbf{R}$, and $\mathbf{V}$ form a right-handed system. Hence,

$$\mathbf{V} = \Omega \times \mathbf{R}. \qquad (8\text{-}2)$$

The result is independent of the origin O, for if a new origin O_1 is chosen and P is specified by a vector $\mathbf{R}_1$ from O_1, then

$$\mathbf{R}_1 = \mathbf{R} + \mathbf{S},$$

where $\mathbf{S}$ is parallel to Ω (see Fig. 17). Hence $\Omega \times \mathbf{S} = \mathbf{O}$, and therefore

$$\Omega \times \mathbf{R}_1 = \Omega \times (\mathbf{R} + \mathbf{S}) = \Omega \times \mathbf{R} + \Omega \times \mathbf{S} = \Omega \times \mathbf{R}.$$

Another example from dynamics illustrates the compactness of vector notation. Let O be a fixed point in a rigid body, and let a force $\mathbf{F}$ be applied at a point R of the body, which is located by the bound vector $\mathbf{R}$ whose origin is at O. The force $\mathbf{F}$ establishes a *torque* or *moment* $\mathbf{T}$ which tends to rotate the body about an axis that passes through O and is normal to the plane of $\mathbf{R}$ and $\mathbf{F}$. The magnitude of $\mathbf{T}$ is given by

$$|\mathbf{T}| = |\mathbf{R}|\,|\mathbf{F}|\sin\,(\mathbf{R},\mathbf{F}).$$

In addition, $\mathbf{R}$, $\mathbf{F}$, and $\mathbf{T}$ form a right-handed system, so that

$$\mathbf{T} = \mathbf{R} \times \mathbf{F}. \qquad (8\text{-}3)$$

That the choice of O is immaterial follows as in the discussion of (8-2). Similarly one shows that $\mathbf{F}$ may slide along its line of action without affecting the result; that is, $\mathbf{F}$ may be regarded as a sliding vector.

To illustrate the use of (8-3), we obtain a formula for the so-called *center of mass* of a system of mass points. The force on a point of mass m in a gravitational field is given by $m\mathbf{F}$, where m is the mass of the point and $\mathbf{F}$ is a vector specifying the strength of the field at the point in question. We assume a uniform field, so that $\mathbf{F}$ is independent of position. From (8-3)

$$(\mathbf{R} - \mathbf{P}) \times m\mathbf{F} \qquad (8\text{-}4)$$

represents the moment about the point [1] P of the gravitational force on a point of mass m at R. If there are n points of masses $m_1, m_2, \ldots, m_n$ located by the vectors $\mathbf{R}_1, \mathbf{R}_2, \ldots, \mathbf{R}_n$, respectively, the total moment about the point P due to all of them is

$$\Sigma(\mathbf{R}_i - \mathbf{P}) \times m_i\mathbf{F} \qquad (8\text{-}5)$$

It is desired to find a single mass point such that its moment (8-4) reproduces the total moment (8-5) for all choices of $\mathbf{F}$ and $\mathbf{P}$. Equating the moments (8-4) and (8-5) leads to

$$[m\mathbf{P} - \Sigma m_i\mathbf{P} - m\mathbf{R} + \Sigma m_i\mathbf{R}_i] \times \mathbf{F} = \mathbf{0}, \qquad (8\text{-}6)$$

after rearrangement. Since $\mathbf{F}$ is arbitrary in (8-6), the factor in brackets must vanish, so that

$$\mathbf{P}(m - \Sigma m_i) = m\mathbf{R} - \Sigma m_i\mathbf{R}_i. \qquad (8\text{-}7)$$

---

[1] The vectors $\mathbf{R}$, $\mathbf{P}$, and $\mathbf{R}_i$ are bound position vectors with a common origin for the points R, P, and R_i, respectively.

The fact that $\mathbf{P}$ is arbitrary in (8-7) now gives

$$m = \Sigma m_i, \qquad m\mathbf{R} = \Sigma m_i \mathbf{R}_i. \tag{8-8}$$

Conversely, (8-8) ensures the validity of (8-7) and hence of (8-6) independently of $\mathbf{F}$ and $\mathbf{P}$.

This discussion was carried out by equating moments only. Equation (8-8) shows, however, that the total gravitational force is also preserved, since the mass of the point equals the total mass of the collection.

The point R with position vector

$$\mathbf{R} = \frac{m_1 \mathbf{R}_1 + m_2 \mathbf{R}_2 + m_n \mathbf{R}_n}{m_1 + m_2 + \cdots + m_n} \tag{8-9}$$

determined by (8-8) is called the *center of mass*. Evidently the collection of points, regarded as a rigid body, would balance about the point R as pivot, for the moment (8-4) is zero when $\mathbf{P} = \mathbf{R}$, and hence the moment (8-5) also vanishes.

Still another example of the use of vectors in mechanics is given by Newton's laws. Relative to an origin O, which is regarded as fixed, let the position of a particle at time t be specified by the bound vector $\mathbf{R}(t)$. The velocity vector $\mathbf{V}$ is $d\mathbf{R}/dt$, as indicated in Sec. 7, and the momentum vector is defined by

$$\mathbf{M} = m\mathbf{V} = m\frac{d\mathbf{R}}{dt}, \tag{8-10}$$

where m is the mass of the particle at time t. In this notation Newton's second law of motion takes the simple form

$$\mathbf{F} = \frac{d\mathbf{M}}{dt}, \tag{8-11}$$

where $\mathbf{F}$ is the force on the particle at time t. If m is constant the result is

$$\mathbf{F} = m\frac{d^2\mathbf{R}}{dt^2}. \tag{8-12}$$

We shall use (8-10) and (8-12) to derive some interesting properties of the center of mass. Suppose given n particles with masses m_i and positions denoted by $\mathbf{R}_i$ ($i = 1$, 2, ..., n), where each m_i is independent of t. The total momentum of the system satisfies

$$\Sigma m_i \frac{d\mathbf{R}_i}{dt} = \frac{d}{dt}\Sigma m_i \mathbf{R}_i = m\frac{d}{dt}\frac{\Sigma m_i \mathbf{R}_i}{m} = m\frac{d\mathbf{R}}{dt}, \tag{8-13}$$

where $m = \Sigma m_i$ is the total mass and where $\mathbf{R}$ locates the center of mass [(8-9)]. Thus, *the total momentum of the system equals that of a single particle which has mass m and moves with the same velocity as the center of mass of the system.*

If (8-13) is differentiated with respect to t, there results

$$\Sigma \mathbf{F}_i = m\frac{d^2\mathbf{R}}{dt^2}$$

when we let $\mathbf{F}_i$ be the force on the ith particle and use (8-12). Since internal forces cancel in pairs by Newton's law of equal and opposite reaction, the sum $\Sigma \mathbf{F}_i$ represents the total *external* force acting on the system.   Hence *the center of mass has the same accelera-tion as a particle of mass m acted on by a force equal to the sum of the external forces acting on the system.*

Example 1.   Parallel forces $\mathbf{F}$, $-\mathbf{F}$ of equal magnitude but opposite direction constitute a *couple*.   Find the total moment, and show that it is the same about every point.

Let $\mathbf{R}$ be a vector from a given point O to a point P on the line of action of $\mathbf{F}$, and $\mathbf{R}_1$ to a point P_1 on the line of action of $-\mathbf{F}$ (Fig. 18).   The total torque is

$$\mathbf{R} \times \mathbf{F} + \mathbf{R}_1 \times (-\mathbf{F}) = (\mathbf{R} - \mathbf{R}_1) \times \mathbf{F} = (\overrightarrow{P_1P}) \times \mathbf{F}.$$

Since this is independent of O, the result follows.   Notice that $\mathbf{F}$ and $-\mathbf{F}$ must be regarded as sliding vectors (Sec. 1) rather than free vectors, since the line of action is fixed.

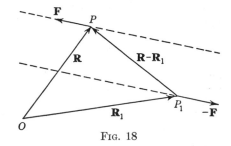

Fig. 18

Example 2.   A system of forces $\mathbf{F}_i$ acting at various points R_i of a rigid body is such that $\Sigma\mathbf{F}_i = \mathbf{0}$.   If the total torque about one point is zero, then the total torque about every point is zero.

From $\Sigma(\mathbf{R}_0 - \mathbf{R}_i) \times \mathbf{F}_i = \mathbf{0}$, say, we are to deduce $\Sigma(\mathbf{R} - \mathbf{R}_i) \times \mathbf{F}_i = \mathbf{0}$.   The two equations may be written

$$\mathbf{R}_0 \times (\Sigma\mathbf{F}_i) = \Sigma\mathbf{R}_i \times \mathbf{F}_i, \tag{8-14}$$

$$\mathbf{R} \times (\Sigma\mathbf{F}_i) = \Sigma\mathbf{R}_i \times \mathbf{F}_i. \tag{8-15}$$

Equation (8-14) gives $\Sigma\mathbf{R}_i \times \mathbf{F}_i = \mathbf{0}$, since $\Sigma\mathbf{F}_i = \mathbf{0}$, and (8-15) follows.

Example 3.   The moment of the momentum vector $\mathbf{M}$ about a point is called the *angular momentum* of the particle about that point.   According to the *principle of angu-lar momentum,* the rate of increase of angular momentum about a point equals the re-sultant torque about that point.   Show that this principle is equivalent to Newton's law, $\mathbf{F} = d\mathbf{M}/dt$.

If $\mathbf{A}$ is the angular momentum about the origin, then $\mathbf{A} = \mathbf{R} \times \mathbf{M}$, where $\mathbf{R}$ gives the position of the point.   Thus

$$\frac{d\mathbf{A}}{dt} = \mathbf{R} \times \frac{d\mathbf{M}}{dt} + \frac{d\mathbf{R}}{dt} \times \mathbf{M}$$

$$= \mathbf{R} \times \frac{d\mathbf{M}}{dt} + \mathbf{V} \times (m\mathbf{V}) = \mathbf{R} \times \frac{d\mathbf{M}}{dt}.$$

The principle of angular momentum $d\mathbf{A}/dt = \mathbf{R} \times \mathbf{F}$ is therefore equivalent to

$$\mathbf{R} \times \frac{d\mathbf{M}}{dt} = \mathbf{R} \times \mathbf{F}. \tag{8-16}$$

If this holds for every choice of origin, that is, for every $\mathbf{R}$, then necessarily $d\mathbf{M}/dt = \mathbf{F}$.   Conversely, if $d\mathbf{M}/dt = \mathbf{F}$, then (8-16) holds for every $\mathbf{R}$.

PROBLEMS

1. Given $\mathbf{A} = \mathbf{i} + 2\mathbf{j} + \mathbf{k}$, $\mathbf{B} = \mathbf{i} - \mathbf{k}$, $\mathbf{C} = 2\mathbf{i} + \mathbf{j}$, with $\mathbf{A}$, $\mathbf{B}$ having their origins at a common point, (*a*) find the work done by a force $\mathbf{A}$ in a displacement $\mathbf{B}$.   (*b*) Find the work done in a displacement from the head of **A** to the head of **B** under a force **C**. (*c*) Find the work done in the displacement **A** subject to simultaneous forces **B** and **C**.

2. In Prob. 1: (*a*) Find the torque about the origin of **A** due to a force **C** through the head of **A**.   (*b*) Find the torque about the head of **A** due to a force **C** acting through the head of **B**.

3. In Prob. 1: (*a*) If the figure formed by **A** and **B** rotates about **A** with angular velocity Ω, find the velocity of the head of **B**.   (*b*) Find the velocity of the head of **A** if the figure formed by **A** and **B** rotates with angular velocity Ω about an axis parallel to **C** through the head of **B**.

4. Two coordinate systems have a common origin at all times, but the second has a vectorial angular velocity Ω relative to the first. Show that $V_1 = V_2 + (\Omega \times R)$, where V_1 and V_2 are the velocity vectors in the first and second systems of a point whose position vector is **R** in the first system.

5. Show that the torque due to two couples is the sum of the torques.

6. Three points labeled 1, 2, 3 have masses 1, 2, 3 and positions $2i + j + 2k, i - k, 3j$, respectively.   (*a*) Find the center of mass.   (*b*) Find the total mass 2, 1, and their center of mass.   From this obtain, again, the center of mass for all three.

7. The vectors **A, B, C, D, E** give the positions of the vertices of a regular pentagon as referred to an origin not necessarily in its plane. Show that their resultant is equal to 5**R**, where **R** gives the position of the center. *Hint:* Place a unit mass at each vertex, and find the center of mass in two ways.

8. (*a*) Show that $F \cdot V$ represents the rate at which work is done on a particle moving with velocity **V** under a force **F**.   (*b*) When the mass is constant, show that

$$(d/dt)(m|V|^2/2) = F \cdot V,$$

so that the rate of increase of kinetic energy equals the rate at which work is done on the particle.

9. Lines and Planes. If **R** is a bound vector with its origin at the origin of coordinates, then the direction numbers x, y, z are the same as the coordinates of the head of **R**, and one may speak indifferently of "the point **R**" or "the vector **R**." This correspondence between vectors and points enables us to use vectors in geometry. Here we consider the geometry of lines and planes, which is especially simple; the following sections are concerned with general curves and surfaces.

Suppose we have given a plane through the point R_0 and perpendicular to the constant vector **A**. If the point **R** is in the plane, then $R - R_0$ is perpendicular to **A**, and conversely (Fig. 19). Hence the equation of the plane is

$$(R - R_0) \cdot A = 0. \tag{9-1}$$

If D is the distance from the point R_1 to the plane, then

$$D = |R_1 - R_0||\cos \theta| = \frac{|R_1 - R_0||A||\cos \theta|}{|A|} = \frac{|(R_1 - R_0) \cdot A|}{|A|}, \tag{9-2}$$

where θ is the angle between **A** and $R_1 - R_0$.

Next, consider a line through the point R_0 and parallel to a constant vector **A**. If the point **R** is on this line, then the vector $R - R_0$ is parallel to **A**, and conversely (Fig. 20).   Hence, the equation of the line is

$$(\mathbf{R} - \mathbf{R}_0) \times \mathbf{A} = 0. \qquad (9\text{-}3)$$

If D is the perpendicular distance from the point $\mathbf{R}_1$ to this line, then

$$D = |\mathbf{R}_1 - \mathbf{R}_0|\,|\sin \theta| = \frac{|\mathbf{R}_1 - \mathbf{R}_0|\,|\mathbf{A}|\,|\sin \theta|}{|\mathbf{A}|} = \frac{|(\mathbf{R}_1 - \mathbf{R}_0) \times \mathbf{A}|}{|\mathbf{A}|}.$$
$$(9\text{-}4)$$

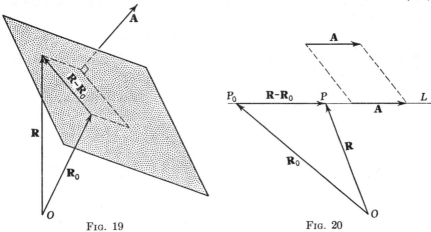

FIG. 19   FIG. 20

In (9-3) the fact that $\mathbf{R} - \mathbf{R}_0$ is parallel to **A** may also be expressed by writing

$$\mathbf{R} - \mathbf{R}_0 = \mathbf{A}t,$$

where t is a scalar.   Thus we obtain the equation of the straight line in a parametric form,

$$\mathbf{R} = \mathbf{R}_0 + \mathbf{A}t, \qquad -\infty < t < \infty, \qquad (9\text{-}5)$$

which is often more useful than (9-3).   It is left to the student to deduce the cartesian equation by setting

$$\mathbf{R}_0 = x_0\mathbf{i} + y_0\mathbf{j} + z_0\mathbf{k}, \qquad \mathbf{A} = a\mathbf{i} + b\mathbf{j} + c\mathbf{k}$$

in (9-5) and equating components.   Eliminating t yields the symmetric form

$$\frac{x - x_0}{a} = \frac{y - y_0}{b} = \frac{z - z_0}{c}, \qquad (9\text{-}6)$$

which may also be found from (9-3).

Example 1.   Show that every equation of form

$$ax + by + cz + d = 0 \qquad a, b, c, d \text{ const} \qquad (9\text{-}7)$$

represents a plane with $\mathbf{A} = a\mathbf{i} + b\mathbf{j} + c\mathbf{k}$ as normal, and conversely.

If $\mathbf{R}$ is a general point and $\mathbf{R}_0$ a fixed point on the locus (9-7), then writing (9-7) in vector form yields

$$\mathbf{R}\cdot\mathbf{A} + d = 0, \qquad \mathbf{R}_0\cdot\mathbf{A} + d = 0.$$

Subtracting these equations we obtain (9-1), which shows that the locus is a plane. On the other hand, (9-1) itself has the form (9-7), with $d = -\mathbf{R}_0\cdot\mathbf{A}$, and hence the converse is also true.

Example 2. Find the equation of a line which passes through the point $\mathbf{i} - \mathbf{j}$ and is parallel to the two planes $x + y = 3$, $2x + y + 3z = 4$.

The respective normals to the planes are $\mathbf{i} + \mathbf{j}$ and $2\mathbf{i} + \mathbf{j} + 3\mathbf{k}$, and hence the line of intersection of the planes is parallel to the cross product:

$$(\mathbf{i} + \mathbf{j}) \times (2\mathbf{i} + \mathbf{j} + 3\mathbf{k}) = 3\mathbf{i} - 3\mathbf{j} - \mathbf{k}.$$

Since this vector is parallel to both planes, it gives the direction of the required line, and hence the equation is

$$\mathbf{R} = \mathbf{i} - \mathbf{j} + (3\mathbf{i} - 3\mathbf{j} - \mathbf{k})t, \qquad -\infty < t < \infty.$$

PROBLEMS

1. (a) Find a vector normal to the plane $x + 2y + 3z = 1$. (b) Find the angle between this plane and the plane $x + y + z + 2 = 0$. (c) What is the distance from the point $3\mathbf{i} + 2\mathbf{j} + \mathbf{k}$ to the plane in (a)? (d) Show that the points $\mathbf{i}$ and $-\mathbf{j} + \mathbf{k}$ lie in the plane in (a). (e) Find a vector lying in the plane in (a). *Hint:* Subtract the vectors of (d). (f) Verify that the vector of (e) is normal to the normal found in (a).

2. (a) Find a vector parallel to the line $\mathbf{R} = \mathbf{i} + \mathbf{k} + (\mathbf{i} + 2\mathbf{j} + 3\mathbf{k})t$. (b) If $\mathbf{R} = \mathbf{i}x + \mathbf{j}y + \mathbf{k}z$ in (a), find x, y, and z in terms of t. (c) In (a), find the distance from the point $\mathbf{i} + 2\mathbf{j} + 3\mathbf{k}$ to the given line. (d) Show that the line (a) intersects the line $\mathbf{R} = 2\mathbf{k} + (3\mathbf{i} + 2\mathbf{j} + \mathbf{k})s$. *Hint:* Equate the two expressions for $\mathbf{R}$, and consider each component. It will be found that all three equations are satisfied by $s = t = \frac{1}{2}$. (e) Find the intersection point in (d). (f) Find the point where the line in (a) intersects the plane $2x - y + 3z = 4$. *Hint:* Substitute the result of (b) into the equation of the plane, find t, then find $\mathbf{R}$.

3. (a) Find the equation of the line common to the two planes $x + 2y + 4z = 1$, $x + y = 3$ in the form $\mathbf{R} = \mathbf{R}_0 + \mathbf{A}t$. *Hint:* Let $z = t$, and solve for x and y in terms of t. (b) Find a vector parallel to the intersection of the planes by use of the cross product as in Example 2. (c) Verify that your answers to (a) and (b) are consistent. (d) Find the equation of all planes perpendicular to both planes. (e) Write the equation of the line which is parallel to both planes and passes through the point $-3\mathbf{i} + \mathbf{k}$.

4. (a) In terms of t, find the square of the distance from the point $\mathbf{i} + 2\mathbf{j} + 3\mathbf{k}$ to a general point on the line $\mathbf{R} = 3\mathbf{i} + 2\mathbf{j} + \mathbf{k} + (\mathbf{i} + \mathbf{j} + \mathbf{k})t$. (b) By differentiating, find the t for which the distance is minimum and the minimum value. (c) Check by the distance formula.

5. In the form (9-5) obtain the equation of a line perpendicular to the plane $x + y + 3z = 0$ at the origin. At what point does this line intersect the plane $y = 3z + 1$?

6. If the lines $\mathbf{R} = \mathbf{R}_0 + \mathbf{A}t$ and $\mathbf{R} = \mathbf{R}_1 + \mathbf{B}t$ are not parallel, then the perpendicular distance between them is

$$D = \frac{|(\mathbf{R}_1 - \mathbf{R}_0) \cdot \mathbf{A} \times \mathbf{B}|}{|\mathbf{A} \times \mathbf{B}|}.$$

Hint: By a suitable figure show that the distance is the length of the projection of $\mathbf{R}_1 - \mathbf{R}_0$ on the common perpendicular to the two lines.

10. Normal Lines and Tangent Planes. If a curve $C: x = x(t)$, $y = y(t)$, $z = z(t)$ lies on a surface which has the equation

$$u(x,y,z) = c, \tag{10-1}$$

where c is constant, then

$$u[x(t),y(t),z(t)] \equiv c \tag{10-2}$$

identically in t. At a fixed point $\mathbf{R}_0 = \mathbf{i}x_0 + \mathbf{j}y_0 + \mathbf{k}z_0$ (Fig. 21) we differentiate (10-2) by the chain rule (Chap. 3, Sec. 4) to obtain

$$\frac{\partial u}{\partial x}\frac{dx}{dt} + \frac{\partial u}{\partial y}\frac{dy}{dt} + \frac{\partial u}{\partial z}\frac{dz}{dt} = 0. \tag{10-3}$$

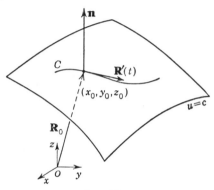

FIG. 21

This may be written as

$$\mathbf{n} \cdot \mathbf{R}'(t) = 0, \tag{10-4}$$

where $\mathbf{R}(t) = \mathbf{i}x(t) + \mathbf{j}y(t) + \mathbf{k}z(t)$ and where

$$\mathbf{n} = \mathbf{i}\frac{\partial u}{\partial x} + \mathbf{j}\frac{\partial u}{\partial y} + \mathbf{k}\frac{\partial u}{\partial z} \qquad \text{at } (x_0,y_0,z_0). \tag{10-5}$$

Since $\mathbf{R}'(t)$ is tangent to the curve C by Sec. 7, it follows from (10-4) that $\mathbf{n}$ is normal to the curve C. And since this is true for every choice of C, the vector $\mathbf{n}$ must be normal to the surface. The tangent plane is the plane perpendicular to $\mathbf{n}$ at $\mathbf{R}_0$, and hence its equation is $\mathbf{n} \cdot (\mathbf{R} - \mathbf{R}_0) = 0$ by Sec. 9.

The assumptions which underlie the foregoing result are clear from the derivation. We assume u differentiable (so that the chain rule holds), and we assume that not all the partial derivatives are zero (otherwise $\mathbf{n} = \mathbf{0}$, and $\mathbf{n}$ does not determine a direction). The analysis shows, then, that $\mathbf{n}$ *is perpendicular to every differentiable curve* $\mathbf{R} = \mathbf{R}(t)$ *which passes through the point* $\mathbf{R}_0$ *and lies in the surface.* It is this property that enables us to consider $\mathbf{n}$ as "normal to the surface."

To illustrate the use of (10-5) we find a normal vector and tangent plane for the ellipsoid
$$x^2 + 2y^2 + 3z^2 = 12$$
at the point $(1,2,-1)$. Since $u = x^2 + 2y^2 + 3z^2$, the partial derivatives are $2x$, $4y$, and $6z$. Evaluating these at $(1,2,-1)$ and substituting in (10-5) give the normal vector
$$\mathbf{n} = 2\mathbf{i} + 8\mathbf{j} - 6\mathbf{k}.$$
The tangent plane is perpendicular to $\mathbf{n}$ and contains the point $(1,2,-1)$. Hence its equation is
$$x + 4y - 3z = 12,$$
as the reader can verify.

Introduction of the tangent plane leads to a simple interpretation of the differential (Chap. 3, Sec. 3). If the equation of a surface is given in the form $z = f(x,y)$, then
$$f(x,y) - z = 0$$
and hence (10-1) holds with $u(x,y,z) = f(x,y) - z$. By (10-5) a normal is
$$\mathbf{n} = \mathbf{i}\frac{\partial f}{\partial x} + \mathbf{j}\frac{\partial f}{\partial y} - \mathbf{k} \tag{10-6}$$
so that the tangent plane has the equation [1]
$$(x - x_0)\frac{\partial f}{\partial x} + (y - y_0)\frac{\partial f}{\partial y} = z - z_0, \tag{10-7}$$
where $\partial f/\partial x$ and $\partial f/\partial y$ are evaluated at (x_0,y_0). If we set $x - x_0 = \Delta x$, $y - y_0 = \Delta y$ and $z - z_0 = \Delta z$ in (10-7) (Fig. 22), there results
$$\frac{\partial f}{\partial x}\Delta x + \frac{\partial f}{\partial y}\Delta y = \Delta z.$$

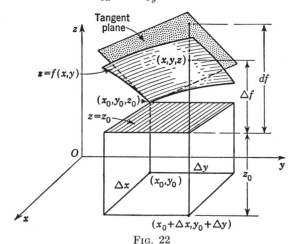

FIG. 22

---

[1] The values x, y, z in (10-7) refer to the tangent plane and must not be confused with the values x, y, z on the surface $z = f(x,y)$.

The left-hand side is simply the differential df, and hence the *differential* for the surface $z = f(x,y)$ equals the *increment* for the tangent plane. The definition of differentiability given in Chap. 3, Sec. 3, now has a simple intuitive meaning; namely, $f(x,y)$ *is differentiable if, and only if, the surface $z = f(x,y)$ is well approximated by its tangent plane.*

PROBLEMS

1. By use of (10-5) find a vector normal to the plane $ax + by + cz + d = 0$. Compare Sec. 9, Example 1.

2. At the point $(2,1,3)$ on the surface $xyz = x^2 + 2$ find (a) a normal vector, (b) an equation for the tangent plane, (c) an equation for the normal line.

3. Show that the surfaces $xyz = 1$ and $x^2 + y^2 - 2z^2 = 0$ intersect at right angles at the point $(1,1,1)$; that is, the tangent planes are perpendicular.

4. The two surfaces $x^2 + y^2 + z^2 = 6$ and $2x^2 + 3y^2 + z^2 = 9$ intersect at $(1,1,2)$. Find the angle between the tangent planes at this point.

5. In Prob. 4 find a vector tangent to the curve in which the surfaces intersect. *Hint:* The required vector is perpendicular to both normals.

11. Frenet's Formulas. It was shown in Sec. 7 that the vector $\mathbf{R}'(t)$ is tangent to the space curve $\mathbf{R} = \mathbf{R}(t)$ and has length $|\mathbf{R}'| = ds/dt$, where s is the arc along the curve. If the parameter itself is equal to the arc, so that $t = s$ and

$$\mathbf{R} = \mathbf{R}(s), \tag{11-1}$$

then $ds/dt = 1$. In this case the vector

$$\mathbf{T} = \frac{d\mathbf{R}}{ds} \tag{11-2}$$

is a tangent vector of *unit length*. From $\mathbf{T}\cdot\mathbf{T} = 1$ we deduce that $d\mathbf{T}/ds$ is perpendicular to $\mathbf{T}$ (Sec. 7, Example 2). Hence we may write

$$\frac{d\mathbf{T}}{ds} = \varkappa\mathbf{N}, \qquad \varkappa > 0, \tag{11-3}$$

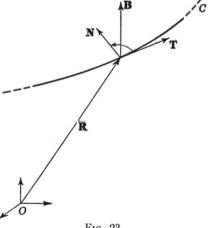

FIG. 23

where $\mathbf{N}$ is a unit vector perpendicular to $\mathbf{T}$ and where $\varkappa$ is a scalar multiplier. The vector $\mathbf{N}$ defined by (11-3) is called the *principal normal*, and the scalar $\varkappa$ is called the *curvature*. The plane of $\mathbf{T}$ and $\mathbf{N}$ is termed the *osculating plane*. We define $\varkappa = 0$ for a straight line.

If we introduce a third unit vector $\mathbf{B}$ defined by $\mathbf{B} = \mathbf{T} \times \mathbf{N}$, then the system $\mathbf{T}, \mathbf{N}, \mathbf{B}$ forms a right-handed set of orthogonal unit vectors, analogous to the vectors $\mathbf{i}, \mathbf{j}, \mathbf{k}$ introduced previously. By Fig. 23,

$$\mathbf{N} \times \mathbf{B} = \mathbf{T}, \qquad \mathbf{B} \times \mathbf{T} = \mathbf{N}, \qquad \mathbf{T} \times \mathbf{N} = \mathbf{B}. \tag{11-4}$$

The vector $\mathbf{B}$ is called the *binormal;* the figure formed by $\mathbf{T}$, $\mathbf{B}$, $\mathbf{N}$ is some-times referred to as the *trihedral* associated with the curve.

Differentiating the relation $\mathbf{B} = \mathbf{T} \times \mathbf{N}$ and using (11-3) give

$$\mathbf{B}' = \mathbf{T} \times \mathbf{N}' + \mathbf{T}' \times \mathbf{N} = \mathbf{T} \times \mathbf{N}' + (\varkappa\mathbf{N}) \times \mathbf{N} = \mathbf{T} \times \mathbf{N}',$$

and hence $\mathbf{B}'$ is perpendicular to $\mathbf{T}$.   It is also perpendicular to $\mathbf{B}$, since $\mathbf{B}\cdot\mathbf{B} = 1$, and therefore $\mathbf{B}'$ is parallel to $\mathbf{N}$:

$$\frac{d\mathbf{B}}{ds} = \tau\mathbf{N}. \tag{11-5}$$

The scalar multiple τ in (11-5) is called the *torsion;* it measures the rate at which the curve twists out of its osculating plane.   We define $\tau = 0$ for a straight line.

To evaluate $d\mathbf{N}/ds$, recall that $\mathbf{N} = \mathbf{B} \times \mathbf{T}$.   Hence

$$\mathbf{N}' = \mathbf{B} \times \mathbf{T}' + \mathbf{B}' \times \mathbf{T} = \varkappa\mathbf{B} \times \mathbf{N} + \tau\mathbf{N} \times \mathbf{T} \tag{11-6}$$

by (11-3) and (11-5).   When we use (11-4), Eq. (11-6) reduces to

$$\frac{d\mathbf{N}}{ds} = -\varkappa\mathbf{T} - \tau\mathbf{B}. \tag{11-7}$$

Equations (11-3), (11-5), and (11-7) are known as the *Frenet-Serret* formulas; they are of fundamental importance in the theory of space curves.

By equating the lengths of the two vectors in (11-3) and recalling $|\mathbf{N}| = 1$ we obtain

$$\varkappa = |\mathbf{T}'| = |\mathbf{R}''|, \qquad ' = \frac{d}{ds}. \tag{11-8}$$

To get a similar formula for τ we differentiate (11-3), obtaining

$$\mathbf{T}'' = \varkappa\mathbf{N}' + \varkappa'\mathbf{N} = \varkappa(-\varkappa\mathbf{T} - \tau\mathbf{B}) + \varkappa'\mathbf{N} \tag{11-9}$$

by (11-7).   Hence, by (11-3), (11-9), and (11-4),

$$\mathbf{T}' \times \mathbf{T}'' = \varkappa\mathbf{N} \times (-\varkappa^2\mathbf{T} - \varkappa\tau\mathbf{B} + \varkappa'\mathbf{N}) = \varkappa^3\mathbf{B} - \varkappa^2\tau\mathbf{T},$$

since $\mathbf{N} \times \mathbf{N} = \mathbf{0}$.   Taking the dot product with $\mathbf{T}$ yields

$$\mathbf{T}\cdot\mathbf{T}' \times \mathbf{T}'' = -\varkappa^2\tau. \tag{11-10}$$

If we solve (11-10) for τ, express $\varkappa^2$ in terms of $\mathbf{R}$ by (11-8), and express $\mathbf{T}$ in terms of $\mathbf{R}$ by (11-2), there results

$$\tau = -\frac{\mathbf{R}'\cdot\mathbf{R}'' \times \mathbf{R}'''}{\mathbf{R}''\cdot\mathbf{R}''}, \tag{11-11}$$

which is the desired formula.   When $\mathbf{R} = \mathbf{i}x(s) + \mathbf{j}y(s) + \mathbf{k}z(s)$, Eqs. (11-8) and (11-11) give, respectively,

$$\varkappa^2 = (x'')^2 + (y'')^2 + (z'')^2, \qquad \varkappa^2\tau = - \begin{vmatrix} x' & y' & z' \\ x'' & y'' & z'' \\ x''' & y''' & z''' \end{vmatrix}. \tag{11-12}$$

It can be shown that $\varkappa(s)$ and $\tau(s)$ determine the curve completely, apart from its position in space.[1]

Since a smooth curve can always be expressed in terms of its arc as parameter, the foregoing theory suffers no loss of generality by assuming $t = s$. In many physical problems, however, it is more fruitful to take the time t as parameter, and this possibility is now to be examined.

Let $\mathbf{R} = \mathbf{R}(t)$ give the position of a moving particle at time t, so that the velocity is $\mathbf{V} = \mathbf{R}'(t)$. With $v = ds/dt$ we have [2]

$$\mathbf{V} = \frac{d\mathbf{R}}{dt} = \frac{d\mathbf{R}}{ds}\frac{ds}{dt} = \mathbf{T}v, \tag{11-13}$$

upon using (11-2). Since (11-3) gives

$$\frac{d\mathbf{T}}{dt} = \frac{d\mathbf{T}}{ds}\frac{ds}{dt} = \varkappa\mathbf{N}v,$$

we get

$$\frac{d\mathbf{V}}{dt} = \mathbf{T}\frac{dv}{dt} + v\frac{d\mathbf{T}}{dt} = \mathbf{T}\frac{dv}{dt} + \varkappa v^2\mathbf{N} \tag{11-14}$$

upon differentiating (11-13). Hence *the acceleration vector* $\mathbf{A} = d\mathbf{V}/dt$ *lies in the osculating plane, its tangential component has magnitude equal to the linear acceleration* dv/dt, *and its normal component has magnitude* $\varkappa v^2$. This is a far-reaching generalization of the familiar results

$$A_{\text{tangential}} = 0, \qquad A_{\text{normal}} = \frac{v^2}{r}$$

for uniform motion in a circle of radius r.

Taking the cross product of (11-13) and (11-14) with $\mathbf{V}$ replaced by $\mathbf{R}'$ we obtain

$$\mathbf{R}' \times \mathbf{R}'' = \varkappa v^3 \mathbf{T} \times \mathbf{N} = \varkappa v^3 \mathbf{D}.$$

Hence, the direction of the binormal is given by $\mathbf{R}' \times \mathbf{R}''$ even when the parameter is t rather than s. Since $\mathbf{B}$ is a unit vector, we have

$$\mathbf{B} = \frac{\mathbf{R}' \times \mathbf{R}''}{|\mathbf{R}' \times \mathbf{R}''|}, \qquad ' = \frac{d}{dt}, \tag{11-15}$$

and similarly, the unit vector $\mathbf{T}$ is obtained from

$$\mathbf{T} = \frac{\mathbf{R}'}{|\mathbf{R}'|}, \qquad ' = \frac{d}{dt}. \tag{11-16}$$

Knowing $\mathbf{B}$ and $\mathbf{T}$ we find $\mathbf{N}$ from

$$\mathbf{N} = \mathbf{B} \times \mathbf{T}. \tag{11-17}$$

[1] See, for example, L. P. Eisenhart, "An Introduction to Differential Geometry," sec. 6, pp. 25–27, Princeton University Press, Princeton, N.J., 1940.

[2] In agreement with the results of Sec. 7, Eq. (11-13) expresses the fact that the velocity is tangent to the orbit and has magnitude equal to the speed.

These formulas enable us to compute the trihedral when the curve is given with an arbitrary parameter t provided $ds/dt > 0$.

Example 1.   Find the equation of the osculating plane at $t = 1$ for the curve $\mathbf{R} = t\mathbf{i} + 2t^2\mathbf{j} + t^3\mathbf{k}$.

Differentiation gives

$$\mathbf{R}'(1) = \mathbf{i} + 4\mathbf{j} + 3\mathbf{k},\ \mathbf{R}''(1) = 4\mathbf{j} + 6\mathbf{k}.$$

Hence by (11-15) the binormal $\mathbf{B}$ is parallel to

$$(\mathbf{i} + 4\mathbf{j} + 3\mathbf{k}) \times (4\mathbf{j} + 6\mathbf{k}) = 12\mathbf{i} - 6\mathbf{j} + 4\mathbf{k}.$$

The osculating plane is normal to $\mathbf{B}$ and contains the point

$$\mathbf{R}(1) = \mathbf{i} + 2\mathbf{j} + \mathbf{k}.$$

Hence its equation is $6x - 3y + 2z = 2$, as the reader can verify.

Example 2.   A curve is a plane curve if, and only if, the torsion is zero.

If the curve is a plane curve, not a straight line, then the osculating plane is well defined and is the plane of the curve.   Hence $\mathbf{B}$ is constant, and the torsion vanishes by (11-5).   Suppose, conversely, that the torsion is zero.   Then $\mathbf{B}$ is constant by (11-5), and therefore, using (11-2),

$$\frac{d}{ds}(\mathbf{B}\cdot\mathbf{R}) = \mathbf{B}\cdot\frac{d\mathbf{R}}{ds} = \mathbf{B}\cdot\mathbf{T} = 0.$$

This gives $\mathbf{B}\cdot\mathbf{R} = \text{const}$, which is the equation of a plane.

Example 3.   Consider the circular helix (Fig. 24) with equation

$$\mathbf{R} = \mathbf{i}a \cos \theta + \mathbf{j}a \sin \theta + \mathbf{k}p\theta, \qquad a,\ p \text{ positive const.} \tag{11-18}$$

Here, the parametric equations are

$$x = a \cos \theta,$$

$$y = a \sin \theta,$$

$$z = p\theta.$$

By (11-8) $\varkappa = |\mathbf{R}''|$, where primes denote differentiation with respect to the arc parameter s.   From (11-18)

$$d\mathbf{R} = -\mathbf{i}a \sin \theta\, d\theta + \mathbf{j}a \cos \theta\, d\theta + \mathbf{k}p\, d\theta,$$

so that

$$ds^2 = d\mathbf{R}\cdot d\mathbf{R} = (a^2 \sin^2 \theta + a^2 \cos^2 \theta + p^2)(d\theta)^2 = (a^2 + p^2)\, d\theta^2$$

and therefore $d\theta/ds = 1/\sqrt{a^2 + p^2} \equiv h$, say.   It follows that

$$\frac{d\mathbf{R}}{ds} = \frac{d\mathbf{R}}{d\theta}\frac{d\theta}{ds} = (-\mathbf{i}a \sin \theta + \mathbf{j}a \cos \theta + \mathbf{k}p)h,$$

$$\frac{d^2\mathbf{R}}{ds^2} = \frac{d}{d\theta}\frac{d\mathbf{R}}{ds}\frac{d\theta}{ds} = (-\mathbf{i}a \cos \theta - \mathbf{j}a \sin \theta)h^2,$$

$$\frac{d^3\mathbf{R}}{ds^3} = \frac{d}{d\theta}\frac{d^2\mathbf{R}}{ds^2}\frac{d\theta}{ds} = (\mathbf{i}a \sin \theta - \mathbf{j}a \cos \theta)h^3.$$

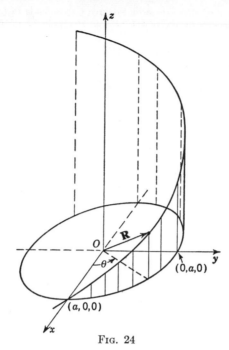

FIG. 24

On making use of formula (11-8) we find

$$\varkappa^2 = (\mathbf{R}'' \cdot \mathbf{R}'') = (a^2 \sin^2 \theta + a^2 \cos^2 \theta)h^4 = a^2 h^4,$$

so that

$$\varkappa = \frac{a}{a^2 + p^2}.$$

According to (11-12) the torsion is

$$\tau = -\frac{h^6}{\varkappa^2} \begin{vmatrix} -a \sin \theta & a \cos \theta & p \\ -a \cos \theta & -a \sin \theta & 0 \\ a \sin \theta & -a \cos \theta & 0 \end{vmatrix} = \frac{-p}{a^2 + p^2}.$$

If $p = 0$, we get a circle of radius a by inspection of (11-18). In this case $\tau = 0$ because the curve is a plane curve and $\varkappa = 1/a$ because the radius is always equal to the constant a. The behavior as $p \to \infty$ may be discussed similarly.

PROBLEMS

1. Given the curve $R(t) = i(t^2 - 1) + 2t\mathbf{j} + (t^2 + 1)\mathbf{k}$. (a) Find a unit tangent at $t = -1$. (b) Find the equation of the normal plane at this point. (c) Find the length of the curve from $t = 0$ to $t = 1$.

2. (a) If $\mathbf{R}(t)$ in Prob. 1 represents an orbit, find the velocity and acceleration at time t. (b) By use of (a) and Eq. (11-13), find the speed v at time t. (c) By use of (a), (b), and (11-14) find the curvature $\varkappa$ and the principal normal $\mathbf{N}$ at time t.

3. If the components of $\mathbf{R}(t)$ are second-degree polynomials in t, then $\mathbf{R} = \mathbf{R}(t)$ is a plane curve. (a) Prove this by use of (11-12) and Example 2. (b) Find the equation of the plane.

4. Show that (a) the tangents to a helix make a fixed angle with the axis of the helix, (b) the principal normal is perpendicular to the axis of the helix.

5. (a) Given a particle moving according to the law $\mathbf{R}(t) = \mathbf{i}t + \mathbf{j}t^2$, find a unit tangent and a unit normal to the orbit at $t = 1$. (b) Find the cartesian components of $\mathbf{V}$ and $\mathbf{A}$ at $t = 1$. (c) By use of the dot product and (a), find the tangential components V_t and A_t of $\mathbf{V}$ and $\mathbf{A}$ at $t = 1$. (d) Find ds/dt as $|\mathbf{R}'(t)|$, and from this find d^2s/dt^2. Compare (c).

6. In Prob. 5, (a) show that $\mathbf{V}_n$, the normal component of $\mathbf{V}$, is zero, and find that of $\mathbf{A}$ at $t = 1$ by use of the dot product and Prob. 5a. (b) By (a) and $\mathbf{A}_n = \varkappa |\mathbf{V}|^2$ find the curvature of the orbit at $t = 1$. (c) Show that the cartesian equation of the orbit is $y = x^2$, and compute the curvature by $\varkappa = y''/(1 + y'^2)^{3/2}$. Compare (b). (d) Explain how to find $\mathbf{A}_n$ in terms of $\mathbf{A}_x$, $\mathbf{A}_y$, and $\mathbf{A}_t$, and use this to check some of your work.

LINEAR VECTOR SPACES AND MATRICES

12. Spaces of Higher Dimensions. There is nothing mysterious about the idea of spaces whose dimensionality is greater than three. In locating objects in the familiar three-dimensional space of our physical intuition, we have found it convenient to introduce a coordinate system and to specify the location of any point in the object by means of three numbers termed the *coordinates of the point*. Thus, if a cartesian system of axes is introduced, we can associate with each point P an ordered triple of labels (x,y,z).

In dealing with the state of gas determined by the pressure p, volume v, and temperature T, it is often useful to visualize the triples of values (p,v,T) as coordinates of points in three-dimensional space, but such a visualization fails when the number of variables characterizing the gas-state exceeds three. Thus, the state of gas may (and generally does) depend not only on the pressure, volume, and temperature, but also on the time t. Although a quadruple of values (p,v,T,t) cannot be represented as a point in a fixed coordinate system in the three-dimensional space, the geometric visualization is of much lesser importance than the *analytic* apparatus developed for coping with the geometric problems. This apparatus (analytic geometry and vector analysis) makes use of the tools of algebra and analysis which involve operations on ordered sets of quantities such as (p,v,T,t) or $(x_1,x_2,\ldots,x_n)$, which are valid regardless of the number of variables appearing in the set.

The habits of using the language associated with geometric thinking are so strong, however, that it is natural to continue speaking figuratively of a quadruple of numbers (p,v,T,t) as representing a point in four-dimensional space and more generally refer to an ordered set of n values $(x_1,x_2,\ldots,x_n)$ as *a point in n-dimensional space*. The values x_1, x_2, $\ldots$, x_n

may be of quite diverse sorts; the first three, for example, may be associated with cartesian coordinates of some point M in three-dimensional physical space, x_4 may represent the magnitude of electric charge located at M, x_5 may stand for the time of observation, and so on. But whatever meaning we choose to attach to the individual values x_i, we can speak of the *n-tuple* $(x_1, x_2, \ldots, x_n)$ as representing a point P in n-dimensional space.

In three-dimensional space we found it useful to associate with every pair of points P_1 and P_2 an entity $\overrightarrow{P_1 P_2}$ which we called a vector **a**, and we have developed a set of rules for operations with vectors which form the basis for the algebra and calculus of vectors.

Although in the initial formulation of these rules we have been guided by geometric considerations, we have distilled out geometry by giving a set of *algebraic* laws (2-1), (2-3), (2-4), (4-3), (4-4), and (4-5) which govern operations with vectors.

We can continue using the suggestive language of three-dimensional vector analysis and say that every pair of points P_1, P_2 in n-dimensional space determines a vector **a**. We further stipulate that in devising the rules for operating on such vectors we adopt the set of algebraic laws (2-1), (2-3), (2-4), (4-3), (4-4), (4-5), which contain no reference to the dimensionality of space, and we define the vector **0** by the relation $\mathbf{a} + \mathbf{0} = \mathbf{0} + \mathbf{a} = \mathbf{a}$ for every vector **a**.

The dimensionality of space, we recall, entered only when we made use of these laws in those calculations which involved the *representations of vectors by components in special coordinate systems*. Thus in Sec. 3 we considered a vector in the plane determined by a pair of noncollinear vectors and introduced the notion of base vectors and the so-called components of the vector along the base vectors. We also saw that a vector in three-dimensional space can be represented uniquely in terms of its components in the directions of three noncoplanar base vectors. These remarks suggest that the dimensionality of space is in some way connected with the number of base vectors needed to represent a given vector by components. In providing a generalization of the representation of vectors by components in spaces of higher dimensions, we need the notion of linear dependence of a set of vectors which we develop next.

13. The Dimensionality of Space. Linear Vector Spaces. The concept of linear dependence of a set of vectors $\mathbf{a}_1$, $\mathbf{a}_2$, $\ldots$, $\mathbf{a}_n$ is intimately connected with the idea of dimensionality of space.

DEFINITION. *A set of n vectors $\mathbf{a}_1$, $\mathbf{a}_2$, $\ldots$, $\mathbf{a}_n$ is linearly dependent if there exists a set of numbers α_1, α_2, $\ldots$, α_n, not all of which are zero, such that*

$$\alpha_1 \mathbf{a}_1 + \alpha_2 \mathbf{a}_2 + \cdots + \alpha_n \mathbf{a}_n = \mathbf{0}. \tag{13-1}$$

If no such numbers exist, the vectors a_1, a_2, ..., a_n *are said to be linearly independent.*[1]

To get at the geometric meaning of this definition consider two vectors

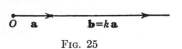

FIG. 25

a and **b** which are like or oppositely directed (Fig. 25). Then we can find a number $k \neq 0$ such that

$$b = k a. \qquad (13\text{-}2)$$

We can write this equation in symmetric form by setting $k = -\alpha/\beta$, so that (13-2) reads

$$\alpha a + \beta b = 0. \qquad (13\text{-}3)$$

Since neither α nor β is zero, it follows from our definition of linear dependence that two collinear vectors are always linearly dependent. Inasmuch as every vector **b** directed along **a** can be represented in the form (13-2), formula (13-2) serves to define a *one-dimensional linear vector space*. We observe that every two vectors in such a space are linearly dependent.

If we consider two noncollinear vectors **a** and **b** (Fig. 26), then every vector **c** in their plane can be represented in the form

$$c = k_1 a + k_2 b \qquad (13\text{-}4)$$

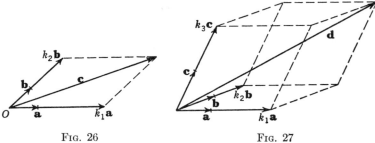

FIG. 26   FIG. 27

by a suitable choice of the constants k_1 and k_2. Equation (13-4) can be written as

$$\alpha a + \beta b + \gamma c = 0, \qquad (13\text{-}5)$$

in which not all constants α, β, γ are zero. Formula (13-4) determines every vector **c** in the plane of **a** and **b**, and it thus defines a *two-dimensional linear vector space*, while formula (13-5) ensures that every three vectors in the two-dimensional space are linearly dependent.

If we take three noncoplanar vectors **a**, **b**, **c** (Fig. 27), we can represent every vector **d** in the form

$$d = k_1 a + k_2 b + k_3 c, \qquad (13\text{-}6)$$

[1] Cf. the definition of linear dependence of a set of functions in Sec. 21, Chap. 1.

from which follows the relation

$$\alpha a + \beta b + \gamma c + \delta d = 0, \tag{13-7}$$

in which α, β, γ, δ are not all zero.

Equation (13-7) states that in a *three-dimensional linear vector space* defined by (13-6), four vectors are invariably linearly dependent.

The foregoing discussion indicates a relationship between the dimensionality of a vector space with the number of linearly independent vectors required to represent any vector in one-, two-, or three-dimensional vector space.

We generalize this relationship by saying that in an n-dimensional linear vector space every vector x can be represented in the form

$$x = k_1 a_1 + k_2 a_2 + \cdots + k_n a_n, \tag{13-8}$$

where a_1, a_2, ..., a_n is any set of n linearly independent vectors. It follows from (13-8) that in such a space every set of more than n vectors is linearly dependent.

We shall call a given set of n linearly independent vectors the *base vectors* (or the *basis*) of the n-dimensional linear vector space, and we shall term the numbers $(k_1, k_2, \ldots, k_n)$ the *measure numbers* associated with the basis a_1, a_2, ..., a_n.

In Sec. 3 we noted that every vector V in three-dimensional vector space can be represented uniquely by taking as a basis any set of three linearly independent vectors a, b, c. But we saw that a special set of mutually orthogonal unit vectors i, j, k when used as a basis greatly simplifies the calculations. This suggests the desirability of representing a vector x in the n-dimensional space in the form (13-8) in which the base vectors a_i are the analogues of the unit vectors i, j, k. The construction of an analogous set of base vectors requires the extension of the concepts of length and orthogonality to sets of vectors in n-dimensional space. In making these extensions we suppose that the scalar product $a \cdot b$ of a and b is a real number, and that $a \cdot a > 0$ unless $a = 0$. Further, the operation of scalar multiplication obeys the laws (4-3) and (4-5).

We recall that in three-dimensional space two vectors a and b are orthogonal if

$$a \cdot b = 0$$

and a is a unit vector if

$$a \cdot a = 1.$$

We extend these definitions to vectors in n-dimensional space and show that when any set of n linearly independent vectors a_1, a_2, ..., a_n is given, one can construct a new set of vectors e_1, e_2, ..., e_n, such that

$$\begin{aligned} e_i \cdot e_j &= 0, \quad \text{if } i \neq j, \\ &= 1, \quad \text{if } i = j. \end{aligned} \tag{13-9}$$

A set of vectors satisfying the conditions (13-9) is called an *orthonormal set*.

Let the set of vectors $\mathbf{a}_1$, $\mathbf{a}_2$, $\ldots$, $\mathbf{a}_n$ be linearly independent, so that the equation

$$\alpha_1 \mathbf{a}_1 + \alpha_2 \mathbf{a}_2 + \cdots + \alpha_n \mathbf{a}_n = \mathbf{0} \qquad (13\text{-}10)$$

can be satisfied only by choosing $\alpha_1 = \alpha_2 = \cdots = \alpha_n = 0$. It follows from (13-10) that $\mathbf{a}_1 \neq \mathbf{0}$, for if it were a zero vector, the choice

$$\alpha_1 = 1, \qquad \alpha_2 = 0, \ldots, \alpha_n = 0$$

would satisfy (13-10) and hence the vectors $\mathbf{a}_i$ would be linearly dependent, thus contradicting our initial assumption.

We shall write

$$\mathbf{a}_i \cdot \mathbf{a}_i \equiv |\mathbf{a}_i|^2$$

and call $|\mathbf{a}_i|$ the *length* of $\mathbf{a}_i$. Now denote the product of $\mathbf{a}_1$ by the reciprocal of its length $|\mathbf{a}_1|$ by $\mathbf{e}_1$, so that

$$\mathbf{e}_1 = \frac{\mathbf{a}_1}{|\mathbf{a}_1|}.$$

Since $\mathbf{e}_1 \cdot \mathbf{e}_1 = 1$, $\mathbf{e}_1$ is a unit vector. The vectors

$$\mathbf{e}_1, \mathbf{a}_2, \ldots, \mathbf{a}_n$$

are obviously linearly independent. Consider next the vector

$$\mathbf{e}_2' = \mathbf{a}_2 - (\mathbf{a}_2 \cdot \mathbf{e}_1)\mathbf{e}_1.$$

The scalar product $\mathbf{e}_2' \cdot \mathbf{e}_1$ is

$$\mathbf{e}_2' \cdot \mathbf{e}_1 = \mathbf{a}_2 \cdot \mathbf{e}_1 - (\mathbf{a}_2 \cdot \mathbf{e}_1)\mathbf{e}_1 \cdot \mathbf{e}_1 = 0,$$

since $\mathbf{e}_1$ is a unit vector. Thus $\mathbf{e}_2'$ is orthogonal to $\mathbf{e}_1$ and the vector

$$\mathbf{e}_2 \equiv \frac{\mathbf{e}_2'}{|\mathbf{e}_2'|}$$

is a unit vector orthogonal to $\mathbf{e}_1$.

The set of vectors

$$\mathbf{e}_1, \mathbf{e}_2, \mathbf{a}_3, \ldots, \mathbf{a}_n$$

is linearly independent, and we construct the vector

$$\mathbf{e}_3' = \mathbf{a}_3 - (\mathbf{a}_3 \cdot \mathbf{e}_1)\mathbf{e}_1 - (\mathbf{a}_3 \cdot \mathbf{e}_2)\mathbf{e}_2$$

which is orthogonal to both $\mathbf{e}_1$ and $\mathbf{e}_2$. The vector

$$\mathbf{e}_3 = \frac{\mathbf{e}_3'}{|\mathbf{e}_3'|}$$

is a unit vector, and the set of vectors

$$\mathbf{e}_1,\ \mathbf{e}_2,\ \mathbf{e}_3,\ \mathbf{a}_4,\ \ldots,\ \mathbf{a}_n$$

is a linearly independent set. We continue the process by forming

$$\mathbf{e}_4' = \mathbf{a}_4 - (\mathbf{a}_4 \cdot \mathbf{e}_1)\mathbf{e}_1 - (\mathbf{a}_4 \cdot \mathbf{e}_2)\mathbf{e}_2 - (\mathbf{a}_4 \cdot \mathbf{e}_3)\mathbf{e}_3$$

which is orthogonal to $\mathbf{e}_1$, $\mathbf{e}_2$, and $\mathbf{e}_3$, and normalize it by dividing it by $|\mathbf{e}_4'|$. The set of vectors

$$\mathbf{e}_1,\ \mathbf{e}_2,\ \mathbf{e}_3,\ \mathbf{e}_4,\ \mathbf{a}_5,\ \ldots,\ \mathbf{a}_n$$

is linearly independent, and a continuation of the procedure yields after n steps the desired set of orthonormal vectors

$$\mathbf{e}_1,\ \mathbf{e}_2,\ \ldots,\ \mathbf{e}_n.$$

14. Cartesian Reference Frames. When the base vectors $\mathbf{i}$, $\mathbf{j}$, $\mathbf{k}$ of Sec. 3 are oriented along the xyz axes, the coordinates of their terminal points are

$$\mathbf{i}:\quad (1,0,0),$$

$$\mathbf{j}:\quad (0,1,0),$$

$$\mathbf{k}:\quad (0,0,1).$$

By analogy we can say that when a set of orthonormal base vectors $\mathbf{e}_1$, $\mathbf{e}_2$, $\ldots$, $\mathbf{e}_n$ is oriented along "a cartesian reference frame in n-dimensional Euclidean space," the terminal points of the base vectors have the coordinates

$$\mathbf{e}_1:\quad (1,0,0,\ldots,0),$$

$$\mathbf{e}_2:\quad (0,1,0,\ldots,0),$$

$$\mathbf{e}_3:\quad (0,0,1,\ldots,0),$$

$$\cdots\cdots\cdots\cdots$$

$$\mathbf{e}_n:\quad (0,0,0,\ldots,1).$$

In this reference frame every vector $\mathbf{x}$ has the representation

$$\mathbf{x} = x_1\mathbf{e}_1 + x_2\mathbf{e}_2 + \cdots + x_n\mathbf{e}_n, \tag{14-1}$$

where the x_i are the *components* of $\mathbf{x}$.

On making use of the distributive law of scalar multiplication, we find that

$$\mathbf{x}\cdot\mathbf{x} = x_1^2 + x_2^2 + \cdots + x_n^2, \tag{14-2}$$

since

$$\mathbf{e}_i\cdot\mathbf{e}_j = \delta_{ij}, \tag{14-3}$$

where the symbol δ_{ij}, the *Kronecker delta*, means

$$\delta_{ij} = 1, \qquad \text{if } i = j,$$

$$= 0, \qquad \text{if } i \neq j.$$

From (14-2) we conclude that the length $|\mathbf{x}|$ of the vector $\mathbf{x}$ is given by the formula

$$|\mathbf{x}| = \sqrt{x_1^2 + x_2^2 + \cdots + x_n^2}.$$

This is the *formula of Pythagoras in n-dimensional Euclidean space.*
Also, if

$$\mathbf{y} = y_1\mathbf{e}_1 + y_2\mathbf{e}_2 + \cdots + y_n\mathbf{e}_n, \tag{14-4}$$

then on forming the scalar product $\mathbf{x}\cdot\mathbf{y}$ we find

$$\mathbf{x}\cdot\mathbf{y} = x_1y_1 + x_2y_2 + \cdots + x_ny_n, \tag{14-5}$$

which has the same structure as formula (4-9).
For the sum of two vectors $\mathbf{x}$, $\mathbf{y}$ with components

$$\mathbf{x}: \ (x_1, x_2, \ldots, x_n),$$

$$\mathbf{y}: \ (y_1, y_2, \ldots, y_n),$$

we have the vector $\mathbf{x} + \mathbf{y}$ with components

$$\mathbf{x} + \mathbf{y}: (x_1 + y_1, \ x_2 + y_2, \ \ldots, \ x_n + y_n), \tag{14-6}$$

and for the product of $\mathbf{x}$ by a scalar α,

$$\alpha\mathbf{x}: (\alpha x_1, \alpha x_2, \ldots, \alpha x_n). \tag{14-7}$$

If we have two vectors $\mathbf{x}$ and $\mathbf{y}$ in Euclidean three-dimensional space, we have a useful inequality

$$(\mathbf{x}\cdot\mathbf{y})^2 \le (\mathbf{x}\cdot\mathbf{x})(\mathbf{y}\cdot\mathbf{y}) \tag{14-8}$$

which follows directly from the fact that

$$\cos^2\theta = \frac{(\mathbf{x}\cdot\mathbf{y})^2}{(\mathbf{x}\cdot\mathbf{x})(\mathbf{y}\cdot\mathbf{y})} \le 1.$$

We show next that the formula (14-8), known as the *Cauchy-Schwarz inequality*, is valid in an *n*-dimensional Euclidean space.
Indeed,

$$(\mathbf{x}\cdot\mathbf{x})(\mathbf{y}\cdot\mathbf{y}) - (\mathbf{x}\cdot\mathbf{y})^2 = \mathbf{y}\cdot\mathbf{y}\left[\mathbf{x}\cdot\mathbf{x} - 2\frac{(\mathbf{x}\cdot\mathbf{y})^2}{\mathbf{y}\cdot\mathbf{y}} + \frac{(\mathbf{x}\cdot\mathbf{y})^2}{\mathbf{y}\cdot\mathbf{y}}\right]$$

$$= |\mathbf{y}|^2 \left|\mathbf{x} - \mathbf{y}\frac{\mathbf{x}\cdot\mathbf{y}}{\mathbf{y}\cdot\mathbf{y}}\right|^2 \ge 0,$$

which proves the inequality (14-8). We note that the equality sign in (14-8) holds if, and only if, $\mathbf{y} = \mathbf{0}$ or $\mathbf{x} = \alpha\mathbf{y}$ for some scalar α.
The formula (14-8) enables us to establish the result

$$|\mathbf{x} + \mathbf{y}| \le |\mathbf{x}| + |\mathbf{y}|, \tag{14-9}$$

analogous to the "triangle inequality" of Prob. 3 in Sec. 3. We compute

$$|\mathbf{x} + \mathbf{y}|^2 = (\mathbf{x} + \mathbf{y}) \cdot (\mathbf{x} + \mathbf{y}) = \mathbf{x} \cdot \mathbf{x} + \mathbf{y} \cdot \mathbf{y} + 2\mathbf{x} \cdot \mathbf{y}$$

$$\leq |\mathbf{x}|^2 + |\mathbf{y}|^2 + 2|\mathbf{x} \cdot \mathbf{y}|. \tag{14-10}$$

But from (14-8)

$$(\mathbf{x} \cdot \mathbf{x})(\mathbf{y} \cdot \mathbf{y}) \geq |\mathbf{x} \cdot \mathbf{y}|^2,$$

so that

$$|\mathbf{x}| \cdot |\mathbf{y}| \geq |\mathbf{x} \cdot \mathbf{y}|. \tag{14-11}$$

The substitution from (14-11) in (14-10) yields

$$|\mathbf{x} + \mathbf{y}|^2 \leq |\mathbf{x}|^2 + |\mathbf{y}|^2 + 2|\mathbf{x}| \cdot |\mathbf{y}| = (|\mathbf{x}| + |\mathbf{y}|)^2,$$

and on extracting the square root we get the inequality (14-9).

In quantum mechanics and in several other branches of physics it is necessary to consider ordered sets of *complex* numbers $(x_1, x_2, \ldots, x_n)$. Such sets can be viewed as components of a vector $\mathbf{x}$ in an n-dimensional *complex vector space*. For the definition of addition of two complex vectors $\mathbf{x}$, $\mathbf{y}$ with components

$$\mathbf{x}: \quad (x_1, x_2, \ldots, x_n),$$

$$\mathbf{y}: \quad (y_1, y_2, \ldots, y_n),$$

we can take formula (14-6) and define the multiplication by a scalar α (real or complex) by (14-7). To make the length $|\mathbf{x}|$ of the complex vector $\mathbf{x}$ real, we adopt as the definition of scalar product of $\mathbf{x}$ and $\mathbf{y}$ the formula

$$\mathbf{x} \cdot \mathbf{y} = \bar{x}_1 y_1 + \bar{x}_2 y_2 + \cdots + \bar{x}_n y_n, \tag{14-12}$$

in which $\bar{x}_i$ denotes the conjugate of the complex number x_i. This formula specializes to (14-5) when the components of vectors are real, since for real numbers $\bar{x}_i = x_i$. We note from (14-12) that

$$\mathbf{y} \cdot \mathbf{x} = x_1 \bar{y}_1 + x_2 \bar{y}_2 + \cdots + x_n \bar{y}_n,$$

so that

$$\mathbf{x} \cdot \mathbf{y} = \overline{\mathbf{y} \cdot \mathbf{x}},$$

since the conjugate of the sum of complex numbers is equal to the sum of their conjugates and the conjugate of the product is the product of the conjugates.

Formula (14-12) yields

$$\mathbf{x} \cdot \mathbf{x} = \bar{x}_1 x_1 + \bar{x}_2 x_2 + \cdots + \bar{x}_n x_n, \tag{14-13}$$

so that $|\mathbf{x}| = \sqrt{\mathbf{x} \cdot \mathbf{x}}$ is a real number.

The definition of linear independence of a set of complex vectors is that given in Sec. 13 where the constants α_i are now in the field of complex numbers.

PROBLEMS

1. If one starts with the definition of a vector $\mathbf{x}$ as an n-tuple of n real or complex numbers $(x_1, x_2, \ldots, x_n)$ and uses for the definition of sum and product the formulas

$$\mathbf{x} + \mathbf{y}: \quad (x_1 + y_1, \ldots, x_n + y_n),$$

$$k\mathbf{x}: \quad (kx_1, \ldots, kx_n),$$

$$\mathbf{x} \cdot \mathbf{y} = \sum_{i=1}^{n} \bar{x}_i y_i,$$

then
$$(\mathbf{x} + \mathbf{y}) \cdot \mathbf{z} = \mathbf{x} \cdot \mathbf{z} + \mathbf{y} \cdot \mathbf{z},$$

$$\mathbf{x} \cdot (\mathbf{y} + \mathbf{z}) = \mathbf{x} \cdot \mathbf{y} + \mathbf{x} \cdot \mathbf{z},$$

$$(k\mathbf{x}) \cdot \mathbf{y} = \bar{k}(\mathbf{x} \cdot \mathbf{y}),$$

$$\mathbf{x} \cdot (k\mathbf{y}) = k(\mathbf{x} \cdot \mathbf{y}).$$

2. Prove that if $\mathbf{a}^{(1)}$, $\mathbf{a}^{(2)}$, $\ldots$, $\mathbf{a}^{(n)}$ is a set of n linearly independent vectors in a complex n-dimensional vector space, then the only vector $\mathbf{x}$ orthogonal to each of the vectors $\mathbf{a}^{(i)}$ is the zero vector.

3. Prove that a set of mutually orthogonal vectors is always linearly independent.

4. Modify the proof of orthogonalization in Sec. 13 so that it applies to a set of linearly independent complex vectors.

15. Summation Convention. Cramer's Rule. In dealing with expressions involving sums of quantities it is often useful to adopt the following summation convention: *If in some expression a certain summation index occurs twice, we omit writing the summation symbol Σ and agree to sum the terms in the expression for all admissible values of the index.*

Thus in a linear form $\sum\limits_{i=1}^{3} a_i x_i$ the summation index i appears twice under the summation symbol Σ, and we shall write $a_i x_i$ to mean $a_1 x_1 + a_2 x_2 + a_3 x_3$. The symbol $\sum\limits_{i=1}^{3} a_{ii} = a_{11} + a_{22} + a_{33}$ will be written simply as a_{ii}. Again, a double sum

$$\sum_{i=1}^{3} \sum_{j=1}^{3} a_{ij} x_i x_j = a_{11} x_1 x_1 + a_{12} x_1 x_2 + a_{13} x_1 x_3 + a_{21} x_2 x_1 + a_{22} x_2 x_2$$
$$+ a_{23} x_2 x_3 + a_{31} x_3 x_1 + a_{32} x_3 x_2 + a_{33} x_3 x_3,$$

which has two repeated summation indices i and j under the summation symbols, will be written as

$$a_{ij} x_i x_j.$$

The range of admissible values of the indices, of course, has to be specified. Thus, the expression

$$a_{ij} x_j, \qquad \begin{cases} i = 1, 2, 3, \\ j = 1, 2, 3, 4 \end{cases}$$

represents *three linear forms*

$$a_{11} x_1 + a_{12} x_2 + a_{13} x_3 + a_{14} x_4,$$

$$a_{21} x_1 + a_{22} x_2 + a_{23} x_3 + a_{24} x_4,$$

$$a_{31} x_1 + a_{32} x_2 + a_{33} x_3 + a_{34} x_4,$$

corresponding to the three possible choices $i = 1, 2, 3$ of the *free index i*. The summation index j is often called the *dummy index* because it can be replaced by any other letter having the same range of summation. The dummy index is analogous to the variable of integration in a definite integral, which can also be changed at will. Thus

$$a_{ij}x_ix_j = a_{kr}x_kx_r,$$

it being understood that the indices i, j, k, r range over the same sets of values. Unless a statement to the contrary is made, we shall suppose that the indices have the range of values from 1 to n. We shall thus write formulas (14-4) and (14-5), for example, as

$$\mathbf{y} = y_i\mathbf{e}_i,$$

$$\mathbf{x}\cdot\mathbf{y} = x_iy_i,$$

and (14-13) as

$$\mathbf{x}\cdot\mathbf{x} = \bar{x}_ix_i.$$

We shall make use of this summation notation among other places in writing formulas for the product of determinants and for the expansion of determinants.

We recall that a determinant

$$|a_{ij}| \equiv \begin{vmatrix} a_{11} & a_{12}\cdots a_{1n} \\ a_{21} & a_{22}\cdots a_{2n} \\ \cdot & \cdot \quad \cdot \quad \cdot \quad \cdot \\ a_{n1} & a_{n2}\cdots a_{nn} \end{vmatrix} \tag{15-1}$$

of order n represents an algebraic sum of $n!$ terms formed from the elements a_{ij} in such a way that one, and only one, element from each row i and each column j appears in each term.[1]

The product of two determinants $|a_{ij}|$ and $|b_{ij}|$, each of the order n, can be written as a single determinant $|c_{ij}|$ of order n in which the element c_{ij} in the ith row and jth column is [2]

$$c_{ij} = a_{ik}b_{jk} = a_{i1}b_{j1} + a_{i2}b_{j2} + \cdots + a_{in}b_{jn}. \tag{15-2}$$

Inasmuch as the value of the determinant $|b_{ij}|$ is unchanged when its rows and columns are interchanged, the value of the determinant

$$|c_{ij}| = |a_{ij}|\,|b_{ij}|$$

with the elements (15-2) is the same as that of the determinant $|c_{ij}|$ with the elements

$$c_{ij} = a_{ik}b_{kj} = a_{i1}b_{1j} + a_{i2}b_{2j} + \cdots + a_{in}b_{nj}. \tag{15-3}$$

---

[1] A discussion of determinants is contained in Appendix A.

[2] Since the number n is *fixed*, the term $a_{in}b_{jn}$ does not represent the sum of terms with respect to n. Here n is *not* a summation index. Cf. Appendix A, Formula (1-10).

If the cofactor [1] of the element a_{ij} in the determinant (15-1) is denoted by A_{ij}, we can expand a_{ij} in terms of the cofactors of elements in any row or column of the determinant. A reference to (1-5) in Appendix A will show that the following formulas include the Laplace developments of (15-1):

$$a_{ij}A_{ik} = \delta_{jk}a, \qquad (15\text{-}4)$$

$$a_{ji}A_{ki} = \delta_{jk}a, \qquad (15\text{-}5)$$

where δ_{jk} is the Kronecker delta and a stands for the value of $|a_{ij}|$; for if in (15-4) $k \neq j$, the expression $a_{ij}A_{ik}$ represents the sum of products of the elements in the jth column by the cofactors of the elements in the kth column. The value of such a sum is zero, since it represents the expansion of a determinant with two like columns. If $j = k$, the sum $a_{ij}A_{ik}$ is the sum of products of the elements in the jth column by the cofactors of those elements, yielding the value $a = |a_{ij}|$. Similar statements apply to (15-5) if we replace the word "column" by "row."

Formula (15-4) enables us to give a compact derivation of Cramer's rule for solving a system of n linear equations

$$a_{ij}x_j = b_i \qquad (15\text{-}6)$$

in n unknowns x_j.

We multiply both members of (15-6) by the cofactors A_{ik} and sum with respect to i. We get

$$a_{ij}A_{ik}x_j = A_{ik}b_i.$$

But by (15-4) this is

$$\delta_{jk}ax_j = A_{ik}b_i.$$

The sum $\delta_{jk}x_j = x_k$, and we conclude that

$$x_k = \frac{A_{ik}b_i}{a} \qquad (15\text{-}7)$$

whenever $a \neq 0$. The numerator in (15-7) is the determinant obtained by replacing the elements in the kth column of $|a_{ij}|$ by the b_i. The reader finding the foregoing calculations too concise will find a more expansive discussion in Sec. 2 of Appendix A.

PROBLEMS

1. Write out the following expressions in full:

(a) $\delta_{ij}a_j$; (b) $\delta_{ij}x_ix_j$; (c) $a_{ij}b_{jk} = \delta_{ik}$; (d) $a_{ijk}x_k$; (e) $\dfrac{\partial f}{\partial x_i}\,dx_i$; (f) $\dfrac{\partial f_j}{\partial x_k}\,dx_k$; (g) δ_{ii}; (h) $a_i = \dfrac{\partial y_i}{\partial x_j}\,b_j$; (i) $a_{ij}a_{ik} = \delta_{jk}$; (j) $a_{ij}x_ix_j$; (k) $\delta_{ij}\delta_{ik}$; (l) $a_{ik}x_k = b_i$. The symbols δ_{ij} denote the Kronecker deltas.

[1] See Appendix A. We recall that the cofactor of a_{ij} is the signed minor M_{ij} of the element a_{ij}, the sign being $(-1)^{i+j}$.

2. Write out the determinants represented by the expansion $a_{i2}A_{i3}$ and $a_{3i}A_{i4}$, where A_{ij} is the cofactor of the element a_{ij} in $|a_{ij}|$. Also write out the determinants represented by $a_{i2}A_{i2}$ and $a_{3i}A_{i3}$.

3. Expand the determinants:

$$(a) \quad \begin{vmatrix} a_{11} & a_{12} & a_{13} & a_{14} \\ 0 & a_{22} & a_{23} & a_{24} \\ 0 & 0 & a_{33} & a_{34} \\ 0 & 0 & 0 & a_{44} \end{vmatrix} ; \qquad (b) \quad \begin{vmatrix} 1 & x_1 & x_1^2 \\ 1 & x_2 & x_2^2 \\ 1 & x_3 & x_3^2 \end{vmatrix} ;$$

$$(c) \quad \begin{vmatrix} 1 & 1 & 1 \\ x_1 & x_2 & x_3 \\ x_1^2 & x_2^2 & x_3^2 \end{vmatrix} ; \qquad (d) \quad \begin{vmatrix} a_1 & 0 & 0 \\ a_2 & b_2 & 0 \\ a_3 & b_3 & c_3 \end{vmatrix} .$$

4. Multiply the determinant (b) in Prob. 3 by the determinants (c) and (d).

16. Matrices. In this section we introduce the concept of a matrix and discuss some rules of operation with matrices which are of value in the study of linear transformations.

An $m \times n$ matrix is an ordered set of mn quantities a_{ij} arranged in a rectangular array of m rows and n columns. If $m = n$, the array is called a *square matrix* of order n. The quantities a_{ij} are called the *elements* of the matrix. Thus, a matrix is an array

$$A \equiv \begin{pmatrix} a_{11} & a_{12} \cdots a_{1n} \\ a_{21} & a_{22} \cdots a_{2n} \\ \cdot & \cdot \quad \cdot \quad \cdot \quad \cdot \\ a_{m1} & a_{m2} \cdots a_{mn} \end{pmatrix}, \tag{16-1}$$

where parentheses are used to enclose the array of elements. We shall denote matrices by capital letters, or when it is desired to exhibit a typical element of the matrix (16-1), we shall write (a_{ij}).

If the order of the elements in (16-1) is changed, or if any element is changed, a different matrix results. For example, a triple of values (a_1, a_2, a_3) representing the cartesian coordinates of a point is a 1×3 matrix. If $a_1 \neq a_2$, the matrix (a_2, a_1, a_3) obviously represents a different point.

Two $m \times n$ matrices $A = (a_{ij})$ and $B = (b_{ij})$ are said to be equal if, and only if, $a_{ij} = b_{ij}$ for each i and j. That is, $A = B$ only when the elements in like positions of the two arrays are equal.

We define the sum $A + B$ of two $m \times n$ matrices $A = (a_{ij})$, $B = (b_{ij})$ to be the array

$$A + B = (a_{ij} + b_{ij}), \tag{16-2}$$

and their difference $A - B$ to be the array

$$A - B = (a_{ij} - b_{ij}).$$

We shall agree to say that the product of the matrix $A = (a_{ij})$ by a constant k, written kA, is a matrix each of whose elements is multiplied by k. Thus $kA = (ka_{ij})$.

If we have an $m \times n$ matrix A and an $n \times p$ matrix B, we define the product of A and B, written AB, by the formula

$$AB = (a_{ij}b_{jk}),\tag{16-3}$$

where, as agreed in Sec. 15, the repeated index j is summed from 1 to n. Thus, the product AB is an $m \times p$ matrix, and we can multiply two matrices only if the number of columns in the first factor is equal to the number of rows in the second.

Example 1.   If

$$A = \begin{pmatrix} 1 & 0 & 2 \\ 2 & -1 & 3 \\ 0 & 5 & 6 \end{pmatrix} \quad \text{and} \quad B = \begin{pmatrix} 2 & -1 & 1 \\ 0 & 1 & 2 \\ 1 & -2 & -1 \end{pmatrix},$$

$$A + B = \begin{pmatrix} 1+2 & 0-1 & 2+1 \\ 2+0 & -1+1 & 3+2 \\ 0+1 & 5-2 & 6-1 \end{pmatrix} = \begin{pmatrix} 3 & -1 & 3 \\ 2 & 0 & 5 \\ 1 & 3 & 5 \end{pmatrix}$$

and

$$AB = \begin{pmatrix} (1)(2)+ & (0)(0)+(2)(1) & (1)(-1)+ & (0)(1)+(2)(-2) & (1)(1)+ & (0)(2)+(2)(-1) \\ (2)(2)+(-1)(0)+(3)(1) & (2)(-1)+(-1)(1)+(3)(-2) & (2)(1)+(-1)(2)+(3)(-1) \\ (0)(2)+ & (5)(0)+(6)(1) & (0)(-1)+ & (5)(1)+(6)(-2) & (0)(1)+ & (5)(2)+(6)(-1) \end{pmatrix}$$

$$= \begin{pmatrix} 4 & -5 & -1 \\ 7 & -9 & -3 \\ 6 & -7 & 4 \end{pmatrix}.$$

Also, if

$$C = \begin{pmatrix} 2 \\ 3 \\ -1 \end{pmatrix},$$

then

$$AC = \begin{pmatrix} 1 & 0 & 2 \\ 2 & -1 & 3 \\ 0 & 5 & 6 \end{pmatrix}\begin{pmatrix} 2 \\ 3 \\ -1 \end{pmatrix} = \begin{pmatrix} (1)(2)+ & (0)(3)+(2)(-1) \\ (2)(2)+(-1)(3)+(3)(-1) \\ (0)(2)+ & (5)(3)+(6)(-1) \end{pmatrix} = \begin{pmatrix} 0 \\ -2 \\ 9 \end{pmatrix}.$$

We observe that the rule (16-2) for the addition of matrices requires that $A + B = B + A$, but it does not follow from (16-3) that the order of factors in the product AB can be interchanged even when the matrices are square.   Indeed, for

$$A = \begin{pmatrix} 0 & 1 \\ 1 & 0 \end{pmatrix} \quad \text{and} \quad B = \begin{pmatrix} -1 & 0 \\ 0 & 1 \end{pmatrix}$$

the rule (16-3) gives

$$AB = \begin{pmatrix} 0 & 1 \\ -1 & 0 \end{pmatrix}, \quad \text{while } BA = \begin{pmatrix} 0 & -1 \\ 1 & 0 \end{pmatrix}.$$

Thus, the multiplication of matrices, in general, is not commutative.

However, if we have two square matrices of order n which have zero elements everywhere except possibly on the main diagonal, then it follows from (16-3) that

$$
\begin{pmatrix} a_1 & 0 & \cdots & 0 \\ 0 & a_2 & \cdots & 0 \\ \cdot & \cdot & \cdot & \cdot \\ 0 & 0 & \cdots & a_n \end{pmatrix} \cdot \begin{pmatrix} b_1 & 0 & \cdots & 0 \\ 0 & b_2 & \cdots & 0 \\ \cdot & \cdot & \cdot & \cdot \\ 0 & 0 & \cdots & b_n \end{pmatrix} = \begin{pmatrix} a_1b_1 & 0 & \cdots & 0 \\ 0 & a_2b_2 & \cdots & 0 \\ \cdot & \cdot & \cdot & \cdot \\ 0 & 0 & \cdots & a_nb_n \end{pmatrix}.
$$

Such matrices are called *diagonal*.

Thus for two diagonal matrices A and B,

$$AB = BA.$$

A diagonal matrix in which all elements along the main diagonal are equal is called a *scalar matrix*. A particular scalar matrix

$$
I = \begin{pmatrix} 1 & 0 & \cdots & 0 \\ 0 & 1 & \cdots & 0 \\ \cdot & \cdot & \cdot & \cdot \\ 0 & 0 & \cdots & 1 \end{pmatrix} \tag{16-4}
$$

is called the *identity* (*or unit*) *matrix*.

We note that if I is the identity matrix and A is any square matrix, then [1]

$$IA = AI = A. \tag{16-5}$$

By analogy with the rules of ordinary algebra, we define the zero matrix O to be the matrix such that

$$O + A = A.$$

It follows from (16-2) that all elements of the zero matrix are zeros. We observe that the product of two matrices may be a zero matrix even when neither of the factors is a zero matrix. Thus, if

$$
A = \begin{pmatrix} 1 & 1 & 0 \\ 0 & 0 & 0 \\ 0 & 1 & 0 \end{pmatrix} \quad \text{and} \quad B = \begin{pmatrix} 0 & 0 & 0 \\ 0 & 0 & 0 \\ 1 & 0 & 0 \end{pmatrix},
$$

then
$$
AB = \begin{pmatrix} 0 & 0 & 0 \\ 0 & 0 & 0 \\ 0 & 0 & 0 \end{pmatrix}.
$$

---

[1] More generally we can show that if $AX = XA$ for *every* matrix A, then X is a scalar matrix. See Prob. 6.

If the matrix is square, it is possible to form from the elements of the matrix a determinant whose elements have the same arrangement as those of the matrix. This determinant is called *the determinant of the matrix*. From any matrix, other matrices can be obtained by striking out a number of rows and columns. Certain of these matrices will be square matrices, and the determinants of these matrices are called *determinants of the matrix*. For an $m \times n$ matrix, there are square matrices of orders 1, 2, ..., p, where p is equal to the smaller of the numbers m and n.

Example 2. The 2×3 matrix

$$A \equiv \begin{pmatrix} a_{11} & a_{12} & a_{13} \\ a_{21} & a_{22} & a_{23} \end{pmatrix}$$

contains the first-order square matrices (a_{11}), (a_{12}), (a_{23}), etc., obtained by striking out any two columns and any one row. It also contains the second-order square matrices

$$\begin{pmatrix} a_{11} & a_{12} \\ a_{21} & a_{22} \end{pmatrix}, \quad \begin{pmatrix} a_{11} & a_{13} \\ a_{21} & a_{23} \end{pmatrix}, \quad \begin{pmatrix} a_{12} & a_{13} \\ a_{22} & a_{23} \end{pmatrix},$$

obtained by striking out any column of A.

In many applications, it is useful to employ the notion of the rank of a matrix A. This is defined in terms of the determinants of A. *A matrix A is said to be of rank r if there is at least one r-rowed determinant of A that is not zero, whereas all determinants of A of order higher than r are zero or nonexistent.*[1]

Example 3. If

$$A \equiv \begin{pmatrix} 1 & 0 & 1 & 3 \\ 2 & 1 & 0 & -2 \\ -1 & -1 & 1 & 5 \end{pmatrix},$$

the third-order determinants are

$$\begin{vmatrix} 1 & 0 & 1 \\ 2 & 1 & 0 \\ -1 & -1 & 1 \end{vmatrix} = 0, \quad \begin{vmatrix} 1 & 0 & 3 \\ 2 & 1 & -2 \\ -1 & -1 & 5 \end{vmatrix} = 0,$$

$$\begin{vmatrix} 1 & 1 & 3 \\ 2 & 0 & -2 \\ -1 & 1 & 5 \end{vmatrix} = 0, \quad \begin{vmatrix} 0 & 1 & 3 \\ 1 & 0 & -2 \\ -1 & 1 & 5 \end{vmatrix} = 0.$$

Since

$$\begin{vmatrix} 1 & 0 \\ 2 & 1 \end{vmatrix} \neq 0,$$

there is at least one second-order determinant different from zero, whereas all third-order determinants of A are zero. Therefore, the rank of A is 2.

It should be observed that a matrix is said to have rank zero if all its elements are zero.

[1] Cf. Appendix A, Sec. 2.

If $A = (a_{ij})$ and $B = (b_{ij})$ are two square matrices, then

$$AB = (a_{ik}b_{kj})$$

and the determinant of the matrix AB is

$$|AB| = |a_{ik}b_{kj}|. \tag{16-6}$$

We note with reference to (15-3) that the elements in the ith row and jth column of the determinant in (16-6) are precisely those that appear in the product of two determinants $|A| = |a_{ij}|$ and $|B| = |b_{ij}|$. Thus

$$|AB| = |A| \cdot |B|, \tag{16-7}$$

or in words, *the determinant $|AB|$ of the product of two matrices A and B is equal to the product of determinants $|A|$ and $|B|$.*

It follows from (16-7) that whenever the product of two matrices is a zero matrix, *then the determinant of at least one of the factors is zero.*

A square matrix whose determinant is zero is called a *singular matrix.*

PROBLEMS

1. Make use of the definitions in Sec. 16 to establish the following theorems for matrices:

(a) $A + B = B + A$;
(c) $(A + B)C = AC + BC$;

(b) $(A + B) + C = A + (B + C)$;
(d) $C(A + B) = CA + CB$.

2. Verify that the matrices A and B in Example 1 of this section do not commute.

3. Multiply:

(a) $\begin{pmatrix} 1 & 2 & 3 \\ 3 & 1 & 2 \\ 1 & 0 & 2 \end{pmatrix} \cdot \begin{pmatrix} 2 \\ 1 \\ 3 \end{pmatrix}$,   (b) $\begin{pmatrix} 1 & 2 & 3 \\ 3 & 1 & 2 \\ 1 & 3 & 2 \end{pmatrix} \cdot \begin{pmatrix} 2 & 0 & 0 \\ 1 & 0 & 0 \\ 3 & 0 & 0 \end{pmatrix}$.

4. Show that $(AB)C = A(BC)$.

5. Determine the ranks of the matrices:

$$A = \begin{pmatrix} 1 & 2 & 3 \\ 1 & 4 & 2 \\ 2 & 6 & 5 \end{pmatrix}; \quad B = \begin{pmatrix} 1 & 0 & 1 \\ 0 & 0 & 1 \\ 1 & 1 & 1 \end{pmatrix}; \quad C = \begin{pmatrix} 2 & -3 & 4 \\ 1 & 2 & -3 \\ 4 & 1 & -2 \end{pmatrix};$$

$$D = \begin{pmatrix} 2 & -4 & 1 \\ 3 & 1 & -2 \end{pmatrix}; \quad E = \begin{pmatrix} k & 0 & 0 \\ 0 & k & 0 \\ 0 & 0 & k \end{pmatrix}.$$

Is $AB = BA$?   Is $AE = EA$?   Are these matrices singular?

6. If $AX = XA$ for every matrix A, show that X is a scalar matrix. *Hint:* Let $X = (x_{ij})$, then since $AX = XA$, $a_{ij}x_{jk} = x_{ij}a_{jk}$ for all choices of a_{ij} and a_{jk}. Now choose $a_{ij} = \delta_{i(p)}\delta_{j(q)}$, where $\delta_{i(p)}$ and $\delta_{j(q)}$ are the Kronecker deltas and p and q have fixed but arbitrary values ranging from 1 to n, and conclude that $x_{ij} = x_{ji} = 0$ if $i \neq j$ and $x_{ii} = x_{jj}$ for each i and j.

17. Linear Transformations. The matrix notation introduced in the preceding section enables us to study effectively properties of linear transformations.

A set of n linear relations

$$y_i = a_{ij}x_j, \qquad i, j = 1, 2, \ldots, n, \tag{17-1}$$

where the a_{ij} are constants, defines a linear transformation of the set of n variables x_i into a new set y_i.

We can regard the quantities $x_1, x_2, \ldots, x_n$ as components (or measure numbers) of some vector $\mathbf{x}$ referred to a set of base vectors $\mathbf{a}_1, \mathbf{a}_2, \ldots, \mathbf{a}_n$ in the n-dimensional vector space. The quantities $y_1, y_2, \ldots, y_n$ can be viewed as components of another vector $\mathbf{y}$ referred to the same basis. The relations (17-1) then represent a transformation of the vector $\mathbf{x}$ into another vector $\mathbf{y}$. Since the lengths of $\mathbf{x}$ and $\mathbf{y}$ and their orientations relative to the base vectors $\mathbf{a}_i$ are different in general, we can look upon the transformation (17-1) as representing a deformation of space.

When the components of $\mathbf{x}$ and $\mathbf{y}$ are represented by the column matrices

$$X = \begin{pmatrix} x_1 \\ x_2 \\ \cdot \\ \cdot \\ \cdot \\ x_n \end{pmatrix}, \qquad Y = \begin{pmatrix} y_1 \\ y_2 \\ \cdot \\ \cdot \\ \cdot \\ y_n \end{pmatrix},$$

the set of relations (17-1) can be written in the form

$$Y = AX, \tag{17-2}$$

where $A = (a_{ij})$ is the matrix of the coefficients in the linear transformation (17-1) and the product AX is computed by the rule (16-3).

If A is a nonsingular matrix, we can solve Eqs. (17-1) for the x_i by Cramer's rule (15-7) and obtain the *inverse* transformation

$$x_i = \frac{A_{ji}}{a} y_j, \tag{17-3}$$

where A_{ij} is the cofactor of the element a_{ij} in the determinant $a = |a_{ij}|$ of the matrix A.

The set of equations (17-3) can be written in matrix notation as

$$X = A^{-1}Y,$$

where A^{-1} is

$$A^{-1} = \begin{pmatrix} \dfrac{A_{11}}{a} & \dfrac{A_{21}}{a} & \cdots & \dfrac{A_{n1}}{a} \\[2mm] \dfrac{A_{12}}{a} & \dfrac{A_{22}}{a} & \cdots & \dfrac{A_{n2}}{a} \\[2mm] \cdot & \cdot & \cdots & \cdot \\[2mm] \dfrac{A_{1n}}{a} & \dfrac{A_{2n}}{a} & \cdots & \dfrac{A_{nn}}{a} \end{pmatrix}. \qquad (17\text{-}4)$$

It is natural to call A^{-1} the *inverse matrix* of A. We note that the inverse matrix can be constructed whenever A is nonsingular, that is, whenever the determinant $|A| \equiv a$ does not vanish.

If we form the product of A and A^{-1}

$$AA^{-1} = \left(a_{ik}\frac{A_{jk}}{a} \right) \qquad (17\text{-}5)$$

and recall [1] that

$$a_{ik}A_{jk} = \delta_{ij}a,$$

we can write (17-5) as

$$AA^{-1} = (\delta_{ij}) = I, \qquad (17\text{-}6)$$

where I is the identity matrix.

Since the determinant of the product of two matrices is equal to the product of their determinants, we conclude from (17-6) that

$$|A^{-1}A| = |A^{-1}| \cdot |A| = |I| = 1,$$

so that

$$|A^{-1}| = \frac{1}{|A|}. \qquad (17\text{-}7)$$

Multiplying (17-6) on the left by A^{-1} and on the right by $(A^{-1})^{-1}$ gives

$$A^{-1}A = I = AA^{-1}. \qquad (17\text{-}8)$$

In addition to the inverse matrix A^{-1} we shall make frequent use of the matrix

$$A' = \begin{pmatrix} a_{11} & a_{21} & \cdots & a_{n1} \\ a_{12} & a_{22} & \cdots & a_{n2} \\ \cdot & \cdot & \cdots & \cdot \\ a_{1n} & a_{2n} & \cdots & a_{nn} \end{pmatrix} \qquad (17\text{-}9)$$

[1] See (15-5), but note the relation of the subscripts on the A_{ij} to the rows and columns in (17-4).

obtained by interchanging the rows and columns in the matrix

$$A = \begin{pmatrix} a_{11} & a_{12} & \cdots & a_{1n} \\ a_{21} & a_{22} & \cdots & a_{2n} \\ \cdot & \cdot & \cdot & \cdot \cdot \cdot & \cdot \\ a_{n1} & a_{n2} & \cdots & a_{nn} \end{pmatrix}. \tag{17-10}$$

The matrix A' is called the *transpose* of A.

On using the laws of addition and multiplication of matrices it is easy to show that

$$(A + B)' = A' + B',$$

$$(kA)' = kA',$$

$$(AB)' = B'A'. \tag{17-11}$$

(Note order.)

If we recall the relation (17-8),

$$A^{-1}A = AA^{-1},$$

and form the transpose

$$(A^{-1}A)' = (AA^{-1})',$$

we get, on making use of (17-11),

$$A'(A^{-1})' = (A^{-1})'A'. \tag{17-12}$$

Multiplying both members of (17-12) on the left by $(A')^{-1}$, we get

$$(A')^{-1}A'(A^{-1})' = (A')^{-1}(A^{-1})'A'.$$

Hence $(A^{-1})' = (A')^{-1}(AA^{-1})' = (A')^{-1}.$

Thus $(A^{-1})' = (A')^{-1}. \tag{17-13}$

The important result embodied in (17-13) states that the *inverse of the transpose of the matrix A is equal to the transpose of its inverse.*

In many calculations it is necessary to compute the inverse of the product of two nonsingular matrices A and B. We can obtain the desired result as follows: Since

$$(AB)(AB)^{-1} = I,$$

or (see Prob. 4, Sec. 16)

$$AB(AB)^{-1} = I,$$

we get, on multiplying both members of this relation on the left by A^{-1},

$$A^{-1}AB(AB)^{-1} = A^{-1}$$

or $B(AB)^{-1} = A^{-1}.$

Multiplying this result on the left by B^{-1}, we get the desired result

$$(AB)^{-1} = B^{-1}A^{-1}. \tag{17-14}$$

(Note order.) This result can be extended in an obvious way to more than two matrices, so that, for example,

$$(ABC)^{-1} = C^{-1}B^{-1}A^{-1}.$$

Example 1. Compute A^{-1} for the matrix

$$A = \begin{pmatrix} 1 & 2 \\ 3 & -1 \end{pmatrix}.$$

Here
$$A_{11} = -1, \qquad A_{12} = -3; \qquad A_{21} = -2, \qquad A_{22} = 1.$$

Since $a = |A| = -7$,

$$A^{-1} = \begin{pmatrix} \tfrac{1}{7} & \tfrac{2}{7} \\ \tfrac{3}{7} & -\tfrac{1}{7} \end{pmatrix}.$$

We note that $|A^{-1}| = -\tfrac{1}{7} = 1/|A|$.

Example 2. If A is a nonsingular matrix, show that the matric equations

$$AX = I \qquad \text{and} \qquad XA = I$$

have unique solutions $X = A^{-1}$.

On multiplying both members of the given equations by A^{-1}, we get

$$A^{-1}AX = A^{-1}I \qquad \text{and} \qquad XAA^{-1} = IA^{-1}.$$

But
$$A^{-1}A = AA^{-1} = I \qquad \text{and} \qquad A^{-1}I = IA^{-1} = A^{-1},$$

so that
$$X = A^{-1}.$$

If we have two successive linear transformations

$$y_i = a_{ij}x_j,$$
$$z_i = b_{ij}y_j, \tag{17-15}$$

the direct transformation from the variables x_i to the z_i is obtained by inserting for the y_j in the second set of Eqs. (17-15) from the first set. We thus get

$$z_i = b_{ij}a_{jk}x_k. \tag{17-16}$$

The transformation (17-16) is called the *product* of the transformations in (17-15). If the variables $(x_1,x_2,\ldots,x_n)$, $(y_1,y_2,\ldots,y_n)$, and $(z_1,z_2,\ldots,z_n)$ are interpreted as components of the vectors **x**, **y**, **z**, represented by column matrices

$$X = \begin{pmatrix} x_1 \\ x_2 \\ \vdots \\ x_n \end{pmatrix}, \qquad Y = \begin{pmatrix} y_1 \\ y_2 \\ \vdots \\ y_n \end{pmatrix}, \qquad Z = \begin{pmatrix} z_1 \\ z_2 \\ \vdots \\ z_n \end{pmatrix},$$

we can write Eqs. (17-15) as

$$Y = AX,$$
$$Z = BY, \qquad (17\text{-}17)$$

and the product transformation (17-16) as

$$Z = BAX. \qquad (17\text{-}18)$$

Thus, when the variables x_i are subjected to a linear transformation (17-15) *with a matrix A and the variables y_i are subjected to a linear transformation with a matrix B, the product transformation has the matrix BA.* Since BA in general is not equal to AB, the order in which the transformations are performed is material.

When it is desired to interpret Eqs. (17-15) as transformations on the components of the vectors $\mathbf{x}$, $\mathbf{y}$, $\mathbf{z}$, Eqs. (17-17) and (17-18) can be written in the forms

$$\mathbf{y} = A\mathbf{x},$$
$$\mathbf{z} = B\mathbf{y}, \qquad (17\text{-}19)$$
$$\mathbf{z} = BA\mathbf{x},$$

where $\mathbf{x}$, $\mathbf{y}$, $\mathbf{z}$ are regarded as the column matrices X, Y, Z, respectively. The matrices in Eqs. (17-19) can be viewed as *operators* transforming a given vector into another vector. Since

$$A(k\mathbf{x}) = kA\mathbf{x}, \qquad k \text{ const},$$

and $\qquad\qquad A(\mathbf{x} + \mathbf{y}) = A\mathbf{x} + A\mathbf{y},$

one often speaks of A as a *linear operator*.

PROBLEMS

1. If

$$A = \begin{pmatrix} 1 & 2 & -1 \\ 3 & 0 & 2 \\ 4 & 5 & 0 \end{pmatrix} \quad \text{and} \quad B = \begin{pmatrix} 1 & 0 & 0 \\ 2 & 1 & 0 \\ 0 & 1 & 3 \end{pmatrix},$$

find A^{-1} and B^{-1}. Verify that $(AB)' = B'A'$ and $(AB)^{-1} = B^{-1}A^{-1}$.

2. Prove that $(ABC)' = C'B'A'$.

3. Prove that $(A^{-1})^{-1} = A$.

4. Prove that if A is singular, there exists no matrix B such that $AB = I$.

5. If $y_1 = x_1 \cos \alpha - x_2 \sin \alpha$, $y_2 = x_1 \sin \alpha + x_2 \cos \alpha$, find A^{-1}, A' and show that $A^{-1} = A'$. If $\mathbf{x}$ is a vector with components (x_1, x_2), what is the geometric relation of $\mathbf{x}$ to $\mathbf{y}$? Write out the inverse transformation $\mathbf{x} = A^{-1}\mathbf{y}$.

6. If $y_1 = x_1 - x_2$, $y_2 = x_1 + x_2$, what is A^{-1}? Is $A^{-1} = A'$? If $\mathbf{x}$ is a vector with components (x_1, x_2), what is the geometric relation of $\mathbf{x}$ to $\mathbf{y}$?

7. If

$$y_1 = \frac{1}{\sqrt{2}} x_1 + \frac{1}{\sqrt{2}} x_3,$$

$$y_2 = x_2,$$

$$y_3 = -\frac{1}{\sqrt{2}} x_1 + \frac{1}{\sqrt{2}} x_3,$$

compute the matrix A' for the inverse transformation and compare it with the given matrix A. If $\mathbf{x}$ is a vector with components (x_1, x_2, x_3) and $\mathbf{y}$ is a vector with components (y_1, y_2, y_3), what is the geometric relation of $\mathbf{x}$ to $\mathbf{y}$?

8. Let

$$A = \begin{pmatrix} 1 & 2 \\ 2 & 3 \end{pmatrix}$$

and consider the vector

$$\mathbf{y} = A\mathbf{x}.$$

Compute $\mathbf{x} = A^{-1}\mathbf{y}$. Is it true that $A' = A^{-1}$?

9. If

$$y_1 = x_1 \cos \alpha + x_2 \sin \alpha,$$

$$y_2 = -x_1 \sin \alpha + x_2 \cos \alpha,$$

and

$$z_1 = y_1 \cos \beta + y_2 \sin \beta,$$

$$z_2 = -y_1 \sin \beta + y_2 \cos \beta,$$

find the product transformation directly and also by computing the product of the matrices as in (17-18). Compute BA and AB, $A^{-1}B^{-1}$, and $(BA)^{-1}$. Also find $(BA)'$ and compare it with $(BA)^{-1}$.

10. If

$$y_1 = 2x_1 + x_2,$$

$$y_2 = x_1 - x_2,$$

and

$$z_1 = y_1 - y_2,$$

$$z_2 = 2y_1 + y_2,$$

perform the calculations required in Prob. 9.

18. Transformation of Base Vectors.

In the preceding section we interpreted the set of linear relations

$$y_i = a_{ij}x_j \tag{18-1}$$

as transformations of components $(x_1, x_2, \ldots, x_n)$ of a vector $\mathbf{x}$ into components $(y_1, y_2, \ldots, y_n)$ of another vector $\mathbf{y}$ when the vectors are referred to the same basis $(\mathbf{a}_i)$, so that

$$\mathbf{x} = x_i\mathbf{a}_i \quad \text{and} \quad \mathbf{y} = y_i\mathbf{a}_i. \tag{18-2}$$

If we introduce a new system of base vectors $\boldsymbol{\alpha}_i$, obtained from the set $\mathbf{a}_i$ by a linear transformation

$$\boldsymbol{\alpha}_i = b_{ij}\mathbf{a}_j, \quad \text{with } |b_{ij}| \neq 0, \tag{18-3}$$

the vectors **x** and **y** in the new reference system will have certain representations

$$\mathbf{x} = \xi_i \boldsymbol{\alpha}_i, \qquad \mathbf{y} = \eta_i \boldsymbol{\alpha}_i. \qquad (18\text{-}4)$$

We raise two questions: (1) What is the relation of the components of vectors in the two representations (18-2) and (18-4) when the base vectors are transformed by (18-3)? (2) What is the form of the transformation of the components ξ_i into η_i which corresponds to the deformation of the vector **x** characterized by Eqs. (18-1)?

To answer the first question we insert from (18-3) in (18-4) and get

$$\mathbf{x} = b_{ij}\xi_i \mathbf{a}_j, \qquad (18\text{-}5)$$

while a reference to (18-2) shows that

$$\mathbf{x} = \mathbf{a}_i x_i \equiv \mathbf{a}_j x_j. \qquad (18\text{-}6)$$

From (18-5) and (18-6) we conclude that

$$x_j = b_{ij}\xi_i. \qquad (18\text{-}7)$$

This formula is the desired relationship connecting the components of **x** when it is referred to two different base systems related by (18-3).

We note that in the transformation (18-3) the summation is on the second index j while in (18-7) it is on the first index. In other words, the matrix of coefficients b_{ij} in (18-7) is the transpose of the matrix (b_{ij}) in (18-3).

If we write the matrix in (18-3) as

$$(b_{ij}) = B,$$

the set of equations (18-7) can be written as

$$\mathbf{x} = B'\boldsymbol{\xi}, \qquad (18\text{-}8)$$

x and $\boldsymbol{\xi}$ being the column matrices with components $(x_1, x_2, \ldots, x_n)$ and $(\xi_1, \xi_2, \ldots, \xi_n)$.

On multiplying (18-8) by $(B')^{-1}$ on the left we get the solution for $\boldsymbol{\xi}$ in the form

$$\boldsymbol{\xi} = (B')^{-1}\mathbf{x}. \qquad (18\text{-}9)$$

Formulas (18-8) and (18-9) give a complete answer to the first question.

The relationship connecting the components $(y_1, y_2, \ldots, y_n)$ with $(\eta_1, \eta_2, \ldots, \eta_n)$ can be represented similarly by

$$\mathbf{y} = B'\boldsymbol{\eta} \qquad \text{and} \qquad \boldsymbol{\eta} = (B')^{-1}\mathbf{y}. \qquad (18\text{-}10)$$

We proceed next to the answer of the question concerning the form of the deformation of space (18-1) in the new reference frame $\boldsymbol{\alpha}_i$.

We write Eqs. (18-1) in matrix form as

$$\mathbf{y} = A\mathbf{x}, \qquad (18\text{-}11)$$

substitute for $\mathbf{x}$ from (18-8) and for $\mathbf{y}$ from (18-10), and obtain

$$B'\boldsymbol{\eta} = AB'\boldsymbol{\xi}. \qquad (18\text{-}12)$$

To solve for $\boldsymbol{\eta}$ we multiply on the left by $(B')^{-1}$ and get

$$\boldsymbol{\eta} = (B')^{-1}AB'\boldsymbol{\xi}. \qquad (18\text{-}13)$$

Thus the relationship between the components $(\xi_1, \xi_2, \ldots, \xi_n)$ and $(\eta_1, \eta_2, \ldots, \eta_n)$ is determined by the matrix

$$S \equiv (B')^{-1}AB'. \qquad (18\text{-}14)$$

Since the matrix S characterizes the same deformation of space as the matrix A, the matrices A and S related in the manner of (18-14) are termed *similar*. To avoid carrying primes, we set $B' = C$, and formula (18-14) then assumes the form

$$S = C^{-1}AC, \qquad (18\text{-}15)$$

and (18-13) becomes

$$\boldsymbol{\eta} = S\boldsymbol{\xi}. \qquad (18\text{-}16)$$

One of the important problems in the theory of linear transformations is to determine a reference frame in which the equations for the deformation of space assume forms which admit of simple interpretations. For example, if it proves possible to find a matrix C such that the matrix S in (18-15) has the diagonal form

$$S = \begin{pmatrix} \lambda_1 & 0 & \cdots & 0 \\ 0 & \lambda_2 & \cdots & 0 \\ \cdot & \cdot & \cdot & \cdot \\ 0 & \cdot & \cdots & \lambda_n \end{pmatrix}, \qquad (18\text{-}17)$$

then Eq. (18-16) shows that

$$\eta_1 = \lambda_1 \xi_1,$$
$$\eta_2 = \lambda_2 \xi_2,$$
$$\vdots$$
$$\eta_n = \lambda_n \xi_n.$$

In three-dimensional space these correspond to simple elongations (or contractions) of the components of the vector in the directions of base vectors $\boldsymbol{\alpha}_i$ determined by the matrix $C = B'$ [see (18-3)].

Whether or not a matrix C reducing A to the diagonal form S can be found clearly depends on the nature of deformation specified by A. In many problems in dynamics and in the theory of elasticity, the deformation matrix A will turn out to be symmetric, and we shall see in Sec. 20 that such matrices can always be diagonalized by finding a suitable matrix C. This fact turns out to be of cardinal importance because it enormously simplifies the analysis of many problems.

In the following section we shall study properties of the matrix A in (18-1) for those transformations that leave the length of every vector $\mathbf{x}$ unchanged. In three dimensions such transformations represent rotations and reflections.

19. Orthogonal Transformations. Let us refer our n-dimensional space to a set of orthonormal base vectors $\mathbf{e}_1$, $\mathbf{e}_2$, ..., $\mathbf{e}_n$, introduced in Sec. 13. Relative to this basis the vector $\mathbf{x}$ has the representation

$$\mathbf{x} = \mathbf{e}_i x_i$$

and its length $|\mathbf{x}|$ can be computed from the formula

$$|\mathbf{x}|^2 = x_i x_i. \tag{19-1}$$

Let us investigate the structure of the matrix A in the class of transformations

$$y_i = a_{ij} x_j \tag{19-2}$$

which leave the length $|\mathbf{x}|$ of the vector unchanged. Now, the square of the length of the vector $\mathbf{y}$ is

$$|\mathbf{y}|^2 = y_i y_i, \tag{19-3}$$

and since we suppose that $|\mathbf{x}| = |\mathbf{y}|$,

$$y_i y_i = x_i x_i. \tag{19-4}$$

We insert in (19-4) from (19-2) and get

$$(a_{ij} x_j)(a_{ik} x_k) = x_i x_i$$

or
$$a_{ij} a_{ik} x_j x_k = \delta_{jk} x_j x_k, \tag{19-5}$$

since
$$\delta_{jk} x_j x_k = x_{kk} = x_i x_i.$$

On equating the coefficients of $x_j x_k$ in (19-5), we get the set of restrictive conditions

$$a_{ij} a_{ik} = \delta_{jk} \tag{19-6}$$

on the coefficients a_{ij} if the transformation (19-2) is to leave the length of every vector unchanged.

Equations (19-6), when written out for $n = 3$, are

$$a_{11}^2 + a_{21}^2 + a_{31}^2 = 1,$$
$$a_{12}^2 + a_{22}^2 + a_{32}^2 = 1,$$
$$a_{13}^2 + a_{23}^2 + a_{33}^2 = 1,$$
$$a_{12}a_{13} + a_{22}a_{23} + a_{32}a_{33} = 0,$$
$$a_{13}a_{11} + a_{23}a_{21} + a_{33}a_{31} = 0,$$
$$a_{11}a_{12} + a_{21}a_{22} + a_{31}a_{32} = 0.$$

The determinant of the matrix in (19-6) is

$$|a_{ij}a_{ik}| = |\delta_{jk}| = 1, \tag{19-7}$$

and if we recall the rule for multiplication of determinants [cf. (15-2)], we conclude from (19-7) that

$$|a_{ij}a_{ik}| = |a_{ij}| \cdot |a_{ij}| = a^2 = 1, \tag{19-8}$$

where a is the determinant of (a_{ij}). Equation (19-8) states that

$$a = \pm 1.$$

In three dimensions the situation when $a = 1$ corresponds to a rotation of space relative to a set of fixed xyz axes determined by the unit vectors **i, j, k**. The circumstance when $a = -1$ corresponds to a transformation of reflection (say, $x = -x, y = -y, z = -z$) or to a reflection followed by a rotation.

A transformation (19-2) in which the coefficients a_{ij} satisfy (19-6) is called an *orthogonal transformation;* it is called the *transformation of rotation* if $|a_{ij}| = 1$, whatever be the dimensionality of space.

If we denote by A' the transpose of $(a_{ij}) = A$ in (19-2), we can write the *orthogonality condition* (19-6) in matrix form as

$$A'A = I. \tag{19-9}$$

On multiplying this by A^{-1} on the right we get

$$A' = A^{-1}. \tag{19-10}$$

Thus, *in an orthogonal transformation the inverse matrix A^{-1} is equal to the transpose A' of A.*

When Eqs. (19-2) are written in the form

$$\mathbf{y} = A\mathbf{x},$$

we can write their solutions for the x_i as

$$\mathbf{x} = A^{-1}\mathbf{y}. \tag{19-11}$$

We conclude from (19-10) that the solutions of Eqs. (19-2), when the transformation is orthogonal, are

$$x_i = a_{ji}y_j. \tag{19-12}$$

In Sec. 17, we saw that the matrix of the product of two linear transformations is the product of the matrices of the component transformations. Using this fact and the property (19-10) it is easy to show that the *product of two orthogonal transformations is an orthogonal transformation.*

PROBLEMS

1. Verify that the transformations

(a)
$$y_1 = x_1 \cos \alpha - x_2 \sin \alpha,$$
$$y_2 = x_1 \sin \alpha + x_2 \cos \alpha,$$

and

(b)
$$y_1 = \frac{1}{\sqrt{2}} x_1 + \frac{1}{\sqrt{2}} x_3,$$

$$y_2 = x_2,$$

$$y_3 = -\frac{1}{\sqrt{2}} x_1 + \frac{1}{\sqrt{2}} x_3,$$

are orthogonal.   Do they represent rotations?

2. Discuss the transformation

$$y_1 = \frac{1}{\sqrt{2}} x_1 - \frac{1}{\sqrt{2}} x_2,$$

$$y_2 = \frac{1}{3\sqrt{2}} x_1 + \frac{1}{3\sqrt{2}} x_2 + \frac{4}{3\sqrt{2}} x_3$$

$$y_3 = \frac{2}{3} x_1 + \frac{2}{3} x_2 - \frac{1}{3} x_3.$$

Find the inverse transformation.

3. Prove that the product of any number of orthogonal transformations is an orthogonal transformation.

4. If A is a symmetric matrix (so that $A' = A$) and S is an orthogonal transformation, prove that the matrix $B = S^{-1}AS$ is symmetric.   Thus, orthogonal transformations do not destroy the symmetry of A.

5. Let

$$A = \begin{pmatrix} 1 & 1 & 0 \\ 1 & 2 & -1 \\ 0 & -1 & 3 \end{pmatrix}$$

and let C be an orthogonal matrix

$$C = \begin{pmatrix} c_{11} & c_{12} & c_{13} \\ c_{21} & c_{22} & c_{23} \\ c_{31} & c_{32} & c_{33} \end{pmatrix}.$$

Write out the set of equations which the c_{ij} must satisfy if $C^{-1}AC = S$, where S is a diagonal matrix.

6. Is the transformation

$$y_1 = 3x_1 - x_2,$$

$$y_2 = -2x_1 + x_2,$$

orthogonal?   Find the inverse transformation.   Determine the components of $\mathbf{x}$: (x_1, x_2) and $\mathbf{y}$: (y_1, y_2) when the base vectors $\mathbf{e}_1$, $\mathbf{e}_2$ are rotated through 45 and 90°.

7. If $y_i = a_{ij}x_j$ is a linear transformation for the components of a complex vector $\mathbf{x}: (x_1, x_2, \ldots, x_n)$, which preserves the length $|\mathbf{x}|$ of the vector, show that $\bar{a}_{ij}a_{ik} = \delta_{jk}$ or $\bar{A}'A = I$, where $\bar{A}$ is the *conjugate matrix* formed by replacing every element a_{ij} of A by $\bar{a}_{ij}$. Transformations such that $\bar{A}' = A^{-1}$ are called *unitary;* they are of great importance in quantum mechanics.

20. The Diagonalization of Matrices. We saw in Sec. 18 that the determination of a nonsingular matrix C such that the given matrix A reduces to the diagonal form S by a similitude transformation $C^{-1}AC$ is equivalent to determining a set of base vectors relative to which the transformation

$$y_i = a_{ij}x_j \tag{20-1}$$

assumes the form

$$\eta_1 = \lambda_1\xi_1, \qquad \eta_2 = \lambda_2\xi_2, \qquad \ldots, \qquad \eta_n = \lambda_n\xi_n. \tag{20-2}$$

We thus seek a solution of the matric equation

$$C^{-1}AC = S \tag{20-3}$$

in which $A = (a_{ij})$ is a given matrix, C the unknown matrix

$$C = \begin{pmatrix} c_{11} & c_{12} & \cdots & c_{1k} & \cdots & c_{1n} \\ c_{21} & c_{22} & \cdots & c_{2k} & \cdots & c_{2n} \\ \cdot & \cdot & \cdot & \cdot & \cdot & \cdot \\ c_{n1} & c_{n2} & \cdots & c_{nk} & \cdots & c_{nn} \end{pmatrix}, \tag{20-4}$$

and S is the diagonal matrix,

$$S = \begin{pmatrix} \lambda_1 & 0 & \cdots & 0 \\ 0 & \lambda_2 & \cdots & 0 \\ \cdot & \cdot & \cdots & \cdot \\ 0 & 0 & \cdots & \lambda_n \end{pmatrix}. \tag{20-5}$$

On multiplying (20-3) on the left by C we get an equivalent matric equation

$$AC = CS, \tag{20-6}$$

provided that the solution of (20-6) yields a nonsingular matrix C.

Now the matric equation (20-6) is equivalent to a system of linear equations

$$a_{ij}c_{jk} = c_{ik}\lambda_k, \qquad \text{no sum on } k, \; k = 1, \ldots, n \tag{20-7}$$

obtained by equating the corresponding elements in the products AC and CS.

For every fixed value of k, the system (20-7) represents a set of n linear *homogeneous* equations for the unknowns $(c_{1k}, c_{2k}, \ldots, c_{nk})$ appearing in the

kth column of (20-4). The fact that the system (20-7) is homogeneous can be made plainer by rewriting it in the form

$$(a_{ij} - \delta_{ij}\lambda_k)c_{jk} = 0, \qquad \text{no sum on } k. \tag{20-8}$$

We recall [1] that a system of homogeneous equations has solutions other than the obvious solution $c_{1k} = c_{2k} = \cdots = c_{nk} = 0$ if, and only if, its determinant [2]

$$|a_{ij} - \lambda\delta_{ij}| = 0. \tag{20-9}$$

On writing out this determinant in full,

$$\begin{vmatrix} a_{11} - \lambda & a_{12} & \cdots & a_{1n} \\ a_{21} & a_{22} - \lambda & \cdots & a_{2n} \\ \cdots\cdots\cdots\cdots\cdots\cdots\cdots \\ a_{n1} & a_{n2} & \cdots & a_{nn} - \lambda \end{vmatrix} = 0, \tag{20-10}$$

we see that (20-10) is an algebraic equation of degree n in λ. Accordingly, there are n roots of this equation, say $\lambda = \lambda_1$, $\lambda = \lambda_2$, ..., $\lambda = \lambda_n$, and corresponding to each root $\lambda = \lambda_k$ ($k = 1, \ldots, n$), the system (20-8) will have a solution

$$(c_{ik}, c_{2k}, \ldots, c_{nk}). \tag{20-11}$$

The solution (20-11) yields the kth column of the matrix C. If the roots $\lambda_1, \lambda_2, \ldots, \lambda_n$ are all distinct, one can prove that the matrix C will be non-singular. [3] When the roots λ_k are not distinct, it is impossible, in general, to reduce A by the similitude transformation (20-3) to the diagonal form, because the desired nonsingular matrix C may not exist. In important special cases, however (for example, when A is a real and symmetric matrix), one can construct C such that S has the diagonal form even when some, or even all, roots are equal.

A brief discussion of this is contained in the following section.

As a matter of terminology, Eq. (20-9) is called the *characteristic equation* and its solutions are *characteristic values* of the matrix (a_{ij}). The solutions (20-11) of the system (20-8) corresponding to these characteristic values are called *characteristic vectors*. [4]

---

[1] Appendix A, Sec. 2.

[2] Note that this determinantal equation when written in matrix form is $|A - \lambda I| = 0$.

[3] Or in the language of vectors, if we regard each column of C as a vector $\mathbf{c}^{(k)}$: $(c_{1k}, c_{2k}, \ldots, c_{nk})$, the vectors $\mathbf{c}^{(k)}(k = 1, 2, \ldots, n)$ will be linearly independent. A simple proof of this is given in I. S. Sokolnikoff, "Tensor Analysis," pp. 33–34, John Wiley & Sons, Inc., New York, 1951.

[4] The hybrid terms *eigenvalues* for the λ_k and *eigenvectors* for the $\mathbf{c}^{(k)}$: $(c_{1k}, c_{2k}, \ldots, c_{nk})$ are used by some writers who do not mind mixing German with English.

Example 1.   Reduce the matrix

$$A = (a_{ij}) = \begin{pmatrix} 1 & -1 \\ -1 & 1 \end{pmatrix} \tag{20-12}$$

to the diagonal form S by the similitude transformation $C^{-1}AC$.
  The characteristic equation (20-9) here is

$$\begin{vmatrix} 1-\lambda & -1 \\ -1 & 1-\lambda \end{vmatrix} = (1-\lambda)^2 - 1 = 0.$$

Its solutions are $\lambda_1 = 0$, $\lambda_2 = 2$.   The desired matrix C in our case has the form

$$C = \begin{pmatrix} c_{11} & c_{12} \\ c_{21} & c_{22} \end{pmatrix}, \tag{20-13}$$

the columns in which satisfy the system of equations (20-8), yielding

$$(a_{11} - \lambda_k)c_{1k} + a_{12}c_{2k} = 0, \qquad \text{no sum on } k,$$
$$a_{21}c_{1k} + (a_{22} - \lambda_k)c_{2k} = 0, \qquad k = 1, 2. \tag{20-14}$$

Since $a_{11} = 1$, $a_{12} = -1$, $a_{21} = -1$, $a_{22} = 1$, we get, on setting $k = 1$ and $\lambda_1 = 0$,

$$c_{11} - c_{21} = 0,$$
$$-c_{11} + c_{21} = 0. \tag{20-15}$$

As is always the case with nontrivial homogeneous systems of equations,[1] there are infinitely many solutions of the system (20-15).   If we set $c_{11} = a$ (any constant), Eqs. (20-15) give $c_{21} = a$.
  Thus the vector $\mathbf{c}^{(1)}$: (c_{11}, c_{21}) appearing in the first column of (20-13) has the components $c_{11} = c_{21} = a$.   Since any matrix C accomplishing the reduction will do, we can take[2] $a = 1$.
  The substitution of $k = 2$ and $\lambda_2 = 2$ in (20-14) yields the system

$$(1 - 2)c_{12} - c_{22} = 0,$$
$$-c_{12} + (1 - 2)c_{22} = 0,$$

or $$-c_{12} - c_{22} = 0.$$

Again there are infinitely many solutions, and if we take $c_{12} = a$, then $c_{22} = -a$.   We can set $a = 1$ if we wish, so that the elements of the second column in (20-13) are $c_{12} = 1$, $c_{22} = -1$.   The desired matrix C, therefore, is

$$C = \begin{pmatrix} 1 & 1 \\ 1 & -1 \end{pmatrix}.$$

The inverse of C is easily found to be

$$C^{-1} = \begin{pmatrix} \tfrac{1}{2} & \tfrac{1}{2} \\ \tfrac{1}{2} & -\tfrac{1}{2} \end{pmatrix},$$

so that $C^{-1}AC$ is

$$\begin{pmatrix} \tfrac{1}{2} & \tfrac{1}{2} \\ \tfrac{1}{2} & -\tfrac{1}{2} \end{pmatrix} \cdot \begin{pmatrix} 1 & -1 \\ -1 & 1 \end{pmatrix} \cdot \begin{pmatrix} 1 & 1 \\ 1 & -1 \end{pmatrix}.$$

---

[1] See Appendix A, Sec. 2.
[2] Usually one normalizes solutions so that the length of the column vector $\mathbf{c}^{(k)}$ is 1. This would correspond to the choice of $a = 1/\sqrt{2}$, since $c_{11}^2 + c_{12}^2 = 1$.

On multiplying these matrices we get

$$S = \begin{pmatrix} 0 & 0 \\ 0 & 2 \end{pmatrix}, \tag{20-16}$$

as we should, since

$$S = \begin{pmatrix} \lambda_1 & 0 \\ 0 & \lambda_2 \end{pmatrix}$$

as we knew from the start [see (20-5)].

If we interpret A as a matrix operator characterizing the deformation of a vector $\mathbf{x}$ into a vector $\mathbf{y}$ [see (18-11)], the result (20-16) states that in a suitable reference frame the components of $\mathbf{x}$ and $\mathbf{y}$ are related by

$$\eta_1 = 0 \cdot \xi_1, \qquad \eta_2 = 2\xi_2.$$

We thus have a deformation of space corresponding to the twofold elongation in the direction of one of the base vectors. In the notation of Sec. 18, $C = B'$, so that one can actually write out Eqs. (18-3) for the transformation of the base vectors. This, however, is seldom required because the essential matter is to determine the deformation characterized by A rather than a reference frame giving a simple form of the deformation.

Example 2.   Determine the characteristic values of the matrix

$$(a_{ij}) = \begin{pmatrix} 1 & -1 & -1 \\ -1 & 1 & -1 \\ -1 & -1 & 1 \end{pmatrix}. \tag{20-17}$$

The characteristic equation this time is

$$\begin{vmatrix} 1-\lambda & -1 & -1 \\ -1 & 1-\lambda & -1 \\ -1 & -1 & 1-\lambda \end{vmatrix} = (1-\lambda)^3 - 3(1-\lambda) - 2 = 0.$$

We easily check that the solutions of this cubic are $\lambda_1 = 2$, $\lambda_2 = 2$, $\lambda_3 = -1$. Since we have a double root $\lambda_1 = \lambda_2 = 2$, the solution of the system (20-8) will enable us to determine only two linearly independent columns of the matrix C. The matrix (20-17), however, is *real* and *symmetric*, and one can, in fact, construct the third column of the matrix C such that

$$C^{-1}AC = S,$$

where
$$S = \begin{pmatrix} \lambda_1 & 0 & 0 \\ 0 & \lambda_2 & 0 \\ 0 & 0 & \lambda_3 \end{pmatrix} = \begin{pmatrix} 2 & 0 & 0 \\ 0 & 2 & 0 \\ 0 & 0 & -1 \end{pmatrix}.$$

However, the theory presented in this section does not explain how this can be accomplished.

PROBLEMS

1. Diagonalize the matrix

$$A = \begin{pmatrix} 2 & 3 \\ -1 & -2 \end{pmatrix}$$

and determine, in the manner of Example 1, the matrix C. Discuss the meaning of A when viewed as an operator characterizing a deformation of space.

2. Find the roots of the characteristic equation for the matrix

$$A = \begin{pmatrix} 3 & 1 \\ -2 & 2 \end{pmatrix}.$$

3. Find a matrix C reducing

$$A = \begin{pmatrix} -1 & 1 & 2 \\ 0 & -2 & 1 \\ 0 & 0 & -3 \end{pmatrix}$$

to the diagonal form by the transformation $C^{-1}AC$.

4. Diagonalize the matrix

$$\begin{pmatrix} 2 & 4 & -6 \\ 4 & 2 & -6 \\ -6 & -6 & -15 \end{pmatrix}.$$

5. Prove that the roots of characteristic equations of all similar matrices are equal. *Hint:* Write the characteristic equation of $C^{-1}AC$ [cf. (20-9)] in the form $|C^{-1}AC - \lambda I| = 0$. But $|C^{-1}AC - \lambda I| = |C^{-1}(A - \lambda I)C| = |A - \lambda I|$, since $|C^{-1}| = 1/|C|$.

21. Real Symmetric Matrices and Quadratic Forms.

Let the matrix $A = (a_{ij})$ in a linear transformation

$$y_i = a_{ij}x_j, \qquad i, j = 1, \ldots, n, \tag{21-1}$$

be real and symmetric, so that $A' = A$ (or $a_{ij} = a_{ji}$). We shall indicate that in this case the matrix A can always be reduced by the transformation $C^{-1}AC$ to the diagonal form S. Moreover, C can be chosen as an orthogonal matrix; that is, a matrix such that $C^{-1} = C'$ [cf. Eq. (19-10)].

Linear transformations with real symmetric matrices dominate the study of deformations of elastic media. Real symmetric matrices also occur in the study of quadratic forms

$$Q(x_1, x_2, \ldots, x_n) \equiv a_{ij}x_ix_j, \qquad i, j = 1, 2, \ldots, n, \tag{21-2}$$

which arise in many problems concerned with vibrations of dynamical systems.

We can always suppose that the coefficients in a quadratic form (21-2) are symmetric because every quadratic form Q can be symmetrized by writing it as

$$Q = \tfrac{1}{2}(a_{ij} + a_{ji})x_ix_j$$
$$= b_{ij}x_ix_j,$$

in which the coefficients

$$b_{ij} = \tfrac{1}{2}(a_{ij} + a_{ji})$$

are obviously symmetric. Henceforth we shall suppose that our quadratic forms have been symmetrized so that $a_{ij} = a_{ji}$.

It will follow from discussion in this section that the problems of reduction of the transformation (21-1) *with symmetric coefficients* to the form

$$\eta_1 = \lambda_1\xi_1, \qquad \eta_2 = \lambda_2\xi_2, \qquad \ldots, \qquad \eta_n = \lambda_n\xi_n \tag{21-3}$$

and of the quadratic form (21-2) to the form

$$Q = \lambda_1 \xi_1^2 + \lambda_2 \xi_2^2 + \cdots + \lambda_n \xi_n^2 \tag{21-4}$$

are mathematically identical.

We first note several properties of quadratic forms. If the variables x_i in (21-2) are subjected to a linear transformation

$$x_i = c_{ij} \xi_j, \tag{21-5}$$

the form (21-2) becomes

$$Q = a_{ij}(c_{ik}\xi_k)(c_{jr}\xi_r)$$

$$= a_{ij} c_{ik} c_{jr} \xi_k \xi_r.$$

We denote the coefficients of $\xi_k \xi_r$ by b_{kr}, so that

$$Q = b_{kr} \xi_k \xi_r, \tag{21-6}$$

where

$$b_{kr} = a_{ij} c_{ik} c_{jr}. \tag{21-7}$$

Since i and j are the summation indices and $a_{ij} = a_{ji}$, we see that the value of b_{kr} is not changed by an interchange of k and r. Thus, we conclude that the symmetry of the coefficients in a quadratic form (21-2) is not destroyed when the variables x_i are changed by a linear transformation (21-5).

If we write (21-7) in the form

$$b_{kr} = c_{ik}(a_{ij} c_{jr}),$$

we see that the sum $a_{ij} c_{jr}$ is an element in the ith row and the rth column of the matrix

$$AC \equiv D,$$

or

$$(a_{ij} c_{jr}) \equiv (d_{ir}).$$

The product $c_{ik}(a_{ij} c_{jr}) = c_{ik} d_{ir}$ is the element in the kth row and the rth column of the matrix $C'D$. Thus we can write (21-7) as

$$B = C'AC. \tag{21-8}$$

The result (21-8) can be stated as a theorem.

THEOREM. *When the variables x_i in a quadratic form (21-2) with a matrix A are subjected to a linear transformation (21-5) with a matrix C, the resulting quadratic form has the matrix $C'AC$.*

If the linear transformation (21-5) is orthogonal, then $C' = C^{-1}$, and hence (21-8) can be written as

$$B = C^{-1}AC. \tag{21-9}$$

We conclude from (21-9) that the *reduction of a symmetric matrix to the diagonal form by an orthogonal transformation calls for a solution of the matric equation*

$$S = C^{-1}AC. \tag{21-10}$$

This equation is identical with that considered in the preceding section. When the roots of the characteristic equation

$$|a_{ij} - \lambda\delta_{ij}| = 0 \tag{21-11}$$

are distinct and real, the method of Sec. 20 enables us to compute a matrix C which can be shown to be orthogonal. As a matter of fact, the desired matrix C can always be found whenever the matrix A is real and symmetric. Moreover, it can be shown that the roots of symmetric real matrices are invariably real.[1]

The fact that the columns of C are linearly independent can be established easily when A is symmetric and the λ_k are all unequal. Let $\mathbf{c}$ be a characteristic vector for λ and let $\mathbf{c}'$ be a characteristic vector for a different value, λ'. Then, from (20-7),

$$a_{ij}c_j = \lambda c_i \quad \text{and} \quad a_{ij}c'_j = \lambda'c'_i.$$

Multiplying these equations by c'_i and c_i, respectively, gives

$$a_{ij}c'_ic_j = \lambda c'_ic_i \quad \text{and} \quad a_{ij}c'_jc_i = \lambda'c_ic'_i$$

after summing on i. Since $a_{ij} = a_{ji}$, the left sides of these equations are equal. Hence by subtraction,

$$0 = \lambda c'_ic_i - \lambda'c_ic'_i = (\lambda - \lambda')c_ic'_i.$$

Since $\lambda \neq \lambda'$ we get $\mathbf{c}\cdot\mathbf{c}' = c_ic'_i = 0$, so that the vectors $\mathbf{c}$ and $\mathbf{c}'$ are orthogonal and thus linearly independent.

If the roots λ_i are all positive, Eq. (21-4) shows that the quadratic form (21-2) assumes positive values for all nonzero values of the variables x_i. Such quadratic forms are called *positive definite*. They appear in numerous investigations in mathematical physics.

An analogue of a symmetric quadratic form (21-2) in which the variables x_i are complex is a *bilinear form* [2]

$$H = a_{ij}\bar{x}_ix_j \tag{21-12}$$

in which $a_{ij} = \bar{a}_{ji}$. Such forms are called *Hermitian,* and their matrices $(a_{ij}) = A$ are *Hermitian matrices.* Since $a_{ij} = \bar{a}_{ji}$, it follows that the elements on the main diagonal of A are necessarily real and that

$$A' = \bar{A}.$$

From the structure of (21-12) it follows that the Hermitian forms assume only real values for arbitrary complex values x_i, for on taking the conjugate of (21-12), we get

$$\bar{H} = \bar{a}_{ij}x_i\bar{x}_j = a_{ji}\bar{x}_jx_i = H,$$

which proves that H is real.

[1] For proofs utilizing the notation of this section, see I. S. Sokolnikoff, "Tensor Analysis," pp. 37–40, John Wiley & Sons, Inc., New York, 1951.
[2] Cf. Prob. 7, Sec. 19.

Hermitian forms occur in quantum mechanics, and a discussion of the reduction of a quadratic form to a sum of squares (21-4) can be generalized to show that (21-12) can be reduced to the form

$$H = \lambda_1 \bar{\xi}_1 \xi_1 + \lambda_2 \bar{\xi}_2 \xi_2 + \cdots + \lambda_n \bar{\xi}_n \xi_n$$

by a linear transformation (21-5) with a *unitary* matrix C defined in Prob. **7** of Sec. 19.

22. Solution of Systems of Linear Equations. In Sec. 15 we derived Cramer's rule for solving the system of equations

$$a_{ij}x_j = b_i. \tag{22-1}$$

When the number of equations in (22-1) is large, Cramer's rule is inefficient, since it requires evaluating determinants of high orders. For this reason all practical methods of solving the system (22-1) depend on reducing it by some process to an equivalent system whose matrix is sufficiently simple to enable one to compute the unknowns without great effort.

The system (22-1) can be written in matrix notation as

$$A\mathbf{x} = \mathbf{b}, \tag{22-2}$$

where $A = (a_{ij})$, $\mathbf{x}$ is the column matrix $(x_1, x_2, \ldots, x_n)$, and $\mathbf{b}$ is the column matrix $(b_1, b_2, \ldots, b_n)$. If A is nonsingular, the solution of (22-2) is

$$\mathbf{x} = A^{-1}\mathbf{b} \tag{22-3}$$

so that the determination of unknowns hinges on constructing the inverse matrix A^{-1}. The development of effective methods for inverting matrices is a major problem of numerical analysis. One of such methods depends on a reduction of the system (22-2) to an equivalent system

$$B\mathbf{x} = \mathbf{c}, \tag{22-4}$$

in which B has the triangular form

$$\begin{pmatrix} 1 & b_{12} & b_{13} & \cdots & b_{1n} \\ 0 & 1 & b_{23} & \cdots & b_{2n} \\ \cdot & \cdot & \cdot & \cdot & \cdot \\ 0 & 0 & 0 & \cdots & 1 \end{pmatrix}$$

in which the elements below the main diagonal are all zero. When the system (22-4) is written out in full, it has the appearance of Eqs. (4-2) in Chap. 9, whose solutions, as shown in Sec. 4, Chap. 9, can be obtained quite readily.[1]

Among other methods for solving the system (22-2) is the method of orthogonalization, the essence of which is as follows. Let us seek a matrix C such that the product

$$CA = D \tag{22-5}$$

---

[1] This is the so-called Gauss reduction method discussed in Chap. 9.

is an orthogonal matrix. Since D is required to be orthogonal, it follows from (19-9) that

$$DD' = D'D = I, \tag{22-6}$$

where D' is the transpose of D.

On multiplying (22-2) on the left by $A'C'C$, we get

$$A'C'CA\mathbf{x} = A'C'C\mathbf{b}, \tag{22-7}$$

and since

$$A'C' = (CA)' = D'$$

by virtue of (17-11) and (22-5), we can write (22-7) as

$$D'D\mathbf{x} = D'C\mathbf{b}.$$

However, by (22-6) $D'D = I$, so that we finally have

$$\mathbf{x} = D'C\mathbf{b}. \tag{22-8}$$

Formula (22-8) gives the solution of the system (22-1) once a matrix C is determined. We do not present the classical procedure for constructing C (known as the Gram-Schmidt method) because of the rather special character of the problem.

CHAPTER 5

VECTOR FIELD THEORY

Coordinates and Functions

Transformation Theorems

Illustrations and Applications

This chapter is concerned with a study of scalar and vector functions defined in the familiar three-dimensional space. It includes a discussion of curvilinear coordinate systems and a derivation of several transformation theorems involving line, surface, and volume integrals. These theorems, usually associated with the names of Gauss, Green, and Stokes, are indispensable in the study of mechanics of fluids, thermodynamics, and electrodynamics and in virtually every branch of mechanics of deformable media.

COORDINATES AND FUNCTIONS

1. Curvilinear Coordinates. The chief advantage of formulating relations among geometrical and physical quantities in the form of vector equations is that the relations so stated are valid in all coordinate systems. Only when one comes to consider a special problem involving numerical computations does it prove desirable to translate vector equations into the language of special coordinate systems that seem best adapted to the problem at hand. For example, in analyzing vibrations of clamped rectangular membranes, it is usually advantageous to express the displacement vector in cartesian coordinates. In the study of heat flow in a sphere, the geometry of the situation suggests the use of spherical coordinates, while problems concerned with the flow of currents in cylindrical conductors may indicate the use of cylindrical or bipolar coordinates. All these coordinate systems are but special cases of the general curvilinear coordinate system which we proceed to describe.

Let us refer a given region R of space to a set of orthogonal cartesian axes y_1, y_2, y_3. We denote the coordinates of any point P in R by (y_1, y_2, y_3) (Fig. 1) instead of the familiar labels (x, y, z). A set of functional relations

$$x_1 = x_1(y_1, y_2, y_3),$$

$$x_2 = x_2(y_1, y_2, y_3), \tag{1-1}$$

$$x_3 = x_3(y_1, y_2, y_3),$$

357

$$\vec{a} = a_1 \, \hat{\imath} + a_2 \hat{\jmath} + a_3 \, \hat{k}$$

connecting the variables y_1, y_2, y_3 with three new variables x_1, x_2, x_3 is said to represent a _transformation of coordinates_. We shall suppose that the functions $x_i(y_1,y_2,y_3)$ $(i = 1, 2, 3)$ are single-valued and are continuously differentiable at all points of the region R and that Eqs. (1-1) can be solved for the y_i to yield the _inverse transformation_

$$x_1 = x_1(y_1, y_2, y_3)$$
$$x_2 = x_2(y_1, y_1, y_3)$$
$$x_3 = x_3(y_1, y_2, y_3)$$

$$y_1 = y_1(x_1,x_2,x_3),$$
$$y_2 = y_2(x_1,x_2,x_3), \qquad (1\text{-}2)$$
$$y_3 = y_3(x_1,x_2,x_3),$$

in which the functions $y_i(x_1,x_2,x_3)$ are single-valued and continuously differentiable with respect to the variables x_i. The transformations (1-1)

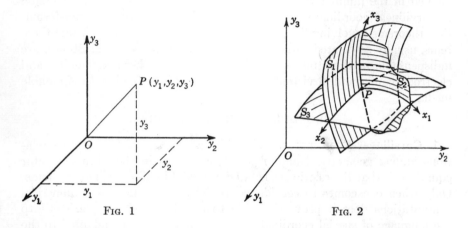

FIG. 1   FIG. 2

and (1-2) with these properties establish a one-to-one correspondence between the triplets of values (y_1,y_2,y_3) and (x_1,x_2,x_3). We shall term the triplet of values (x_1,x_2,x_3), corresponding to a given point $P(y_1,y_2,y_3)$, the _curvilinear coordinates_ of P, and shall say that Eqs. (1-1) define a _curvilinear coordinate system_ x_1,x_2,x_3. The reason for this terminology is the following: If we set in (1-1) $x_1 = c_1$ (a constant), the equation

$$x_1(y_1,y_2,y_3) = c_1 \qquad (1\text{-}3)$$

represents a certain surface S_1. Similarly, equations

$$x_2(y_1,y_2,y_3) = c_2, \qquad (1\text{-}4)$$

and

$$x_3(y_1,y_2,y_3) = c_3, \qquad (1\text{-}5)$$

represent surfaces S_2 and S_3. These surfaces, shown in Fig. 2, intersect at the point P whose cartesian coordinates (y_1,y_2,y_3) can be obtained by solving Eqs. (1-3) to (1-5) for the y_i.

The surfaces S_i are called *coordinate surfaces*, and their intersections pair by pair are *coordinate lines* x_1, x_2, x_3. Thus, the x_1 coordinate line is the line of intersection of the surfaces $x_2 = c_2$ and $x_3 = c_3$. Along this line the only variable that changes is x_1, since $x_2 = c_2$ and $x_3 = c_3$ along the line x_1. Similarly, along the x_2 coordinate line the only variable that changes is x_2, while along the x_3 line the only variable that changes is x_3.

A very special case of the set of Eqs. (1-1) is

$$x_1 = y_1,$$
$$x_2 = y_2, \qquad (1\text{-}6)$$
$$x_3 = y_3.$$

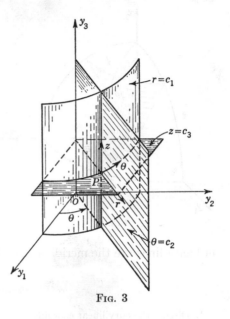

If we set $x_i = c_i$ $(i = 1, 2, 3)$ in (1-6), we get three planes $y_i = c_i$ perpendicular to the y coordinate axes. These planes intersect at the point (c_1, c_2, c_3). The coordinate surfaces in this case are planes, and their intersections pair by pair are straight lines parallel to the coordinate axes.

As a more interesting example consider a transformation

$$y_1 = r \cos \theta,$$
$$y_2 = r \sin \theta, \qquad (1\text{-}7)$$
$$y_3 = z,$$

FIG. 3

which is of the form (1-2) if we set $x_1 = r$, $x_2 = \theta$, $x_3 = z$. The inverse of (1-7) is

$$r = + \sqrt{y_1^2 + y_2^2},$$

$$\theta = \tan^{-1} \frac{y_2}{y_1}, \qquad (1\text{-}8)$$

$$z = y_3,$$

and it is single-valued if we take $0 \leq \theta < 2\pi$ and $r > 0$. The surface $r = c_1$ is a circular cylinder $y_1^2 + y_2^2 = c_1^2$ whose axis coincides with the y_3 axis (Fig. 3). The surface $\theta = c_2$ is the plane $y_2 = (\tan c_2) y_1$ containing the y_3 axis, while the surface $z = c_3$ is the plane $y_3 = c_3$ perpendicular to the y_3 axis. The r, θ, and z coordinate lines are shown in Fig. 3, and we recognize that the curvilinear coordinate system r, θ, z is the familiar system of cylindrical coordinates.

As a final example, consider the transformation

$$y_1 = \rho \sin \theta \cos \phi,$$

$$y_2 = \rho \sin \theta \sin \phi, \qquad (1\text{-}9)$$

$$y_3 = \rho \cos \theta,$$

with the inverse

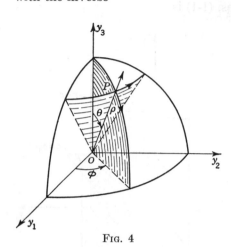

FIG. 4

$$\rho = \sqrt{y_1^2 + y_2^2 + y_3^2},$$

$$\theta = \tan^{-1} \frac{\sqrt{y_1^2 + y_2^2}}{y_3}, \qquad (1\text{-}10)$$

$$\phi = \tan^{-1} \frac{y_2}{y_1},$$

which is single-valued if we suppose that $\rho > 0,\ 0 < \theta < \pi,\ 0 \le \phi < 2\pi$.

The transformation defines a spherical system of coordinates. The coordinate surfaces $\rho = \text{const}$, $\theta = \text{const}$, and $\phi = \text{const}$ are, respectively, spheres, cones, and planes, shown in Fig. 4. The coordinate lines are the meridians, the lines of parallels, and the radial lines.

PROBLEMS

1. Discuss the curvilinear coordinates determined by

$$y_1 = x_1 + x_2 + x_3,$$

$$y_2 = x_1 - x_2 + x_3,$$

$$y_3 = 2x_1 + x_2 - x_3.$$

2. Show by geometry that the coordinate lines in cylindrical and spherical coordinate systems intersect at right angles.

2. Metric Coefficients. In this section we introduce an abridged notation which will enable us to write many formulas compactly and without loss of clarity. Thus, we shall write the set of three equations of transformation (1-1) in the form

$$x_i = x_i(y_1, y_2, y_3), \qquad i = 1, 2, 3, \qquad (2\text{-}1)$$

and their inverse (1-2) as

$$y_i = y_i(x_1, x_2, x_3). \qquad (2\text{-}2)$$

Throughout this section we shall suppose that the Latin indices i, j, k have the range of values 1, 2, 3.

If $P(y_1, y_2, y_3)$ is any point referred to a set of cartesian axes y (Fig. 5), its position vector $\mathbf{r}$ can be written in the form

$$\mathbf{r} = \mathbf{i}_1 y_1 + \mathbf{i}_2 y_2 + \mathbf{i}_3 y_3, \tag{2-3}$$

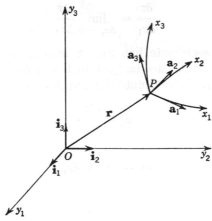

FIG. 5

where the $\mathbf{i}_1$, $\mathbf{i}_2$, $\mathbf{i}_3$ are the unit base vectors, which in Chap. 4 we denoted by $\mathbf{i}$, $\mathbf{j}$, $\mathbf{k}$.

The square of the element of arc ds along some curve C has the form

$$(ds)^2 = (dy_1)^2 + (dy_2)^2 + (dy_3)^2, \tag{2-4}$$

and since

$$d\mathbf{r} = \mathbf{i}_1 \, dy_1 + \mathbf{i}_2 \, dy_2 + \mathbf{i}_3 \, dy_3, \tag{2-5}$$

we can write (2-4) as a scalar product

$$(ds)^2 = \sum_{i=1}^{3} dy_i \, dy_i = d\mathbf{r} \cdot d\mathbf{r}. \tag{2-6}$$

If we replace the y_i in (2-3) by their values in terms of the xs with the aid of (2-2), $\mathbf{r}$ becomes a function of the variables x_i and we can write

$$d\mathbf{r} = \frac{\partial \mathbf{r}}{\partial x_1} \, dx_1 + \frac{\partial \mathbf{r}}{\partial x_2} \, dx_2 + \frac{\partial \mathbf{r}}{\partial x_3} \, dx_3 \tag{2-7}$$

$$\equiv \sum_{i=1}^{3} \frac{\partial \mathbf{r}}{\partial x_i} \, dx_i$$

Now, the symbol

$$\frac{\partial \mathbf{r}(x_1, x_2, x_3)}{\partial x_i}$$

denotes the derivative of $\mathbf{r}$ with respect to a particular variable x_i ($i =$ 1, 2, 3) when the remaining variables are held fast. Thus, if we fix the variables x_2 and x_3 by setting $x_2 = c_2$ and $x_3 = c_3$, $\mathbf{r}$ becomes a function of x_1 alone, and hence the terminus of $\mathbf{r}$ is constrained to move along the x_1 coordinate line in the x coordinate system determined by Eqs. (2-1). Consequently, the vector

$$\frac{\partial \mathbf{r}}{\partial x_1} = \lim_{\Delta x_1 \to 0} \frac{\Delta \mathbf{r}}{\Delta x_1}$$

is tangent to the coordinate line x_1. Similarly, we conclude that the vectors $\partial \mathbf{r}/\partial x_2$ and $\partial \mathbf{r}/\partial x_3$ are tangent to the x_2 and x_3 coordinate lines, respectively (Fig. 5). If we denote these vectors by $\mathbf{a}_i$, so that

$$\mathbf{a}_i = \frac{\partial \mathbf{r}}{\partial x_i}, \tag{2-8}$$

we can write (2-7) as

$$d\mathbf{r} = \sum_{i=1}^{3} \mathbf{a}_i \, dx_i \tag{2-9}$$

and hence Eq. (2-6) assumes the form

$$(ds)^2 = \left(\sum_{i=1}^{3} \mathbf{a}_i \, dx_i \right) \cdot \left(\sum_{i=1}^{3} \mathbf{a}_i \, dx_i \right). \tag{2-10}$$

On expanding the scalar product in (2-10), we see that formula (2-10) can be written as

$$(ds)^2 = \sum_{i=1}^{3} \sum_{j=1}^{3} \mathbf{a}_i \cdot \mathbf{a}_j \, dx_i \, dx_j$$

and hence, with g_{ij} defined by

$$\mathbf{a}_i \cdot \mathbf{a}_j \equiv g_{ij}, \tag{2-11}$$

we can write it as

$$(ds)^2 = \sum_{i=1}^{3} \sum_{j=1}^{3} g_{ij} \, dx_i \, dx_j. \tag{2-12}$$

In expanded form this reads

$$(ds)^2 = g_{11}(dx_1)^2 + g_{12} \, dx_1 \, dx_2 + g_{13} \, dx_1 \, dx_3$$
$$+ g_{21} \, dx_2 \, dx_1 + g_{22}(dx_2)^2 + g_{23} \, dx_2 \, dx_3$$
$$+ g_{31} \, dx_3 \, dx_1 + g_{32} \, dx_3 \, dx_2 + g_{33}(dx_3)^2. \tag{2-13}$$

Since $\mathbf{a}_i \cdot \mathbf{a}_j = \mathbf{a}_j \cdot \mathbf{a}_i$, we see from the definition (2-11) that $g_{ij} = g_{ji}$. Thus the *quadratic differential form* (2-13) is symmetric.

For reasons which will appear presently, the coefficients g_{ij} in this quadratic form are called *metric coefficients*. We shall see that they can be computed directly from Eqs. (2-2) without first calculating the vectors $\mathbf{a}_i$.

The vectors $\mathbf{a}_i$, which were found to be tangent to the coordinate lines x_i at a given point P, are called *base vectors* in the curvilinear coordinate system x. Any vector $\mathbf{A}$ with the origin at P can be resolved into components A_1, A_2, A_3 along the directions of the vectors $\mathbf{a}_1$, $\mathbf{a}_2$, $\mathbf{a}_3$ (Fig. 6). Thus, the base vectors $\mathbf{a}_i$ play the same role in the system x as the base vectors $\mathbf{i}_1$, $\mathbf{i}_2$, $\mathbf{i}_3$ do in the cartesian system y. It should be noted, however, that while the magnitudes and directions of cartesian base vectors are fixed, the vectors $\mathbf{a}_i$, in general, vary from point to point in space.

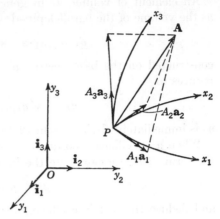

FIG. 6

From the definition (2-11) we see on setting $i = j = 1$ that the length of $\mathbf{a}_1$ is $|\mathbf{a}_1| = \sqrt{g_{11}}$. Similarly, $|\mathbf{a}_2| = \sqrt{g_{22}}$ and $|\mathbf{a}_3| = \sqrt{g_{33}}$. These vectors are orthogonal if, and only if,

$$g_{12} = g_{21} = \mathbf{a}_1 \cdot \mathbf{a}_2 = 0,$$

$$g_{31} = g_{13} = \mathbf{a}_1 \cdot \mathbf{a}_3 = 0,$$

$$g_{23} = g_{32} = \mathbf{a}_2 \cdot \mathbf{a}_3 = 0.$$

A curvilinear coordinate system for which these relations hold is called *orthogonal*, and we note that in an orthogonal system the quadratic form (2-13) has the structure

$$(ds)^2 = g_{11}(dx_1)^2 + g_{22}(dx_2)^2 + g_{33}(dx_3)^2. \tag{2-14}$$

To get at the meaning of the coefficients g_{11}, g_{22}, and g_{33}, we note that when an element of arc ds is directed along the x_1 coordinate line, $dx_2 = dx_3 = 0$, since along the x_1 line x_2 and x_3 do not vary. Thus, (2-14) gives in this case

$$(ds_1)^2 = g_{11}(dx_1)^2,$$

so that

$$ds_1 = \sqrt{g_{11}}\, dx_1. \tag{2-15}$$

Thus, the length of the arc element ds_1 along the x_1 coordinate line is obtained by multiplying the differential of x_1 by $\sqrt{g_{11}}$. Similarly we find that the differentials of arc ds_i along the x_2 and x_3 coordinate lines are

$$ds_2 = \sqrt{g_{22}}\, dx_2, \qquad ds_3 = \sqrt{g_{33}}\, dx_3. \tag{2-16}$$

Since the ds_i and the dx_i are real, we conclude that $g_{11} \geq 0$, $g_{22} \geq 0$, $g_{33} \geq 0$. In orthogonal cartesian coordinates $(ds)^2$ is given by the formula (2-4), and hence in such a system $g_{11} = g_{22} = g_{33} = 1$.

An element of volume $d\tau$ in general curvilinear coordinates is defined as the volume of the parallelepiped

$$d\tau = |a_1 \cdot a_2 \times a_3| \, dx_1 \, dx_2 \, dx_3 \qquad (2\text{-}17)$$

constructed on the base vectors a_i. If the system is orthogonal, (2-17) reduces to

$$d\tau = \sqrt{g_{11}g_{22}g_{33}} \, dx_1 \, dx_2 \, dx_3, \qquad (2\text{-}18)$$

as is immediately obvious from (2-15) and (2-16).

When a curvilinear coordinate system x is determined by equations of the form (2-1), we can write the inverse transformation (2-2) as

$$y_k = y_k(x_1, x_2, x_3) \qquad (2\text{-}19)$$

and deduce the metric coefficients g_{ij} as follows: On differentiating Eqs. (2-19) with respect to x_i we get

$$dy_k = \sum_{i=1}^{3} \frac{\partial y_k}{\partial x_i} \, dx_i. \qquad (2\text{-}20)$$

But in cartesian coordinates

$$ds^2 = \sum_{k=1}^{3} dy_k \, dy_k,$$

and the substitution from (2-20) in this formula yields [1]

$$ds^2 = \sum_{k=1}^{3} \left[\sum_{i=1}^{3} \frac{\partial y_k}{\partial x_i} \, dx_i \sum_{j=1}^{3} \frac{\partial y_k}{\partial x_j} \, dx_j \right]$$

$$= \sum_{i=1}^{3} \sum_{j=1}^{3} \left(\sum_{k=1}^{3} \frac{\partial y_k}{\partial x_i} \frac{\partial y_k}{\partial x_j} \right) dx_i \, dx_j. \qquad (2\text{-}21)$$

On comparing (2-21) with (2-12), we see that

$$g_{ij} = \sum_{k=1}^{3} \frac{\partial y_k}{\partial x_i} \frac{\partial y_k}{\partial x_j}, \qquad i, j = 1, 2, 3. \qquad (2\text{-}22)$$

This is the desired formula for the calculation of metric coefficients.

To illustrate the use of (2-22) consider a coordinate system defined by Eqs. (1-7), which we write in the form

---

[1] Note that the summation index can be changed at will so that

$$\sum_{i=1}^{3} \frac{\partial y_k}{\partial x_i} \, dx_i \equiv \sum_{j=1}^{3} \frac{\partial y_k}{\partial x_j} \, dx_j$$

$$y_1 = x_1 \cos x_2,$$

$$y_2 = x_1 \sin x_2,$$

$$y_3 = x_3,$$

to agree with the notation used in this section. From (2-22) we have

$$g_{11} = \left(\frac{\partial y_1}{\partial x_1}\right)^2 + \left(\frac{\partial y_2}{\partial x_1}\right)^2 + \left(\frac{\partial y_3}{\partial x_1}\right)^2$$

$$= \cos^2 x_2 + \sin^2 x_2 + 0 = 1,$$

$$g_{22} = \left(\frac{\partial y_1}{\partial x_2}\right)^2 + \left(\frac{\partial y_2}{\partial x_2}\right)^2 + \left(\frac{\partial y_3}{\partial x_2}\right)^2$$

$$= x_1^2 \sin^2 x_2 + x_1^2 \cos x_2^2 + 0 = x_1^2,$$

$$g_{33} = \left(\frac{\partial y_1}{\partial x_3}\right)^2 + \left(\frac{\partial y_2}{\partial x_3}\right)^2 + \left(\frac{\partial y_3}{\partial x_3}\right)^2$$

$$= 0 + 0 + 1 = 1,$$

$$g_{12} = \frac{\partial y_1}{\partial x_1}\frac{\partial y_1}{\partial x_2} + \frac{\partial y_2}{\partial x_1}\frac{\partial y_2}{\partial x_2} + \frac{\partial y_3}{\partial x_1}\frac{\partial y_3}{\partial x_2}$$

$$= \cos x_2(-x_1 \sin x_2) + \sin x_2(x_1 \cos x_2) + 0 = 0.$$

We find in the same way that $g_{23} = g_{13} = 0$. Hence the system under consideration is orthogonal. The expression for ds^2 is

$$ds^2 = \sum_{i=1}^{3} \sum_{j=1}^{3} g_{ij}\, dx_i\, dx_j$$

$$= (dx_1)^2 + x_1^2(dx_2)^2 + (dx_3)^2,$$

which is a familiar formula for the square of the arc element in cylindrical coordinates if we recall that $x_1 = r$, $x_2 = \theta$, $x_3 = z$. Since this system is orthogonal, the element of volume is given by (2-18), which in our case yields

$$d\tau = r\, dr\, d\theta\, dz.$$

Example: Obtain expressions for the elements of arc and volume in the coordinate system x defined by

$$y_1 = x_1 + x_2 + x_3,$$

$$y_2 = x_1 - x_2 - x_3, \qquad\qquad (2\text{-}23)$$

$$y_3 = 2x_1 + x_2 - x_3,$$

and discuss the system.

On making use of formula (2-22) we find as in the preceding illustration that

$$g_{11} = 6, \qquad g_{22} = 3, \qquad g_{33} = 3, \qquad g_{12} = 2, \qquad g_{23} = 1, \qquad g_{13} = -2.$$

Hence

$$ds^2 = 6(dx_1)^2 + 4\,dx_1\,dx_2 - 4\,dx_1\,dx_3 + 2\,dx_2\,dx_3 + 3(dx_2)^2 + 3(dx_3)^2.$$

The system is clearly not orthogonal, and to compute $d\tau$ we shall make use of formula (2-17). Now

$$\mathbf{r} = \mathbf{i}_1 y_1 + \mathbf{i}_2 y_2 + \mathbf{i}_3 y_3$$

$$= \mathbf{i}_1(x_1 + x_2 + x_3) + \mathbf{i}_2(x_1 - x_2 - x_3) + \mathbf{i}_3(2x_1 + x_2 - x_3)$$

and hence the base vectors $\mathbf{a}_i = \partial \mathbf{r}/\partial x_i$ are

$$\mathbf{a}_1 = \mathbf{i}_1 + \mathbf{i}_2 + 2\mathbf{i}_3,$$

$$\mathbf{a}_2 = \mathbf{i}_1 - \mathbf{i}_2 + \mathbf{i}_3,$$

$$\mathbf{a}_3 = \mathbf{i}_1 - \mathbf{i}_2 - \mathbf{i}_3.$$

Thus,

$$d\tau = |\mathbf{a}_1 \cdot \mathbf{a}_2 \times \mathbf{a}_3|\,dx_1\,dx_2\,dx_3 = \begin{vmatrix} 1 & 1 & 2 \\ 1 & -1 & 1 \\ 1 & -1 & -1 \end{vmatrix} dx_1\,dx_2\,dx_3 = 4\,dx_1\,dx_2\,dx_3.$$

On solving (2-23) for the x_i we get

$$x_1 = \tfrac{1}{2}y_1 + \tfrac{1}{2}y_2,$$

$$x_2 = -\tfrac{1}{4}y_1 - \tfrac{3}{4}y_2 + \tfrac{1}{2}y_3,$$

$$x_3 = \tfrac{3}{4}y_1 + \tfrac{1}{4}y_2 - \tfrac{1}{2}y_3.$$

The coordinate surfaces $x_i = c_i$ are planes, and the coordinate lines x_i are therefore straight lines.

The system in this example is a special case of an *affine coordinate system* determined by the transformation

$$y_i = a_{i1}x_1 + a_{i2}x_2 + a_{i3}x_3, \qquad i = 1, 2, 3, \tag{2-24}$$

in which the a_{ij} are constants. Affine transformations (2-24) occur in the study of elastic deformations, in dynamics of rigid bodies, and in many other branches of mathematical physics.

PROBLEMS

1. Discuss in the manner of the preceding example a coordinate system x determined by

$$y_1 = \frac{1}{\sqrt{6}}\,x_1 + \frac{2}{\sqrt{6}}\,x_2 + \frac{1}{\sqrt{6}}\,x_3,$$

$$y_2 = \frac{1}{\sqrt{2}}\,x_1 - \frac{1}{\sqrt{3}}\,x_2 + \frac{1}{\sqrt{3}}\,x_3,$$

$$y_3 = \frac{1}{\sqrt{2}}\,x_1 - \frac{1}{\sqrt{2}}\,x_3.$$

2. Compute the metric coefficients appropriate to a spherical coordinate system defined by Eqs. (1-9), and thus show that

$$(ds)^2 = (d\rho)^2 + \rho^2(d\theta)^2 + \rho^2 \sin^2\theta(d\phi)^2$$

and

$$d\tau = \rho^2 \sin\theta \, d\rho \, d\theta \, d\phi.$$

3. If $\mathbf{R} = \mathbf{i}x + \mathbf{j}y + \mathbf{k}z$ is the position vector of a moving point $P(x,y,z)$ in cartesian coordinates, show that the *unit* base vectors $\mathbf{e}_r$, $\mathbf{e}_\theta$, $\mathbf{e}_z$ in cylindrical coordinates (r,θ,z) [see (1-7)] are

$$\mathbf{e}_r = \mathbf{i}\cos\theta + \mathbf{j}\sin\theta, \qquad \mathbf{e}_\theta = -\mathbf{i}\sin\theta + \mathbf{j}\cos\theta, \qquad \mathbf{e}_z = \mathbf{k}.$$

Show that $\mathbf{R} = r\mathbf{e}_r + z\mathbf{e}_z$, compute $d\mathbf{R}/dt$ and $d^2\mathbf{R}/dt^2$, and thus show that the velocity $\mathbf{v}$ and the acceleration $\mathbf{a}$ of the point P are

$$\mathbf{v} = \frac{dr}{dt}\mathbf{e}_r + r\frac{d\theta}{dt}\mathbf{e}_\theta + \frac{dz}{dt}\mathbf{e}_z,$$

$$\mathbf{a} = \left[\frac{d^2r}{dt^2} - r\left(\frac{d\theta}{dt}\right)^2\right]\mathbf{e}_r + \frac{1}{r}\frac{d}{dt}\left(r^2\frac{d\theta}{dt}\right)\mathbf{e}_\theta + \frac{d^2z}{dt^2}\mathbf{e}_z.$$

4. If $\mathbf{R} = \mathbf{i}x + \mathbf{j}y + \mathbf{k}z$ is the position vector of $P(x,y,z)$ in cartesian coordinates, show that the *unit* base vectors $\mathbf{e}_\rho$, $\mathbf{e}_\theta$, $\mathbf{e}_\phi$ in spherical coordinates defined by Eqs. (1-9) are

$$\mathbf{e}_\rho = \mathbf{i}\sin\theta\cos\phi + \mathbf{j}\sin\theta\sin\phi + \mathbf{k}\cos\theta,$$

$$\mathbf{e}_\theta = \mathbf{i}\cos\theta\cos\phi + \mathbf{j}\cos\theta\sin\phi - \mathbf{k}\sin\theta,$$

$$\mathbf{e}_\phi = -\mathbf{i}\sin\phi + \mathbf{j}\cos\phi.$$

5. If the position vector $\mathbf{R}$ of a moving point P in spherical coordinates is written as $\mathbf{R} = \rho\mathbf{e}_\rho$, where $\mathbf{e}_\rho$ is the unit vector in the direction of the increasing coordinate ρ, use the results of Prob. 4 to show that

$$\mathbf{v} = \frac{d\mathbf{R}}{dt} = \frac{d\rho}{dt}\mathbf{e}_\rho + \rho\frac{d\theta}{dt}\mathbf{e}_\theta + \rho\sin\theta\frac{d\phi}{dt}\mathbf{e}_\phi.$$

3. Scalar and Vector Fields. Gradient.

If in some region of space a scalar $u(P)$ is defined at every point, we say that $u(P)$ is a *scalar point function*. An example of such a function is the temperature at any point in a solid. A function $\mathbf{v}(P)$ defining a vector at every point P of the given region is a *vector point function*. An example of vector point function is the velocity at any point P of a fluid. The regions of definition of scalar and vector point functions are sometimes called *fields*, and one thus speaks of scalar and vector fields. Unless otherwise noted, we shall assume that $u(P)$ and $\mathbf{v}(P)$ are single-valued functions.

To facilitate calculations involving scalar and vector point functions, it is often convenient to refer the region of their definition to a special coordinate system x. If this is done, the coordinates of P can be denoted by (x_1,x_2,x_3) and $u(P)$ and $\mathbf{v}(P)$ can be denoted by $u(x_1,x_2,x_3)$ and $\mathbf{v}(x_1,x_2,x_3)$, respectively. As explained in the preceding section, $\mathbf{v}(x_1,x_2,x_3)$ can then be represented in terms of its components $v_i(x_1,x_2,x_3)$ $(i = 1, 2, 3)$ along the appropriate base vectors at (x_1, x_2, x_3). It should be noted, however, that the introduction of coordinate systems is a matter of convenience and that $u(P)$ and $\mathbf{v}(P)$ depend only on the choice of P in the field and not on any special reference frame selected to locate P. The fact that scalar and vector point functions are independent of coordinate systems is spoken of as *invariance*, and we shall see that it is possible to associate with $u(P)$ and $\mathbf{v}(P)$ certain new scalar and vector functions which have important invariant significance.

We say that $u(P)$ and $\mathbf{v}(P)$ are *continuous* at P if

$$\lim_{P' \to P} u(P') = u(P) \qquad \text{and} \qquad \lim_{P' \to P} \mathbf{v}(P') = \mathbf{v}(P)$$

for every choice of P' in the neighborhood of P. Functions continuous at every point of the region are said to be continuous in the region.

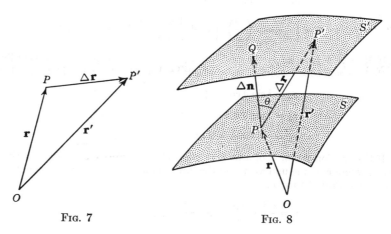

FIG. 7   FIG. 8

Let $u(P)$ be a continuous scalar function in the given region. We select a point O in this region for the origin of position vectors $\mathbf{r} \equiv \overrightarrow{OP}$. If P' is some point in the neighborhood of P, we denote $\overrightarrow{OP'}$ by $\mathbf{r}'$ and write (Fig. 7)

$$\mathbf{r}' \equiv \mathbf{r} + \Delta\mathbf{r}. \quad \text{this is vectorially odd.}$$

The difference quotient

$$\frac{u(P') - u(P)}{|\Delta\mathbf{r}|} \equiv \frac{u(P') - u(P)}{\Delta s}, \tag{3-1}$$

where $|\Delta\mathbf{r}| = \Delta s$, gives an approximate space rate of change of $u(P)$, and we can study the limit of (3-1) as P' is made to approach P along the rectilinear path $\Delta\mathbf{r}$. If this limit exists, we shall write

$$\lim_{\Delta s \to 0} \frac{u(P') - u(P)}{\Delta s} = \frac{du}{ds} \tag{3-2}$$

and call it the *directional derivative of* $u(P)$ in the direction specified by $\Delta\mathbf{r}$. A different choice of P' yields a different vector $\Delta\mathbf{r}$ and in general a different value for du/ds at P.

A set of points for which $u(P)$ has a constant value c determines a surface S called a *level surface;* we assume that at each point of S there is a uniquely determined tangent plane. Let us consider a pair of such surfaces S and S' determined by $u = c$ and $u = c + \Delta c$, where Δc is a small change in c (Fig. 8). If P is a point on S and P' on S', the change $\Delta u \equiv u(P') - u(P)$ is Δc, and this is independent of the position of P' on S'. But the average space rate of change

$$\frac{u(P') - u(P)}{|\Delta\mathbf{r}|} \equiv \frac{\Delta u}{\Delta s} \tag{3-3}$$

clearly depends on the magnitude of $\Delta\mathbf{r}$. The limit of this ratio as $\Delta\mathbf{r}$ is made to approach zero by making $\Delta c \to 0$ is the directional derivative (3-2) in the fixed direction determined by $\Delta\mathbf{r}$. The greatest space rate of change of u will occur when P' is taken on the normal $\overrightarrow{PQ} \equiv \Delta\mathbf{n}$ to the surface S (Fig. 8), since for this position of P' the denominator $|\Delta\mathbf{r}|$ in (3-3) is not greater than $|\Delta\mathbf{n}|$. Indeed,

$$\Delta\mathbf{n} \cong \Delta\mathbf{r}\cos\theta, \tag{3-4}$$

where θ is the angle between the normal $\overrightarrow{PQ}$ to S and $\overrightarrow{PP'}$.

On taking account of (3-4), we conclude that

$$\frac{du}{dn} = \frac{1}{\cos\theta}\frac{du}{ds} \equiv \frac{du}{ds}\sec\theta. \tag{3-5}$$

The derivative du/dn in the direction of the normal to the level surface $u = $ const is called the *normal derivative of* $u(P)$.

If $\mathbf{n}$ is a unit vector at P, pointing in the direction for which $\Delta u > 0$, we can construct a vector, called the *gradient of* u, namely,

$$\operatorname{grad} u \equiv \mathbf{n}\frac{du}{dn}. \tag{3-6}$$

This vector represents in both the direction and magnitude the *greatest space rate of increase* of $u(P)$, provided, of course, that $du/dn \neq 0$. The gradient vector (3-6) is clearly independent of the choice of coordinate systems and hence is an invariant. If we introduce the familiar cartesian coordinates xyz and denote $u(P)$ by $u(x,y,z)$, then, as in Chap. 3, Sec. 8,

$$\frac{du}{ds} = \frac{\partial u}{\partial x}\frac{dx}{ds} + \frac{\partial u}{\partial y}\frac{dy}{ds} + \frac{\partial u}{\partial z}\frac{dz}{ds}, \tag{3-7}$$

where $dx/ds = \cos(x,s)$, $dy/ds = \cos(y,s)$, $dz/ds = \cos(z,s)$ are the direction cosines of the unit vector $\mathbf{s}$ in the direction of the arc element $d\mathbf{s}$ (Fig. 9). In this case the position vector $\mathbf{r}$ or P is

$$\mathbf{r} = \mathbf{i}x + \mathbf{j}y + \mathbf{k}z$$

and

$$\mathbf{s} = \frac{d\mathbf{r}}{ds} = \mathbf{i}\frac{dx}{ds} + \mathbf{j}\frac{dy}{ds} + \mathbf{k}\frac{dz}{ds}. \tag{3-8}$$

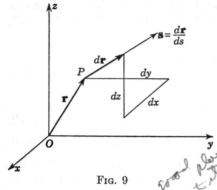

FIG. 9

We see that (3-7) can be written as the scalar product of the vector

$$\nabla u \equiv \mathbf{i}\frac{\partial u}{\partial x} + \mathbf{j}\frac{\partial u}{\partial y} + \mathbf{k}\frac{\partial u}{\partial z} \tag{3-9}$$

and the unit vector $\mathbf{s}$ in (3-8). Thus,

$$\frac{du}{ds} = \nabla u \cdot \mathbf{s}. \tag{3-10}$$

Inasmuch as the greatest value of du/ds is assumed when the direction of $\mathbf{s}$ coincides with that of the normal $\mathbf{n}$ to the level surface $u = $ const, we conclude that

$$\nabla u = \operatorname{grad} u, \tag{3-11}$$

for the right-hand member of (3-10) can be interpreted as the component of the vector ∇u in the direction $\mathbf{s}$ and the maximum component du/ds is obtained when $\mathbf{s}$ is directed along ∇u.

It follows from (3-9) and (3-11) that a formula for calculating grad $\mathbf{u}$ in cartesian coordinates is

$$\operatorname{grad} u = \mathbf{i}\frac{\partial u}{\partial x} + \mathbf{j}\frac{\partial u}{\partial y} + \mathbf{k}\frac{\partial u}{\partial z}. \tag{3-12}$$

On comparing (3-6) and (3-12), we see that

$$|\operatorname{grad} u| = \left|\frac{du}{dn}\right| = \sqrt{\left(\frac{\partial u}{\partial x}\right)^2 + \left(\frac{\partial u}{\partial y}\right)^2 + \left(\frac{\partial u}{\partial z}\right)^2}.$$

Formula (3-9) suggests a definition of the differential vector operator ∇, called *del* or *nabla*,

$$\nabla \equiv \mathbf{i}\frac{\partial}{\partial x} + \mathbf{j}\frac{\partial}{\partial y} + \mathbf{k}\frac{\partial}{\partial z}, \tag{3-13}$$

analogous to the scalar differential operator D introduced in Chap. 1, Sec. 23. The product of ∇ and the scalar $u(x,y,z)$ is interpreted to mean

note that V_x is coeffecient of i in $\vec{v}$ + dv_x was...
der of coeffecient of i in $\vec{v}$ ... ... to s.

(3-9). The reader will show that

$$\nabla(u + v) = \nabla u + \nabla v,$$

$$\nabla(uv) = u\nabla v + v\nabla u,$$

(3-14)

whenever u and v are scalar functions of (x,y,z). A formula for grad u in orthogonal curvilinear coordinates is deduced in Sec. 13.

The directional derivative dv/ds of a vector point function $\mathbf{v}(P)$ is defined by formula (3-2) in which $u(P)$ is replaced by $\mathbf{v}(P)$. When $\mathbf{v}(P)$ is expressed in the form

$$\mathbf{v} = \mathbf{i}v_x + \mathbf{j}v_y + \mathbf{k}v_z,$$

(3-15)

where $\mathbf{i}$, $\mathbf{j}$, $\mathbf{k}$ are the base vectors in the system x,y,z, *is de $q \times y \, z =$*

here are not partial *$xy + yz + xz$*

or they are just

$$\frac{d\mathbf{v}}{ds} = \mathbf{i}\frac{dv_x}{ds} + \mathbf{j}\frac{dv_y}{ds} + \mathbf{k}\frac{dv_z}{ds}.$$

(3-16)

or w/respect to s. *← this $\nabla w \cdot s$*

We have already employed a similar formula in Chap. 4, Sec. 7, to calculate the derivatives of the position vector $\mathbf{R} = \mathbf{i}x + \mathbf{j}y + \mathbf{k}z$ with respect to the time parameter t.

Example 1. Find the directional derivative of $u = xyz^2$ at $(1,0,3)$ in the direction of the vector $\mathbf{i} - \mathbf{j} + \mathbf{k}$. Compute the greatest rate of change of u and the direction of the maximum rate of increase of u.

On substituting $u = xyz^2$ in (3-9), we find that the gradient u is given by

$$\nabla u = \mathbf{i}yz^2 + \mathbf{j}xz^2 + \mathbf{k}2xyz.$$

At $(1,0,3)$

$$\nabla u = \mathbf{i}0 + \mathbf{j}9 + \mathbf{k}0 = 9\mathbf{j}.$$

Thus, the greatest rate of change $|\nabla u| = 9$, and the direction of the maximum rate of change is along the y axis. Since the unit vector $\mathbf{s}$ in the direction of the vector $\mathbf{i} - \mathbf{j} + \mathbf{k}$ is

$$\mathbf{s} = \frac{1}{\sqrt{3}}(\mathbf{i} - \mathbf{j} + \mathbf{k}),$$

we find on using (3-10) that the desired directional derivative is

$$\frac{du}{ds} = \nabla u \cdot \mathbf{s} = 9\mathbf{j} \cdot \frac{1}{\sqrt{3}}(\mathbf{i} - \mathbf{j} + \mathbf{k}) = -\frac{9}{\sqrt{3}}.$$

Example 2. Find the unit normals to the surface $x^2 - y^2 + z^2 = 6$ at $(1,2,3)$.

The surface in this example is a level surface for the function $u = x^2 - y^2 + z^2$. Since the gradient of u is normal to the level surface $u = $ const, we have by (3-11)

$$\text{grad } u = \nabla u = \mathbf{i}2x - \mathbf{j}2y + \mathbf{k}2z,$$

which at $(1,2,3)$ has the value

$$\nabla u = \mathbf{i}2 - \mathbf{j}4 + \mathbf{k}6.$$

when $\nabla v = dv_x \, i + dv_y \, j + d v_z \, k$

But this vector is directed along the unit normal $\mathbf{n}$ to $u = x^2 - y^2 + z^2 = 6$ in the direction of increasing u. Hence

$$\mathbf{n} = \frac{\nabla u}{|\nabla u|} = \frac{1}{\sqrt{56}}(\mathbf{i}2 - \mathbf{j}4 + \mathbf{k}6).$$

The direction of the other unit normal vector is opposite to this.

PROBLEMS

1. Compute the directional derivative of $u = x^2 + y^2 + z^2$ at $(1,2,3)$ in the direction of the line

$$\frac{x}{3} = \frac{y}{4} = \frac{z}{5}.$$

Find the maximum rate of increase of u at $(1,2,3)$; at $(0,1,2)$.

2. Find grad u if (a) $u = (x^2 + y^2 + z^2)^{-1/2}$, (b) $u = \log(x^2 + y^2 + z^2)$.

3. Find the directional derivative of $u = x^2y - y^2z - xyz$ at $(1,-1,0)$ in the direction of the vector $\mathbf{i} - \mathbf{j} + 2\mathbf{k}$.

4. Find the directional derivative of $u = xyz$ at $(1,2,3)$ in the direction from $(1,2,3)$ to $(1,-1,-3)$.

5. Find the unit normal vector in the direction of the exterior normal to the surface $x^2 + 2y^2 + z^2 = 7$ at $(1,-1,2)$.

6. Find the unit vectors normal to $xyz = 2$ at $(1,-1,-2)$.

7. Show that $\nabla r^n = nr^{n-2}\mathbf{r}$, where $\mathbf{r} = \mathbf{i}x + \mathbf{j}y + \mathbf{k}z$ and $r = |\mathbf{r}|$.

8. Use the result of Prob. 7 to compute the directional derivative of $u = (x^2 + y^2 + z^2)^{3/2}$ at $(-1,1,2)$ in the direction of the vector $\mathbf{i} - 2\mathbf{j} + \mathbf{k}$.

9. Compute the directional derivative of

$$\mathbf{v} = \mathbf{i}(x^2 - y^2) + \mathbf{j}(xyz - 1) + \mathbf{k}z$$

at $(1,2,0)$ in the direction from $(1,2,0)$ to $(0,0,0)$.

4. Integration of Vector Functions.

Integrals of vector functions with the integrands consisting of scalar products of vectors are defined in the usual manner. Thus if $\mathbf{v}(P)$ is a continuous vector point function specified along a curve C joining a pair of points P_0, P', and if $\mathbf{r}(P)$ is the position vector of P on C, then the integral

$$\int_{P_0}^{P'} \mathbf{v} \cdot d\mathbf{r} \tag{4-1}$$

is defined as the limit of a sum constructed as follows. Let C, which we suppose to be sectionally smooth,[1] be divided into n arc elements Δs_i by inserting the points P_i (Fig. 10). We form the sum

$$\sum_{i=1}^{n} \mathbf{v}(P_i) \cdot \Delta\mathbf{r}_i, \tag{4-2}$$

[1] This means that C consists of a finite number of segments with continuously changing tangents. The term *piecewise smooth* is also used.

where $\Delta \mathbf{r}_i = \mathbf{r}_{i+1} - \mathbf{r}_i$, and compute the limit of this sum as $n \to \infty$ and every $|\Delta \mathbf{r}_i| \to 0$. The continuity of $\mathbf{v}(P)$ and the smoothness of C suffice to show that the limit of (4-2) exists, and we define the *line integral* (4-1) to be this limit.

If $\mathbf{v}(P)$ is defined in some region containing several paths joining P_0 and P, then the integral (4-1) will ordinarily have different values when computed along different paths. In exceptional circumstances, discussed in the following sections, these values may turn out to be equal.

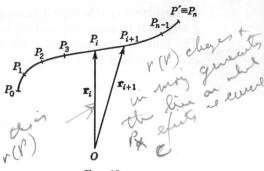

FIG. 10

If we introduce the xyz coordinate system and write

$$\mathbf{v}(P) = \mathbf{v}(x,y,z) \equiv \mathbf{i}v_x(x,y,z) + \mathbf{j}v_y(x,y,z) + \mathbf{k}v_z(x,y,z),$$

$$d\mathbf{r} \equiv \mathbf{i}\,dx + \mathbf{j}\,dy + \mathbf{k}\,dz,$$

the integral (4-1) becomes

$$\int_{P_0}^{P'} [v_x(x,y,z)\,dx + v_y(x,y,z)\,dy + v_z(x,y,z)\,dz]. \qquad (4\text{-}3)$$

When the equations of C are given in parametric form

$$\left.\begin{array}{l} x = x(t), \\ y = y(t), \\ z = z(t), \end{array}\right\} \qquad t_0 < t < t', \qquad (4\text{-}4)$$

where the values t_0, t' of the parameter t correspond to the end points P_0, P' of C, the integral (4-3) can be expressed as a definite integral[1] $\int_{t_0}^{t'} F(t)\,dt$ and evaluated by the usual means.

Similarly, the surface integral

$$\int_{\Sigma} \mathbf{v} \cdot \mathbf{n}\, d\sigma \qquad (4\text{-}5)$$

where $\mathbf{n}$ is a unit normal specified at all points of a sufficiently smooth surface [2] Σ, can be defined as the limit of the sum

---

[1] See the examples at the end of this section. The equivalence of the integral (4-3) and the ordinary Riemann integral, when (4-4) holds, is easily seen by comparing the sums of which these integrals are the respective limits.

[2] We assume that the surface Σ is two-sided and that $\mathbf{n}$ is directed toward one side. This normal we elect to call *positive*. If the surface is closed, it is customary to regard the exterior normal as positive.

$$\lim_{k \to \infty} \sum_{i=1}^{k} \mathbf{v}(P_i) \cdot \mathbf{n}(P_i) \, \Delta\sigma_i. \tag{4-6}$$

In constructing this sum it is supposed that the surface Σ is divided into k elements of areas $\Delta\sigma_i$ and P_i is chosen somewhere in the element $\Delta\sigma_i$. The limit is then computed by increasing the number k of elements in such a way that the maximum diameter of every $\Delta\sigma_i$ approaches zero.

Formally one is tempted to extend these "limits of the sum" definitions to such symbols as

$$\int_{P_0}^{P'} \mathbf{v}(P) \, ds, \qquad \int_{\Sigma} \mathbf{v}(P) \, d\sigma, \qquad \int_{\tau} \mathbf{v}(P) \, d\tau, \tag{4-7}$$

in which $\mathbf{v}(P)$ is a vector function and ds, $d\sigma$, and $d\tau$, respectively, are the elements of arc length, surface, and volume. Thus, there is a temptation to define the volume integral $\int_{\tau} \mathbf{v}(P) \, d\tau$ by the formula

$$\int_{\tau} \mathbf{v}(P) \, d\tau = \lim_{k \to \infty} \sum_{i=1}^{k} \mathbf{v}(P_i) \, \Delta\tau_i, \tag{4-8}$$

in which it is imagined that the volume τ is divided into elements of volume $\Delta\tau_i$. A definition such as (4-8) requires forming sums $\sum_{i=1}^{k} \mathbf{v}(P_i) \, \Delta\tau_i$ of the *bound* vectors $\mathbf{v}(P_i)$ which are determined at different points of the body. There is a question if the rules for addition of free vectors given in Chap. 4, Sec. 2, can be used to provide a sensible definition of (4-8). Without going into details we state it as a fact that the definition (4-8) makes sense in those geometries where the distance between a pair of points is given by the Pythagorean formula.[1]

If $\mathbf{v}(P)$ is expressed in terms of its cartesian components as $\mathbf{v} = \mathbf{i}v_x(x,y,z) + \mathbf{j}v_y(x,y,z) + \mathbf{k}v_z(x,y,z)$, the integrals in (4-7) can be reduced to the evaluation of three ordinary integrals by writing, for example,

$$\int_{\tau} \mathbf{v}(P) \, d\tau = \mathbf{i}\int_{\tau} v_x \, d\tau + \mathbf{j}\int_{\tau} v_y \, d\tau + \mathbf{k}\int_{\tau} v_z \, d\tau.$$

No such simple means of evaluating integrals of the type (4-7) are available in curvilinear coordinates because the base vectors in curvilinear coordinate systems vary from point to point in space. This remark may serve to explain why cartesian coordinates are so prominent in calculations involving vectors.

Line integrals of the form

$$\int_{C} [P(x,y,z) \, dx + Q(x,y,z) \, dy + R(x,y,z) \, dz], \tag{4-9}$$

which is identical with (4-3), are frequently defined without reference to vectors, but as we shall see, the definition adopted here has many interesting and immediate physical interpretations.

[1] Spaces so metrized are called Euclidean, and it is only with such that we are concerned in this book.

Example 1. Evaluate the integral $\int_C \mathbf{r} \cdot d\mathbf{r}$ when C is the helical path

$$x = \cos t,$$

$$y = \sin t, \tag{4-10}$$

$$z = t,$$

joining the points determined by $t = 0$ and $t = \pi/2$ and also when C is the straight line joining these points.

Since $\mathbf{r} = \mathbf{i}x + \mathbf{j}y + \mathbf{k}z$, we get, on using (4-10),

$$r = \mathbf{i} \cos t + \mathbf{j} \sin t + \mathbf{k}t,$$

$$d\mathbf{r} = (-\mathbf{i} \sin t + \mathbf{j} \cos t + \mathbf{k}) \, dt.$$

Hence
$$\int_C \mathbf{r} \cdot d\mathbf{r} = \int_0^{\pi/2} t \, dt = \frac{\pi^2}{8}. \tag{4-11}$$

If the path C is a straight line joining the same points $(1,0,0)$ and $(0,1,\pi/2)$, we can write its equation in vector form as

$$\mathbf{r} = \mathbf{r}_1 + (\mathbf{r}_2 - \mathbf{r}_1)t, \tag{4-12}$$

where $\mathbf{r}_1$ and $\mathbf{r}_2$ are the position vectors of $(1,0,0)$ and $(0,1,\pi/2)$, respectively (Fig. 11).

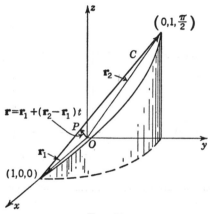

Fig. 11

The parameter t clearly varies between 0 and 1, since for $t = 0$, (4-12) yields $\mathbf{r} = \mathbf{r}_1$ and for $t = 1$, $\mathbf{r} = \mathbf{r}_2$. But $\mathbf{r}_1 = \mathbf{i}$, $\mathbf{r}_2 = \mathbf{j} + (\pi/2)\mathbf{k}$, so that (4-12) reduces to

$$\mathbf{r} = \mathbf{i} + \left(\mathbf{j} + \frac{\pi}{2}\mathbf{k} - \mathbf{i} \right) t.$$

Hence
$$\int_C \mathbf{r} \cdot d\mathbf{r} = \int_0^1 \left[-1 + \left(2 + \frac{\pi^2}{4} \right) t \right] dt = \frac{\pi^2}{8}.$$

This is the same value as we got for the helical path. In the following section we shall see why this particular integral is independent of the path.

Example 2. Compute the value of $\int_C \mathbf{v} \cdot d\mathbf{r}$, where $\mathbf{v} = \mathbf{i}y + \mathbf{j}2x$ and C is the straight line joining $(0,1)$ and $(1,0)$. Discuss also when C is the arc of a circle centered at the origin.

Since $\mathbf{r} = \mathbf{i}x + \mathbf{j}y$, we have $d\mathbf{r} = \mathbf{i}\,dx + \mathbf{j}\,dy$ and therefore

$$\int_C \mathbf{v} \cdot d\mathbf{r} = \int_C (y\,dx + 2x\,dy). \tag{4-13}$$

To evaluate this integral along the rectilinear path in Fig. 12, we write the equation of the path in the form

$$y = -x + 1 \qquad\qquad \tag{4-14}$$

and insert (4-14) in (4-13). Since $dy = -dx$, we get

$$\int_C \mathbf{v} \cdot d\mathbf{r} = \int_0^1 [(-x+1)\,dx - 2x\,dx] = \int_0^1 (1 - 3x)\,dx = -\tfrac{1}{2}.$$

The integration here is performed so that the path C is traced from the point $(0,1)$ to $(1,0)$.

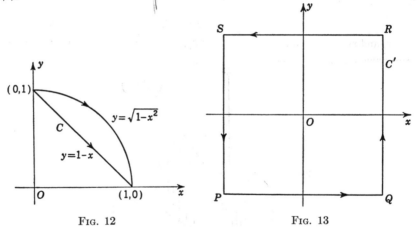

FIG. 12   FIG. 13

To compute the value of the integral (4-13) over the circular path C' joining the same two points, we note that $y = \sqrt{1 - x^2}$ along C', $dy = -x\,dx/\sqrt{1 - x^2}$, so that

$$\int_{C'} \mathbf{v} \cdot d\mathbf{r} = \int_0^1 \left[\sqrt{1 - x^2}\,dx - \frac{2x^2}{\sqrt{1 - x^2}}\,dx \right]$$

$$= \int_0^1 \frac{1 - 3x^2}{\sqrt{1 - x^2}}\,dx = -\frac{\pi}{4}.$$

Again, the path C' is traced out from $(0,1)$ to $(1,0)$. If the direction of description of C' is reversed, so that the circle is traced out from $(1,0)$ to $(0,1)$, the limits in the integral must be interchanged and we get $+\pi/4$ for the value of the integral.

Example 3. Evaluate $\int_C \mathbf{v} \cdot d\mathbf{r}$, where $\mathbf{v} = (\mathbf{i}y - \mathbf{j}x)/(x^2 + y^2)$ and C is the circular path $x^2 + y^2 = 1$ described counterclockwise.

This integral can be evaluated as in the preceding example by substituting in the integrand $y = \sqrt{1 - x^2}$ for points on the upper half of the circle C and $y = -\sqrt{1 - x^2}$ on the lower half. It is simpler, however, to write the equations of the path in parametric form

$$\left.\begin{array}{l} x = \cos\theta, \\ y = \sin\theta, \end{array}\right\} \quad 0 \le \theta \le 2\pi. \tag{4-15}$$

We thus get

$$\mathbf{r} = \mathbf{i}x + \mathbf{j}y = \mathbf{i}\cos\theta + \mathbf{j}\sin\theta,$$

$$d\mathbf{r} = (-\mathbf{i}\sin\theta + \mathbf{j}\cos\theta)\, d\theta;$$

$$\mathbf{v} = \frac{\mathbf{i}\sin\theta - \mathbf{j}\cos\theta}{\sin^2\theta + \cos^2\theta} = \mathbf{i}\sin\theta - \mathbf{j}\cos\theta.$$

Hence

$$\int_C \mathbf{v}\cdot d\mathbf{r} = \int_0^{2\pi} (-\sin^2\theta - \cos^2\theta)\, d\theta = -2\pi.$$

If the path is traced in the clockwise direction, we get $+2\pi$.

It may prove instructive to evaluate this integral over the square C' formed by the lines $x = \pm 1$, $y = \pm 1$ (Fig. 13).

The integral over C' is equal to the sum of four integrals evaluated over the paths PQ, QR, RS, SP.

Now along PQ, $y = -1$, $dy = 0$, $\mathbf{r} = \mathbf{i}x - \mathbf{j}$, $d\mathbf{r} = \mathbf{i}\, dx$, and $\mathbf{v} = (-\mathbf{i} - \mathbf{j}x)/(x^2 + 1)$.

Hence

$$\int_{PQ} \mathbf{v}\cdot d\mathbf{r} = \int_{-1}^{1} \frac{-dx}{x^2 + 1} = -\tan^{-1}x \Big|_{-1}^{1} = -\frac{\pi}{2}.$$

Along the path QR, $x = 1$, $\mathbf{r} = \mathbf{i} + \mathbf{j}y$, $d\mathbf{r} = \mathbf{j}\, dy$, $\mathbf{v} = (\mathbf{i}y - \mathbf{j})/(1 + y^2)$, so that

$$\int_{QR} \mathbf{v}\cdot d\mathbf{r} = \int_{-1}^{1} \frac{-dy}{1 + y^2} = -\frac{\pi}{2}.$$

In a similar way we find that

$$\int_{RS} \mathbf{v}\cdot d\mathbf{r} = \int_{SP} \mathbf{v}\cdot d\mathbf{r} = -\frac{\pi}{2},$$

so that the integral

$$\int_{C'} \mathbf{v}\cdot d\mathbf{r} = 4\left(-\frac{\pi}{2}\right) = -2\pi.$$

This time we obtained the same result as we did for the circular path. In Sec. 5 we shall see that this is not an accident and that the value of this integral for every closed path enclosing the origin is -2π.

PROBLEMS

1. Evaluate the integral in Example 2 over the path C consisting of straight-line segments joining the points $(0,1)$, $(0,0)$, $(1,0)$ in that order.

2. Evaluate the integral in Example 1 over the polygonal path joining the points $(1,0,0)$, $(1,1,0)$, $(1,1,\pi/2)$ in that order.

3. Compute the value of the integral $\int_C (xy\,dx - y\,dy + dz)$ over the following paths:

    (a) Straight line joining $(0,0,0)$ and $(1,1,1)$,
    (b) Straight line joining $(0,0,1)$ and $(0,1,1)$,
    (c) Straight line joining $(0,0,0)$ and $(1,2,3)$.

Note that this integral has the form $\int_C \mathbf{v} \cdot d\mathbf{r}$.

4. Compute the integral $\int_C \mathbf{v} \cdot d\mathbf{r}$ where $\mathbf{v} = \mathbf{i}x - \mathbf{j}y + \mathbf{k}z$ over the helical path in Example 1. Also evaluate it over the rectilinear path.

5. Compute the work W done in displacing a particle of unit mass in a constant gravitational field $\mathbf{F} = -\mathbf{k}g$ along the following paths:

    (a) Straight line joining $(0,0,0)$ and $(1,1,1)$,
    (b) A polygonal path joining $(0,0,0)$, $(1,1,0)$, $(1,1,1)$ in that order. *Hint:* $W = \int_C \mathbf{F} \cdot d\mathbf{r}$.

5. Line Integrals Independent of the Path.

A special case of line integral

$$\int_C \mathbf{v} \cdot d\mathbf{r} = \int_C [v_x(x,y,z)\,dx + v_y(x,y,z)\,dy + v_z(x,y,z)\,dz], \quad (5\text{-}1)$$

in which $\mathbf{v}(x,y,z)$ is known to be the gradient of some *single-valued* scalar $u(x,y,z)$ specified in the region R containing C, frequently appears in applications. Now, if $\mathbf{v} = \nabla u$, then

$$\mathbf{v} \cdot d\mathbf{r} = \nabla u \cdot d\mathbf{r} = \frac{\partial u}{\partial x}\,dx + \frac{\partial u}{\partial y}\,dy + \frac{\partial u}{\partial z}\,dz$$

$$= du, \qquad (5\text{-}2)$$

and thus the integrand in (5-1) is an exact differential. We can, therefore, write

$$\int_C \mathbf{v} \cdot d\mathbf{r} = \int_{P_0}^{P} du = u(P) - u(P_0), \qquad (5\text{-}3)$$

where P_0 and P are the end points of the path C.

    This result is unique since u, by hypothesis, is single-valued. Moreover, since it depends only on the end points P_0 and P, we see that the value of the integral in (5-3) is independent of the path joining these points. If C_1 and C_2 are two different paths shown in Fig. 14, then

$$\int_{P_0}^{P} \nabla u \cdot d\mathbf{r} \Big|_{C_1} = \int_{P_0}^{P} \nabla u \cdot d\mathbf{r} \Big|_{C_2}. \qquad (5\text{-}4)$$

But along C_2,

$$\int_{P_0}^{P} = -\int_{P}^{P_0},$$

and we can therefore write (5-4) as

$$\int_{P_0}^{P} \nabla u \cdot d\mathbf{r} + \int_{P}^{P_0} \nabla u \cdot d\mathbf{r} = 0$$
$$C_1 \qquad\qquad C_2$$

or

$$\int_{C} \nabla u \cdot d\mathbf{r} = 0, \qquad\qquad (5\text{-}5)$$

where C is the closed path formed by C_1 and C_2.

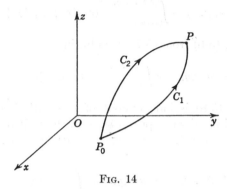

FIG. 14

The results embodied in (5-3) and (5-5) can be stated as a theorem.

THEOREM I. *The line integral* $\int_C \nabla u \cdot d\mathbf{r}$, *in which u is a single-valued continuously differentiable function in a given region R, is independent of the path, and hence it vanishes for every closed path drawn in R.*

At first glance Theorem I appears to contradict the result in Example 3 of Sec. 4, where the integral $\int_C \mathbf{v} \cdot d\mathbf{r}$ with $\mathbf{v} = (\mathbf{i}y - \mathbf{j}x)/(x^2 + y^2)$ was considered. It is easy to check that $\mathbf{v} = -\nabla \tan^{-1}(y/x)$, so that in this case $u = -\tan^{-1}(y/x)$. This integral does not vanish when evaluated over any closed path including the origin because the function $\tan^{-1}(y/x)$ is multiple-valued. Also, the continuity requirement of the theorem is not fulfilled by $\mathbf{v} = \nabla u$ at $(0,0)$.

We can also establish another important theorem which is a converse of Theorem I.

THEOREM II. *If a vector point function* $\mathbf{v}$ *is continuous in a given region R, and if the integral* $\int_C \mathbf{v} \cdot d\mathbf{r}$ *is independent of the path, then a single-valued scalar u exists such that* $\mathbf{v} = \nabla u$ *in R.*

We shall prove this theorem by actual construction of the function $u(x,y,z)$ fulfilling the conditions of this theorem.

By hypothesis, the integral $\int_C \mathbf{v} \cdot d\mathbf{r}$ when evaluated over any curve C joining $P_0(x_0,y_0,z_0)$ with $P(x,y,z)$ is independent of the path and thus defines a single-valued function

$$u(x,y,z) = \int_{(x_0,y_0,z_0)}^{(x,y,z)} (v_x \, dx + v_y \, dy + v_z \, dz). \tag{5-6}$$

We shall show that this function is, indeed, such that $\mathbf{v} = \nabla u$.

On replacing x by $x + \Delta x$ in (5-6), we get

$$u(x + \Delta x, y, z) = \int_{(x_0,y_0,z_0)}^{(x+\Delta x, \, y, \, z)} (v_x \, dx + v_y \, dy + v_z \, dz) \tag{5-7}$$

and on subtracting (5-6) from (5-7), we obtain

$$u(x + \Delta x, y, z) - u(x,y,z) = \int_{(x,y,z)}^{(x+\Delta x, \, y, \, z)} (v_x \, dx + v_y \, dy + v_z \, dz). \tag{5-8}$$

The integral in (5-8) is independent of the path joining (x,y,z) with $(x + \Delta x, \, y, \, z)$, and it suits our purposes to evaluate it over the rectilinear path $y = $ const, $z = $ const. Over such a path $dy = dz = 0$, and hence (5-8) yields

$$u(x + \Delta x, y, z) - u(x,y,z) = \int_x^{x+\Delta x} v_x(x,y,z) \, dx. \tag{5-9}$$

But by the mean-value theorem for integrals

$$\int_x^{x+\Delta x} v_x(x,y,z) \, dx = v_x(\xi,y,z) \, \Delta x \tag{5-10}$$

where $x \leq \xi \leq x + \Delta x$. The substitution from (5-10) in (5-9), on dividing by Δx, gives

$$\frac{u(x + \Delta x, y, z) - u(x,y,z)}{\Delta x} = v_x(\xi,y,z).$$

Now, if we let $\Delta x \to 0$, we get

$$\frac{\partial u}{\partial x} = v_x(x,y,z) \tag{5-11}$$

by recalling the definition of partial derivative and by the fact that v_x is continuous. In a similar way we prove that

$$\frac{\partial u}{\partial y} = v_y(x,y,z) \tag{5-12}$$

and

$$\frac{\partial u}{\partial z} = v_z(x,y,z). \tag{5-13}$$

But the statements (5-11) to (5-13) are equivalent to the vector equation $\nabla u = \mathbf{v}$, and the theorem is thus proved.

It should be carefully noted that the key hypothesis which ensured the existence of a single-valued function u such that $\mathbf{v} = \nabla u$ is that the integral $\int_C \mathbf{v} \cdot d\mathbf{r}$ is independent of the path. The integrand $\mathbf{v} \cdot d\mathbf{r} = v_x \, dx + v_y \, dy + v_z \, dz$ may be an exact differential of a multivalued function u, in which case the integral $\int_C \mathbf{v} \cdot d\mathbf{r}$ may depend on the path.

A differential form

$$v_x(x,y,z) \, dx + v_y(x,y,z) \, dy + v_z(x,y,z) \, dz, \tag{5-14}$$

in which v_x, v_y, v_z are continuously differentiable single-valued functions, is said to be *exact* if

$$v_x \, dx + v_y \, dy + v_z \, dz \equiv \frac{\partial u}{\partial x} \, dx + \frac{\partial u}{\partial y} \, dy + \frac{\partial u}{\partial z} \, dz, \tag{5-15}$$

where u is not necessarily single-valued. We can deduce a set of necessary conditions for (5-14) to be an exact differential as follows: If there exists a function $u(x,y,z)$ such that (5-15) is true, then on setting $x = $ const, $y = $ .const, $z = $ const, in turn, we get

$$v_x = \frac{\partial u}{\partial x}, \qquad v_y = \frac{\partial u}{\partial y}, \qquad v_z = \frac{\partial u}{\partial z}. \tag{5-16}$$

Differentiating the first of Eqs. (5-16) with respect to y and the second with respect to x, we get

$$\frac{\partial v_x}{\partial y} = \frac{\partial^2 u}{\partial x \, \partial y}, \qquad \frac{\partial v_y}{\partial x} = \frac{\partial^2 u}{\partial y \, \partial x}.$$

But the mixed partial derivatives in these expressions are equal, since $\partial v_x/\partial y$ and $\partial v_y/\partial x$ are continuous by hypothesis (see Sec. 2, Chap. 3). Thus

$$\frac{\partial v_x}{\partial y} = \frac{\partial v_y}{\partial x}. \tag{5-17}$$

In a similar way we obtain two more relations

$$\frac{\partial v_y}{\partial z} = \frac{\partial v_z}{\partial y}, \qquad \frac{\partial v_z}{\partial x} = \frac{\partial v_x}{\partial z}. \tag{5-18}$$

The relations (5-17) and (5-18) give a necessary condition to be satisfied by the functions v_x, v_y, v_z in (5-15) if that differential form is to be an exact differential of some function $u(x,y,z)$. We shall see in Sec. 12 that these conditions suffice to ensure the existence of a function u such that (5-14) is equal to du. However, the conditions (5-17) and (5-18) do not guarantee that u is single-valued. The question naturally arises: What supplementary conditions must be adjoined to Eqs. (5-17) and (5-18) to ensure that u is single-valued? A complete answer to this question is complex because it depends not only on the differentiability properties of v_x, v_y, v_z but also on the geometry of the region in which these functions are defined. If the region of definition of these functions is simply connected and sufficiently regular to permit the use of certain integral transformation theorems discussed in Secs. 9 to 11, then $u(x,y,z)$ determined from the formula

$$u(x,y,z) = \int_{(x_0,y_0,z_0)}^{(x,y,z)} (v_x \, dx + v_y \, dy + v_z \, dz) \qquad (5\text{-}19)$$

is single-valued. We describe these restrictions on the character of the region in the following section.

PROBLEMS

1. Show that the integral $\int_C \mathbf{r} \cdot d\mathbf{r}$ is independent of the path and find its value when computed over the rectilinear path joining $(0,0,0)$ and $(1,1,1)$. *Hint:* $\mathbf{r} \cdot d\mathbf{r} = d(\tfrac{1}{2}r^2)$.

2. Show that $(y - x^2) \, dx + (x + y^2) \, dy$ is an exact differential du, and find $u(x,y)$.

3. Show that the conditions (5-17) and (5-18) for an exact differential can be written in symmetric form as

$$\nabla \times \mathbf{v} \equiv \begin{vmatrix} \mathbf{i} & \mathbf{j} & \mathbf{k} \\ \dfrac{\partial}{\partial x} & \dfrac{\partial}{\partial y} & \dfrac{\partial}{\partial z} \\ v_x & v_y & v_z \end{vmatrix} = 0.$$

4. (a) Is $yz \, dx + zx \, dy + xy \, dz$ an exact differential du? If so, find $u(x,y,z)$. (b) Evaluate the integral $\int_C (yz \, dx + zx \, dy + xy \, dz)$ over the rectilinear path joining $(0,0,0)$ to a fixed point (x,y,z).

5. If $\mathbf{v} = \mathbf{i}\dfrac{x}{x^2 + y^2} + \mathbf{j}\dfrac{y}{x^2 + y^2}$, show that $\int_C \mathbf{v} \cdot d\mathbf{r} = 0$ for every closed path that does not include the origin. What is the value of this integral over the circular path $x^2 + y^2 = 1$? Find u such that $du = \nabla u \cdot d\mathbf{r}$.

6. Compute $\int_C \nabla u \cdot d\mathbf{r}$ where $u = \log (x^2 + y^2)$ and C is the circle $x^2 + y^2 = 1$.

7. Find a function u such that

$$du = \frac{x}{x^2 - y^2} \, dx - \frac{y}{x^2 - y^2} \, dy \qquad \text{if } x^2 > y^2.$$

8. If $\mathbf{v} = \nabla \dfrac{1}{r}$, compute $\int_{(x_0,y_0,z_0)}^{(x,y,z)} \nabla \dfrac{1}{r} \cdot d\mathbf{r}$ over some simple path that does not pass through $(0,0,0)$.

TRANSFORMATION THEOREMS

6. Simply Connected Regular Regions. The validity of several important theorems on the transformation of surface and volume integrals presented in the following sections hinges on the regularity and connectivity of domains of definition of functions appearing in the integrals. A careful characterization of such domains is extremely involved and is quite out of place in this book, but in order to aid the reader in understanding the circumstances under which the theorems in question are valid, we give a qualitative discussion.

We shall say that a given region is *connected* if every two points of it can be joined by a smooth curve that lies entirely in the region. A region is *simply connected* provided that every simple closed curve [1] drawn in its interior can be shrunk to a point by continuous deformation without crossing the boundaries of the region.

Thus, the interior of a square is simply connected, but the interior of a ring bounded by two concentric circles C_1 and C_2 is not (Fig. 15) because a closed curve C surrounding C_2 cannot be shrunk to a point without crossing C_2. Also, the interior of a sphere is simply connected, and so is the interior of the region bounded by two concentric spheres, but the interior of a torus (an anchor ring) is not simply connected. A region that is not simply connected is called *multiply connected*.

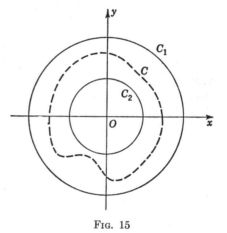

Fig. 15

In dealing with bounded three-dimensional regions we shall say that the bounding surface S is *smooth* if at each point P of the surface one can erect a normal $\mathbf{n}(P)$ which changes continuously as P moves along the surface. A surface that can be subdivided by smooth curves into a finite number of pieces each of which is smooth is called *sectionally smooth* or *piecewise smooth*. The surface of a cube is an example of a piecewise smooth surface.

The surfaces which we shall consider have two sides, although not all surfaces are two-sided. A one-sided surface can be formed, for example, by gluing the ends of a long strip in such a way that the upper side of one end of the strip is joined onto the under side of the other end (Fig. 16). If two oppositely directed normals $\overrightarrow{PN}$ and $\overrightarrow{PN'}$ are drawn at any point P of the surface, then the normal $\overrightarrow{PN}$ when carried along the path $PABCP$ will coincide with $\overrightarrow{PN'}$. It may be noted that this surface has a simple closed curve as its boundary.

---

[1] We recall that a simple closed curve is a closed curve consisting of a finite number of nonintersecting smooth curves.

We shall suppose that all surfaces with which we deal are two-sided,

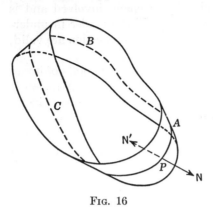

Fig. 16

piecewise smooth, and such that for some orientation of cartesian axes the projections on the coordinate planes consist of the interiors of simple closed curves. Such surfaces we shall term *regular*. If a region is a union of finitely many regions each bounded by a regular surface, it will also be called *regular*.

Regions bounded by a cone, a sphere, or a cube are regular simply connected regions. The interior of a torus is an example of a regular multiply connected region.

7. Divergence. Let a continuously differentiable vector point function $\mathbf{v}(P)$ be defined in a regular simply connected region R bounded by a closed surface σ. The surface integral of the component of $\mathbf{v}$ in the direction of the exterior unit normal $\mathbf{n}(P)$ to σ is called the *flux* of $\mathbf{v}$ over σ. Thus, the flux F is

$$F = \int_{\sigma} \mathbf{v} \cdot \mathbf{n} \, d\sigma. \qquad (7\text{-}1)$$

When $\mathbf{v}$ is the velocity of an incompressible fluid, the scalar F represents the amount of fluid issuing from σ per unit time. The points of the region at which the fluid is generated are termed *sources*, and those where it is absorbed are *sinks*. When the total strength of the sources is greater than that of the sinks, the flux is positive; when the strength is less, the flux is negative.

Consider, now, a volume element τ containing within it a point P, and denote the bounding surface of τ by σ. Then the flux of $\mathbf{v}$ over σ per unit volume is

$$\frac{\int_{\sigma} \mathbf{v} \cdot \mathbf{n} \, d\sigma}{\tau}. \qquad (7\text{-}2)$$

If we let the volume τ shrink to zero in such a way that the maximum diameter tends to zero, the quotient (7-2) will have a limit called the *divergence* of $\mathbf{v}$ at P. We denote the divergence of $\mathbf{v}$ by div $\mathbf{v}(P)$ so that

$$\operatorname{div} \mathbf{v}(P) = \lim_{\tau \to 0} \frac{\int_{\sigma} \mathbf{v} \cdot \mathbf{n} \, d\sigma}{\tau}. \qquad (7\text{-}3)$$

This quantity is a measure of the strength of the source at P.

Inasmuch as the volume τ is arbitrary, the existence and, indeed, the meaning of the limit in (7-3) are not quite obvious mathematically. One may let τ approach zero while staying similar to itself, or one may let τ become arbitrarily thin compared with its length, and so on. It is tolerably clear when suitable restrictions are imposed that all these processes yield a unique limit L, independent of the shape of τ. Moreover, the convergence is uniform in the following sense: Given any $\epsilon > 0$, there is a $\delta > 0$ such that

$$\left| \frac{\int_\sigma \mathbf{v} \cdot \mathbf{n}\, d\sigma}{\tau} - L \right| < \epsilon, \tag{7-3a}$$

provided the maximum diameter of τ is less than δ. For rectangular solids τ this fact is established in the next few paragraphs, though the proof in the general case is not presented here.

To calculate div $\mathbf{v}$ in cartesian coordinates we consider a volume τ in the shape of a rectangular parallele-piped with center at $P(x,y,z)$ and with edges Δx, Δy, Δz (Fig. 17). The flux of $\mathbf{v}$ over the surface of this parallelepiped is easily computed. Since $\mathbf{v} = \mathbf{i}v_x + \mathbf{j}v_y + \mathbf{k}v_z$, the normal component $\mathbf{v} \cdot \mathbf{n}$ of $\mathbf{v}$ over the face $ABCD$ is v_x. Hence the outflow over that face is $(v_x)_{x+\frac{1}{2}\Delta x}\, \Delta y\, \Delta z$, where $(v_x)_{x+\frac{1}{2}\Delta x}$ is the mean value of v_x over $ABCD$. Similarly, the out-flow over the parallel face $EFGH$ is

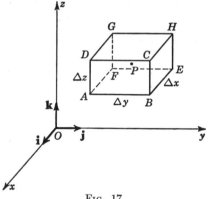

FIG. 17

$$(-v_x)_{x-\frac{1}{2}\Delta x}\, \Delta y\, \Delta z,$$

where the minus sign appears because the exterior normal to $EFGH$ is $-\mathbf{i}$ and hence $\mathbf{v} \cdot \mathbf{n} = -v_x$.

Thus the net outflow over a pair of faces parallel to the yz plane is

$$\left[(v_x)_{x+\frac{1}{2}\Delta x} - (v_x)_{x-\frac{1}{2}\Delta x}\right]\Delta y\, \Delta z \equiv v_x \Big|_{x-\frac{1}{2}\Delta x}^{x+\frac{1}{2}\Delta x} \Delta y\, \Delta z.$$

Proceeding in the same way with the remaining faces we get for the total outflow

$$\int_\sigma \mathbf{v} \cdot \mathbf{n}\, d\sigma = v_x \Big|_{x-\frac{1}{2}\Delta x}^{x+\frac{1}{2}\Delta x} \Delta y\, \Delta z + v_y \Big|_{y-\frac{1}{2}\Delta y}^{y+\frac{1}{2}\Delta y} \Delta x\, \Delta z + v_z \Big|_{z-\frac{1}{2}\Delta z}^{z+\frac{1}{2}\Delta z} \Delta x\, \Delta y.$$

Dividing by $\tau = \Delta x\, \Delta y\, \Delta z$ and taking the limit give

$$\operatorname{div} \mathbf{v}(P) = \lim \left\{ \frac{v_x \Big|_{x-\frac{1}{2}\Delta x}^{x+\frac{1}{2}\Delta x}}{\Delta x} + \frac{v_y \Big|_{y-\frac{1}{2}\Delta y}^{y+\frac{1}{2}\Delta y}}{\Delta y} + \frac{v_z \Big|_{z-\frac{1}{2}\Delta z}^{z+\frac{1}{2}\Delta z}}{\Delta z} \right\} \tag{7-4}$$

as Δx, Δy, and Δz approach zero in any manner. Now, the three limits in (7-4) are the respective partial derivatives, so that we obtain the important formula

$$\operatorname{div} \mathbf{v}(P) = \frac{\partial v_x}{\partial x} + \frac{\partial v_y}{\partial y} + \frac{\partial v_z}{\partial z}. \tag{7-5}$$

The fact that the limits are partial derivatives is suggested by the definition of partial derivative (cf. Chap. 3, Sec. 2). Further discussion is required, however, because the functions v_x, v_y, v_z are *mean values*. By the theorem of the mean [see Eq. (3-7), Chap. 3]

$$\frac{G(x + \tfrac{1}{2}\,\Delta x,\, y_1,\, z_1) - G(x - \tfrac{1}{2}\,\Delta x,\, y_1,\, z_1)}{\Delta x} = G_1(\xi, y_1, z_1),$$

where G_1 stands for $\partial G/\partial x$ and where ξ is between $x - \tfrac{1}{2}\,\Delta x$ and $x + \tfrac{1}{2}\,\Delta x$. If G_1 is continuous, then

$$|G_1(\xi, y_1, z_1) - G_1(x, y, z)|$$

is as small as we please *provided only that*

$$|\xi - x| \leq \tfrac{1}{2}\,\Delta x, |y - y_1| \leq \tfrac{1}{2}\,\Delta y, |z - z_1| \leq \tfrac{1}{2}\,\Delta z$$

with Δx, Δy, and Δz sufficiently small. Hence the mean value

$$\frac{1}{\Delta y\,\Delta z} \int_{z-\frac{1}{2}\,\Delta z}^{z+\frac{1}{2}\,\Delta z} \int_{y-\frac{1}{2}\,\Delta y}^{y+\frac{1}{2}\,\Delta y} G_1(\xi, y_1, z_1)\,dy_1\,dz_1$$

is as close as we please to $G_1(x, y, z)$, and the limit is therefore $G_1(x, y, z)$. Applying this result to (7-4) with $G = v_x$ gives $\partial v_x/\partial x$ for the first limit, and the others follow by symmetry.

The analysis shows that we may let Δx, Δy, and Δz approach zero in any manner. For instance, if $\Delta x \to 0$ first, then $\Delta y \to 0$, and finally $\Delta z \to 0$, the volume becomes a plane, a line, and finally a point. On the other hand if we set

$$\Delta x = ah, \qquad \Delta y = bh, \qquad \Delta z = ch$$

where a, b, c are constant, and let $h \to 0$, then the volume stays similar to itself. Not only is the same limit obtained in all such cases, but the departure from that limit is seen to be uniformly small, provided only that

$$\max\{|\Delta x|, |\Delta y|, |\Delta z|\}$$

is small. The remarks made in connection with (7-3a) are thus verified in this case.

In terms of the differential operator

$$\nabla = \mathbf{i}\,\frac{\partial}{\partial x} + \mathbf{j}\,\frac{\partial}{\partial y} + \mathbf{k}\,\frac{\partial}{\partial z}$$

introduced in Sec. 3, we can consider a symbolic scalar product

$$\nabla \cdot \mathbf{v} = \left(\mathbf{i}\,\frac{\partial}{\partial x} + \mathbf{j}\,\frac{\partial}{\partial y} + \mathbf{k}\,\frac{\partial}{\partial z}\right) \cdot (\mathbf{i}v_x + \mathbf{j}v_y + \mathbf{k}v_z)$$

$$\equiv \frac{\partial v_x}{\partial x} + \frac{\partial v_y}{\partial y} + \frac{\partial v_z}{\partial z}.$$

On comparing this with (7-5) we see that

$$\operatorname{div} \mathbf{v} = \nabla \cdot \mathbf{v}. \tag{7-6}$$

We can also define the *Laplacian operator* ∇^2 by the formula

$$\nabla^2 = \nabla \cdot \nabla = \left(\mathbf{i}\frac{\partial}{\partial x} + \mathbf{j}\frac{\partial}{\partial y} + \mathbf{k}\frac{\partial}{\partial z} \right) \cdot \left(\mathbf{i}\frac{\partial}{\partial x} + \mathbf{j}\frac{\partial}{\partial y} + \mathbf{k}\frac{\partial}{\partial z} \right)$$

$$= \frac{\partial^2}{\partial x^2} + \frac{\partial^2}{\partial y^2} + \frac{\partial^2}{\partial z^2} \tag{7-7}$$

and observe that if $\mathbf{v} = \nabla u$, then

$$\operatorname{div} \nabla u = \nabla \cdot \nabla u = \nabla^2 u. \tag{7-8}$$

Furthermore, if the symbol $\nabla \times \mathbf{v}$ is defined by the rule for computing vector products, we get

$$\nabla \times \mathbf{v} = \begin{vmatrix} \mathbf{i} & \mathbf{j} & \mathbf{k} \\ \dfrac{\partial}{\partial x} & \dfrac{\partial}{\partial y} & \dfrac{\partial}{\partial z} \\ v_x & v_y & v_z \end{vmatrix}$$

$$= \mathbf{i}\left(\frac{\partial v_z}{\partial y} - \frac{\partial v_y}{\partial z} \right) + \mathbf{j}\left(\frac{\partial v_x}{\partial z} - \frac{\partial v_z}{\partial x} \right) + \mathbf{k}\left(\frac{\partial v_y}{\partial x} - \frac{\partial v_x}{\partial y} \right). \tag{7-9}$$

It is worth observing that the condition $\nabla \times \mathbf{v} = 0$ requires that each component of the vector $\nabla \times \mathbf{v}$ be zero. We can therefore write Eqs. (5-17) and (5-18) (which ensure the existence of a scalar u such that $\mathbf{v} = \nabla u$) in the compact form $\nabla \times \mathbf{v} = \mathbf{0}$.

In Sec. 13 we shall deduce a formula for div $\mathbf{v}$ analogous to (7-5) when the vector $\mathbf{v}$ is referred to an arbitrary orthogonal curvilinear coordinate system. It is important to note that the definition (7-3) is independent of the choice of coordinates, so that div $\mathbf{v}$ is an invariant.

Example: If $\mathbf{v} = \mathbf{i}3x^2 + \mathbf{j}5xy^2 + \mathbf{k}xyz^3$, compute div $\mathbf{v}$ at $(1,2,3)$ and $\nabla \times \mathbf{v}$ at (x,y,z).
Since $v_x = 3x^2$, $v_y = 5xy^2$, $v_z = xyz^3$, the substitution in (7-5) yields div $\mathbf{v} = 6x + 10xy + 3xyz^2$. At the point $(1,2,3)$ div $\mathbf{v} = 6 + 20 + 54 = 80$. If $\mathbf{v}$ is interpreted as the velocity vector of fluid particles, we conclude that the point $(1,2,3)$ is a source of the fluid.

To compute $\nabla \times \mathbf{v}$ we use formula (7-9) and find

$$\nabla \times \mathbf{v} = \mathbf{i}(xz^3 - 0) + \mathbf{j}(0 - yz^3) + \mathbf{k}(5y^2 - 0).$$

Since this vector is not identically zero, we conclude that no scalar function $u(x,y,z)$ exists such that $\mathbf{v} = \nabla u$.

PROBLEMS

1. Find $\operatorname{div} \mathbf{v}$ if (a) $\mathbf{v} = \mathbf{i}x + \mathbf{j}y + \mathbf{k}z$, (b) $\mathbf{v} = \mathbf{i}(x/r) + \mathbf{j}(y/r) + \mathbf{k}(z/r)$, where $r = \sqrt{x^2 + y^2 + z^2} \neq 0$. (c) $\mathbf{v} = \mathbf{i}(z - y) + \mathbf{j}(x - z) + \mathbf{k}(y - x)$.

2. Compute $\nabla^2(1/r)$ and $\nabla^2 r$, where $r = \sqrt{x^2 + y^2 + z^2}$.

3. Show that (a) $\operatorname{div}(\mathbf{u} + \mathbf{v}) = \operatorname{div}\mathbf{u} + \operatorname{div}\mathbf{v}$, (b) $\operatorname{div}(u\mathbf{v}) = \nabla \cdot (u\mathbf{v}) = \nabla u \cdot \mathbf{v} + u \nabla \cdot \mathbf{v}$, (c) $\operatorname{div}(\mathbf{u} \times \mathbf{v}) = \nabla \cdot (\mathbf{u} \times \mathbf{v}) = \mathbf{v} \cdot (\nabla \times \mathbf{u}) - \mathbf{u} \cdot (\nabla \times \mathbf{v})$.

4. Show that $\operatorname{div}(\mathbf{r} \times \mathbf{a}) = 0$ if $\mathbf{r} = \mathbf{i}x + \mathbf{j}y + \mathbf{k}z$ and $\mathbf{a}$ is a constant vector.

5. Find $\operatorname{div}(u\mathbf{v})$ if $u = x^2 + y^2 + z^2$ and $\mathbf{v} = \mathbf{i}x + \mathbf{j}y + \mathbf{k}z$. Also find $\operatorname{div}(\nabla u \times \mathbf{v})$.

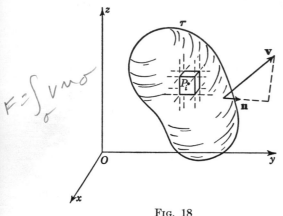

FIG. 18

8. The Divergence Theorem. An important relationship connecting the surface integral (7-1) for the flux of a vector field with the volume integral of its divergence is deduced in this section. The resulting integral transformation theorem, known as the *Gauss* or *divergence theorem*, is fundamental to all developments in mechanics of continuous media.

Let a continuously differentiable vector function $\mathbf{v}(P)$ be defined in a regular simply connected region τ bounded by the surface σ. We subdivide τ into k volume cells $\Delta\tau_i$ in the shape of rectangular boxes and parts of boxes (Fig. 18) and compute the divergence

$$\operatorname{div} \mathbf{v}(P_i) = \lim_{\Delta\tau_i \to 0} \frac{\int_{\Delta\sigma_i} (\mathbf{v}\cdot\mathbf{n})\,d\sigma}{\Delta\tau_i} \tag{8-1}$$

for each cell $\Delta\tau_i$. [The role of τ and σ in (7-3) is now taken by $\Delta\tau_i$ and $\Delta\sigma_i$.] On recalling the definition of limit, we can rewrite (8-1) in the form

$$\int_{\Delta\sigma_i} \mathbf{v}\cdot\mathbf{n}\,d\sigma = (\operatorname{div}\mathbf{v})_i\,\Delta\tau_i + \epsilon_i\Delta\tau_i, \tag{8-2}$$

where the $\epsilon_i \to 0$ as $\Delta\tau_i \to 0$ and where $(\operatorname{div}\mathbf{v})_i \equiv \operatorname{div}\mathbf{v}(P_i)$. We next form the sum

$$\sum_{i=1}^{k} \int_{\Delta\sigma_i} \mathbf{v}\cdot\mathbf{n}\,d\sigma = \sum_{i=1}^{k} (\operatorname{div}\mathbf{v})_i\,\Delta\tau_i + \sum_{i=1}^{k} \epsilon_i\,\Delta\tau_i \tag{8-3}$$

over all the cells and observe that the surface integrals in (8-3) over the interfaces of adjacent cells vanish, since the exterior normals $\mathbf{n}$ to the common faces of the boxes point in opposite directions. Thus the surviving terms in the sum on the left in (8-3) correspond to surface elements belonging to the exterior surface σ, and hence this sum is equal to $\int_\sigma \mathbf{v} \cdot \mathbf{n} \, d\sigma$.

The sum $\sum\limits_{i=1}^{k} (\operatorname{div} \mathbf{v})_i \, \Delta\tau_i$ approximates the volume integral $\int_\tau \operatorname{div} \mathbf{v} \, d\tau$,
and indeed, the approximation can be made as close as we wish by suitably decreasing the size (that is, the maximum diameter) of the cells.[1] The sum of terms $\sum\limits_{i=1}^{k} \epsilon_i \, \Delta\tau_i$ involves products of small quantities ϵ_i and $\Delta\tau_i$, and it becomes arbitrarily small [2] in the course of the process described. We thus conclude from (8-3) that

$$\int_\sigma \mathbf{v} \cdot \mathbf{n} \, d\sigma = \int_\tau \operatorname{div} \mathbf{v} \, d\tau. \tag{8-4}$$

The result embodied in this formula is the *divergence theorem*. This theorem expresses certain surface integrals as volume integrals, and since it contains no reference to any special coordinate system, the result is true in all coordinate systems. In particular, if $\mathbf{v}$ and $\mathbf{n}$ are expressed in terms of their cartesian components

$$\mathbf{n} = \mathbf{i} \cos (x,n) + \mathbf{j} \cos (y,n) + \mathbf{k} \cos (z,n),$$

we can write (8-4), on recalling (7-5), as

$$\int_\sigma [v_x \cos (x,n) + v_y \cos (y,n) + v_z \cos (z,n)] \, d\sigma = \int_\tau \left(\frac{\partial v_x}{\partial x} + \frac{\partial v_y}{\partial y} + \frac{\partial v_z}{\partial z} \right) d\tau.$$

$$\tag{8-5}$$

Example 1. Verify the theorem (8-4) for $\mathbf{v} = \mathbf{i}(x/r) + \mathbf{j}(y/r) + \mathbf{k}(z/r)$, where $r = \sqrt{x^2 + y^2 + z^2}$ and the region τ is the sphere $x^2 + y^2 + z^2 \le a^2$.

We readily find that

$$\frac{\partial v_x}{\partial x} = \frac{r^2 - x^2}{r^3}, \qquad \frac{\partial v_y}{\partial y} = \frac{r^2 - y^2}{r^3}, \qquad \frac{\partial v_z}{\partial z} = \frac{r^2 - z^2}{r^3}$$

so that by (7-5)

$$\operatorname{div} \mathbf{v} = \frac{3r^2 - r^2}{r^3} = \frac{2}{r}.$$

Now

$$\int_\tau \operatorname{div} \mathbf{v} \, d\tau = \int_\tau \frac{2}{r} \, d\tau$$

[1] Of course, the number of cells k must increase without limit as this process is carried out.

[2] This is true by virtue of the uniformity emphasized earlier [see (7-3a)]. Thus, given $\epsilon > 0$, we can make the subdivision so fine that $|\epsilon_i| < \epsilon$ for all the ϵ_is at once. In that case

$$|\Sigma \epsilon_i \, \Delta\tau_i| < \epsilon\Sigma \, \Delta\tau_i = \epsilon V,$$

where V is the volume of the region.

and it is easy to evaluate this integral in spherical coordinates, since in spherical coordinates $d\tau = r^2 \sin \theta \, d\theta \, d\phi \, dr$ (see Prob. 2, Sec. 2). We have

$$\int_\tau \operatorname{div} \mathbf{v} \, d\tau = \int_\tau \frac{2}{r} \, d\tau = 8 \int_0^a \int_0^{\pi/2} \int_0^{\pi/2} \frac{2}{r} r^2 \sin \theta \, d\theta \, d\phi \, dr = 4\pi a^2.$$

On the other hand

$$\int_\sigma \mathbf{v} \cdot \mathbf{n} \, d\sigma = \int_\sigma 1 \cdot d\sigma = 4\pi a^2,$$

since $\mathbf{v} \cdot \mathbf{n} = 1$, for $\mathbf{n} = \mathbf{i}(x/r) + \mathbf{j}(y/r) + \mathbf{k}(z/r)$ is directed along the radius of the sphere.

Example 2. Prove with the aid of the divergence theorem the relation

$$\int_\tau \nabla u \, d\tau = \int_\sigma u \mathbf{n} \, d\sigma, \tag{8-6}$$

where u is a continuously differentiable scalar point function.

Now in cartesian coordinates

$$\mathbf{n} = \mathbf{i} \cos (x,n) + \mathbf{j} \cos (y,n) + \mathbf{k} \cos (z,n)$$

$$= \mathbf{i}(\mathbf{n} \cdot \mathbf{i}) + \mathbf{j}(\mathbf{n} \cdot \mathbf{j}) + \mathbf{k}(\mathbf{n} \cdot \mathbf{k})$$

and

$$\nabla u = \mathbf{i} \frac{\partial u}{\partial x} + \mathbf{j} \frac{\partial u}{\partial y} + \mathbf{k} \frac{\partial u}{\partial z},$$

so that (8-6) is equivalent to the three equations

$$\int_\tau \frac{\partial u}{\partial x} \, d\tau = \int_\sigma (\mathbf{i}u) \cdot \mathbf{n} \, d\sigma,$$

$$\int_\tau \frac{\partial u}{\partial y} \, d\tau = \int_\sigma (\mathbf{j}u) \cdot \mathbf{n} \, d\sigma,$$

$$\int_\tau \frac{\partial u}{\partial z} \, d\tau = \int_\sigma (\mathbf{k}u) \cdot \mathbf{n} \, d\sigma.$$

But these are the special cases of formula (8-5) applied to vectors $\mathbf{v} = \mathbf{i}u$, $\mathbf{v} = \mathbf{j}u$, $\mathbf{v} = \mathbf{k}u$, and thus the correctness of (8-6) is established.

Formula (8-6) can serve as a basis for a definition of ∇u in the form

$$\nabla u = \lim_{\tau \to 0} \frac{\int_\sigma u \mathbf{n} \, d\sigma}{\tau} \tag{8-7}$$

analogous to (7-3).

PROBLEMS

1. Prove that $\int_\sigma \mathbf{r} \cdot \mathbf{n} \, d\sigma = 3\tau$, where $\mathbf{r}$ is the position vector of a point on the surface of a regular simply connected region of volume τ. *Hint:* Apply the divergence theorem to the surface integral.

2. Compute $\int_\sigma \mathbf{v} \cdot \mathbf{n} \, d\sigma$, where σ is the surface of the cylinder $x^2 + y^2 = a^2$ bounded by the planes $z = 0$, $z = b$, and where $\mathbf{v} = \mathbf{i}x - \mathbf{j}y + \mathbf{k}z$.

$h =$

3. Find $\int_\sigma \mathbf{r} \cdot \mathbf{n} \, d\sigma$, where $\mathbf{r}$ is the position vector of points on the surface of the ellipsoid $(x^2/a^2) + (y^2/b^2) + (z^2/c^2) = 1$.

4. Find the value of $\int_\sigma \mathbf{v} \cdot \mathbf{n} \, d\sigma$, where $\mathbf{v} = r^2(\mathbf{i}x + \mathbf{j}y + \mathbf{k}z)$, $r^2 = x^2 + y^2 + z^2$, and σ is the surface of the sphere $x^2 + y^2 + z^2 = a^2$. Compute the integral directly and also with the aid of the divergence theorem.

5. If $\mathbf{v} = \nabla u$ and $\nabla^2 u = \rho$, where ρ is a specified scalar point function, show that

$$\int_\sigma \frac{du}{dn} \, d\sigma = \int_\tau \rho \, d\tau.$$

Hint: Recall that

$$\frac{du}{dn} = \nabla u \cdot \mathbf{n}.$$

6. Use the divergence theorem to show that

$$\int_\tau \operatorname{div} (u \, \nabla v) d\tau = \int_\sigma u \, \nabla v \cdot \mathbf{n} \, d\sigma.$$

Show that this equation can be written as

$$\int_\tau u\nabla^2 v \, d\tau = \int_\sigma u \frac{dv}{dn} \, d\sigma - \int \nabla u \cdot \nabla v \, d\tau.$$

This important relation is known as *Green's first identity*.

7. Using Prob. 6 obtain the symmetrical form of Green's identity, namely,

$$\int_\tau (u\nabla^2 v - v\nabla^2 u) \, d\tau = \int_\sigma \left(u \frac{dv}{dn} - v \frac{du}{dn} \right) d\sigma,$$

which is also known as *Green's second identity*. (It is assumed in this identity that both u and v have continuous second derivatives.) Green's identities are perhaps the most frequently encountered transformation formulas in mathematical physics.

8. If the twice-differentiable function u satisfies Laplace's equation $\nabla^2 u = 0$, what is the value of $\int_\sigma \frac{du}{dn} \, d\sigma$? *Hint:* Set $v = 1$ in Green's second identity, Prob. **7**.

9. Green's Theorem. Line Integral in the Plane. Because of the importance in applications of line integrals defined over plane curves, we deduce here a special form of the divergence theorem commonly called *Green's theorem in the plane.* Let a vector function

$$\mathbf{v} = \mathbf{i}v_x(x,y) + \mathbf{j}v_y(x,y) \quad (9\text{-}1)$$

with continuously differentiable components v_x, v_y be defined in the plane region R bounded by a simple closed curve C (Fig. 19). If we construct a right cylinder of height h with base R and apply formula (8-5)

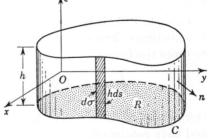

FIG. 19

to the region τ bounded by this cylinder, we get

$$\int_{\sigma} [v_x \cos (x,n) + v_y \cos (y,n)] \, d\sigma = \int_{\tau} \left(\frac{\partial v_x}{\partial x} + \frac{\partial v_y}{\partial y} \right) d\tau. \qquad (9\text{-}2)$$

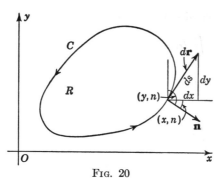

FIG. 20

The exterior unit normals $\mathbf{n}$ to the top and bottom bases of the cylinder are $\mathbf{k}$ and $-\mathbf{k}$, respectively, and hence $\cos (x,n) = \cos (y,n) = 0$ on the bases of the cylinder. The contribution to the surface integral in (9-2) from the bases is, therefore, zero, and the integral need be evaluated only over the lateral surface. The element of surface $d\sigma$ of the lateral surface is $d\sigma = h \, ds$, where ds is the arc element of C, and the volume element $d\tau$ can be taken in the form $d\tau = h \, dx \, dy$. We can thus write (9-2) as

$$\int_C [v_x \cos (x,n) + v_y \cos (y,n)] h \, ds = \iint_R \left(\frac{\partial v_x}{\partial x} + \frac{\partial v_y}{\partial y} \right) h \, dy \, dx, \quad (9\text{-}3)$$

where n is the exterior normal to C. But from Fig. 20

$$\cos (x,n) = \frac{dy}{ds}, \qquad \cos (y,n) = -\frac{dx}{ds}, \qquad (9\text{-}4)$$

so that on dividing by h, Eq. (9-3) yields

$$\int_C (v_x \, dy - v_y \, dx) = \iint_R \left(\frac{\partial v_x}{\partial x} + \frac{\partial v_y}{\partial y} \right) dx \, dy, \qquad (9\text{-}5)$$

where in tracing C the region R remains on the left; that is, the path C is described in the positive direction.

Formula (9-5) is Green's theorem in the plane. The function $-v_y(x,y)$ is sometimes denoted by $M(x,y)$ and $v_x(x,y)$ by $N(x,y)$, so that (9-5) assumes the form

$$\int_C (M \, dx + N \, dy) = -\iint_R \left(\frac{\partial M}{\partial y} - \frac{\partial N}{\partial x} \right) dx \, dy. \qquad (9\text{-}6)$$

Our restrictions on v_x and v_y demand that $M(x,y)$ and $N(x,y)$ be continuous and have continuous partial derivatives in the plane region R.

We see that if $\partial M / \partial y = \partial N / \partial x$ at all points of R, then $\int_C (M \, dx + N \, dy) = 0$ over every simple closed curve C drawn in R. Conversely, if the line integral in (9-6) vanishes for every simple closed path C in R, then

$$\iint_R \left(\frac{\partial M}{\partial y} - \frac{\partial N}{\partial x} \right) dx\, dy = 0 \qquad (9\text{-}7)$$

for every region R. This enables us to prove that

$$\frac{\partial M}{\partial y} = \frac{\partial N}{\partial x} \qquad (9\text{-}8)$$

at every point of R; for suppose that

$$\frac{\partial M}{\partial y} - \frac{\partial N}{\partial x} \neq 0 \qquad (9\text{-}9)$$

at some point P, and for definiteness let this difference be positive. Since $(\partial M/\partial y) - (\partial N/\partial x)$ is continuous, there is a small region R' including P throughout which the integrand in (9-7) is positive. But this means that the integral is also positive, and since (9-7) is known to yield zero for *every* region R, we have a contradiction. Thus, the hypothesis (9-9) is untenable.

We summarize these results as a theorem.

THEOREM. *A necessary and sufficient condition for the line integral $\int_C (M\, dx + N\, dy)$ to vanish for every simple closed path drawn in a simply connected region R, where M, N, $\partial M/\partial y$, and $\partial N/\partial x$ are continuous, is that $\partial M/\partial y = \partial N/\partial x$ at all points of R.*

The vanishing of the integral

$$\int_C (M\, dx + N\, dy) \qquad (9\text{-}10)$$

over every closed path is equivalent to the statement that this integral is independent of the path, and it follows from Sec. 5 that the expression $M\, dx + N\, dy$ is an exact or total differential du of a single-valued function $u(x,y)$ determined by the formula [cf. Eq. (5-6)]

$$u(x,y) = \int_{(x_0, y_0)}^{(x,y)} (M\, dx + N\, dy). \qquad (9\text{-}11)$$

We recognize condition (9-8) to be identical with (5-17).

The theorem (9-6) can be extended to suitable plane multiply connected domains in the following way. If R is a doubly connected region bounded externally by a contour C_0 and internally by a contour C_1 (Fig. 21), we introduce a "cut" C joining some point P_0 on C_0 with P_1 on C_1. The cut C can be visualized as a slit in the region R, forming the boundary $C + C_0 + C_1$ of the slit region. The slit region R is simply connected, and if we apply formula (9-6) to it, we get

$$-\iint_R \left(\frac{\partial M}{\partial y} - \frac{\partial N}{\partial x}\right) dy\, dx$$

$$= \oint_{C_0} (M\, dx + N\, dy) + \int_{P_0}^{P_1} (M\, dx + N\, dy)$$

$$+ \oint_{C_1} (M\, dx + N\, dy) + \int_{P_1}^{P_0} (M\, dx + N\, dy). \quad (9\text{-}12)$$

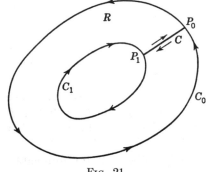 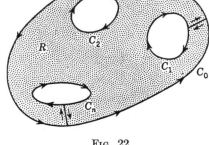

FIG. 21   FIG. 22

The arrows on the integrals in (9-12) refer to the direction of integration along C_0 and C_1 as shown in Fig. 21, and the integrals $\int_{P_0}^{P_1}$ and $\int_{P_1}^{P_0}$ are evaluated along C in the direction indicated by the limits. Inasmuch as $\int_{P_0}^{P_1} = -\int_{P_1}^{P_0}$, Eq. (9-12) reduces to

$$-\iint_R \left(\frac{\partial M}{\partial y} - \frac{\partial N}{\partial x}\right) dy\, dx$$

$$= \oint_{C_0} (M\, dx + N\, dy) + \oint_{C_1} (M\, dx + N\, dy). \quad (9\text{-}13)$$

An obvious extension of this result to the region R bounded externally by C_0 and internally by n contours C_i (Fig. 22) yields

$$-\iint_R \left(\frac{\partial M}{\partial y} - \frac{\partial N}{\partial x}\right) dy\, dx$$

$$= \oint_{C_0} (M\, dx + N\, dy) + \sum_{i=1}^{n} \oint_{C_i} (M\, dx + N\, dy). \quad (9\text{-}14)$$

An important result follows directly from formula (9-14) if it is supposed that continuously differentiable functions M and N are such that

$$\frac{\partial M}{\partial y} = \frac{\partial N}{\partial x} \qquad\qquad (9\text{-}15)$$

in the region R. If (9-15) holds in R, the double integral in (9-14) vanishes and we get

$$\oint_{C_0} (M\ dx + N\ dy) = - \sum_{i=1}^{n} \oint_{C_i} (M\ dx + N\ dy)$$

$$= \sum_{i=1}^{n} \oint_{C_i} (M\ dx + N\ dy).$$

Thus, the line integral over the exterior contour C_0 taken in the counter-clockwise direction is equal to the sum of the line integrals over the interior contours C_i taken in the same direction. In particular, if there is only one interior contour C_1 (Fig. 21), we conclude that

$$\int_{C_0} (M\ dx + N\ dy) = \int_{C_1} (M\ dx + N\ dy). \tag{9-16}$$

This integral need not vanish. If, however, continuously differentiable functions M and N are also defined in the region interior to C_1 and satisfy the condition (9-15) in that region, then the value of the integral $\int_{C_1} (M\ dx + N\ dy)$ is zero, inasmuch as the integral on the left in (9-16) vanishes by theorem (9-6).

PROBLEMS

1. Show that the following integrals are independent of the path and find their values:

(a) $\displaystyle\int_{(0,1)}^{(1,2)} [(x^2 + y^2)\ dx + 2xy\ dy]$,

(b) $\displaystyle\int_{(0,0)}^{(1,1)} \left[\frac{1 - y^2}{(1 + x)^3}\ dx + \frac{y}{(1 + x)^2}\ dy \right]$, $x \neq -1$,

(c) $\displaystyle\int_{(0,0)}^{(\pi/2,\pi/2)} (y \cos x\ dx + \sin x\ dy)$,

(d) $\displaystyle\int_{(0,0)}^{(\frac{1}{2},\frac{1}{2})} \left[\frac{xy\ dx}{\sqrt{1 - x^2}} - \sqrt{1 - x^2}\ dy \right]$, $x^2 < 1$,

(e) $\displaystyle\int_{(1,1)}^{(2,3)} (x + 1)\ dx + (y + 1)\ dy$.

2. Write each of the integrals in Prob. 1 in the form $\int \mathbf{v} \cdot d\mathbf{r}$, and determine $u(x,y)$ such that $\nabla u = \mathbf{v}$.

3. Find the value of

$$\int_C \left(\frac{-y\ dx}{x^2 + y^2} + \frac{x\ dy}{x^2 + y^2} \right),$$

where C bounds the region interior to the circle $x^2 + y^2 = 4$ and exterior to the circle $x^2 + y^2 = 1$. What is the value of the integral (a) over the circle $x^2 + y^2 = 4$? (b) Over the circle $x^2 + y^2 = 1$?

4. Compute the integral

$$\iint_R \text{div } \mathbf{v}\ dx\ dy,$$

where $\mathbf{v} = \mathbf{i}x + \mathbf{j}y$ over the region R bounded by the circles $x^2 + y^2 = 1$ and $x^2 + y^2 = 4$.

5. Use formula (9-13) to evaluate the integral $\int_C (-y\,dx + x\,dy)$, where C is the path bounding the region R in Prob. 4. What is the value of this integral over the path $x^2 + y^2 = 1$? Over the path $x^2 + y^2 = 4$?

10. Curl of a Vector Field. We saw in Sec. 7 that with every continuously differentiable vector function $\mathbf{v}(P)$ one can associate a scalar div $\mathbf{v}(P)$ defined by the formula

$$\operatorname{div} \mathbf{v}(P) = \lim_{\tau \to 0} \frac{\int_\sigma \mathbf{n} \cdot \mathbf{v}\,d\sigma}{\tau} \tag{10-1}$$

which has a simple physical meaning.

We show next that $\mathbf{v}(P)$ can also be associated with a vector field called curl $\mathbf{v}$, defined by an analogous formula

$$\operatorname{curl} \mathbf{v}(P) = \lim_{\tau \to 0} \frac{\int_\sigma \mathbf{n} \times \mathbf{v}\,d\sigma}{\tau}. \tag{10-2}$$

We shall see that curl $\mathbf{v}(P)$ bears an interesting relation to the concept of *circulation* in the vector field.

Let $\mathbf{v}(P)$ be defined in some regular three-dimensional region R, and let C be a simple closed curve in R bounding a plane area A. At a given point P of A we construct a unit normal $\boldsymbol{\nu}$ so directed that $\boldsymbol{\nu}$ points in the direction of an advancing right-hand screw when C is traversed in the positive sense (Fig. 23). We then construct a right cylinder of small height

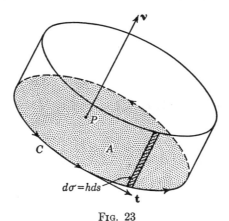

Fig. 23

h with elements parallel to $\boldsymbol{\nu}$ and with base A and denote its surface by σ and its volume by τ.

*n∥v ∴ n×v=0
by def of x product
since sin θ ⊖ =0
+ line ⊖ =0*

Since $\boldsymbol{v}$ is a constant vector, formula (10-2) yields

$$\boldsymbol{v}\cdot\operatorname{curl}\boldsymbol{v} = \lim_{\tau \to 0} \frac{\int_{\sigma}\boldsymbol{v}\cdot\mathbf{n}\times\mathbf{v}\,d\sigma}{\tau}.$$ (10-3)

But along the bases of the cylinder $\boldsymbol{v}$ is parallel to the normal $\mathbf{n}$, and hence the triple scalar product $\boldsymbol{v}\cdot\mathbf{n}\times\mathbf{v}$ vanishes over the bases. Accordingly, the integral in (10-3) need be computed only over the lateral surface of the cylinder. We can thus write

$$\boldsymbol{v}\cdot\operatorname{curl}\boldsymbol{v} = \lim_{\tau \to 0} \frac{\int_{C}\boldsymbol{v}\cdot\mathbf{n}\times\mathbf{v}h\,ds}{\tau},$$ (10-4)

since $d\sigma = h\,ds$.

But $\boldsymbol{v}\cdot\mathbf{n}\times\mathbf{v} = \mathbf{v}\cdot\boldsymbol{v}\times\mathbf{n}$ by Chap. 4, Eq. (6-4), and $\boldsymbol{v}\times\mathbf{n} = \mathbf{t}$ along C, where $\mathbf{t}$ is the unit tangent vector to C. Thus the integrand in (10-4) can be written

$$\boldsymbol{v}\cdot\mathbf{n}\times\mathbf{v}h\,ds = \mathbf{v}\cdot\boldsymbol{v}\times\mathbf{n}h\,ds = \mathbf{v}\cdot\mathbf{t}h\,ds = h\mathbf{v}\cdot d\mathbf{r}$$

where $d\mathbf{r}$ is the differential of the position vector $\mathbf{r}$ of a point on C. If we further note that $\tau = hA$, we can rewrite (10-4) as

$$\boldsymbol{v}\cdot\operatorname{curl}\boldsymbol{v} = \lim_{A \to 0} \frac{\int_{C}\mathbf{v}\cdot d\mathbf{r}}{A}.$$ (10-5)

The line integral $\int_{C}\mathbf{v}\cdot d\mathbf{r}$ is called the *circulation of* $\mathbf{v}$ *along* C. If $\mathbf{v}$ represents the velocity of a fluid, then $\mathbf{v}\cdot d\mathbf{r} = \mathbf{v}\cdot\mathbf{t}\,ds$ takes account of the tangential component of velocity $\mathbf{v}$ and a fluid particle moving with this velocity circulates along C. A particle moving with velocity $\mathbf{v}\cdot\mathbf{n}$ normal to C, on the other hand, crosses C. That is, it flows either into or out of the region bounded by C. Hence formula (10-5) provides a measure of *the circulation per unit area* at the point P. This formula can be used to compute the cartesian components of the vector curl $\mathbf{v}$ by taking $\boldsymbol{v}$ successively as the $\mathbf{i}$, $\mathbf{j}$, $\mathbf{k}$ base vectors and by evaluating the limit in the right-hand member. It is somewhat simpler, however, to get the formula for curl $\mathbf{v}$ in cartesian coordinates from the definition (10-2) with the aid of the divergence theorem.[1]

Now the components of $\mathbf{n}\times\mathbf{v}$ in cartesian coordinates are $\mathbf{n}\times\mathbf{v}\cdot\mathbf{i}$, $\mathbf{n}\times\mathbf{v}\cdot\mathbf{j}$, $\mathbf{n}\times\mathbf{v}\cdot\mathbf{k}$. Consequently,

$$\mathbf{n}\times\mathbf{v} = \mathbf{i}(\mathbf{n}\times\mathbf{v}\cdot\mathbf{i}) + \mathbf{j}(\mathbf{n}\times\mathbf{v}\cdot\mathbf{j}) + \mathbf{k}(\mathbf{n}\times\mathbf{v}\cdot\mathbf{k})$$
$$\equiv \mathbf{i}(\mathbf{n}\cdot\mathbf{v}\times\mathbf{i}) + \mathbf{j}(\mathbf{n}\cdot\mathbf{v}\times\mathbf{j}) + \mathbf{k}(\mathbf{n}\cdot\mathbf{v}\times\mathbf{k}).$$ (10-6)

---

[1] Also the uniformity of approach mentioned in connection with (7-3a) will then yield the same kind of uniformity for (10-2).

On inserting from (10-6) in (10-2) we get

$$\text{curl } \mathbf{v} = \mathbf{i} \lim_{\tau \to 0} \frac{\int_\sigma (\mathbf{n} \cdot \mathbf{v} \times \mathbf{i}) \, d\sigma}{\tau} + \mathbf{j} \lim_{\tau \to 0} \frac{\int_\sigma (\mathbf{n} \cdot \mathbf{v} \times \mathbf{j}) \, d\sigma}{\tau}$$

$$+ \mathbf{k} \lim_{\tau \to 0} \frac{\int_\sigma (\mathbf{n} \cdot \mathbf{v} \times \mathbf{k}) \, d\sigma}{\tau}. \quad (10\text{-}7)$$

But a comparison of the right-hand member of (10-7) with (10-1) enables us to rewrite (10-7) in the form

$$\text{curl } \mathbf{v} = \mathbf{i} \text{ div } (\mathbf{v} \times \mathbf{i}) + \mathbf{j} \text{ div } (\mathbf{v} \times \mathbf{j}) + \mathbf{k} \text{ div } (\mathbf{v} \times \mathbf{k}). \quad (10\text{-}8)$$

On inserting

$$\mathbf{v} = \mathbf{i} v_x + \mathbf{j} v_y + \mathbf{k} v_z$$

in (10-8) we get

$$\text{curl } \mathbf{v} = \mathbf{i} \text{ div } (\mathbf{j} v_z - \mathbf{k} v_y) + \mathbf{j} \text{ div } (\mathbf{k} v_x - \mathbf{i} v_z) + \mathbf{k} \text{ div } (\mathbf{i} v_y - \mathbf{j} v_x),$$

and a simple calculation making use of formula (7-5) yields the desired result

$$\text{curl } \mathbf{v} = \mathbf{i} \left(\frac{\partial v_z}{\partial y} - \frac{\partial v_y}{\partial z} \right) + \mathbf{j} \left(\frac{\partial v_x}{\partial z} - \frac{\partial v_z}{\partial x} \right) + \mathbf{k} \left(\frac{\partial v_y}{\partial x} - \frac{\partial v_x}{\partial y} \right). \quad (10\text{-}9)$$

If we recall the expression (3-13) for the symbolic vector ∇, we can write (10-9) compactly as

$$\text{curl } \mathbf{v} = \begin{vmatrix} \mathbf{i} & \mathbf{j} & \mathbf{k} \\ \dfrac{\partial}{\partial x} & \dfrac{\partial}{\partial y} & \dfrac{\partial}{\partial z} \\ v_x & v_y & v_z \end{vmatrix} \equiv \nabla \times \mathbf{v}. \quad (10\text{-}10)$$

An analogous formula for curl $\mathbf{v}$ in orthogonal curvilinear coordinates is given in Sec. 13, and several useful relations involving the use of the curl operator are recorded in Prob. 1.

Example: Compute curl $\mathbf{v}$ if $\mathbf{v} = \mathbf{i} xyz + \mathbf{j} xyz^2 + \mathbf{k} x^3 yz$.
The substitution of $v_x = xyz$, $v_y = xyz^2$, $v_z = x^3 yz$ in (10-9) yields

$$\text{curl } \mathbf{v} = \mathbf{i}(x^3 z - 2xyz) + \mathbf{j}(xy - 3x^2 yz) + \mathbf{k}(yz^2 - xz).$$

PROBLEMS

1. Show that under suitable hypothesis on continuity of the derivatives:

(a) $\operatorname{curl}(\mathbf{A} + \mathbf{B}) = \operatorname{curl}\mathbf{A} + \operatorname{curl}\mathbf{B}$;

(b) $\operatorname{div}\operatorname{curl}\mathbf{A} = \nabla \cdot \nabla \times \mathbf{A} = 0$;

(c) $\operatorname{curl}\operatorname{curl}\mathbf{A} = \nabla\operatorname{div}\mathbf{A} - \nabla^2\mathbf{A}$, where $\nabla^2\mathbf{A} \equiv \mathbf{i}\nabla^2 A_x + \mathbf{j}\nabla^2 A_y + \mathbf{k}\nabla^2 A_z$;

(d) $\operatorname{curl}\nabla u = \nabla \times (\nabla u) = 0$;

(e) $\operatorname{curl}(u\mathbf{A}) = \nabla \times (u\mathbf{A}) = u\nabla \times \mathbf{A} + \nabla u \times \mathbf{A}$;

(f) $\operatorname{div}(\mathbf{A} \times \mathbf{B}) = \mathbf{B}\cdot\operatorname{curl}\mathbf{A} - \mathbf{A}\cdot\operatorname{curl}\mathbf{B}$;

(g) $\operatorname{curl}(\mathbf{A} \times \mathbf{B}) = \mathbf{A}\nabla\cdot\mathbf{B} - \mathbf{B}\nabla\cdot\mathbf{A} + (\mathbf{B}\cdot\nabla)\mathbf{A} - (\mathbf{A}\cdot\nabla)\mathbf{B}$, where $(\mathbf{A}\cdot\nabla)\mathbf{B} \equiv \mathbf{C}$ is the vector with components

$$C_x = A_x\frac{\partial B_x}{\partial x} + A_y\frac{\partial B_x}{\partial y} + A_z\frac{\partial B_x}{\partial z},$$

$$C_y = A_x\frac{\partial B_y}{\partial x} + A_y\frac{\partial B_y}{\partial y} + A_z\frac{\partial B_y}{\partial z},$$

$$C_z = A_x\frac{\partial B_z}{\partial x} + A_y\frac{\partial B_z}{\partial y} + A_z\frac{\partial B_z}{\partial z}.$$

2. Compute $\operatorname{curl}\mathbf{A}$ if $r = \sqrt{x^2 + y^2 + z^2}$ and

(a) $\mathbf{A} = \mathbf{i}x + \mathbf{j}y + \mathbf{k}z$, (b) $\mathbf{A} = \mathbf{i}(x/r) + \mathbf{j}(y/r) + \mathbf{k}(z/r)$, (c) $\mathbf{A} = \mathbf{r}r^n$, where $\mathbf{r} = \mathbf{i}x + \mathbf{j}y + \mathbf{k}z$.

3. If $\mathbf{a}$ is a constant vector and $\mathbf{r} = \mathbf{i}x + \mathbf{j}y + \mathbf{k}z$, show that

(a) $\nabla(\mathbf{a}\cdot\mathbf{r}) = \mathbf{a}$, (b) $\nabla \times (\mathbf{a} \times \mathbf{r}) = 2\mathbf{a}$.

4. Let a rigid body rotate with constant angular velocity Ω about some axis through a point O in the body. If $\mathbf{r}$ is the position vector of a point $P(x,y,z)$ relative to a set of axes fixed at O, the velocity $\mathbf{v}$ of P is $\mathbf{v} = \mathbf{v}_0 + \Omega \times \mathbf{r}$, where $\mathbf{v}_0$ is the velocity of O relative to some reference frame fixed in space (cf. Sec. 8, Chap. 4). Show that $\operatorname{curl}\mathbf{v} = 2\Omega$, so that the angular velocity Ω at any instant of time is equal to one-half the curl of the velocity field. Note that the velocity $\mathbf{v}_0$ is independent of the coordinates (x,y,z) of points in the body.

5. Show from geometrical considerations that the angle $d\theta$ subtended at the origin by an element ds of a curve is $d\theta = (\mathbf{n}\cdot\mathbf{r}/r^2)\,ds$.

6. A solid angle ω subtended by a surface σ is measured by the area subtended by the angle on a unit sphere S with center at the vertex of ω. Show that

$$\omega = -\int_\sigma \mathbf{n}\cdot\nabla\frac{1}{r}\,d\sigma,$$

where $\mathbf{r}$ is the position vector of points on σ measured from the vertex of ω and $\mathbf{n}$ is the unit normal to σ. *Hint:* Apply the divergence theorem to a volume formed by the bundle of rays issuing from the solid angle and by the areas cut out by these rays on S and on σ.

7. Referring to Prob. 6, show from geometrical considerations that

$$d\omega = \frac{\mathbf{n}\cdot\mathbf{r}}{r^3}\,d\sigma.$$

11. Stokes's Theorem.   This useful integral transformation theorem enables one to reduce the evaluation of certain surface integrals to the calculation of line integrals.

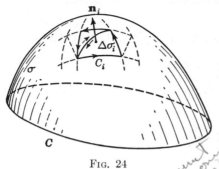

Fig. 24

Let R be a three-dimensional region in which $\mathbf{v}(P)$ is a continuously differentiable vector function and σ a regular open surface embedded in R. We suppose that the edge of σ is a simple closed curve C (Fig. 24).   Then it is true that

$$\int_{\sigma} \mathbf{n} \cdot \text{curl } \mathbf{v} \, d\sigma = \int_{C} \mathbf{v} \cdot d\mathbf{r}, \quad (11\text{-}1)$$

where $\mathbf{n}$ is a unit normal to σ and the line integral over C is evaluated in the direction determined by the chosen positive orientation of $\mathbf{n}$.

To establish formula (11-1), which is known as *Stokes's theorem*, we follow a procedure similar to that used in Sec. 8 to prove the divergence theorem.   We subdivide σ into k approximately planar elements of area $\Delta\sigma_i$, each bounded by a simple contour C_i (say triangular) (see Fig. 24). Then formula (10-5) with $\mathbf{v}$ replaced by $\mathbf{n}_i$ and A by $\Delta\sigma_i$ when applied to the element bounded by C_i yields

$$\mathbf{n}_i \cdot \text{curl } \mathbf{v}(P_i) \, \Delta\sigma_i = \int_{C_i} \mathbf{v} \cdot d\mathbf{r} + \epsilon_i \, \Delta\sigma_i. \qquad (11\text{-}2)$$

On summing these expressions over the entire surface σ we get

$$\sum_{i=1}^{k} \mathbf{n}_i \cdot \text{curl } \mathbf{v}(P_i) \, \Delta\sigma_i = \sum_{i=1}^{k} \int_{C_i} \mathbf{v} \cdot d\mathbf{r} + \sum_{i=1}^{k} \epsilon_i \, \Delta\sigma_i. \qquad (11\text{-}3)$$

But the line integrals in (11-3) when summed over the common boundaries of adjacent elements cancel out, since such boundaries are traversed twice in opposite directions.   The surviving terms yield the line integral $\int_{C} \mathbf{v} \cdot d\mathbf{r}$ over the boundary C.   If the number k of elements $\Delta\sigma_i$ is allowed to increase indefinitely, so that the greatest linear dimensions of the $\Delta\sigma_i$ tend to zero, the sum on the left becomes the surface integral $\int_{\sigma} \mathbf{n} \cdot \text{curl } \mathbf{v} \, d\sigma$.   The sum $\sum_{i=1}^{k} \epsilon_i \, \Delta\sigma_i$ tends to zero as in the discussion of (8-3).[1]   Thus, formula (11-1) is correct.   It should be noted that once a positive direction for the normal $\mathbf{n}$ has been agreed upon, the positive direction of description of the contours C_i, and hence of C, is determined by the right-hand-screw convention.

---

[1] That is, if all $|\epsilon_i|$ are less than ϵ, this sum is less than ϵS, where S is the area of σ.

how is M found?

If σ is a closed surface, the sum of the line integrals over the contours C_i is zero, and in that event $\int_\sigma \mathbf{n} \cdot \operatorname{curl} \mathbf{v} \, d\sigma = 0$.

We note further that if $\operatorname{curl} \mathbf{v} = \mathbf{0}$ in R, then $\int_C \mathbf{v} \cdot d\mathbf{r} = 0$ for an *arbitrary* closed contour C. Hence the line integral $\int_{P_0}^{P} \mathbf{v} \cdot d\mathbf{r}$ is independent of the path and thus defines a function $u(P)$, such that $du = \mathbf{v} \cdot d\mathbf{r}$. We can show conversely [1] that if the line integral in (11-1) vanishes for every closed path C in R, then $\operatorname{curl} \mathbf{v} = \mathbf{0}$ throughout R. Reference to (10-9) shows that the condition $\operatorname{curl} \mathbf{v} = \mathbf{0}$ is identical with Eqs. (5-17) and (5-18), ensuring that $\mathbf{v} \cdot d\mathbf{r} = du$.

Example: Evaluate $\int_\sigma \mathbf{n} \cdot \operatorname{curl} \mathbf{v} \, d\sigma$ over the surface $z = +\sqrt{a^2 - x^2 - y^2}$ if

$$\mathbf{v} = \mathbf{i}2y - \mathbf{j}x + \mathbf{k}z.$$

The surface in this example is a hemisphere of radius a, and it is clear that

$$\mathbf{n} = \mathbf{i}\frac{x}{r} + \mathbf{j}\frac{y}{r} + \mathbf{k}\frac{z}{r},$$

where $\mathbf{r} = \mathbf{i}x + \mathbf{j}y + \mathbf{k}z$ is the position vector for points on the hemisphere. We readily check that

$$\operatorname{curl} \mathbf{v} = \begin{vmatrix} \mathbf{i} & \mathbf{j} & \mathbf{k} \\ \dfrac{\partial}{\partial x} & \dfrac{\partial}{\partial y} & \dfrac{\partial}{\partial z} \\ 2y & -x & z \end{vmatrix} = -3\mathbf{k}.$$

Hence $\int_\sigma \mathbf{n} \cdot \operatorname{curl} \mathbf{v} \, d\sigma = -3 \int_\sigma \dfrac{z}{a} \, d\sigma.$

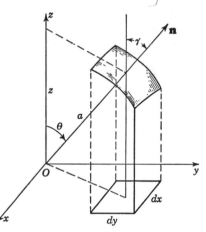

FIG. 25

This integral can be easily evaluated by noting that (Fig. 25) $d\sigma = \sec \gamma \, dx \, dy$, where γ is the angle between the normal $\mathbf{n}$ and the positive direction of the z axis (cf. Chap. 3, Sec. 17). But from Fig. 25, $\sec \gamma = \sec \theta = a/z$, so that

$$-3 \int_\sigma \frac{z}{a} \, d\sigma = -3 \iint_A dx \, dy = -3\pi a^2, \tag{11-4}$$

since the region of integration A is a circle of radius a. The reader will check this result by taking $d\sigma = a^2 \sin \theta \, d\theta \, d\phi$ as the element of area of the surface of the sphere in spherical coordinates.

To obtain the result (11-4) from Stokes's theorem (11-1) we compute $\int_C \mathbf{v} \cdot d\mathbf{r}$, where C is the boundary of the circle $x^2 + y^2 = a^2$. Since $d\mathbf{r} = \mathbf{i} \, dx + \mathbf{j} \, dy + \mathbf{k} \, dz$, we have

$$\int_C \mathbf{v} \cdot d\mathbf{r} = \int_C (2y \, dx - x \, dy + z \, dz). \tag{11-5}$$

[1] See the corresponding discussion in Sec. 9.

But along C we have $dz = 0$, and the equation of C may be taken in the form

$$x = a \cos \phi,$$

$$y = a \sin \phi, \qquad 0 \leq \phi \leq 2\pi.$$

We thus get for (11-5)

$$\int_C \mathbf{v} \cdot d\mathbf{r} = -\int_0^{2\pi} a^2 (2 \sin^2 \phi + \cos^2 \phi) \, d\phi = -3\pi a^2.$$

PROBLEMS

1. Show that for the special case of a plane region bounded by a simple closed curve C, Stokes's theorem reduces to Green's theorem (9-6).

2. If $\mathbf{v} = \mathbf{i}y + \mathbf{j}z + \mathbf{k}x$ and σ is the surface of the paraboloid $z = 1 - x^2 - y^2$, $z \geq 0$, compute $\int_\sigma \mathbf{n} \cdot \text{curl } \mathbf{v} \, d\sigma$.

3. What is the value of the surface integral $\int_\sigma \mathbf{n} \cdot \text{curl } \mathbf{v} \, d\sigma$ if $\mathbf{v} = \mathbf{i}y^2 + \mathbf{j}xy + \mathbf{k}xz$ and σ is the hemisphere $x^2 + y^2 + z^2 = 1$, $z \geq 0$? Evaluate this integral directly and by Stokes's theorem.

4. Compute $\int_C \mathbf{v} \cdot d\mathbf{r}$ if $\mathbf{v} = \mathbf{i}(x^2 + y^2) + \mathbf{j}(x^2 + z^2) + \mathbf{k}y$ and C is the circle $x^2 + y^2 = 4$ in the plane $z = 0$.

5. Prove that the area A of the plane region bounded by a simple closed curve C in the xy plane is given by

$$A = \frac{1}{2} \int_C (x \, dy - y \, dx)$$

when C is described in the positive direction. *Hint:* Use Green's theorem (9-6).

6. Verify Stokes's theorem if $\mathbf{v} = \mathbf{i}y^2 + \mathbf{j}xy - \mathbf{k}xz$ and σ is the hemisphere $z = \sqrt{a^2 - x^2 - y^2}$.

ILLUSTRATIONS AND APPLICATIONS

12. Solenoidal and Irrotational Fields. Let a continuously differentiable vector function $\mathbf{v}(P)$ be specified in a region R. If curl $\mathbf{v} = \mathbf{0}$ at every point of R, we say that $\mathbf{v}(P)$ is an *irrotational vector field*. If $\mathbf{v}(P)$ is such that div $\mathbf{v} = 0$, the field is said to be *solenoidal*. The importance of solenoidal and irrotational vectors in applications derives from the fact that every continuously differentiable vector function $\mathbf{v}(P)$ defined in a regular simply connected region R can be expressed as the sum of two vector functions, one of which is solenoidal and the other irrotational. We do not prove this fact here because it depends on demonstrating the existence of solutions of certain partial differential equations,[1] and it would carry us too far in the study of potential theory. Accordingly, we limit our discussion to proofs of two basic theorems concerned with solenoidal and irrotational vector fields.

[1] See Prob. 6. A discussion of the system of equations in question is contained in M. Mason and W. Weaver, "The Electromagnetic Field," pp. 352–365, University of Chicago Press, Chicago, 1932.

Handwritten at top of page:

$\operatorname{div} \mathbf{v} = \nabla \cdot \mathbf{v} = 0$ solonoidal

$\operatorname{curl} \mathbf{v} = 0 = \nabla \times \mathbf{v} = 0$ urotational

THEOREM I. *A necessary and sufficient condition that a continuously differentiable vector* $\mathbf{v}(P)$ *be irrotational in a simply connected regular region* R *is that* $\mathbf{v} = \nabla u$, *where* u *is a single-valued scalar function with continuous second derivatives.*

We suppose, first, that $\mathbf{v} = \nabla u$; then

$$\operatorname{curl} \mathbf{v} = \operatorname{curl} \nabla u = \begin{vmatrix} \mathbf{i} & \mathbf{j} & \mathbf{k} \\ \dfrac{\partial}{\partial x} & \dfrac{\partial}{\partial y} & \dfrac{\partial}{\partial z} \\ \dfrac{\partial u}{\partial x} & \dfrac{\partial u}{\partial y} & \dfrac{\partial u}{\partial z} \end{vmatrix} = 0,$$

as follows at once on expanding the determinant and noting the equality of the mixed partial derivatives of $u(x,y,z)$.

Conversely, if we suppose that curl $\mathbf{v} = 0$ in R, then it follows from the concluding paragraph of Sec. 11 that $du = \mathbf{v} \cdot d\mathbf{r}$ and hence $\mathbf{v} = \nabla u$.

THEOREM II. *The continuously differentiable vector function* $\mathbf{v}(P)$ *is solenoidal in a region bounded by a regular surface if, and only if, it is equal to the curl of some vector* $\mathbf{w}$ *with continuous second derivatives.*

Let us suppose, first, that $\mathbf{v} = \operatorname{curl} \mathbf{w}$. Then

$$\operatorname{div} \mathbf{v} = \operatorname{div} \operatorname{curl} \mathbf{w} \equiv 0,$$

as follows from a simple calculation [1] making use of formulas (7-5) and (10-9). Conversely, if div $\mathbf{v} = 0$, we show that a vector $\mathbf{w}$ can be constructed such that $\mathbf{v} = \operatorname{curl} \mathbf{w}$. It suffices to show that the system of equations curl $\mathbf{w} = \mathbf{v}$, or

$$\frac{\partial w_z}{\partial y} - \frac{\partial w_y}{\partial z} = v_x,$$

$$\frac{\partial w_x}{\partial z} - \frac{\partial w_z}{\partial x} = v_y, \tag{12-1}$$

$$\frac{\partial w_y}{\partial x} - \frac{\partial w_x}{\partial y} = v_z,$$

has a solution for w_x, w_y, w_z whenever

$$\frac{\partial v_x}{\partial x} + \frac{\partial v_y}{\partial y} + \frac{\partial v_z}{\partial z} = 0. \tag{12-2}$$

[1] See Prob. 1b, Sec. 10.

We show how to construct one such solution in rectangular domains. If we take $w_x \equiv 0$, then the second and third of Eqs. (12-1) require that

$$\frac{\partial w_z}{\partial x} = -v_y(x,y,z), \qquad \frac{\partial w_y}{\partial x} = v_z(x,y,z). \tag{12-3}$$

On integrating (12-3) with respect to x and treating y and z as constants, we get

$$w_z = -\int_{x_0}^{x} v_y(x,y,z) \, dx + \phi(y,z),$$

$$w_y = \int_{x_0}^{x} v_z(x,y,z) \, dx + \psi(y,z), \tag{12-4}$$

where ϕ and ψ are arbitrary differentiable functions of y and z. If we insert these solutions in the first of Eqs. (12-1), we get

$$v_x = -\int_{x_0}^{x} \left(\frac{\partial v_y}{\partial y} + \frac{\partial v_z}{\partial z} \right) dx + \frac{\partial \phi}{\partial y} - \frac{\partial \psi}{\partial z}. \tag{12-5}$$

But from (12-2)

$$\frac{\partial v_y}{\partial y} + \frac{\partial v_z}{\partial z} = -\frac{\partial v_x}{\partial x},$$

so that (12-5) yields

$$v_x = \int_{x_0}^{x} \frac{\partial v_x}{\partial x} \, dx + \frac{\partial \phi}{\partial y} - \frac{\partial \psi}{\partial z}$$

$$= v_x(x,y,z) - v_x(x_0,y,z) + \frac{\partial \phi}{\partial y} - \frac{\partial \psi}{\partial z}.$$

This equation can be satisfied by taking $\psi \equiv 0$ and

$$\phi(y,z) = \int_{y_0}^{y} v_x(x_0,y,z) \, dy. \tag{12-6}$$

Thus, one solution of the system (12-1) and (12-2) is

$$w_x = 0,$$

$$w_y = \int_{x_0}^{x} v_z(x,y,z) \, dx,$$

$$w_z = -\int_{x_0}^{x} v_y(x,y,z) \, dx + \int_{y_0}^{y} v_x(x_0,y,z) \, dy. \tag{12-7}$$

The proof clearly indicates that $\mathbf{w}$ is not unique. Indeed, if we take $\mathbf{w}$ with components given by (12-7) and add to it ∇u, where u is an arbitrary scalar function with continuous second derivatives, then

$$\text{curl } (\mathbf{w} + \nabla u) = \text{curl } \mathbf{w}$$

inasmuch as curl $\nabla u \equiv 0$.[1]

---

[1] Conversely, if curl $\mathbf{w}_1 = \mathbf{v}$, then curl $(\mathbf{w}_1 - \mathbf{w}) = 0$ and $\mathbf{w}_1 - \mathbf{w} = \nabla u$ by Theorem I. Thus every solution $\mathbf{w}_1$ is representable in the form $\mathbf{w} + \nabla u$, where $\mathbf{w}$ is the particular solution found in the text.

We remark in conclusion that whenever the divergence and curl of a vector function $\mathbf{v}$ are specified in the interior of a regular simply connected region and the normal component of $\mathbf{v}$ is known over the surface bounding the region, then there is just one vector function $\mathbf{v}$ satisfying these conditions. This uniqueness theorem is important in many applications. The reader may prove it by following suggestions given in Prob. 7 below.

PROBLEMS

1. Show that $\mathbf{v} = \mathbf{i}2xyz + \mathbf{j}x^2z + \mathbf{k}x^2y$ is irrotational, and find $u(x,y,z)$ such that $\mathbf{v} = \nabla u$.

2. Show that $\mathbf{v} = \mathbf{i}(z - y) + \mathbf{j}(x - z) + \mathbf{k}(y - x)$ is solenoidal, and find $\mathbf{w}(x,y,z)$ such that $\mathbf{v} = \operatorname{curl} \mathbf{w}$.

3. Is $\mathbf{v} = \mathbf{i}(y^2 + 2xz^2 - 1) + \mathbf{j}2xy + \mathbf{k}2x^2z$ irrotational? If so, find u such that $\mathbf{v} = \nabla u$.

4. Is $\mathbf{v} = \mathbf{i}(x^3z - 2xyz) + \mathbf{j}(xy - 3x^2yz) + \mathbf{k}(yz^2 - xz)$ solenoidal? If so, find a $\mathbf{w}$ such that $\mathbf{v} = \operatorname{curl} \mathbf{w}$.

5. Prove that $\mathbf{v} = r^n\mathbf{r}$, where $\mathbf{r} = \mathbf{i}x + \mathbf{j}y + \mathbf{k}z$, is irrotational. Is it solenoidal?

6. Let $\mathbf{w} = \mathbf{u} + \mathbf{v}$, where $\mathbf{u}$ is irrotational and $\mathbf{v}$ solenoidal in a given suitably restricted region R. Then there exists a vector $\mathbf{q}$ such that $\mathbf{v} = \operatorname{curl} \mathbf{q}$ and a scalar ϕ such that $\mathbf{u} = \nabla\phi$. Show that ϕ and $\mathbf{q}$ satisfy the following partial differential equations:

$$\nabla^2\phi = \operatorname{div} \mathbf{w}, \qquad \nabla \operatorname{div} \mathbf{q} - \nabla^2\mathbf{q} = \operatorname{curl} \mathbf{w}.$$

7. If $\mathbf{v}$ is a continuously differentiable vector function defined in a regular simply connected region R bounded by the surface σ and if

$$\operatorname{curl} \mathbf{v} = \mathbf{f}(x,y,z), \qquad \operatorname{div} \mathbf{v} = g(x,y,z)$$

in R and $\mathbf{v} \cdot \mathbf{n} = h(x,y,z)$ on σ, show that $\mathbf{v}$ is uniquely determined in R by these conditions.

Outline of the Solution. Assume that there are two such vectors, $\mathbf{v} = \mathbf{v}_1$ and $\mathbf{v} = \mathbf{v}_2$. With $\mathbf{w} = \mathbf{v}_1 - \mathbf{v}_2$, show that there is a u such that $\mathbf{w} = \nabla u$, and deduce $\nabla^2 u = 0$. By applying the divergence theorem to the vector $u\nabla u$, show that $\int_R (\nabla u) \cdot (\nabla u)\, d\tau = 0$. Since $(\nabla u) \cdot (\nabla u) \geq 0$, this integral can vanish only if $\nabla u \equiv 0$.

13. Gradient, Divergence, and Curl in Orthogonal Curvilinear Coordinates.

In this section we record the expressions for the gradient, divergence, curl, and Laplacian in orthogonal curvilinear coordinates. These can be obtained from the definitions (7-3), (8-7), and (10-2) in a manner so similar to that used to obtain formulas valid in cartesian coordinates that we dispense with the details of calculations.

As in Sec. 1, we suppose that a transformation

$$y_i = y_i(x_1,x_2,x_3), \qquad i = 1, 2, 3,$$

wherein the variables y_i are cartesian, defines a curvilinear coordinate system x. We suppose that the coordinates x_i are orthogonal so that the quadratic differential form (2-13) has the structure

$$(ds)^2 = g_{11}(dx_1)^2 + g_{22}(dx_2)^2 + g_{33}(dx_3)^2.$$

We denote the *unit base vectors* along the x_i coordinate lines by $\mathbf{e}_1$, $\mathbf{e}_2$, $\mathbf{e}_3$ and represent a vector $\mathbf{v}(P)$ in the form

$$\mathbf{v} = \mathbf{e}_1 v_1 + \mathbf{e}_2 v_2 + \mathbf{e}_3 v_3. \tag{13-1}$$

The volume element $d\tau$ formed by the coordinate surfaces $x_i = \text{const}$ and $x_i + dx_i = \text{const}$ (Fig. 26) has the shape of a rectangular parallel-epiped with edges [1] $ds_i = \sqrt{g_{ii}}\, dx_i$. Hence the areas $d\sigma_{ij}$ of its faces are

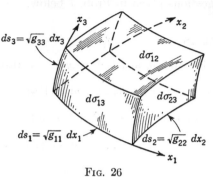

FIG. 26

$$d\sigma_{12} = \sqrt{g_{11}g_{22}}\, dx_1\, dx_2,$$

$$d\sigma_{13} = \sqrt{g_{11}g_{33}}\, dx_1\, dx_3, \tag{13-2}$$

$$d\sigma_{23} = \sqrt{g_{22}g_{33}}\, dx_2\, dx_3,$$

and its volume $d\tau$ is

$$d\tau = \sqrt{g_{11}g_{22}g_{33}}\, dx_1\, dx_2\, dx_3. \tag{13-3}$$

To compute div $\mathbf{v}$ we calculate the flux $\int_\sigma \mathbf{n}\cdot\mathbf{v}\, d\sigma$ over the surface of the volume element $d\tau$ and divide it by its volume (13-3). A calculation like that performed in Sec. 7 yields the result

$$\text{div } \mathbf{v} = \frac{1}{h_1 h_2 h_3}\left[\frac{\partial(v_1 h_2 h_3)}{\partial x_1} + \frac{\partial(v_2 h_1 h_3)}{\partial x_2} + \frac{\partial(v_3 h_1 h_2)}{\partial x_3}\right] \tag{13-4}$$

where $h_i \equiv \sqrt{g_{ii}}$.

A similar but slightly longer computation also yields the formula

$$\text{curl } \mathbf{v} = \mathbf{e}_1 \frac{1}{h_3 h_2}\left[\frac{\partial(h_3 v_3)}{\partial x_2} - \frac{\partial(h_2 v_2)}{\partial x_3}\right]$$

$$+ \mathbf{e}_2 \frac{1}{h_1 h_3}\left[\frac{\partial(h_1 v_1)}{\partial x_3} - \frac{\partial(h_3 v_3)}{\partial x_1}\right] + \mathbf{e}_3 \frac{1}{h_1 h_2}\left[\frac{\partial(h_2 v_2)}{\partial x_1} - \frac{\partial(h_1 v_1)}{\partial x_2}\right], \tag{13-5}$$

which can be written more compactly as

$$\text{curl } \mathbf{v} = \frac{1}{h_1 h_2 h_3}\begin{vmatrix} h_1\mathbf{e}_1 & h_2\mathbf{e}_2 & h_3\mathbf{e}_3 \\ \dfrac{\partial}{\partial x_1} & \dfrac{\partial}{\partial x_2} & \dfrac{\partial}{\partial x_3} \\ h_1 v_1 & h_2 v_2 & h_3 v_3 \end{vmatrix}. \tag{13-6}$$

[1] See Sec. 2.

Finally, the formula for the gradient of a scalar $u(x_1,x_2,x_3)$, as follows from (8-7), is [1]

$$\nabla u = \frac{\mathbf{e}_1}{h_1} \frac{\partial u}{\partial x_1} + \frac{\mathbf{e}_2}{h_2} \frac{\partial u}{\partial x_2} + \frac{\mathbf{e}_3}{h_3} \frac{\partial u}{\partial x_3}. \tag{13-7}$$

Inasmuch as div $\nabla u = \nabla^2 u$, it is easy to check that the substitution of $\mathbf{v} = \nabla u$ in (13-4) yields

$$\nabla^2 u = \frac{1}{h_1 h_2 h_3} \left[\frac{\partial}{\partial x_1} \left(\frac{h_2 h_3}{h_1} \frac{\partial u}{\partial x_1} \right) + \frac{\partial}{\partial x_2} \left(\frac{h_1 h_3}{h_2} \frac{\partial u}{\partial x_2} \right) + \frac{\partial}{\partial x_3} \left(\frac{h_1 h_2}{h_3} \frac{\partial u}{\partial x_3} \right) \right].$$

$$\tag{13-8}$$

In cylindrical coordinates defined by the transformation

$$x = r \cos \theta,$$

$$y = r \sin \theta,$$

$$z = z,$$

the metric coefficients are [2]

$$g_{11} = 1, \qquad g_{22} = r^2, \qquad g_{33} = 1,$$

so that

$$h_1 = 1, \qquad h_2 = r, \qquad h_3 = 1.$$

Accordingly, formulas (13-4) and (13-8) yield

$$\text{div } \mathbf{v} = \frac{1}{r} \frac{\partial (r v_r)}{\partial r} + \frac{1}{r} \frac{\partial v_\theta}{\partial \theta} + \frac{\partial v_z}{\partial z},$$

$$\nabla^2 u = \frac{1}{r} \frac{\partial \left(r \frac{\partial u}{\partial r} \right)}{\partial r} + \frac{1}{r^2} \frac{\partial^2 u}{\partial \theta^2} + \frac{\partial^2 u}{\partial z^2},$$

where

$$\mathbf{v} = \mathbf{r}_1 v_r + \mathbf{\theta}_1 v_\theta + \mathbf{k} v_z$$

$\mathbf{r}_1$, $\mathbf{\theta}_1$, $\mathbf{k}$ being unit vectors in the direction of increasing r, θ, and z (Fig. 3). In spherical coordinates determined by

$$x = \rho \sin \theta \cos \phi,$$

$$y = \rho \sin \theta \sin \phi,$$

$$z = \rho \cos \theta,$$

---

[1] Henceforth we shall use the symbol ∇u to mean grad u in curvilinear coordinates as well as in cartesian.

[2] See Sec. 2.

$h_1 = 1$, $h_2 = \rho$, $h_3 = \rho \sin \theta$, as follows from Prob. 2 in Sec. 2.   On making use of (13-4) and (13-8) we find that in spherical coordinates

$$\operatorname{div} \mathbf{v} = \frac{1}{\rho^2} \frac{\partial(\rho^2 v_\rho)}{\partial \rho} + \frac{1}{\rho \sin \theta} \frac{\partial(\sin \theta \, v_\theta)}{\partial \theta} + \frac{1}{\rho \sin \theta} \frac{\partial v_\phi}{\partial \phi},$$

$$\nabla^2 u = \frac{1}{\rho^2} \frac{\partial\left(\rho^2 \dfrac{\partial u}{\partial \rho}\right)}{\partial \rho} + \frac{1}{\rho^2 \sin \theta} \frac{\partial\left(\sin \theta \dfrac{\partial u}{\partial \theta}\right)}{\partial \theta} + \frac{1}{\rho^2 \sin^2 \theta} \frac{\partial^2 u}{\partial \phi^2},$$

where
$$\mathbf{v} = \boldsymbol{\rho}_1 v_\rho + \boldsymbol{\theta}_1 v_\theta + \boldsymbol{\phi}_1 v_\phi,$$

and $\boldsymbol{\rho}_1$, $\boldsymbol{\theta}_1$, $\boldsymbol{\phi}_1$ are the unit vectors in the direction of increasing coordinate lines shown in Fig. 4.

PROBLEMS

1. Write out the expressions for ∇u in spherical and cylindrical coordinates.

2. What is the form of ∇^2 in parabolic coordinates (u,v,ϕ) for which

$$(ds)^2 = (u^2 + v^2)[(du)^2 + (dv)^2] + u^2 v^2 (d\phi)^2?$$

3. The force $\mathbf{F}$ per unit charge due to a dipole of constant strength p is

$$\mathbf{F} = \mathbf{r}_1(2p \cos \theta / r^3) + \boldsymbol{\theta}_1(p \sin \theta / r^3),$$

where r, θ are polar coordinates.   Compute $\operatorname{div} \mathbf{F}$ and $\operatorname{curl} \mathbf{F}$.

14. Conservative Force Fields.

In the concluding sections of this chapter we illustrate the use of vector analysis in the treatment of several problems drawn from mechanics, hydrodynamics, and the theory of heat flow in solids.

When a particle of matter is displaced along a path C in a given field of force $\mathbf{F}$, the work W expended in moving it is determined by the integral

$$W = \int_C \mathbf{F} \cdot d\mathbf{r}. \tag{14-1}$$

The integral (14-1), in general, will have different values for different paths joining the same two points in the force field.   If (14-1) is independent of the path, the field $\mathbf{F}$ is said to be *conservative*.

We show next that the force field determined by Newton's inverse-square law of attraction is conservative.[1]   According to Newton's law a particle of mass m located at a point P is acted on by a force $\mathbf{F}$ whose magnitude is proportional to m and inversely proportional to the square of the distance r from P to the center of attraction O.   Thus,

$$\mathbf{F} = -\frac{km}{r^2} \mathbf{r}_1, \tag{14-2}$$

---

[1] A similar discussion applies to electrostatic force fields determined by Coulomb's law, since the mathematical structures of Newton's and Coulomb's laws are identical.

where $\mathbf{r}_1$ is the unit vector directed from O to P. The positive constant k is determined experimentally; it clearly depends on the choice of units of measure of $\mathbf{F}$. Physically the law (14-2) represents the force of attraction of the mass m at P by a unit mass located at O.

If we rewrite (14-2) in the form

$$\mathbf{F} = -\frac{km}{r^3}\mathbf{r}, \qquad (14\text{-}3)$$

where $\mathbf{r} = r\mathbf{r}_1$, and insert it in the work integral (14-1), we get for the work done in displacing the particle from P_1 to P_2 along the path C,

$$W = \int_C -\frac{km}{r^3}\mathbf{r}\cdot d\mathbf{r}. \qquad (14\text{-}4)$$

But $\mathbf{r}\cdot d\mathbf{r} = \tfrac{1}{2}d(\mathbf{r}\cdot\mathbf{r}) = r\,dr$, so that we can write (14-4) as

$$W = \int_C -\frac{km}{r^2}\,dr = \int_C km\,d\left(\frac{1}{r}\right) = km\left[\frac{1}{r}\right]_{P_1}^{P_2}. \qquad (14\text{-}5)$$

The integral (14-5) is clearly independent of the path joining P_1 and P_2, and if we denote $\mathbf{r}(P_2)$ by r_2 and $\mathbf{r}(P_1)$ by r_1 (Fig. 27), we can write

$$W = km\left(\frac{1}{r_2} - \frac{1}{r_1}\right).$$

The scalar function

$$u \equiv \frac{km}{r} \qquad (14\text{-}6)$$

appearing in (14-5) is known as the *gravitational potential*. It is easy to check that

$$\nabla u = \nabla\left(\frac{km}{r}\right) = -\frac{km}{r^3}\mathbf{r} = \mathbf{F}. \quad (14\text{-}7)$$

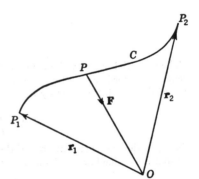

FIG. 27

The function $u(P)$ in (14-6) is continuous at all points except when $r = 0$, and since div $\nabla u = \nabla^2 u$, we readily find that the gravitational potential (14-6) satisfies Laplace's equation

$$\nabla^2 u = 0$$

except when $r = 0$.

The gravitational potential at a point P due to a continuous distribution of mass of density ρ is defined by the integral

$$u(P) = \int_\tau \frac{k\rho\,d\tau}{r}, \qquad (14\text{-}8)$$

where r is the distance from the element of mass $dm = \rho\,d\tau$ to the point P.

The force of attraction of the unit mass located at P by the body is determined by the formula $\mathbf{F} = \nabla u$.

The study of the properties of the scalar function $u(P)$ defined by (14-8) is in the province of potential theory, and we shall encounter it once more in Chap. 6.

Example: Let us compute the gravitational potential $u(P)$ of a thin homogeneous spherical shell of radius a at a point P whose distance from the center of the shell is R (Fig. 28).

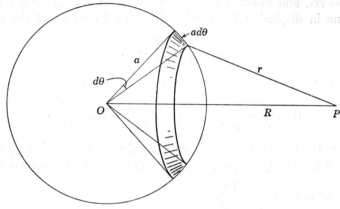

FIG. 28

The potential at P can be computed by summing potentials of the ring-shaped elements of matter bounded by the cones with the semivertical angles θ and $\theta + d\theta$. The area of the zone intercepted by these cones is $2\pi a \sin \theta \, a \, d\theta$, so that

$$u(P) = \int_0^\pi \frac{k\rho 2\pi a^2 \sin \theta \, d\theta}{r}, \qquad (14\text{-}9)$$

where ρ is the mass per unit area of the shell.

From the cosine law of trigonometry

$$r = \sqrt{a^2 + R^2 - 2aR \cos \theta},$$

and we can write (14-9) as

$$u(P) = 2\pi k\rho a^2 \int_0^\pi \frac{\sin \theta \, d\theta}{\sqrt{a^2 + R^2 - 2aR \cos \theta}}$$

$$= \frac{2\pi k\rho a}{R} [\sqrt{(R+a)^2} - \sqrt{(R-a)^2}], \qquad \text{if } R > a,$$

$$= \frac{2\pi k\rho a}{R} [\sqrt{(R+a)^2} - \sqrt{(a-R)^2}], \qquad \text{if } R < a.$$

If P is outside the shell, $R > a$, and we have the result

$$u(P) = \frac{4\pi k\rho a^2}{R} \equiv \frac{kM}{R}, \qquad (14\text{-}10)$$

where $M = 4\pi a^2 \rho$ is the mass of the shell.

When P is inside the shell, $R < a$, and we get

$$u(P) = 4\pi k\rho a, \qquad (14\text{-}11)$$

a constant.

The result (14-10) can be stated as a theorem.

THEOREM. *The potential (and hence the force of attraction* $\mathbf{F} = \nabla u$) *produced by a thin spherical shell at a point exterior to the shell is the same as if the mass of the shell were concentrated at its center.*

The potential due to a solid sphere of constant density ρ at a point outside the sphere can be deduced at once from (14-10) by supposing the sphere to consist of thin concentric shells. We conclude that this potential has the same form as (14-10) with M replaced by the mass of the sphere. Accordingly, the force of attraction produced by a solid homogeneous sphere on a unit mass at a point P outside the sphere has the magnitude kM/R^2. This force is directed toward the center of the sphere.

From (14-11) we see that the force of attraction at a point inside the shell is zero.

The integral (14-8) becomes improper if P is within the solid, for in that case, $r = \sqrt{(x - \xi)^2 + (y - \eta)^2 + (z - \zeta)^2}$ becomes zero when the integration variables (ξ, η, ζ) coincide with the coordinates (x,y,z) of P. However, the concepts of potential and gravitational attraction can be shown to have a meaning even when P is a point in the interior of a homogeneous solid.[1]

15. Steady Flow of Fluids. Let C be a curve in the xy plane over which a sheet of homogeneous fluid of depth 1 is flowing. The lines of flow of the fluid particles are indicated in Fig. 29 by curved arrows, and we suppose that the flow pattern is identical in all planes parallel to the xy plane. A flow of this sort is called two-dimensional.

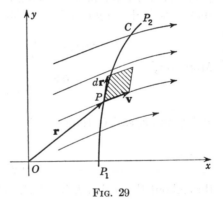

FIG. 29

The problem is to determine the amount of fluid that crosses C per unit time. We denote by $\mathbf{v}$ the velocity of the fluid particles at a point P on C and compute the volume dV of fluid crossing an element $d\mathbf{r}$ of C per unit time. Since the depth of the fluid is 1, this volume is equal to the volume of the parallelepiped

$$dV = \mathbf{k} \cdot \mathbf{v} \times d\mathbf{r},$$

where $\mathbf{k}$ is the unit vector perpendicular to the xy plane. The volume V crossing C per unit time, therefore, is

$$V = \int_C \mathbf{k} \cdot \mathbf{v} \times d\mathbf{r}.$$

---

[1] See in this connection Sec. 20, Chap. 1, and I. S. Sokolnikoff, "Tensor Analysis," sec. 89, John Wiley & Sons, Inc., New York, 1951, where it is shown that the potential u satisfies Poisson's equation $\nabla^2 u = -4\pi\rho$.

$K_i \mathbf{v} \times d\mathbf{r} = (k \cdot \mathbf{v} \, d\mathbf{r})$

$K = 0i + 0j + 1k$

But by Chap. 4, Eq. (6-2),

$$\mathbf{k \cdot v \times} d\mathbf{r} = \begin{vmatrix} 0 & 0 & 1 \\ v_x & v_y & 0 \\ dx & dy & 0 \end{vmatrix} = v_x \, dy - v_y \, dx,$$

since $\mathbf{v} = \mathbf{i}v_x + \mathbf{j}v_y$ and $d\mathbf{r} = \mathbf{i} \, dx + \mathbf{j} \, dy$.

Accordingly,

$$V = \int_C (v_x \, dy - v_y \, dx). \tag{15-1}$$

If C is a closed curve and the fluid is incompressible, the net amount of fluid crossing C is zero, because as much fluid enters the region bounded by C as leaves it. Thus a steady flow of an incompressible fluid is characterized by the equation

$$\int_C (v_x \, dy - v_y \, dx) = 0, \tag{15-2}$$

where the integral is evaluated over any closed curve C not enclosing the points at which the fluid is generated or absorbed. But Eq. (15-2) implies that $-v_y \, dx + v_x \, dy$ is an exact differential $d\Psi(x,y)$ of the function

$$\Psi(x,y) = \int_{(x_0,y_0)}^{(x,y)} (-v_y \, dx + v_x \, dy). \tag{15-3}$$

Moreover,[1]

$$\frac{\partial \Psi}{\partial x} = -v_y, \qquad \frac{\partial \Psi}{\partial y} = v_x, \tag{15-4}$$

and v_x and v_y satisfy the condition

$$\frac{\partial(-v_y)}{\partial y} = \frac{\partial v_x}{\partial x} \tag{15-5}$$

throughout the region R in which (15-2) holds. Equation (15-5) is a consequence of (15-2); it states, in effect, that there is no fluid created or destroyed in the region R. For this reason it is called the *equation of continuity.* Since

$$\text{div } \mathbf{v} = \frac{\partial v_x}{\partial x} + \frac{\partial v_y}{\partial y},$$

$(\mathbf{v} = \mathbf{i}v_x + \mathbf{j}v_y)$

we can write (15-5) in vector form as

$$\text{div } \mathbf{v} = 0, \tag{15-6}$$

which is consistent with the meaning attached to the symbol div $\mathbf{v}$ in Sec. 7.

[1] See Sec. 5.

$\dfrac{\partial vx}{\partial t} = -\dfrac{\partial vy}{\partial y}$ hence div $v = 0$

The function $\Psi(x,y)$ defined by (15-3) is the *stream function*, and the tracks of the particles of fluid, or *streamlines*, are determined by the equation $\Psi(x,y) = $ const. The velocity field satisfying (15-6), we recall, is said to be solenoidal. If the flow $\mathbf{v}$ is irrotational, then curl $\mathbf{v} = \mathbf{0}$ and there exists a scalar function $\Phi(x,y)$ such that [1]

$$\mathbf{v} = \nabla\Phi, \tag{15-7}$$

or
$$v_x = \frac{\partial\Phi}{\partial x}, \qquad v_y = \frac{\partial\Phi}{\partial y}. \tag{15-8}$$

The function $\Phi(x,y)$ determined by the integral

$$\Phi(x,y) = \int_{(x_0,y_0)}^{(x,y)} (v_x\,dx + v_y\,dy) \equiv \int_{P_0}^{P} \mathbf{v}\cdot d\mathbf{r}$$

is called the *velocity potential* because of the relations (15-8). We emphasize the fact that the condition for the existence of $\Phi(x,y)$ is

$$\text{curl } \mathbf{v} = \mathbf{0}$$

or in scalar form

$$\frac{\partial v_x}{\partial y} = \frac{\partial v_y}{\partial x}. \tag{15-9}$$

If the flow is both irrotational and solenoidal, the relations (15-4) and (15-8) hold and we conclude that

$$\frac{\partial\Phi}{\partial x} = \frac{\partial\Psi}{\partial y}, \qquad \frac{\partial\Phi}{\partial y} = -\frac{\partial\Psi}{\partial x} \quad \text{in } R. \tag{15-10}$$

These are the celebrated *Cauchy-Riemann equations* which we shall encounter again in Chap. 7.

Furthermore, if div $\mathbf{v} = 0$ and $\mathbf{v}$ is given by (15-7), we see that

$$\text{div } \nabla\Phi = \nabla^2\Phi = 0. \tag{15-11}$$

Thus, the velocity potential Φ satisfies Laplace's equation throughout any region containing no sources or sinks.

On differentiating the first of Eqs. (15-10) with respect to y and the second with respect to x and on equating $\partial^2\Phi/\partial x\,\partial y$ to $\partial^2\Phi/\partial y\,\partial x$, we find that the stream function $\Psi(x,y)$ also satisfies the equation

$$\nabla^2\Psi = 0.$$

The practical importance of these results is stressed in Chap. 7, Secs. 19 to 21.

The foregoing considerations can be extended to the three-dimensional flows as indicated in Sec. 17.

---

[1] See Sec. 12.

PROBLEMS

1. Show that the gravitational field determined by (14-2) is both solenoidal and irrotational except at (0,0,0).

2. Show that the velocity field

$$v = i \frac{x}{x^2 + y^2} + j \frac{y}{x^2 + y^2}$$

is solenoidal in any region which does not contain the origin (0,0). Is it irrotational? Verify that the velocity potential $\Phi = \log r = \frac{1}{2} \log (x^2 + y^2)$ and the stream function $\Psi = \tan^{-1}(y/x) = \theta$. Compute the circulation around a circular path enclosing the origin, and thus obtain a physical interpretation of results in Probs. 5 and 6 of Sec. 5 and Prob. 3 of Sec. 9.

3. Discuss a two-dimensional flow for which the velocity potential $\Phi = cx$. What is the stream function Ψ for this flow? Plot the curves $\Phi = $ const and $\Psi = $ const.

4. Discuss a two-dimensional flow for which the stream function is $\Psi = 2xy$. Find the velocity potential Φ, and sketch the curves $\Phi = $ const and $\Psi = $ const.

5. If **v** and **w** are irrotational vector fields, show that $v \times w$ is solenoidal.

6. Show that the streamlines are orthogonal to the lines $\Phi = $ const.

7. Show that when the three-dimensional flow **v** is irrotational, the streamlines satisfy the equations

$$\frac{dx}{v_x} = \frac{dy}{v_y} = \frac{dz}{v_z}.$$

8. If the velocity potential of the two-dimensional flow is $\Phi = x^2 - y^2$, find **v** and obtain the equations of the streamlines. Is this flow solenoidal? Is it irrotational?

9. Show with the aid of the Cauchy-Riemann equations that when the stream function $\Psi(x,y)$ is given, the velocity potential Φ is determined by

$$\Phi(x,y) = \int_{(x_0,y_0)}^{(x,y)} \left(\frac{\partial \Psi}{\partial y} dx - \frac{\partial \Psi}{\partial x} dy \right).$$

10. Use the result given in the preceding problem to calculate $\Phi(x,y)$ if (a) $\Psi = x^3 - 3xy^2$, (b) $\Psi = -y/(x^2 + y^2)$, $x \neq 0$, $y \neq 0$.

16. Equation of Heat Flow.

The following derivation of the Fourier equation of heat flow illustrates admirably the use of the divergence theorem in mathematical physics.

It is known from empirical results that heat will flow from points at higher temperatures to those at lower temperatures. At any point the rate of decrease of temperature varies with the direction, and it is generally assumed that the amount of heat ΔH crossing an element of surface $\Delta \sigma$ in Δt sec is proportional to the greatest rate of decrease of the temperature u; that is,

$$\Delta H \doteq k \, \Delta \sigma \, \Delta t \left| \frac{du}{dn} \right|.$$

Define the vector **q**, representing the flow of heat, by the formula

$$q = -k \, \nabla u, \tag{16-1}$$

where k is a constant of proportionality known as the thermal conductivity of a substance. [The units of k are cal/(cm-sec °C).] The negative sign is chosen in the definition because heat flows from points of higher temperature to those of lower, and the vector ∇u is directed normally to the level surface $u = \text{const}$ in the direction of increasing u.

Then the total amount of heat H flowing out in Δt sec from an arbitrary volume τ bounded by a closed surface σ is

$$H \doteq -\Delta t \int_\sigma k \frac{du}{dn} \, d\sigma = \Delta t \int_\sigma \mathbf{q} \cdot \mathbf{n} \, d\sigma, \qquad (16\text{-}2)$$

since $\mathbf{q} \cdot \mathbf{n} = -k \, du/dn$ by (16-1).

On the other hand, the amount of heat lost by the body τ can be calculated as follows: In order to increase the temperature of a volume element by $\Delta u°$, one must supply an amount of heat that is proportional to the increase in temperature and to the mass of the volume element. Hence

$$\Delta H \doteq c \, \Delta u \, \rho \, \Delta\tau \doteq c \frac{\partial u}{\partial t} \, \Delta t \, \rho \, \Delta\tau,$$

where c is the specific heat of the substance [cal/(g °C)] and ρ is its density. Therefore, the total loss of heat from the volume τ in Δt sec is

$$H \doteq -\Delta t \int_\tau \frac{\partial u}{\partial t} c\rho \, d\tau. \qquad (16\text{-}3)$$

Equating (16-2) and (16-3) gives

$$\int_\sigma \mathbf{q} \cdot \mathbf{n} \, d\sigma = -\int_\tau \frac{\partial u}{\partial t} c\rho \, d\tau. \qquad (16\text{-}4)$$

Applying the divergence theorem to the left-hand member of (16-4) yields

$$\int_\tau \operatorname{div} \mathbf{q} \, d\tau = -\int_\tau \frac{\partial u}{\partial t} c\rho \, d\tau,$$

and since $\mathbf{q} = -k\nabla u$, the foregoing equation assumes the form

$$\int_\tau \left[\operatorname{div} (-k\nabla u) + c\rho \frac{\partial u}{\partial t} \right] d\tau \equiv 0. \qquad (16\text{-}5)$$

Now, if k is a constant,

$$\operatorname{div} (k\nabla u) = k\nabla^2 u$$

and (16-5) becomes

$$\int_\tau \left(-k\nabla^2 u + c\rho \frac{\partial u}{\partial t} \right) d\tau \equiv 0. \qquad (16\text{-}6)$$

Since this integral must vanish for an arbitrary volume τ and the integrand is a continuous function, it follows that the integrand must be equal to zero, for if such were not the case, τ could be so chosen as to be a region throughout which the integrand has constant sign. But if the integrand had one sign throughout this region, then the integral would have the same sign and would not vanish as required by (16-6).

Therefore,

$$-k\nabla^2 u + c\rho\,\frac{\partial u}{\partial t} = 0$$

or

$$\frac{\partial u}{\partial t} = h^2\nabla^2 u, \qquad (16\text{-}7)$$

where

$$h^2 \equiv \frac{k}{c\rho}.$$

Equation (16-7) was developed by Fourier in 1822 and is of basic importance in the study of heat conduction in solids. A similar equation occurs in the study of current flow in conductors and in problems dealing with diffusion in liquids and gases.

It follows from (16-7) that a steady distribution of temperatures is characterized by the solution of Laplace's equation

$$\nabla^2 u = 0.$$

It was assumed in this derivation that the body is free from sources and sinks. If there are sources of heat continuously distributed within τ, then it is necessary to add to the right-hand member of (16-3) the integral

$$\int_\tau f(x,y,z,t)\,d\tau,$$

where $f(x,y,z,t)$ is a function representing the strengths of the sources. The reader will show that in this case one is led to the equation

$$\frac{\partial u}{\partial t} = h^2\nabla^2 u + \frac{f}{c\rho},$$

provided that the thermal conductivity of the substance is constant. Thus the presence of sources leads to a nonhomogeneous partial differential equation.

17. Equations of Hydrodynamics. Consider a region of space containing a fluid, and let $\mathbf{v}$ denote the velocity of a typical particle of the fluid. The amount Q of fluid crossing an arbitrary closed surface σ drawn in the region can be calculated by determining the flow across a typical element $\Delta\sigma$ of the surface σ. A particle of fluid is displaced in Δt sec through a distance $\mathbf{v}\,\Delta t$, and since only the component of the vector $\mathbf{v}$

normal to the element $\Delta\sigma$ contributes to the flow across this element, the amount ΔQ of the fluid crossing $\Delta\sigma$ is

$$\Delta Q \doteq \rho\mathbf{v}\cdot\mathbf{n}\,\Delta\sigma\,\Delta t,$$

where ρ is the density of the fluid (Fig. 30).

The entire amount Q of fluid flowing out of the volume τ, which is bounded by σ, in Δt sec is

$$Q \doteq \Delta t \int_\sigma \rho\mathbf{v}\cdot\mathbf{n}\,d\sigma.$$

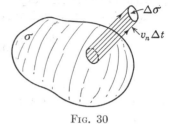

On the other hand, the quantity of the fluid originally contained in τ will have diminished by the amount

$$Q \doteq -\Delta t \int_\tau \frac{\partial\rho}{\partial t}\,d\tau,$$

FIG. 30

for the change in mass in Δt sec is nearly equal to $(\partial\rho/\partial t)\,\Delta t\,\Delta\tau$, and the negative sign is taken because ρ is a decreasing function of t.

Equating these two expressions for Q gives

$$\int_\sigma \rho\mathbf{v}\cdot\mathbf{n}\,d\sigma = -\int_\tau \frac{\partial\rho}{\partial t}\,d\tau, \tag{17-1}$$

and the application of the divergence theorem to the left-hand member of this equation yields

$$\int_\tau \operatorname{div}(\rho\mathbf{v})\,d\tau = -\int_\tau \frac{\partial\rho}{\partial t}\,d\tau$$

or

$$\int_\tau \left[\operatorname{div}(\rho\mathbf{v}) + \frac{\partial\rho}{\partial t}\right] d\tau = 0.$$

Since the integrand is continuous and the volume τ is arbitrary, one can conclude that

$$\frac{\partial\rho}{\partial t} + \operatorname{div}(\rho\mathbf{v}) = 0. \tag{17-2}$$

This is the basic equation of hydrodynamics, known as the *equation of continuity*. It merely expresses the law of conservation of matter.

It has been assumed that there are no sources or sinks within the region occupied by the fluid. If matter is created at the rate $k\rho(x,y,z,t)$, then the right-hand member of (17-1) should include a term that accounts for the increase of mass per second due to such sources, namely,

$$\int_\tau k\rho\,d\tau.$$

In this event the equation of continuity reads

$$\frac{\partial \rho}{\partial t} + \text{div } (\rho \mathbf{v}) = k\rho.$$

The constant of proportionality k is sometimes called the growth factor.

The density $\rho(x,y,z,t)$ of the fluid at the location (x,y,z) of the fluid particle depends on t explicitly and on x,y,z implicitly, since the particle coordinates change with time as the particle is displaced. Thus,

$$\frac{d\rho}{dt} = \frac{\partial \rho}{\partial t} + \frac{\partial \rho}{\partial x}\frac{dx}{dt} + \frac{\partial \rho}{\partial y}\frac{dy}{dt} + \frac{\partial \rho}{\partial z}\frac{dz}{dt}. \tag{17-3}$$

In this equation, $d\rho/dt$ means the rate of change of density as one moves with the fluid, whereas $\partial \rho/\partial t$ is the rate of change of density at a fixed point.

Upon noting that

$$\mathbf{v} = \mathbf{i}\frac{dx}{dt} + \mathbf{j}\frac{dy}{dt} + \mathbf{k}\frac{dz}{dt}$$

and

$$\nabla \rho = \mathbf{i}\frac{\partial \rho}{\partial x} + \mathbf{j}\frac{\partial \rho}{\partial y} + \mathbf{k}\frac{\partial \rho}{\partial z},$$

we can write the formula (17-3) as

$$\frac{d\rho}{dt} = \frac{\partial \rho}{\partial t} + \mathbf{v} \cdot \nabla \rho. \tag{17-4}$$

Substituting from (17-2) in (17-4) gives

$$\frac{d\rho}{dt} = - \text{div } (\rho \mathbf{v}) + \mathbf{v} \cdot \nabla \rho. \tag{17-5}$$

But div $(\rho \mathbf{v}) = \mathbf{v} \cdot \nabla \rho + \rho$ div $\mathbf{v}$ (see Prob. 3b, Sec. 7), so that (17-5) becomes

$$\frac{d\rho}{dt} = -\rho \text{ div } \mathbf{v},$$

or

$$\text{div } \mathbf{v} = -\frac{1}{\rho}\frac{d\rho}{dt}. \tag{17-6}$$

It is clear from (17-6) that div $\mathbf{v}$ is equal to the relative rate of change of the density ρ at any point of the fluid. Therefore, if the fluid is incompressible, the velocity field is characterized by the equation

$$\text{div } \mathbf{v} = 0. \tag{17-7}$$

If the flow of fluid is irrotational, then curl $\mathbf{v} = \mathbf{0}$, and one is assured that there exists a scalar function Φ such that

$$\mathbf{v} = \nabla\Phi.$$

Substituting this in (17-7) gives the differential equation to be satisfied by Φ, namely,

$$\nabla^2\Phi \equiv \frac{\partial^2\Phi}{\partial x^2} + \frac{\partial^2\Phi}{\partial y^2} + \frac{\partial^2\Phi}{\partial z^2} = 0. \tag{17-8}$$

The function Φ is called the *velocity potential*. A similar result was obtained in Sec. 15 for the two-dimensional flow.

If the fluid is ideal, that is, such that the force due to pressure on any surface element is always directed normally to that surface element, one can easily derive Euler's equations of hydrodynamics. Denote the pressure at any point of the fluid by p; then the force acting on a surface element $\Delta\sigma$ is $-p\mathbf{n}\,\Delta\sigma$, and the resultant force acting on an arbitrary closed surface σ is

$$-\int_\sigma p\mathbf{n}\,d\sigma.$$

The negative sign is chosen because the force due to pressure acts in the direction of the interior normal, whereas $\mathbf{n}$ denotes the unit exterior normal.

Let the body force, per unit mass, acting on the masses contained within the region τ be $\mathbf{F}$; then the resultant of the body forces is

$$\int_\tau \mathbf{F}\rho\,d\tau.$$

Hence, the resultant $\mathbf{R}$ of the body and surface forces is

$$\begin{aligned}
\mathbf{R} &= \int_\tau \mathbf{F}\rho\,d\tau - \int_\sigma p\mathbf{n}\,d\sigma \\
&= \int_\tau \mathbf{F}\rho\,d\tau - \int_\tau \nabla p\,d\tau,
\end{aligned} \tag{17-9}$$

where the last step is obtained by making use of (8-6).

From Newton's law of motion, the resultant force is equal to

$$\mathbf{R} = \int_\tau \rho\,\frac{d^2\mathbf{r}}{dt^2}\,d\tau, \tag{17-10}$$

where $\mathbf{r} = \mathbf{i}x + \mathbf{j}y + \mathbf{k}z$ is the position vector of the masses relative to the origin of cartesian coordinates. It follows from (17-9) and (17-10) that

$$\int_\tau \left(\mathbf{F}\rho - \nabla p - \rho\,\frac{d^2\mathbf{r}}{dt^2} \right) d\tau = 0,$$

and since the volume element is arbitrary and the integrand is continuous,

$$\rho \frac{d^2\mathbf{r}}{dt^2} = \mathbf{F}\rho - \nabla p. \tag{17-11}$$

This is the desired equation in vector form, and it is basic in hydro- and aerodynamical applications.

In books on hydrodynamics, the cartesian components of the velocity vector $d\mathbf{r}/dt$ are usually denoted by u, v, and w, so that

$$\frac{d\mathbf{r}}{dt} = \mathbf{i}u + \mathbf{j}v + \mathbf{k}w = \mathbf{i}\frac{dx}{dt} + \mathbf{j}\frac{dy}{dt} + \mathbf{k}\frac{dz}{dt}.$$

Since u, v, and w are functions of the coordinates of the point (x,y,z) and of the time t, it follows that

$$\frac{d^2\mathbf{r}}{dt^2} = \mathbf{i}\left(\frac{\partial u}{\partial t} + \frac{\partial u}{\partial x}\frac{dx}{dt} + \frac{\partial u}{\partial y}\frac{dy}{dt} + \frac{\partial u}{\partial z}\frac{dz}{dt}\right)$$

$$+ \mathbf{j}\left(\frac{\partial v}{\partial t} + \frac{\partial v}{\partial x}\frac{dx}{dt} + \frac{\partial v}{\partial y}\frac{dy}{dt} + \frac{\partial v}{\partial z}\frac{dz}{dt}\right)$$

$$+ \mathbf{k}\left(\frac{\partial w}{\partial t} + \frac{\partial w}{\partial x}\frac{dx}{dt} + \frac{\partial w}{\partial y}\frac{dy}{dt} + \frac{\partial w}{\partial z}\frac{dz}{dt}\right).$$

Substituting this expression in (17-11) and setting $\mathbf{F} = \mathbf{i}F_x + \mathbf{j}F_y + \mathbf{k}F_z$ lead to three scalar equations, which are associated with the name of Euler:

$$\frac{\partial u}{\partial t} + \frac{\partial u}{\partial x}u + \frac{\partial u}{\partial y}v + \frac{\partial u}{\partial z}w = F_x - \frac{1}{\rho}\frac{\partial p}{\partial x},$$

$$\frac{\partial v}{\partial t} + \frac{\partial v}{\partial x}u + \frac{\partial v}{\partial y}v + \frac{\partial v}{\partial z}w = F_y - \frac{1}{\rho}\frac{\partial p}{\partial y}, \tag{17-12}$$

$$\frac{\partial w}{\partial t} + \frac{\partial w}{\partial x}u + \frac{\partial w}{\partial y}v + \frac{\partial w}{\partial z}w = F_z - \frac{1}{\rho}\frac{\partial p}{\partial z}.$$

It is possible to show with the aid of these equations (and by making some simplifying assumptions) that the propagation of sound is governed approximately by the wave equation

$$\frac{\partial^2 s}{\partial t^2} = a^2 \nabla^2 s.$$

In this equation, a is the velocity of sound and s is related to the density ρ of the medium by the formula

$$s = \frac{\rho}{\rho_0} - 1,$$

where ρ_0 is the density of the medium at rest.

CHAPTER 6

PARTIAL DIFFERENTIAL EQUATIONS

The Vibrating String

Solution by Series

Solution by Integrals

Elliptic, Parabolic, and Hyperbolic Equations

Equations containing partial derivatives arise in many branches of mathematical physics. Fluid flow, heat transfer, wave motion, electromagnetic theory, elasticity, quantum mechanics, nuclear physics, and meteorology are but a few of the fields that involve a study of such equations. In this chapter we give representative examples, indicating some of the more important methods of solution. In contrast to the theory of ordinary differential equations, it will be seen that now the general solution is seldom sought. The main problem, rather, is to find that particular solution which satisfies the determinative conditions (the so-called initial values and boundary values) of the specific problem in hand.

THE VIBRATING STRING

1. Arbitrary Functions: One-dimensional Waves. A *partial differential equation of order n* is an equation containing partial derivatives of order n but no higher derivatives. For example, each of the three equations

$$\frac{\partial^2 u}{\partial t^2} = a^2 \frac{\partial^2 u}{\partial x^2}, \qquad \frac{\partial u}{\partial t} = \alpha^2 \frac{\partial^2 u}{\partial x^2}, \qquad \frac{\partial^2 u}{\partial x^2} + \frac{\partial^2 u}{\partial y^2} + \frac{\partial^2 u}{\partial z^2} = 0 \qquad \leftarrow \text{La Place}$$

is a partial differential equation of order 2. In this chapter we shall often use the subscript notation for derivatives, so that the foregoing expressions can be written more briefly as

$$u_{tt} = a^2 u_{xx}, \qquad u_t = \alpha^2 u_{xx}, \qquad u_{xx} + u_{yy} + u_{zz} = 0. \qquad (1\text{-}1)$$

A function u that satisfies a given partial differential equation is called a *solution* of the equation. For example, the function

$$u = \cos x \cos at \qquad (1\text{-}2)$$

is a solution of the first Eq. (1-1), because (1-2) gives

$$u_x = -\sin x \cos at, \qquad u_t = \cos x(-a \sin at),$$

$$u_{xx} = -\cos x \cos at, \qquad u_{tt} = \cos x(-a^2 \cos at) = a^2 u_{xx}.$$

425

The reader will recall that the general solution of an ordinary differential equation contains arbitrary constants; for example, the general solution of $y'' + y = 0$ is

$$y = c_1 \sin x + c_2 \cos x,$$

which has the arbitrary constants c_1 and c_2. We shall see that many important partial differential equations have solutions which contain arbitrary functions and, conversely, the elimination of arbitrary functions from a given expression often leads to a partial differential equation.

As an illustration of this fact let

$$u = f(x + y), \tag{1-3}$$

where f is an arbitrary differentiable function. If the argument of f is denoted by $s = x + y$, then

$$u = f(x + y) = f(s)$$

and the chain rule [1] gives

$$u_x = \frac{\partial u}{\partial x} = \frac{df}{ds}\frac{\partial s}{\partial x} = \frac{df}{ds} \cdot 1 = f'(s).$$

Similarly, $u_y = f'(s)$, and hence u satisfies

$$u_x = u_y \tag{1-4}$$

for any and all choices of the differentiable function f.

Conversely, let $u(x,y)$ be a solution of (1-4). If we set $s = x + y$, then

$$u(x,y) = u(x, s - x) \equiv U(x,s).$$

The chain rule gives

$$u_x = U_x \frac{\partial x}{\partial x} + U_s \frac{\partial s}{\partial x} = U_x + U_s$$

and, similarly, $u_y = U_s$. Substituting into (1-4) we get

$$U_x + U_s = U_s,$$

which shows that $U_x = 0$. It follows that U is a function of s only,

$$U = f(s) = f(x + y),$$

and hence the same is true of u. Thus, (1-3) follows from (1-4).

For an example containing two arbitrary functions, let

$$U = f_1(r) + f_2(s), \qquad f_1 \text{ and } f_2 \text{ differentiable}, \tag{1-5}$$

where r and s are the independent variables. Then $U_r = f_1'(r)$, and hence

$$U_{rs} = 0. \tag{1-6}$$

[1] The reader may find it advisable to review Chap. 3, Sec. 4.

(The reader can verify that also $U_{sr} = 0$.) Conversely, from (1-6) we have

$$\frac{\partial}{\partial s}(U_r) = 0$$

so that U_r is independent of s:

$$U_r = h(r), \qquad \text{a function of } r \text{ only.} \qquad (1\text{-}7)$$

If we write $f_1(r) = \int h(r)\, dr$, then Eq. (1-7) yields

$$\frac{\partial}{\partial r}[U - f_1(r)] = 0,$$

so that $U - f_1(r) = f_2(s)$, a function of s only. Thus, U has the form (1-5).

An important example of the elimination of arbitrary functions arises from the situation shown in Fig. 1. If t is time, it is seen that $f_1(x - at)$

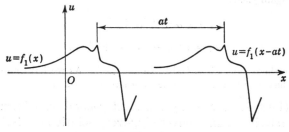

FIG. 1

represents a wave form which propagates in the positive x direction with velocity a and with no change in shape, that is, with no *dispersion*. In a similar manner, $f_2(x + at)$ represents a wave form which propagates in the opposite direction with velocity a. The most general one-dimensional wave without dispersion is a superposition of two such, namely,

$$u = f_1(x - at) + f_2(x + at). \qquad (1\text{-}8)$$

Suppose, now, that $u(x,t)$ is given by (1-8), with f_1 and f_2 twice differentiable. If we set

$$x - at = r, \qquad x + at = s, \qquad (1\text{-}9)$$

then $u = f_1(r) + f_2(s)$, and by the chain rule

$$u_x = \frac{\partial u}{\partial x} = \frac{\partial(f_1 + f_2)}{\partial r}\frac{\partial r}{\partial x} + \frac{\partial(f_1 + f_2)}{\partial s}\frac{\partial s}{\partial x} = f_1'(x - at) + f_2'(x + at).$$

The reader may verify similarly that

$$u_t = f_1'(x - at)(-a) + f_2'(x + at)(a).$$

Differentiating again gives

$$u_{xx} = f_1''(x - at) + f_2''(x + at),$$

$$u_{tt} = f_1''(x - at)(-a)^2 + f_2''(x + at)(a)^2,$$

and hence u satisfies the partial differential equation

$$u_{tt} = a^2 u_{xx}. \quad \text{wave eq}$$
$$\tag{1-10}$$

We show conversely that every solution $u(x,t)$ of (1-10) has the form (1-8) and thus represents the superposition of two waves propagating with velocity a. The substitution (1-9) gives

$$u(x,t) = U(r,s)$$

so that, by using the chain rule as in the previous discussion,

$$u_x = U_r + U_s, \qquad u_t = -aU_r + aU_s.$$

Differentiating again yields

$$u_{xx} = U_{rr} + 2U_{rs} + U_{ss},$$

$$u_{tt} = a^2 U_{rr} - 2a^2 U_{rs} + a^2 U_{ss}.$$

If we substitute these values into (1-10) we get (1-6). As we have already seen, this ensures that U has the form (1-5), and hence u has the form (1-8).

Equation (1-10) is satisfied by the most general one-dimensional wave motion with velocity a; and conversely, every solution of (1-10) represents such a motion. For this reason (1-10) is called the *wave equation*. Together with its analogues in two and three dimensions, (1-10) is an important aid in the study of many vibration phenomena.

Example: Standing Waves. The motion given by

$$f_1(x - at) = A \sin k(x - at), \qquad A, k \text{ const}, \tag{1-11}$$

represents a sine wave of amplitude A and wavelength $\lambda = 2\pi/k$, moving to the right with velocity a. The *period* T is the time required for the wave to progress a distance equal to one wavelength, so that $\lambda = aT$ or

$$T = \frac{\lambda}{a} = \frac{2\pi}{ka}.$$

Similarly, a motion described by

$$f_2(x + at) = A \sin k(x + at) \tag{1-12}$$

represents a sine wave, of the same amplitude and period, moving with velocity a to the left. The superposition of (1-11) and (1-12) gives

$$u = A \sin k(x - at) + A \sin k(x + at)$$

which becomes

$$u = (2A \cos kat) \sin kx \tag{1-13}$$

when we recall the trigonometric identities

$$\sin k(x \pm at) = \sin kx \cos kat \pm \cos kx \sin kat.$$

The expression (1-13) may be regarded as a sinusoid $\sin kx$ whose amplitude $2A \cos kat$ varies with the time t in a simply harmonic manner. Several curves of (1-13) are sketched in Fig. 2 for various values of t. The points $n\pi/k$ remain fixed throughout the motion

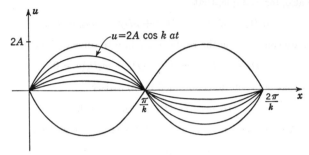

FIG. 2

and are called *nodes*. Although the result was obtained by superposing two traveling waves, the wave form (1-13) does not appear to travel either to the left or the right, and (1-13) is said to represent a *standing wave*.

The number f of oscillations or *cycles* made by the wave per unit time is called the *frequency*. From the definition of the period T, it follows that $f = 1/T$.

PROBLEMS

1. If $u = f(y/x)$ with f differentiable, show that

$$xu_x + yu_y = 0 \qquad \text{for } x \neq 0.$$

2. Show by direct differentiation that $u = \sin kx \sin kat$ satisfies the one-dimensional wave equation for every choice of the constant k, and express this function in the form (1-8).

3. (a) By computing u_x, u_y, and u_{xy} obtain a second-order partial differential equation for $u = f_1(x)f_2(y)$. (b) Show that your result is equivalent to $(\log u)_{xy} = 0$, and explain.

4. For many functions the chain rule applies even when the argument is complex. Assuming this, show that

$$u = f_1(x + iy) + f_2(x - iy), \qquad i^2 = -1,$$

satisfies *Laplace's equation* $u_{xx} + u_{yy} = 0$.

5. Let $f(x + iy) = u(x,y) + iv(x,y)$, where u and v are real. Using the chain rule, show that u and v satisfy the *Cauchy-Riemann equations*

$$u_x = v_y, \qquad u_y = -v_x.$$

6. Show that $u = f(\alpha y - \beta x)$ satisfies

$$\alpha u_x + \beta u_y = 0$$

if f is differentiable and α, β are constant.

The Linear Equation with Constant Coefficients

7. The operators D_x^n and D_y^n are defined by

$$D_x^n = \frac{\partial^n}{\partial x^n}, \qquad D_y^n = \frac{\partial^n}{\partial y^n}$$

and we agree also, for example, that

$$(\alpha D_x + \beta D_y)u \equiv \alpha D_x u + \beta D_y u \equiv \alpha u_x + \beta u_y.$$

(a) If m_i are constant use the result of Prob. 6 to solve each of the equations

$$(D_x - m_1 D_y)u = 0, \qquad (D_x - m_2 D_y)u = 0.$$

(b) Show that both solutions obtained in (a) satisfy

$$(D_x - m_1 D_y)(D_x - m_2 D_y)u = 0. \qquad (1\text{-}14)$$

Hint: Since m_i are constant, Eq. (1-14) may also be written

$$(D_x - m_2 D_y)(D_x - m_1 D_y)u = 0.$$

(c) Deduce that a solution of (1-14), containing two arbitrary functions, is

$$u = F_1(y + m_1 x) + F_2(y + m_2 x), \qquad m_1 \neq m_2,$$

$$u = F_1(y + m_1 x) + x F_2(y + m_1 x), \qquad m_1 = m_2.$$

Hint: Since the equation is linear and homogeneous, the sum of the two solutions in (b) is again a solution. The result for $m_1 = m_2$ may be verified by direct substitution.

[Similar results hold in general. The solution of

$$(D_x - m D_y)^r u = 0$$

can be shown to be

$$u = F_1(y + mx) + x F_2(y + mx) + \cdots + x^{r-1} F_r(y + mx)$$

and the solution for several such factors is obtained by addition (cf. Chap. 1, Sec. 21). The process gives the "general solution" in that the number of arbitrary functions equals the order of the equation.]

8. The fourth-order equation

$$\frac{\partial^4 u}{\partial x^4} + 2\frac{\partial^4 u}{\partial x^2\, \partial y^2} + \frac{\partial^4 u}{\partial y^4} = 0$$

occurs in the study of elastic plates. Show that the general solution is

$$u = F_1(y - ix) + x F_2(y - ix) + F_3(y + ix) + x F_4(y + ix).$$

Hint: The equation may be written

$$(D_x^4 + 2 D_x^2 D_y^2 + D_y^4)u = 0$$

so that the decomposition into linear factors gives

$$(D_x + i D_y)(D_x + i D_y)(D_x - i D_y)(D_x - i D_y)u = 0.$$

Use the result of Prob. 7.

9. As in Probs. **7** and **8**, solve:

(a) $u_{xx} - a^2 u_{yy} = 0$;

(b) $u_{xx} + u_{xy} = 2u_{yy}$;

(c) $u_{xx} + u_{yy} = 0$;

(d) $u_{xx} + u_{yy} = 2u_{xy}$.

10. Consider the equation

$$u_{xx} + 4u_{xy} - 5u_{yy} = f(x,y).$$

(a) By the method of Prob. **7** obtain a general solution when $f = 0$.

(b) By assuming $u = cy^4$, where c is a constant to be determined, obtain a particular solution when $f = y^2$.

(c) Similarly, obtain a particular solution when $f = x$.

(d) By addition of the results (a), (b), (c) obtain the general solution when $f = y^2 + x$.

11. As in Prob. **10**, obtain the general solution: (a) $2z_{xx} + z_{xy} - z_{yy} = 1$; (b) $z_{xx} - a^2 z_{yy} = x^2$; (c) $z_{xx} + 3z_{xy} + 2z_{yy} = x + y$.

2. Derivation of a Differential Equation. Consider a flexible, elastic string stretched between two supports on the x axis (Fig. 3). To obtain

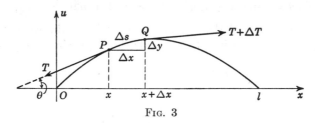

FIG. 3

a differential equation for the motion, let $u(x,t)$ represent the vertical distance from the point x on the x axis to the string at time t. We shall apply Newton's law,

$$\text{(Mass)(acceleration of center of mass)} = \text{force}, \qquad (2\text{-}1)$$

to the short piece of string between x and $x + \Delta x$.

The mass of the short piece is

$$\text{Mass} = \bar{\rho}\, \Delta s$$

where $\bar{\rho}$ is the mean density and Δs the length. The vertical component of acceleration for the short piece is

$$\text{Vertical acceleration} = \frac{\partial^2 \bar{u}}{\partial t^2}$$

if $\bar{u}$ is the height of the center of mass above the x axis. To compute the vertical component of force we let T be the tension, and we introduce the angle θ between the tension vector and the x axis. By Fig. 3 the vertical component is

$$\text{Vertical force due to tension} = (T \sin \theta)\Big|_{x+\Delta x} - (T \sin \theta)\Big|_{x}.$$

If there is an additional vertical force $F_1(x,t)\,\Delta x$ due to other causes, substituting into (2-1) yields

$$\bar{\rho}\,\Delta s\,\frac{\partial^2 \bar{u}}{\partial t^2} = (T \sin \theta)\Big|_{x+\Delta x} - (T \sin \theta)\Big|_x + F_1(x,t)\,\Delta x.$$

Upon dividing by Δx and letting $\Delta x \to 0$ we get

$$\rho\,\frac{\partial s}{\partial x}\frac{\partial^2 u}{\partial t^2} = \frac{\partial}{\partial x}(T \sin \theta) + F_1(x,t) \tag{2-2}$$

if the required derivatives are continuous.

To obtain a simpler equation, note that the definition of arc length yields [1]

$$\frac{\partial s}{\partial x} = \left[1 + \left(\frac{\partial u}{\partial x}\right)^2\right]^{\frac{1}{2}} \sim 1$$

and also [2]

$$\sin \theta = \tan \theta (1 + \tan^2 \theta)^{-\frac{1}{2}} = u_x(1 + u_x^2)^{-\frac{1}{2}} \sim u_x,$$

if $u_x^2 \ll 1$. Moreover, if the displacement u is small, we can consider $T = $ const. Substituting into (2-2) yields the approximate equation

$$\rho u_{tt} = T u_{xx} + F_1(x,t).$$

This in turn may be written

$$u_{tt} = a^2 u_{xx} + F(x,t), \tag{2-3}$$

where $a = \sqrt{T/\rho}$ and $F(x,t) = \rho^{-1}F_1(x,t).$

Equation (2-3) will be considered in the sequel under the assumption that ρ, and hence a, is constant.

When the force function $F(x,t)$ is zero, the vibrations of the string are termed *free vibrations*. By (2-3) the equation for free vibrations is

$$u_{tt} = a^2 u_{xx} \tag{2-4}$$

and hence the solution has the form (1-8). According to the discussion in Sec. 1, the motion can always be regarded as a superposition of two waves moving with velocity

$$a = \sqrt{\frac{T}{\rho}} \tag{2-5}$$

---

[1] The symbol $\sim$ (read "is asymptotic to") means that the ratio of the two sides tends to 1. A discussion of this useful notation is given in Chap. 1, Sec. 2.

[2] The fact that the string is flexible means that the tension vector is tangent to the string, so that

$$\tan \theta = \text{slope of curve} = \frac{\partial u}{\partial x}.$$

in opposite directions. Later we shall determine the precise form of these waves by considering the initial state of the string, that is, the state at $t = 0$, together with the conditions at the end points, $x = 0$ and $x = l$.

Inasmuch as the constant a in (2-4) involves only the ratio T/ρ, two strings may behave similarly even if made of different materials. For example, a string with density 2ρ under tension $2T$ behaves like a string with density ρ and tension T, since both yield the same value for a. An equivalence of two different physical systems such as this is sometimes called a *principle of similitude*.

The study of similitude belongs to an interesting branch of mathematical physics known as *dimensional analysis*. Although a general development [1] will not be given here, we shall describe the underlying idea as it applies to (2-5).

Equation (2-5) relates three quantities a, T, and ρ which are expressed in different physical units. In the mks system [2]

$$a = \left[\frac{\text{meters}}{\text{second}}\right], \qquad \rho = \left[\frac{\text{kilograms}}{\text{meter}}\right], \qquad T = \left[\frac{\text{kilogram-meters}}{(\text{second})^2}\right], \qquad (2\text{-}6)$$

where the square bracket is used to indicate that the measuring unit, rather than the value, is being described. The value of a for use in (2-5) is the *number* of such measuring units, that is, the number of meters per second, and similarly for ρ and T.

If we decide to measure lengths in centimeters rather than in meters, then the value of a will be increased by a factor 100. In other words, $100a$ cm per sec is the same as a m per sec. Similarly T will be multiplied by 100, but ρ will be divided by 100, since the length unit for ρ in (2-6) occurs in the denominator. (Indeed, ρ kg per m is clearly the same as 0.01ρ kg per cm.) Hence when a string has a wave velocity a, density ρ, and tension T in the old system (2-6), then the same string has velocity, density, and tension

$$100a, \quad \frac{\rho}{100}, \quad 100T \qquad (2\text{-}7)$$

in the new system. Substituting into (2-5) yields

$$100a = \sqrt{\frac{100T}{\rho/100}}$$

which is consistent with (2-5), as it should be. One does not get a contradictory result by measuring all lengths in centimeters rather than in meters.

When we change meters into centimeters, we divide the unit of length by 100. More generally, one might divide the unit by an arbitrary positive constant α. The new values of a, ρ, and T would be, respectively,

$$\alpha a, \quad \frac{\rho}{\alpha}, \quad \alpha T, \qquad (2\text{-}8)$$

[compare (2-7)]. Similar changes may be made in the units of mass or of time. Equa-

---

[1] The reader is referred to P. W. Bridgman, "Dimensional Analysis," Yale University Press, New Haven, Conn., 1931, and S. Drobot, The Foundations of Dimensional Analysis, *Studia Math.*, **14**:84–99 (1954).

[2] The mks units for T can be found from Newton's law (2-1), since T is a force.

tion (2-5) remains self-consistent under such changes, as the reader can verify. The question arises: Is (2-5) the *only* functional relationship

$$a = f(\rho, T) \tag{2-9}$$

which is consistent under such changes? If so, then we would have a proof of the functional relation (2-5), assuming merely that there is a functional relation of *some* kind.

To investigate this possibility, suppose (2-9) holds where f is an unknown function and where a, T, and ρ stand for the numbers of their respective units of measurement in (2-6). If the unit of length is divided by α, then (2-8) gives

$$\alpha a = f\left(\frac{\rho}{\alpha}, \alpha T\right)$$

upon substitution into (2-9). Since α is arbitrary we may choose $\alpha = \rho$ to find

$$\rho a = f(1, \rho T). \tag{2-10}$$

If we now divide the unit of mass by β, the value of a is unchanged but ρ and T become $\beta\rho$ and βT, respectively [see (2-6)]. Substituting into (2-10) yields

$$\beta\rho a = f(1, \beta^2 \rho T).$$

Upon choosing $\beta^2 = (\rho T)^{-1}$, we get

$$(\rho T)^{-\frac{1}{2}}\rho a = f(1,1),$$

so that

$$a = c\sqrt{\frac{T}{\rho}}, \tag{2-11}$$

where $c = f(1,1)$ is a *constant*, independent of a, ρ, and T.

Finally, if we divide the unit of time by γ, the new values of a, ρ, and T are given by (2-6) as a/γ, ρ, and T/γ^2. Substituting into (2-11) gives

$$\frac{a}{\gamma} = c\sqrt{\frac{T/\gamma^2}{\rho}},$$

which reduces to (2-11) again. Thus, no new information is obtained by changing the unit of time, and the constant c in (2-11) cannot be found by dimensional analysis. But we can determine c by considering the limiting case of small oscillations. The partial differential equation (2-4) is then valid, and (2-5) shows that $c = 1$.

PROBLEMS

1. The displacement of a certain string is

$$u(x,t) = f_1(x - at) + f_2(x + at).$$

What is the physical meaning of the condition $u(0,t) \equiv 0$? If $u(0,t) \equiv 0$, express f_1 in terms of f_2, and thus deduce

$$u(x,t) = f_2(x + at) - f_2(-x + at).$$

2. (*a*) Find $f(x - at)$ when $f(x) = (1 + x^2)^{-1}$; when $f(x) = \sin kx$; when $f(x) = e^x$. In each case compute also $f'(x - at)$. *Hint:* Substitute $x - at$ for x in the expressions for $f(x)$. (*b*) If $u(x,t) = f(x - at) + f(x + at)$, find $u(0,t)$, $u(x,0)$, and $u(l,1/a)$ for each $f(x)$ in part (*a*) of this problem.

3. In the derivation of (2-3) we observed that $\sin \theta \sim u_x$, but we used this result in the form $(\sin \theta)_x \sim (u_x)_x$. (a) By differentiating the exact formula

$$\sin \theta = u_x(1 + u_x^2)^{-\frac{1}{2}}$$

with respect to x, show that $(\sin \theta)_x \sim u_{xx}$ is correct provided u_{xx} is bounded. Also show that the error is of the order of u_x^2 in this case. (b) By considering $u = 1 + x$, $v = 1 + 2x$ near $x = 0$, show that the equation $u \sim v$ does not always enable us to conclude $u_x \sim v_x$. (In other words: If two functions approximate each other the derivatives need not approximate each other and a separate investigation must be given.)

4. Show that the small longitudinal vibrations of a uniform long rod satisfy the differential equation

$$\frac{\partial^2 u}{\partial t^2} = \frac{E}{\rho} \frac{\partial^2 u}{\partial x^2},$$

where u is the displacement of a point originally at a distance x from the end of the rod, E is the modulus of elasticity, and ρ is the density. *Hint:* From the definition of Young's modulus E, the force on a cross-sectional area q at a distance x units from the end of the rod is $Eq(\partial u/\partial x)$, since $\partial u/\partial x$ is the extension per unit length. On the other hand, the force on an element of the rod of length Δx is $\rho q\, \Delta x\, \partial^2 \bar{u}/\partial t^2$.

5. If the rod of Prob. 4 is made of steel for which $E = 22 \times 10^8$ g per cm^2 and whose specific gravity is 7.8, show that the velocity of propagation of sound in steel is nearly 5.3×10^5 cm per sec, which is about sixteen times as great as the velocity of sound in air. Note that in the cgs system E must be expressed in dynes per square centimeter.

6. Show that the differential equation of the transverse vibrations of an elastic rod carrying a load of $p(x)$ lb per unit length is

$$EI \frac{\partial^4 y}{\partial x^4} = p(x) - m \frac{\partial^2 y}{\partial t^2},$$

where E = modulus of elasticity

$\quad\quad I$ = moment of inertia of cross-sectional area of rod about a horizontal transverse axis through center of gravity

$\quad m$ = mass per unit length

Hint: For small deflections the bending moment M about a horizontal transverse axis at a distance x from the end of the rod is given by the Euler formula $M = EI\, d^2y/dx^2$, and the shearing load $p(x)$ is given by $d^2M/dx^2 = p(x)$.

3. Initial Conditions.   In the previous section the wave equation

$$u_{tt} = a^2 u_{xx}, \qquad a = \text{const}, \tag{3-1}$$

was derived for small displacements of a uniform flexible string. According to Sec. 1 the general solution of (3-1) is

$$u(x,t) = f_1(x - at) + f_2(x + at) \tag{3-2}$$

where f_1 and f_2 are arbitrary twice-differentiable functions.[1] We shall

---

[1] Actually, (3-2) is meaningful whenever f_1 and f_2 are well defined, and hence, conditions of differentiability are not emphasized in the sequel. A nondifferentiable function (such as the function shown in Fig. 4) is regarded as being a "solution" of (3-1) if it can be approximated, with arbitrary precision, by smooth solutions. See: I. G. Petrovsky, "Partial Differential Equations," p. 65, Cambridge University Press, New York, 1954.

now see that these functions can be determined from the initial conditions, that is, from the conditions at time $t = 0$. It is convenient to regard the string as infinite and the conditions as given for $-\infty < x < \infty$. The effect of the end points $x = 0$ and $x = l$ will be considered in Sec. 5.

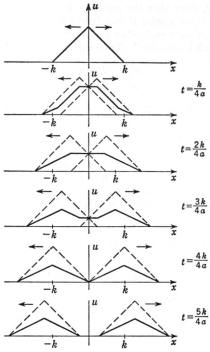

FIG. 4. Ordinates on the resultant wave are obtained by forming one-half the sum of the oppositely moving waves shown by the dashed lines.

CASE I. *Initial Impulse* 0. Assume that the string is released from rest and that the initial shape is given by a known function $f(x)$. (Such a situation arises when the string is plucked, as in a harpsichord.) In symbols,

$$u(x,0) = f(x), \qquad u_t(x,0) = 0, \tag{3-3}$$

where the second Eq. (3-3) expresses the fact that the vertical velocity $\partial u / \partial t$ is initially 0 for each point x of the string. By (3-2) we get

$$u_t(x,t) = -af_1'(x - at) + af_2'(x + at) \tag{3-4}$$

upon using the chain rule as in Sec. 1. Since $u_t(x,0) = 0$, Eq. (3-4) gives

$$f_1'(x) = f_2'(x)$$

after dividing by a. It follows that $f_2(x) = f_1(x) + c$, where c is constant.

Using this equality with x replaced by $x + at$ we see that (3-2) may be written

$$u(x,t) = f_1(x - at) + f_1(x + at) + c. \tag{3-5}$$

This step is sometimes puzzling when encountered for the first time; namely, from

$$f_2(x) = f_1(x) + c$$

how can we deduce $f_2(x + at) = f_1(x + at) + c$? The conclusion follows because the first equation holds *for all values of* x (and the conclusion would not follow otherwise). One cannot simply set $x = x + at$, because that would lead to $at = 0$. But one can reason as follows: We have $f_2(x) = f_1(x) + c$ for all x. Hence $f_2(s) = f_1(s) + c$ for all s, and the choice $s = x + at$ yields the desired result.

So far we have used only the second initial condition (3-3). To ensure the first condition, $u(x,0) = f(x)$, we set $t = 0$ in (3-5) and equate the result to $f(x)$, thus:

$$f_1(x) + f_1(x) + c = f(x).$$

It follows that $f_1(x) = \frac{1}{2}f(x) - \frac{1}{2}c$, and substituting into (3-5) gives the final answer:

$$u(x,t) = \frac{1}{2}f(x - at) + \frac{1}{2}f(x + at). \tag{3-6}$$

The displacement $u(x,t)$ in (3-6) is the sum of two waves, each of the form $\frac{1}{2}f(x)$, which travel in opposite directions with the velocity a. Initially (that is, for $t = 0$) these waves coincide, but with the passage of time they diverge, the wave $\frac{1}{2}f(x - at)$ moving to the right and the other to the left. In particular, if the waves are of finite extent, then any given point of the string is at rest in the initial position after the passage of both waves. The situation is illustrated schematically in Fig. 4 when $f(x)$ is a triangular wave on $(-k,k)$.

CASE II. *Initial Displacement* 0. Suppose, next, that the initial displacement is 0 but that the initial velocity is not 0. (Such a situation arises when the string is struck, as in a piano.) If the initial velocity is $g(x)$ at point x of the string, the initial conditions are now

$$u(x,0) = 0, \qquad u_t(x,0) = g(x). \tag{3-7}$$

The first Eq. (3-7) gives

$$f_1(x) + f_2(x) = 0,$$

when we recall (3-2), so that $f_2(x) = -f_1(x)$ for all values of x. Using this equality with x replaced by $x + at$, we see that (3-2) may be written

$$u(x,t) = f_1(x - at) - f_1(x + at). \tag{3-8}$$

Differentiating (3-8) with respect to t and setting $t = 0$ yield

$$u_t(x,0) = -af_1'(x) - af_1'(x) = g(x)$$

when we use the second condition (3-7). It follows that

$$f_1(x) = -\frac{1}{2a} \int_0^x g(s)\, ds + c, \tag{3-9}$$

where c is constant, and hence (3-8) gives the final answer

$$u(x,t) = -\frac{1}{2a} \int_0^{x-at} g(s)\, ds + \frac{1}{2a} \int_0^{x+at} g(s)\, ds.$$

The result may be expressed more compactly as

$$u(x,t) = \frac{1}{2a} \int_{x-at}^{x+at} g(s)\, ds. \tag{3-10}$$

Equation (3-8), like (3-6), represents a superposition of two waves traveling in opposite directions. Here, however, the shapes of the waves are determined by $f_1(x)$ and $-f_1(x)$, which are mirror images of each other in the x axis. Moreover, the shapes are not found directly by the initial condition but are obtained through the integration (3-9). For this reason the waves may be of infinite extent even when the initial impulse $u_t(x,0) = g(x)$ is confined to a finite portion $-k < x < k$ of the string. Indeed, for such a choice of $g(x)$ formula (3-10) shows that any given point x of the string eventually suffers a permanent displacement

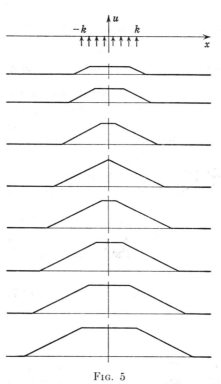

$$\frac{1}{2a} \int_{-k}^{k} g(s)\, ds. \tag{3-11}$$

This is the case because when $at > k + |x|$, the interval $(x - at, x + at)$ contains the interval $(-k,k)$. Inasmuch as $g(x) = 0$ outside the interval $(-k,k)$, the integral (3-10) is then equal to (3-11). Since each given point of the string eventually moves the same distance (3-11), the

FIG. 5

part of the string that is again at rest forms a straight line parallel to the original string. It is most interesting that this happens *regardless of the choice of $g(x)$,* provided only that $g(x) = 0$ outside some finite interval. Graphical illustration is given in Fig. 5 for the case $g(x) = 1$ on $(-k,k)$.

CASE III. *Arbitrary Initial Conditions.* Suppose, now, that both the initial displacement and the initial velocity are given by arbitrary functions of x, so that the initial conditions are

$$u(x,0) = f(x), \qquad u_t(x,0) = g(x). \tag{3-12}$$

This problem can be solved by superposition of the two solutions previously obtained. Indeed, let $v(x,t)$ and $w(x,t)$ satisfy the wave equation (3-1) and the respective initial conditions

$$v(x,0) = f(x), \qquad v_t(x,0) = 0,$$
$$w(x,0) = 0, \qquad w_t(x,0) = g(x). \tag{3-13}$$

Then the function

$$u(x,t) = v(x,t) + w(x,t) \tag{3-14}$$

satisfies the wave equation because v and w do, and addition of the relations (3-13) shows that u satisfies (3-12). Since the wave equation was solved in the previous discussion subject to initial conditions of the type (3-13), addition of the two solutions obtained formerly gives the solution desired now. That is,

$$u(x,t) = \frac{1}{2}f(x - at) + \frac{1}{2}f(x + at) + \frac{1}{2a} \int_{x-at}^{x+at} g(s)\,ds. \tag{3-15}$$

The expression (3-15) is known as *d'Alembert's formula;* it satisfies (3-1) and (3-12), hence gives the motion of a string subjected to arbitrary initial displacements and velocities.

The formula (3-15) can also be used to find the displacement of a semi-infinite string $(0 \leq x < \infty)$ fixed at $x = 0$. If the initial displacement and velocity of a semi-infinite string are

$$u(x,0) = f(x), \qquad u_t(x,0) = g(x), \qquad x \geq 0, \tag{3-16}$$

we can imagine an infinite string for which the initial conditions in the interval $(0,\infty)$ coincide with (3-16) and in the interval $(-\infty,0)$ are determined by

$$u(x,0) = -f(|x|), \qquad u_t(x,0) = -g(|x|), \qquad x \leq 0. \tag{3-17}$$

The point $x = 0$ of an infinite string, moving in accord with (3-16) and (3-17), will obviously be at rest, and the behavior of the infinite string for $x \geq 0$ will be identical with that of the semi-infinite string.

The superposition method does yield a solution of the problem but does not establish the uniqueness of that solution. We shall now show that every solution of (3-1) and (3-12) can be represented in the form $v + w$, with v and w as in (3-13). Since v and w were already shown to be unique, it will follow that u is also unique.

Indeed, let $u(x,t)$ be a solution of the wave equation (3-1) which satisfies the initial conditions (3-12). Let $v(x,t)$ be the unique solution of (3-1) satisfying the first conditions (3-13). Then the function $w(x,t)$ defined by

$$w(x,t) = u(x,t) - v(x,t)$$

satisfies (3-1) and the second set of initial conditions (3-13), as the reader can verify. It follows that w is uniquely determined and hence $u(x,t)$ is also uniquely determined. Because of uniqueness, (3-15) describes *the behavior of the string.* Without uniqueness, we could only say that (3-15) describes *a possible behavior of the string.*

PROBLEMS

1. The displacement of a string is given by the traveling wave

$$u(x,t) = \sin (x - at).$$

What are the initial displacement and velocity? Verify, by actual substitution into (3-15), that your initial values yield the correct result, $u(x,t) = \sin (x - at)$.

2. For a freely vibrating string the initial displacement and velocity are, respectively, $\sin x$ and $\cos 2x$. Find the displacement and velocity of the point $x = 0$ when $t = \pi$. *Hint:* First find $u(x,t)$ from (3-15).

3. A freely vibrating string was subjected to an initial displacement $6 \cos 5x$ and initial velocity 0. One second later it is found that the point $x = 0$ is displaced three units from the equilibrium position; that is, $u(0,1) = 3$. What can you say about the velocity of propagation for waves on this string?

4. The initial velocity of a freely vibrating string is xe^{-x^2}. For what choice of the initial displacement (if any) does the resulting motion represent a traveling wave traveling in the positive x direction? *Hint:* It is desired that $u(x,t) = f_1(x - at)$. Determine f_1 from the initial velocity, and then determine the initial displacement from f_1.

5. Solve Prob. 4 with the words "velocity" and "displacement" interchanged.

6. A stretched infinite string is struck so that its segment $-1 \le x \le 1$ is given an initial velocity 1. Use (3-15) to find the displacement and sketch the displacement curves for $t = 1/a$ and $t = 2/a$.

7. The initial displacement and velocity of a semi-infinite string are $u(x,0) = \sin x$, $u_t(x,0) = 0$, $0 \le x < \infty$. Find $u(x,t)$ for $t > 0$. Also find $u(x,t)$ if $u(x,0) = 0$, $u_t(x,0) = -2a \cos x$, $0 \le x < \infty$.

4. Characteristics. A physical interpretation may be given not only by plotting $u(x,t)$ versus x for a succession of values of t, but also by considering the xt plane. Each point of the xt plane represents a definite position on the string at a definite time t. If we take $t = 0$ to be the present time, then the half planes $t < 0$ and $t > 0$ give the past [1] and future, respectively.

Since the speed of propagation is a, the disturbance at (x,t) will reach a point (x_0,t_0) given by

---

[1] Although it is not appropriate to permit $t < 0$ when the string is plucked or struck at $t = 0$, it is appropriate if the string has been in motion for some time and the initial conditions are determined by high-speed photography. We could then take the viewpoint that we are trying to ascertain the past history of the string by observations on the present.

$$\frac{x - x_0}{t - t_0} = a \quad \text{or} \quad \frac{x - x_0}{t - t_0} = -a, \qquad (4\text{-}1)$$

for the direct wave $f_1(x - at)$ and the opposite wave $f_2(x + at)$, respectively. Equations (4-1) may be written

$$x - at = x_0 - at_0, \quad x + at = x_0 + at_0. \qquad (4\text{-}2)$$

If we draw the two lines (4-2) through the point (x_0, t_0), as shown in Fig. 6,
their intersection with the x axis
(that is, $t = 0$) gives those points on
the string for which the initial condition contributes to the disturbance at (x_0, t_0). The lines (4-2) are
called the *characteristics* of the partial differential equation (3-1).

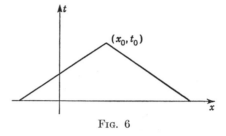

FIG. 6

Along the first line (4-2), $x - at$
is constant, and hence $f_1(x - at)$ is
constant. Thus, the deflection due
to the direct wave is the same at all points of the first characteristic (4-2).
The second line serves the same purpose for the opposite wave, and we
can say, briefly, that the disturbance travels along the characteristics.

If the initial disturbance is confined to some interval (x_1, x_2), then we
have the situation shown in Fig. 7. The xt plane is divided by the charac-

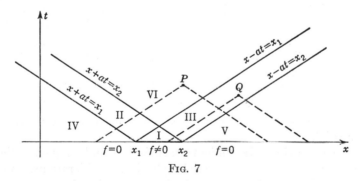

FIG. 7

teristics into six regions. In region I the points receive the disturbance
from both waves, in II only from the opposite wave, and in III only from
the direct wave. The points in IV and V are too far away to receive any
disturbance at the corresponding times, and the points in VI are at rest
because both waves have passed. That is, if P is a point in the region
VI, then the characteristics through P (shown dashed in the figure) intersect the x axis outside the interval (x_1, x_2). Hence the initial displacement at these points is zero, and we need consider the initial impulse only.

Since the characteristics intersect outside the interval (x_1,x_2), the displacement at P due to the initial impulse is given by the constant value (3-11).

We have seen that the initial conditions determine both the direct wave and the opposite wave at each point on the x axis where these conditions are given. Since the disturbance propagates along the characteristics the following theorem is suggested:

THEOREM I.   *Let u and u_t be given on the interval (x_1,x_2) in Fig. 8, and*

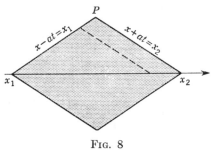

FIG. 8

suppose $u_{tt} = a^2 u_{xx}$. Then $u(x,t)$ is uniquely determined in the shaded region but is not uniquely determined at any other point.

Both the initial displacement and the initial velocity have to be specified in Theorem I, just as one would expect intuitively. It is a remarkable fact that the *displacement alone* (without the velocity) will determine the solution, provided this displacement is given along two intersecting characteristics in the xt plane. Indeed, let $u(x,t)$ be given along (x_1,P) in Fig. 8. Since the direct wave $f_1(x - at)$ is constant on (x_1,P), we can ascertain the shape of the reverse wave $f_2(x + at)$ along (x_1,P). This, in turn, gives $f_2(x + at)$ along (x_1,x_2), because the disturbance $f_2(x + at)$ propagates from (x_1,x_2) to (x_1,P) along the characteristics parallel to (x_2,P) (see the dashed line in the figure). In just the same way, when $u(x,t)$ is given on (x_2,P), we can determine the shape of the direct wave $f_1(x - at)$ on (x_1,x_2). Thus, we are led to the following theorem:

THEOREM II.   *Let u be specified along the two intersecting characteristics (x_1,P) and (x_2,P) in Fig. 8, and suppose that $u_{tt} = a^2 u_{xx}$. Then $u(x,t)$ is uniquely determined in the shaded region but is not uniquely determined at any other point.*

Theorems I and II are the fundamental existence and uniqueness theorem for the wave equation, deduced here by physical considerations. A simple mathematical proof of the same results is given in Sec. 25.

5. Boundary Conditions.   We now suppose that the freely vibrating string is not infinite but is stretched between two points of support (Fig. 3). When the supports are on the x axis and do not move, the situation is described by

$$u(0,t) = 0, \qquad u(l,t) = 0 \qquad \text{for all } t. \tag{5-1}$$

These are called *boundary conditions*, because they refer to the boundary points of the interval $(0,l)$ in which our physical problem is defined. Although the boundary conditions obviously do not determine the motion uniquely, they do enable us to establish some of the most interesting and important properties of the motion. Hence, in this section we see what can be deduced from (5-1) alone. In the next section we use (5-1) together with appropriate initial conditions.

Physically, one would expect the string to act like an infinite string until the disturbance created by the ends reaches the point of observation. In terms of Fig. 7, the ends $x = 0$ and $x = l$ have no effect in the region I provided the points $x = 0$ and $x = l$ lie outside the interval (x_1, x_2). When the disturbance reaches an end point, however, it is reflected, and the reflected wave must eventually be taken into account.

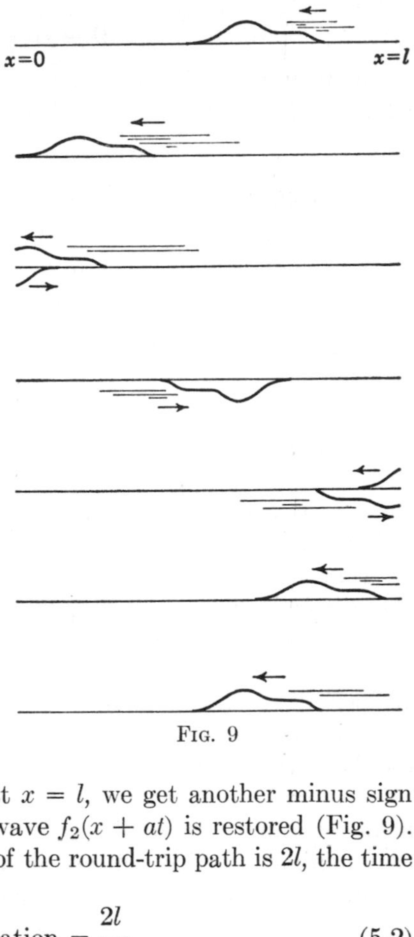

Because the end point is fixed the incident and reflected waves have algebraic sum 0 at the end point, and hence there is a 180° phase shift. A wave of type $f_2(x + at)$ becomes a wave of type $-f_2(-x + at)$ upon reflection at $x = 0$, for example (see Fig. 9). The change of sign in f_2 expresses the phase shift, and the change of sign in x indicates that the reflected wave

$$g(x - at) \equiv -f_2(-x + at)$$

propagates in the opposite direction.

FIG. 9

When the wave is reflected again at $x = l$, we get another minus sign in each case, and hence the original wave $f_2(x + at)$ is restored (Fig. 9). Since the velocity is a and the length of the round-trip path is $2l$, the time for a round trip is

$$\text{Period of vibration} = \frac{2l}{a}. \tag{5-2}$$

In terms of $f_2(at)$ the periodicity condition means that

$$f_2(at) = f_2\left[a\left(t + \frac{2l}{a} \right) \right] = f_2(at + 2l).$$

Similar remarks apply to $f_1(x)$, and hence we expect that both $f_1(x)$ and $f_2(x)$ will be periodic functions [1] with period $2l$.

[1] A function $f(x)$ has period p if $f(x + p) \equiv f(x)$, where p is a nonzero constant.

To discuss the boundary conditions mathematically, let us think of the finite string as being in reality an infinite string which vibrates in such a way that the points $x = 0$ and $x = l$ remain fixed. The formula

$$u(x,t) = f_1(x - at) + f_2(x + at) \qquad (5\text{-}3)$$

holds for all solutions of the wave equation. Letting $x = 0$ gives

$$0 = f_1(-at) + f_2(at)$$

when we use the first boundary condition $u(0,t) = 0$. This shows that $f_2(s) = -f_1(-s)$ for all s, and hence (5-3) becomes

$$u(x,t) = f_1(x - at) - f_1(-x - at). \qquad (5\text{-}4)$$

Thus the effect of the boundary condition at $x = 0$ is to reduce the number of arbitrary functions from two to one.

The second boundary condition applied to (5-4) gives

$$0 = f_1(l - at) - f_1(-l - at)$$

or, if we set $s = -l - at$,

$$0 = f_1(s + 2l) - f_1(s). \qquad (5\text{-}5)$$

Since t is arbitrary, so is s, and hence $f_1(x)$ has period $2l$. (This agrees with the surmise we had formed on physical grounds.) In view of (5-4), we can summarize our result as follows:

THEOREM I. *Suppose an infinite string vibrates freely in such a way that the points $x = 0$ and $x = l$ remain fixed. Then the displacement $u(x,t)$ is periodic both in space and in time. The two periods are, respectively, $2l$ for x and $2l/a$ for t if a is the velocity of propagation.*

Hence if a string is stretched between two fixed points, the free vibrations are periodic *no matter what the initial conditions may be.* Since a periodic vibration is generally perceived as musical, this fact is of great importance for the development of musical instruments.

Theorem I asserts that the motion will repeat after a time $2l/a$. Hence if the minimum t period of a vibrating string is determined by observation, that minimum period will not be longer than $2l/a$. It may be shorter, however. For instance, the function

$$u(x,t) = \sin 2\pi x/l \cos 2\pi at/l$$

satisfies (5-1) and the wave equation, hence represents free vibrations of a string of length l. But the minimum t period of this function is l/a rather than $2l/a$. The shorter period is explained by the fact that $u(\tfrac{1}{2}l,t) \equiv 0$; that is, the center of the string is a node. The center does not move, and the string acts like two strings of length $l/2$ placed end to end. We shall now show that there is always at least one node if the period is smaller than that given by Theorem I.

THEOREM II. *If the string considered in Theorem I has an x period 2p or t period 2p/a, where 0 < p < l, then the point x = p must be a node.*

Suppose, first, that the x period is $2p$. Then, in particular,

$$u(p,t) = u(-p,t). \tag{5-6}$$

On the other hand (5-4) gives $u(x,t) = -u(-x,t)$; hence

$$u(p,t) = -u(-p,t). \tag{5-7}$$

By addition of (5-6) and (5-7) we get $u(p,t) = 0$, which shows that $x = p$ is a node.

Suppose, next, that the t period is $2p/a$. The equation

$$u\left(x, t + \frac{2p}{a}\right) = u(x,t)$$

combines with (5-4) to give

$$f_1(x - at - 2p) - f_1(-x - at - 2p) = f_1(x - at) - f_1(-x - at).$$

If we let $x + at = 0$ and $x - at - 2p = s$, the equation reduces, after rearrangement, to

$$f_1(s + 2p) - f_1(s) = c, \tag{5-8}$$

where $c = f_1(0) - f_1(-2p)$ is constant. Equation (5-8) shows that $f_1(s)$ increases by the amount c whenever s increases by $2p$. If $c \neq 0$, it follows that $|f_1(s)|$ is unbounded. However, $f_1(s)$ has period $2l$ by (5-5), hence is bounded, and this shows that $c = 0$ in (5-8). The choice $s = -p - at$ in (5-8) with $c = 0$ leads to the desired result:

$$u(p,t) = f_1(p - at) - f_1(-p - at) = 0.$$

To illustrate the use of Theorem II, suppose a 2-in.-diameter steel cable 100 ft long is observed to vibrate without nodes at the rate of two complete cycles per second. According to Theorem I the t period is $2l/a$ or possibly less. But Theorem II shows that the period is not less, since the motion was observed to have no fixed points. Hence

$$\frac{1}{2} = 2\frac{100}{a}$$

which gives $a = 400$ fps. This is the velocity with which waves are propagated along the cable. Since the density of steel is about 480 lb per ft^3, the weight of 1 ft of cable is

$$480\pi(\tfrac{1}{12})^2 1 = (\tfrac{10}{3})\pi \doteq 10 \text{ lb per ft.}$$

This gives $\rho = \tfrac{10}{32}$ slug for the linear density, and hence the tension is

$$T = a^2\rho = (400)^2(\tfrac{10}{32}) = 50,000 \text{ lb.}$$

PROBLEMS

1. An infinite string vibrates freely in such a way that the two points $x = 0$ and $x = l$ remain fixed; that is, $u(0,t) = u(l,t) = 0$. Are any other points of the string necessarily fixed? Which ones?

2. Suppose a freely vibrating string of length l has just one node at $x = p$ between 0 and l. Show that the node must be at the mid-point. (The analogous result for n nodes is also true.) *Hint:* If $p < l/2$, apply Prob. 1 to the two points $x = 0$, $x = p$. If $p > l/2$, apply Prob. 1 to the two points $x = p$, $x = l$.

3. A cable of length l ft is made of a material with density d lb per ft^3. It is found that the cable makes 10 complete oscillations in t sec. Show that the cross-sectional stress is

$$\sigma = 0.087d \left(\frac{l}{t}\right)^2 \quad \text{psi}$$

provided the oscillations do not have a node between 0 and l. How would the result change if the mid-point remains fixed during the observed oscillations but no other point remains fixed?

4. Let $h(t)$ be a given function of t. (a) What is the physical meaning of the boundary condition $u(l,t) = h(t)$? (b) Describe a physical problem that would lead to the boundary conditions $u(x,0) = 0$, $u[x,h(t)] = 0$.

6. Initial and Boundary Conditions. We shall now consider the free vibrations of a string satisfying the boundary conditions

$$u(0,t) = 0, \qquad u(l,t) = 0 \qquad \text{for all } t, \tag{6-1}$$

together with the initial conditions

$$u(x,0) = f(x), \qquad u_t(x,0) = g(x) \qquad \text{for } 0 < x < l. \tag{6-2}$$

As in the preceding section we regard the finite string as being an infinite string with nodes $x = 0$, $x = l$. According to (5-4) and (5-5), the boundary conditions give

$$u(x,t) = f_1(x - at) - f_1(-x - at) \tag{6-3}$$

where $f_1(x)$ has period $2l$, and conversely, (6-3) ensures (6-1). The initial conditions (6-2) are prescribed on $(0,l)$ for the infinite string, and our task is to assign initial conditions outside the interval $(0,l)$ in such a way that the solution has the form (6-3).

Denoting the unknown initial conditions for the infinite string by $f_0(x)$ and $g_0(x)$, we have

$$f_0(x) = f(x), \qquad g_0(x) = g(x), \qquad 0 < x < l, \tag{6-4}$$

because the infinite string is to agree with the finite string on $(0,l)$. Upon setting $t = 0$ in (6-3) we get

$$f_0(x) = f_1(x) - f_1(-x).$$

Similarly, differentiating (6-3) with respect to t and putting $t = 0$ give

$$g_0(x) = -af_1'(x) + af_1'(-x).$$

These expressions show that [1]

---

[1] A function $\phi(x)$ is *even* if $\phi(-x) \equiv \phi(x)$, *odd* if $\phi(x) \equiv -\phi(x)$. An analytical and graphical discussion of such functions is given in Chap. 2, Sec. 19.

$$f_0(x) \text{ and } g_0(x) \text{ are odd functions.} \qquad (6\text{-}5)$$

Hence, f_0 and g_0 are determined on $(-l,l)$ by their values on $(0,l)$.

Finally, since $f_0(x)$ and $g_0(x)$ are expressed in terms of the function $f_1(x)$, which has period $2l$, we see that

$$f_0(x) \text{ and } g_0(x) \text{ have period } 2l. \qquad (6\text{-}6)$$

Thus, f_0 and g_0 are known everywhere as soon as they are known on $(-l,l)$.

According to (3-15), the solution is

$$u(x,t) = \frac{1}{2}f_0(x - at) + \frac{1}{2}f_0(x + at) + \frac{1}{2a}\int_{x-at}^{x+at} g_0(s)\, ds. \qquad (6\text{-}7)$$

If $f_0(x)$ and $g_0(x)$ in (6-7) are determined by (6-4) to (6-6), it is easily verified that this function $u(x,t)$ satisfies the wave equation, the initial conditions (6-2), and the boundary conditions (6-1). Thus, (6-7) is a simple and explicit expression for the motion of a vibrating string with fixed end points.

The correspondence between the finite string and the infinite string leads to an interesting geometrical construction for getting the disturbance at any point P of the strip $0 < x < l$ in the xt plane (Fig. 10). For the infinite string the disturbance at P is found by drawing characteristics as in Sec. 4 (see solid lines in Fig. 10). Since the initial

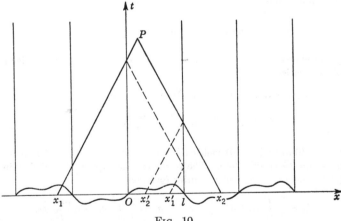

FIG. 10

conditions for the infinite string are obtained from those for the finite string by (6-4) to (6-6), the same result may be found by following the dashed lines in Fig. 10. To take account of (6-5), however, we must introduce a changed sign upon each reflection at the boundary. The disturbance at P arises from the initial disturbance at x_1' and x_2', subject to the above-mentioned convention regarding sign. This reflection of the characteristics in the boundary lines $x = 0$, $x = l$ is quite analogous to the reflection of waves at the end points of the string.

The procedure illustrated in Fig. 10 is an example of the *method of images*, so called because the initial conditions for the infinite string are obtained from those for the finite string by forming repeated mirror images in the lines $t = 0$, $x = 0$, and $x = l$.

Example: Discuss the free oscillations of a string of length l which satisfies the initial conditions

$$u(x,0) = f_n \sin \frac{n\pi x}{l}, \qquad u_t(x,0) = 0,$$

where n is an integer and f_n is constant.

Since $\sin n\pi x/l$ is odd and has period $2l$, we may take

$$f_0(x) = f_n \sin \frac{n\pi x}{l}, \qquad g_0(x) = 0$$

as initial conditions for the associated infinite string. Equation (6-7) now yields the solution

$$u(x,t) = \frac{f_n}{2} \sin \frac{n\pi(x - at)}{l} + \frac{f_n}{2} \sin \frac{n\pi(x + at)}{l}$$

$$= f_n \sin \frac{n\pi x}{l} \cos \frac{n\pi at}{l}. \tag{6-8}$$

If the initial displacement is given by a Fourier series, so that [1]

$$u(x,0) = f(x) = \Sigma f_n \sin \frac{n\pi x}{l}, \qquad u_t(x,0) = 0$$

then superposition of the corresponding solutions (6-8) yields

$$u(x,t) = \Sigma f_n \sin \frac{n\pi x}{l} \cos \frac{n\pi at}{l}. \tag{6-9}$$

Similarly, by choosing $f_0(x) = 0$, $g_0(x) = g_n \sin n\pi x/l$ in (6-7), the reader can verify that the solution satisfying

$$u(x,0) = 0, \qquad u_t(x,0) = g(x) = \Sigma g_n \sin \frac{n\pi x}{l}$$

is
$$u(x,t) = \Sigma \frac{g_n l}{n\pi a} \sin \frac{n\pi x}{l} \sin \frac{n\pi at}{l}. \tag{6-10}$$

Superposition of (6-9) and (6-10) yields the general *Fourier-series solution* of the wave equation satisfying (6-1) and (6-2). The result can be expressed explicitly in terms of $f(x)$ and $g(x)$ by means of the Euler-Fourier formulas

$$f_n = \frac{2}{l} \int_0^l f(x) \sin \frac{n\pi x}{l}\, dx, \qquad g_n = \frac{2}{l} \int_0^l g(x) \sin \frac{n\pi x}{l}\, dx.$$

Because of convergence questions the Fourier-series solution is somewhat less general than (6-7), and it is hopelessly inferior to (6-7) for numerical computation. But Fourier series have great usefulness in that they apply to many problems in which the preceding

---

[1] Throughout Chap. 6 we use Σ as an abbreviation for $\displaystyle\sum_{n=1}^{\infty}$. A brief review of this *sigma notation* is given in Chap. 2, Sec. 2, and Fourier series are discussed in Chap. 2, Secs. 18 to 25.

methods fail. Examples are given for the vibrating string in the next section and for other physical systems in the sections to follow.

PROBLEMS

1. Show that the expression (6-8) satisfies the appropriate (a) differential equation, (b) initial conditions, (c) boundary conditions.

2. The initial displacement of a freely vibrating string of length l is

$$f(x) = \frac{2bx}{l}, \qquad 0 < x < \frac{1}{2}l,$$

$$f(x) = 2b - \frac{2bx}{l}, \qquad \frac{1}{2}l < x < l,$$

and the initial velocity is $g(x) = 0$. (a) Sketch $f(x)$ and $f_0(x)$. (b) Using (6-7) and your sketch, find the displacement of the mid-point of the string when $at = l/4$.

3. (a) Express $f(x)$ in Prob. 2 as a Fourier sine series. (b) By (a) and (6-9) show that the displacement of the string in Prob. 2 is

$$u(x,t) = \frac{8b}{\pi^2} \left(\frac{1}{1^2} \sin \frac{\pi x}{l} \cos \frac{\pi at}{l} - \frac{1}{3^2} \sin \frac{3\pi x}{l} \cos \frac{3\pi at}{l} + \cdots \right).$$

(c) Obtain an infinite-series representation for the displacement of the mid-point when $at = l/4$.

7. Damped Oscillations.

The foregoing discussion was concerned with free vibrations, so that $F(x,t) = 0$ in (2-3). It was indicated that the displacement $u(x,t)$ is always periodic in time and hence the amplitude remains constant. But, in fact, the oscillations gradually die down when a string is vibrating in air, and this behavior is to be analyzed next.

The reason for the decrease in amplitude is that the air resists the motion of an object moving through it. When there is no relative velocity, there is no resistance; when there is high velocity, there is high resistance. If the resistance is assumed proportional to the velocity, we have

$$F(x,t) = -2bu_t(x,t), \qquad b > 0, \text{ const}, \tag{7-1}$$

in (2-3). The minus sign is used because the force resists the motion, hence is directed opposite to the velocity. Our partial differential equation is now

$$u_{tt} - a^2 u_{xx} = -2bu_t \tag{7-2}$$

and the solutions of (7-2) for $b > 0$ represent the damped oscillations of the string. As before, one has the initial and boundary conditions

$$u(x,0) = f(x), \qquad u_t(x,0) = g(x), \tag{7-3}$$

$$u(0,t) = 0, \qquad u(l,t) = 0. \tag{7-4}$$

Equation (7-2) cannot be solved by the method of the preceding sections but can be solved by Fourier series. Thus, since the solution $u(x,t)$ is a twice-differentiable function of x for each t, we may expand $u(x,t)$ in a Fourier sine series

$$u(x,t) = \Sigma b_n(t) \sin \frac{n\pi x}{l}, \qquad 0 < x < l. \tag{7-5}$$

A sine series is chosen rather than a cosine series because such a series automatically satisfies the boundary conditions (7-4). To satisfy the initial conditions we require

$$f(x) = \Sigma b_n(0) \sin \frac{n\pi x}{l}, \qquad g(x) = \Sigma b'_n(0) \sin \frac{n\pi x}{l}. \tag{7-6}$$

These relations show that $b_n(0)$ and $b'_n(0)$ must be the Fourier coefficients of $f(x)$ and $g(x)$. That is, if

$$f_n = \frac{2}{l} \int_0^l f(x) \sin \frac{n\pi x}{l} \, dx, \qquad g_n = \frac{2}{l} \int_0^l g(x) \sin \frac{n\pi x}{l} \, dx \tag{7-7}$$

then multiplying (7-6) by $\sin n\pi x/l$ and integrating from 0 to l yield

$$b_n(0) = f_n, \qquad b'_n(0) = g_n. \tag{7-8}$$

We must still satisfy the differential equation. Upon substituting the terms (7-5) into (7-2) we get

$$\Sigma b''_n \sin \frac{n\pi x}{l} + a^2 \Sigma b_n \left(\frac{n\pi}{l}\right)^2 \sin \frac{n\pi x}{l} = -2b \Sigma b'_n \sin \frac{n\pi x}{l},$$

which gives a set of ordinary differential equations

$$b''_n + 2bb'_n + \left(\frac{n\pi a}{l}\right)^2 b_n = 0 \tag{7-9}$$

when the coefficient of $\sin n\pi x/l$ is equated to zero.

Equation (7-9) may be solved as in Chap. 1 by assuming that $b_n = e^{\alpha t}$. It is found that

$$b_n(t) = C_0 e^{-bt} \cos \omega_n t + C_1 e^{-bt} \sin \omega_n t, \tag{7-10}$$

where

$$\omega_n^2 = \left(\frac{n\pi a}{l}\right)^2 - b^2. \tag{7-11}$$

The arbitrary constants C_0 and C_1 are determined from (7-8) as

$$C_0 = f_n, \qquad C_1 = (g_n + bf_n)\omega_n^{-1}.$$

Substituting (7-10) into (7-5) yields the final answer

$$u(x,t) = e^{-bt} \Sigma \left[f_n \cos \omega_n t + (g_n + bf_n) \frac{\sin \omega_n t}{\omega_n} \right] \sin \frac{n\pi x}{l}.$$

Conditions (7-2)–(7-4) are satisfied if the term-by-term differentiation is legitimate, for instance, if $f'''(x)$ and $g''(x)$ are bounded.[1] When $b = 0$, the solution agrees with the sum of (6-9) and (6-10), as it should. According to (7-11), the damping reduces the frequency of the corresponding terms in the series for undamped vibrations. If $b < \pi a/l$, all the terms are oscillatory and they have the same damping factor e^{-bt}. But for larger values of b the first few terms may have ω_n pure imaginary. The corresponding trigonometric functions become hyperbolic functions, and the terms in question are not oscillatory. If $\omega_n = 0$, which may happen in this latter case, we replace $(\sin \omega_n t)/\omega_n$ by its limit t [cf. Chap. 1, Sec. 32].

PROBLEMS

1. A string of length l vibrating in air satisfies the initial conditions $u(x,0) = f_1 \sin \pi x/l$, $u_t(x,0) = 0$. Show that the displacement of the mid-point can be written in the form

$$u(\tfrac{1}{2}l,t) = Ae^{-bt} \cos(\omega t + \phi), \qquad A, \omega, \phi \text{ const.}$$

2. Referring to Prob. 1, sketch the curves $y = \pm Ae^{-bt}$ and $y = u(\tfrac{1}{2}l,t)$ in a single neat diagram. Thus describe an experimental procedure for determining b. (When the oscillations are rapid and b is small, one can speak of the mean amplitude at a given time t. If the amplitude is A_0 at time t_0 and A_1 at time $t_0 + \tau$, the reader can verify that

$$b = \tau^{-1} \log \frac{A_0}{A_1}.$$

Since A_0 and A_1 can be found by placing a scale behind the oscillating string, this gives a method for comparing the viscosity of gases.)

8. Forced Oscillations and Resonance. Sometimes the force function $F(x,t)$ does not involve the unknown displacement u, as in (7-1), but is determined independently. (For example, consider the gravitational force on a horizontal vibrating string.) The corresponding mathematical problem is

$$u_{tt} - a^2 u_{xx} = F(x,t), \qquad u(x,0) = f(x), \qquad u_t(x,0) = g(x),$$

$$u(0,t) = 0, \qquad u(l,t) = 0. \tag{8-1}$$

Associated with this problem are two simpler problems,

$$v_{tt} - a^2 v_{xx} = F(x,t), \qquad v(x,0) = 0, \qquad v_t(x,0) = 0,$$

$$v(0,t) = 0, \qquad v(l,t) = 0, \tag{8-2}$$

and $\quad w_{tt} - a^2 w_{xx} = 0, \qquad w(x,0) = f(x), \qquad w_t(x,0) = g(x),$

$$w(0,t) = 0, \qquad w(l,t) = 0. \tag{8-3}$$

Equation (8-2) describes purely forced vibrations, and (8-3) describes free vibrations. Now, if v satisfies (8-2) and w satisfies (8-3), it is easily seen

---

[1] See Chap. 2, Sec. 25, Theorem III.

that $u = v + w$ satisfies (8-1). Also, uniqueness in the latter problem yields uniqueness in the former. Since (8-3) was solved in Sec. 6, we need consider (8-2) only. This system will now be solved formally on the assumption that $F(x,t)$ has a Fourier series,

$$F(x,t) = \Sigma B_n(t) \sin \frac{n\pi x}{l}. \tag{8-4}$$

The coefficients are given by the Euler-Fourier formulas,

$$B_n(t) = \frac{2}{l} \int_0^l F(\xi,t) \sin \frac{n\pi\xi}{l} \, d\xi. \tag{8-5}$$

Substituting (8-4) and the Fourier series

$$u(x,t) = \Sigma b_n(t) \sin \frac{n\pi x}{l} \tag{8-6}$$

into the differential equation (8-1) gives

$$\Sigma b_n'' \sin \frac{n\pi x}{l} + \Sigma \omega_n^2 b_n \sin \frac{n\pi x}{l} = \Sigma B_n \sin \frac{n\pi x}{l},$$

where $\omega_n = n\pi a/l$ [compare (7-11)]. If we equate the coefficients of $\sin n\pi x/l$, we get

$$b_n'' + \omega_n^2 b_n = B_n. \tag{8-7}$$

These equations are to be solved subject to the initial conditions

$$b_n(0) = 0, \qquad b_n'(0) = 0, \tag{8-8}$$

which result from the initial conditions in (8-2). By the method of Chap. 1, Sec. 28 [cf. also Eq. (33-9) in Chap. 1], the solution of (8-7) and (8-8) is

$$b_n(t) = \omega_n^{-1} \int_0^t B_n(\lambda) \sin \omega_n(t - \lambda) \, d\lambda. \tag{8-9}$$

Determining $B_n(\lambda)$ by (8-5), $b_n(t)$ by (8-9), and $u(x,t)$ by (8-6) yields an explicit formula

$$u(x,t) = \Sigma \frac{2}{n\pi a} \sin \frac{n\pi x}{l} \int_0^t \int_0^l \sin \frac{n\pi\xi}{l} \sin \frac{n\pi a}{l} (t - \lambda) F(\xi,\lambda) \, d\xi \, d\lambda$$

when ω_n is replaced by its value $n\pi a/l$.

If we have both damping and forcing, then (8-7) contains an extra term $2bb_n'$ as in (7-9). This leads to a different formula (8-9), but in other respects the analysis is unchanged. Thus, the method of Fourier series enables us to find the damped oscillations of a string with arbitrary initial conditions and force function.

If $F(x,t)$ is periodic in t, there may be resonance, and this important phenomenon will now be discussed for the special case (cf. Chap. 1, Sec. 33)

$$F(x,t) = a(x) \sin \omega t + b(x) \cos \omega t. \tag{8-10}$$

[In the general case $F(x,t)$ is a sum of terms like (8-10), since the assumed periodicity enables us to express $F(x,t)$ as a Fourier series in t.] With $F(x,t)$ as in (8-10) the form of $B_n(t)$ can be determined by inspection of (8-5). Substitution into (8-7) then gives an equation of form

$$b_n'' + \omega_n^2 b_n = \alpha \sin \omega t + \beta \cos \omega t, \tag{8-11}$$

where α and β are constant.

If $\omega^2 \neq \omega_n^2$, the solutions of (8-11) are all bounded, but if $\omega = \omega_n$, the particular integral involves the functions

$$t \sin \omega t, \; t \cos \omega t$$

which increase indefinitely with t. Hence in that case the term

$$b_n(t) \sin \frac{n\pi x}{l} \tag{8-12}$$

in the Fourier series for $u(x,t)$ becomes strongly emphasized as t increases, and we say, briefly, that the oscillation (8-12) is *resonant*.

A physical explanation is readily given in terms of the results of Sec. 5. Thus, the condition $\omega = \omega_n$ can be written as

$$\frac{2\pi}{\omega} = \frac{2l}{na}.$$

This asserts that the period of $F(x,t)$ in (8-10) is equal to the period for free oscillations of a string of length l/n. And l/n is precisely the distance between nodes for a vibration of the type (8-12).

Example: A cord stretched between the fixed points $x = 0$ and $x = l$ is initially supported so that it forms a horizontal straight line. Discuss the oscillations when the support is suddenly removed.

The force function $F_1(x,t)$ in Sec. 2 is $-g\rho$, and hence the partial differential equation is

$$u_{tt} - a^2 u_{xx} = -g, \tag{8-13}$$

while the boundary and initial conditions are

$$u(0,t) = u(l,t) = 0,$$

$$u(x,0) = u_t(x,0) = 0. \tag{8-14}$$

If we succeed in finding a particular solution $u = v(x)$ of (8-13) which satisfies the boundary conditions

$$v(0) = v(l) = 0, \tag{8-15}$$

then the solution of (8-13) can be written as

$$u(x,t) = w(x,t) + v(x) \qquad (8\text{-}16)$$

where, as follows from (8-13) and (8-14), $w(x,t)$ satisfies

$$w_{tt} - a^2 w_{xx} = 0, \qquad w(0,t) = 0, \qquad w(l,t) = 0, \qquad w(x,0) = -v(x),$$
$$w_t(x,0) = 0. \qquad (8\text{-}17)$$

Since the desired particular solution $v(x)$ is to be independent of t, the choice $u(x,t) = v(x)$ in (8-13) yields $a^2 v'' = g$, so that

$$v(x) = -\frac{g}{2a^2}\, x(l - x), \qquad (8\text{-}18)$$

when the integration constants are determined so as to satisfy (8-15). This particular solution corresponds to the equilibrium position of the string under gravity. The solution of the system (8-17) can now be written down with the aid of (6-7) as

$$w(x,t) = \tfrac{1}{2}f_0(x - at) + \tfrac{1}{2}f_0(x + at),$$

where $f_0(x)$ is odd, has period $2l$, and is defined for $0 < x < l$ by

$$f_0(x) = -v(x) = \frac{g}{2a^2}\, x(l - x).$$

The required solution is $u = v + w$.

By interpreting $f_0(x)$, $f_0(x - at)$, and $f_0(x + at)$ graphically one finds that $w(x,t)$ is largest on $0 < x < l$ when $at = 0, 2l, 4l, \ldots$ and then $w(x,t) = f_0(x)$. Similarly, $w(x,t)$ is least when $at = l, 3l, 5l, \ldots$ and then $w(x,t) = -f_0(x)$. It follows that the cord oscillates between the horizontal position $u = 0$ and the position $u = 2v(x)$ in which each point is twice as low as the equilibrium position (8-18). The period is $2l/a$.

PROBLEMS

1. A horizontal cable 100 ft long sags 5 ft when at rest under gravity. If the cable is disturbed so that it oscillates without nodes, what is the frequency of the oscillations? *Hint:* See (8-18).

2. A string of length l is subjected to a force $F(x,t) = \sin \omega t \sin \pi x/l$, where ω is constant. Find the displacement $u(x,t)$ if the string was initially at rest in the equilibrium position. Be sure to distinguish the cases $\omega \neq n\pi a/l$ and $\omega = n\pi a/l$.

3. Show that the equilibrium shape of a string under a force $F(x)$ is described by

$$u = \frac{x}{a^2 l} \int_0^l \int_0^\xi F(s)\, ds\, d\xi - \frac{1}{a^2} \int_0^x \int_0^\xi F(s)\, ds\, d\xi.$$

4. Show that the function

$$v(x,t) = -\frac{1}{4a^2} \int_0^{x+at} \int_0^{x-at} F\left[\frac{1}{2}(r + s), \frac{1}{2a}(r - s) \right] ds\, dr$$

satisfies $v_{tt} - a^2 v_{xx} = F(x,t)$. *Hint:* Let $x + at = r$, $x - at = s$, $v(x,t) = V(r,s)$. Then, as in Sec. 1, $-4a^2 V_{rs} = F(x,t)$.

5. If $v(x,t)$ is the function obtained in Prob. 4, let $w(x,t)$ be determined by

$$w_{tt} - a^2 w_{xx} = 0, \qquad w(x,0) = f(x) - v(x,0), \qquad w_t(x,0) = g(x) - v_t(x,0),$$

(cf. Sec. 3).   Then $u = v + w$ satisfies

$$u_{tt} - a^2 u_{xx} = F(x,t), \qquad u(x,0) = f(x), \qquad u_t(x,0) = g(x).$$

6. Solve the Example in the text by means of Fourier series.

SOLUTION BY SERIES

9. Heat Flow in One Dimension.   The foregoing discussion of the vibrating string enabled us to survey the field of partial differential equations and to illustrate a number of important methods.   Prominent among these is the method of infinite series, which will now be explored more fully and used in a variety of applications.   We begin with a problem from the theory of heat conduction.

Consider a section cut from an insulated, uniform bar by two parallel planes Δx units apart (Fig. 11), and suppose that the temperature of one

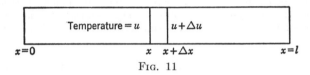

$$x=0 \qquad\qquad x \quad x+\Delta x \qquad\qquad x=l$$
Fig. 11

of the planes is u while that of the second plane is $u + \Delta u$.   It is known from experiment that heat flows from the plane at higher temperature to that at the lower, the amount of heat flowing per unit area per second being approximately

$$\text{Rate of flow} \doteq -k\frac{\Delta u}{\Delta x}. \tag{9-1}$$

Here k is a constant called the *thermal conductivity* of the material; its dimensions in the cgs system are $\text{cal}/(\text{cm-sec } °\text{C})$.   In the limit as $\Delta x \to 0$, Eq. (9-1) can be regarded as an exact equality, so that

$$\text{Rate of flow} = -k u_x. \tag{9-2}$$

On the other hand, if c is the heat capacity of the medium and ρ its density, the amount of heat in the section from x to $x + \Delta x$ is

$$(c\rho A\ \Delta x)\bar{u}, \tag{9-3}$$

where A is the cross-sectional area and where $\bar{u}$ is the mean value of u over the interval $(x, x + \Delta x)$.   For a time interval $(t, t + \Delta t)$ the increase in amount of heat in the section $(x, x + \Delta x)$ can be computed from (9-3) and also from (9-2).   The computation yields [1]

---

[1] It is supposed that no heat is generated within the material and that k, ρ, and c are constant over the relevant range of temperatures.   If ρ is measured in grams per cubic centimeter, the dimensions of c are $\text{cal}/(\text{g } °\text{C})$.

$$c\rho A\ \Delta x\ \bar{u}(x, t + \Delta t) - c\rho A\ \Delta x\ \bar{u}(x,t)$$

$$= kA\ \Delta t\ \overline{u_x}(x + \Delta x, t) - kA\ \Delta t\ \overline{u_x}(x,t),$$

where $\overline{u_x}$ is the mean value of u_x in the time interval $(t, t + \Delta t)$. Dividing by $c\rho A\ \Delta x\ \Delta t$ we obtain

$$\frac{\bar{u}(x,t + \Delta t) - \bar{u}(x,t)}{\Delta t} = \frac{k}{c\rho}\frac{\overline{u_x}(x + \Delta x, t) - \overline{u_x}(x,t)}{\Delta x} \tag{9-4}$$

and letting $\Delta x \to 0$, $\Delta t \to 0$ now gives

$$u_t = \alpha^2 u_{xx}, \qquad \alpha^2 = \frac{k}{c\rho}, \tag{9-5}$$

if we recall the definition of partial derivative.

The fact that (9-4) involves mean values causes no trouble when u_t and u_{xx} are continuous; see the discussion of Eq. (7-4), Chap. 5. Thus, (9-5) follows *without approximation* from appropriate physical assumptions. This contrasts to the wave equation $u_{tt} = a^2 u_{xx}$, which is only an approximate statement of Newton's law for the vibrating string.

We shall now solve (9-5) under the assumption that the initial temperature is a prescribed function $f(x)$,

$$u(x,0) = f(x), \qquad 0 < x < l, \tag{9-6}$$

which can be represented by a convergent Fourier series. The ends of the bar are assumed to have the temperature zero:

$$u(0,t) = u(l,t) = 0, \qquad t \geq 0. \tag{9-7}$$

Since u_{xx} must exist if u satisfies (9-5), we know that $u(x,t)$ has a Fourier series in x for each fixed $t > 0$:

$$u(x,t) = \Sigma b_n(t) \sin \frac{n\pi x}{l}. \tag{9-8}$$

Here, a sine series is chosen because such a series automatically satisfies the requirement (9-7). Proceeding tentatively, assume that (9-8) can be differentiated term by term to give

$$\Sigma b_n'(t) \sin \frac{n\pi x}{l} = \alpha^2 \Sigma b_n(t) \left(\frac{n\pi}{l}\right)^2 \left(-\sin \frac{n\pi x}{l}\right) \tag{9-9}$$

upon substitution into (9-5). Equation (9-9) is satisfied if the coefficients of $\sin n\pi x/l$ on each side are equated:

$$b_n' = -\left(\frac{\alpha n\pi}{l}\right)^2 b_n.$$

Upon integration this gives

$$b_n(t) = c_n e^{-(\alpha n\pi/l)^2 t},$$

where the c_n are constant, and hence (9-8) becomes

$$u(x,t) = \Sigma c_n e^{-(\alpha n\pi/l)^2 t} \sin \frac{n\pi x}{l}. \tag{9-10}$$

The initial condition (9-6) yields

$$f(x) = u(x,0) = \Sigma c_n \sin \frac{n\pi x}{l}. \tag{9-11}$$

Since the Fourier series for $f(x)$ converges to $f(x)$ by hypothesis, Eq. (9-11) is assured if c_n are the Fourier coefficients,

$$c_n = \frac{2}{l} \int_0^l f(x) \sin \frac{n\pi x}{l} \, dx.$$

The only questionable step in the foregoing discussion was the term-by-term differentiation, but this step can now be justified. Differentiating (9-10) term by term actually does give

$$u_{xx} = -\Sigma c_n e^{-(\alpha n\pi/l)^2 t} \left(\frac{n\pi}{l}\right)^2 \sin \frac{n\pi x}{l}$$

$$\tag{9-12}$$

$$u_t = -\Sigma c_n e^{-(\alpha n\pi/l)^2 t} \left(\frac{\alpha n\pi}{l}\right)^2 \sin \frac{n\pi x}{l}$$

because the series (9-12) are *uniformly convergent* when $t \geq \delta > 0$. (See Chap. 2, Sec. 7, Theorem IV. The uniform convergence follows from the convergence of

$$\Sigma n^2 e^{-(\alpha n\pi/l)^2 \delta},$$

since the Fourier coefficients c_n are bounded.) Hence, (9-10) is a solution of the problem. We cannot yet say that (9-10) is *the* solution, because there might be another solution— necessarily different from the one we found—for which the term-by-term differentiation is not permissible. A uniqueness theorem is established, however, in Sec. 24.

Because of the exponential factors the series (9-10) is rapidly convergent and affords a useful means of computing the temperature. By contrast, the series obtained in Sec. 6 for solutions of the wave equation converges no better than the series for the initial values $f(x)$ and $g(x)$. The physical significance of this difference in the two cases is discussed in Sec. 27.

Example 1. Find the steady-state temperature of a uniform bar. It is required that $u(x,t)$ be independent of t, whence by (9-5)

$$\alpha^2 u_{xx} = u_t = 0.$$

Hence, $u = c_0 + c_1 x$, where c_0 and c_1 are constant. If the temperatures at the ends are, respectively, u_0 and u_1, we can determine the constants and thus obtain the formula

$$u(x,t) = u_0 + \frac{x}{l}(u_1 - u_0). \tag{9-13}$$

The rate of heat flow is given by (9-2) and (9-13) as

$$-k\frac{u_1 - u_0}{l} \tag{9-14}$$

and hence, (9-1) holds without approximation in the steady state.

Example 2. A rod of length 5 has the end $x = 0$ at $0°$, the end $x = 5$ at $10°$, and the initial temperature is $f(x)$. Find the temperature distribution.

If $v(x,t)$ is the unknown temperature at point x and time t, we let

$$u = v - 2x, \tag{9-15}$$

where $2x$ is the steady-state temperature determined from (9-13). Then $\alpha^2 u_{xx} = u_t$, $u(x,0) = f(x) - 2x$, $u(0,t) = u(5,t) = 0$. Hence u is given by (9-10), where the c_ns are the Fourier coefficients of $f(x) - 2x$. When we have found u, Eq. (9-15) gives v.

We have noted that the value $2x$ introduced in (9-15) is the steady-state temperature as determined by Example 1. The same method enables us to replace any constant boundary conditions by the homogeneous conditions $u(0,t) = u(l,t) = 0$. That is, if the unknown temperature $v(x,t)$ satisfies

$$v(0,t) = v_0, \qquad v(l,t) = v_1, \qquad v_0 \text{ and } v_1 \text{ const}, \tag{9-16}$$

we define u to be the difference between v and the steady-state temperature:

$$u(x,t) = v(x,t) - \left[v_0 + \frac{x}{l}(v_1 - v_0)\right].$$

Then $u(0,t) = u(l,t) = 0$, and hence u can be determined by the method of the text. A similar use of the steady-state solution was made in the Example, Sec. 8.

PROBLEMS

1. Compute the loss of heat per day per square meter of a large concrete wall whose thickness is 25 cm if one face is kept at $0°C$ and the other at $30°C$. Use $k = 0.002$, and assume steady-state conditions. *Hint:* The wall can be thought to be composed of bars 25 cm long perpendicular to the wall faces. By symmetry, no heat flows through the sides of these bars in the steady state, and hence (9-14) can be applied.

2. An insulated metal rod 1 m long has its ends kept at $0°C$ and its initial temperature is $50°C$. What is the temperature in the middle of the rod at any subsequent time? Use $k = 1.02$, $c = 0.06$, and $\rho = 9.6$.

3. Let the rod of Prob. 2 have one of its ends kept at $0°C$ and the other at $10°C$. If the initial temperature of the rod is $50°C$, find the temperature of the rod at any later time. *Hint:* See Example 2.

4. An insulated bar with unit cross-sectional area has its ends kept at temperature 0, and the initial temperature is $f(x) = c_n \sin n\pi x/l$, where c_n is constant and n is an integer. (*a*) Show that the amount of heat present in the bar initially is $2lc\rho c_n/n\pi$ if n is odd and 0 if n is even. (*b*) Show that the net rate of flow out of the bar across the ends is $2kc_n(n\pi/l)e^{-(\alpha n\pi/l)^2 t}$ when n is odd and 0 when n is even. *Hint:* The rate of flow out of the bar at the end $x = 0$ is $+ku_x$, not $-ku_x$. (c) How much heat flows out of the bar in the time from $t = 0$ to t?   Evaluate as $t \to \infty$, compare (a), and explain.

   5. By addition of the results in Prob. 4 obtain similar results for the bar with arbitrary initial temperature $f(x)$.

10. Other Boundary Conditions. Separation of Variables.   In the fore-going section the differential equation

$$u_t = \alpha^2 u_{xx} \tag{10-1}$$

was obtained for the temperature $u(x,t)$ of an insulated bar at point x and time t.   The initial condition was

$$u(x,0) = f(x), \qquad 0 < x < l, \tag{10-2}$$

and the ends were held at constant temperature.

   If, instead, the ends are *insulated*, the boundary conditions are

$$u_x(0,t) = 0, \qquad u_x(l,t) = 0. \tag{10-3}$$

Equations (10-3) are appropriate because by (9-2) they state that the rate of flow across the ends is zero.   We shall now consider the problem posed by (10-1)–(10-3).

   The boundary conditions (10-3) are satisfied automatically if we express $u(x,t)$ as a cosine series:

$$u(x,t) = \frac{1}{2} a_0(t) + \Sigma a_n(t) \cos \frac{n\pi x}{l}. \tag{10-4}$$

Thus, u_x in (10-4) is a sine series (assuming that one can differentiate term by term), and we have already noted that the sine series vanishes at $x = 0$ and l.

   Substituting (10-4) into the differential equation (10-1) gives

$$\frac{1}{2} a_0' = 0, \qquad a_n' = -\alpha^2 \left(\frac{n\pi}{l} \right)^2 a_n, \tag{10-5}$$

just as in the derivation of (9-9).   Solving (10-5) and substituting into (10-4), we find

$$u(x,t) = \frac{1}{2} c_0 + \Sigma c_n e^{-(n\pi\alpha/l)^2 t} \cos \frac{n\pi x}{l}, \tag{10-6}$$

where the c_ns are constant.   The initial condition (10-2) shows that the c_ns are the Fourier cosine coefficients,

$$c_n = \frac{2}{l} \int_0^l f(x) \cos \frac{n\pi x}{l}\, dx, \tag{10-7}$$

and the problem is solved.[1]

   [1] The solution can be verified, if desired, as in the previous section.

separatn of var

We shall now solve this same problem by an important method known as *separation of variables*. It will prove interesting to compare the various stages of the solution with the answer, (10-6).

The desired solution (10-6) is a sum of terms each of which has the form

$$X(x)T(t). \tag{10-8}$$

In the method of separating variables the idea is to construct functions of the form (10-8) which satisfy the differential equation and the boundary conditions. By superposition of these functions (10-8), one then satisfies the initial conditions. The fact that there is a solution of the type (10-6) gives good reason for expecting the method to succeed.

Substituting (10-8) into (10-1) yields

$$XT' = \alpha^2 X''T,$$

where the prime denotes differentiation with respect to the appropriate variable. Dividing by XT we get

$$\frac{T'}{T} = \alpha^2 \frac{X''}{X}. \tag{10-9}$$

The variables x and t in (10-9) are *separated*, in that the left side is a function of t alone and the right side is a function of x alone. It follows that each side must be constant, independent of both x and t. A brief investigation of the effect of changing sign in (10-10) shows that XT can satisfy (10-3) only if the constant is zero or a negative number $-p^2$. Thus,

$$\frac{T'}{T} = -p^2, \qquad \alpha^2 \frac{X''}{X} = -p^2. \tag{10-10}$$

Independent solutions of (10-10) are [1]

$$T = e^{-p^2 t}; \qquad X = \cos \frac{p}{\alpha} x, \qquad X = \sin \frac{p}{\alpha} x. \tag{10-11}$$

The boundary condition $u_x(0,t) = 0$ for $u = XT$ requires that $X'(0) = 0$, and hence the appropriate choice of X in (10-11) is

$$X = \cos \frac{p}{\alpha} x. \tag{10-12}$$

Similarly, the condition $u_x(l,t) = 0$ gives $X'(l) = 0$, so that

$$p = \frac{n\pi\alpha}{l}, \tag{10-13}$$

[1] It is suggested that the reader compare XT at this and subsequent stages with the general term of (10-6).

$u_t = a^2 u_{xx}$

$u_x(0,t) = u_x(l,t) = 0$

where n is an integer. By (10-11)–(10-13) we see that the function

$$T(t)X(x) = e^{-(n\pi\alpha/l)^2 t} \cos \frac{n\pi x}{l} \tag{10-14}$$

satisfies the differential equation and the boundary conditions. To satisfy *put in series form.* the initial conditions we form a superposition of terms (10-14). The resulting series is precisely the series (10-6), and the solution is completed as before.

The merit of the separation method is that it produced the functions $\cos(n\pi x/l)$ by direct consideration of the differential equation. If some other functions had been more appropriate, the method would have produced those other functions instead. This fact will now be illustrated by an example.

According to Newton's law of cooling, a body radiates heat at a rate proportional to the difference between the temperature u of the radiating body and the temperature u_0 of the surrounding medium. Thus, if our insulated rod of length l has the end $x = 0$ maintained at temperature 0 while the other end radiates into a medium of temperature $u_0 = 0$, the corresponding boundary conditions are

$$u(0,t) = 0, \qquad u_x(l,t) = -hu(l,t), \tag{10-15}$$

where h is constant. [The second condition (10-15) states that the rate of flow $-ku_x$ is proportional to $u(l,t) - 0$, and this agrees with Newton's law.] If $h = 0$, there is no radiation and we have the condition for an insulated end as discussed previously. But if $h > 0$, which we now assume, the problem is essentially different from those considered hitherto. The difference results from the fact that (10-15) cannot be satisfied in any simple way by an ordinary Fourier series.

Actually, as we show next, the appropriate functions for the problem (10-1), (10-2), and (10-15) are not $\sin(n\pi x/l)$ or $\cos(n\pi x/l)$ but are $\sin \beta_n x$, where the β_ns are the positive roots of the transcendental equation [1]

$$\beta \cos \beta l = -h \sin \beta l. \tag{10-16}$$

Although one could hardly expect to discover the sequence $\sin \beta_n x$ by a priori considerations, it is produced automatically by the method of separating variables. The solution to the problem is found to be

$$u(x,t) = \Sigma c_n e^{-\alpha^2 \beta_n^2 t} \sin \beta_n x, \tag{10-17}$$

[1] Since the equation is equivalent to $\tan \beta l = -\beta/h$ when $h \neq 0$, its roots can be obtained graphically by considering the intersection of the curves $y = \tan \beta l$ and $y = -\beta/h$. Cf. Example 2, Sec. 2, Chap. 9.

where c_n is given in terms of the initial values by

$$c_n = \frac{\int_0^l f(x) \sin \beta_n x \, dx}{\int_0^l \sin^2 \beta_n x \, dx}. \tag{10-18}$$

To obtain this solution by separating variables, observe that the substitution $u = X(x)T(t)$ leads to functions of the type (10-11), exactly as in the former case. Here, however, the condition $u(0,t) = 0$ gives $X(0) = 0$, so that we require the sine rather than the cosine. The resulting expression

$$T(t)X(x) = e^{-p^2 t} \sin \frac{p}{\alpha} x$$

becomes $\qquad\qquad e^{-\alpha^2 \beta^2 t} \sin \beta x \tag{10-19}$

if we set $p = \alpha\beta$, and this form will be more convenient for our purposes. The function (10-19) satisfies (10-1) and the first boundary condition (10-15) for all values of the constant β. To satisfy the second condition (10-15) we must choose β so that

$$e^{-\alpha^2 \beta^2 t} \beta \cos \beta l = -h e^{-\alpha^2 \beta^2 t} \sin \beta l, \tag{10-20}$$

and this leads to (10-16). The resulting functions

$$e^{-\alpha^2 \beta_n^2 t} \sin \beta_n x$$

satisfy both boundary conditions (10-15) and also satisfy the differential equation (10-1). If a suitable superposition (10-17) is found to satisfy the initial condition, our problem will be solved.

Setting $t = 0$ in (10-17) gives

$$f(x) = \Sigma c_n \sin \beta_n x. \tag{10-21}$$

As in Chap. 2, Sec. 22, Example 1, we can show that the functions $\sin \beta_n x$ are orthogonal on $(0,l)$, and hence the c_ns are given by (10-18). The solution can be verified by the method of Sec. 9 if $f(x)$ admits an expansion (10-21). Since an analogue of Dirichlet's theorem holds for the sequence $\sin \beta_n x$, Eq. (10-21) is not a serious restriction on $f(x)$.

PROBLEMS

1. If $f(x) \equiv g(t)$, where x and t are independent variables, show that $f(x)$ and $g(t)$ are constant. *Hint:* Let $t = t_0$, a fixed value.

2. Attempt to satisfy the conditions (10-3) by choosing a positive constant $+p^2$ instead of $-p^2$ in (10-10).

3. By using the functions (10-11) solve

$$u_t = \alpha^2 u_{xx}, \qquad u(0,t) = u(l,t) = 0, \qquad u(x,0) = f(x).$$

4. (a) Describe a physical situation which would lead to

$$u_t = \alpha^2 u_{xx}, \qquad u(0,t) = u_x(l,t) = 0, \qquad u(x,0) = f(x).$$

(b) Solve by separating variables [cf. (10-11)]. (c) Verify that your result agrees with (10-16)–(10-18) for $h = 0$.

5. Solve Prob. 4 by the method of images.

Outline of the Solution. Consider a rod of length $2l$ with ends at temperature 0. Let the initial temperature $f_0(x)$ agree with $f(x)$ on $(0,l)$, and let $f_0(x)$ be symmetric about $x = l$ (Fig. 12). By symmetry, no heat flows across the center, and hence the left

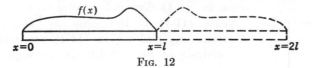

$$f(x)$$

$$x=0 \qquad\qquad x=l \qquad\qquad x=2l$$

Fig. 12

half of the long rod behaves like the rod of Prob. 4. The temperature $u_0(x,t)$ for the long rod can be found from (9-10).

6. The vertical displacement $u(x,t)$ of a vibrating string with fixed end points satisfies

$$u_{tt} = a^2 u_{xx}, \qquad u(0,t) = u(l,t) = 0.$$

By setting $u(x,t) = X(x)T(t)$ and separating variables, obtain solutions of the form

$$\sin\frac{n\pi a t}{l}\sin\frac{n\pi x}{l} \text{ and } \cos\frac{n\pi a t}{l}\sin\frac{n\pi x}{l}.$$

7. In Prob. 6, express $u(x,t)$ as an infinite series if

$$u(x,0) = f(x), \qquad u_t(x,0) = 0.$$

8. In Prob. 6, express $u(x,t)$ as an infinite series if

$$u(x,0) = 0, \qquad u_t(x,0) = g(x).$$

11. Heat Flow in a Solid. By a procedure similar to that of Sec. 9 one can establish the equation

$$u_t = \alpha^2(u_{xx} + u_{yy} + u_{zz}), \qquad \alpha^2 \equiv \frac{k}{c\rho}, \qquad (11\text{-}1)$$

for the temperature [1] $u = u(x,y,z,t)$ in a uniform solid at time t. This is the three-dimensional form of the equation

$$u_t = \alpha^2 u_{xx} \qquad (11\text{-}2)$$

obtained previously for heat conduction in a rod. The state of the solid at time $t = 0$ gives the initial condition; the state of the surface for $t > 0$ gives the boundary condition. For instance, if the surface radiates according to Newton's law, the boundary condition is

$$-k\frac{\partial u}{\partial n} = e(u - u_0), \qquad (11\text{-}3)$$

where u_0 is the temperature of the surrounding medium, e the *emissivity*,

[1] See the derivation in Chap. 5, Sec. 16. A similar equation governs diffusion and the drying of porous solids, with u equal to the concentration of the diffusing substance. Because of this analogy many problems on diffusion and heat conduction are mathematically indistinguishable. The constant α^2 in (11-1) is often called the *diffusivity*.

and $\partial u/\partial n$ the derivative in the direction of the outward normal. When $e = 0$, Eq. (11-3) means that the body is insulated.

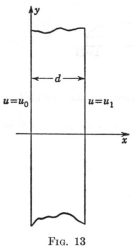

FIG. 13

Sometimes there is so much symmetry that u in (11-1) does not depend on y or z. In this case (11-1) is the same as (11-2), since the terms u_{yy} and u_{zz} in (11-1) are zero, and the analysis of Secs. 9–10 can be applied without change.

As a specific illustration consider a uniform plate extending from the plane $x = 0$ to the plane $x = d$ (Fig. 13). Let $u = u_0$ on the surface $x = 0$ and $u = u_1$ on the surface $x = d$, where u_0 and u_1 are constant. If the plate is infinite, or if the edges are far away from the points being considered, the symmetry suggests that u depends on x only and, hence, that (11-2) holds. The steady-state temperature is then given by Example 1, Sec. 9, as

$$u = u_0 + \frac{x}{d}(u_1 - u_0).$$

Since the rate of flow is $-ku_x$, the amount of heat Q flowing across the area A in t sec is

$$Q = ktA\,\frac{u_0 - u_1}{d}.$$

If the flow of heat is steady, so that u is independent of time, then $u_t = 0$ and (11-1) reduces to

$$u_{xx} + u_{yy} + u_{zz} = 0. \qquad (11\text{-}4)$$

This is known as *Laplace's equation;* it occurs in a variety of physical problems. The corresponding two-dimensional form is

$$u_{xx} + u_{yy} = 0, \qquad u = u(x,y). \qquad (11\text{-}5)$$

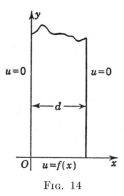

FIG. 14

To illustrate the use of (11-5) we shall discuss the steady-state temperature in an infinitely long metal strip of width d (see Fig. 14). If the sides of the strip have the temperature zero and the bottom edge has the temperature $f(x)$, the boundary conditions are

$$u(0,y) = 0, \qquad u(d,y) = 0, \qquad u(x,0) = f(x). \qquad (11\text{-}6)$$

We assume besides that (11-5) holds for $0 < x < d$, $y > 0$.

It is a surprising fact that these conditions do not suffice to determine the temperature.[1] However, one expects the temperature to approach zero as one moves away from the bottom edge, so that

$$\lim_{y \to \infty} u(x,y) = 0 \qquad \text{uniformly in } x. \tag{11-7}$$

If this condition is explicitly required, the solution can be shown to be unique (see Sec. 24).

Although the problem can be solved very simply by Fourier series, we prefer to show how the desired functions are generated by the method of separating variables. The choice $u = X(x)Y(y)$ in (11-5) gives

$$\frac{X''}{X} = -\frac{Y''}{Y} \tag{11-8}$$

after dividing by XY. Since the variables in (11-8) are separated, each side is a constant. The boundary conditions applied to XY show (after some calculation) that the constant must be a negative number $-p^2$, and hence (11-8) gives

$$\frac{X''}{X} = -p^2, \qquad \frac{Y''}{Y} = p^2.$$

Since $(-p)^2 = p^2$, we can assume that $p > 0$ with no loss of generality. Linearly independent solutions of these equations are, respectively,

$$\cos px, \sin px \qquad \text{and} \qquad e^{py}, e^{-py}.$$

Since $u(0,y) = 0$ requires that $X(0) = 0$, we reject the cosine, and in view of (11-7) we reject the solution e^{py}. Hence the function XY takes the form

$$XY = e^{-py} \sin px. \tag{11-9}$$

The boundary condition $u(d,y) = 0$ gives $p = n\pi/d$, where n is an integer. Forming a linear combination of the resulting solutions (11-9) we get

$$u(x,y) = \Sigma c_n e^{-(n\pi/d)y} \sin \frac{n\pi x}{d} \tag{11-10}$$

and the condition $u(x,0) = f(x)$ now shows that the c_ns are the Fourier coefficients

$$c_n = \frac{2}{d} \int_0^d f(x) \sin \frac{n\pi x}{d} \, dx.$$

The solution can be verified, if desired, as in Sec. 9.

---

[1] The trouble is that the other end of the strip must be taken into account even though it is infinitely far away. This purpose is served by (11-7).

The foregoing derivation obscures an important point which will now be discussed more fully. Although the solutions

$$e^{py} \quad \text{and} \quad e^{-py}$$

can be chosen for the equation $Y'' = p^2Y$, these are not the only possibilities. Another pair of independent solutions, for example, is

$$\cosh py \quad \text{and} \quad \sinh py.$$

If, now, we try to decide which of these functions satisfies (11-7) it will be found that neither one does.

What is really involved is the following: The *general* solution of $Y'' = p^2Y$ is

$$Y = ae^{py} + be^{-py},$$

where a and b are constant. By (11-7) we get $a = 0$, and hence $Y = be^{-py}$. The reader can verify that if

$$Y = a_0 \cosh py + b_0 \sinh py,$$

the condition (11-7) will give $a_0 + b_0 = 0$, and again Y is a multiple of e^{-py}. Similar remarks apply to the construction of $X(x)$ and to the derivation of (10-14).

Just as in the case of the rod, this problem involving a strip can be given a three-dimensional interpretation. That is, the strip need not be thin provided there is no variation of temperature across its thickness. By letting the thickness approach infinity, we get a semi-infinite plate. (In Fig. 14 the plate extends infinitely far toward and away from the reader; the area outlined in the figure is the *cross section* of the plate, not a frontal view.) The boundary-value problem for the plate is

$$u_{xx} + u_{yy} + u_{zz} = 0, \qquad 0 < x < d, \, y > 0, \, -\infty < z < \infty, \quad (11\text{-}11)$$

$$u(0,y,z) = 0, \qquad u(d,y,z) = 0, \qquad u(x,0,z) = f(x), \quad (11\text{-}12)$$

$$\lim_{y \to \infty} u(x,y,z) = 0 \qquad \text{uniformly in } x \text{ and } z. \quad (11\text{-}13)$$

If we assume u independent of z, the resulting problem is the same as that formerly considered, hence has the unique solution (11-10).

The fact that $u(x,y,z)$ is independent of z does not follow from the physical symmetry but requires the condition (11-13). Indeed the function

$$u = \sin \frac{\pi x}{d} \sin \frac{\pi y}{d} e^{\sqrt{2}\,\pi z/d}$$

satisfies (11-11) and (11-12) with $f(x) = 0$ and yet depends on z. Reduction of the dimension by omitting a variable is really an application of *uniqueness*. If we verify that (11-10) satisfies the problem (11-11) to (11-13), *and that the problem has no other solution*, then it is true that u must be independent of z.

PROBLEMS

1. A refrigerator door is 10 cm thick and has the outside dimensions 60 by 100 cm. If the temperature inside the refrigerator is $-10°C$ and outside is $20°C$, and if $k = 0.0002$, find the gain of heat per day across the door by assuming the flow of heat to be of the same nature as that across an infinite plate.

2. If $f(x) = 1$ and $d = \pi$, show that (11-10) gives

$$u = \frac{4}{\pi}\left(e^{-y}\sin x + \frac{1}{3}e^{-3y}\sin 3x + \frac{1}{5}e^{-5y}\sin 5x + \cdots\right).$$

3. In Prob. 2 compute the temperature at the following points: $(\pi/2,1)$, $(\pi/3,2)$, $(\pi/4,10)$.

4. Derive (11-10) by assuming a Fourier series

$$u(x,y) = \Sigma b_n(y)\sin\frac{n\pi x}{d}.$$

5. A semi-infinite plate 10 cm in thickness has its faces kept at 0°C and its base kept at 100°C. What is the steady-state temperature at any point of the plate?

6. The faces of an infinite slab 10 cm thick are kept at temperature 0°C. If the initial temperature of the slab is 100°C, what is the state of the temperature at any subsequent time?

7. A large rectangular iron plate (Fig. 15) is heated throughout to 100°C and is placed in contact with and between two like plates each at 0°C. The outer faces of these outside plates are maintained at 0°C. Find the temperature of the inner faces of the two plates and the temperature at the mid-point of the inner plate 10 sec after the plates have been put together. Given: $\alpha = 0.2$ cgs unit. *Hint:* The boundary and initial conditions are

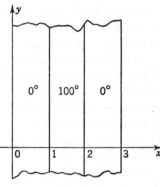

FIG. 15

$$u(0,t) = 0, \qquad u(3,t) = 0, \qquad u(x,0) = f(x),$$

where $f(x) = 0$ for $0 < x < 1$ and $2 < x < 3$ but $f(x) = 100$ for $1 < x < 2$.

12. The Dirichlet Problem. The Laplace equation

$$u_{xx} + u_{yy} + u_{zz} = 0 \qquad (12\text{-}1)$$

was obtained in Sec. 11 for steady-state heat flow. We shall show how the same equation arises in electrostatics and gravitation.[1]

It is a consequence of Coulomb's law that the potential due to a point charge q at (x_1,y_1,z_1) is

$$u = \frac{q}{r} \qquad \text{taking } u = 0 \text{ at } r = \infty, \qquad (12\text{-}2)$$

where r is the distance from the charge to the point (x,y,z) at which u is computed. Thus,

$$r^2 = (x - x_1)^2 + (y - y_1)^2 + (z - z_1)^2, \qquad r > 0. \qquad (12\text{-}3)$$

[1] A more complete discussion is given in Chap. 5, Sec. 14. The relation of Laplace's equation and fluid flow is developed in Chap. 5, Secs. 15 and 17, and in Chap. 7, Sec. 19.

The potential due to a distribution of n point charges q_i is given by addition,

$$u = \sum_{i=1}^{n} \frac{q_i}{r_i}, \qquad (12\text{-}4)$$

and the potential due to a distribution of continuous charge of density ρ in a body τ can be obtained from an expression like (12-4) by passing to the limit.

It is easily shown that $1/r$ satisfies Laplace's equation (12-1), and hence the same is true of u in (12-4) provided no r_i is zero. This latter condition means that there is no charge at the point of observation. One would expect, therefore, that the potential due to a continuous charge distribution will also satisfy (12-1) if there is no charge at the point of observation. This is actually the case, and that is the reason why Laplace's equation plays such a prominent role in electrostatics. Although a more sophisticated treatment may be given, it all comes down to the same thing; namely, $1/r$ satisfies (12-1), and the potential is given by some sort of superposition process applied to $1/r$.

Since the gravitational potential satisfies (12-2) (where q is the mass of the attracting mass point), the study of gravitation also leads to Laplace's equation. In view of its many applications, the Laplace equation (12-1) is profitably regarded as a field of study in its own right. Such a study leads the way to a branch of analysis known as *potential theory*.

An important problem in potential theory is the *Dirichlet problem*, which can be stated as follows: Suppose given a body τ in (x,y,z) space, together with assigned values $f(x,y,z)$ on the surface of τ. Find a function u which satisfies Laplace's equation in τ and is equal to $f(x,y,z)$ on the surface. The foregoing discussion gives a number of physical interpretations. For instance, if u is temperature, the Dirichlet problem is to find the steady-state temperature in a uniform solid when the temperature on the surface is given. But if u is the electrostatic potential, the problem is to find the potential inside a closed surface when the potential on the surface is known. Interpretations in terms of diffusion, fluid flow, and gravitation can also be given.

Since solutions of Laplace's equation are often called *harmonic functions*, Dirichlet's problem can be stated as follows: Find a function which is harmonic in a given region and assumes preassigned values on the boundary. In two dimensions a harmonic function $u(x,y)$ satisfies

$$u_{xx} + u_{yy} = 0. \qquad (12\text{-}5)$$

The region in Dirichlet's problem is now a plane region, and its boundary is a curve. The physical interpretation refers to phenomena in a thin plane sheet, or it refers to three-dimensional phenomena which show no dependence on z. The latter condition is to be expected when there is cylindrical symmetry, that is, when all planes $z =$ const exhibit the same geometry and boundary conditions.

We shall now solve the Dirichlet problem for a circle. It turns out that the problem is greatly simplified by use of polar coordinates appropriate to the circular symmetry. With

$$x = r \cos \theta, \qquad y = r \sin \theta, \qquad u(x,y) \equiv U(r,\theta),$$

an elementary calculation shows that (12-5) becomes

$$(rU_r)_r + \frac{1}{r} U_{\theta\theta} = 0 \tag{12-6}$$

(see Prob. 2). The boundary condition can be expressed as

$$U(R,\theta) = f(\theta), \tag{12-7}$$

where $f(\theta)$ is a known function of θ and R is the radius of the circle.

For each value of r it is clear that U has period 2π in θ, since u is single-valued, and therefore U has a Fourier series

$$U(r,\theta) = \frac{a_0(r)}{2} + \Sigma[a_n(r) \cos n\theta + b_n(r) \sin n\theta]. \tag{12-8}$$

Proceeding tentatively, we substitute (12-8) into (12-6) to obtain

$$\left(\frac{ra_0'}{2}\right)' + \Sigma[(ra_n')' \cos n\theta + (rb_n')' \sin n\theta]$$

$$- \frac{1}{r} \Sigma(a_n n^2 \cos n\theta + b_n n^2 \sin n\theta) = 0.$$

Since the coefficients of $\cos n\theta$ and of $\sin n\theta$ must vanish,

$$(ra_n')' = \frac{1}{r} n^2 a_n, \qquad n = 0, 1, 2, \ldots,$$

$$(rb_n')' = \frac{1}{r} n^2 b_n, \qquad n = 1, 2, 3, \ldots.$$

These equations are both of form

$$r(ry')' = n^2 y$$

which is readily solved by the method of Chap. 1, Sec. 30. Specifically, the substitution $y = r^a$ gives

$$r(ar^a)' = n^2 r^a,$$

whence $a = \pm n$. Since $a_n(r)$ and $b_n(r)$ must be finite at $r = 0$, the minus sign is excluded, and

$$a_n(r) = a_n r^n, \qquad b_n(r) = b_n r^n,$$

where a_n and b_n are constant. Hence by (12-8)

$$U(r,\theta) = \frac{a_0}{2} + \Sigma(a_n r^n \cos n\theta + b_n r^n \sin n\theta). \qquad (12\text{-}9)$$

Putting $r = R$ and using the boundary condition (12-7) give

$$f(\theta) = \frac{a_0}{2} + \Sigma(a_n R^n \cos n\theta + b_n R^n \sin n\theta). \qquad (12\text{-}10)$$

If $f(\theta)$ has a convergent Fourier series, the validity of (12-10) is ensured by choosing $a_n R^n$ and $b_n R^n$ to be the Fourier coefficients of f:

$$a_n R^n = \frac{1}{\pi} \int_{-\pi}^{\pi} f(\phi) \cos n\phi \, d\phi,$$

$$ \qquad (12\text{-}11)$$

$$b_n R^n = \frac{1}{\pi} \int_{-\pi}^{\pi} f(\phi) \sin n\phi \, d\phi.$$

The problem is now solved, but a simpler form can be found as follows: Substituting (12-11) into (12-9) gives

$$U(r,\theta) = \frac{1}{\pi} \int_{-\pi}^{\pi} \left[\frac{1}{2} + \Sigma \left(\frac{r}{R}\right)^n \cos n(\theta - \phi)\right] f(\phi) \, d\phi, \qquad (12\text{-}12)$$

when we note that

$$\cos n\theta \cos n\phi + \sin n\theta \sin n\phi = \cos(n\theta - n\phi)$$

and interchange the order of summation and integration. The series in brackets in (12-12) can be summed as in Chap. 2, Sec. 17, Prob. 6. The result is the *Poisson formula for a circle* [1]

$$U(r,\theta) = \frac{1}{2\pi} \int_{-\pi}^{\pi} \frac{R^2 - r^2}{R^2 - 2rR \cos(\theta - \phi) + r^2} f(\phi) \, d\phi. \qquad (12\text{-}13)$$

If $f(\phi)$ is piecewise continuous and bounded, one can differentiate under the integral sign for $r < R$ to find that (12-6) holds. Also, it can be shown that (12-13) gives

$$\lim_{r \to R-} U(r,\theta) = f(\theta) \qquad (12\text{-}14)$$

provided f is continuous at θ. Hence (12-13) is a solution. In view of the derivation, it is remarkable that (12-14) holds even when the Fourier series for f does not converge to f.

The expression (12-13) gives the steady-state temperature of a thin uniform insulated disk in terms of the temperature at the boundary. Or

[1] Another derivation is given in Chap. 7, Sec. 21.

(12-13) can be interpreted as giving the temperature in a circular cylinder when the temperature of the surface is $f(\theta)$ independent of z. On the other hand the formula also gives the electrostatic potential in terms of its values on the boundary, and so on.

Example: Let $u(x,y)$ be harmonic in a plane region, and let C be a circle contained entirely in the region. Show that the value of u at the center of C is the average of the values on the circumference.

Without loss of generality we can take the center to be at the origin. Equation (12-13) then gives, with $r = 0$,

$$u(0,0) = U(0,\theta) = \frac{1}{2\pi} \int_{-\pi}^{\pi} f(\phi)\, d\phi. \tag{12-15}$$

Since $f(\phi)$ stands for the values of u on the boundary, this is the required result.

PROBLEMS

1. (a) Verify that $1/r$ in (12-2) satisfies the Laplace equation (12-1). *Hint:* $rr_x = x - x_1$. Using this, find $(1/r)_{xx}$. (b) Verify that $\log r$ satisfies the two-dimensional Laplace equation (12-5).

2. If $u(x,y) = U(r,\theta)$ with $x = r \cos \theta$, $y = r \sin \theta$, show that

$$u_{xx} + u_{yy} = r^{-1}(rU_r)_r + r^{-2}U_{\theta\theta}.$$

Hint: $U_r = u_x \cos \theta + u_y \sin \theta$, $U_\theta = u_x(-r \sin \theta) + u_y(r \cos \theta)$. Similarly, compute $(rU_r)_r$ and $(U_\theta)_\theta$.

3. Derive (12-10) by considering $U = R(r)\Theta(\theta)$ and separating variables.

4. Give two physical interpretations of the following Dirichlet problem for a semicircle, where $u(x,y) = U(r,\theta)$ as in (12-6):

$$u_{xx} + u_{yy} = 0, \qquad x^2 + y^2 < 1,\, y > 0,$$

$$U(1,\theta) = g(\theta), \qquad 0 \le \theta \le \pi,$$

$$U(r,0) = U(r,\pi) = 0, \qquad 0 \le r \le 1.$$

5. Solve Prob. 4 by the method of images. *Hint:* For $0 < \theta < \pi$, define $f(\theta) = g(\theta)$, $f(-\theta) = -g(\theta)$ and use (12-13).

6. Obtain a formula analogous to (12-13) for the region $r > R$. (Assume that $|U(r,\theta)|$ is bounded as $r \to \infty$ and, hence, that positive values of n in the discussion of the text may be rejected.)

7. Interpret the result of Prob. 6 physically in terms of an infinite metal plate with a hole whose edges have a prescribed temperature.

13. Spherical Symmetry. Legendre Functions.

Let it be required to determine the steady-state temperature in a uniform solid sphere of radius unity when one half of the surface is kept at the constant temperature $0°C$ and the other half at the constant temperature $1°C$. By the discussion of Sec. 11, the temperature u within the sphere satisfies Laplace's equation

$$u_{xx} + u_{yy} + u_{zz} = 0. \tag{13-1}$$

Symmetry suggests the use of spherical coordinates (r,θ,ϕ) with origin at the center of the given unit sphere (Fig. 16). Since

$$x = r \sin \theta \cos \phi,$$

$$y = r \sin \theta \sin \phi,$$

$$z = r \cos \theta,$$

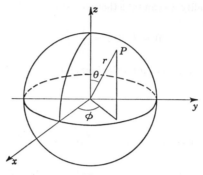

FIG. 16

Laplace's equation can be shown to be [1]

$$r(rU)_{rr} + (U_\theta \sin \theta)_\theta \csc \theta + U_{\phi\phi} \csc^2 \theta = 0, \qquad (13\text{-}2)$$

where $u(x,y,z) = U(r,\theta,\phi)$. If the plane separating the unequally heated hemispheres is the xy plane, the symmetry suggests that U will be independent of ϕ, so that (13-2) becomes

$$r(rU)_{rr} + (U_\theta \sin \theta)_\theta \csc \theta = 0. \qquad (13\text{-}3)$$

The boundary conditions are

$$u = 1 \quad \text{for } 0 < \theta < \tfrac{1}{2}\pi, \quad \text{when } r = 1,$$
$$u = 0 \quad \text{for } \tfrac{1}{2}\pi < \theta < \pi, \quad \text{when } r = 1. \qquad (13\text{-}4)$$

We shall use the method of separating variables. Substituting the form

$$U = R(r)\Theta(\theta)$$

into (13-3) gives two ordinary differential equations,

$$r(rR)'' - \alpha R = 0, \qquad ' = \frac{d}{dr},$$

$$(\Theta' \sin \theta)' \csc \theta + \alpha\Theta = 0, \qquad ' = \frac{d}{d\theta}, \qquad (13\text{-}5)$$

[1] See Chap. 5, Sec. 13, or proceed as in Prob. 2 of the preceding section.

where α is an arbitrary constant. The first of these equations can be solved by assuming that $R = r^m$ as in Chap. 1, Sec. 30. One obtains the linearly independent solutions

$$R = r^m, \qquad R = r^{-(m+1)},$$

where m satisfies the quadratic equation

$$m(m+1) = \alpha. \tag{13-6}$$

Changing the independent variable in (13-5) from θ to x by means of

$$x = \cos \theta, \qquad \Theta(\theta) = P(x),$$

and replacing α by the expression (13-6), we get Legendre's equation

$$(1 - x^2)P'' - 2xP' + m(m+1)P = 0, \qquad ' = \frac{d}{dx}. \tag{13-7}$$

When m is a nonnegative integer, a solution of (13-7) is the Legendre polynomial $P_m(x) = P_m(\cos \theta)$. Thus, one is led to consider solutions of (13-3) which have the form

$$r^m P_m(\cos \theta) \qquad \text{or} \qquad r^{-(m+1)} P_m(\cos \theta).$$

The second of these expressions is rejected because it becomes infinite as $r \to 0$, and we attempt to build up the desired solution u by forming a series

$$u = \sum_{m=0}^{\infty} A_m r^m P_m (\cos \theta). \tag{13-8}$$

Each term of this series satisfies (13-3).

When $r = 1$, Eq. (13-8) becomes

$$u = \sum_{m=0}^{\infty} A_m P_m (\cos \theta), \qquad r = 1, \tag{13-9}$$

and if it is possible to choose the constants A_m in such a way that (13-9) satisfies the boundary condition (13-4), then (13-8) will be a solution of the problem. Since $x = \cos \theta$, the boundary condition requires

$$F(x) = \sum_{m=0}^{\infty} A_m P_m(x), \tag{13-10}$$

where $F(x) = 0$ for $-1 < x < 0$, and $F(x) = 1$ for $0 < x < 1$. Now, it was stated in Chap. 2, Sec. 22, that the expansion (13-10) is possible for suitably restricted functions $F(x)$ and that the coefficients are given by

$$A_m = \left(m + \frac{1}{2}\right) \int_{-1}^{1} F(x) P_m(x)\, dx.$$

By means of this formula, the solution is found to be

$$u = \tfrac{1}{2} + \tfrac{3}{4}rP_1(\cos\theta) - \tfrac{7}{16}r^3P_3(\cos\theta) + \tfrac{11}{32}r^5P_5(\cos\theta) - \cdots.$$

It is possible to establish that (13-8) is actually a solution, though the demonstration requires a detailed knowledge of Legendre functions.[1] The uniqueness theorem established in Sec. 24 shows that there is no other solution, and hence the foregoing procedure can be justified. In particular it was permissible to take m as a nonnegative integer and to use the polynomial solution of (13-7) rather than one of the infinite-series solutions.

PROBLEMS FOR REVIEW

1. As an infinite series, express the steady-state temperature in a circular plate of radius a which has one half of its circumference at 0°C and the other half at 100°C.

2. By (12-13), find the temperature of the plate considered in Prob. 1.

3. By separating variables in polar coordinates find the steady-state temperature in a semicircular plate of radius a if the bounding diameter is kept at the temperature 0°C and the circumference is kept at the temperature 100°C.

4. Interpret the following Dirichlet problem physically, and solve:

$$u_{xx} + u_{yy} = 0, \qquad 0 < x < 1, 0 < y < 1,$$

$$u(0,y) = u(1,y) = u(x,0) = 0, \qquad u(x,1) = f(x).$$

5. Derive (13-5) from (13-3).

14. The Rectangular Membrane. Double Fourier Series.

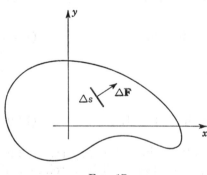

FIG. 17

Let a uniform elastic membrane be stretched over a fixed, plane, bounding curve (Fig. 17). To explain what is meant by the *tension*, we consider the force $\Delta\mathbf{F}$ exerted by the membrane on one side of a small straight slit of length Δs. The membrane is said to be under *uniform tension* T if this force is directed perpendicular to the slit in the plane of the membrane and has magnitude $T\,\Delta s$ independent of the location and orientation of the slit. A similar definition applies when the membrane does not lie in a plane except that we must let $\Delta s \to 0$:

$$T = \lim_{\Delta s \to 0} \frac{|\Delta\mathbf{F}|}{\Delta s}.$$

The role taken by the plane of the membrane in the first case is now taken by the tangent plane at the point in question.

[1] One must show that the series obtained by differentiating (13-8) are uniformly convergent for $r < 1 - \delta$ and that the boundary condition is verified as $r \to 1$.

Let the coordinate system be so chosen that the bounding curve of the membrane lies in the xy plane. The vertical displacement of any point in the membrane at time t is denoted by $u = u(x,y,t)$. To obtain a differential equation for the motion, we consider a small, nearly square portion of the membrane bounded by vertical planes through the points

$$(x,y,0),\ (x + \Delta x,\ y,\ 0),\ (x,\ y + \Delta y,\ 0),\ (x + \Delta x,\ y + \Delta y,\ 0)$$

(see Fig. 18). Applying Newton's law to the small portion gives the approximate equation

$$u_{tt} = \gamma^2(u_{xx} + u_{yy}), \qquad \gamma^2 = \frac{T}{\rho}, \tag{14-1}$$

where ρ is the surface density. This equation describes *small* oscillations of the *freely vibrating* membrane. Its derivation is similar to the corresponding derivation for a vibrating string (Sec. 2).

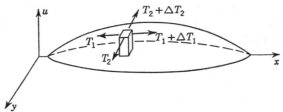

FIG. 18

The problem of the vibrating membrane is solved when we have found the solution of (14-1) which satisfies appropriate initial and boundary conditions. We shall now consider the case of a clamped rectangular membrane with sides of lengths a and b (Fig. 19). The boundary conditions are

$$
\begin{aligned}
u = 0 \quad &\text{for } x = 0 \text{ and for } x = a, \quad &0 \le y \le b, \\
u = 0 \quad &\text{for } y = 0 \text{ and for } y = b, \quad &0 \le x \le a.
\end{aligned} \tag{14-2}
$$

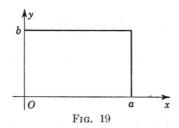

FIG. 19

To determine the solution uniquely we also specify the initial displacement and initial velocity:

$$u(x,y,0) = f(x,y), \qquad u_t(x,y,0) = g(x,y). \tag{14-3}$$

The assumption that
$$u = X(x)Y(y)T(t)$$
in (14-1) yields
$$\gamma^2 \left(\frac{X''}{X} + \frac{Y''}{Y} \right) = \frac{T''}{T} \tag{14-4}$$

upon division by XYT. Since the variables are separated, the terms in (14-4) are constant. It can be shown that these constants are negative, so that we may write
$$\frac{X''}{X} = -p^2, \qquad \frac{Y''}{Y} = -q^2, \qquad \frac{T''}{T} = -\omega^2,$$

with $\gamma^2(p^2 + q^2) = \omega^2$ by (14-4).

Since $X'' + p^2 X = 0$, the function $X(x)$ is a linear combination of $\sin px$ and $\cos px$. The cosine is rejected because the condition $u = 0$ at $x = 0$ gives $X(0) = 0$, and we must have $p = m\pi/a$, where m is an integer, because the condition $u = 0$ at $x = a$ gives $X(a) = 0$. In just the same way it is found that
$$Y = \sin qy,$$

where $q = n\pi/b$ for an integer n. Thus, the desired oscillation has the form
$$\sin \frac{m\pi x}{a} \sin \frac{n\pi y}{b} (A \cos \omega_{mn}t + B \sin \omega_{mn}t), \tag{14-5}$$

where A and B are constant and where $\omega_{mn} = \omega$ is given by
$$\omega_{mn}^2 = \left(\frac{\pi m\gamma}{a} \right)^2 + \left(\frac{\pi n\gamma}{b} \right)^2.$$

The functions (14-5) satisfy the differential equation and the boundary condition. To satisfy the initial conditions (14-3) we try a superposition, using different constants A and B for each choice of m and n:
$$u(x,y,t) = \sum_{m,n=1}^{\infty} (A_{mn} \cos \omega_{mn}t + B_{mn} \sin \omega_{mn}t) \sin \frac{m\pi x}{a} \sin \frac{n\pi y}{b}. \tag{14-6}$$

Since the initial displacement is $f(x,y)$, we must determine A_{mn} so that
$$f(x,y) = \sum_{m,n=1}^{\infty} A_{mn} \sin \frac{m\pi x}{a} \sin \frac{n\pi y}{b}.$$

Multiplying this *double Fourier series* by $\sin (m\pi x/a) \sin (n\pi y/b)$ and integrating over the rectangle give the formula
$$A_{mn} = \frac{4}{ab} \int_0^a \int_0^b f(x,y) \sin \frac{m\pi x}{a} \sin \frac{n\pi y}{b} dx \, dy,$$

just as in the corresponding discussion for single Fourier series (Chap. 2, Sec. 18). Similarly, differentiating (14-6) with respect to t and setting $t = 0$ give

$$B_{mn} = \frac{4}{ab\omega_{mn}} \int_0^a \int_0^b g(x,y) \sin \frac{m\pi x}{a} \sin \frac{n\pi y}{b} \, dx \, dy$$

when we use the second initial condition (14-3).

The general term of the series (14-6) is a periodic function of time with period $2\pi/\omega_{mn}$. The corresponding frequencies

$$\frac{\omega_{mn}}{2\pi} = \frac{\gamma}{2} \left[\left(\frac{m}{a}\right)^2 + \left(\frac{n}{b}\right)^2 \right]^{\frac{1}{2}} \qquad \text{cps} \qquad (14\text{-}7)$$

are called *characteristic frequencies*, and the associated oscillations (14-5) are called *modes*. The *fundamental mode* is the mode of lowest frequency, obtained by setting $m = n = 1$.

Similar terminology applies to the vibrating string (Secs. 2–6). If the length of the string is a and the equation of motion is

$$u_{tt} = \gamma^2 u_{xx},$$

the characteristic frequencies may be written in the form

$$\frac{\omega_m}{2\pi} = \frac{\gamma}{2} \left[\left(\frac{m}{a}\right)^2 \right]^{\frac{1}{2}} \qquad (14\text{-}8)$$

analogous to (14-7). The modes are described by

$$u = \sin \frac{m\pi x}{a} (A \cos \omega_m t + B \sin \omega_m t)$$

and the *fundamental* is the mode obtained for $m = 1$. The three-dimensional analogue of (14-7) and (14-8) is discussed in Prob. 2.

In Sec. 8 it was shown for the vibrating string that the *characteristic* frequencies agree with the *resonant* frequencies, and a similar behavior is found for vibration phenomena in general. It is also true in general that the vibration can be expressed as a superposition of individual modes. This fact is illustrated by (14-6) and by the Fourier-series solution for the vibrating string.

The behavior of the vibrating membrane differs from that of the string in one respect. For each characteristic frequency of vibration of the string the corresponding mode is such that the string is divided into equal parts by the nodes whose positions are fixed. When a membrane oscillates with a given characteristic frequency, there are also points on the membrane which remain at rest. Such points form *nodal lines*. The position and the shape of the nodal lines, however, need not be the same for a given frequency.

As an illustration consider a rectangular membrane with $a = b$. The frequency equation (14-7) then yields

$$\omega_{mn} = \frac{\gamma\pi}{a}\sqrt{m^2 + n^2}$$

$$= \alpha\sqrt{m^2 + n^2}, \qquad \alpha \equiv \frac{\gamma\pi}{a}. \tag{14-9}$$

For $m = n = 1$, we get from (14-6) the fundamental mode

$$u_{11} = (A_{11}\cos\omega_{11}t + B_{11}\sin\omega_{11}t)\sin\frac{\pi x}{a}\sin\frac{\pi y}{a},$$

where $\omega_{11} = \alpha\sqrt{2}$. Since $u_{11} = 0$ for all t only when $x = 0$, $y = 0$, $x = a$, $y = a$, there are no nodal lines in the interior of the membrane for this frequency. If we take $m = 1$, $n = 2$ and $m = 2$, $n = 1$, we get two modes:

$$u_{12} = (A_{12}\cos\omega_{12}t + B_{12}\sin\omega_{12}t)\sin\frac{\pi x}{a}\sin\frac{2\pi y}{a},$$

$$\tag{14-10}$$

$$u_{21} = (A_{21}\cos\omega_{21}t + B_{21}\sin\omega_{21}t)\sin\frac{2\pi x}{a}\sin\frac{\pi y}{a},$$

with the same frequency, since $\omega_{21} = \omega_{12} = \alpha\sqrt{5}$. For $y = a/2$, $u_{12} \equiv 0$ and for $x = a/2$, $u_{21} \equiv 0$. These nodal lines are shown in Fig. 20. By forming linear combinations of the modes in (14-10) we can get oscillations with the same frequency but with different nodal lines. Thus, if we take $A_{12} = A_{21} = 0$ and form $u_{12} + u_{21}$, we get

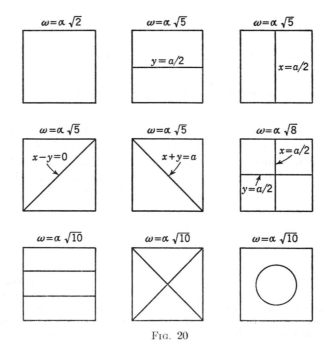

FIG. 20

$$u_{12} + u_{21} = \sin \omega_{12}t \left(B_{12} \sin \frac{\pi x}{a} \sin \frac{2\pi y}{a} + B_{21} \sin \frac{2\pi x}{a} \sin \frac{\pi y}{a} \right)$$

$$= (\sin \omega_{12}t) 2 \sin \frac{\pi x}{a} \sin \frac{\pi y}{a} \left(B_{12} \cos \frac{\pi y}{a} + B_{21} \cos \frac{\pi x}{a} \right).$$

For this oscillation the nodal lines in the interior of the membrane are determined by

$$B_{12} \cos \frac{\pi y}{a} + B_{21} \cos \frac{\pi x}{a} = 0. \qquad (14\text{-}11)$$

Equation (14-11) for $B_{12} = B_{21}$ yields the nodal line $x + y = a$ and for $B_{12} = -B_{21}$, the line $x - y = 0$ (see Fig. 20). Different nodal lines can be obtained by forming different linear combinations of the modes (14-10).

The reader will show that for $m = n = 2$, all oscillations have the same nodal lines $x = a/2$, $y = a/2$, while infinitely many different nodal lines can be obtained by forming different linear combinations of the modes u_{13} and u_{31}. A few of these are shown in Fig. 20.

Since the nodal lines may be regarded as the boundaries of new membranes contained in the original one, the character of oscillation of membranes of different shapes can be deduced from the examination of nodal lines (see Prob. 3).

Nodal lines can be observed experimentally by sprinkling a fine powder on the vibrating membrane.

PROBLEMS

1. Suppose the initial conditions for the rectangular membrane considered in the text are

$$u(x,y,0) = 0.1 \sin \frac{\pi x}{a} \sin \frac{\pi y}{b}, \qquad u_t(x,y,0) = 0.$$

(a) What is the frequency of the oscillation? (b) What is the maximum speed attained by the mid-point of the membrane?

2. Analysis of a microwave resonant cavity leads to the equation

$$u_{tt} = \gamma^2 (u_{xx} + u_{yy} + u_{zz})$$

with the boundary condition $u = 0$ or $\partial u / \partial n = 0$ on suitable portions of the planes

$$x = 0, \qquad x = a, \qquad y = 0, \qquad y = b, \qquad z = 0, \qquad z = c$$

(see Fig. 21). By assuming $u = XYZT$ show that the characteristic frequencies are

$$\frac{\omega_{mnp}}{2\pi} = \frac{\gamma}{2} \left[\left(\frac{m}{a} \right)^2 + \left(\frac{n}{b} \right)^2 + \left(\frac{p}{c} \right)^2 \right]^{\frac{1}{2}},$$

where m, n, and p are integers.

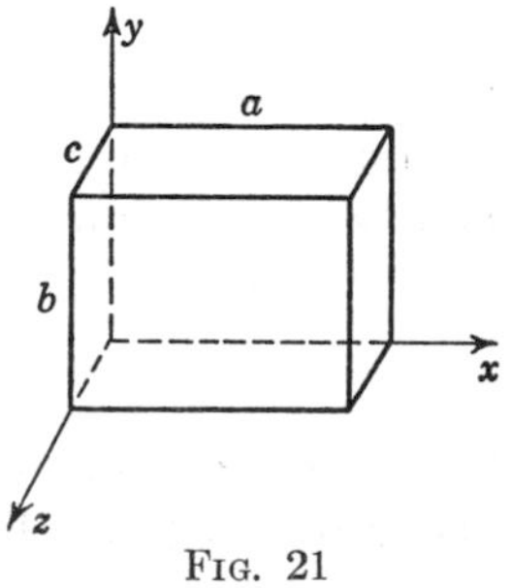

3. A curve in the xy plane along which $u = 0$ for all t is called a *nodal line*. (a) Sketch the nodal lines for the oscillation (14-5). (b) Sketch the nodal line for the oscillation

$$\left(\sin \frac{\pi x}{a} \sin \frac{2\pi y}{b} + \sin \frac{2\pi x}{a} \sin \frac{\pi y}{b} \right) (A \cos \omega_{21}t + B \sin \omega_{21}t)$$

Fig. 21

which arises by adding the modes $m = 1$, $n = 2$ and $m = 2$, $n = 1$. *Hint*: $\sin 2\theta = 2 \sin \theta \cos \theta$. (c) Thus obtain one solution for the problem of a triangular membrane.

15. The Circular Membrane. Bessel Functions. To discuss the oscillations of a circular membrane with fixed edges we introduce cylindrical coordinates (r,θ,u). With

$$u(x,y,t) = U(r,\theta,t) \qquad (15\text{-}1)$$

the equation of motion (14-1) takes the form (cf. Sec. 12, Prob. 2)

$$U_{tt} = \gamma^2[U_{rr} + r^{-1}U_r + r^{-2}U_{\theta\theta}]. \qquad (15\text{-}2)$$

If the boundary is the circle $r = a$, then the boundary condition is

$$U(a,\theta,t) = 0. \qquad (15\text{-}3)$$

To make the problem definite we also introduce initial conditions

$$U(r,\theta,0) = f(r), \qquad U_t(r,\theta,0) = 0 \qquad (15\text{-}4)$$

which state, respectively, that the initial shape of the membrane is given by $f(r)$ and that the initial velocity is zero.

Since the initial shape is independent of θ, the solution presumably involves r and t only. Thus, we consider expressions of the form $R(r)T(t)$ when applying the separation method. Substituting into (15-2) gives

$$\frac{1}{T}\frac{d^2T}{dt^2} = \gamma^2 \left(\frac{1}{R}\frac{d^2R}{dr^2} + \frac{1}{rR}\frac{dR}{dr} \right) \qquad (15\text{-}5)$$

after division by RT. Since the left-hand member of (15-5) depends on t alone and the right-hand member on r alone, each side must be constant. It can be shown that the constant is not positive, hence may be written as $-\omega^2$. Thus (15-5) leads to

$$T'' + \omega^2 T = 0, \qquad ' = \frac{d}{dt}, \qquad (15\text{-}6)$$

$$R'' + r^{-1}R' + k^2R = 0, \qquad ' = \frac{d}{dr}, \qquad (15\text{-}7)$$

where $k = \omega/\gamma$.

Equation (15-6) is the familiar equation for simple harmonic motion, and Eq. (15-7) can be reduced to the Bessel equation by the substitution $x = kr$. Hence, (15-7) has a solution

$$R = J_0(x) = J_0(kr).$$

The other solutions of (15-7) are rejected because they become infinite at $r = 0$, and we are led to the functions

$$J_0(kr) \sin \omega t \qquad \text{or} \qquad J_0(kr) \cos \omega t.$$

Since $u_t = 0$ when $t = 0$, we reject the solution involving the sine. The boundary condition (15-3) applied to our elementary solution RT now gives

$$J_0(ka) \cos \omega t = 0$$

for all t. This requires that ka be a root of the equation $J_0(x) = 0$ (see Fig. 22). If the positive roots of $J_0(x)$ are denoted by x_n, the appropriate

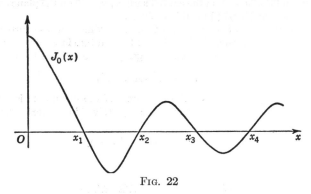

$$\text{FIG. 22}$$

choices of k are given by $k_n = x_n/a$. Since $\omega = k\gamma$, our elementary solutions have the form

$$RT = J_0(k_n r) \cos k_n \gamma t.$$

These functions satisfy the differential equation (15-2), the boundary condition (15-3), and the second initial condition (15-4). To satisfy the first initial condition we try to represent U as a linear combination of such terms:

$$U = \sum_{n=1}^{\infty} A_n J_0(k_n r) \cos k_n \gamma t. \qquad (15\text{-}8)$$

When $t = 0$, the initial condition requires that

$$f(r) = \sum_{n=1}^{\infty} A_n J_0(k_n r).$$

The problem of expanding an arbitrary function in series of Bessel functions was discussed in Chap. 2, Sec. 22. It was shown that the coefficients are given by

$$A_n = \frac{2}{a^2 [J_0'(k_n a)]^2} \int_0^a f(r) J_0(k_n r) r \, dr \qquad (15\text{-}9)$$

provided the series is uniformly convergent (but see also Chap. 2, Sec. 23).

In the terminology of the preceding section, the solution (15-8) is expressed by means of the modes. The characteristic frequencies are

$$\frac{\omega_n}{2\pi} = \frac{k_n \gamma}{2\pi} = \frac{x_n \gamma}{2\pi a}$$

and the fundamental is described by $J_0(k_1 r) \cos k_1 \gamma t$.

PROBLEMS

1. The oscillations of a cylindrical resonant cavity satisfy

$$u_{tt} = \gamma^2(u_{xx} + u_{yy} + u_{zz}), \qquad 0 \leq r < a, 0 < z < b$$

with boundary condition $u = 0$ on the curved surface, $u_z = 0$ on the plane ends. Obtain solutions of the form $R(r)Z(z)T(t)$ for this problem.

2. Find the distribution of temperature in a long cylinder whose surface is kept at the constant temperature zero and whose initial temperature in the interior is unity.

3. An elastic membrane subject to uniform gas pressure satisfies the equation

$$u_{tt} + p = \gamma^2(u_{xx} + u_{yy}),$$

where p is a constant depending on the pressure. If the membrane is circular, show how to reduce this problem to a problem of the type solved in the text. *Hint:* Consider the function

$$U(r,\theta,t) = u - \frac{p}{4\gamma^2}(r^2 - a^2).$$

SOLUTION BY INTEGRALS

16. The Fourier Transform. For many partial differential equations the desired solution can be expressed as an integral involving the initial or boundary values. This possibility was already illustrated by formula (3-10) for displacement of a vibrating string and by the solution of the Dirichlet problem given in (12-13). We shall now describe a systematic method of obtaining integral formulas.

The function $g(s)$ defined by

$$\mathbf{T}f = \lim_{a \to \infty} \frac{1}{\sqrt{2\pi}} \int_{-a}^{a} e^{-ixs}f(x)\,dx = g(s) \tag{16-1}$$

is called the *Fourier transform* of $f(x)$; the operator $\mathbf{T}$ is called the *Fourier transform operator*. The inverse operator $\mathbf{T}^{-1}$ is obtained by changing the sign of i, so that the foregoing equation may also be written

$$\mathbf{T}^{-1}g = \lim_{a \to \infty} \frac{1}{\sqrt{2\pi}} \int_{-a}^{a} e^{ixs}g(s)\,ds = f(x). \tag{16-2}$$

When such is the case, the symbol $\mathbf{T}$ satisfies the easily remembered equations

$$\mathbf{T}\mathbf{T}^{-1}f = f, \qquad \mathbf{T}^{-1}\mathbf{T}f = f. \tag{16-3}$$

If the limits in (16-1) and (16-2) are regarded in the sense of mean convergence (Chap. 2, Sec. 23), and if the integrals are regarded as Lebesgue integrals (Appendix C), then (16-1) gives (16-2) and (16-2) gives (16-1) provided either of the integrals

$$\int_{-\infty}^{\infty} |f(x)|^2\,dx \qquad \text{or} \qquad \int_{-\infty}^{\infty} |g(s)|^2\,ds \tag{16-4}$$

is finite.[1] Both integrals (16-4) then have the same value. In many physical problems the common value represents the total power or energy present in the system.

To illustrate the use of the Fourier transform, we shall solve the problem

$$u_t = \alpha^2 u_{xx}, \qquad t > 0, \ -\infty < x < \infty, \tag{16-5}$$

$$u(x,0) = f(x), \qquad -\infty < x < \infty, \tag{16-6}$$

$$u(x,t) \to 0, \qquad \text{as } t \to \infty. \tag{16-7}$$

Physically, this system describes the temperature $u(x,t)$ of an infinitely long bar at point x and time t when the initial temperature $u(x,0)$ is known. The trial solution $u = e^{px+qt}$ with p and q constant leads to

$$qe^{px+qt} = \alpha^2 p^2 e^{px+qt}$$

when substituted into (16-5). Hence $q = \alpha^2 p^2$, and the trial solution is

$$e^{px+\alpha^2 p^2 t}.$$

We choose p^2 negative because of (16-7). Thus $p = is$, where s is real, and the trial solution is now

$$e^{isx-\alpha^2 s^2 t} = e^{isx} e^{-\alpha^2 s^2 t}. \tag{16-8}$$

We shall satisfy the initial condition (16-6) by forming a linear combination [2] of solutions (16-8). Thus

$$\frac{1}{\sqrt{2\pi}} e^{isx} e^{-\alpha^2 s^2 t} g(s)$$

is a solution of (16-5) no matter what value $g(s)$ may have, and the integral

$$u(x,t) = \frac{1}{\sqrt{2\pi}} \int_{-\infty}^{\infty} e^{isx} e^{-\alpha^2 s^2 t} g(s) \, ds$$

is also a solution, provided we can differentiate under the integral sign. By (16-2) the latter expression can be written

$$u(x,t) = \mathbf{T}^{-1} e^{-\alpha^2 s^2 t} g(s). \tag{16-9}$$

Setting $t = 0$ and using the initial condition (16-6) give

$$f(x) = \mathbf{T}^{-1} g(s),$$

[1] This important theorem, known as *Plancherel's theorem*, is proved in E. C. Titchmarsh, "Introduction to the Theory of Fourier Integrals," Chap. 3, Oxford University Press, London, 1937. For a heuristic discussion of the relation between (16-1) and (16-2) see Chap. 2, Secs. 20 and 21, of the present text.

[2] This procedure is analogous to the formation of Fourier series in the method of separating variables.

so that $Tf = TT^{-1}g = g$. Substituting into (16-9) we get the final answer,

$$u(x,t) = T^{-1}e^{-\alpha^2 s^2 t}Tf. \tag{16-10}$$

This is an explicit formula for the temperature $u(x,t)$ in terms of the initial temperature $f(x)$.

As another example we shall solve the Dirichlet problem for a half plane. Several physical interpretations were given in Sec. 12; the mathematical formulation is

$$u_{xx} + u_{yy} = 0, \qquad y > 0, \ -\infty < x < \infty, \tag{16-11}$$

$$u(x,0) = f(x), \qquad -\infty < x < \infty, \tag{16-12}$$

$$u(x,y) \to 0, \qquad \text{as } y \to \infty. \tag{16-13}$$

The function e^{px+qy} satisfies (16-11) if $p^2 + q^2 = 0$. We choose q real and negative because of (16-13), and hence p is pure imaginary, $p = is$. The trial solution is now

$$e^{isx-|s|y},$$

when we note that $q^2 = s^2$ and that q is negative. This function satisfies (16-11) and (16-13). To satisfy (16-12) we form a linear combination as in the previous example, thus:

$$u(x,y) = \frac{1}{\sqrt{2\pi}} \int_{-\infty}^{\infty} e^{isx}e^{-|s|y}g(s)\,ds \equiv T^{-1}e^{-|s|y}g.$$

Setting $y = 0$ we get $f = T^{-1}g$ by (16-12). Hence $g = Tf$, and the solution [1] is

$$u(x,y) = T^{-1}e^{-|s|y}Tf. \tag{16-14}$$

As a final example we shall consider the problem

$$u_{tt} = a^2 u_{xx}, \qquad u(x,0) = f(x), \qquad u_t(x,0) = g(x)$$

which describes waves on an infinite string (cf. Secs. 2 and 3). The trial solution e^{isx+qt} yields the two expressions

$$e^{isx}e^{iast} \qquad \text{and} \qquad e^{isx}e^{-iast}.$$

Forming a general linear combination, we get

$$u(x,t) = T^{-1}e^{iast}g_1(s) + T^{-1}e^{-iast}g_2(s), \tag{16-15}$$

where g_1 and g_2 are to be determined from the initial conditions.

If (16-15) can be differentiated under the integrals which are implied in T^{-1}, the result is

$$u_t(x,t) = T^{-1}iase^{iast}g_1(s) - T^{-1}iase^{iast}g_2(s). \tag{16-16}$$

[1] Formulas of the type (16-10) and (16-14) are discussed in R. M. Redheffer, Operators and Initial-value Problems, *Proc. Am. Math. Soc.*, **4** (August, 1953).

Setting $t = 0$ in (16-15) and (16-16) now gives, respectively,

$$f = \mathbf{T}^{-1} g_1 + \mathbf{T}^{-1} g_2, \qquad g = \mathbf{T}^{-1} ias g_1 - \mathbf{T}^{-1} ias g_2,$$

or, after operating on the equations with $\mathbf{T}$,

$$g_1 + g_2 = \mathbf{T}f, \qquad ias(g_1 - g_2) = \mathbf{T}g.$$

Solving for g_1 and g_2,

$$g_1 = \frac{1}{2} \mathbf{T}f + \frac{1}{2ias} \mathbf{T}g, \qquad g_2 = \frac{1}{2} \mathbf{T}f - \frac{1}{2ias} \mathbf{T}g, \qquad (16\text{-}17)$$

and this gives the final answer upon substitution into (16-15).

The foregoing result can be deduced from d'Alembert's formula (3-15). However, the method of Fourier transforms also applies when d'Alembert's method fails (cf. Probs. 1 and 2).

PROBLEMS

1. According to Sec. **7** the equation for damped motion of waves on a string is

$$u_{tt} - a^2 u_{xx} = -2bu_t.$$

Obtain a family of solutions of the type

$$u(x,t) = \mathbf{T}^{-1} e^{-bt} e^{t(b^2 - a^2 s^2)^{1/2}} g_1(s) + \mathbf{T}^{-1} e^{-bt} e^{-t(b^2 - a^2 s^2)^{1/2}} g_2(s)$$

by starting with $u = e^{isx+qt}$ and forming a linear combination.

2. Formulate appropriate initial conditions for Prob. 1, and use them to determine g_1 and g_2.

3. The displacement $u(x,t)$ of a long, stiff rod satisfies

$$EI \frac{\partial^4 u}{\partial x^4} = f(x,t), \qquad f = \text{force},$$

when the mass is negligible (cf. Sec. 2, Prob. 6). Let $U(s,t)$ be the transform of u with respect to the variable x, and let $F(s,t)$ be the transform of f. Neglecting convergence questions, show that $EIs^4 U = F$, and thus obtain the solution in the form

$$u(x,t) = (EI)^{-1} \mathbf{T}^{-1} s^{-4} \mathbf{T}f.$$

Hint: Write out the expressions

$$u(x,t) = \mathbf{T}^{-1} U(s,t), \qquad f(x,t) = \mathbf{T}^{-1} F(s,t)$$

in full, and substitute into the differential equation.

4. If the mass of the rod in the preceding example is m, the equation of motion is

$$EI \frac{\partial^4 u}{\partial x^4} + m \frac{\partial^2 u}{\partial t^2} = f(x,t).$$

Show that $u = \mathbf{T}^{-1} U$, where $U = U(s,t)$ satisfies the ordinary differential equation

$$m \frac{d^2 U}{dt^2} + s^4 EIU = F(s,t).$$

17. Waves in a Half Plane. The Fourier transform can be used to solve the two-dimensional wave equation

$$\gamma^2(u_{xx} + u_{yy}) = u_{tt}, \qquad \gamma = \text{const}, \qquad (17\text{-}1)$$

and the result has an interesting physical interpretation. We suppose that the time dependence is harmonic, so that

$$u(x,y,t) = U(x,y)e^{-i\omega t}, \qquad (17\text{-}2)$$

where ω is constant. Substituting in (17-1) gives the *scalar wave equation*

$$U_{xx} + U_{yy} + k^2 U = 0, \qquad k = \frac{\omega}{\gamma}. \qquad (17\text{-}3)$$

This equation will now be solved in the half plane $y > 0$ subject to the additional conditions

$$U(x,0) = f(x), \qquad U(x,y) \to 0 \qquad \text{as } y \to \infty. \qquad (17\text{-}4)$$

Physically, the solution describes the radiation field of an antenna [1] when the aperture illumination is $f(x)$ (see Fig. 23).

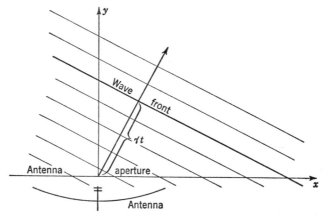

FIG. 23

By substituting the function $e^{ixs + qy}$ into (17-3) we obtain solutions

$$e^{isx} e^{\pm iy\sqrt{k^2 - s^2}}. \qquad (17\text{-}5)$$

Because of the second condition (17-4) the coefficient of y in (17-5) has a negative real part when s is large; we shall indicate this by dropping the

[1] Formulation of (17-3) in this context and discussion of the conditions for a unique solution can be found in treatises on electromagnetic theory.

minus sign. Forming a linear combination of expressions (17-5) as in the preceding section,

$$U(x,y) = \frac{1}{\sqrt{2\pi}} \int_{-\infty}^{\infty} e^{isx} e^{iy\sqrt{k^2-s^2}} g(s) \, ds = \mathbf{T}^{-1} e^{iy\sqrt{k^2-s^2}} g.$$

For $y = 0$ the first condition (17-4) yields $g = \mathbf{T}f$, and hence

$$U(x,y) = \mathbf{T}^{-1} e^{iy\sqrt{k^2-s^2}} \mathbf{T}f. \tag{17-6}$$

Multiplying by $e^{-i\omega t}$ as in (17-2), we get the corresponding solution of (17-1).

The discussion of (17-1) given here contrasts to that given in connection with the vibrating membrane (Sec. 14). For the membrane we specified the initial values of u and u_t, and we obtained a series involving infinitely many oscillation frequencies. Here, on the contrary, the frequency $\omega/2\pi$ was prescribed in advance. By (17-2) the initial conditions are

$$u(x,y,0) = U(x,y), \qquad u_t(x,y,0) = -i\omega U(x,y)$$

and the first condition cannot be specified arbitrarily, inasmuch as $U(x,y)$ satisfies (17-3).

To interpret the solution physically, we have

$$u(x,y,t) = \mathbf{T}^{-1} e^{-i\omega t + iy\sqrt{k^2-s^2}} g(s)$$

by combining (17-2) and (17-6), with $\mathbf{T}f = g(s)$. Writing out in full,

$$u(x,y,t) = \frac{1}{\sqrt{2\pi}} \int_{-\infty}^{\infty} e^{i(xs + y\sqrt{k^2-s^2} - \omega t)} g(s) \, ds. \tag{17-7}$$

For simplicity we shall suppose that $g(s) = 0$ when $|s| > k$. The limits $(-\infty,\infty)$ of the integral can then be replaced by $(-k,k)$. If we now introduce a variable θ,

$$s = k \sin \theta, \qquad \sqrt{k^2 - s^2} = k \cos \theta, \tag{17-8}$$

we get

$$u(x,y,t) = \frac{1}{\sqrt{2\pi}} \int_{-\pi/2}^{\pi/2} e^{i(kx \sin \theta + ky \cos \theta - \omega t)} g(k \sin \theta) k \cos \theta \, d\theta.$$

This formula expresses the solution as a superposition of functions of the form

$$e^{i(kx \sin \theta + ky \cos \theta - \omega t)}. \tag{17-9}$$

In the next paragraph it will be seen that (17-9) represents a plane wave traveling with velocity γ in the direction θ (Fig. 23). Hence, *the Fourier transform procedure gives the plane-wave expansion of the antenna field.* The amplitude of the wave moving in a given direction θ is

$$g(k \sin \theta) \, k \cos \theta \, d\theta,$$

where $g(s)$ is the Fourier transform of the aperture illumination.

To see that (17-9) represents a plane wave we examine the (x,y) locus on which (17-9) is constant. Without essential loss of generality we confine our attention, in particular, to the locus along which the exponent is zero. The equation of this locus is

$$x \sin \theta + y \cos \theta = \frac{\omega}{k} t = \gamma t, \qquad (17\text{-}10)$$

when we divide by k and replace k by its value (17-3).

The wave front (17-10) is clearly a straight line, and the wave fronts for different ts are all parallel. In fact, their common perpendicular makes an angle θ with the y axis. Since the distance from the line (17-10) to the origin is γt, the velocity of propagation is the constant γ, and hence the desired result is established. It is possible to give a similar discussion for the part of the integral (17-7) with $|s| > k$, though we shall not do so here.

18. The Convolution Theorem. The *convolution* $f * g$ of two functions f and g is defined by

$$f * g = \lim_{a \to \infty} \frac{1}{\sqrt{2\pi}} \int_{-a}^{a} f(\xi)g(x - \xi)\, d\xi = \frac{1}{\sqrt{2\pi}} \int_{-\infty}^{\infty} f(\xi)g(x - \xi)\, d\xi \quad (18\text{-}1)$$

if the limit exists either in the ordinary sense or in the sense of mean convergence. The importance of the operation (18-1) rests on the following theorem:

CONVOLUTION THEOREM. *Let f, g, $|f|^2$ and $|g|^2$ be integrable, and let all infinite integrals be interpreted in the sense of mean convergence. Then the product of the transforms equals the transform of the convolution. In symbols,*

$$\mathbf{T}(f * g) = (\mathbf{T}f)(\mathbf{T}g). \qquad (18\text{-}2)$$

Although a complete proof requires knowledge of Lebesgue integration and mean convergence, the result can be made plausible as follows. We have

$$\mathbf{T}(f * g) = \frac{1}{\sqrt{2\pi}} \int_{-\infty}^{\infty} \left[\frac{1}{\sqrt{2\pi}} \int_{-\infty}^{\infty} f(\xi)g(x - \xi)\, d\xi \right] e^{-ixs}\, dx$$

$$= \frac{1}{2\pi} \int_{-\infty}^{\infty} \left[\int_{-\infty}^{\infty} g(x - \xi)e^{-ixs}\, dx \right] f(\xi)\, d\xi$$

provided the order of integration may be inverted. If the variable x in the inner integral is changed to $t = x - \xi$, we get

$$\frac{1}{2\pi} \int_{-\infty}^{\infty} \left[\int_{-\infty}^{\infty} g(t)e^{-i(t+\xi)s}\, dt \right] f(\xi)\, d\xi = \left(\frac{1}{\sqrt{2\pi}} \int_{-\infty}^{\infty} f(\xi)e^{-i\xi s}\, d\xi \right) \left(\frac{1}{\sqrt{2\pi}} \int_{-\infty}^{\infty} g(t)e^{-its}\, dt \right),$$

and this is $(\mathbf{T}f)(\mathbf{T}g)$.

By means of the convolution theorem some of the foregoing results can be greatly simplified. Taking the transform of the formula (16-10) with respect to x gives

$$\mathbf{T}u = e^{-\alpha^2 s^2 t}\mathbf{T}f \qquad (18\text{-}3)$$

for the temperature $u(x,t)$ of a rod when the initial temperature is $f(x)$. By consulting a table of Fourier transforms or by using the result of Prob. 1,

$$e^{-\alpha^2 s^2 t} = \mathbf{T}g(x), \qquad \text{where } g(x) = (2\alpha^2 t)^{-\frac{1}{2}} e^{-x^2/(4\alpha^2 t)}.$$

Hence, the result (18-3) may be written

$$\mathbf{T}u = (\mathbf{T}f)(\mathbf{T}g) = \mathbf{T}(f * g)$$

when we recall (18-2). Taking the inverse transform now yields

$$u(x,t) = f * g = (4\pi\alpha^2 t)^{-\frac{1}{2}} \int_{-\infty}^{\infty} f(\xi) e^{-(x-\xi)^2/(4\alpha^2 t)} \, d\xi. \qquad (18\text{-}4)$$

The advantage of this formula is that it involves only a single integration whereas (16-10) requires two integrations. Since the integral is rapidly convergent when t is not too large, (18-4) is well suited for numerical computation.

To obtain a physical interpretation of (18-4), let the rod have the initial temperature zero except for a short piece on the interval $(x_0 - \epsilon, x_0 + \epsilon)$ (see Fig. 24). If Q cal of heat is uniformly distributed over this element of the rod, the corresponding initial temperature f is given by

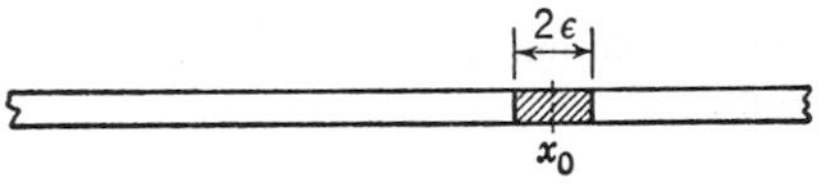

FIG. 24

$$Q = 2\epsilon c\rho f, \qquad x_0 - \epsilon < x < x_0 + \epsilon$$

where c is the heat capacity and ρ the linear density. By (18-4) the resulting temperature at point x and time t is

$$u(x,t) = \frac{Q}{c\rho(4\pi\alpha^2 t)^{\frac{1}{2}}} \frac{1}{2\epsilon} \int_{x_0-\epsilon}^{x_0+\epsilon} e^{-(x-\xi)^2/(4\alpha^2 t)} \, d\xi.$$

Letting $\epsilon \to 0$ and using the mean-value theorem we get

$$\frac{Q}{c\rho(4\pi\alpha^2 t)^{\frac{1}{2}}} e^{-(x-x_0)^2/(4\alpha^2 t)}. \qquad (18\text{-}5)$$

This gives the temperature distribution for an instantaneous source of strength Q at the point x_0. Now, Eq. (18-4) *represents the temperature in the general case as a superposition of such sources.* The source at $x = \xi$ has the strength

$$Q = c\rho f(\xi) \, d\xi.$$

As we shall see in the next section, this physical interpretation enables us to solve a variety of problems in heat flow with the greatest ease.

Example: Let $u(x,y)$ be harmonic for $y > 0$ and satisfy the additional conditions

$$u(x,0) = f(x), \qquad u(x,y) \to 0 \text{ as } y \to \infty.$$

Show that u is given by the *Poisson formula for a half plane:*

$$u(x,y) = \frac{y}{\pi} \int_{-\infty}^{\infty} \frac{f(\xi)}{(x - \xi)^2 + y^2} \, d\xi. \tag{18-6}$$

Since this problem is the same as that in (16-11) to (16-13), the solution is given by (16-14). Taking the transform of (16-14),

$$\mathbf{T}u = e^{-|s|y}\mathbf{T}f. \tag{18-7}$$

The convolution theorem can be applied if we express $e^{-|s|y}$ as a Fourier transform. To this end we compute the inverse transform

$$\mathbf{T}^{-1}e^{-|s|y} = \frac{1}{\sqrt{2\pi}} \int_0^{\infty} e^{isx}e^{-sy} \, ds + \frac{1}{\sqrt{2\pi}} \int_{-\infty}^0 e^{isx}e^{sy} \, ds$$

$$= \frac{1}{\sqrt{2\pi}} \left(\frac{1}{y - ix} + \frac{1}{y + ix} \right). \tag{18-8}$$

This shows that $e^{-|s|y} = \mathbf{T}g$, where g is the function (18-8):

$$g = \frac{1}{\sqrt{2\pi}} \frac{2y}{x^2 + y^2}.$$

The convolution theorem applied to (18-7) now gives $u = f * g$, and that is the desired result.

PROBLEMS

1. Let $I(x) = \mathbf{T}^{-1}e^{-cs^2}$, where c is constant. (*a*) Differentiate, and integrate the result by parts to obtain

$$\frac{dI}{dx} = -\frac{x}{2c} I.$$

(*b*) Using Eq. (10-1), Chap. 8, find the value of $I(0)$. (*c*) Thus deduce the formula

$$\mathbf{T}^{-1}e^{-cs^2} = (2c)^{-\frac{1}{2}}e^{-x^2/4c}.$$

(In particular, $e^{-x^2/2}$ and $e^{-s^2/2}$ are transforms of each other.)

2. Obtain the temperature distribution for a rod extending from $x = 0$ to $x = \infty$ if the initial temperature is $f(x)$ and the end $x = 0$ is insulated. *Hint:* Consider a rod extending from $-\infty$ to ∞, with initial temperature $f_0(x)$ defined by

$$f_0(x) \text{ even}, \qquad f_0(x) = f(x) \qquad \text{for } x > 0.$$

Compare Prob. 5, Sec. 10.

3. By taking $f_0(x)$ odd in Prob. 2, find the temperature distribution when the end $x = 0$ is not insulated but is kept at the temperature zero.

4. A rod extending from $x = 0$ to $x = l$ has the initial temperature distribution $f(x)$. By regarding this rod as part of an infinite rod with the initial temperature $f_0(x)$, find the temperature $u(x,t)$ when (*a*) both ends are insulated, (*b*) both ends are kept at the temperature zero. *Hint:* Let $f_0(x)$ have period $2l$. This method of satisfying boundary conditions was used for the vibrating-string problem in Sec. 6.

19. The Source Functions for Heat Flow. According to (18-5) the function

$$\frac{Q}{\rho c (4\pi \alpha^2 t)^{\frac{1}{2}}} e^{-r^2/4\alpha^2 t}, \qquad r^2 = x^2, \tag{19-1}$$

represents the temperature distribution due to an instantaneous source of strength Q at the origin. Equation (19-1) applies to the one-dimensional heat equation $\alpha^2 u_{xx} = u_t$. The corresponding result for two dimensions is

$$\frac{Q}{\rho c (4\pi \alpha^2 t)} e^{-r^2/4\alpha^2 t}, \qquad r^2 = x^2 + y^2, \tag{19-2}$$

and for three dimensions it is

$$\frac{Q}{\rho c (4\pi \alpha^2 t)^{\frac{3}{2}}} e^{-r^2/4\alpha^2 t}, \qquad r^2 = x^2 + y^2 + z^2. \tag{19-3}$$

In these formulas r is *the distance from the source to the point of observation* and t is *the length of time that has elapsed* since the heat was released. The value of ρ is, respectively, the linear, surface, or volume density.

The functions (19-1) to (19-3) are solutions, respectively, of

$$\alpha^2 u_{xx} = u_t, \ \alpha^2 (u_{xx} + u_{yy}) = u_t, \ \alpha^2 (u_{xx} + u_{yy} + u_{zz}) = u_t.$$

Also they give the limit 0 as $t \rightarrow 0$ through positive values, provided $r \neq 0$. Hence the initial temperature distribution is concentrated entirely at the origin. By integrating over the whole space it can be shown in each case that the total amount of heat present is Q when $t > 0$. For these reasons, the physical interpretation as a *point source of strength Q* is fully justified.

The expressions (19-1) to (19-3) indicate that heat travels with infinite speed. Even if r is large, we get a *positive* temperature for each positive t, no matter how small, but the initial temperature was zero. By contrast, the disturbance associated with the wave equation travels with finite speed (cf. Secs. 2 and 4.)

To illustrate the use of (19-3) let us find $u(x,y,z,t)$ when the initial temperature

$$u(x_1,y_1,z_1,0) = f(x_1,y_1,z_1)$$

is given at each point (x_1,y_1,z_1) of space. Instead of this distribution we introduce a source of strength

$$Q = c\rho f(x_1,y_1,z_1) \, dx_1 \, dy_1 \, dz_1 \tag{19-4}$$

at (x_1,y_1,z_1). The temperature at point (x,y,z) and time t due to *one* such source is given by (19-3), with Q as in (19-4) and with r the distance from (x,y,z) to the source:

$$r^2 = (x_1 - x)^2 + (y_1 - y)^2 + (z_1 - z)^2.$$

The temperature at (x,y,z) due to *all* the sources is given by superposition:

$$u(x,y,z,t) = (4\pi\alpha^2 t)^{-\frac{3}{2}} \int_{-\infty}^{\infty} \int_{-\infty}^{\infty} \int_{-\infty}^{\infty} e^{-r^2/4\alpha^2 t} f(x_1,y_1,z_1)\, dx_1\, dy_1\, dz_1. \quad (19\text{-}5)$$

As another illustration we shall find the temperature due to a point source which emits heat continually. Let $Q(t)$ represent the strength of the source, so that the amount of heat emitted in time interval $(t_1, t_1 + dt_1)$ is approximately $Q(t_1)\, dt_1$. The heat at the present time t due to the source at time t_1 is

$$\frac{Q(t_1)\, dt_1}{\rho c [4\pi\alpha^2(t - t_1)]^{\frac{3}{2}}} e^{-r^2/[4\alpha^2(t-t_1)]}$$

when we recall that t in (19-3) stands, not for the time, but for the *elapsed* time. Adding the contributions from the source at all values of t_1 prior to t gives

$$u = \frac{1}{\rho c} \int_{-\infty}^{t} \frac{1}{[4\pi\alpha^2(t - t_1)]^{\frac{3}{2}}} e^{-r^2/[4\alpha^2(t-t_1)]} Q(t_1)\, dt_1. \quad (19\text{-}6)$$

If $Q(t)$ is a constant Q, the integral can be evaluated explicitly by the change of variable

$$s^2 = \frac{r^2}{4\alpha^2(t - t_1)};$$

the result is

$$u = \frac{Q}{4\pi\alpha^2\rho c} \frac{1}{r}. \quad (19\text{-}7)$$

This represents the temperature due to a continuous uniform source of heat at a distance r from the point of observation. Since the conditions are steady state, the solution satisfies Laplace's equation. (Compare Sec. 12, where the function $1/r$ was obtained in connection with electrostatics and gravitation.)

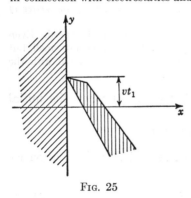

FIG. 25

Example: A line contact is pressed against the plane $x = 0$ with constant normal force F per unit length, the coefficient of friction being a constant μ. At time $t = 0$ it starts to slide in a direction perpendicular to its length with constant velocity v (see Fig. 25). Obtain the temperature in the medium $x \le 0$, assuming this temperature to have been zero initially and neglecting heat loss at the surface $x = 0$.

This problem arises in the theory of milling, leather glazing, and lathe turning. To solve it, let the line contact be initially coincident with the z axis, so that its height at time t_1 is $y = vt_1$. The heat generated by friction per unit length is $F\mu\, dy$, and hence the heat generated per unit length in the time interval dt_1 is

$$Q = F\mu v\, dt_1.$$

Using this value of Q in the result (19-2) we obtain

$$\frac{F\mu v\, dt_1}{4\rho c\alpha^2 \pi (t - t_1)} e^{-[x^2+(y-vt_1)^2]/4\alpha^2(t-t_1)}$$

for the contribution, at the point (x,y,z) and at the present time t, due to motion of the line contact in the time interval $(t_1, t_1 + dt_1)$. [The reader is reminded that t in (19-2) stands for the elapsed time and $x^2 + y^2$ in (19-2) is the square of the distance from the point of observation to the line source.] Superposition yields the final answer:

$$u(x,y,z,t) = \frac{F\mu v}{4\rho c \alpha^2 \pi} \int_0^t \frac{e^{-[x^2 + (y - vt_1)^2]/4\alpha^2(t - t_1)}}{t - t_1}\, dt_1.$$

PROBLEMS

1. Show that (19-2) can be obtained by integrating (19-3) with respect to z and (19-1) by integrating (19-2) with respect to y. Interpret physically.

2. What initial- or boundary-value problem is solved by (19-5)? By (19-6)?

3. By use of (19-2) solve the initial-value problem

$$\alpha^2(u_{xx} + u_{yy}) = u_t, \qquad u(x,y,0) = f(x,y).$$

4. Find the temperature distribution $u(x,y,z,t)$ for $x > 0$ due to a time-dependent distribution $f(y,z,t)$ on the plane $x = 0$. Take the initial temperature as zero for $x > 0$.

5. State and solve the two-dimensional analogue of Prob. 4; the one-dimensional analogue.

20. A Singular Integral. We shall now derive an integral formula which can be used in the study of many partial differential equations. The discussion depends on certain theorems of vector analysis [1] summarized in the following paragraph.

In the *divergence theorem*

$$\int_\tau (\nabla \cdot \mathbf{A})\, d\tau = \int_\sigma \mathbf{A}_n\, d\sigma, \qquad \begin{cases} d\tau = \text{volume element} \\ d\sigma = \text{surface element} \end{cases} \tag{20-1}$$

the choice $\mathbf{A} = u\nabla v$ yields *Green's first identity*

$$\int_\tau [u\nabla^2 v + (\nabla u \cdot \nabla v)]\, d\tau = \int_\sigma u\, \frac{\partial v}{\partial n}\, d\sigma \tag{20-2}$$

when we recall that $(\nabla v)_n = \partial v/\partial n$, the normal derivative. Writing (20-2) with u and v interchanged and subtracting give *Green's symmetric identity*

$$\int_\tau (u\nabla^2 v - v\nabla^2 u)\, d\tau = \int_\sigma \left(u\, \frac{\partial v}{\partial n} - v\, \frac{\partial u}{\partial n} \right) d\sigma. \tag{20-3}$$

The conditions for validity of these identities are discussed in Chap. 5. For our present purposes we need an appropriate form of (20-3) when v does not satisfy the continuity conditions there required.

---

[1] The reader may find it advisable to review Chap. 5, Secs. 8 to 10. Unless otherwise indicated, the functions considered in Secs. 20 to 22 are twice continuously differentiable in the region τ and on its boundary. The surface of τ is assumed smooth, so that the normal is a continuous function of position.

To this end, we show that

$$\lim_{a \to 0} \int_{\sigma_1} \frac{f(Q)}{a^c} \, d\sigma = \begin{cases} 4\pi f(P), & \text{for } c = 2, \\ 0, & \text{for } c < 2, \end{cases} \qquad (20\text{-}4)$$

where f is continuous, c is constant, and the region of integration σ_1 is the surface of a sphere of radius a centered at P. Now, the integral (20-4) may be written

$$\int_{\sigma_1} \frac{f(Q)}{a^c} \, d\sigma = \int_{\sigma_1} \frac{f(P)}{a^c} \, d\sigma + \int_{\sigma_1} \frac{f(Q) - f(P)}{a^c} \, d\sigma = I_1 + I_2.$$

Since the area of the sphere is $4\pi a^2$, we have, as $a \to 0$,

$$I_1 = \frac{f(P)}{a^c} \int_{\sigma_1} d\sigma = \frac{f(P)}{a^c} 4\pi a^2 \to \begin{cases} 4\pi f(P), & \text{for } c = 2, \\ 0, & \text{for } c < 2. \end{cases}$$

Since a surface integral does not exceed the area of the surface times the maximum value of the integrand, we have

$$|I_2| \le 4\pi a^2 \frac{\max|f(Q) - f(P)|}{a^c} \le 4\pi \max|f(Q) - f(P)|.$$

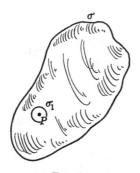

FIG. 26

If f is continuous, this tends to zero as $a \to 0$, and (20-4) follows.

Let us now apply (20-3) to the function

$$v = w + \frac{1}{r}, \qquad r = r(P,Q), \qquad (20\text{-}5)$$

where w is twice continuously differentiable and where r is the distance from a fixed point P to the variable point of integration, Q. The region of integration is to be the region inside a given closed surface σ and outside a small sphere σ_1 of radius a centered at P (see Fig. 26). In this region $r \ne 0$ and (20-3) can be applied without hesitation.

According to (20-5) we have

$$\nabla^2 v = \nabla^2 w + \nabla^2 \frac{1}{r} = \nabla^2 w. \qquad (20\text{-}6)$$

On σ_1 the outward normal n is directed along the radius into the sphere, so that

$$\frac{\partial}{\partial n} \frac{1}{r} = -\frac{\partial}{\partial r} \frac{1}{r} = \frac{1}{r^2} = \frac{1}{a^2}.$$

Since $r = a$ on σ_1, the foregoing equation and (20-5) give

$$\frac{\partial v}{\partial n} = \frac{\partial w}{\partial n} + \frac{1}{a^2}, \qquad v = w + \frac{1}{a}, \qquad \text{on } \sigma_1. \qquad (20\text{-}7)$$

The surface integral in (20-3) can be written as an integral over σ plus an integral over σ_1. By inspection of (20-7) the integral over σ_1 is

$$\int_{\sigma_1} \left[u \left(\frac{\partial w}{\partial n} + \frac{1}{a^2} \right) - \left(w + \frac{1}{a} \right) \frac{\partial u}{\partial n} \right] d\sigma. \qquad (20\text{-}8)$$

This becomes $4\pi u(P)$ as $a \to 0$, in view of (20-4). If we use this result and (20-6) in (20-3), we obtain the desired formula

$$4\pi u(P) = \int_\tau (u\nabla^2 w - v\nabla^2 u) \, d\tau + \int_\sigma \left(v \frac{\partial u}{\partial n} - u \frac{\partial v}{\partial n} \right) d\sigma \qquad (20\text{-}9)$$

upon letting $a \to 0$. When P is exterior to τ, the same formula is valid, except that $4\pi u(P)$ must be replaced by 0.

Since the volume integral in (20-9) is taken over the whole region τ, it includes the point P at which $v = \infty$. The meaning of the integral is clear from the derivation, but we shall show directly that a singularity of the type $1/r$ in a volume integral causes no convergence difficulties. If τ_1 is the interior of the sphere with surface σ_1, we have

$$\int_{\tau_1} \frac{1}{r} \, d\tau = \int_0^a \frac{1}{r} 4\pi r^2 \, dr = 2\pi a^2.$$

This is clearly finite and in fact tends to zero as $a \to 0$.

21. The Poisson Equation. If u has continuous second derivatives, then the Laplacian $\nabla^2 u$ is a continuous function of position. We shall denote this function by $-4\pi\rho(x,y,z)$, so that

$$\nabla^2 u = -4\pi\rho. \qquad (21\text{-}1)$$

The choice $v = 1/r$, $w = 0$ in (20-9) now yields the *Poisson formula*

$$u(P) = \int_\tau \frac{\rho}{r} \, d\tau + \frac{1}{4\pi} \int_\sigma \left(\frac{1}{r} \frac{\partial u}{\partial n} - u \frac{\partial}{\partial n} \frac{1}{r} \right) d\sigma \qquad (21\text{-}2)$$

when we divide by 4π. As before, $r = r(P,Q)$ is the distance from P to the variable point of integration Q. The formula (21-2) holds for every function having continuous second derivatives in τ and on its boundary.[1]

We now change our viewpoint. Instead of starting with u and defining ρ by (21-1), we suppose that ρ is given in advance. Equation (21-1) is now a partial differential equation for the unknown function u; it is

---

[1] Provided the boundary is simple enough to permit the use of (20-9). This condition on τ is hereby postulated once for all.

called the *Poisson equation*. The foregoing considerations show that if u satisfies the Poisson equation, then u is given by the Poisson formula. The interest of the formula is that it yields the values of u throughout the interior of τ in terms of u and $\partial u/\partial n$ on the surface only.

For a physical interpretation, let u be the electrostatic potential due to a charge distribution of density ρ. The fact that the potential satisfies Poisson's equation is established in treatises on electrostatics,[1] so that this interpretation is consistent with (21-1). Since q/r represents the potential due to a charge q at a distance r from the point of observation, the term

$$\frac{1}{r}(\rho\, d\tau), \qquad \text{where } r = r(P,Q) \text{ and } \rho = \rho(Q),$$

represents the potential at P due to the charges within the volume element $d\tau$ at Q. Hence the first term of (21-2),

$$\int_\tau \frac{1}{r}(\rho\, d\tau),$$

represents the potential at P due to charges within the body τ. Similarly the second term in (21-2),

$$\int_\sigma \frac{1}{r}\left(\frac{1}{4\pi}\frac{\partial u}{\partial n}\, d\sigma\right),$$

represents the potential at P due to a certain surface-charge distribution on the surface σ.

To interpret the term

$$\int_\sigma \left(\frac{\partial}{\partial n}\frac{1}{r}\right)\left(-\frac{u}{4\pi}\, d\sigma\right) \qquad\qquad (21\text{-}3)$$

in (21-2), we consider the configuration shown in Fig. 27. Here, a charge $-q$ is introduced at the point Q on the surface σ and a charge $+q$ at a distance Δn along the outward normal $\mathbf{n}$ to σ. The distance from $-q$ to P is r, and the distance from q to P is denoted by r_1. If we take $q = m/\Delta n$, where m is constant, the potential at P is

$$q\frac{1}{r_1} - q\frac{1}{r} = q\Delta\frac{1}{r} = m\frac{\Delta(1/r)}{\Delta n} \rightarrow m\frac{\partial}{\partial n}\frac{1}{r}$$

as $\Delta n \rightarrow 0$. [That the limit is $m\,\partial(1/r)/\partial n$ follows from the *definition* of normal derivative, without calculation.] The limiting configuration of Fig. 27 is called a *dipole*; the constant m is called the *moment* of the dipole. We have thus found the desired interpretation of (21-3); namely, (21-3) represents the potential due to a surface distribu-

---

[1] The case $\rho = 0$ in (21-1) is discussed in Chap. 5, Sec. 14. A detailed analysis of the conditions under which Poisson's equation holds may be found in O. D. Kellogg, "Foundations of Potential Theory," p. 156, Springer-Verlag OHG, Berlin, 1929.

tion of dipoles having the moments $-u \, d\sigma/4\pi$. A surface distribution of dipoles such as this is called a *double layer*.

Since the volume integral in (21-2) is extended only over τ, it does not take account of the charges outside τ. That purpose is served by the surface integral in (21-2). From this viewpoint (21-2) shows that *the charges outside τ can be replaced by a suitable surface charge and double layer on σ*, without changing the potential within τ. If τ increases beyond all bounds, the limiting value of the surface integral can be thought to represent the influence of the charges at infinity.

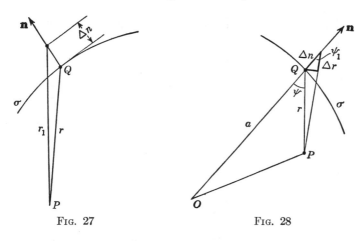

FIG. 27   FIG. 28

In many important problems there are no charges at infinity, so that the limiting value of the surface integral is zero. To investigate this possibility, let σ be a large sphere of radius a centered at the origin O. By inspection of the differential triangle in Fig. 28,

$$\Delta r \sim \Delta n \cos \psi_1 \sim \Delta n \cos \psi, \qquad \text{as } \Delta n \to 0$$

where ψ is the angle between OQ and PQ. The definition of normal derivative leads to

$$\frac{\partial r}{\partial n} = \lim \frac{\Delta r}{\Delta n} = \cos \psi \tag{21-4}$$

and hence

$$\frac{\partial}{\partial n}\frac{1}{r} = -\frac{1}{r^2}\frac{\partial r}{\partial n} = -\frac{\cos \psi}{r^2}. \tag{21-5}$$

If P is fixed and $a \to \infty$, it is easily seen that $r \sim a$ uniformly with respect to the point Q on σ. Hence $1/r$ has the order of magnitude $1/a$, and by (21-5) the normal derivative has the order of magnitude $1/a^2$. Now, the surface integral in (21-2) does not exceed $4\pi a^2$ times the maximum of the integrand. By the foregoing remarks, the integral therefore tends to zero as $a \to \infty$ if

$$a \max \left| \frac{\partial u}{\partial n} \right| \to 0 \qquad \text{and} \qquad \max |u| \to 0, \qquad \text{as } a \to \infty. \quad (21\text{-}6)$$

In this case (21-2) leads to the simple formula

$$u = \int \frac{\rho}{r} d\tau, \qquad \text{integrated over all space.} \qquad (21\text{-}7)$$

Referred to spherical coordinates [1] (r,θ,ϕ) the normal derivative $\partial u/\partial n$ in (21-6) is the radial derivative $\partial u/\partial r$, and $a = r$. Thus (21-6) is equivalent to

$$\lim_{r \to \infty} r \frac{\partial u}{\partial r} = 0, \qquad \lim_{r \to \infty} u = 0, \qquad \text{uniformly in } \theta \text{ and } \phi. \quad (21\text{-}8)$$

By substituting (21-5) into the integral and regrouping terms one finds that (21-8) may be replaced by the weaker condition

$$\lim_{r \to \infty} \left(r \frac{\partial u}{\partial r} + u \right) = 0, \qquad \lim_{r \to \infty} \frac{u}{r} = 0, \qquad \text{uniformly in } \theta \text{ and } \phi. \quad (21\text{-}9)$$

That is, if u satisfies (21-1) and (21-9), then u can be represented in the form (21-7). When $\rho = 0$ outside a bounded region, an altogether different procedure [2] shows that the second condition (21-8) also suffices.

Example: If the region τ is a sphere of radius r_0 centered at P, every solution of Poisson's equation satisfies

$$u(P) = \frac{1}{4\pi r_0^2} \int_\sigma u \, d\sigma + \int_\tau \left(\frac{1}{r} - \frac{1}{r_0} \right) \rho \, d\tau. \qquad (21\text{-}10)$$

Here $r = r(P,Q)$ is the distance from P to the variable point of integration Q. To prove (21-10) we choose $w = -1/r_0$ in (20-5) and note that on σ

$$v = 0, \qquad \frac{\partial v}{\partial n} = \frac{\partial v}{\partial r} = -\frac{1}{r^2} = -\frac{1}{r_0^2}.$$

The desired result follows at once from (20-9). The special case $\rho = 0$ in (21-10) yields the AVERAGE-VALUE THEOREM: *If a function is harmonic throughout a sphere, its value at the center of the sphere equals the average of the values on the surface.* This fact is of central importance in the study of harmonic functions.

The merit of taking $w = -1/r_0$ in (20-5) is that then $v = 0$ on σ. Hence the term involving $\partial u/\partial n$ in the surface integral (20-9) drops out. The possibility of making such a choice of v will be systematically exploited in Sec. 23.

---

[1] The r in (21-8) has no relation to the $r = r(P,Q)$ that appears elsewhere in this discussion.

[2] See H. B. Phillips, "Vector Analysis," p. 158, John Wiley & Sons, Inc., New York, 1933.

PROBLEMS

1. If u is harmonic, show that the choice $u = v$ in (20-2) gives

$$\int_\tau (u_x^2 + u_y^2 + u_z^2)\, d\tau = \int_\sigma u\, \frac{\partial u}{\partial n}\, d\sigma.$$

2. Show that a solution of Poisson's equation in a closed bounded surface σ is wholly determined by its boundary values and that it is determined, apart from an additive constant, by the boundary values of the normal derivative. *Hint:* If u_1 and u_2 are two solutions, apply Prob. 1 to $u = u_1 - u_2$ and then use the result of Prob. 4.

3. Let u be harmonic in a region τ, and suppose u assumes its maximum value u_0 at an interior point P. Show that $u = u_0$ throughout every sphere contained in τ and centered at P. *Hint:* If $M(u)$ denotes the mean value on the surface of such a sphere, then $u_0 = M(u)$ and hence $M(u_0 - u) = 0$. Now use Prob. 4.

4. Let $f(Q)$ be continuous and nonnegative in a region τ. If $\int_\tau f\, d\tau = 0$, then $f \equiv 0$. Similarly for surface integrals. *Hint:* If $f = \epsilon > 0$ at an interior point P, then by continuity $f \geq \epsilon/2$ throughout some sphere τ_1 of radius $\delta > 0$ centered at P. But this gives $\int_\tau f\, d\tau \geq \int_{\tau_1} f\, d\tau \geq \int_{\tau_1} (\epsilon/2)\, d\tau > 0$.

22. The Helmholtz Formula. The *Helmholtz equation*

$$\nabla^2 u + k^2 u = 0 \tag{22-1}$$

is obtained by separating variables in the wave equation (Sec. 14) or by requiring harmonic time dependence (Sec. 17). A brief calculation [1] shows that (22-1) has the solution e^{ikr}/r, where r is the distance from a fixed point P to a variable point Q. If we set

$$v = \frac{e^{ikr}}{r}, \qquad w = v - \frac{1}{r} \tag{22-2}$$

it follows that $\nabla^2 w = \nabla^2 v = -k^2 v$ for $r \neq 0$. Hence

$$u\nabla^2 w - v\nabla^2 u = u(-k^2 v) - v(-k^2 u) = 0, \tag{22-3}$$

provided $r \neq 0$ and provided u satisfies (22-1). Substituting (22-2) into (20-9) with due regard to (22-3) now yields the *Helmholtz formula*

$$u(P) = \frac{1}{4\pi} \int_\sigma \left[\frac{e^{ikr}}{r} \frac{\partial u}{\partial n} - u \frac{\partial}{\partial n}\left(\frac{e^{ikr}}{r} \right) \right] d\sigma. \tag{22-4}$$

This expresses the solution u of (22-1) as an integral involving the boundary values of u and $\partial u/\partial n$.

Sometimes the region τ is bounded and (22-1) holds at points exterior to τ. To see if (22-4) remains valid in this case, we construct a sphere τ_1

[1] Let the Laplacian be referred to spherical coordinates with origin at P.

centered at the origin and having a radius a so large that τ is contained entirely within τ_1 (Fig. 29). Formula (22-4) applied to the region between τ and the surface σ_1 of the sphere gives

$$4\pi u(P) = \int_\sigma \left[\frac{e^{ikr}}{r} \frac{\partial u}{\partial n} - u \frac{\partial}{\partial n} \left(\frac{e^{ikr}}{r} \right) \right] d\sigma + \int_{\sigma_1} \left[\frac{e^{ikr}}{r} \frac{\partial u}{\partial n} - u \frac{\partial}{\partial n} \left(\frac{e^{ikr}}{r} \right) \right] d\sigma.$$

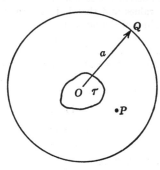

Fɪɢ. 29

In the first integral the outer normal for the region of integration is the inner normal for τ. With this understanding we see that (22-4) holds in the present case, provided the integral over σ_1 tends to zero as $a \to \infty$.

To investigate the behavior as $a \to \infty$, note that on σ_1

$$\frac{\partial}{\partial n} \frac{e^{ikr}}{r} = \frac{\partial}{\partial r} \frac{e^{ikr}}{r} \frac{\partial r}{\partial n} = \frac{e^{ikr}}{r} \left(ik - \frac{1}{r} \right) \cos \psi$$

by (21-4). Hence the integral over σ_1 becomes, after rearrangement,

$$\int_{\sigma_1} \frac{e^{ikr}}{r} \left[\frac{\partial u}{\partial n} - iku + iku(1 - \cos \psi) + \frac{1}{r} u \cos \psi \right] d\sigma. \qquad (22\text{-}5)$$

As $a \to \infty$ with P fixed, we have $a \sim r$. Also, the law of cosines applied to Fig. 28 shows that $a^2(1 - \cos \psi)$ remains bounded. Hence, the integral will tend to 0 provided

$$a \max \left| \frac{\partial u}{\partial n} - iku \right| \to 0 \qquad \text{and} \qquad \max |u| \to 0, \qquad \text{as } a \to \infty.$$

This assumes k real, so that $|e^{ikr}| = 1$.

In spherical coordinates (r,θ,ϕ) the result of the foregoing discussion may be summarized as follows: *Formula* (22-4) *applies to the exterior of the bounded region τ provided*

$$r \left(\frac{\partial u}{\partial r} - iku \right) \to 0 \qquad \text{and} \qquad u \to 0 \qquad (22\text{-}6)$$

as $r \to \infty$, *uniformly in* θ *and* ϕ. In just the same way it is found that (21-2) applies to the exterior of the bounded region τ provided (22-6) holds with $k = 0$.

Equation (22-6) with $k = 0$ is sometimes called the *Dirichlet condition.* It is the same as (21-8), hence means that there are no charges at infinity. Equation (22-6) with $k \neq 0$ is called the *Sommerfeld radiation condition;* it means that there are no sources of radiation at infinity.

Although (22-6) is the form usually given, it is unnecessarily restrictive. A more careful analysis of (22-5) shows that (22-6) may be replaced by the weaker condition

$$r \left(\frac{\partial u}{\partial r} - iku + \frac{u}{r} \right) \to 0 \quad \text{and} \quad \frac{u}{r} \to 0, \tag{22-7}$$

which reduces to (21-9) when $k = 0$.

23. The Functions of Green and Neumann. The Laplace equation can be obtained by setting $\rho = 0$ in Poisson's equation (21-1) or by setting $k = 0$ in the Helmholtz equation (22-1). The corresponding integral formulas, (21-2) and (22-4), both reduce to

$$u(P) = \frac{1}{4\pi} \int_{\sigma} \left(\frac{1}{r} \frac{\partial u}{\partial n} - u \frac{\partial}{\partial n} \frac{1}{r} \right) d\sigma. \tag{23-1}$$

This expresses every harmonic function in τ as an integral involving the boundary values and the boundary values of the normal derivative. However, a harmonic function is determined by the *boundary values alone,* without any reference to the normal derivative.[1] We shall now obtain a formula, similar to (23-1), in which $\partial u / \partial n$ is not present.

Such a formula can be found by an appropriate choice of v in (20-9). Since $\nabla^2 u = 0$, the volume integral in (20-9) will drop out if

$$\nabla^2 w = 0 \quad \text{throughout } \tau. \tag{23-2}$$

And the term involving $\partial u / \partial n$ in (20-9) will drop out if $v = 0$ on σ. By (20-5), that condition is equivalent to

$$w = -\frac{1}{r} \quad \text{on } \sigma. \tag{23-3}$$

Evidently, (23-2) and (23-3) determine w uniquely. Since the function $r = r(P,Q)$ involves the fixed point P, the boundary condition (23-3) makes w, and hence v, depend on P. The function v obtained in this way is called *Green's function* and is denoted by $G(P,Q)$. Thus,

$$G(P,Q) = v = w + \frac{1}{r} \tag{23-4}$$

[1] See Sec. 21. Prob. 2.

where $r = r(P,Q)$ and where w satisfies (23-2) and (23-3). The formula (20-9) now yields

$$u(P) = -\frac{1}{4\pi}\int_\sigma u\,\frac{\partial v}{\partial n}\,d\sigma = -\frac{1}{4\pi}\int_\sigma u\,\frac{\partial G}{\partial n}\,d\sigma, \qquad (23\text{-}5)$$

with G given by (23-4). The differentiation and integration in (23-5) are with respect to Q.

What we have shown is the following: Let u satisfy

$$\nabla^2 u = 0 \text{ in } \tau, \qquad u = f \text{ on } \sigma. \qquad (23\text{-}6)$$

If the region τ has the Green function G, then

$$u(P) = -\frac{1}{4\pi}\int_\sigma f(Q)\,\frac{\partial G}{\partial n}\,d\sigma. \qquad (23\text{-}7)$$

When a continuous function f is given in advance, it can be shown, conversely, that the function u in (23-7) satisfies (23-6). In other words, *formula* (23-7) *solves the Dirichlet problem.* The general Dirichlet problem is thus reduced to the special Dirichlet problems [1] that have to be solved in constructing Green's function.

To interpret Green's function physically, let a unit charge be placed at the point P interior to a closed, grounded conducting surface σ. Since P is the only charge present, the potential has the form $v = w + 1/r$, where $\nabla^2 w = 0$. Since the conductor σ is a grounded equipotential, $v = 0$ on σ, and hence, v agrees with the v in the foregoing paragraph. *Thus,* $G(P,Q)$ *is the potential at Q due to a unit charge at P in the grounded conducting surface σ.* Because of this interpretation the existence of Green's function is very plausible on physical grounds.[2]

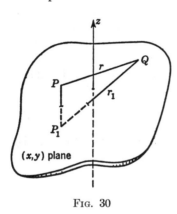

FIG. 30

The physical interpretation not only suggests that $G(P,Q)$ exists but gives a method of finding it in many cases. As an illustration, we shall construct Green's function for the half space $z > 0$ (Fig. 30). Let a charge $q = 1$ be placed at P and a charge $q = -1$ at P_1, the mirror image of P in the plane $z = 0$. By symmetry the potential $v = 0$ when $z = 0$, and hence v is Green's function. If r is the distance from P to Q and r_1 the distance from P_1 to Q, the potential is

---

[1] One problem for each choice of P.

[2] A proof of the existence for all regions likely to be met in practice is given in O. D. Kellogg, "Foundations of Potential Theory," chap. 11, Springer-Verlag OIIG, Berlin, 1929.

$$G(P,Q) = \frac{1}{r} - \frac{1}{r_1}.$$

As in the derivation of (21-5),

$$\frac{\partial G}{\partial n} = -\frac{2 \cos \psi}{r^2} \quad \text{on } z = 0,$$

where ψ is the angle between PQ and the normal to $z = 0$. Substituting into (23-7) yields the *Poisson formula for a half space,*

$$u(x,y,z) = \frac{1}{2\pi} \int_\sigma \int f \frac{\cos \psi}{r^2} \, d\sigma = \frac{z}{2\pi} \int_{-\infty}^{\infty} \int_{-\infty}^{\infty} \frac{f(x_1,y_1)}{[(x - x_1)^2 + (y - y_1)^2 + z^2]^{3/2}} \, dx_1 \, dy_1.$$

This formula represents a harmonic function for $z > 0$, which reduces to $f(x,y)$ when $z = 0$.

In terms of heat flow, the Dirichlet problem is to compute the steady-state temperature in a solid when the temperature on the surface is known. Sometimes the rate of heat flow across the surface is prescribed rather than the temperature. The problem which arises in this way is called *the Neumann problem;* it leads to the equations

$$\nabla^2 u = 0 \text{ in } \tau, \qquad \frac{\partial u}{\partial n} = g \text{ on } \sigma. \tag{23-8}$$

If (23-8) is to have a solution, we must restrict g so that the rate of flow into τ equals the rate out; otherwise, a steady-state temperature cannot be expected. It is clear physically that the appropriate condition is

$$\int_\sigma g \, d\sigma = 0 \tag{23-9}$$

and indeed, the choice $v = 1$ in (20-3) shows that (23-9) follows from (23-8).

When g satisfies (23-9), the problem is still not well posed because it has infinitely many solutions. That is, (23-8) involves the derivatives only, so that u can be altered by an additive constant. To make the solution unique we require that

$$\int_\sigma u \, d\sigma = 0. \tag{23-10}$$

Properly stated, the *Neumann problem* is to solve (23-8) when (23-9) and (23-10) hold.

By means of (20-9) we can develop a *Neumann function* $N(P,Q)$ analogous to the Green function $G(P,Q)$ of the foregoing paragraphs. As before the condition

$$\nabla^2 w = 0 \qquad \text{throughout } \tau \tag{23-11}$$

makes the volume integral (20-9) drop out. To get rid of the surface integral involving u, we require that $\partial v/\partial n$ be constant [1] on σ, and we recall (23-10). Since $v = w + 1/r$, this requirement is

$$\frac{\partial w}{\partial n} = -\frac{\partial}{\partial n}\frac{1}{r} + \text{const.} \tag{23-12}$$

To make w unique we require also that

$$\int_\sigma w \, d\sigma = 0. \tag{23-13}$$

The *Neumann function* is

$$N(P,Q) \equiv v = w + \frac{1}{r} \tag{23-14}$$

where w satisfies (23-11) to (23-13). The solution u of (23-8) can evidently be expressed in the form

$$u(P) = \frac{1}{4\pi}\int_\sigma gv \, d\sigma = \frac{1}{4\pi}\int_\sigma g(Q)N(P,Q) \, d\sigma. \tag{23-15}$$

When g is given in advance, it can be shown, conversely, that the function (23-15) satisfies (23-8). Hence, if we solve the particular Neumann problems involved in the construction of $N(P,Q)$, we can solve the general Neumann problem for the region.

Physically, the Neumann function represents the heat flow due to a source of strength 4π at P when the heat flows out at a uniform rate across the boundary. This shows that the condition

$$\frac{\partial v}{\partial n} = 0 \qquad \text{on } \sigma \tag{23-16}$$

analogous to (23-3) cannot be required in general; when the region is bounded, (23-16) violates the principle of conservation of heat. For *unbounded* regions (23-16) is possible, as we see by considering the *Neumann function for a half plane*,

$$N(P,Q) = \frac{1}{r} + \frac{1}{r_1}. \tag{23-17}$$

It is left for the reader to verify that (23-17) satisfies (23-16) on the plane $z = 0$ and to solve the Neumann problem.

ELLIPTIC, PARABOLIC, AND HYPERBOLIC EQUATIONS

24. Classification and Uniqueness. If a, b, and c are real continuous functions of x and y, and if H is a continuous function of the indicated arguments, the partial differential equation

$$az_{xx} + 2bz_{xy} + cz_{yy} = H(x,y,z,z_x,z_y) \tag{24-1}$$

[1] See remarks at the end of this section.

includes many equations of mathematical physics. It is convenient to classify equations of the type (24-1) according to the sign of the *discriminant*, $b^2 - ac$. When $b^2 - ac < 0$, the equation is said to be *elliptic;* when $b^2 - ac = 0$, it is *parabolic;* and when $b^2 - ac > 0$, it is *hyperbolic.* This nomenclature is suggested by analogy with the conic

$$ax^2 + 2bxy + cy^2 = H, \qquad a, b, c, H \text{ const,}$$

which is an ellipse, a parabola, or a hyperbola according to the sign of $b^2 - ac$.

As typical illustrations, the reader can verify that

$$u_{xx} + u_{yy} = 0, \qquad u_{xx} = u_y, \qquad u_{xx} - u_{yy} = 0 \qquad (24\text{-}2)$$

are elliptic, parabolic, and hyperbolic equations, respectively. The first of these is Laplace's equation; the second [1] is the equation for heat flow; the third [2] describes the motion of waves on a string. The general equation (24-1) in the elliptic, parabolic, or hyperbolic case has much in common with the corresponding Eq. (24-2), and that is the reason why the classification is important. We shall now discuss the conditions for unique determination of u.

CASE I. *Elliptic Equation.* Physical considerations suggest that a solution of Laplace's equation is wholly determined by its boundary values. That is, if u_1 and u_2 satisfy

$$u_{xx} + u_{yy} = 0 \qquad (24\text{-}3)$$

in a bounded region τ, and if $u_1 = u_2$ on the boundary, then $u_1 = u_2$ in τ. A mathematical proof is readily given, assuming that the function $u = u_1 - u_2$ is continuous in τ and on the boundary.

Without loss of generality, let the region τ lie between the lines $x = 0$ and $x = 1$ (so that $\cos x \neq 0$ in τ). If v is defined by

$$u = v \cos x,$$

a short calculation shows that (24-3) yields

$$v_{xx} + v_{yy} - 2v_x \tan x - v = 0. \qquad (24\text{-}4)$$

Suppose that $v > 0$ at an interior point P_0. Then v assumes a positive maximum at an interior point P_1 (since $v = 0$ on the boundary and v is continuous). At P_1 we have

$$v > 0, \qquad v_x = 0, \qquad v_{xx} \leq 0, \qquad v_{yy} \leq 0,$$

and hence (24-4) cannot hold. This contradiction shows that $v \leq 0$ throughout the region. Similarly, $v \geq 0$, and hence $v \equiv 0$. It follows that $u \equiv 0$, as was to be proved. The same method can be used in three dimensions; the only change is that (24-4)

[1] Let $y = \alpha^2 t$ in (9-5).
[2] Let $y = at$ in (2-4).

has an extra term v_{zz}. A decidedly less elementary proof (which applies also to the Neumann problem) was given in Sec. 21, Prob. 2.

What we have actually shown is that if the harmonic function u satisfies $u \leq 0$ on the boundary, then the same inequality holds at interior points. Considering $u - m$ instead of u yields the following significant result:[1]

MAXIMUM PRINCIPLE. *Let u be harmonic in a bounded region τ and let m be constant. If $u \leq m$ throughout the boundary of τ, then $u \leq m$ throughout τ.*

This theorem is true for the general equation [2] (24-1), provided (24-1) is elliptic and $H \geq 0$.

CASE II. *Parabolic Equation.* Let u be the temperature of a thin rod extending from $x = 0$ to $x = l$. With $y = \alpha^2 t$ the equation of heat conduction is

$$u_{xx} = u_y, \qquad 0 < x < l, \qquad 0 < y < \infty. \qquad (24\text{-}5)$$

As typical initial and boundary conditions, we assume that

$$u(x,0) = f(x), \qquad u(0,y) = g(y), \qquad u(l,y) = h(y). \qquad (24\text{-}6)$$

These conditions give the initial temperature and the temperature of the two ends. In the xy plane, (24-6) specifies the value of u on the boundary of a certain semi-infinite rectangle (Fig. 31). The physical interpretation suggests that u is thereby determined within the rectangle, and we shall now show that this is, in general, the case.

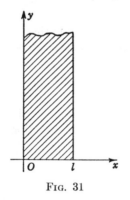

FIG. 31

Let u_1 and u_2 satisfy (24-5) and (24-6). The function

$$u = u_1 - u_2$$

then satisfies (24-5) and (24-6) with $f = g = h = 0$. For simplicity, we shall suppose that u is continuous and bounded in the region of Fig. 31 and on its boundary, though these conditions could be weakened.

If v is defined by $u = ve^y$, substitution in (24-5) yields

$$v_{xx} = v_y + v. \qquad (24\text{-}7)$$

Suppose that $v = v_0 > 0$ at some point P_0 of the rectangle in Fig. 31. We know that $v = 0$ on the three sides of this rectangle, and since u is bounded, the equation $v = e^{-y}u$ shows that $v < v_0$ if y is large enough. It follows that v assumes a positive maximum at some interior point P_1. At P_1,

$$v_y = 0, \qquad v_{xx} \leq 0, \qquad v > 0$$

and hence (24-7) cannot hold. This contradiction shows that $v \leq 0$, everywhere. Similarly, $v \geq 0$, and hence $v \equiv 0$. It follows that $u_1 \equiv u_2$.

[1] Cf. Sec. 21, Prob. 3.

[2] See: H. Bateman, "Partial Differential Equations of Mathematical Physics," p. 135, Cambridge University Press, London, 1932.

The method of proving this *uniqueness theorem* leads, just as in the foregoing discussion, to a MAXIMUM PRINCIPLE: *If $u \leq m$ on the boundary of the rectangle in Fig. 31, then $u \leq m$ throughout the rectangle.* A physical interpretation is readily given.

PROBLEMS

1. For what values of the constant k is $u_{xx} + k u_{xy} + u_{yy} = 0$ elliptic?   Parabolic? Hyperbolic?

2. In what regions of the xy plane is

$$(1 + y)u_{xx} + 2x u_{xy} + (1 - y)u_{yy} = u_x$$

elliptic?   Parabolic?   Hyperbolic?

3. Show that the solution of the elliptic equation

$$u_{xx} + u_{yy} = -ku$$

is not always uniquely determined by the boundary values.   *Hint:* Let the region be the square $0 \leq x \leq \pi, 0 \leq y \leq \pi$, and separate variables.   For a physical interpretation, see Sec. 14.

4. A *characteristic value* for a region τ is a constant λ such that the problem

$$u_{xx} + u_{yy} + u_{zz} + \lambda u = 0 \text{ in } \tau, \qquad u = 0 \text{ on the boundary}$$

has a solution other than the trivial solution $u = 0$.   Show that a characteristic value is always positive.   *Hint:* If $u \not\equiv 0$, then u has a positive maximum or a negative minimum at some interior point P.

5. The semi-infinite strip $0 < x < \pi, y > 0$ has its edges kept at the constant temperature $u = 0$, whereas its end $y = 0$ is kept at the temperature $u = \sin x$.   In the steady state the temperature u satisfies $u_{xx} + u_{yy} = 0$, and also

$$u(0,y) = 0, \qquad u(\pi,y) = 0, \qquad u(x,0) = \sin x.$$

(*a*) By the method of separating variables obtain infinitely many distinct solutions to this problem.   (*b*) Show that only one of these solutions satisfies $\lim_{y \to \infty} u(x,y) = 0$ uniformly in x.   (*c*) If condition (*b*) is imposed, show that the problem has, in fact, only one solution.   *Hint:* Use the maximum principle.

25. Further Discussion of Uniqueness.   Continuing the study of (24-1) we consider the hyperbolic equation

$$u_{xx} - u_{yy} = 0. \tag{25-1}$$

Since solutions of (25-1) do not satisfy the maximum principle, the foregoing methods cannot be used here.

CASE IIIa.   *Hyperbolic Equation, First Problem.*   Let the value and normal derivative of u in (25-1) be given on an interval (a,b) of the x axis (Fig. 32).   Thus,

$$u(x,0) = f(x), \qquad u_y(x,0) = g(x), \qquad a < x < b.$$

If $G(x) = \int_a^x g(s)\, ds$, d'Alembert's formula (3-15) yields an expression

$$2u(x,y) = f(x + y) + G(x + y) + f(x - y) - G(x - y), \tag{25-2}$$

which will now be used to discuss the uniqueness of u.

By hypothesis, $f(x)$ and $G(x)$ are determined for $a < x < b$ but not outside this interval. Hence

$$f(x + y) + G(x + y) \text{ is determined for } a < x + y < b,$$
$$f(x - y) - G(x - y) \text{ is determined for } a < x - y < b,$$

(25-3)

but not elsewhere. In the xy plane, the loci

$$a < x + y < b, \qquad a < x - y < b$$

represent two strips, bounded by the two pairs of lines

$$x + y = a, \qquad x + y = b \qquad \text{and} \qquad x - y = a, \qquad x - y = b \quad (25\text{-}4)$$

(Fig. 32). Both expressions (25-3), and hence u in (25-2), are uniquely determined in the intersection of these strips, but only there. This shows that the region of determinacy is the doubly shaded region in the figure.[1]

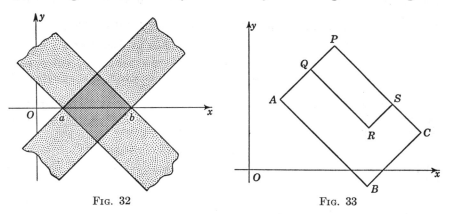

Fig. 32   Fig. 33

Similar behavior is found for the general hyperbolic equation, the role of the lines (25-4) being taken by the *characteristics* introduced in Sec. 29. It is often possible to express u by an integral formula involving the initial value and normal derivative. The method requires construction of the *Riemann function*,[2] which is in some respects analogous to the Green function of Sec. 23.

CASE IIIb. *Hyperbolic Equation, Second Problem.* The equation $u_{xx} = u_{yy}$ has the general solution

$$u(x,y) = f_1(x - y) + f_2(x + y) \tag{25-5}$$

as was shown in Sec. 1. If u is given on two adjacent sides of the rectangle in Fig. 33, we shall use (25-5) to show that u is determined in the whole rectangle.[3]

---

[1] Cf. Theorem I, Sec. 4.

[2] See A. G. Webster, "Partial Differential Equations of Mathematical Physics," p. 248, Teubner Verlagsgesellschaft, Leipzig, 1927.

[3] Cf. Theorem II, Sec. 4.

Choose a point R in the rectangle, and draw RQ and RS parallel to the sides of the rectangle, as in the figure. With P the apex of the rectangle, $x - y$ is constant on PQ and $x - y$ is also constant on SR. Hence the same is true of $f_1(x - y)$:

$$f_1(x - y) = \alpha \text{ at } P \text{ and } Q, \qquad f_1(x - y) = \beta \text{ at } R \text{ and } S.$$

Similarly,

$$f_2(x + y) = \gamma \text{ at } P \text{ and } S, \qquad f_2(x + y) = \delta \text{ at } Q \text{ and } R.$$

By using these values in (25-5) we can verify the identity

$$u(R) = u(Q) + u(S) - u(P). \tag{25-6}$$

This shows that u is determined by the data at every point in the rectangle and at no point outside the rectangle.

By a procedure known as *Picard's method*, the problem just discussed can often be solved for the general hyperbolic equation (24-1). It is supposed that the equation has the form [1]

$$u_{xy} = H(x,y,u,u_x,u_y) \tag{25-7}$$

and for simplicity we assume the homogeneous boundary conditions

$$u(x,0) = 0, \qquad u(0,y) = 0, \qquad 0 \le x \le a, 0 \le y \le b. \tag{25-8}$$

Thus, $u = 0$ on two adjacent sides of the rectangle in Fig. 34. The conditions (25-8) enable us to write (25-7) in the form

$$u(x,y) = \int_0^x \int_0^y H(x_1,y_1,u,u_x,u_y) \, dx_1 \, dy_1$$

where the arguments of u, u_x, and u_y in the integral are x_1 and y_1.

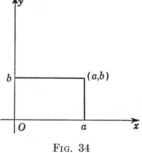

FIG. 34

Picard's method consists of choosing a first approximation $u^{(0)}$, evaluating the integral, and using the result as the second approximation $u^{(1)}$. A similar process yields $u^{(2)}$, and so on. If $u^{(n)}$ is the nth approximation, the next approximation is

$$u^{(n+1)}(x,y) = \int_0^x \int_0^y H(x_1,y_1,u^{(n)},u_x^{(n)},u_y^{(n)}) \, dx_1 \, dy_1. \tag{25-9}$$

Subject to mild restrictions on H it can be shown [2] that the solution is

[1] See Sec. 29, Case III.

[2] R. Courant and D. Hilbert, "Methoden der mathematischen Physik," vol. II, p. 317, I. Springer-Verlag OHG, Berlin, 1937.

given by

$$u(x,y) = \lim_{n \to \infty} u^{(n)}(x,y).$$

As an illustration, let the equation be

$$u_{xy} = 1 + u.$$

By (25-9),

$$u^{(n+1)} = \int_0^x \int_0^y [1 + u^{(n)}] \, dx_1 \, dy_1 = xy + \int_0^x \int_0^y u^{(n)} \, dx_1 \, dy_1.$$

Starting with $u^{(0)} = 0$, we get $u^{(1)} = xy$, $u^{(2)} = xy + (xy)^2/4$,

$$u^{(3)} = xy + \int_0^x \int_0^y \left[x_1 y_1 + \frac{(x_1 y_1)^2}{4} \right] dx_1 \, dy_1 = xy + \frac{(xy)^2}{(2!)^2} + \frac{(xy)^3}{(3!)^2}$$

and so on. Evidently, the process gives

$$u(x,y) = \sum_{n=1}^{\infty} \frac{(xy)^n}{(n!)^2}.$$

That this is a solution can be verified by actual substitution.

26. The Associated Difference Equations. Let h be a positive number and $u = u(x,y)$ a function of x and y. The *difference operators* Δ_x and Δ_y are defined by

$$\Delta_x u = \frac{u(x + h, y) - u(x,y)}{h}, \qquad \Delta_y u = \frac{u(x, y + h) - u(x,y)}{h}. \qquad (26\text{-}1)$$

Passing to the limit as $h \to 0$, we get the partial derivatives; that is,

$$\lim_{h \to 0} \Delta_x u = u_x, \qquad \lim_{h \to 0} \Delta_y u = u_y \qquad (26\text{-}2)$$

when the limits exist. If the *second differences* are defined by

$$\Delta_{xx} u = \frac{u(x + h, y) - 2u(x,y) + u(x - h, y)}{h^2}$$

$$\Delta_{yy} u = \frac{u(x, y + h) - 2u(x,y) + u(x, y - h)}{h^2} \qquad (26\text{-}3)$$

it can be shown, in general, that

$$\lim_{h \to 0} \Delta_{xx} u = u_{xx}, \qquad \lim_{h \to 0} \Delta_{yy} u = u_{yy}$$

(see Prob. 1).   Hence the three *difference equations*

$$\Delta_{xx} u - \Delta_{yy} u = 0, \qquad \Delta_{xx} u = \Delta_y u, \qquad \Delta_{xx} u + \Delta_{yy} u = 0$$

as $h \to 0$ become the respective differential equations

$$u_{xx} - u_{yy} = 0, \qquad u_{xx} = u_y, \qquad u_{xx} + u_{yy} = 0.$$

The correspondence of difference equations and differential equations is important because there are numerical methods of solving the former which are especially adapted to high-speed computers (cf. Chap. 9, Sec. 19). As $h \to 0$, the solution of the difference equation generally tends to the solution of the corresponding differential equation. This fact gives a means of numerical approximation which has been extensively exploited. Because of space limitations we shall consider merely the determinacy of the solutions, our objective being to clarify further the distinction among elliptic, parabolic, and hyperbolic equations.

CASE I. *Elliptic Equation.* Using (26-3) the reader can verify that

$$\Delta_{xx}u + \Delta_{yy}u = 0 \tag{26-4}$$

can be written in the form

$$u(x,y) = \tfrac{1}{4}[u(x + h, y) + u(x - h, y) + u(x, y + h) + u(x, y - h)]. \tag{26-5}$$

This equation gives a relation between the five values of u at the five neighboring lattice points [1] illustrated in Fig. 35; in fact, *the value at the*

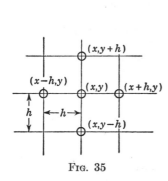

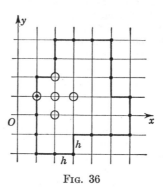

FIG. 35   FIG. 36

central lattice point is the arithmetic mean of the values at the four neighbors. The corresponding property for Laplace's equation is the average-value theorem given in the example of Sec. 21.

To state the Dirichlet problem for the difference equation (26-4) we say that a point is *interior* to a region if its four neighbors are points of the region. A *boundary point* is a point for which at least one neighbor belongs to the region and at least one does not. For instance the points • in Fig. 36 are boundary points. In the *Dirichlet problem* a function u satisfying (26-4) is given at every boundary point, and it is required to find u at the interior points. We shall now establish both the existence and the uniqueness of the solution.[2]

Suppose, then, that u is known at every lattice point bounding a given region (Fig. 36). If we write down the equation (26-5) for each interior

---

[1] That is, points of the form (mh,nh) with integers m and n.

[2] The region is assumed bounded, so that the number of interior points is a *finite* number n.

point (x,y), we obtain a system of n linear equations in n unknowns. It will be seen presently that the determinant of this system is not zero, and hence there is one, and only one, solution. On the other hand, if the values are not prescribed at *every* boundary point, there are always more unknowns than equations, and the solution is not determined uniquely. These properties are analogous to those obtained previously for the Laplace equation.

To show that the determinant is not zero, we shall analyze the special case in which the boundary values are zero. In this case the system of linear equations obtained by writing (26-4) at each interior point is homogeneous. *If the determinant is zero*, the system will have a solution other than the trivial solution $u \equiv 0$. Without loss of generality we can suppose that this nontrivial solution u is positive at some point.

Let the maximum value of u over all the lattice points be denoted by $m > 0$, and let P be a point where $u = m$. Evidently P cannot be on the boundary, since $u > 0$ at P. Hence, P is interior, and the value of u at P is the average of the values at the four neighbors. Now $u \leq m$ at these neighbors, since m is the maximum. If $u < m$ at any neighbor, then the average is $<m$, so that $u(P) < m$. This contradiction shows that $u = m$ at the four neighbors of P.

We can now repeat the process, starting with one of these four neighbors instead of P. Proceeding in this way we find that $u = m$ at every lattice point. But that is impossible, since $u = 0 \neq m$ on the boundary. Hence the assumption that the determinant was zero led to a contradiction.

PROBLEMS

1. (*a*) Show that $\Delta_{xx}u(x,y) = \Delta_x[\Delta_x u(x - h,\ y)]$. (*b*) If u has a Taylor series expansion about the point (x,y), show that $\Delta_{xx}u \to u_{xx}$ as $h \to 0$. *Hint:* Use the first six terms of $u(x + h,\ y + k) = a + bh + ck + \cdots$.

2. Suppose $\Delta_{xx}u + \Delta_{yy}u = 0$, and suppose u is known for $x = 0$ and for $x = h$ $(y = h, 2h, 3h, \ldots)$. In what region of the xy plane is u determined? *Hint:* See Fig. 35.

3. Let $\Delta_{xx}u + \Delta_{yy}u = 0$, and suppose $u(0,y) = 1$ for all y, $u(2h,y) = 2$ for all y, $u(h,0) = u(h,4h) = 0$. Find $u(h,2h)$.

27. Further Discussion of Difference Equations.

According to the foregoing discussion, the elliptic case leads to a set of simultaneous equations for determination of the unknown function u. In the parabolic and hyperbolic cases, as we shall now see, the values of u can be obtained successively.

CASE II. *Parabolic Equation.* By (26-1) and (26-3) the equation

$$\Delta_{xx}u = \Delta_y u \tag{27-1}$$

takes the form

$$u(x + h,\ y) - (2 - h)\ u(x,y) + u(x - h,\ y) = hu(x,\ y + h). \tag{27-2}$$

This shows that if u is known at the three collinear points in Fig. 37, then u can be found at the fourth point.

By analogy with the problem of heat flow discussed in Sec. 24, let u be given at the points • on the boundary of the semi-infinite rectangle in Fig. 38. Referring to Fig. 37, we see that u can be found at the lattice points with $y = h$ in the rectangle. Repetition gives u for $y = 2h$, and so on. Thus, u is determined throughout the rectangle, just as in the case of Fig. 31. The process works equally well when the rod is infinite and u is given at all the lattice points on the x axis.

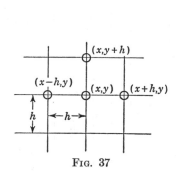

FIG. 37

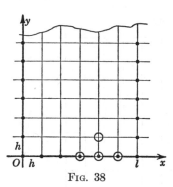

FIG. 38

Because the pattern of Fig. 37 points upward, so to speak, it is impossible to proceed in the *negative y* direction when the rod is infinite. The very first step leads to a system of infinitely many equations in infinitely many unknowns. Inasmuch as $y = \alpha^2 t$, where t is time, this fact expresses the irreversibility of thermodynamic processes.

Further insight into the one-directional character of t is given by (9-10) and (18-4). In general, these expressions are infinitely differentiable for $t > 0$ but divergent for $t < 0$. This behavior of the heat equation contrasts to that of the wave equation. As we have repeatedly observed and will see again in the sequel, the latter is meaningful for negative t.

CASE IIIa. *Hyperbolic Equation, First Problem.* Writing the equation

$$\Delta_{xx}u - \Delta_{yy}u = 0 \tag{27-3}$$

in the form

$$u(x + h, y) + u(x - h, y) - u(x, y + h) - u(x, y - h) = 0 \quad (27\text{-}4)$$

we see that the corresponding pattern is that shown in Fig. 39. If u is given at any three of the four lattice points, then (27-4) gives u at the fourth point. Inasmuch as the pattern is symmetric, one can proceed in the positive y direction and in the negative y direction with equal ease.

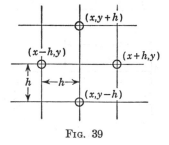

FIG. 39

To discuss the analogue of the initial-value problem (Sec. 25, Case IIIa), let u and $\Delta_y u$ be given in an interval of lattice points on the x axis. This is equivalent to specifying u itself on two adjacent rows of lattice points, as indicated by the black dots in Fig. 40. Considering Fig. 39 in conjunction with Fig. 40, we see that the region of determination for u consists of the lattice points in the square. The analogy with Fig. 32 is evident.

CASE III*b*. *Hyperbolic Equation, Second Problem.* If u is given on two adjacent sides of a rectangle as shown in Fig. 41, we can apply Fig. 39,

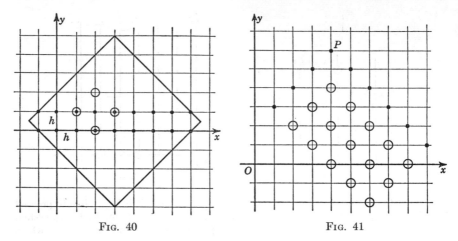

FIG. 40   FIG. 41

starting at P. It will be found that u is determined at the indicated points O, and at no others. This behavior corresponds to that found in Sec. 25, Case III*b*.

PROBLEMS

1. In Fig. 38 let $u = 0$ on the vertical rows of points •, and $u = 1$ on the horizontal row •, for $0 < x < l$. Assuming $h = 1$ in (27-2) find $u(h,6h)$.

2. In Fig. 40 let $u = 1,0,0,2,0,0,3,0,0$ on the bottom row of points • (in order), and let $\Delta_y u = 0$ at these points. Find $u(3h,5h)$.

3. Let $u(P) = 0$ in Fig. 41. Find the value of u at the opposite corner if $u = 0$ at the points • on the left of P, and $u = 2$ at the points • on the right of P.

28. An Example: Flow of Electricity in a Cable.

Many physical problems lead to an equation that changes type, according to the values of the physical parameters. Since the character of the solutions undergoes a corresponding change, this phenomenon has great practical importance. As an illustration we shall consider the flow of electricity in linear conductors (such as telephone wires or submarine cables) in which the current may leak to ground.

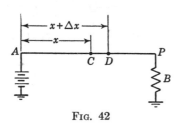

FIG. 42

Let a long, imperfectly insulated cable (Fig. 42) carry an electric current whose source is at A. The current is assumed to flow to the receiving end at P through the load B and to return through the ground. It is assumed that the leaks occur along the entire length of the cable because of imperfections in the insulating sheath. Let the distance, measured along the length of the cable, be denoted by x; then the emf V (volts) and the current I (amperes) are functions of x and t. The resistance of the cable will be denoted by R (ohms per mile), and the conductance from sheath to ground by G (mhos per mile). It is known that the cable acts as an electrostatic condenser, and the capacitance of the cable to ground per unit length is assumed to be C (farads per mile); the inductance per mile will be denoted by L (henrys per mile).

Consider an element CD of the cable of length Δx. If the emf is V at C and $V + \Delta V$ at D, then the change in voltage across the element Δx is produced by the resistance and the inductance drops, so that one can write

$$\Delta V \doteq - \left(IR\, \Delta x + \frac{\partial I}{\partial t} L\, \Delta x \right).$$

The negative sign signifies that the voltage is a decreasing function of x. Dividing through by Δx and passing to the limit as $\Delta x \to 0$ give the equation for the voltage:

$$\frac{\partial V}{\partial x} = -IR - L\frac{\partial I}{\partial t}. \tag{28-1}$$

The decrease in current, on the other hand, is due to the leakage and the action of the cable as a condenser. Hence, the drop in current ΔI across the element Δx of the cable is

$$\Delta I \doteq -VG\, \Delta x - \frac{\partial V}{\partial t} C\, \Delta x,$$

so that

$$\frac{\partial I}{\partial x} = -VG - C\frac{\partial V}{\partial t}. \tag{28-2}$$

Equations (28-1) and (28-2) are simultaneous partial differential equations for the voltage and current. The voltage V can be eliminated from these equations by differentiating (28-2) with respect to x to obtain

$$I_{xx} = -V_x G - CV_{tx}.$$

Substituting for V_x from (28-1) gives

$$I_{xx} = IRG + LGI_t - CV_{tx}$$

from which V_{tx} can be eliminated by using the expression for V_{xt} obtained by differentiating (28-1). Thus one is led to

$$I_{xx} - LCI_{tt} = (LG + RC)I_t + IRG. \tag{28-3}$$

A similar calculation shows that (28-3) is also satisfied by the voltage V. Evidently, (28-3) is hyperbolic when $LC \neq 0$ but parabolic when $LC = 0$.

When the cable is lossless, $R = G = 0$. Equation (28-3) and the corresponding equation for V are, then,

$$I_{xx} = LCI_{tt}, \qquad V_{xx} = LCV_{tt}. \tag{28-4}$$

Comparing the equation for wave motion (Sec. 1), we see that the cable propagates electromagnetic waves with velocity

$$a = (LC)^{-1/2}.$$

The hyperbolic equation (28-4) is appropriate if the frequency is high and the loss is low.

For an audio-frequency submarine cable it is more appropriate to take $G = L = 0$. The equations are then parabolic:

$$I_{xx} = RCI_t, \qquad V_{xx} = RCV_t. \tag{28-5}$$

Instead of representing waves, the propagation of V and I is now identical with the flow of heat in rods. Comparing with (9-5) gives

$$\alpha = (RC)^{-1/2}.$$

Example: Consider a submarine cable l miles in length, and let the voltage at the source A, under steady-state conditions, be 12 volts and at the receiving end R be 6 volts. At a certain instant $t = 0$, the receiving end is grounded, so that its potential is reduced to zero, but the potential at the source is maintained at its constant value of 12 volts. Determine the current and voltage in the line subsequent to the grounding of the receiving end.

It is required to find V in (28-5) subject to the boundary conditions

$$V(0,t) = 12, \qquad V(l,t) = 0, \qquad t \geq 0. \tag{28-6}$$

The initial condition is

$$V(x,0) = 12 - 6\frac{x}{l} \tag{28-7}$$

since the steady-state solution of (28-5) is a linear function of x (Sec. 9, Example 1).

The voltage $V(x,t)$ subsequent to the grounding can be thought of as being made up of a steady-state [1] voltage $V_S(x)$ and a transient voltage $V_T(x,t)$ which decreases rapidly with time. Thus,

$$V(x,t) = V_S(x) + V_T(x,t). \tag{28-8}$$

Since $V_S(x)$ is linear, its value is given by the boundary conditions as

$$V_S(x) = 12 - 12\frac{x}{l}. \tag{28-9}$$

Equations (28-6) and (28-7) now yield

$$V_T(0,t) = V_T(l,t) = 0, \qquad V_T(x,0) = \frac{6x}{l}.$$

[1] Compare Sec. 9, Example 2.

Since V_T satisfies (28-5), we can use the solution of the heat equation (9-10) with $\alpha^2 = 1/RC$. The result is

$$V_T(x,t) = \sum_{n=1}^{\infty} \left(\frac{2}{l} \int_0^l \frac{6}{l} x_1 \sin \frac{n\pi x_1}{l} \, dx_1 \right) e^{-(1/RC)(n\pi/l)^2 t} \sin \frac{n\pi x}{l}.$$

The function V is now given by (28-8).

PROBLEMS

1. By using (28-1) with $L = 0$, find I in the Example.

2. Find the emf in the cable whose length is 100 miles and whose characteristics are as follows: $R = 0.3$ ohm per mile, $C = 0.08$ μf per mile, $L = 0$, $G = 0$. If the voltage at the source is 6 volts and at the terminal end 2 volts, what is the voltage after the terminal end has been suddenly grounded? [Use (28-5).]

3. Using (28-5), find the current in a cable 1,000 miles long, whose potential at the source, under steady-state conditions, is 1,200 volts and at the terminal end is 1,100 volts. What is the current in the cable after the terminal end has been suddenly grounded? Use $R = 2$ ohms per mile and $C = 3 \cdot 10^{-7}$ farad per mile.

29. Characteristics and Canonical Form.

If a, b, c are continuous functions of x and y, with $a \neq 0$, then the partial differential equation

$$au_{xx} + 2bu_{xy} + cu_{yy} = H(x,y,u,u_x,u_y) \tag{29-1}$$

can be simplified by use of the equation

$$a \, dy^2 - 2b \, dy \, dx + c \, dx^2 = 0. \tag{29-2}$$

Setting $dy = p \, dx$ in (29-2) and solving the resulting quadratic give

$$p = a^{-1}[b + (b^2 - ac)^{1/2}] \quad \text{or} \quad p = a^{-1}[b - (b^2 - ac)^{1/2}]. \tag{29-3}$$

Since $p = dy/dx$, Eqs. (29-3) are ordinary differential equations of the first order, and hence the solutions may be expected to contain an arbitrary constant c. If the solutions are written in the form

$$X(x,y) = c \quad \text{or} \quad Y(x,y) = c, \tag{29-4}$$

the resulting curves (29-4) are called the *characteristics* of (29-1).

For example, when (29-1) is the wave equation

$$a^2 u_{xx} - u_{tt} = 0 \tag{29-5}$$

the differential equation (29-2) is

$$a^2 \, dt^2 - dx^2 = 0.$$

Since this reduces to $dx/dt = \pm a$, the characteristics are the straight lines

$$x - at = c, \qquad x + at = c.$$

It was shown in Sec. 1 that the change of variable

$$r = x - at, \qquad s = x + at, \qquad u(x,t) = U(r,s)$$

reduces (29-5) to the form $U_{rs} = 0$, and a physical interpretation of the characteristics was given in Sec. 4.

Equation (29-1) is said to be in *canonical form* if it has one of the three forms

$$u_{xx} + u_{yy} = H, \qquad u_{xx} = H, \qquad u_{xy} = H$$

where H is a function of x, y, u, u_x, and u_y. It is a basic fact that *the reduction to canonical form can be achieved by means of the characteristics,* and we shall now describe [1] the procedure.

CASE I.   *Elliptic Equation.*   When $b^2 - ac < 0$, the two values of p in (29-3) are conjugate complex, and hence the same is true of X and Y in (29-4). That is,

$$X = r(x,y) + is(x,y), \qquad Y = r(x,y) - is(x,y)$$

where r and s are real. In this case the reduction can be achieved by choosing r and s as new independent variables. If $u(x,y) = U(r,s)$, Eq. (29-1) gives an equation for U in which the second derivatives occur as $U_{rr} + U_{ss}$.

CASE II.   *Parabolic Equation.*   When $b^2 - ac = 0$ the two values of p in (29-3) are real and equal. Hence the same is true of X and Y in (29-4). In this case the reduction can be achieved by the change of variable

$$r = X(x,y), \qquad s = \text{any function independent of } X.$$

The second derivatives of U now occur as U_{ss}.

CASE III.   *Hyperbolic Equation.*   When $b^2 - ac > 0$, the roots (29-3) are real and unequal, and the same is true of X and Y. The reduction is achieved by taking

$$r = X(x,y), \qquad s = Y(x,y)$$

as new independent variables. The second derivatives of U occur only as U_{rs}.

To illustrate the procedure we shall consider the equation

$$u_{xx} - kxu_{xy} + 4x^2u_{yy} = 0 \tag{29-6}$$

when $k = 0$, 4, or 5. According to (29-3),

$$p = -\tfrac{1}{2}kx \pm (\tfrac{1}{4}k^2x^2 - 4x^2)^{\frac{1}{2}}. \tag{29-7}$$

When $k = 0$, this gives $p = \pm 2ix$. The equations $y' = \pm 2ix$ have the solutions

$$y - ix^2 = c, \qquad y + ix^2 = c$$

---

[1] A proof may be found in A. G. Webster, "Partial Differential Equations of Mathematical Physics," p. 242, Teubner Verlagsgesellschaft, Leipzig, 1927.

where c is constant. Taking real and imaginary parts,

$$r = y, \qquad s = x^2.$$

With $u(x,y) = U(r,s)$, the derivatives are

$$u_{xx} = 4x^2 U_{ss} + 2U_s, \qquad u_{xy} = 2xU_{sr}, \qquad u_{yy} = U_{rr}$$

and substitution into (29-6) with $k = 0$ gives the canonical form

$$U_{rr} + U_{ss} = -(2x^2)^{-1}U_s = -(2s)^{-1}U_s.$$

When $k = 4$, the two roots (29-7) are both $p = -2x$. Solving this differential equation we see that (29-4) is

$$y + x^2 = c, \qquad y + x^2 = c.$$

Since $y + x^2$ and y are independent, we can take

$$r = y + x^2, \qquad s = y.$$

It is left for the reader to show that the canonical form is

$$U_{ss} = -(2x^2)^{-1}U_r = -(2r - 2s)^{-1}U_r. \tag{29-8}$$

Finally, the case $k = 5$ leads to two distinct real roots $p = -x$, $p = -4x$. Setting $p = dy/dx$ and solving,

$$y + \tfrac{1}{2}x^2 = c, \qquad y + 2x^2 = c.$$

The change of variable

$$r = y + \tfrac{1}{2}x^2, \qquad s = y + 2x^2$$

now leads to the canonical form

$$U_{rs} = (6s - 6r)^{-1}(U_r + 4U_s). \tag{29-9}$$

PROBLEMS

1. Derive (29-8) and (29-9).

2. Describe the behavior of the characteristics of (28-3) as LC varies from zero to infinity.

3. Reduce to canonical form

$$3u_{xy} = u_{xx} + 2u_{yy}, \qquad 2u_{xy} = u_{xx} + u_{yy}, \qquad 2u_{xy} = u_{xx} + 2u_{yy}.$$

30. Characteristics and Discontinuities. The function $u = f(x - at)$ represents a wave propagating in the positive x direction with velocity a. If $f(x)$ has the form shown [1] in Fig. 43, the motion exhibits a *wave front* (Fig. 44), whose locus can be found by setting the argument of f equal to c:

$$x - at = c.$$

In the xt plane, we recognize that this equation describes a characteristic of the wave equation (29-5).

[1] The intent is $f(x) = 0$ for $x > c$, $f'(c) = 0$, $f''(c+) - f''(c-) \neq 0$.

Discontinuities of the type just considered arise in many investigations, ranging from the theory of the cracking of glass to the theory of super-sonic flight. The locus of the discontinuity is always a characteristic, as we shall presently see, and hence, the foregoing example is typical of the general case.

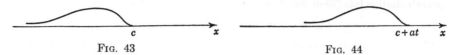

FIG. 43   FIG. 44

Since the locus is a characteristic, a discontinuity of the type in question may arise on two families of curves for hyperbolic equations, it may arise on one family for parabolic equations, and it cannot arise for elliptic equations. For example, the equations of fluid flow are elliptic at velocities less than the velocity of sound in the fluid. But at velocities exceeding the velocity of sound the equations become hyperbolic, and the fact that a discontinuity is now possible permits the formation of a *shock wave*.

To discuss these questions mathematically, consider a solution surface $u = u(x,y)$ satisfying (29-1). We suppose that u is continuous and has continuous first derivatives but has a discontinuity in one of the second derivatives on a certain curve C. This single solution is to be regarded as two solutions $u_1(x,y)$, $u_2(x,y)$ which are tangent along the curve C but do not have equal second derivatives along C. We let the surfaces defined by u_1 and u_2 extend past C, so that their first derivatives are well defined on C.

The symbol ( ) denotes the *jump* of the function in the parentheses; that is,

$$(u) = u_1 - u_2 \qquad \text{evaluated on } C. \qquad (30\text{-}1)$$

Differentiating (30-1) with respect to x gives

$$(u_x) = u_{1x} - u_{2x} = (u)_x \qquad (30\text{-}2)$$

and similarly for other derivatives. Our hypothesis is that

$$(u) = (u_x) = (u_y) = 0 \qquad (30\text{-}3)$$

but that one of the quantities (u_{xx}), (u_{xy}), or (u_{yy}) is not zero.

Differentiating the relation $(u_x) = 0$ with respect to x by the chain rule yields

$$(u_{xx}) + (u_{xy})y' = 0 \qquad (30\text{-}4)$$

when we recall that y is a function of x on C and take due account of (30-2). Similarly, differentiating $(u_y) = 0$ with respect to x yields

$$(u_{yx}) + (u_{yy})y' = 0. \qquad (30\text{-}5)$$

Taking the ( ) of the partial differential equation (29-1), we get

$$a(u_{xx}) + 2b(u_{xy}) + c(u_{yy}) = (H) = 0 \qquad (30\text{-}6)$$

when H is continuous.   The fact that $(H) = 0$ follows from (30-3) if we recall that H does not involve the higher derivatives of u.

Equations (30-4), (30-5), and (30-6) are three linear homogeneous equations in the three unknowns (u_{xx}), $(u_{xy}) = (u_{yx})$, and (u_{yy}).   By hypothesis not all these unknowns are zero, and hence, the coefficient determinant must vanish:

$$\begin{vmatrix} 1 & y' & 0 \\ 0 & 1 & y' \\ a & 2b & c \end{vmatrix} = 0. \qquad (30\text{-}7)$$

Expansion of this determinant yields the characteristic equation (29-2), so that C must be a characteristic curve.   Conversely, if C is a characteristic, the determinant (30-7) is zero, the related homogeneous equations have a nontrivial solution, and a discontinuity is possible.

Example: Fundamental Solutions.   A *fundamental solution* of a partial differential equation is a solution of the form $f[\lambda(x,y)]$, when λ is a *fixed* function and f an *arbitrary* function.   For example, the equation $u_{xx} = u_{yy}$ has the fundamental solutions

$$f_1(x - y) \qquad \text{and} \qquad f_2(x + y) \qquad (30\text{-}8)$$

in which $\lambda = x - y$ and $\lambda = x + y$, respectively.   We shall now see that *if* (29-1) *has the fundamental solution* $f[\lambda(x,y)]$, *then the curves*

$$\lambda(x,y) = c, \qquad c \text{ const} \qquad (30\text{-}9)$$

are characteristics.   For proof, it suffices to choose the arbitrary function f so that $f''(x)$ is continuous except at $x = c$.   Then the function $u = f[\lambda(x,y)]$ has a discontinuity of the type previously considered on the locus $\lambda(x,y) = c$, and the desired result follows.

This explains why the techniques used in Secs. 1 to 6 to study the wave equation are not applicable to Laplace's equation.   Namely, d'Alembert's method is based on the fundamental solutions (30-8) and the Laplace equation, being elliptic, has no such solutions.

CHAPTER 7

COMPLEX VARIABLE

Analytic Aspects

Geometric Aspects

Applications

This chapter contains a concise presentation of the rudiments of complex-variable theory with an indication of its many uses in the solution of important problems of physics and engineering. This theory, with roots in potential theory and hydrodynamics, is among the most fertile and beautiful of mathematical creations. Its unfolding left a deep imprint on the whole of mathematics and on several branches of mathematical physics. To an applied mathematician this theory is a veritable mine of effective tools for the solution of important problems in heat conduction, elasticity, hydrodynamics, and the flow of electric currents.

ANALYTIC ASPECTS

1. Complex Numbers. The analysis in the preceding chapters was concerned principally with functions of real variables, that is, such variables as can be represented graphically by points on a number axis, say the x axis of the cartesian coordinate system. The reader is familiar with the fact that calculation of the zeros of the function $f(x) = ax^2 + bx + c$, when the discriminant $b^2 - 4ac$ is negative, necessitates the introduction of complex numbers of the form $u + iv$, where u and v are real numbers and i is a number such that $i^2 = -1$.

A number of the form $u + iv$ can be represented by a point in a plane referred to a pair of orthogonal x and y axes if it is agreed that the number u represents the abscissa and v the ordinate of the point (Fig. 1). No confusion is likely to arise if the point (u,v), associated with the number $u + iv$, is labeled simply $u + iv$. It is clear that the point (u,v) can be located by the terminus of a vector z whose origin is at the origin O of the coordinate system. In this manner a one-to-one correspondence is established between the totality of vectors in the xy plane and the complex numbers.

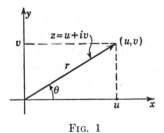

Fɪɢ. 1

527

The vector z may be thought to represent the resultant of two vectors, one of which is of magnitude u and directed along the x axis and the other of magnitude v and directed along the y axis. Thus,

$$z = u + iv,$$

where u is spoken of as the real part of the complex number z and v as the imaginary part. Therefore, if the points of the plane are referred to a pair of coordinate axes, one can establish a correspondence between the pair of real numbers (u,v) and a single complex number $u + iv$. In this case the xy plane is called the plane of a complex variable, the x axis is called the *real axis*, and the y axis is called the *imaginary axis*.

If v vanishes, then

$$z = u + 0 \cdot i = u$$

is a number corresponding to some point on the real axis. Accordingly, this mode of representation of complex numbers (due to Gauss and Argand) includes as a special case the usual way of representing real numbers on the number axis.

The equality of two complex numbers,

$$a + ib = c + id,$$

is interpreted to be equivalent to the two equations

$$a = c \quad \text{and} \quad b = d.$$

In particular, $a + ib = 0$ is true if, and only if, $a = 0$ and $b = 0$.

If the polar coordinates of the point (u,v) (Fig. 1) are (r,θ), then

$$u = r \cos \theta \quad \text{and} \quad v = r \sin \theta$$

so that

$$r = \sqrt{u^2 + v^2} \quad \text{and} \quad \theta = \tan^{-1} \frac{v}{u}.$$

The number r is called the *modulus*, or *absolute value*, and θ is called the *argument*, or *phase angle*, of the complex number $z = u + iv$. It is clear that the argument of a complex number is not unique, and if one writes it as $\theta + 2k\pi$, where $0 \le \theta < 2\pi$ and $k = 0, \pm 1, \pm 2, \ldots$, then θ is called the *principal argument* of z. The modulus of the complex number z is frequently denoted by using absolute-value signs, so that

$$r = |z| = |u + iv| = \sqrt{u^2 + v^2},$$

and the argument θ is denoted by the symbol

$$\theta = \arg z.$$

The student is assumed to be familiar with the fundamental algebraic operations on complex numbers, and these will not be entered upon in detail here. It should be recalled that (cf. Chap. 2, Sec. 15)

$$z_1 + z_2 = (x_1 + iy_1) + (x_2 + iy_2) = (x_1 + x_2) + i(y_1 + y_2),$$

$$z_1 \cdot z_2 = (x_1 + iy_1)(x_2 + iy_2) = (x_1x_2 - y_1y_2) + i(x_1y_2 + x_2y_1),$$

$$\frac{z_1}{z_2} = \frac{x_1 + iy_1}{x_2 + iy_2} = \frac{x_1x_2 + y_1y_2}{x_2^2 + y_2^2} + i\,\frac{x_2y_1 - x_1y_2}{x_2^2 + y_2^2},$$

provided that $|z_2| = \sqrt{x_2^2 + y_2^2} \neq 0$.

On representing complex numbers z_1 and z_2 by vectors, we can see at once from Fig. 2 that they obey the familiar "parallelogram law of addition" formulated in Chap. 4.

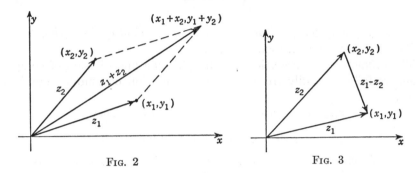

FIG. 2   FIG. 3

From elementary geometric considerations we deduce that

$$|z_1 + z_2| \leq |z_1| + |z_2|; \tag{1-1}$$

that is, *the modulus of the sum of two complex numbers is less than or equal to the sum of the moduli.* This follows at once from Fig. 2 on recalling that the sum of two sides of a triangle is not less than the third side.

Also,

$$|z_1 + z_2| \geq |z_1| - |z_2|; \tag{1-2}$$

that is, *the modulus of the sum is greater than or equal to the difference of the moduli.* This follows from the fact that the length of one side of a triangle is not less than the difference of two other sides.

Equations (1-1) and (1-2) yield a useful inequality,

$$|z_1| - |z_2| \leq |z_1 - z_2| \leq |z_1| + |z_2|, \tag{1-3}$$

indicated in Fig. 3.

When calculations are carried out with complex numbers, the notion of the *conjugate complex number* is useful. We define the conjugate $\bar{z}$ of the number $z = x + iy$ by the formula

$$\bar{z} = x - iy.$$

The application of the rules for addition, multiplication, and division of complex numbers yields the following theorems:

(a)
$$\overline{z_1 + z_2} = \bar{z}_1 + \bar{z}_2,$$
(1-4)

or, in words, *the conjugate of the sum of two complex numbers is equal to the sum of the conjugates;*

(b)
$$\overline{z_1 z_2} = \bar{z}_1 \bar{z}_2,$$
(1-5)

that is, *the conjugate of the product is equal to the product of the conjugates;*

(c)
$$\overline{\left(\frac{z_1}{z_2}\right)} = \frac{\bar{z}_1}{\bar{z}_2},$$
(1-6)

or *the conjugate of the quotient is equal to the quotient of the conjugates.*

We note that if $\bar{z} = z$, then z is real.

The geometric interpretation of multiplication and division of complex numbers follows readily from polar representation of complex numbers. Thus,

$$z_1 z_2 = r_1(\cos\theta_1 + i\sin\theta_1)r_2(\cos\theta_2 + i\sin\theta_2)$$
$$= r_1 r_2[\cos(\theta_1 + \theta_2) + i\sin(\theta_1 + \theta_2)].$$
(1-7)

That is, *the modulus of the product is equal to the product of the moduli and the argument of the product is equal to the sum of the arguments.*

Also,

$$\frac{z_1}{z_2} = \frac{r_1(\cos\theta_1 + i\sin\theta_1)}{r_2(\cos\theta_2 + i\sin\theta_2)} = \frac{r_1}{r_2}[\cos(\theta_1 - \theta_2) + i\sin(\theta_1 - \theta_2)],$$
(1-8)

as follows on multiplying the numerator and denominator in (1-8) by $\cos\theta_2 - i\sin\theta_2$. Thus, *the modulus of the quotient is the quotient of the moduli and the argument of the quotient is obtained by subtracting the argument of the denominator from that of the numerator.*

On extending formula (1-7) to the product of n complex numbers

$$z_k = r_k(\cos\theta_k + i\sin\theta_k), \qquad k = 1, 2, \ldots, n,$$

we get

$$z_1 z_2 \ldots z_n = r_1 r_2 \ldots r_n[\cos(\theta_1 + \theta_2 + \cdots + \theta_n) + i\sin(\theta_1 + \theta_2 + \cdots + \theta_n)]$$

and, in particular, if all zs are equal,

$$z^n = [r(\cos\theta + i\sin\theta)]^n = r^n(\cos n\theta + i\sin n\theta).$$
(1-9)

Formula (1-9) is known as the *de Moivre formula*, and we have shown that it is valid for any positive integer n. We can show that it is also valid for negative and fractional values of n.

Indeed, from (1-8) we deduce that

$$\frac{1}{z} = \frac{\cos 0 + i \sin 0}{r(\cos \theta + i \sin \theta)} = \frac{1}{r}[\cos(-\theta) + i \sin(-\theta)],$$

and since (1-9) is known to hold for positive integers n,

$$\left(\frac{1}{z}\right)^n = z^{-n} = \left(\frac{1}{r}\right)^n [\cos(-\theta) + i \sin(-\theta)]^n$$

$$= r^{-n}[\cos(-n\theta) + i \sin(-n\theta)].$$

This establishes the result (1-9) for negative integers n.

To prove the validity of (1-9) for fractional values of n, it suffices to show that it holds when the integer n is replaced by $1/n$, for on raising the result to an integral power m, we obtain the desired formula for fractional exponents.

Let

$$w \equiv z^{1/n} = \sqrt[n]{z}, \tag{1-10}$$

so that w is a solution of equation

$$w^n = z. \tag{1-11}$$

On introducing polar representations,

$$
\begin{aligned}
w &= R(\cos \varphi + i \sin \varphi), \\
z &= r(\cos \theta + i \sin \theta),
\end{aligned}
\tag{1-12}
$$

where θ is the principal argument of z, we can write (1-11) with the aid of (1-9) as

$$w^n = R^n(\cos n\varphi + i \sin n\varphi) = r(\cos \theta + i \sin \theta).$$

We conclude from this that

$$R^n = r, \qquad n\varphi = \theta \pm 2k\pi, \qquad k = 0, 1, 2, \ldots,$$

and thus

$$R = \sqrt[n]{r}, \qquad \varphi = \frac{\theta \pm 2k\pi}{n}, \qquad k = 0, 1, 2, \ldots.$$

Hence, from (1-12),

$$w = \sqrt[n]{r}\left(\cos \frac{\theta \pm 2k\pi}{n} + i \sin \frac{\theta \pm 2k\pi}{n}\right),$$

and on recalling (1-10), we see that

$$z^{1/n} = [r(\cos \theta + i \sin \theta)]^{1/n} = r^{1/n}\left(\cos \frac{\theta \pm 2k\pi}{n} + i \sin \frac{\theta \pm 2k\pi}{n}\right). \tag{1-13}$$

Since $\cos{(\theta \pm 2k\pi)}/n$ and $\sin{(\theta \pm 2k\pi)}/n$ have the same values for two integers k differing by a multiple of n, the formula (1-13) yields just n distinct values for $\sqrt[n]{z}$, namely,

$$\sqrt[n]{z} = r^{1/n}\left(\cos\frac{\theta + 2k\pi}{n} + i\sin\frac{\theta + 2k\pi}{n}\right), \qquad k = 0, 1, 2, \ldots, n-1.$$
$$(1\text{-}14)$$

The validity of formula (1-9) for fractional values of n follows directly from (1-14) upon raising $z^{1/n}$ to an integral power m.

We illustrate the use of formula (1-14) by two examples.

Example 1. Compute $\sqrt[n]{1}$. In this case $z = 1$ and its principal argument $\theta = 0$. Formula (1-14) then yields

$$\sqrt[n]{1} = \cos\frac{2k\pi}{n} + i\sin\frac{2k\pi}{n}, \qquad k = 0, 1, \ldots, n-1.$$

If we plot these n roots of unity, we see that they coincide with the vertices of a regular polygon of n sides inscribed in the unit circle, with one vertex of the polygon at $z = 1$. Figure 4 shows this for $n = 6$.

Example 2. Find all roots of $\sqrt[3]{1+i}$. Since $1 + i = \sqrt{2}\,[\cos{(\pi/4)} + i\sin{(\pi/4)}]$, formula (1-14) gives

$$\sqrt[3]{1+i} = \sqrt[6]{2}\left(\cos\frac{(\pi/4) + 2k\pi}{3} + i\sin\frac{(\pi/4) + 2k\pi}{3}\right), \qquad k = 0, 1, 2.$$

Thus the desired roots are

$$w_1 = \sqrt[6]{2}(\cos{\tfrac{1}{12}2\pi} + i\sin{\tfrac{1}{12}2\pi}),$$

$$w_2 = \sqrt[6]{2}(\cos{\tfrac{3}{4}\pi} + i\sin{\tfrac{3}{4}\pi}),$$

$$w_3 = \sqrt[6]{2}(\cos{\tfrac{17}{12}2\pi} + i\sin{\tfrac{17}{12}2\pi}).$$

These roots are represented in Fig. 5.

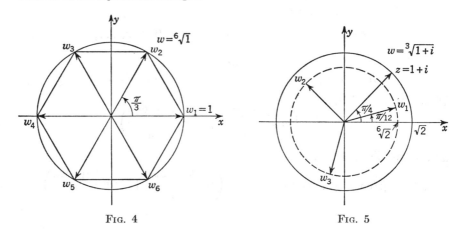

FIG. 4   FIG. 5

The reader unskilled in simple calculations involving complex numbers is urged to work out the representative problems in the following list before proceeding to the next section. The symbols Re (z) and Im (z) used in some problems in this list denote, respectively, the real and imaginary parts of a complex number z.

PROBLEMS

1. Find the moduli and principal arguments of the following numbers, and represent the numbers graphically:

(a) $1 + i\sqrt{3}$, (b) $2 + 2i$, (c) -2, (d) i^3, (e) $\dfrac{1}{1+i}$, (f) $\dfrac{1+i}{1-i}$, (g) $\dfrac{3}{(i-\sqrt{3})^2}$,

(h) $(1 - i)^4$.

2. Write the following complex numbers in the form $a + bi$:

(a) $(1 - \sqrt{3}\,i)^3$, (b) $\dfrac{(1+i)^2}{1-i}$, (c) $\dfrac{2 - \sqrt{3}\,i}{1+i}$.

3. Find the cubes of the following numbers:

(a) 1, (b) $\frac{1}{2}(-1 + i\sqrt{3})$, (c) $\frac{1}{2}(-1 - i\sqrt{3})$.

4. Find the cube roots of i, and represent them graphically.

5. Find all solutions of the equation $z^4 + 1 = 0$.

6. Verify that $z^2 - 2z + 2 = 0$ has the roots $z = 1 \pm i$.

7. Compute and represent graphically the following numbers:

(a) $\sqrt[3]{1}$, (b) $\sqrt[4]{1}$, (c) $\sqrt[5]{1}$, (d) $\sqrt[6]{1}$.

8. Find all the fifth roots of $1 + i$, and represent them graphically.

9. Use de Moivre's formula $[r(\cos\theta + i\sin\theta)]^n = r^n(\cos n\theta + i\sin n\theta)$ to obtain $\cos 2\theta = \cos^2\theta - \sin^2\theta$ and $\sin 2\theta = 2\sin\theta\cos\theta$.

10. Write the following numbers in the form $a + bi$:

(a) $\sqrt{i}$, (b) $\sqrt{1 - i}$, (c) $\dfrac{1}{\sqrt{1+i}}$.

11. Prove that (a) $z_1 + z_2 = z_2 + z_1$, (b) $z_1 z_2 = z_2 z_1$, (c) $z_1(z_2 + z_3) = z_1 z_2 + z_1 z_3$.

12. Show that if $z_1 z_2 = 0$, then $z_1 = 0$ or $z_2 = 0$.

13. Prove formulas (1-4), (1-5), and (1-6).

14. Find $|z|$, $\bar{z}$, Re (z), and Im (z) for the following:

(a) $z = 1 - 2i$; (b) $z = 3 + 4i$; (c) $z = \dfrac{1 - 2i}{3 + 4i}$.

15. Show that (a) $\overline{iz} = -i\bar{z}$, (b) $|\bar{z}^3| = |z|^3$.

16. What is the locus of points for which

(a) $|z| = 1$?   (b) $|z| < 1$?   (c) $|z| \geq 1$?

Hint: $|z| = \sqrt{x^2 + y^2}$.

17. If $z = x + iy$, what is the locus of points for which

(a) Re $(z) \geq 1$?   (b) Im $(z) > 1$?   (c) Re $(z^2) = 1$?

18. If $z = x + iy$, describe the loci:

(a) $|z - 1| = 2$; (b) $\dfrac{1}{|z|} = $ const; (c) $\left|\dfrac{z-1}{z+1}\right| = $ const.

19. Under what conditions does one have the relation

(a) $|z_1 + z_2| = |z_1| + |z_2|$?   (b) $|z_1 + z_2| = |z_1| - |z_2|$?

20. If $z = x + iy$, write the following in the form $u + iv$:

(a) z^2, (b) $\dfrac{1}{z}$, (c) $\dfrac{1}{1-z}$, (d) $z^2 + z - 1$, (e) $\dfrac{1}{z+i}$.

2. Functions of a Complex Variable. A complex quantity $z = x + iy$ in which x and y are real variables is called a *complex variable*. We shall speak of the plane in which the variable z is represented as the z plane. If in some region of this plane for each $z = x + iy$ one or more complex numbers $w = u + iv$ are determined, we say that w is a function of z and write

$$w = u + iv = f(z).$$

Thus, $$w = x^2 - y^2 + i2xy = (x + iy)^2 = z^2$$

is a function of z defined throughout the z plane. Also,

$$w = u + iv = x - iy = \bar{z}$$

is a function of z. In fact, every expression of the form $u(x,y) + iv(x,y)$ in which u and v are real functions of x and y is a function of z, since $x \equiv \frac{1}{2}(z + \bar{z})$ and $y \equiv (1/2i)(z - \bar{z})$ are functions of z.

A complex function $w = f(z)$ is *single-valued* if for each z in a given region of the z plane there is determined only one value of w. If more than one value of w corresponds to z, the function $w = f(z)$ is *multiple-valued*. Thus

$$w = x^2 - y^2 + i2xy = z^2$$

and $$w = x^2 - y^2 - i2xy = \bar{z}^2$$

are single-valued functions of z. The function $w = \sqrt{z}$ for each $z \neq 0$ determines two complex numbers, for on setting $z = r(\cos \theta + i \sin \theta)$ and recalling formula (1-14), we get

$$w = r^{\frac{1}{2}} \left(\cos \frac{\theta + 2k\pi}{2} + i \sin \frac{\theta + 2k\pi}{2} \right), \qquad k = 0, 1,$$

so that $$w_1 = r^{\frac{1}{2}} \left(\cos \frac{\theta}{2} + i \sin \frac{\theta}{2} \right),$$

$$w_2 = r^{\frac{1}{2}} \left[\cos \left(\frac{\theta}{2} + \pi \right) + i \sin \left(\frac{\theta}{2} + \pi \right) \right].$$

Thus $w = \sqrt{z}$ is not single-valued.

The functions in the foregoing examples are defined throughout the z plane. The function $w = 1/z$ is not defined at the origin $z = 0$, while $w = 1/(|z| - 1)$ is not defined when $|z| = 1$, that is, when the points z lie on the circle of radius 1 with center at the origin.

Of course, $w = f(z)$ may be defined by different formulas in different regions of the plane, or it may not be defined at all in certain regions.

In dealing with regions of the z plane we shall distinguish interior points from those that lie on the boundaries of the region. A characteristic property of the interior points is that about each interior point P one can draw a circle with center at P and with nonzero radius r so small that the circle contains only those points that belong to the region. The points on the boundary of the region are not interior because every circle with the boundary point as its center includes points that do not belong to the region.

A region consisting only of interior points is said to be *open*. An example of such a region is the circular region whose points z satisfy the condition $|z| < R$. When the boundary of the region is included in the region, the region is called *closed*. An example of a closed region is the region consisting of points z such that $|z| \leq R$.

If every point of the region is at a finite distance from the origin, the region is said to be *finite* or *bounded*. Thus all points of the bounded region lie within a circle $|z| = R$ if the radius R is chosen sufficiently large. The region consisting of all points in the z plane is *unbounded*, and so is the region consisting of the points satisfying the condition $|z| \geq 1$.

A plane region is *simply connected* if *every* closed curve drawn in the region encloses only points of the region. Thus, a region bounded by an ellipse is a simply connected region, while a region bounded by a pair of concentric circles is not simply connected. A region that is not simply connected is called *multiply connected*.

PROBLEMS

1. Express the following functions in the form $u(x,y) + iv(x,y)$:

(a) $z^2 - z + 1$, (b) $\dfrac{1}{z}$, (c) $\dfrac{1}{z-1}$, (d) $\dfrac{z-i}{z+i}$, (e) $\dfrac{1}{z^2+i}$, (f) $z + \frac{1}{2}(z - \bar{z})$, (g) $\dfrac{1}{z\bar{z}}$,

(h) $\dfrac{z^2 - 2z + 1}{z + 2}$.

2. Describe the regions in the z plane defined by the following conditions: (a) Re $(z) < 3$; (b) Im $(z) \geq 1$; (c) $|z| \geq 1$; (d) $1 \leq |z| < 2$; (e) $|z - 1| < 1$; (f) $|z - z_0| \leq 1$; (g) $|z + i| > 2$.

3. Elementary Complex Functions. In Sec. 1 we defined the operations of addition, multiplication, division, and root extraction for complex numbers. These suffice to determine, for any z, values of such algebraic expressions as

$$w = \frac{a_0 z^m + a_1 z^{m-1} + \cdots + a}{b_0 z^n + b_1 z^{n-1} + \cdots + b}$$

in which the powers m and n may be integers or fractions. However, they do not provide direct means for defining the complex counterparts of the real elementary transcendental [1] functions e^x, $\sin x$, $\log x$, $\tan^{-1} x$, etc.

---

[1] A variable w satisfying the equation $P(z,w) = 0$, where P is a polynomial in z and w, is called an *algebraic* function of z. A function that is not algebraic is called *transcendental*. The trigonometric and logarithmic functions and their inverses are called *elementary transcendental functions*.

A useful definition of a complex function such as e^z, for example, must specialize to e^x when z assumes real values. Also, it is desirable to preserve the familiar law of exponents $e^{z_1}e^{z_2} = e^{z_1+z_2}$.

A definitive formula for e^z that fulfills these criteria is

$$e^z = e^{x+iy} = e^x(\cos y + i \sin y). \tag{3-1}$$

Moreover, as we shall presently see, it suggests sensible definitions for all the other elementary transcendental functions. We note first that for $x = 0$ the definition (3-1) yields

$$e^{iy} = \cos y + i \sin y. \tag{3-2}$$

On replacing y by $-y$ we get

$$e^{-iy} = \cos y - i \sin y. \tag{3-3}$$

Adding and subtracting (3-2) and (3-3) we get the *Euler formulas*

$$\cos y = \tfrac{1}{2}(e^{iy} + e^{-iy}),$$
$$\sin y = \frac{1}{2i}(e^{iy} - e^{-iy}). \tag{3-4}$$

These formulas suggest that we define the trigonometric functions of z as follows:

$$\cos z = \frac{1}{2}(e^{iz} + e^{-iz}), \qquad \sin z = \frac{1}{2i}(e^{iz} - e^{-iz}), \qquad \tan z = \frac{\sin z}{\cos z},$$

$$\cot z = \frac{1}{\tan z}, \qquad \sec z = \frac{1}{\cos z}, \qquad \csc z = \frac{1}{\sin z}. \tag{3-5}$$

Using these definitions it is easy to check [1] that *all* the familiar formulas of analytic trigonometry remain valid when real arguments are replaced by the complex ones. For example,

$$\sin^2 z + \cos^2 z = 1,$$

$$\sin (z_1 + z_2) = \sin z_1 \cos z_2 + \cos z_1 \sin z_2,$$

and so on.

The logarithm of a complex number z is defined in the same way as in real variable analysis. Thus,

$$w = \log z \tag{3-6}$$

means that

$$z = e^w, \tag{3-7}$$

---

[1] See Prob. 1 at the end of this section. Also, cf. alternative definitions of e^z, $\sin z$, and $\cos z$ in Sec. 17, Chap. 2.

where e is the base of natural logarithms. Setting $w = u + iv$ in (3-7) gives

$$z = e^{u+iv} = e^u(\cos v + i \sin v) \tag{3-8}$$

by (3-1). On the other hand, we can write z as

$$z = x + iy = r(\cos \theta + i \sin \theta),$$

so that (3-8) gives

$$r(\cos \theta + i \sin \theta) = e^u(\cos v + i \sin v).$$

It follows from this that

$$e^u = r, \qquad v = \theta + 2k\pi, \qquad k = 0, \pm 1, \pm 2, \ldots. \tag{3-9}$$

Since u and v are real, we conclude from (3-9) that $u = \text{Log } r$, where the symbol Log is used to denote the logarithm encountered in real-variable theory. We can thus write (3-6) in the form

$$w = u + iv = \log z = \text{Log } r + (\theta + 2k\pi)i \tag{3-10}$$

or
$$\log z = \frac{1}{2}\text{Log }(x^2 + y^2) + i \tan^{-1}\frac{y}{x}, \tag{3-11}$$

since $r = \sqrt{x^2 + y^2}$ and $\theta + 2k\pi = \tan^{-1}(y/x)$.

Thus $\log z$ has infinitely many values corresponding to the different choices of the arguments θ of z. Setting $k = 0$ in (3-10) and assuming that $0 \leq \theta < 2\pi$, we get a single-valued function

$$\log z = \text{Log } r + \theta i, \qquad 0 \leq \theta < 2\pi,$$

which is called the *principal value* of $\log z$. If z is real and positive, the principal value of $\log z$ equals $\text{Log } r$.

The definition (3-10) serves to define complex and irrational powers c of the variable z by the formula

$$z^c = e^{c \log z} \tag{3-12}$$

which is equivalent to the statement that $\log z^c = c \log z$. Inasmuch as $\log z$ is infinitely-many-valued, it follows that z^c, in general, is an infinitely-many-valued function.[1] The hyperbolic functions of z are defined by the formulas

$$\sinh z = \frac{1}{2}(e^z - e^{-z}), \qquad \cosh z = \frac{1}{2}(e^z + e^{-z}), \qquad \tanh z = \frac{\sinh z}{\cosh z},$$

$$\text{sech } z = \frac{1}{\cosh z}, \qquad \text{csch } z = \frac{1}{\sinh z}. \tag{3-13}$$

---

[1] Note, however, that z^c is single-valued when c is an integer.

These functions are clearly single-valued. The inverse trigonometric and inverse hyperbolic functions are defined in the same way as in real-variable analysis, and they are multiple-valued.[1]

Example 1. Compute e^{1-i}.
On setting $x = 1$ and $y = -1$ in the formula (3-1) we get

$$e^{1-i} = e[\cos(-1) + i\sin(-1)]$$

$$= e(\cos 1 - i\sin 1).$$

Since $\cos 1 = 0.54030$, $\sin 1 = 0.84147$, and $e = 2.718$,

$$e^{1-i} = 2.718(0.5403 - i0.8415)$$

$$= 1.469 - i2.287$$

to three decimal places.
Example 2. Compute $\sin(1 - i)$.
Since

$$\sin z = \frac{1}{2i}(e^{iz} - e^{-iz})$$

and $z = 1 - i$, we have

$$\sin(1 - i) = \frac{1}{2i}(e^{i+1} - e^{-i-1})$$

$$= \frac{1}{2i}\{e(\cos 1 + i\sin 1) - e^{-1}[\cos(-1) + i\sin(-1)]\}$$

$$= \frac{e - e^{-1}}{2i}\cos 1 + \frac{e + e^{-1}}{2}\sin 1.$$

We can obtain the same result by making use of the addition formulas of trigonometry. Thus,

$$\sin(1 - i) = \sin 1 \cos(-i) + \cos 1 \sin(-i)$$

$$= \sin 1 \cos i - \cos 1 \sin i.$$

But by (3-5)

$$\cos i = \frac{1}{2}(e^{-1} + e^1), \qquad \sin i = \frac{1}{2i}(e^{-1} - e^1).$$

Substitution in the foregoing formula yields the result obtained from the definition of $\sin z$.
Example 3. Compute $\log(1 + i)$.
Since $1 + i = \sqrt{2}\,[\cos(\pi/4) + i\sin(\pi/4)]$,

$$\log(1 + i) = \text{Log}\,\sqrt{2} + \left(\frac{\pi}{4} + 2k\pi\right)i, \qquad k = 0, \pm 1, \pm 2, \ldots,$$

by (3-10). The principal value is got by setting $k = 0$.
Example 4. Compute 2^i.
By (3-12),

$$2^i = e^{i\log 2}.$$

[1] See Probs. **7** and **8**.

But $\log 2 = \text{Log } 2 + i2\pi k$. Hence

$$2^i = e^{i \,\text{Log } 2 - 2\pi k}, \qquad k = 0, \pm 1, \pm 2, \ldots .$$

Example 5. Compute i^i.

By (3-12),

$$i^i = e^{i \log i}.$$

But $\log i = \text{Log } 1 + i[(\pi/2) + 2k\pi] = i[(\pi/2) + 2k\pi]$, and hence

$$i^i = e^{-(\pi/2 + 2k\pi)}, \qquad k = 0, \pm 1, \pm 2, \ldots .$$

Example 6. Find all solutions of the equation $\cos z - 2 = 0$.
We have $\cos z = 2$, which gives, successively,

$$\frac{e^{iz} + e^{-zi}}{2} = 2,$$

$$e^{iz} + e^{-iz} = 4,$$

$$e^{2iz} - 4e^{iz} + 1 = 0.$$

Solving for e^{iz},

$$e^{iz} = \frac{4 \pm \sqrt{16 - 4}}{2}$$

$$= 2 \pm \sqrt{3}.$$

Hence

$$iz = \log (2 \pm \sqrt{3})$$

and

$$z = \frac{1}{i} \log (2 \pm \sqrt{3}).$$

Since $\log (2 \pm \sqrt{3})$ is infinitely-many-valued, there are infinitely many values of z.

PROBLEMS

1. Verify the following: (a) $e^{z_1} e^{z_2} = e^{z_1 + z_2}$; (b) $\sin^2 z + \cos^2 z = 1$; (c) $\cos (z_1 + z_2)$ $= \cos z_1 \cos z_2 - \sin z_1 \sin z_2$; (d) $\cos iz = \cosh z$; (e) $\sin iz = i \sinh z$.

2. If a and b are real integers, show that $(re^{i\theta})^{a+bi} = r^a e^{-b\theta}[\cos (a\theta + b \text{ Log } r) + i \sin (a\theta + b \text{ Log } r)]$.

3. Compute (a) $\cos (2 + i)$, (b) 1^i, (c) $(1 + i)^i$, (d) 2^{1+i}, (e) i^{-i}.

4. Express in the form $a + bi$, where a and b are real: (a) $1/(z - 1)$, (b) $1/(z^2 + i)$, (c) $\sin (1 + i)$, (d) e^{z^2}, (e) $e^{1/z}$.

5. Find the principal values and represent the numbers graphically: (a) $\log (-4)$, (b) $\log (5i)$, (c) $\log (1 + i)$, (d) $\log i$, (e) i^i, (f) e^{1+i}, (g) $\sin 2i$.

6. Find all solutions of the following equations: (a) $e^z + 1 = 0$; (b) $\sin z - 2 = 0$; (c) $\cos^{-1} z = 2$; (d) $\cos z - 1 = 0$.

7. The inverse functions are defined as solutions of the equation $z = f(w)$ for w in terms of z. Thus, $w = \sin^{-1} z$ if $z = \sin w = (e^{iw} - e^{-iw})/2i$. Obtain e^{iw} in this example by solving the equation $e^{2iw} - 2ize^{iw} - 1 = 0$. The result is $e^{iw} = iz \pm \sqrt{1 - z^2}$. Hence $w = \sin^{-1} z = -i \log (iz \pm \sqrt{1 - z^2})$. Show in the same way that

$$\tan^{-1} z = \frac{i}{2} \log \frac{i + z}{i - z} \qquad \text{and} \qquad \cos^{-1} z = -i \log (z \pm \sqrt{z^2 - 1}).$$

8. Refer to Prob. **7** and show that:

(a) $\sinh^{-1} z = \log (z + \sqrt{z^2 + 1})$, (b) $\cosh^{-1} z = \log (z + \sqrt{z^2 - 1})$,

(c) $\tanh^{-1} z = \dfrac{1}{2} \log \dfrac{1 + z}{1 - z}$.

9. For complex numbers a, b, c in what sense and in what circumstances is it true that $(ab)^c = a^c b^c$?

4. Analytic Functions of a Complex Variable. We say that a point $z = x + iy$ approaches a fixed point $z_0 = x_0 + iy_0$ if $x \to x_0$ and $y \to y_0$. Let $f(z)$ be a *single-valued* function defined in some neighborhood of the point $z = z_0$. By the *neighborhood* of z_0 we mean the set of *all points in a sufficiently small circular region with center at* z_0. As $z \to z_0$, the function $f(z)$ may tend to a definite value w_0. We say, then, that the limit of $f(z)$ as z approaches z_0 is w_0 and write

$$\lim_{z \to z_0} f(z) = w_0.$$

In particular, if $f(z_0) = w_0$, we say that $f(z)$ is *continuous* at $z = z_0$.

It is not difficult to prove that if $f(z) = u(x,y) + iv(x,y)$ is continuous at $z_0 = x_0 + iy_0$, then its real and imaginary parts u and v are continuous functions at (x_0,y_0), and conversely.

Let $w = f(z)$ be continuous at every point of some region in the z plane. The complex quantities w and z can be represented on separate complex planes, called the w and z planes. The relationship $w = f(z)$ sets up a correspondence between the points (x,y) in the z plane and the points (u,v) in the w plane (see Figs. 6 and 7), so that the corresponding points (u,v) fill some region R' in the w plane.

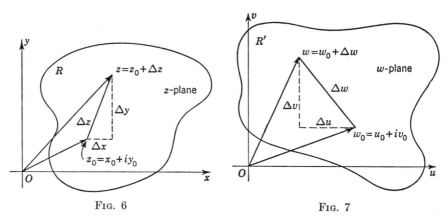

FIG. 6   FIG. 7

If $z_0 = x_0 + iy_0$ and $z = z_0 + \Delta z$ are two points in the z plane with $\Delta z = \Delta x + i\,\Delta y$, the corresponding points in the w plane are $w_0 = u_0 + iv_0$ and $w = w_0 + \Delta w$, where $\Delta w \equiv \Delta u + i\,\Delta v$. The change Δw in the value of $w_0 = f(z_0)$ corresponding to the increment Δz in z_0 is

$$\Delta w = f(z_0 + \Delta z) - f(z_0)$$

and we define the derivative dw/dz [or $f'(z)$] by a familiar formula

$$f'(z_0) = \lim_{\Delta z \to 0} \frac{\Delta w}{\Delta z} = \lim_{\Delta z \to 0} \frac{f(z_0 + \Delta z) - f(z_0)}{\Delta z}. \qquad (4\text{-}1)$$

It is most important to note that in this formula $z = z_0 + \Delta z$ can assume any position in the neighborhood of z_0 and Δz can approach zero along any one of the infinitely many paths joining z with z_0. Hence, if the derivative $f'(z_0)$ is to have a unique value, we must demand that the limit in (4-1) be independent of the way in which Δz is made to approach zero. This restriction greatly narrows down the class of complex functions that possess derivatives.

For example, if

$$w = z\bar{z},$$

then on replacing z by $z + \Delta z$ and $\bar{z}$ by $\bar{z} + \overline{\Delta z}$, we get

$$w + \Delta w = (z + \Delta z)(\bar{z} + \overline{\Delta z}) = z\bar{z} + \bar{z}\,\Delta z + z\,\overline{\Delta z} + \overline{\Delta z}\,\Delta z.$$

Hence
$$\Delta w = \bar{z}\,\Delta z + z\,\overline{\Delta z} + \overline{\Delta z}\,\Delta z$$

and
$$\frac{\Delta w}{\Delta z} = \bar{z} + z\,\frac{\overline{\Delta z}}{\Delta z} + \overline{\Delta z}. \qquad (4\text{-}2)$$

We show next that this quotient, in general, has no unique limit as Δz is made to approach zero along different paths. Since $z = x + iy$,

$$\Delta z = \Delta x + i\,\Delta y, \qquad \overline{\Delta z} = \Delta x - i\,\Delta y$$

and we can write (4-2) as

$$\frac{\Delta w}{\Delta z} = x - iy + (x + iy)\,\frac{\Delta x - i\,\Delta y}{\Delta x + i\,\Delta y} + \Delta x - i\,\Delta y. \qquad (4\text{-}3)$$

If we now let Δz in (4-3) approach zero along the path QRP (Fig. 8), so that first $QR = \Delta y \to 0$ and then $PR = \Delta x \to 0$, we get

$$\lim_{\Delta z \to 0} \frac{\Delta w}{\Delta z} = 2x.$$

But if we take the path $QR'P$ and first allow $QR' = \Delta x \to 0$ and then $R'P = \Delta y \to 0$, we obtain

$$\lim_{\Delta z \to 0} \frac{\Delta w}{\Delta z} = -2iy.$$

Except for $x = y = 0$, these limits are distinct, and hence $w = z\bar{z}$ has no derivative except possibly at $z = 0$. As a matter of fact, it is possible to show that this function does have a derivative (whose value is zero) only at the point $z = 0$.

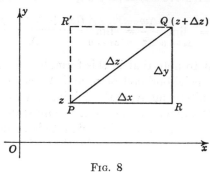

FIG. 8

On the other hand, if we consider

$$w = z^2$$

then $w + \Delta w = (z + \Delta z)^2 = z^2 + 2z\,\Delta z + (\Delta z)^2$, so that

$$\frac{\Delta w}{\Delta z} = \frac{2z\,\Delta z + (\Delta z)^2}{\Delta z} = 2z + \Delta z.$$

The limit of this quotient as $\Delta z \to 0$ is invariably $2z$, whatever may be the path along which $\Delta z \to 0$. In this example the derivative exists and its value is $2z$.

We obtain next a set of conditions which real and imaginary parts of

$$w = f(z) \equiv u(x,y) + iv(x,y)$$

must fulfill if $f(z)$ is to have a unique derivative at a given point $z = x + iy$. Since $\Delta w = \Delta u + i\,\Delta v$ and $\Delta z = \Delta x + i\,\Delta y$, we get from (4-1)

$$f'(z) = \lim_{\Delta z \to 0} \frac{\Delta u + i\,\Delta v}{\Delta z}$$

$$= \lim_{\substack{\Delta z \to 0 \\ \Delta y \to 0}} \frac{\Delta u + i\,\Delta v}{\Delta x + i\,\Delta y}. \qquad (4\text{-}4)$$

Now, if we let $\Delta z \to 0$ by first allowing $\Delta y \to 0$ and then $\Delta x \to 0$, we get from (4-4)

$$f'(z) = \lim_{\Delta x \to 0} \left(\frac{\Delta u}{\Delta x} + i\,\frac{\Delta v}{\Delta x} \right)$$

$$\equiv \frac{\partial u}{\partial x} + i\,\frac{\partial v}{\partial x}. \qquad (4\text{-}5)$$

If, on the other hand, we compute the limit in (4-4) by making first $\Delta x \to 0$ and then $\Delta y \to 0$, we obtain

$$f'(z) = \lim_{\Delta y \to 0} \left(\frac{1}{i} \frac{\Delta u}{\Delta y} + \frac{\Delta v}{\Delta y} \right)$$

$$\equiv \frac{\partial v}{\partial y} - i \frac{\partial u}{\partial y}. \tag{4-6}$$

Hence, if the derivatives in (4-5) and (4-6) are to have identical values at a given point z for these two particular modes of approach of Δz to zero, we must have

$$\frac{\partial u}{\partial x} = \frac{\partial v}{\partial y}, \qquad \frac{\partial v}{\partial x} = -\frac{\partial u}{\partial y}. \tag{4-7}$$

Equations (4-7) are known as the *Cauchy-Riemann equations*, and the foregoing calculation shows that they constitute *necessary conditions* for the existence of a unique derivative of $f(z) = u(x,y) + iv(x,y)$ at $z = x + iy$. These equations also turn out to be *sufficient*[1] if one *further assumes* the continuity of partial derivatives in (4-7) at the point (x,y).

Complex functions which have derivatives only at isolated points in the z plane are of minor interest in applications in comparison with those that have derivatives *throughout the neighborhood of the given point*. We say that *a function $f(z)$ is analytic* (or holomorphic) *at a given point $z = z_0$ if it has a derivative $f'(z)$ at $z = z_0$ and at every point in the neighborhood of z_0.* It can be shown that the following theorem[2] is true.

THEOREM. *A necessary and sufficient condition for $f(z) = u(x,y) + iv(x,y)$ to be analytic at $z_0 = x_0 + iy_0$ is that $u(x,y)$ and $v(x,y)$ together with their partial derivatives be continuous and satisfy Eqs. (4-7) in the neighborhood of (x_0,y_0).*

The points of the region where $f(z)$ ceases to be analytic are called *singular* points of $f(z)$.

It is easy to show that familiar rules for differentiating sums, products, and quotients of real functions remain valid for analytic functions.[3] Also the formulas for differentiating elementary complex functions, defined in Sec. 3, are identical with the corresponding formulas in the calculus of real variables. We give a derivation of several such formulas in the following examples.[4]

---

[1] A demonstration of this is given in several standard texts. See, for example, E. C. Titchmarsh, "The Theory of Functions," 2d ed., p. 68, Oxford University Press, London, 1939.

[2] This theorem can be deduced with the aid of the strong form of Cauchy's theorem stated in Sec. 5.

[3] See Prob. 1.

[4] See also Prob. 2.

Example 1.   Show that $de^z/dz = e^z$.

If $w = e^z = e^{x+iy}$, then the definition (3-1) yields

$$w = u + iv = e^x(\cos y + i \sin y).$$

Here, $u = e^x \cos y$, $v = e^x \sin y$, and it follows that

$$\frac{\partial u}{\partial x} = e^x \cos y, \qquad \frac{\partial u}{\partial y} = -e^x \sin y,$$

$$\frac{\partial v}{\partial x} = e^x \sin y, \qquad \frac{\partial v}{\partial y} = e^x \cos y.$$

Since Eqs. (4-7) are satisfied and the partial derivatives are continuous, dw/dz can be calculated with the aid of either (4-5) or (4-6).   Then,

$$\frac{dw}{dz} = e^x \cos y + ie^x \sin y$$

$$= e^x(\cos y + i \sin y) = e^z.$$

Example 2.   Show that $(d \log z)/dz = 1/z$ if $z \neq 0$.

The function $w = \log z$, as noted in Sec. 3, is multiple-valued.   However any branch of this function got by fixing the value of k in (3-10) is single-valued, and the application of Cauchy-Riemann equations (4-7) to it shows that it is an analytic function except at $z = 0$.   On fixing k we get from $w = \log z$ a single-valued function

$$z = e^w$$

whose derivative with respect to w by Example 1 is

$$\frac{dz}{dw} = e^w = z.$$

Hence $$\frac{dw}{dz} = \frac{d \log z}{dz} = \frac{1}{z}, \qquad \text{if } z \neq 0.$$

The point $z = 0$ is a singular point of $w = \log z$, since the derivative at that point ceases to exist.

Example 3.   Show that $dz^n/dz = nz^{n-1}$ for all values of n (real or complex).

If $w = z^n$, then

$$\log w = n \log z.$$

On differentiating this with respect to z, we get

$$\frac{1}{w}\frac{dw}{dz} = \frac{n}{z}.$$

Hence $$\frac{dw}{dz} = n\frac{w}{z} = nz^{n-1},$$

since $w = z^n$.   This derivative ceases to exist at $z = 0$ if $n < 1$.

PROBLEMS

1. Show that

(a) $\dfrac{d}{dz}(f_1 \pm f_2) = f_1'(z) \pm f_2'(z)$, (b) $\dfrac{d}{dz}(f_1 f_2) = f_1 f_2' + f_2 f_1'$,

(c) $\dfrac{d}{dz}\left(\dfrac{f_1}{f_2}\right) = \dfrac{f_2 f_1' - f_1 f_2'}{(f_2)^2}$, (d) $\dfrac{d}{dz}\{f_1[f_2(z)]\} = \dfrac{df_1}{df_2}\dfrac{df_2}{dz}$,

whenever f_1 and f_2 are analytic functions.

2. Show that

(a) $\dfrac{d(\cos z)}{dz} = -\sin z$, (b) $\dfrac{d(\sin z)}{dz} = \cos z$, (c) $\dfrac{d(\tan z)}{dz} = \sec^2 z$,

(d) $\dfrac{d(\tan^{-1} z)}{dz} = \dfrac{1}{1+z^2}$, (e) $\dfrac{d(\sinh z)}{dz} = \cosh z$, (f) $\dfrac{da^z}{dz} = a^z \log a$.

3. Determine where each of the following functions fails to be analytic: (a) $z^2 + 2z$, (b) $z/(z+1)$, (c) $1/z + (z-1)^2$, (d) $\tan z$, (e) $1/[(z-1)(z+1)]$, (f) $z\bar{z}$, (g) $e^{\bar{z}}$, (h) $x^2 - y^2 - 2ixy$, (i) $x/(x^2 + y^2) + iy/(x^2 + y^2)$, (j) $|z|$, (k) $\tan^{-1} z$.

5. Integration of Complex Functions. Cauchy's Integral Theorem.

We define the integral $\int_C f(z)\,dz$ of a complex function $f(z) = u(x,y) + iv(x,y)$ along a path C in terms of real line integrals as follows:

$$\int_C f(z)\,dz \equiv \int_C (u + iv)(dx + i\,dy)$$

$$= \int_C (u\,dx - v\,dy) + i\int_C (v\,dx + u\,dy). \qquad (5\text{-}1)$$

Real integrals of this type were studied in Chap. 5, Sec. 4, where it was observed that they exist when the functions $u(x,y)$ and $v(x,y)$ are continuous and the path C is sufficiently smooth.

The integral in (5-1) can also be defined in a manner of Sec. 4, Chap. 5, by the formula

$$\int_C f(z)\,dz \equiv \lim_{\substack{n \to \infty \\ \max|z_i - z_{i-1}| \to 0}} \sum_{i=1}^{n} f(\varsigma_i)(z_i - z_{i-1}). \qquad (5\text{-}2)$$

It is supposed that the curve C is divided into n segments by points z_i and that ς_i is some point of the ith segment. The limit is then computed as the number of segments is allowed to increase indefinitely in such a way that the length of the largest segment tends to zero. The fact that the definitions (5-1) and (5-2) are equivalent follows from consideration of Sec. 4, Chap. 5.

As an illustration of the use of formula (5-1) consider the integral

$$\int_C \bar{z}^2\,dz, \qquad (5\text{-}3)$$

where the path C is a straight line joining the points $z = 0$ and $z = 1 + 2i$ (Fig. 9). Since $\bar{z}^2 = (x - iy)^2 = x^2 - y^2 - i2xy$, we get, on substituting $u = x^2 - y^2$, $v = -2xy$ in (5-1),

$$\int_C \bar{z}^2 \, dz = \int_C [(x^2 - y^2) \, dx + 2xy \, dy] + i \int_C [-2xy \, dx + (x^2 - y^2) \, dy].$$

$$(5\text{-}4)$$

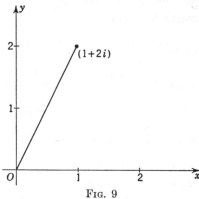

FIG. 9

But the cartesian equation of C is $y = 2x$, and hence (5-4) can be reduced to the evaluation of two definite integrals:

$$\int \bar{z}^2 \, dz = \int_0^1 5x^2 \, dx + i \int_0^1 - 10x^2 \, dx = \tfrac{5}{3} - i^{10}\!\tfrac{10}{3}.$$

The value of the integral (5-4) depends on the path C joining the given points $z = 0$, $z = 1 + 2i$, for according to Sec. 9, Chap. 5, a necessary and sufficient condition that the line integral

$$\int_C M \, dx + N \, dy \qquad\qquad (5\text{-}5)$$

be independent of the path in a simply connected region R is that

$$\frac{\partial M}{\partial y} = \frac{\partial N}{\partial x} \qquad\qquad (5\text{-}6)$$

throughout R. We further recall that in deducing the condition (5-6) with the aid of Green's theorem it was supposed that $M(x,y)$, $N(x,y)$, and their partial derivatives in (5-6) are continuous functions throughout the region. It is readily checked that Eq. (5-6) is not satisfied by the functions appearing in the line integrals in (5-4).

If, however, $f(z) = u + iv$ in (5-1) is an analytic function, then the Cauchy-Riemann equations (4-7) demand that

$$\frac{\partial u}{\partial x} = \frac{\partial v}{\partial y}, \qquad \frac{\partial v}{\partial x} = -\frac{\partial u}{\partial y}. \qquad (5\text{-}7)$$

Reference to (5-6) shows that these conditions are precisely those that ensure the independence of the path of the line integrals in (5-1), provided that the partial derivatives in (5-7) are continuous functions in the given simply connected region R. Thus, if we suppose that $f(z)$ is analytic in the given simply connected region and $f'(z)$ is continuous there, then the integral

$$\int_C f(z)\, dz$$

is independent of the path joining any pair of points in the region. If the path C is closed, then the value of this integral is zero. We thus have a theorem, first deduced by Cauchy, which is of cardinal importance in the study of analytic functions. Although the foregoing proof assumes the continuity of $f'(z)$, the theorem can actually be established [1] under the sole hypothesis that $f'(z)$ exists at each point of the region, and we state it in this strong form.

CAUCHY'S INTEGRAL THEOREM. *If $f(z)$ is analytic at all points within and on a closed curve C, then $\int_C f(z)\, dz = 0$.*

We conclude this section by deducing, from definition (5-2), a useful inequality furnishing an upper bound for the value of the complex integral $\int_C f(z)\, dz$. Inasmuch as the modulus of the sum of complex numbers is never greater than the sum of the moduli,

$$\left| \int_C f(z)\, dz \right| \leq \int_C |f(z)| \cdot |dz|.$$

Now, if the modulus $|f(z)|$ of $f(z)$ along C does not exceed in value some positive number M, then

$$\left| \int_C f(z)\, dz \right| \leq M \int_C |dz| = M \int_C |dx + i\, dy| = M \int_C ds = ML \quad (5\text{-}8)$$

where L is the length of C.

As an illustration of the use of the inequality (5-8) we apply it to deduce an upper bound for the integral (5-3). The modulus of $\bar{z}^2$ takes its maximum at the point $z = 1 + 2i$. Hence we can take M in (5-3) as $|1 + 2i|^2 = 5$, and (5-8) then yields

$$\left| \int_C \bar{z}^2\, dz \right| \leq 5\sqrt{5},$$

inasmuch as $L = \sqrt{5}$ for the rectilinear path in (5-3).

[1] See Titchmarsh, *op. cit.*, pp. 75–83. In a somewhat different development of the subject one deduces the continuity of $f'(z)$ from Cauchy's theorem, not the other way about. We shall see in Sec. 7 that the theorem actually implies existence and continuity of derivatives of all orders.

PROBLEMS

1. Find the value of the integral $\int_C z^2\, dz$ along the rectilinear path joining the points $z = 0$ and $z = 2 + i$. Show that this integral is independent of the path.

2. Find the value of the integral $\int_C \bar{z}\, dz$ along the rectilinear path $y = x$ joining the points $(0,0)$ and $(1,1)$ and also along the parabola $y = x^2$ joining the same points.

3. Show that the integral $\int_C \bar{z}\, dz$ evaluated over the path $|z| = 1$ in a counterclockwise direction yields $2\pi i$. Note that $z = e^{i\theta}$ and $\bar{z} = e^{-i\theta}$ along the path $|z| = 1$.

4. Find the value of the integral $\int_{-1}^{1} \frac{z - 1}{z}\, dz$, where the path is the upper half of the circle $|z| = 1$. Calculate the value of this integral over the lower half of the circle $|z| = 1$.

5. Show that $\int_C (1 + z^2)\, dz$ is independent of the path C, and evaluate this integral when C is the boundary of the square with vertices at the points $z = 0$, $z = 1$, $z = 1 + i$, and $z = i$.

6. What is the value of the integral $\int_C e^{iz}\, dz$ where C is the boundary of the square in Prob. 5?

7. Find the value of the integral $\int_0^{\pi i} e^z\, dz$ over any path joining $z = 0$ and $z = \pi i$.

8. Use formula (5-8) to show that:

(a) $\left| \int_i^{2+i} z^2\, dz \right| < 10$, (b) $\left| \int_i^{2+i} \frac{dz}{z^2} \right| < 2$, (c) $\left| \int_{-i}^{i} (x^2 + iy^2)\, dz \right| < 2$,

where paths are straight lines joining the points appearing in the limits of these integrals.

6. Cauchy's Integral Theorem for Multiply Connected Regions.

In establishing Cauchy's integral theorem in the preceding section we assumed

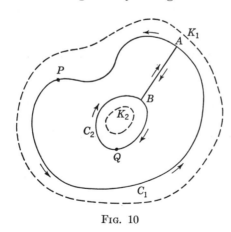

FIG. 10

that the region bounded by the curve C is simply connected. It is easy to extend this theorem to multiply connected domains in the manner of Sec. 9, Chap. 5. Thus consider, for definiteness, a doubly connected region (Fig. 10) bounded by closed curves C_1 and C_2, where C_2 lies entirely within C_1. We assume that $f(z)$ is analytic in the region exterior to C_2 and interior to C_1 and analytic on C_2 and C_1. The requirement of analyticity on C_1 and C_2 implies that the function $f(z)$ is analytic in an extended region (indicated by the dashed curves K_1 and K_2) that contains the curves C_1 and C_2.

If some point A of the curve C_1 is joined to a point B of C_2 by a crosscut

AB, then the region becomes simply connected and the theorem of Cauchy is applicable. Integrating in the positive direction gives

$$\oint_{APA} f(z)\, dz + \int_{AB} f(z)\, dz + \oint_{BQB} f(z)\, dz + \int_{BA} f(z)\, dz = 0, \quad (6\text{-}1)$$

where the subscripts on the integrals indicate the directions of integration along C_1, the crosscut AB, and C_2. Since the second and the fourth integrals in (6-1) are calculated over the same path in opposite directions, their sum is zero and one has

$$\oint_{C_1} f(z)\, dz + \oint_{C_2} f(z)\, dz = 0, \quad (6\text{-}2)$$

where the integral along C_1 is traversed in the counterclockwise direction and that along C_2 in the clockwise direction. Changing the order of integration in the second integral in (6-2) gives

$$\oint_{C_1} f(z)\, dz = \oint_{C_2} f(z)\, dz. \quad (6\text{-}3)$$

We see that the values of the integral of $f(z)$ over two different paths C_1 and C_2 are equal, but they need not be zero inasmuch as $f(z)$ may not be analytic at every point of the region bounded by C_2. But whatever may be the value of the integral over the path C_2, it is the same as its value over the path C_1. An important *principle of the deformation of contours* follows at once from this observation: *The integral of an analytic function over any closed curve C_1 has the same value over any other curve C_2 into which C_1 can be continuously deformed without passing over singular points of $f(z)$.*

We shall see that this principle will enable us to simplify the computation of integrals of analytic functions.

The foregoing results can be extended in an obvious way to yield the following theorem:

THEOREM. *If $f(z)$ is analytic in a closed multiply connected region bounded by the exterior curve C and the interior curves C_1, C_2, ..., C_n, then the integral over the exterior curve C is equal to the sum of the integrals over the interior curves provided that the integration over all the contours is performed in the same direction.*

It should be noted that the requirement of analyticity of $f(z)$ in the *closed* region implied that $f(z)$ be analytic on all contours forming its boundary.

Before considering applications of the theorem of this section to specific problems, we deduce an important result which will enable us to compute many integrals by a method which is vastly simpler than that developed in Sec. 5.

7. The Fundamental Theorem of Integral Calculus. Let $f(z)$ be analytic in a simply connected region R (Fig. 11), and let C be a curve joining two

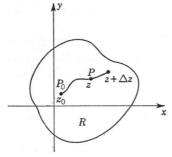

points P_0 and P of the region determined by the complex numbers z_0 and z. We consider the integral

$$\int_{z_0}^{z} f(z) \, dz \qquad (7\text{-}1)$$

along C. Since $f(z)$ is analytic, the integral (7-1) is independent of the path, and its value is completely determined by the choice of z_0 and z. If z_0 is fixed, the integral (7-1) defines a function

Fig. 11

$$F(z) = \int_{z_0}^{z} f(z) \, dz \qquad (7\text{-}2)$$

for every choice of z in R.

To emphasize the fact that the integration variable z plays a distinct role from the variable z appearing in the upper limit of the integral, we can rewrite (7-2) as

$$F(z) = \int_{z_0}^{z} f(\zeta) \, d\zeta. \qquad (7\text{-}3)$$

We prove next that $F(z)$ is an analytic function and, moreover, its derivative at any point z has the value of the function in the integrand at that point. That is,

$$F'(z) = f(z).$$

We can use (7-3) to compute the difference quotient

$$\frac{F(z + \Delta z) - F(z)}{\Delta z} = \frac{1}{\Delta z} \left[\int_{z_0}^{z+\Delta z} f(\zeta) \, d\zeta - \int_{z_0}^{z} f(\zeta) \, d\zeta \right]$$

$$= \frac{1}{\Delta z} \left[\int_{z_0}^{z} f(\zeta) \, d\zeta + \int_{z}^{z+\Delta z} f(\zeta) \, d\zeta - \int_{z_0}^{z} f(\zeta) \, d\zeta \right]$$

$$= \frac{1}{\Delta z} \int_{z}^{z+\Delta z} f(\zeta) \, d\zeta, \qquad (7\text{-}4)$$

and rewrite (7-4) by adding and subtracting $f(z)$ in the integrand:

$$\frac{F(z + \Delta z) - F(z)}{\Delta z} = \frac{1}{\Delta z} \int_{z}^{z+\Delta z} [f(\zeta) - f(z) + f(z)] \, d\zeta$$

$$= \frac{1}{\Delta z} [f(z) \int_{z}^{z+\Delta z} d\zeta] + \frac{1}{\Delta z} \int_{z}^{z+\Delta z} [f(\zeta) - f(z)] \, d\zeta.$$

But $\displaystyle\int_z^{z+\Delta z} d\zeta = \Delta z$, so that

$$\frac{F(z + \Delta z) - F(z)}{\Delta z} = f(z) + \frac{1}{\Delta z} \int_z^{z+\Delta z} [f(\zeta) - f(z)] \, d\zeta. \qquad (7\text{-}5)$$

Now if

$$\lim_{\Delta z \to 0} \frac{1}{\Delta z} \int_z^{z+\Delta z} [f(\zeta) - f(z)] \, d\zeta = 0, \qquad (7\text{-}6)$$

then it would follow from (7-5) that $F'(z) = f(z)$. The fact that the limit in (7-6) is, indeed, zero follows at once from the estimate (5-8), for if $M = \max |f(\zeta) - f(z)|$ on the path joining z and Δz, then

$$\left| \frac{1}{\Delta z} \int_z^{z+\Delta z} [f(\zeta) - f(z)] \, d\zeta \right| \leq M.$$

But since $f(z)$ is continuous, $M \to 0$ as $\Delta z \to 0$.

Any function $F_1(z)$ such that $F_1'(z) = f(z)$ is called a *primitive* or an *indefinite integral* of $f(z)$. As in real calculus, it is easy to prove that if $F_1(z)$ and $F_2(z)$ are any two indefinite integrals of $f(z)$, then they can differ only by a constant.[1]

Hence, if $F_1(z)$ is an indefinite integral of $f(z)$, it follows that

$$F(z) = \int_{z_0}^z f(z) \, dz = F_1(z) + C.$$

To evaluate C, set $z = z_0$; then, since $\displaystyle\int_{z_0}^{z_0} f(z) \, dz = 0$, $C = -F_1(z_0)$. Thus

$$F(z) = \int_{z_0}^z f(z) \, dz = F_1(z) - F_1(z_0). \qquad (7\text{-}7)$$

The statement embodied in (7-7) establishes the connection between line and indefinite integrals and is called the *fundamental theorem of integral calculus* because of its importance in the evaluation of line integrals. It states that *the value of the line integral of an analytic function is equal to the difference in the values of any primitive at the end points of the path of integration.*

[1] Proof: Since $F_1'(z) = F_2'(z) = f(z)$, it is evident that

$$F_1'(z) - F_2'(z) = \frac{d(F_1 - F_2)}{dz} \equiv \frac{dG}{dz} = 0.$$

But if $dG/dz = 0$, it means that $G'(z) = (\partial u/\partial x) + i(\partial v/\partial x) = (\partial v/\partial y) - i(\partial u/\partial y) = 0$, so that $\partial u/\partial x = \partial v/\partial x = \partial u/\partial y = \partial v/\partial y = 0$, and thus u and v do not depend on x and y.

Example 1. As an illustration of the use of formula (7-7) consider the evaluation of

$$\int_C z^2 \, dz \tag{7-8}$$

along some path C joining $z = 0$ and $z = 2 + i$. Inasmuch as $f(z) = z^2$ is analytic throughout the finite z plane, the integral (7-8) is independent of the path. Moreover, since $F(z) = \frac{1}{3}z^3$ is an indefinite integral for $f(z) = z^2$, we can write

$$\int_0^{2+i} z^2 \, dz = \frac{1}{3} z^3 \Big|_0^{2+i} = \frac{1}{3} (2 + i)^3.$$

The reader should contrast this computation with calculations required for solving this in Prob. 1, Sec. 5.

Example 2. Evaluate $\int_C e^z \, dz$ over some path C joining $z = 0$ and $z = \pi i$. Since e^z is analytic, we get at once from (7-7)

$$\int_0^{\pi i} e^z \, dz = e^z \Big|_0^{\pi i} = e^{\pi i} - 1 = -2.$$

We indicate the nature of required calculations if this integral were to be computed by the method of Sec. 5. We first separate the integrand into real and imaginary parts,

$$e^z = e^{x+iy} = e^x \cos y + i e^x \sin y,$$

and form two real line integrals

$$\int_C e^z \, dz = \int_C (e^x \cos y + i e^x \sin y)(dx + i \, dy)$$

$$= \int_C (e^x \cos y \, dx - e^x \sin y \, dy) + i \int_C (e^x \sin y \, dx + e^x \cos y \, dy).$$

Since these line integrals are independent of the path, they may be evaluated over any convenient path joining the points $(0,0)$ and $(0,\pi)$ corresponding to $z = 0$ and $z = \pi i$. The result of such calculations would yield -2, as the reader can verify.

Example 3. Discuss the integral $\int_C (z - a)^m \, dz$, where m is an integer and a is a constant.

The function $f(z) = (z - a)^m$ is obviously analytic at all points of the z plane as long as m is a positive integer. If $m < 0$, we write $m = -n$ and consider

$$f(z) = \frac{1}{(z - a)^n}, \tag{7-9}$$

where n is a positive integer.

To evaluate $\int_{z_0}^z (z - a)^m \, dz$ for $m > 0$, we note that

$$F(z) = \frac{(z - a)^{m+1}}{m + 1}$$

is an indefinite integral for $f(z) = (z - a)^m$. Accordingly

$$\int_{z_0}^z (z - a)^m \, dz = \frac{(z - a)^{m+1}}{m + 1} \Big|_{z_0}^z. \tag{7-10}$$

If, in particular, the path C is closed, so that the limits in (7-10) coincide, we conclude that the value of the integral is zero. This result also follows from Cauchy's theorem, since $f(z) = (z - a)^m$ is analytic for all values of z when $m > 0$.

We consider next the integral

$$\int_C \frac{dz}{(z-a)^n}, \qquad n > 0. \tag{7-11}$$

and note first that if the path C passes through the point $z = a$, the integrand becomes meaningless at $z = a$. In this book [1] we shall not consider in detail integrals over those paths that go through singular points of the integrands, but special types of such integrals will occur in Sec. 22.

If C is a closed path and a is not in the region R enclosed by C, the integrand in (7-11) is analytic in the closed region R. Hence, by Cauchy's theorem the value is zero. If, however, a lies in R, Cauchy's theorem does not apply, since $f(z) = 1/(z-a)^n$ ceases being analytic at $z = a$. The integral (7-11) can, of course, be evaluated by the method of Sec. 5 once the equation of C is specified. However, it is wise to simplify calculations by making use of the principle of deformation of contours. This principle states that when $z = a$ is in the interior of C,

$$\oint_C \frac{dz}{(z-a)^n} = \oint_\gamma \frac{dz}{(z-a)^n},$$

where γ is a circle with center at a and with radius ρ so small that γ lies within C (Fig. 12). But the integral over γ is easily evaluated. Setting $z - a = \rho e^{i\theta}$, we get $dz = \rho e^{i\theta} i \, d\theta$ on observing that ρ is constant on γ. Hence

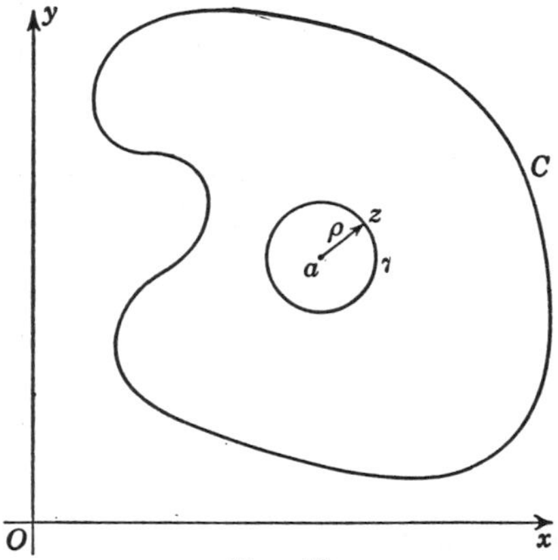

Fig. 12

$$\oint_C \frac{dz}{(z-a)^n} = \oint_\gamma \frac{\rho e^{i\theta} i \, d\theta}{\rho^n e^{in\theta}} = \frac{i}{\rho^{n-1}} \int_0^{2\pi} e^{(1-n)\theta i} \, d\theta = \frac{i}{\rho^{n-1}} \frac{e^{(1-n)\theta i}}{i(1-n)} \Big|_0^{2\pi} = 0, \qquad \text{if } n \neq 1. \tag{7-12}$$

If $n = 1$, we get

$$\int_C \frac{dz}{z-a} = i \int_0^{2\pi} d\theta = 2\pi i. \tag{7-13}$$

In evaluating the integral (7-12), we noted that the integrand $e^{(1-n)\theta i} \, d\theta$, for $n \neq 1$, is the differential of $e^{(1-n)\theta i}/i(1-n)$, and we made use of the fundamental theorem of integral calculus.

Example 4. Evaluate the integral $\int_C \dfrac{dz}{z^2 - 1}$, where C is the circle $x^2 + y^2 = 4$.

The function

$$f(z) = \frac{1}{z^2 - 1} \equiv \frac{1}{(z-1)(z+1)} \tag{7-14}$$

[1] When $z = a$ lies on the path of integration, the integral in (7-11) is an *improper* complex integral and it calls for special considerations analogous to those required to treat improper real integrals. Certain types of improper complex integrals are of interest in applications. See, for example, N. I. Muskhelishvili, "Singular Integral Equations," P. Noordhoff, N.V., Groningen, Netherlands, 1953.

has two singular points $z = 1$ and $z = -1$, both of which lie within the given circle $|z| \leq 2$ (Fig. 13). If we delete these points from the circular region C by circles γ_1 and γ_2 of sufficiently small radii, $f(z)$ will be analytic in the triply connected domain exterior to γ_1 and γ_2 and interior to C. Then Cauchy's theorem for multiply connected domains permits us to write

$$\int_C f(z)\, dz = \int_{\gamma_1} f(z)\, dz + \int_{\gamma_2} f(z)\, dz. \tag{7-15}$$

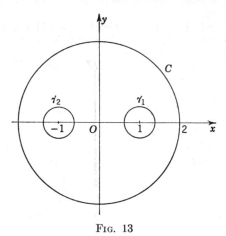

FIG. 13

The integrals in the right-hand member in (7-15) are readily evaluated. Since

$$\frac{1}{(z-1)(z+1)} \equiv \frac{1}{2}\frac{1}{z-1} - \frac{1}{2}\frac{1}{z+1},$$

we get

$$\int_{\gamma_1} \frac{1}{(z-1)(z+1)}\, dz = \frac{1}{2}\int_{\gamma_1} \frac{dz}{z-1} - \frac{1}{2}\int_{\gamma_1} \frac{dz}{z+1}. \tag{7-16}$$

If the radius of γ_1 is such that γ_1 contains within it $z = +1$ but not $z = -1$, then

$$\int_{\gamma_1} \frac{dz}{z-1} = 2\pi i,$$

by (7-13), and

$$\int_{\gamma_1} \frac{dz}{z+1} = 0,$$

by Cauchy's integral theorem, for $1/(z+1)$ has no singularities within γ_1. Thus, the first integral on the right in (7-15) has the value πi. An entirely similar calculation shows

$$\int_{\gamma_2} \frac{1}{(z-1)(z+1)}\, dz = -\pi i.$$

Therefore, $$\int_C \frac{1}{(z-1)(z+1)}\, dz = (\pi i) + (-\pi i) = 0,$$

even though the integrand is not analytic in the region $|z| \leq 2$.

PROBLEMS

1. Show that $\int_{z_0}^{z} z\, dz = \frac{1}{2}(z^2 - z_0^2)$ for all paths joining z_0 with z.

2. Evaluate the integral $\int_C (z - a)^{-1}\, dz$, where C is a simple closed curve and a is interior to C, by expressing it as a sum of two real line integrals over C. *Hint:* Set $z - a = \rho e^{\theta i}$; then $dz = e^{\theta i}(d\rho + i\rho\, d\theta)$.

3. Evaluate $\int_C z^{-2}\, dz$ where the path C is the upper half of the unit circle whose center is at the origin. What is the value of this integral if the path is the lower half of the circle?

4. Evaluate $\int_C z^{-1}\, dz$, where C is the path of Prob. 3.

5. Evaluate $\int_C (z^2 - 2z + 1)\, dz$, where C is the circle $x^2 + y^2 = 2$.

6. Discuss the integral $\int_C \dfrac{z + 1}{z^2}\, dz$, where C is a path enclosing the origin.

7. What is the value of the integral $\int_C (1 + z^2)^{-1}\, dz$, where C is the circle $x^2 + y^2 = 9$?

8. Discuss Prob. 7 by noting that

$$\frac{1}{1 + z^2} = \frac{1}{2i}\left(\frac{1}{z - i} - \frac{1}{z + i}\right)$$

and evaluating the integrals over the unit circles whose centers are at $z = i$ and $z = -i$. Note the theorem of Sec. 6.

9. Show that the integrals $(a) \int_C \dfrac{z\, dz}{z - 2}$, $(b) \int_C \sin z\, dz$, $(c) \int_C z e^z\, dz$, $(d) \int_C z^{-2}\, dz$ vanish if C is the unit circle $|z| = 1$.

10. Evaluate the integral $\int_C \dfrac{1}{1 - z^2}\, dz$ along the following paths C: $(a)\ |z| = \frac{1}{2}$, $(b)\ |z| = 2$, $(c)\ |z - 1| = 1$, $(d)\ |z + 1| = 1$. *Hint:* Decompose the integrand into partial fractions as in Prob. 8.

8. Cauchy's Integral Formula.

In this section we deduce with the aid of Cauchy's theorem the remarkable fact that *every analytic function $f(z)$ is completely determined in the interior of the given closed region R when the values of $f(z)$ are specified on its boundary.*

Let $f(z)$ be analytic in a simply connected region R and on its boundary C. If a is an interior point of R, then the function

$$\frac{f(z)}{z - a} \tag{8-1}$$

is analytic in R with the possible exception of the point $z = a$. If this point is excluded from the region by enclosing it in a circle γ of radius ρ and with center at a (Fig. 12), then (8-1) will surely be analytic in the region exterior to γ and interior to C.

It follows, then, from (6-3) that

$$\int_C \frac{f(z)}{z-a}\,dz = \int_\gamma \frac{f(z)}{z-a}\,dz \tag{8-2}$$

where the paths C and γ are described in the same sense. Now the integral in the right-hand member of (8-2) can be written as

$$\int_\gamma \frac{f(z)}{z-a}\,dz = \int_\gamma \frac{f(z)-f(a)}{z-a}\,dz + f(a)\int_\gamma \frac{dz}{z-a}. \tag{8-3}$$

But by (7-13)

$$\int_\gamma \frac{dz}{z-a} = 2\pi i, \tag{8-4}$$

and we shall show next that the first integral on the right in (8-3) has the value zero. Indeed, if we take $z - a = \rho e^{i\theta}$, then, as long as z is on γ, $dz = i\rho e^{i\theta}\,d\theta$, and therefore

$$\int_\gamma \frac{f(z)-f(a)}{z-a}\,dz = i\int_\gamma [f(z)-f(a)]\,d\theta. \tag{8-5}$$

Let the maximum of $|f(z)-f(a)|$ be M; then by (5-8)

$$\left|\int_\gamma \frac{f(z)-f(a)}{z-a}\,dz\right| \le M\int_0^{2\pi} d\theta = 2\pi M. \tag{8-6}$$

The radius ρ is arbitrary, and if we make it sufficiently small, then $\max |f(z)-f(a)|$ can be made as small as we wish, since $f(z)$ is a continuous function. Accordingly, $M \to 0$ as $\rho \to 0$. On the other hand, from the principle of deformation of contours, the value of the integral (8-6) is *independent* of the radius ρ. Since $M \to 0$ when $\rho \to 0$, we conclude that the value of the integral (8-5) is zero.

Accordingly, (8-3), together with (8-4), gives the result

$$\int_C \frac{f(z)}{z-a}\,dz = 2\pi i f(a). \tag{8-7}$$

We recall that the point a is any interior point of the region R bounded by C and z is the variable of integration on the contour C. If we denote the variable of integration by ζ and let z be any interior point, we can rewrite formula (8-7) as

$$f(z) = \frac{1}{2\pi i}\int_C \frac{f(\zeta)\,d\zeta}{\zeta - z}. \tag{8-8}$$

Formula (8-8) permits us to calculate the value of $f(z)$ at any interior point from specified boundary values $f(\zeta)$ on the contour C. It is known as *Cauchy's integral formula*. This formula can be extended in the manner of Sec. 6 to multiply connected domains bounded by the exterior contour C_0 and m interior contours C_1, C_2, ..., C_m. The integration in (8-8) is then performed in the clockwise sense over the interior contours and counterclockwise over the exterior contour C_0.

It is not difficult to show with the aid of formula (8-8) that an analytic function $f(z)$ has not only continuous first derivatives in the region but also derivatives of all orders. Thus an analytic function can be differentiated infinitely many times.

In fact, if we consider an integral of *Cauchy's type*,

$$F(z) = \frac{1}{2\pi i} \int_C \frac{f(\zeta)}{\zeta - z} d\zeta, \tag{8-9}$$

where $f(\zeta)$ is any continuous (not necessarily analytic) complex function, then this integral defines an analytic function $F(z)$. To show this we merely have to prove that $F(z)$ has a derivative at every point of the region R bounded by C. We form the difference quotient with the aid of (8-9) and get

$$F'(z) = \lim_{\Delta z \to 0} \frac{F(z + \Delta z) - F(z)}{\Delta z}$$

$$= \lim_{\Delta z \to 0} \frac{1}{\Delta z} \left[\frac{1}{2\pi i} \int_C \frac{f(\zeta)\, d\zeta}{\zeta - (z + \Delta z)} - \frac{1}{2\pi i} \int_C \frac{f(\zeta)\, d\zeta}{\zeta - z} \right]$$

$$= \lim_{\Delta z \to 0} \left[\frac{1}{2\pi i} \int_C \frac{f(\zeta)\, d\zeta}{(\zeta - z - \Delta z)(\zeta - z)} \right].$$

On taking the limit as $\Delta z \to 0$ under the integral sign, which is legitimate if $f(\zeta)$ is continuous, we get

$$F'(z) = \frac{1}{2\pi i} \int_C \frac{f(\zeta)}{(\zeta - z)^2} d\zeta.$$

Continuing in the same way, we find

$$F''(z) = \frac{2!}{2\pi i} \int_C \frac{f(\zeta)}{(\zeta - z)^3} d\zeta,$$

$$\cdots \cdots \cdots \cdots \cdots \cdots$$

$$F^{(n)}(z) = \frac{n!}{2\pi i} \int_C \frac{f(\zeta)}{(\zeta - z)^{n+1}} d\zeta.$$

We have thus shown that $F(z)$ defined by (8-9) has derivatives of all orders even when nothing is said about the relation of the values of $F(z)$ on the boundary C to the function $f(\zeta)$ appearing in the integrand. In the special case when $f(\zeta) = F(\zeta)$, we have a formula for the nth derivative of the analytic function $f(z)$ at any interior point of R in terms of the values of $f(z)$ on C:

$$f^{(n)}(z) = \frac{n!}{2\pi i} \int_C \frac{f(\zeta)}{(\zeta - z)^{n+1}} \, d\zeta, \qquad n = 0, 1, 2, \ldots. \qquad (8\text{-}10)$$

We conclude this section by noting some important consequences of formula (8-7). Let the path C be the circle $|z - a| = \rho$ with center at $z = a$ and with radius ρ. Suppose that the maximum value of the modulus of $f(z)$ on this circle is M; then by (5-8)

$$|f(a)| \leq \frac{1}{2\pi} \frac{M}{\rho} 2\pi\rho = M.$$

This result is independent of the radius ρ. Consequently $|f(z)|$ at the center a of the circle is not greater than its maximum value on the boundary. Using this result one can prove that if $f(z)$ is analytic in a given region R bounded by a curve C, and if M is the maximum value of $|f(z)|$ on C, then $|f(z)| < M$ at each interior point of R unless $|f(z)| = M$ throughout the region. This result is known as the *maximum modulus theorem*.[1] The fact that $|f(z)| \leq M$ follows from Sec. 24, Chap. 6, if we note that $\log |f(z)|$ is harmonic.

Example 1. Find the value of the integral $\int_C \frac{\sin z}{z} \, dz$ if C is the ellipse $x^2 + 4y^2 = 1$.

Since $\sin z$ is analytic in the region bounded by C, formula (8-7) yields, upon setting $f(z) = \sin z$ and $a = 0$,

$$\int_C \frac{\sin z}{z} \, dz = 2\pi i(\sin 0) = 0.$$

Example 2. Evaluate the integral $\int_C \frac{e^{-z}}{z + 1} \, dz$ over the circular path $|z| = 2$.

The point $z = -1$ lies within the given circle, and since e^{-z} is analytic within C, formula (8-7) yields

$$\int_C \frac{e^{-z}}{z + 1} \, dz = 2\pi i e^{-z} \Big|_{z=-1} = e2\pi i.$$

Example 3. Find the value of the integral

$$\int_C \frac{\tan z}{[z - (\pi/4)]^2} \, dz,$$

where C is the circle $|z| = 1$.

The point $z = \pi/4$ lies within C, and we note that $\tan z$ is analytic for $|z| \leq 1$. From (8-10)

$$f'(a) = \frac{1}{2\pi i} \int \frac{f(z)}{(z - a)^2} \, dz.$$

Hence

$$\int \frac{\tan z}{[z - (\pi/4)]^2} \, dz = 2\pi i \left(\frac{d \tan z}{dz} \right)_{z=\pi/4} = 2\pi i \sec^2 \frac{\pi}{4} = 4\pi i.$$

---

[1] See proof, for example, in E. C. Titchmarsh, "The Theory of Functions," 2d ed., p. 164, Oxford University Press, London, 1939.

PROBLEMS

1. If $f(z) = \int_C \dfrac{3\zeta^2 + 7\zeta + 1}{\zeta - z}\, d\zeta$, where C is the circle of radius 2 about the origin, find the value of $f(1 - i)$.

2. Apply Cauchy's integral formula to Prob. 7, Sec. 7. Use the integrand in the form given in Prob. 8, Sec. 7.

3. Evaluate the following integrals over the closed path C formed by the lines $x = \pm 1$, $y = \pm 1$: (a) $\int_C \dfrac{\sin z}{z}\, dz$, (b) $\int_C \dfrac{\cos z}{z}\, dz$, (c) $\int_C \dfrac{e^z}{z - \frac{1}{2}i}\, dz$, (d) $\int_C (\sin z + e^z)\, dz$,

(e) $\int_C \dfrac{\cosh z}{z}\, dz$.

4. Evaluate with the aid of Cauchy's integral formula

$$\int_C \frac{3\zeta^2 + \zeta}{\zeta^2 - 1}\, d\zeta,$$

where C is the circle $|\zeta| = 2$. *Hint:* Decompose the integrand into partial fractions.

5. What is the value of the integral of Prob. 4 when evaluated over the circle $|\zeta - 1| = 1$? *Hint:* Note that $(3\zeta^2 + \zeta)/(\zeta + 1)$ is analytic for $|\zeta - 1| \leq 1$.

6. Evaluate $\int_C \dfrac{3z^2 + 2z - 1}{z}\, dz$, where C is the circle $|z| = 1$.

7. Can $|f(z)|$ assume a minimum value at an interior point of a region within which $f(z)$ is analytic? Consider $f(z) = z$.

8. Can $|f(z)|$ assume a nonzero minimum at an interior point of a region within which $f(z)$ is analytic? *Hint:* Consider $1/f(z)$.

9. Harmonic Functions.

We saw in the preceding section that a function analytic at a given point of the region has derivatives of all orders at that point. It follows from this that the real and imaginary parts of an analytic function $f(z) = u + iv$ have partial derivatives of all orders throughout the region where $f(z)$ is analytic, for by (4-5) and (4-6)

$$f'(z) = \frac{\partial u}{\partial x} + i\frac{\partial v}{\partial x} = \frac{\partial v}{\partial y} - i\frac{\partial u}{\partial y}$$

and since $f'(z)$ is also analytic,

$$f''(z) = \frac{\partial^2 u}{\partial x^2} + i\frac{\partial^2 v}{\partial x^2} = \frac{\partial^2 v}{\partial x\, \partial y} - i\frac{\partial^2 u}{\partial x\, \partial y} = -\frac{\partial^2 u}{\partial y^2} - i\frac{\partial^2 v}{\partial y^2}.$$

The fact that $f''(z)$ is analytic enables us to differentiate again to obtain the third partial derivatives, and so on.

Inasmuch as the existence of the third partial derivatives ensures the equality of mixed partial derivatives of the second order, we can show that the real and imaginary parts of an analytic function satisfy Laplace's equation throughout the region of analyticity of $f(z)$; for on differentiating the first of Cauchy-Riemann equations (4-7) with respect to y and the second with respect to x, we get

$$\frac{\partial^2 u}{\partial y \, \partial x} = \frac{\partial^2 v}{\partial y^2}, \qquad \frac{\partial^2 v}{\partial x^2} = - \frac{\partial^2 u}{\partial x \, \partial y}$$

and adding these we find

$$\frac{\partial^2 v}{\partial x^2} + \frac{\partial^2 v}{\partial y^2} = 0.$$

The fact that u also satisfies Laplace's equation

$$\frac{\partial^2 u}{\partial x^2} + \frac{\partial^2 u}{\partial y^2} = 0$$

follows similarly from the differentiation of the first of Eqs. (4-7) with respect to x and the second with respect to y.

Any real function $u(x,y)$ with continuous second partial derivatives which satisfies Laplace's equations in a given region is called *harmonic* in that region. Thus the real and imaginary parts of a function analytic in the region R are harmonic functions. Two harmonic functions $u(x,y)$, $v(x,y)$ such that $u + iv$ is an analytic function $f(z)$ are said to be *conjugate harmonics*. We shall show next that if one harmonic function is given, its conjugate harmonic can be determined to within a constant of integration. For, let $u(x,y)$ be given in R. Then if $v(x,y)$ is a conjugate harmonic, these functions satisfy the Cauchy-Riemann equations

$$\frac{\partial u}{\partial x} = \frac{\partial v}{\partial y}, \qquad \frac{\partial u}{\partial y} = - \frac{\partial v}{\partial x}. \tag{9-1}$$

Hence

$$dv = \frac{\partial v}{\partial x} dx + \frac{\partial v}{\partial y} dy = - \frac{\partial u}{\partial y} dx + \frac{\partial u}{\partial x} dy$$

and, since $\partial u / \partial x$ and $\partial u / \partial y$ are known from $u(x,y)$, we have

$$v(x,y) = \int_{(x_0,y_0)}^{(x,y)} \left(- \frac{\partial u}{\partial y} dx + \frac{\partial u}{\partial x} dy \right), \tag{9-2}$$

where the integral can be evaluated over any path joining an arbitrary point (x_0,y_0) of R with (x,y). Since the value of the line integral (9-2) depends on the choice of (x_0,y_0), it is clear that $v(x,y)$ is determined only to within an arbitrary constant. The integral is independent of the path inasmuch as

$$\frac{\partial}{\partial y} \left(- \frac{\partial u}{\partial y} \right) = \frac{\partial}{\partial x} \left(\frac{\partial u}{\partial x} \right),$$

and this equation is true because $u(x,y)$ is harmonic. It should be noted that when the region R is not simply connected, the function $v(x,y)$ may turn out to be multiple-valued.[1]

The connection of analytic functions with Laplace's equations is one of the principal reasons for the importance of the theory of functions of complex variables in applied mathematics.

In the preceding section we noted the maximum modulus theorem for analytic functions. This theorem enables us to prove the important fact that the *maximum values of harmonic functions (which are not mere constants) are invariably assumed on the boundary of the region.*

Let u be harmonic in the region R whose boundary is C. If v is a conjugate harmonic, then $u + iv$ is an analytic function, and therefore the function

$$e^{u+iv} = e^u(\cos v + i \sin v)$$

is also analytic. But the maximum of $|e^{u+iv}| \equiv e^u$ is assumed on the boundary C of R by the maximum modulus theorem. Since e^u takes on its maximum on the boundary C, $u(x,y)$ must assume its maximum on C.

Example: The function $u = x^2 - y^2$ is harmonic in every region. Obtain a conjugate harmonic v.

Inserting u in the formula (9-2) yields

$$v(x,y) = \int_{(x_0,y_0)}^{(x,y)} (2y\,dx + 2x\,dy) = 2\int_{(x_0,y_0)}^{(x,y)} d(xy) = 2xy + c,$$

where $c = -2x_0y_0$.

In this problem the integrand is so simple that we wrote its differential by inspection. In a more complicated case it may prove more expedient to evaluate the integral over some convenient path rather than reduce the integrand to the form of a differential of some function.

PROBLEMS

1. Prove that $v = 3x^2y - y^3$ is harmonic, and find a conjugate harmonic u.

2. Find an analytic function $f(z) = u + iv$ if:

   (a) $u = x$;
   (b) $u = \cosh y \cos x$;
   (c) $u = x/(x^2 + y^2)$;
   (d) $u = e^x \cos y$;
   (e) $u = \log \sqrt{x^2 + y^2}$.

10. Taylor's Series. In this section we are concerned with the power-series representation of analytic functions. The reader is advised to review Secs. 8, 9, and 16 of Chap. 2 dealing with the properties of power series.

Here we recall that when the power series $\sum\limits_{k=0}^{\infty} a_k z^k$ converges for $z = z_1$, it converges absolutely and uniformly in every closed circular region $|z| \leq r$, where $r < |z_1|$. A circle of radius r such that $\Sigma a_k z^k$ converges for

[1] See Sec. 5, Chap. 5.

$|z| < r$ and diverges for every $|z| > r$ is called the *circle of convergence*, and the number r is the *radius of convergence*. The radius of convergence can frequently be determined with the aid of the ratio test. Thus

$$r = \lim_{n \to \infty} \left| \frac{a_{n-1}}{a_n} \right|$$

whenever this limit exists.[1]

Example: The series $\sum_{n=1}^{\infty} \frac{(-1)^n z^n}{n}$ has the radius of convergence $r = 1$, since

$$\lim_{n \to \infty} \left| \frac{a_{n-1}}{a_n} \right| = \lim_{n \to \infty} \frac{n-1}{n} = 1.$$

The series $\sum_{n=0}^{\infty} n! z^n$ converges only for $z = 0$, since in this case

$$\lim_{n \to \infty} \left| \frac{a_{n-1}}{a_n} \right| = \lim_{n \to \infty} \frac{1}{n} = 0.$$

On the other hand, the series $\sum_{n=0}^{\infty} \frac{z^n}{n!}$ converges for all values of z, since

$$\lim_{n \to \infty} \left| \frac{a_{n-1}}{a_n} \right| = \lim_{n \to \infty} \frac{n!}{(n-1)!} = \infty.$$

We saw in Sec. 9, Chap. 2, that with every real function $f(x)$ having derivatives of all orders at a given point $x = a$, we can associate the power series

$$\sum_{n=0}^{\infty} a_n (x - a)^n$$

with $a_n = f^{(n)}(a)/n!$ which usually converges to $f(x)$ in some interval about the point $x = a$. However, the existence of infinitely many derivatives at $x = a$ does not ensure the convergence of the series $\Sigma a_n(x - a)^n$ to $f(x)$. To ensure convergence, the remainder in the Taylor formula (9-1) of Chap. 2 must approach zero.

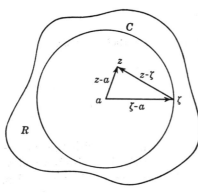

Inasmuch as every function $f(z)$ which is analytic at $z = a$ has infinitely many derivatives at that point, we can write down the series

$$\sum_{n=0}^{\infty} \frac{f^{(n)}(a)}{n!} (z - a)^n$$

Fig. 14

which converges in some circular region $|z - a| \leq r$. The question is: Does such a series invariably converge to $f(z)$?

We prove next (in contradistinction to the situation with the correspond-

[1] See Sec. 8, Chap. 2.

ing real series) that analytic functions can always be represented by power series.

Let $f(z)$ be analytic in some region R, and let C be a circle lying wholly in R and having its center at a. If z is any point interior to C (Fig. 14), then it follows from Cauchy's integral formula that

$$f(z) = \frac{1}{2\pi i} \int_C \frac{f(\zeta)}{\zeta - z} d\zeta$$

$$= \frac{1}{2\pi i} \int_C \frac{f(\zeta)}{\zeta - a} \left[\frac{1}{1 - (z - a)/(\zeta - a)} \right] d\zeta. \qquad (10\text{-}1)$$

But by long division

$$\frac{1}{1 - t} = 1 + t + t^2 + \cdots + t^{n-1} + \frac{t^n}{1 - t},$$

and substituting this expression with $t = (z - a)/(\zeta - a)$ in (10-1) leads to

$$f(z) = \frac{1}{2\pi i} \left[\int_C \frac{f(\zeta)}{\zeta - a} d\zeta + (z - a) \int_C \frac{f(\zeta)}{(\zeta - a)^2} d\zeta + \cdots \right.$$

$$\left. + (z - a)^{n-1} \int_C \frac{f(\zeta)}{(\zeta - a)^n} d\zeta \right] + R_n,$$

where

$$R_n = \frac{(z - a)^n}{2\pi i} \int_C \frac{f(\zeta)}{(\zeta - a)^n (\zeta - z)} d\zeta.$$

Making use of (8-10) gives

$$f(z) = f(a) + f'(a)(z - a) + \frac{f''(a)}{2!} (z - a)^2$$

$$+ \cdots + \frac{f^{(n-1)}(a)}{(n - 1)!} (z - a)^{n-1} + R_n. \qquad (10\text{-}2)$$

By taking n sufficiently large, the modulus of R_n may be made as small as desired. In order to show this, let the maximum value of $|f(\zeta)|$ on C be M, the radius of the circle C be r, and the modulus of $z - a$ be ρ. Then $|\zeta - z| \geq r - \rho$, as shown in Fig. 14, and

$$|R_n| = \frac{|z - a|^n}{2\pi} \left| \int_C \frac{f(\zeta)}{(\zeta - a)^n (\zeta - z)} d\zeta \right|$$

$$\leq \frac{\rho^n}{2\pi} \frac{M 2\pi r}{r^n (r - \rho)} = \frac{Mr}{r - \rho} \left(\frac{\rho}{r} \right)^n.$$

Since $\rho/r < 1$, it follows that $\lim\limits_{n \to \infty} |R_n| = 0$ for every z interior to C. Thus, one can write the infinite series

$$f(z) = f(a) + f'(a)(z - a) + \frac{f''(a)}{2!}(z - a)^2 + \cdots + \frac{f^{(n)}(a)}{n!}(z - a)^n + \cdots$$

$$(10\text{-}3)$$

which converges to $f(z)$ at every point z interior to the circle $|z - a| = r$. The series (10-3) is the Taylor series of $f(z)$ expanded about the point $z = a$. As in Chap. 2, Sec. 9, one can prove that the representation (10-3) is unique.

Let $z = z_0$ be the singular point of $f(z)$ nearest $z = a$; then $f(z)$ is analytic in the circular region $|z - a| < r_0$, where $r_0 = |z_0 - a|$. This circular region will then be the circle of convergence of the series (10-3) inasmuch as the series diverges for $|z - a| > r_0$. It should be noted, however, that there may be points of the region R where $f(z)$ is analytic which lie outside the circle of convergence of this series. However, one can always choose a new point a about which the expansion is performed so that the circle of convergence of Taylor's series about that particular point contains within it the desired value of z as long as $f(z)$ is analytic at z. In this manner the region R can be covered by a set of overlapping circles each of which is associated with some Taylor-series representation of $f(z)$.

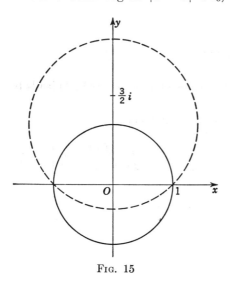

FIG. 15

For example, if $f(z) = 1/(1 - z)$, then the expansion of $f(z)$ about $z = 0$ yields

$$f(z) = 1 + z + z^2 + \cdots.$$

The circle of convergence of this series is $|z| = 1$. But $f(z) = 1/(1 - z)$ is analytic at $z = (\frac{3}{2})i$ (Fig. 15), which lies outside the circle $|z| = 1$. If we take $a = i$, the formula (10-3) yields the series whose circle of convergence is $|z - i| = \sqrt{2}$, and this circle includes the point $z = (\frac{3}{2})i$. The reader may find it instructive to deduce the expansion for $f(z) = 1/(1 - z)$ in powers of $z - i$ and determine the radius of convergence with the aid of the ratio test.

PROBLEMS

1. Expand $f(z) = 1/(1 - z)$ in Taylor's series about (a) $z = 0$, (b) $z = -1$, (c) $z = i$, and draw the circles of convergence for each of the series. What relation do the radii of convergence of these series bear to the distance from the point $z = 1$ to the point about which the series expansion is obtained?

2. Expand $f(z) = \log z$ in the Taylor series about $z = 1$, and determine the radius of convergence.

3. Obtain the Taylor expansion about $z = 0$ for the following functions, and determine the radii of convergence of the resulting series: (a) e^z, (b) $\sin z$, (c) $\cos z$, (d) $\log (1 + z)$, (e) $\cosh z$.

4. Expand $f(z) = \sinh z$ in Taylor's series about the point $z = \pi i$, and determine the radius of convergence of the resulting series.

5. Discuss the validity of the expansion $(1 + z)^m = 1 + mz + [m(m - 1)/2!]z^2 + \cdots$ for arbitrary values of m.

6. Verify the expansions:

(a) $\dfrac{1}{z^2} = \displaystyle\sum_{n=0}^{\infty} (n + 1)(z + 1)^n \qquad$ for $|z + 1| < 1$,

(b) $e^z = e \displaystyle\sum_{n=0}^{\infty} \dfrac{(z - 1)^n}{n!} \qquad$ for $|z| < \infty$.

11. Laurent's Expansion. We have just shown that a function $f(z)$ which is analytic at a given point a can be represented in the neighborhood of that point in a power series. Moreover, this series represents $f(z)$ in the interior of the circular region centered at a and whose radius is equal to the distance of a from the nearest singular point $f(z)$. In this section we prove a more general theorem due to Laurent.

LAURENT'S THEOREM. *A function $f(z)$ analytic in the interior and on the boundary of the circular ring determined by $|z - a| = R_1$ and $|z - a| = R_2$, with $R_2 < R_1$ (Fig. 16), can be represented at every interior point of the ring in the form*

$$f(z) = \sum_{n=0}^{\infty} a_n (z - a)^n + \sum_{n=1}^{\infty} \frac{a_{-n}}{(z - a)^n}, \qquad (11\text{-}1)$$

where $\qquad a_n = \dfrac{1}{2\pi i} \displaystyle\oint_{C_1} \dfrac{f(\zeta)}{(\zeta - a)^{n+1}} \, d\zeta, \qquad n = 0, 1, 2, \ldots, \qquad (11\text{-}2)$

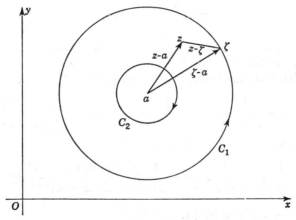

FIG. 16

$$a_{-n} = \frac{1}{2\pi i} \oint_{C_2} \frac{f(\zeta)}{(\zeta - a)^{-n+1}} d\zeta, \qquad n = 1, 2, \ldots, \qquad (11\text{-}3)$$

C_1 and C_2 being the boundaries of the ring.

To prove the theorem we recall that Cauchy's formula (8-8), when applied to the circular ring, enables us to write

$$f(z) = \frac{1}{2\pi i} \oint_{C_1} \frac{f(\zeta)}{\zeta - z} d\zeta - \frac{1}{2\pi i} \oint_{C_2} \frac{f(\zeta)\, d\zeta}{\zeta - z}, \qquad (11\text{-}4)$$

where z is any point in the interior of the ring.

We show next that the integrals in the right-hand member of (11-4) can be represented by the series appearing in (11-1). We begin with the integral over C_1 and note that if ζ is on C_1 and z is in the ring, then

$$\frac{1}{\zeta - z} \equiv \frac{1}{\zeta - a} \frac{1}{1 - (z - a)/(\zeta - a)} = \frac{1}{\zeta - a} \sum_{n=0}^{\infty} \frac{(z - a)^n}{(\zeta - a)^n},$$

since[1] $|z - a|/|\zeta - a| < 1$. Thus,

$$\frac{1}{\zeta - z} = \sum_{n=0}^{\infty} \frac{(z - a)^n}{(\zeta - a)^{n+1}} \qquad (11\text{-}5)$$

and hence

$$\frac{1}{2\pi i} \oint_{C_1} \frac{f(\zeta)\, d\zeta}{\zeta - z} d\zeta = \frac{1}{2\pi i} \oint_{C_1} \sum_{n=0}^{\infty} \frac{f(\zeta)(z - a)^n}{(\zeta - a)^{n+1}} d\zeta.$$

Since integration of the series term by term can be justified as in the discussion of (10-1), we can write

$$\frac{1}{2\pi i} \oint_{C_1} \frac{f(\zeta)\, d\zeta}{\zeta - z} d\zeta = \frac{1}{2\pi i} \sum_{n=0}^{\infty} (z - a)^n \oint_{C_1} \frac{f(\zeta)}{(\zeta - a)^{n+1}} d\zeta$$

$$\equiv \sum_{n=0}^{\infty} a_n (z - a)^n,$$

where we define a_n by the formula (11-2). This establishes the equality of the first terms in the right-hand members of (11-1) and (11-4).

We consider next the second integral in (11-4). If ζ is on C_2, then

$$\frac{1}{\zeta - z} = -\frac{1}{z - a} \frac{1}{1 - (\zeta - a)/(z - a)} = -\sum_{n=0}^{\infty} \frac{(\zeta - a)^n}{(z - a)^{n+1}},$$

since $|\zeta - a|/|z - a| < 1$ in this case. Hence

$$\frac{1}{2\pi i} \oint_{C_2} \frac{f(\zeta)}{\zeta - z} d\zeta = -\frac{1}{2\pi i} \oint_{C_2} \sum_{n=0}^{\infty} \frac{f(\zeta)(\zeta - a)^n}{(z - a)^{n+1}} d\zeta$$

[1] Note that $\dfrac{1}{1 - t} = \sum_{n=0}^{\infty} t^n$ if $|t| < 1$.

and the integration of the series term by term now yields

$$\frac{1}{2\pi i}\oint_{C_2}\frac{f(\zeta)}{\zeta - z}\,d\zeta = -\frac{1}{2\pi i}\sum_{n=0}^{\infty}\frac{1}{(z-a)^{n+1}}\oint_{C_2}f(\zeta)(\zeta - a)^n\,d\zeta$$

$$\equiv -\sum_{n=1}^{\infty}\frac{a_{-n}}{(z-a)^n},$$

where we set

$$a_{-n} = \frac{1}{2\pi i}\oint_{C_2}\frac{f(\zeta)}{(\zeta - a)^{-n+1}}\,d\zeta,\qquad n = 1, 2, \ldots.$$

This establishes the equality of the second terms in the right-hand members of (11-1) and (11-4), and the theorem is proved.

We note that if $f(z)$ is also analytic in the interior of the circle C_2, then the integrand in (11-3) is an analytic function and hence $a_{-n} = 0$ by Cauchy's integral theorem. In this case (11-1) reduces to the Taylor series, since

$$a_n = \frac{1}{2\pi i}\oint_{C_1}\frac{f(\zeta)}{(\zeta - a)^{n+1}}\,d\zeta = \frac{f^{(n)}(a)}{n!}$$

by (8-10).

We can write the series (11-1) more compactly as

$$f(z) = \sum_{n=-\infty}^{\infty} a_n(z - a)^n, \tag{11-6}$$

where the a_n can be computed from the formula

$$a_n = \frac{1}{2\pi i}\oint_{\Gamma}\frac{f(\zeta)}{(\zeta - a)^{n+1}}\,d\zeta,\qquad n = 0, \pm 1, \pm 2, \ldots \tag{11-7}$$

and Γ is any simple closed path [1] which lies in the ring and encloses C_2. It is possible to prove that the representation of $f(z)$ in a given circular ring in the series (11-6) is unique.[2] Hence if one obtains for $f(z)$ a representation

$$f(z) = \sum_{n=-\infty}^{\infty} b_n(z - a)^n$$

in a certain ring with the center at a, the coefficients b_n in this representation must be identical with those given by formula (11-7). This frequently enables one to deduce the Laurent series without evaluating the integrals (11-7).

[1] Recall that the integrals (11-2) and (11-3) have the same values when calculated over any path Γ into which C_1 and C_2 may be deformed without leaving the ring.

[2] See, for example, E. C. Titchmarsh, "The Theory of Functions," p. 101, 2d ed., Oxford University Press, London, 1939.

For example, let $f(z) = e^z/z^2$, and let it be required to obtain the expansion

$$\frac{e^z}{z^2} = \sum_{n=-\infty}^{\infty} a_n z^n.$$

Since $e^z = 1 + z + (z^2/2!) + \cdots + (z^n/n!) + \cdots$, we have for any $z \neq 0$

$$\frac{e^z}{z^2} = \frac{1}{z^2} + \frac{1}{z} + \frac{1}{2!} + \cdots + \frac{z^{n-2}}{n!} + \cdots.$$

This is a Laurent expansion about the origin; hence it is *the* Laurent expansion about the origin.

The Laurent expansion for $e^{1/z}$, valid for all $|z| > 0$, can be obtained from the series $e^u = 1 + u + (u^2/2!) + \cdots$ by letting $u = 1/z$.

As another illustration, consider

$$f(z) = \frac{z}{(z-1)(z-3)}. \tag{11-8}$$

This function has two singular points: $z = 1$ and $z = 3$. To obtain the Laurent series $\sum_{n=-\infty}^{\infty} a_n(z-1)^n$ valid in the neighborhood of $z = 1$, we can proceed as follows. Set $\phi(z) \equiv z/(z-3)$, and expand $\phi(z)$ in Taylor's series about $z = 1$. The result is

$$\frac{z}{z-3} = -\frac{1}{2} - 3 \sum_{n=1}^{\infty} \frac{(z-1)^n}{2^{n+1}}. \tag{11-9}$$

Since $z = 3$ is a singular point of $\phi(z)$, we conclude that (11-9) converges as long as $|z-1| < 2$. On multiplying this series by $1/(z-1)$, we get

$$\frac{z}{(z-1)(z-3)} = -\frac{1}{2(z-1)} - 3 \sum_{n=1}^{\infty} \frac{(z-1)^{n-1}}{2^{n+1}},$$

which is valid for $0 < |z-1| < 2$.

To obtain the expansion of $f(z)$ in (11-8) about $z = 3$, we set $\phi(z) = z/(z-1)$, expand it in Taylor's series about $z = 3$, and multiply the result by $1/(z-3)$.

The expansion for $f(z)$ in (11-8) valid for $|z| > 3$ can be deduced as follows: We decompose $f(z)$ into partial fractions and find

$$\frac{z}{(z-1)(z-3)} = \frac{-\frac{1}{2}}{z-1} + \frac{\frac{3}{2}}{z-3}. \tag{11-10}$$

But
$$\frac{1}{z-1} = \frac{1}{z}\frac{1}{1-(1/2)} = \frac{1}{z}\left(1 + \frac{1}{z} + \frac{1}{z^2} + \cdots\right) \quad \text{for } |z| > 1$$

and
$$\frac{1}{z-3} = \frac{1}{z}\frac{1}{1-(3/z)} = \frac{1}{z}\left(1 + \frac{3}{z} + \frac{3^2}{z^2} + \cdots\right) \quad \text{for } |z| > 3.$$

Substitution of these series in (11-10) yields the desired expansion.

The reader may find it instructive to obtain the same expansion by writing

$$f(z) = \frac{z}{(z-1)(z-3)} = \frac{1}{z}\frac{1}{1-(1/z)}\frac{1}{1-(3/z)} \tag{11-11}$$

and forming the product of the appropriate series for the factors in the right-hand member of (11-11).

PROBLEMS

1. Obtain Laurent's expansions for $f(z) = 1/[z(1 - z)^2]$: (a) about $z = 0$, (b) about $z = 1$.

2. Obtain Laurent's expansion for e^{-1/z^2} valid for $|z| > 0$.

3. Expand in Laurent's series about $z = 1$: (a) $(z - 1)^2$, (b) $1/(z - 1)^2$, (c) $(z - 1)^2 + [1/(z - 1)^2]$.

4. Obtain Laurent's expansion for $f(z) = 1/[(z - 1)(z - 2)]$ valid in the following regions: (a) $|z - 1| < 1$, (b) $|z| > 2$, (c) $1 < |z| < 2$. Note that in (b) and (c) the desired expansions have the forms $\sum_{n=-\infty}^{\infty} a_n z^n$. *Hint:* Show that

$$f(z) \equiv \frac{1}{z - 2} - \frac{1}{z - 1} \quad \text{and} \quad \frac{1}{z - 1} = \frac{1}{z}\sum_{n=0}^{\infty} \frac{1}{z^n} \quad \text{for } |z| > 1,$$

$$\frac{1}{z - 2} = -\frac{1}{2}\sum_{n=0}^{\infty} \left(\frac{z}{2}\right)^n \quad \text{for } |z| < 2, \qquad \frac{1}{z - 2} = \frac{1}{z}\sum_{n=0}^{\infty} \left(\frac{2}{z}\right)^n \quad \text{for } |z| > 2.$$

5. Show that $f(z) = 1/[z^2(1 - z)]$ has the following expansions:

(a) $\sum_{n=0}^{\infty} z^{n-2}$, valid for $0 < |z| < 1$,

(b) $\sum_{n=0}^{\infty} \frac{-1}{z^{n+3}}$, valid for $|z| > 1$.

12. Singular Points. Residues.

If $z = a$ is a singular point of an analytic function $f(z)$ and the neighborhood of $z = a$ contains no other singular points of $f(z)$, the singularity at $z = a$ is said to be *isolated*.

Thus, $f(z) = 1/z$ has an isolated singular point $z = 0$ because the region $|z| = \rho > 0$ contains no singular points other than $z = 0$ within it. The function

$$f(z) = \frac{z - 1}{z(z^2 + 1)}$$

has three isolated singular points: $z = 0$, $z = i$, $z = -i$. The function

$$f(z) = e^{1/(z^2-1)}$$

has two isolated singular points: $z = 1$ and $z = -1$. Not all singular points of analytic functions are isolated, however. For example,

$$f(z) = \frac{1}{\sin (1/z)} \tag{12-1}$$

has a singularity whenever $z = \pm(1/k\pi)$, $k = 1, 2, \ldots$. These singular points are isolated. But (12-1) also has a singular point $z = 0$, which is not isolated, for, no matter how small the radius ρ of the circle $|z| = \rho$ may be, this circle contains infinitely many singular points $z = \pm(1/k\pi)$ in its interior.

The function $\log z$ has a singularity at $z = 0$, and so does $\sqrt{z}$. These singularities are not isolated because every circle $|z| = \rho$ includes part of the positive real axis, upon crossing which the single-valued branches of $\log z$ and $\sqrt{z}$ suffer discontinuities if the real axis is chosen to be the cut, as in Secs. 16 and 17. The points at which the branches of a multiple-valued function assume equal values are called the *branch points*. For the present we shall restrict our considerations to single-valued functions.

If $z = a$ is an isolated singular point of $f(z)$, then in the *neighborhood* of $z = a$ the function $f(z)$ can be represented by the Laurent series

$$f(z) = \sum_{n=0}^{\infty} a_n(z - a)^n + \sum_{n=1}^{\infty} \frac{a_{-n}}{(z - a)^n}. \tag{12-2}$$

Some coefficients in (12-2) may vanish, and there are two nontrivial cases that present themselves:

1. The expansion (12-2) contains at most a finite number m of terms with negative powers of $z - a$, so that (12-2) reads

$$f(z) = \sum_{n=0}^{\infty} a_n(z - a)^n + \frac{a_{-1}}{z - a} + \frac{a_{-2}}{(z - a)^2} + \cdots + \frac{a_{-m}}{(z - a)^m}. \tag{12-3}$$

2. The expansion (12-2) contains infinitely many terms with negative powers of $z - a$.

The type of singularity at $z = a$ characterized by the representation (12-3) is called a *pole of order* m. A pole of order 1 is also called a *simple pole*. When the expansion (12-2) has infinitely many terms with negative powers of $z - a$, the point $z = a$ is called an *essential singular point* of $f(z)$. We shall see in Sec. 14 that the behavior of a function in the neighborhood of a pole differs radically from that at an essential singular point.

We note from (12-3) that whenever $f(z)$ has a pole of order m, one can define a function [1]

$$\phi(z) = (z - a)^m f(z), \qquad z \neq a,$$

$$\phi(a) = a_{-m},$$

which is analytic at $z = a$, but the function $(z - a)^{m-1}f(z)$ is not analytic at $z = a$. This property is used sometimes to define a pole of order m.

The coefficient a_{-1} in the Laurent representation (12-2) of $f(z)$ in the neighborhood of an isolated singular point $z = a$ plays an important role in the evaluation of integrals of analytic functions. This coefficient is called the *residue* of $f(z)$ at $z = a$.

When the singularity at $z = a$ is a *pole* of order m, the residue at a can

[1] When $z = a$, the function $\phi(z)$ assumes the indeterminate form $0/0$. We agree to define $\phi(a) = \lim_{z \to a} \phi(z)$.

be determined without deducing the Laurent expansion. Thus, on multi-plying (12-3) by $(z - a)^m$, we get

$$\phi(z) \equiv (z - a)^m f(z)$$

$$= a_{-m} + a_{-m+1}(z - a) + \cdots + a_{-1}(z - a)^{m-1} + a_0(z - a)^m + \cdots$$

$$(12\text{-}4)$$

where $a_{-m} \neq 0$. Since this is a power-series representation of $\phi(z)$, the coefficient a_{-1} in it must be the coefficient of the term $(z - a)^{m-1}$ in the Taylor expansion of $\phi(z)$ about $z = a$. Thus

$$a_{-1} = \frac{1}{(m - 1)!} \left. \frac{d^{m-1}[(z - a)^m f(z)]}{dz^{m-1}} \right|_{z=a} . \qquad (12\text{-}5)$$

We formulate this result as a useful theorem:

THEOREM. *If* $\phi(z) = (z - a)^m f(z)$ *is analytic at* $z = a$ *and* $\phi(a) \neq 0$, *then* $f(z)$ *has a pole of order* m *at* $z = a$ *with the residue given by* (12-5).

As a special case of this theorem we note that when the pole at $z = a$ is simple, the residue at a is given by the formula

$$a_{-1} = \lim_{z \to a} f(z)(z - a). \qquad (12\text{-}6)$$

Example 1. Obtain the residues at the singular points of $f(z) = (1 + z)/[z(2 - z)]$. This function has a simple pole at $z = 0$ inasmuch as

$$\phi(z) = z \frac{1 + z}{z(2 - z)} = \frac{1 + z}{2 - z}$$

is analytic and does not vanish at $z = 0$. Also

$$\phi(z) = (z - 2) \frac{1 + z}{z(2 - z)} = -\frac{z + 1}{z}$$

is analytic at $z = 2$ and does not vanish for $z = 2$. Hence $f(z)$ also has a simple pole at $z = 2$.

The residues at these points can therefore be computed with the aid of the formula (12-6). We find that the residue at $z = 0$ is $\frac{1}{2}$ and at $z = 2$ it is $-\frac{3}{2}$.

Example 2. The function

$$f(z) = \frac{e^z}{z^2 + 1} = \frac{e^z}{(z + i)(z - i)}$$

obviously has simple poles at $z = -i$ and $z = i$. Therefore the residue at $z = i$ is

$$a_{-1} = \lim_{z \to i} (z - i) \frac{e^z}{(z + i)(z - i)} = \lim_{z \to i} \frac{e^z}{z + i} = \frac{e^i}{2i}.$$

Similarly, the residue at $z = -i$ is found to be $-e^{-i}/2i$.

Example 3. The function $f(z) = 1/[z(z + 1)^2]$ has a simple pole at $z = 0$, since

$$\phi(z) = z \frac{1}{z(z + 1)^2} = \frac{1}{(z + 1)^2}$$

is analytic at $z = 0$ and $\phi(0) \neq 0$. Therefore, the residue at $z = 0$ is

$$a_{-1} = \lim_{z \to 0} \frac{1}{(z+1)^2} = 1.$$

The singularity of $f(z)$ at $z = -1$ is a pole of order 2, since

$$\phi(z) = (z+1)^2 \frac{1}{z(1+z)^2} = \frac{1}{z}$$

is analytic at $z = -1$ and $\phi(-1) = -1$. We can therefore compute the residue at $z = -1$ with the aid of (12-5). We get

$$a_{-1} = \frac{1}{1!}\frac{d}{dz}\left(\frac{1}{z}\right)_{z=-1} = -\frac{1}{z^2}\Big|_{z=-1} = -1.$$

Example 4. The function $(\sin z)/z^4$ has a pole of order 3 at $z = 0$ as the reader can easily check with the aid of the theorem of this section. Hence the residue at $z = 0$ can be computed by using formula (12-5). It is simpler, however, in this case, to write out the Laurent expansion in the neighborhood of $z = 0$ and obtain the residue from it. Since $\sin z = z - (z^3/3!) + (z^5/5!) - \cdots$,

$$\frac{\sin z}{z^4} = \frac{1}{z^3} - \frac{1}{3!}\frac{1}{z} + \frac{z}{5!} - \cdots \qquad \text{for } |z| > 0.$$

It is clear from this that the singularity at $z = 0$ is a pole of order 3 with the residue $-1/3!$.

Example 5. The function

$$f(z) = \cos \frac{1}{z-1}$$

has an isolated singular point at $z = 1$. This point, however, is not a pole, for on noting that

$$\cos u = 1 - \frac{u^2}{2!} + \frac{u^4}{4!} - \cdots$$

we conclude by the substitution $u = 1/(z-1)$ that for $|z-1| > 0$,

$$\cos \frac{1}{z-1} = 1 - \frac{1}{2!(z-1)^2} + \frac{1}{4!(z-1)^4} - \cdots.$$

This is the desired Laurent expansion about $z = 1$. Since it has infinitely many negative powers of $z - 1$, the point $z = 1$ is an essential singular point. Inasmuch as the term $(z-1)^{-1}$ does not appear in the expansion, the residue a_{-1} at $z = 1$ is zero.

PROBLEMS

1. Obtain the Laurent expansions in the neighborhood of the singular points of the following functions, and thus obtain the residues:

(a) $\dfrac{\cos z}{z^3}$, (b) e^{-1/z^2}, (c) $\dfrac{1}{1-z}$, (d) $\dfrac{z}{1-z}$, (e) $\dfrac{e^{-z}}{z^2}$, (f) $z^2 e^{1/z}$, (g) $\dfrac{1-e^{2z}}{z^4}$, (h) $\dfrac{e^z}{(z-1)^2}$,

(i) $\dfrac{1}{1-z^2}$, (j) $\dfrac{1}{z(z-1)}$, (k) $\cot z$, (l) $\tan z$.

2. Whenever possible, determine the residues at the poles of the functions in Prob. 1 by means of formula (12-5).

3. Obtain the residues in Examples 1, 2, and 3 of this section by deducing appropriate Laurent's series.

4. Prove the following theorem: If $f(z) = g(z)/h(z)$ is the quotient of two functions analytic at $z = a$ such that $g(a) \neq 0$, $h(a) = 0$, and $h'(a) \neq 0$, then $f(z)$ has a simple pole at $z = a$ with the residue $g(a)/h'(a)$. *Hint:* Examine the quotient of the Taylor expansions of $g(z)$ and $h(z)$ about $z = a$.

5. Use the theorem of Prob. 4 to show that $f(z) = \cot z = \cos z/\sin z$ has simple poles at $z = \pm k\pi$, $k = 0, 1, 2, \ldots$.

6. Note that $f(z) = 1/(2 - z) + 1/(z - 1)$ has the Laurent expansion

$$f(z) = \sum_{n=0}^{\infty} \frac{1}{2^{n+1}} z^n + \sum_{n=1}^{\infty} \frac{1}{z^n}$$

valid in the ring $1 < |z| < 2$. This expansion has the term $1/z$. Does it follow that $z = 0$ is a singular point of $f(z)$ with the residue equal to 1?

13. Residue Theorem.

Let $f(z)$ be analytic in the given closed region R bounded by C, except at the isolated singular points $z = z_1$, $z = z_2$, $\ldots, z = z_m$. If these points z_k are enclosed by circles Γ_k $(k = 1, 2, \ldots, m)$, so that $f(z)$ is analytic in the multiply connected region bounded by C and the Γ_k, we know that

$$\oint_C f(z)\, dz = \oint_{\Gamma_1} f(z)\, dz + \oint_{\Gamma_2} f(z)\, dz + \cdots + \oint_{\Gamma_m} f(z)\, dz. \qquad (13\text{-}1)$$

But from (11-7), on setting $n = -1$, we see that

$$(a_{-1})_k = \frac{1}{2\pi i} \oint_{\Gamma_k} f(z)\, dz \qquad (13\text{-}2)$$

where $(a_{-1})_k$ is the residue of $f(z)$ at $z = z_k$. We can thus write (13-1) in the form

$$\oint_C f(z)\, dz = 2\pi i \sum_{k=1}^{m} (a_{-1})_k. \qquad (13\text{-}3)$$

The result embodied in this formula is known as the RESIDUE THEOREM: *The integral of $f(z)$ over a contour C containing within it only isolated singular points of $f(z)$ is equal to $2\pi i$ times the sum of the residues at these points.*

Inasmuch as the residues of $f(z)$, as demonstrated in the preceding section, can often be easily calculated, we see that formula (13-3) provides a simple means for evaluating integrals of analytic functions with isolated singularities.

Example 1. Evaluate $\displaystyle\int_C \frac{1+z}{z(2-z)}\, dz$, where C is the circle $|z| = 1$.

The only singular point of the integrand enclosed by C is $z = 0$. In Example 1 of Sec. 12 we saw that the residue of the integrand at $z = 0$ is $\frac{1}{2}$. Hence the value of the integral is $(2\pi i)\frac{1}{2} = \pi i$. The value of this integral over any path C enclosing $z = 0$ and $z = 2$ is $2\pi i(\frac{1}{2} - \frac{3}{2}) = -2\pi i$, since the residues at these points are $\frac{1}{2}$ and $-\frac{3}{2}$.

Example 2.   Evaluate $\int_C \dfrac{e^z}{z^2 + 1}\, dz$ over the circular path $|z| = 2$.

The residues of the integrand at $z = i$ and $z = -i$ were computed in Example 2, Sec. 12. Hence the value of the integral is

$$2\pi i \left(\frac{e^i}{2i} - \frac{e^{-i}}{2i} \right) = 2\pi i \sin 1.$$

Example 3.   Evaluate $\int_C \cos \left(\dfrac{1}{z - 1} \right) dz$.

We saw in Example 5 of Sec. 12 that $z = 1$ is an essential singular point with the residue zero. Hence the value of the integral is zero for every closed path C which does not pass through $z = 1$. If $z = 1$ lies on C, the integral is improper and other means have to be employed to determine its value.

PROBLEMS

1. Use results of Prob. 1, Sec. 12, to obtain values of the following integrals where C is the circle $|z| = 2$:

(a) $\int_C \dfrac{\cos z}{z^3}\, dz$, (b) $\int_C \dfrac{z\, dz}{1 - z}$, (c) $\int_C z^2 e^{1/z}\, dz$, (d) $\int_C \dfrac{1 - e^{2z}}{z^4}\, dz$, (e) $\int_C \dfrac{e^z}{(z - 1)^2}\, dz$,

(f) $\int_C \dfrac{1}{1 - z^2}\, dz$, (g) $\int_C \dfrac{1}{z(z - 1)}\, dz$.

2. Determine the residues of $f(z) = \dfrac{z - 2}{z(z - 1)}$ at $z = 0$ and $z = 1$, and thus evaluate the integral $\int_C \dfrac{z - 2}{z(z - 1)}\, dz$, where C is the circle $|z| = 2$.

3. Evaluate the integrals $\int_{C_i} \dfrac{z + 1}{z^2 - 2z}\, dz$ $(i = 1, 2)$, where C_1 is the circle $|z| = 1$ and C_2 is the circle $|z| = 3$.

4. Find the value of $\int_C \dfrac{z + 1}{(z - 2)^2}\, dz$, where (a) C is the circle $|z| = 1$, (b) C is the circle $|z| = 3$.

14. Behavior of $f(z)$ at Poles and Essential Singular Points. From Laurent's representation (12-3) of $f(z)$ in the neighborhood of a pole $z = a$, we easily conclude that $|f(z)|$ becomes infinite as $z \to a$. The behavior of $|f(z)|$ with an essential singularity at $z = a$ is different because the expansion (12-2) has infinitely many terms with negative powers of $z - a$. While it is true that in this case $|f(z)|$ as $z \to a$ is also unbounded, the function $|f(z)|$ oscillates as $z \to a$. Indeed, it was shown by E. Picard that in the neighborhood of an essential singular point, $f(z)$ assumes any preassigned value, with the possible exception of one value, infinitely many times. A discussion of this would carry us too far in the study of analytic functions, and we merely illustrate this behavior by an example. Since

$$e^{1/z} = 1 + \frac{1}{z} + \frac{1}{2!z^2} + \cdots, \qquad |z| > 0,$$

$f(z) = e^{1/z}$ has an essential singular point at $z = 0$. We show that if A is any complex number not zero, there are infinitely many values of z in the neighborhood of $z = 0$ such that

$$e^{1/z} = A, \qquad (14\text{-}1)$$

for on taking the logarithm of (14-1) we get infinitely many solutions

$$z = \frac{1}{\text{Log } |A| + i(\phi + 2k\pi)}, \qquad k = 0, \pm1, \pm2, \ldots,$$

where ϕ is the principal argument of A.

GEOMETRIC ASPECTS

15. Geometric Representation. The usefulness of graphical representation of real-valued functional relationships in the familiar three-dimensional space is too obvious to require emphasis. The customary mode of representing real functions by curves and surfaces fails, however, when one encounters functions of more than two independent variables. Thus, a relationship $u = f(x,y,z)$ containing three independent real variables x, y, z requires a four-dimensional space for geometric representation. Similar difficulties arise when one attempts to represent graphically complex functions $w = f(z)$, with $z = x + iy$. For, to each pair of values (x,y), there correspond two values (u,v) in $w = u + iv$, and in order to plot a quadruplet of real values (u,v,x,y) we need a four-dimensional space.

However, a different mode of visualizing the relationship $w = f(z)$ which utilizes two separate complex planes for the representation of z and w is possible. The relationship $w = f(z)$ then establishes a connection between the points of a given region R in the z plane and another region R' determined by $w = f(z)$ in the w plane.

On separating $w = f(z)$ into real and imaginary parts one obtains two real functions

$$\begin{aligned} u &= u(x,y), \\ v &= v(x,y), \end{aligned} \qquad (15\text{-}1)$$

which can be viewed as the equations of a transformation that maps a specified set of points in the xy plane into another set of points (u,v) in the uv plane.

We turn now to this mode of studying complex functions.

Example 1. Let $w = z + a$, where $a = h + ik$ is a complex constant. We set $w = u + iv$, $z = x + iy$, and get

$$u + iv = x + iy + h + ik$$
$$= (x + h) + i(y + k).$$

Hence
$$u = x + h,$$
$$(15\text{-}2)$$
$$v = y + k.$$

Formulas (15-2) are the familiar equations defining a *translation*, and the relationship $w = z + a$ can be visualized as representing a rigid displacement of points in the z plane, where each point is moved h units in the direction of the x axis and k units in the direction of the y axis.

Example 2. To study the function $w = az$, where a is a constant, it is convenient to use polar coordinates.

We set $z = re^{i\theta}$, $w = \rho e^{i\phi}$, $a = Ae^{i\alpha}$ and get

$$\rho e^{i\phi} = Are^{i(\alpha+\theta)}.$$

Hence
$$\rho = Ar, \qquad \phi = \alpha + \theta. \qquad (15\text{-}3)$$

We see from (15-3) that the modulus of w is got by multiplying the modulus of z by A. Also the argument ϕ of w is got by adding a constant angle α to the argument θ of z. We can visualize the transformation (15-3) as representing a stretching in the ratio $A:1$ accompanied by a rotation through an angle α. A square with the center at the origin in the z plane is thus deformed into a square, a circle of radius R is transformed into a circle of radius AR, and more generally any figure is transformed into a similar figure enlarged by the factor A. If $A = 1$, we have a pure rotation through an angle α.

The same conclusions can be reached (but less readily) by setting $w = u + iv$, $z = x + iy$, $a = a_1 + ia_2$ and by deducing from $w = az$ the transformation

$$u = a_1x - a_2y,$$
$$v = a_2x + a_1y,$$

in cartesian coordinates.

Example 3. To study the relationship $w = 1/z$, $z \neq 0$, we again use polar coordinates. On setting $w = \rho e^{i\phi}$, $z = re^{i\theta}$, we get $\rho e^{i\phi} = (1/r)e^{-i\theta}$, so that

$$\rho = \frac{1}{r}, \qquad \phi = -\theta. \qquad (15\text{-}4)$$

It is clear from (15-4) that the unit circle $|z| = 1$ is transformed into the unit circle $|w| = 1$ in the w plane. Since $\phi = -\theta$, the corresponding points on these circles are got by reflection in the axis of reals (Fig. 17). As the point A traces out the circle $|z| = 1$ in

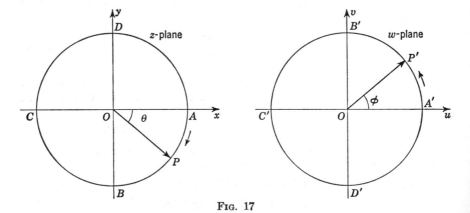

Fig. 17

the clockwise direction, the corresponding point A' in the w plane traces out the circle $|w| = 1$ in the counterclockwise direction. Points in the interior of $|z| = 1$ are mapped into points in the exterior of $|w| = 1$, except that the transformation of the point $z = 0$ is not defined by $w = 1/z$. Points in the neighborhood of $z = 0$ map into points at a great distance from the origin of the w plane, since $\rho = 1/r$. To complete the correspondence of points, we can introduce a new point $w = \infty$ as the correspondent of $z = 0$. The point $w = \infty$ is called the *point at infinity*. If we consider the inverse transformation $z = 1/w$, we see that $w = 0$ corresponds to $z = \infty$.

The reader can show that the equations of transformation defined by $w = 1/z$ in cartesian coordinates have the form

$$u = \frac{x}{x^2 + y^2}, \qquad v = -\frac{y}{x^2 + y^2},$$

with the inverse

$$x = \frac{u}{u^2 + v^2}, \qquad y = -\frac{v}{u^2 + v^2}. \tag{15-5}$$

PROBLEMS

1. Discuss the transformations defined by (a) $w = (1 + i)z$, (b) $w = 1/(z - 1)$, (c) $w = i/z$, (d) $w = az + b$.

2. Show that every circle in the z plane maps by the transformation $w = 1/z$ into a circle in the w plane if one considers straight lines as the limiting cases of circles. *Hint:* Write the general equation of the circle in cartesian coordinates, and make use of (15-5).

3. Show that the *bilinear transformation*

$$w = \frac{az + b}{cz + d}, \qquad \text{with } ad - bc \neq 0,$$

can be decomposed into successive transformations $z' = cz + d$, $z'' = 1/z'$, $w = (a/c) + [(bc - ad)/c]z''$, which are the type studied in Examples 1, 2, and 3. Then conclude (see Prob. 2) that a bilinear transformation transforms circles into circles. Discuss the case when $ad - bc = 0$.

16. Functions $w = z^n$ and $z = \sqrt[n]{w}$. Let us study next the mapping determined by the function

$$w = z^2. \tag{16-1}$$

If we set $z = re^{i\theta}$ and $w = \rho e^{i\phi}$, we get

$$\rho e^{i\phi} = r^2 e^{i2\theta},$$

so that

$$\rho = r^2,$$

$$\phi = 2\theta. \tag{16-2}$$

It is clear from (16-2) that the upper half of the z plane maps into the whole w plane, for when z is in the upper half plane, the range of variation of θ is $0 \leq \theta < \pi$. Since $\phi = 2\theta$, we see that the arguments of the corresponding points in the w plane vary from 0 to 2π. Points on the upper half of the circle $|z| = r$ map into the entire circle $|w| = r^2$ (Fig. 18). The half ray OA in the z plane maps into the half ray $O'A'$ in the w plane. A radial line OB, making an angle θ with the x axis, goes over into a radial line $O'B'$, making an angle $\phi = 2\theta$ with the u axis. The interior of the quadrant OAC of the circle $|z| = 1$ maps into the interior of the semicircle $|w| = 1$ in the upper half of the w plane with the boundary ABC going over into the boundary $A'B'C'$. The segment OF of the negative real axis in the z plane maps into the segment $O'F'$ along the positive u axis. To distinguish points on the positive u axis that correspond to points on the ray OA from those on OF, we can imagine that the w plane is slit

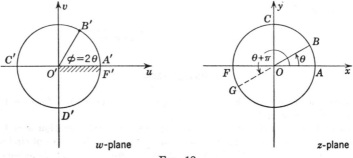

w-plane z-plane

FIG. 18

along the positive u axis and suppose that the points corresponding to OA lie on the upper bank of the slit $O'A'$ and that those corresponding to OF lie on the lower bank $O'F'$.

The transformation of points determined by (16-1) can be visualized as a fanwise stretching of the upper half of the z plane in which the sector OAB opens into a sector $O'A'B'$ and the half circle $OACF$ is deformed into the whole circle $|w| = 1$. The semicircles of radius r in the z plane go over into full circles of radius $\rho = r^2$ in the w plane. Points in the lower half of the circle $|z| = 1$ map into the whole circle $|w| = 1$, inasmuch as the replacement of θ by $\theta + \pi$ in (16-2) yields $\phi = 2\theta + 2\pi$. Thus, two distinct points B and G with the arguments θ and $\theta + \pi$ in the z plane correspond to one and the same point B' in the w plane.

This is to be expected, since, on solving (16-1) for z, we get

$$z = \sqrt{w}, \tag{16-3}$$

which is a double-valued function. If we set $w = \rho e^{i\phi}$ in (16-3), we get two values

$$z = \sqrt{\rho}\, e^{i(\phi/2)}, \qquad z = \sqrt{\rho}\, e^{i[(\phi/2)+\pi]} = -\sqrt{\rho}\, e^{i(\phi/2)}. \tag{16-4}$$

For points along the u axis, the argument $\phi = 0$. Points on the upper bank of the slit $O'A'$ in Fig. 18 correspond to $z = \sqrt{\rho}$, and those of the lower bank $O'F'$ to $z = -\sqrt{\rho}$. Thus, along the slit, $z = \sqrt{w}$ is a discontinuous function unless $\rho = 0$.

The function

$$w = z^n, \qquad n \text{ a positive integer}, \tag{16-5}$$

can be studied in the same way. On setting $z = re^{i\theta}$, $w = \rho e^{i\phi}$ we find

$$\rho = r^n, \qquad \phi = n\theta. \tag{16-6}$$

This time a wedge of angle $2\pi/n$ in the z plane (Fig. 19) maps into the

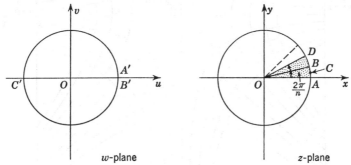

FIG. 19

whole of the w plane, and a circular arc ACB of radius R goes over into a full circle $|w| = R^n$. An adjacent wedge OBD of angle $2\pi/n$ also maps into the whole w plane. If we divide the z plane into a set of n adjoining wedges, each of angle $2\pi/n$, the entire z plane will be mapped into the w plane n times.

Corresponding to a given point $w \neq 0$, there will be n values of z determined by the n roots

$$z = \sqrt[n]{w} = \rho^{1/n}\left[\left(\cos\frac{\phi}{n} + \frac{2\pi k}{n}\right) + i\sin\left(\frac{\phi}{n} + \frac{2\pi k}{n}\right)\right], \tag{16-7}$$

with $k = 0, 1, \ldots, n - 1$. Each of these roots lies in one of the wedges into which the z plane is divided.

Some further insight into the character of mapping by means of (16-1) can be gained by studying the maps of lines $u = \text{const}$, $v = \text{const}$. If we set $z = x + iy$ in (16-1), we find

$$u = x^2 - y^2,$$
$$v = 2xy, \tag{16-8}$$

so that the lines $u = \text{const}$, $v = \text{const}$ map into orthogonal hyperbolas $x^2 - y^2 = \text{const}$, $2xy = \text{const}$. Some of these are shown in Fig. 20, in which the corresponding points are labeled by like letters.

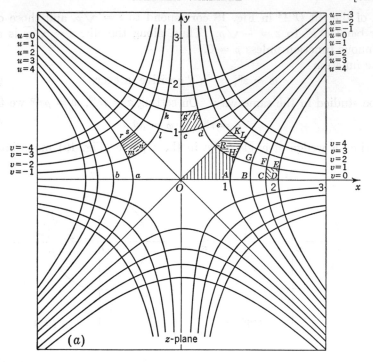

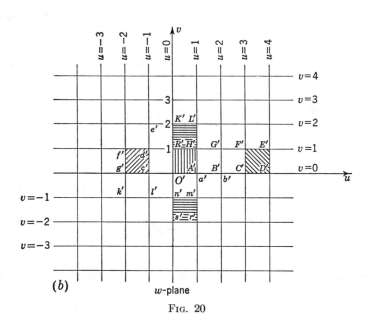

Fig. 20

17. The Functions $w = e^z$ **and** $z = \log w$. If we set $w = u + iv$ and $z = x + iy$ in

$$w = e^z, \tag{17-1}$$

we get

$$u + iv = e^{x+iy} = e^x(\cos y + i \sin y).$$

Hence

$$u = e^x \cos y, \qquad v = e^x \sin y. \tag{17-2}$$

It follows from these equations that

$$u^2 + v^2 = e^{2x},$$

$$\frac{v}{u} = \tan y. \tag{17-3}$$

Accordingly, the lines $x = $ const map into the circles $u^2 + v^2 = $ const in the w plane, and the lines $y = $ const map into the radial lines $v/u = $ const.
Since

$$e^{z+2k\pi i} = e^z e^{2k\pi i} = e^z, \qquad k = 0, \pm 1, \pm 2, \ldots, \tag{17-4}$$

we see that $w = e^z$ has an imaginary period [1] $2\pi i$. Hence, if the z plane is divided into horizontal strips of width 2π, with the initial strip determined by $0 \leq y \leq 2\pi$ (Fig. 21), the relations (17-4) ensure that the behavior

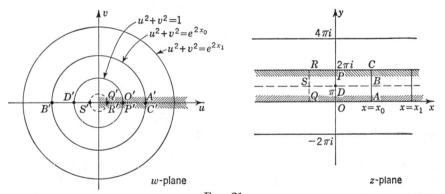

w-plane   z-plane

Fig. 21

of $w = e^z$ in every strip $2k\pi \leq y \leq 2(k+1)\pi$, $k = \pm 1, \pm 2, \ldots$, is identical with that in the initial strip. Consequently, we can confine our attention to the behavior of $w = e^z$ in the initial strip $0 \leq y \leq 2\pi$.

A segment AC of a straight line $x = x_0$ in the initial strip maps by (17-3) into a circle $u^2 + v^2 = e^{2x_0}$. The points $A(x_0, 0)$, $C(x_0, 2\pi)$ correspond to the same point $u = e^{2x_0}$, $v = 0$ on the u axis. The segment OP of the

---

[1] As for real functions, we say that $f(z)$ is periodic of period a if $f(z + a) = f(z)$.

y axis maps into the unit circle $u^2 + v^2 = 1$, since along OP $x = 0$; the half strip $x > 0$, $0 \leq y \leq 2\pi$, maps into the region $|w| > 1$. If $x < 0$, a segment such as QR in Fig. 21 maps into a circle whose radius is less than 1. The half strip $x < 0$, $0 \leq y \leq 2\pi$, goes into the interior of the circle $|w| = 1$. Points on the lines $y = 0$, $y = 2\pi$, forming the boundaries of the strip, map into points on the positive u axis. If we slit the w plane along the positive u axis, then the points on the upper bank of the slit correspond to points on the line $y = 0$ and those on the lower bank to points on $y = 2\pi$. The interior of the rectangle $OACP$ in Fig. 21 corresponds to the interior of the ring between the circles $u^2 + v^2 = 1$ and $u^2 + v^2 = e^{x_0}$.

We further note that a point moving along the x axis away from the origin O in the positive direction has for its image a point in the w plane that moves in the positive direction along the u axis away from the image O' on the unit circle. A point moving *away* from O in the direction of the negative x axis has for its image a point moving from O' *toward* the origin of the w plane.

If we consider some definite point w_0 in the w plane, the equation

$$w_0 = e^z \tag{17-5}$$

has for its solution

$$z = \log w_0 = \text{Log}\,|w_0| + i(\phi_0 + 2k\pi), \qquad k = 0, \pm1, \pm2, \ldots, \tag{17-6}$$

where ϕ_0 is the principal argument of w_0. All these values of z differ only by the imaginary part, and therefore there is just one solution of (17-5) in each strip $2k\pi \leq y \leq 2(k+1)\pi$. The function

$$z = \log w$$

is therefore infinitely-many-valued. If we restrict our attention to the slit w plane so that the argument ϕ of w lies between 0 and 2π, the mapping from the w plane to the z plane will be single-valued with just one image of $\log w$ in the fundamental strip $0 \leq y \leq 2\pi$ of the z plane.

To study the map of $w = \log z$ we interchange the roles of the z and w planes in the foregoing discussion. We remark in conclusion that inasmuch as all trigonometric functions of z are defined in terms of e^z, a study of the mapping properties of such functions is reducible to the study of mapping by $w = e^{az}$.

PROBLEMS

1. Discuss in detail mapping by the function $w = z^3$.

2. Show that the function

$$w = a\left(z + \frac{1}{z}\right), \qquad a > 0,$$

maps the circles $|z| = $ const into confocal ellipses and the radial lines $\arg z = \theta = $ const into confocal hyperbolas.

3. Prove that $\sin z$ and $\tan z$ are periodic functions.

4. Show that the curves $u(x,y) = $ const, $v(x,y) = $ const in (16-8) intersect at right angles (Fig. 20).

18. Conformal Maps. We noted in Sec. 15 that the relationship $w = f(z)$ can be viewed as a mapping that sets up a correspondence between the points of the z and w planes. If $w = f(z)$ is analytic in some region R of the z plane, and if C is a curve in R, there is a remarkable connection between C and its image C' in the corresponding region R' in the w plane (Fig. 22). Consider a pair of points z and $z + \Delta z$ on C, and let the arc

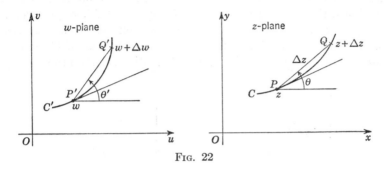

FIG. 22

length between them be $\Delta s = PQ$. The corresponding points in the region R' are denoted by w and $w + \Delta w$, and the arc length between them by $\Delta s' = P'Q'$. Since the ratio of the arc lengths has the same limit as the ratio of the lengths of the corresponding chords,

$$\lim_{\Delta z \to 0} \frac{\Delta s'}{\Delta s} = \lim_{\Delta z \to 0} \frac{|\Delta w|}{|\Delta z|} = \lim_{\Delta z \to 0} \left| \frac{\Delta w}{\Delta z} \right| = \left| \frac{dw}{dz} \right|. \qquad (18\text{-}1)$$

We shall exclude from consideration those points of R at which $dw/dz = 0$ because at such points the correspondence of values of z and w ceases to be one to one.[1]

Formula (18-1) shows that an element of arc through P, on being transformed to the w plane, suffers a change in length such that the magnification ratio is equal to the modulus of dw/dz at P. *This ratio is the same for all curves passing through P*, but ordinarily it varies from point to point in the z plane, since $|dw/dz|$ need not have the same value at all points of the z plane.

We shall see next that the argument of dw/dz determines the orientation of the element of arc $\Delta s'$ relative to Δs. The argument θ of Δz (Fig. 22)

---

[1] If $dw/dz = f'(z) = 0$ at some point P of R, then $dz/dw = 1/f'(z)$ is not defined at the corresponding point P' for the inverse function $z = F(w)$. Thus $F(w)$ is not analytic at P'. Indeed, it can be shown that a necessary and sufficient condition for the existence of a unique differentiable solution of $w = f(z)$ at the point $z = z_0$ is precisely $f'(z_0) \neq 0$.

is the angle made by the chord PQ with the positive direction of the x axis, while the argument θ' of Δw is the angle made by the corresponding chord $P'Q'$ with the u axis.

Hence, the difference between the angles θ' and θ is equal to

$$\arg \Delta w - \arg \Delta z = \arg \frac{\Delta w}{\Delta z}$$

since the difference of the arguments of two complex numbers is equal to the argument of their quotient. As $\Delta z \to 0$, the vectors Δz and Δw tend to coincide with the tangents to C at P and C' at P', respectively, and hence $\arg dw/dz$ is the angle of rotation of the element of arc $\Delta s'$ relative to Δs. It follows immediately from this statement that if C_1 and C_2 are two curves which intersect at P at an angle τ (Fig. 23), then the correspond-

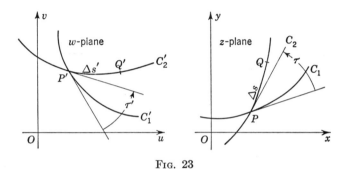

Fig. 23

ing curves C_1' and C_2' in the w plane also intersect at an angle τ, for the tangents to these curves are rotated through the same angle.

A transformation that preserves angles is called *conformal*, and thus one can state the following theorem:

THEOREM. *The mapping performed by an analytic function $f(z)$ is conformal at all points of the z plane where $f'(z) \neq 0$.*

The angle-preserving property of the transformation by analytic functions has many important physical applications. We shall indicate several of these in the remaining sections of this chapter, and we merely note here that a number of results deducible analytically from Sec. 15, Chap. 5, follow directly from geometric considerations.

For example, if an incompressible fluid with a velocity potential $\Phi(x,y)$ flows over a plane (so that $v_x = \partial\Phi/\partial x$, $v_y = \partial\Phi/\partial y$), then it is known [1] that the streamlines $\Psi(x,y) = $ const are directed at right angles to the equipotential curves $\Phi(x,y) = $ const.

[1] See Sec. 15, Chap. 5, and particularly Prob. 6 of that section.

The orthogonality of the curves $\Phi = $ const and $\Psi = $ const in the z plane follows at once from the conformal properties of transformations by analytic functions. It was shown [1] that the functions Φ and Ψ satisfy the Cauchy-Riemann equations. One can therefore assert that Φ and Ψ are the real and imaginary parts, respectively, of some analytic function $w = f(z)$; that is,

$$f(z) = \Phi(x,y) + i\Psi(x,y).$$

But the curves $\Phi = $ const and $\Psi = $ const represent a net of orthogonal lines (Fig. 24) parallel to the coordinate axes in the w plane, and they are

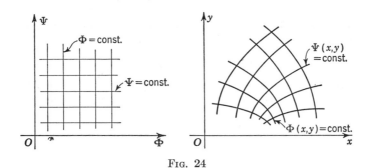

FIG. 24

transformed by the analytic function $w = \Phi(x,y) + i\Psi(x,y)$ into a net of orthogonal curves in the z plane.

We saw in Sec. 9 that the real and imaginary parts of every analytic function $f(z) = u(x,y) + iv(x,y)$ are harmonic; that is, they satisfy Laplace's equation in the region where $f(z)$ is analytic. Since solutions of Laplace's equation are demanded in numerous practical problems, analytic functions serve as a useful apparatus for producing such solutions. For example, if we take

$$w = u + iv = \sin z = \sin (x + iy)$$

then
$$u + iv = \sin x \cos iy + \cos x \sin iy$$

$$= \sin x \cosh y + i \cos x \sinh y.$$

The harmonic functions $u = \sin x \cosh y$, $v = \cos x \sinh y$ are of special interest in deducing solutions of Laplace's equation in rectangular regions.[2]

Further importance of conformal transformation by analytic functions derives from the fact that a harmonic function remains harmonic when subjected to such a transformation. If a function $\phi(u,v)$ satisfies Laplace's

[1] See Eq. (15-10), Sec. 15, Chap. 5.
[2] See, for example, Sec. 20.

equation

$$\frac{\partial^2 \phi}{\partial u^2} + \frac{\partial^2 \phi}{\partial v^2} = 0 \tag{18-2}$$

in some region R' of the uv plane, then ϕ still satisfies Laplace's equation, in the appropriate region R of the xy plane, when the variables u, v in $\phi(u,v)$ are related to x, y by an analytic function

$$w = u + iv = f(z). \tag{18-3}$$

To see this, construct an analytic function

$$F(w) = \phi(u,v) + i\psi(u,v) \tag{18-4}$$

by calculating the conjugate $\psi(u,v)$ of the harmonic function $\phi(u,v)$.

The substitution from (18-3) in (18-4) yields

$$F[f(z)] = \Phi(x,y) + i\Psi(x,y), \tag{18-5}$$

which is analytic in the region R of the xy plane into which the region R' is mapped by (18-3). The function $\Phi(x,y)$, being the real part of the analytic function $F[f(z)]$, is harmonic.

This property of the transformation of harmonic functions by means of analytic functions is of the utmost practical importance; for, suppose that we are required to find a solution $\phi(u,v)$ of Laplace's equation (18-2) such that on the boundary C' of some complicated region R' in the uv plane, $\phi(u,v)$ assumes specified values. If it should prove possible to find a function $w = f(z)$ which maps the region R' conformally into some simple region R (a circle, for example) in the z plane, it may be relatively easy to determine the transform $\Phi(x,y)$ of $\phi(u,v)$ in the region R with proper values of Φ on the boundary C.

If $\Phi(x,y)$ is so determined, the function $\phi(u,v)$ can be obtained by replacing the variables in $\Phi(x,y)$ by their values in terms of u and v. It is a remarkable fact, first discovered by Riemann, that every simply connected region R' (with more than one boundary point) can be mapped conformally onto the unit circle $|z| \le 1$ in such a way that the boundary C' corresponds to the circular boundary $|z| = 1$.

We shall sketch this mode of solution of the Dirichlet problem in Sec. 21.

PROBLEMS

1. Obtain solutions of Laplace's equation from (a) $w = \cos z$, (b) $w = e^z$, (c) $w = z^3$, (d) $w = \log z$, (e) $w = 1/z$.

2. Construct the conjugate harmonic functions $v(x,y)$ for the following functions: (a) $u = \cos x \cosh y$; (b) $u = e^x \cos y$; (c) $u = y + e^x \cos y$; (d) $u = \cosh x \cos y$.

3. Examine the mapping by $w = z^2$ and $w = z^3$ at $z = 0$. Is it conformal at $z = 0$? Examine the behavior of the maps of rays issuing from $z = 0$. What are the ratios of magnification of the arc elements at $z = 1$, $z = 1 + i$, $z = i$?

APPLICATIONS

19. Steady Flow of Ideal Fluids. We discussed the flow of nonviscous incompressible fluids in Sec. 15 of Chap. 5, where we introduced the concept of the velocity potential $\Phi(x,y)$ and the stream function $\Psi(x,y)$. These functions were shown to be related by the Cauchy-Riemann equations

$$\frac{\partial \Phi}{\partial x} = \frac{\partial \Psi}{\partial y}, \qquad \frac{\partial \Phi}{\partial y} = -\frac{\partial \Psi}{\partial x}. \tag{19-1}$$

It follows from (19-1) that

$$F(z) = \Phi(x,y) + i\Psi(x,y) \tag{19-2}$$

is an analytic function of a complex variable $z = x + iy$. We shall call $F(z)$ the *complex potential* and show that its derivative is related simply to the velocity vector $\mathbf{v} = \nabla \Phi$ of the fluid particles.

By (4-5),

$$\frac{dF}{dz} = \frac{\partial \Phi}{\partial x} + i\frac{\partial \Psi}{\partial x} \tag{19-3}$$

and, since $\mathbf{v} = \nabla \Phi$, so that

$$v_x = \frac{\partial \Phi}{\partial x}, \qquad v_y = \frac{\partial \Phi}{\partial y} = -\frac{\partial \Psi}{\partial x},$$

we can write (19-3) in the form

$$\frac{dF}{dz} = v_x - iv_y. \tag{19-4}$$

We shall see in Sec. 21 that because of the simplicity of the complex-variable theory in comparison with the theory of real functions, it is often simpler to calculate the complex potential $F(z)$ than it is to determine either of the real functions $\Phi(x,y)$ or $\Psi(x,y)$. This determination depends on certain so-called *boundary conditions*, which are now to be described. We first recall [1] that since $\mathbf{v} = \nabla \Phi$ is orthogonal to the curves $\Phi(x,y) = $ const and these curves are orthogonal to the curves $\Psi(x,y) = $ const, the vector $\mathbf{v}$ is tangent to the curves $\Psi(x,y) = $ const. Hence these curves, called *streamlines*, are the paths of the fluid particles. When a sheet of fluid flows past an impenetrable obstacle C (cf. Fig. 25, Sec. 20), the fluid particles must flow along the obstacle and hence the boundary C must coincide with one of the streamlines. Thus the equation of one of the streamlines, say

$$\Psi(x,y) = k, \tag{19-5}$$

must coincide with the equation of the boundary C.

---

[1] See Sec. 3, Chap. 5, and Sec. 18 of this chapter.

To determine $\Psi(x,y)$ we must then seek a solution of Laplace's equation

$$\nabla^2\Psi(x,y) = 0 \qquad (19\text{-}6)$$

in the region exterior to the obstacle, which is such that on the boundary C Ψ takes on a constant value.

This suggests an indirect mode of solution of the steady-fluid-flow problems. One examines the shapes of curves $\Psi(x,y) = $ const for various harmonic functions $\Psi(x,y)$, and if a particular curve $\Psi(x,y) = k$ coincides with the boundary C of an obstacle of special technical interest, then the function $\Psi(x,y)$ solves a special problem.

It follows from these remarks that any streamline $\Psi(x,y) = $ const can be regarded as a rigid boundary of some obstacle.

Instead of determining the stream function $\Psi(x,y)$, we can equally well determine a harmonic function $\Phi(x,y)$ which on the boundary C satisfies the condition

$$\frac{d\Phi}{dn} = 0, \qquad (19\text{-}7)$$

where $\mathbf{n}$ is the unit normal to C, for the statement that the obstacle is rigid implies that the normal component v_n of $\mathbf{v}$ must vanish along C, since no particles of fluid can cross C. But $v_n = \mathbf{n}\cdot\mathbf{v}$, and since $\mathbf{v} = \nabla\Phi$ and

$$\frac{d\Phi}{dn} = \mathbf{n}\cdot\nabla\Phi = v_n,$$

we see that (19-7) must hold on C.

It should be noted that we have assumed in the foregoing that there are no sources or sinks in the region and that the fluid is incompressible. Moreover, the flow is irrotational, and hence $\Phi(x,y)$ and $\Psi(x,y)$ are single-valued functions. These considerations can be extended to the more general situation in which circulation is present. However, as we shall see from examples in the following section, the complex potential $F(z)$ will then no longer be a single-valued function of z.

PROBLEM

Deduce from the boundary condition (19-7) that $d\Psi/ds = 0$ along C, so that $\Psi = $ const on C. *Hint:* Note that $d\Phi/dn = (\partial\Phi/\partial x)(dx/dn) + (\partial\Phi/\partial y)(dy/dn)$. Make use of (19-1), and observe that $dx/dn = dy/ds$, $dy/dn = -dx/ds$ on C.

20. The Method of Conjugate Functions. We observed in the preceding section that every analytic function $F(z) = u(x,y) + iv(x,y)$ can be associated with some flow pattern of an incompressible fluid. In fact, every such function determines two flow patterns, since either of the harmonic functions $u(x,y)$, $v(x,y)$ can be regarded as determining the stream-lines.

The simplest example of an irrotational flow is furnished by the function

$$F(z) = cz \equiv \Phi + i\Psi,$$

where c is a real constant. Since $z = x + iy$, we have $\Phi = cx$, $\Psi = cy$, and thus the curves $\Psi = \text{const}$ are straight lines parallel to the x axis. The formula (19-4) for the velocity of the fluid yields $v_x = c$, $v_y = 0$, so that the flow is parallel to the x axis. Since div $\mathbf{v} = 0$ and curl $\mathbf{v} = 0$, there are no sources or sinks in the region and the flow is irrotational.

As a more interesting example, consider

$$F(z) = c\left(z + \frac{a^2}{z}\right) = \Phi + i\Psi, \qquad c > 0, a^2 > 0. \qquad (20\text{-}1)$$

If we set $z = re^{i\theta}$ in (20-1), we easily find that

$$\Phi = c\left(r + \frac{a^2}{r}\right)\cos\theta, \qquad \Psi = c\left(r - \frac{a^2}{r}\right)\sin\theta.$$

For $r = a$, we have $\Psi = 0$, and hence the boundary of the circle $r = a$ is a streamline. The pattern of streamlines is shown in Fig. 25 by the solid lines, and the curves $\Phi = \text{const}$ are indicated by the dashed lines.

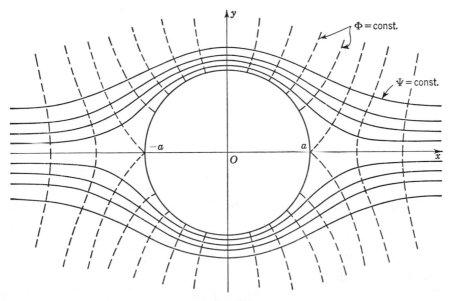

FIG. 25

This flow pattern corresponds to a flow around a circular cylinder. The velocity components are determined from

$$F'(z) = v_x - iv_y = c\left(1 - \frac{a^2}{z^2}\right).$$

It is easy to verify that div $\mathbf{v} = 0$ and curl $\mathbf{v} = \mathbf{0}$, so that the flow is irrotational. The points for which $v_x = v_y = 0$ are $z = \pm a$. These are called the *stagnation points*.

Let us investigate next the flow pattern determined by

$$F(z) = c \log z = u + iv, \qquad z = re^{i\theta}, \qquad (20\text{-}2)$$

where c is a real constant.

If we consider only the one branch of this multiple-valued function for which $0 \le \theta < 2\pi$, we get

$$F(z) = c(\text{Log } r + i\theta),$$

so that $\qquad\qquad u = c \text{ Log } r, \qquad v = c\theta, \qquad 0 \le \theta < 2\pi.$

If we set $\Psi = c\theta$, then the streamlines $\Psi = \text{const}$ are the radial lines and the curves $\Phi = \text{const}$ are circles c Log $r = \text{const}$ (Fig. 26). By Eq.

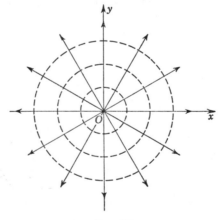

Fig. 26

(15-1) of Chap. 5, the amount of the fluid crossing per second any closed curve C is

$$V = \int_C (v_x \, dy - v_y \, dx) = \int_C \left(\frac{\partial \Psi}{\partial x} \, dx + \frac{\partial \Psi}{\partial y} \, dy\right) = \int_C d\Psi.$$

But $\Psi = c\theta$, so that

$$V = c \int_C d\theta.$$

This integral vanishes for any path that does not enclose the origin. If the origin $z = 0$ is within C, then $V = 2\pi c$. Hence for $c > 0$, the flow is outward and we have a source of strength $2\pi c$ at the origin. For $c < 0$, we have a sink of the same strength. Thus, div $\mathbf{v} = 0$ at all points except $z = 0$.

The circulation J is given by the integral [1]

$$J = \int_C (v_x \, dx + v_y \, dy) = \int_C d\Phi$$

and since $\Phi = c \operatorname{Log} r$, $J = 0$ and the flow is irrotational.

If, however, we take $\Phi = c\theta$ and $\Psi = c \operatorname{Log} r$, the roles of the curves $\Phi = \mathrm{const}$ and $\Psi = \mathrm{const}$ in the preceding discussion are interchanged. We thus conclude that for this flow the circulation $J = 2\pi c$ if C encloses the origin. This corresponds to the situation described as a *point vortex* at the origin.

The reader will find it of interest to study the function

$$\Phi + i\Psi = c \left(z + \frac{a^2}{z} \right) - ic' \log z, \qquad a > 0, c > 0,$$

for which $\Psi = \mathrm{const}$ when $|z| = a$. The function $\Psi(x,y)$ represents a flow around a circular cylinder $r = a$ with the circulation $2\pi c'$.

As further examples of functions yielding useful solutions of interesting physical problems consider the following:

1. *The Transformation $w = \cosh z$.* Here

$$w = \frac{e^z + e^{-z}}{2} = \cosh z.$$

Thus,

$$u + iv = \cosh (x + iy) = \cosh x \cosh iy + \sinh x \sinh iy$$

$$= \cosh x \cos y + i \sinh x \sin y,$$

so that

$$u = \cosh x \cos y,$$

$$v = \sinh x \sin y,$$

or

$$\frac{u^2}{\cosh^2 x} + \frac{v^2}{\sinh^2 x} = 1,$$

$$\frac{u^2}{\cos^2 y} - \frac{v^2}{\sin^2 y} = 1.$$

[1] See Sec. 10, Chap. 5.

This transformation is shown in Fig. 27, and it may be used to obtain the electrostatic field due to an elliptic cylinder, the electrostatic field due to a charged plane from which a strip has been removed, the circulation of liquid around an elliptic cylinder, the flow of liquid through a slit in a plane, etc.

The transformation from the z plane to the w plane may be described geometrically as follows: Consider the horizontal strip of the z plane between

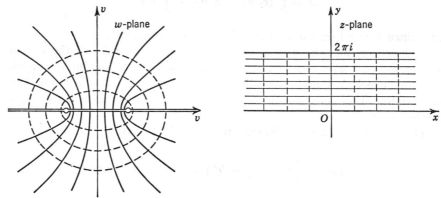

FIG. 27

the lines $y = 0$ and $y = \pi$, and think of these lines as being broken and pivoted at the points where $x = 0$. Rotate the strip 90° counterclockwise, and at the same time fold each of the broken lines $y = 0$ and $y = \pi$ back on itself, the strip thus being doubly "fanned out" so as to cover the entire w plane.

It is interesting to note that this same transformation $w = \cosh z$ can be used to solve a hydrodynamic problem of a different sort. When liquid seeps through a porous soil, it is found that the component in any direction of the velocity of the liquid is proportional to the negative pressure gradient in that same direction. Thus, in a problem of two-dimensional flow the velocity components (u,v) are

$$u = -k \frac{\partial p}{\partial x}, \qquad v = -k \frac{\partial p}{\partial y}.$$

If these values are inserted in the equation of continuity, namely, in the equation

$$\frac{\partial u}{\partial x} + \frac{\partial v}{\partial y} = 0,$$

the result is

$$\nabla^2 p \equiv \frac{\partial^2 p}{\partial x^2} + \frac{\partial^2 p}{\partial y^2} = 0.$$

Suppose, then, one considers the problem of the seepage flow under a gravity dam which rests on material that permits such seepage. One seeks (see Fig. 28) a function p that satisfies Laplace's equation and that

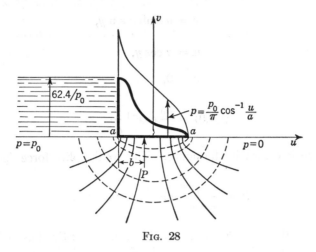

$$62.4/p_0$$

$$p = \frac{p_0}{\pi} \cos^{-1} \frac{u}{a}$$

$$p = p_0 \qquad\qquad p = 0$$

Fig. 28

satisfies certain boundary conditions on the surface of the ground. That is, the pressure must be uniform on the surface of the ground upstream from the heel of the dam and zero on the surface of the ground down-stream from the toe of the dam. If we choose a system of cartesian co-ordinates u, v with origin at the mid-point of the base of the dam (Fig. 28) and u axis on the surface of the ground, then it is easily checked that the function $p(u,v) = p_0 y(u,v)/\pi$, where

$$w = u + iv = a \cosh (x + iy),$$

satisfies the demands of the problem. In fact, it was seen in the study of the transformation $w = \cosh z$ that the line $y = \pi$ of the z plane folds up to produce the portion to the left of $u = -1$ of the u axis in the w plane and the line $y = 0$ of the z plane folds up to produce the portion to the right of $u = +1$ of the u axis. The introduction of the factor a in the transformation merely makes the width of the base of the dam $2a$ rather than 2. These remarks show that $p(u,v)$ reduces to the constant π on the surface of the ground upstream from the heel of the dam. If the head above the dam is such as to produce a hydrostatic pressure p_0, one merely has to set

$$p(u,v) = \frac{p_0 y(u,v)}{\pi}.$$

One can now find the distribution of uplift pressure across the base of the dam. In fact, the base of the dam is the representation, in the uv plane, of the line $x = 0$, $0 \leq y \leq \pi$, of the xy plane. Hence, on the base of the dam the equations

$$u = a \cosh x \cos y,$$

$$v = a \sinh x \sin y,$$

reduce to

$$u = a \cos y,$$

$$v = 0,$$

so that

$$p(u,0) = \frac{p_0}{\pi} \cos^{-1} \frac{u}{a}.$$

This curve is drawn in the figure. The total uplift force (per foot of dam) is

$$P = \frac{p_0}{\pi} \int_{-a}^{+a} \cos^{-1} \frac{u}{a}\, du = p_0 a,$$

which is what the uplift pressure would be if the entire base of the dam were subjected to a head just one-half of the head above the dam or if the pressure decreased uniformly (linearly) from the static head p_0 at the heel to the value zero at the toe. The point of application of the resultant uplift is easily calculated to be at a distance $b = 3a/4$ from the heel of the dam.[1]

2. *The Transformation $w = z + e^z$.* One has

$$u + iv = x + iy + e^{x+iy}$$

$$= x + iy + e^x(\cos y + i \sin y),$$

so that

$$u = x + e^x \cos y,$$

$$v = y + e^x \sin y.$$

This transformation is shown in Fig. 29. If one considers the portion of the z plane between the lines $y = \pm\pi$, then the portion of the strip to the right of $x = -1$ is to be "fanned out" by rotating the portion of $y = +1$ (to the right of $x = -1$) counterclockwise and the portion of $y = -1$ (to the right of $x = -1$) clockwise until each line is folded back on itself. This transformation gives the electrostatic field at the edge of a parallel-plate condenser, the flow of liquid out of a channel into an open sea, etc.

---

[1] Some material in Secs. 18 to 20 is taken by permission from a lecture by Dr. Warren Weaver printed in the October, 1932, issue of the *American Mathematical Monthly*.

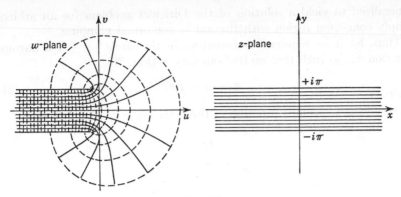

FIG. 29

PROBLEMS

1. Study the flow determined by the complex potential $w = cz^2$ in a quadrant $x \geq 0$, $y \geq 0$. The function $\Psi = 2cxy$ can be associated with the flow of fluid around a corner.

2. Study the flow determined by the complex potential $w = c \sin z$ in the semi-infinite region $|x| \leq \pi/2$, $y \geq 0$.

21. The Problem of Dirichlet.

The procedure for reducing solutions of physical problems described in the preceding section is indirect. It depends on the examination of various harmonic functions that satisfy the boundary conditions appearing in specific physical situations.

In this section we outline a general procedure for constructing harmonic functions which assume preassigned boundary values. Thus, let it be required to determine a solution of Laplace's equation

$$\nabla^2 \Phi(x,y) = 0 \qquad (21\text{-}1)$$

which on the boundary C of a given simply connected region R assumes preassigned continuous values

$$\Phi = \phi(s). \qquad (21\text{-}2)$$

The variable s in (21-2) may be thought to be the arc-parameter s measured along C from some fixed point.

The boundary-value problem characterized by Eqs. (21-1) and (21-2) is known as the *Dirichlet problem*, and it can be shown that the solution of it exists and is unique whenever the boundary C is sufficiently smooth. These conditions are usually met in physical problems.

We first outline a solution of this problem for the case when the region R is the unit circle $|z| \leq 1$ and later indicate how this solution can be generalized to yield a solution of the Dirichlet problem for an arbitrary simply connected region with the aid of conformal mapping.

Thus, let it be required to construct in the circle $|z| \leq 1$ a harmonic function $\Phi(x,y)$ such that on its boundary γ (Fig. 30)

$$\Phi(x,y) = f(\theta), \tag{21-3}$$

where $f(\theta)$ is a specified function of the polar angle θ.

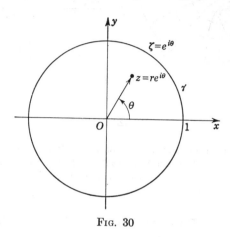

Fig. 30

Instead of determining $\Phi(x,y)$, it proves more convenient to determine an analytic function

$$F(z) = \Phi(x,y) + i\Psi(x,y), \qquad |z| \leq 1 \tag{21-4}$$

whose real part takes on preassigned values (21-3) and then compute $\Phi(x,y)$ by separating $F(z)$ into its real and imaginary parts. Now, since [1] $F(z) + \overline{F(z)} = 2\Phi(x,y)$, we can write the boundary condition (21-3) in the form

$$F(\zeta) + \overline{F(\zeta)} = 2f(\theta) \tag{21-5}$$

where $\zeta = e^{i\theta}$ represents the values of $z = re^{i\theta}$ on the boundary γ. If we now multiply both members of (21-5) by $\dfrac{1}{2\pi i} \dfrac{d\zeta}{\zeta - z}$, where z is an interior point of the circle, and integrate over γ, we get [2]

---

[1] We use bars to denote the conjugate values, so that $\overline{F(z)} = \Phi(x,y) - i\Psi(x,y)$.

[2] To prove that the conditions (21-5) and (21-6) are equivalent, one must impose certain continuity restrictions on $f(\theta)$ usually met in the physical problems. See, for example, I. S. Sokolnikoff, "Mathematical Theory of Elasticity," 2d ed., p. 143, McGraw-Hill Book Company, Inc., New York, 1956.

$$\frac{1}{2\pi i}\int_\gamma \frac{F(\zeta)}{\zeta - z}\,d\zeta + \frac{1}{2\pi i}\int_\gamma \frac{\overline{F(\zeta)}}{\zeta - z}\,d\zeta = \frac{1}{\pi i}\int_\gamma \frac{f(\theta)}{\zeta - z}\,d\zeta. \qquad (21\text{-}6)$$

By Cauchy's integral formula, the first integral in the left-hand member of (21-6) is equal to $F(z)$. We show next that the second integral has a constant value $\overline{F(0)}$ as long as $|z| \leq 1$. On expanding $F(\zeta)$ in Maclaurin's series, we get

$$F(z) = F(0) + F'(0)z + \frac{1}{2!}F''(0)z^2 + \cdots + \frac{1}{n!}F^{(n)}(0)z^n + \cdots \qquad (21\text{-}7)$$

which is convergent for all $|z| \leq 1$, since $F(z)$ is assumed to be analytic in $|z| \leq 1$.

If we set $z = \zeta$ in (21-7) and form the conjugate $\overline{F(\zeta)}$, we get

$$\overline{F(\zeta)} = \overline{F(0)} + \overline{F'(0)}\,\bar\zeta + \frac{1}{2!}\overline{F''(0)}\,\bar\zeta^2 + \cdots + \frac{1}{n!}\overline{F^{(n)}(0)}\,\bar\zeta^n \cdots.$$

But on the circle γ, $\bar\zeta = e^{-i\theta} = 1/e^{i\theta} = 1/\zeta$, so that

$$\overline{F(\zeta)} = \overline{F(0)} + \overline{F'(0)}\frac{1}{\zeta} + \frac{1}{2!}\overline{F''(0)}\frac{1}{\zeta^2} + \cdots + \frac{1}{n!}\overline{F^n(0)}\frac{1}{\zeta^n} + \cdots. \qquad (21\text{-}8)$$

The substitution of this series in the numerator of the second integral in (21-6) then yields a series of integrals of the form

$$\frac{1}{n!}\frac{1}{2\pi i}\int_\gamma \frac{\overline{F^n(0)}}{(\zeta - z)\zeta^n}\,d\zeta, \qquad n = 0, 1, \ldots.$$

But the application of the residue theorem shows that these integrals vanish for $n \geq 1$, and for $n = 0$ we get

$$\frac{1}{2\pi i}\int_\gamma \frac{\overline{F(0)}}{\zeta - z}\,d\zeta = \overline{F(0)} \equiv a_0 - ib_0.$$

Thus (21-6) can be written in the form

$$F(z) = \frac{1}{\pi i}\int_\gamma \frac{f(\theta)}{\zeta - z}\,d\zeta - a_0 + ib_0, \qquad (21\text{-}9)$$

where $a_0 + ib_0 = F(0)$.

The real part a_0 of $F(0)$ can be determined explicitly in terms of the prescribed values $f(\theta)$ on γ, for on setting $z = 0$ in (21-9), we get

$$a_0 + ib_0 = \frac{1}{\pi i}\int_\gamma \frac{f(\theta)}{\zeta}\,d\zeta - a_0 + ib_0$$

and therefore

$$a_0 = \frac{1}{2\pi i} \int_\gamma \frac{f(\theta)}{\zeta} d\zeta.$$

But $\zeta = e^{i\theta}$, so that $d\zeta/\zeta = i\, d\theta$ and hence

$$a_0 = \frac{1}{2\pi} \int_0^{2\pi} f(\theta) \, d\theta. \tag{21-10}$$

Accordingly, the real part of $F(z)$ is determined uniquely when $f(\theta)$ is known. The real part of $F(z)$ is the desired harmonic function $\Phi(x,y)$. Since $\zeta = e^{i\theta}$, $f(\theta)$ can be expressed as a function of ζ, say $g(\zeta)$, and we see that the integral in (21-9) has the form

$$\int_\gamma \frac{g(\zeta)}{\zeta - z} d\zeta.$$

Integrals of this type can frequently be evaluated in closed form with the aid of the theory of residues.

Formula (21-9) thus solves the general Dirichlet problem for the circular region.

We indicate next how the Dirichlet problem for an arbitrary simply connected region R can be solved when the function

$$w = w(z) \tag{21-11}$$

mapping the region R in the complex w plane conformally onto the circle $|z| \leq 1$ is known. Let $w = u + iv$; then the desired harmonic function $\Phi(u,v)$, assuming the prescribed values

$$\Phi(u,v) = \phi(s) \tag{21-12}$$

on the boundary C of R, is the real part of some analytic function

$$\mathfrak{F}(w) \equiv \Phi(u,v) + i\Psi(u,v). \tag{21-13}$$

On substituting in $\mathfrak{F}(w)$ from (21-11), we get

$$\mathfrak{F}[w(z)] \equiv F(z),$$

which is analytic in the circle $|z| \leq 1$.

The values of the real part of $F(z)$ on the boundary γ of the unit circle are known, since the values of $\Phi(u,v)$ on the boundary C are specified by (21-12) and the points on C are mapped into points on γ by (21-11). We can thus write the boundary condition (21-12) in the form

$$\Phi = f(\theta) \qquad \text{on } \gamma.$$

The substitution of $f(\theta)$ in formula (21-9) then yields $F(z)$. To obtain the desired function $\Phi(u,v)$, we must calculate the real part of $\mathfrak{F}(w)$, which can be determined from $F(z)$ by expressing z in terms of w with the aid of (21-11).

It is clear that the solution of the problem of Dirichlet for an arbitrary simply connected domain hinges on the construction of a suitable mapping function (21-11). The fact that such a function exists is guaranteed by Riemann's theorem mentioned in the concluding paragraphs of Sec. 18. During the past 30 years considerable attention has been given to the problem of developing effective methods for constructing conformal maps for simply connected domains.[1] A formula for conformal mapping of a polygonal region on the unit circle (or alternatively, in the upper half of the complex plane) has been supplied [2] by H. A. Schwarz (1843–1921) and E. B. Christoffel (1829–1900).

During recent years extensive applications of complex variables to broad classes of problems in the theory of elasticity have been made.[3]

PROBLEMS

1. Use formula (21-9) to compute harmonic functions $\Phi(x,y)$ in the circular region $x^2 + y^2 = 1$, which assume on its boundary the following values: (a) $\Phi = x^2 + y^2$, (b) $\Phi = x^2 - y^2$, (c) $\Phi = \cos^3 \theta$, where θ is the polar angle. *Hint:* Note that $x = \frac{1}{2}(z + \bar{z})$, $y = (1/2i)(z - \bar{z})$ and that on the boundary of the unit circle $\bar{z} = 1/z$.

2. Set $z = re^{i\phi} \equiv r(\cos \phi + i \sin \phi)$, $\zeta = e^{i\theta} \equiv \cos \theta + i \sin \theta$ in (21-9); take account of (21-10); and show that the real part Φ of $F(z)$ is

$$\Phi(r,\phi) = \frac{1}{2\pi} \int_0^{2\pi} \frac{(1 - r^2)f(\theta)\,d\theta}{1 - 2r \cos(\theta - \phi) + r^2}.$$

This formula, giving the values of harmonic function Φ at every interior point (r,ϕ) of the unit circle in terms of the assigned boundary values $f(\theta)$, is known as *Poisson's integral formula*. (Cf. Chap. 6, Sec. 12.) Because of the difficulty of evaluating real integrals, this formula is generally less useful than the Schwarz formula (21-9).

22. Evaluation of Real Integrals by the Residue Theorem.

Formula (21-9) and the problems in Sec. 21 suggest the use of contour integration of complex functions in the calculation of certain real integrals.

Thus, consider a real integral

$$\int_0^{2\pi} F(\sin \theta, \cos \theta)\,d\theta \tag{22-1}$$

---

[1] There is a vast literature on this subject, and we cite only a book by L. V. Kantorovich and V. I. Krylov, "Approximate Methods of Higher Analysis," Groningen, 1958, containing a comprehensive survey of the problem in chap. 5. A useful catalogue of mapping functions is contained in the "Dictionary of Conformal Representation," Dover Press, New York, 1952, compiled by H. Kober.

[2] This formula is contained in most books on complex-variable theory. See, for example, R. V. Churchill, "Introduction to Complex Variables and Applications," chap. 10, McGraw-Hill Book Company, Inc., New York, 1948.

[3] See Sokolnikoff, *op. cit.*

in which F is the quotient of two polynomials in $\sin \theta$ and $\cos \theta$. The evaluation of such integrals, as we shall presently see, can be reduced to the calculation of the integral of a rational function of z along the unit circle $|z| = 1$. Since rational functions have no singularities other than poles, the residue theorem (13-3) provides a simple means for evaluating integrals of the form (22-1).

We set $z = e^{i\theta}$, so that $dz = e^{i\theta}i\, d\theta$

or
$$d\theta = \frac{dz}{iz}, \tag{22-2}$$

and we recall Euler's formulas,

$$\cos \theta = \frac{z + z^{-1}}{2}, \qquad \sin \theta = \frac{z - z^{-1}}{2i}. \tag{22-3}$$

On inserting from (22-2) and (22-3) in (22-1) we get the integral

$$\int_C R(z)\, dz \tag{22-4}$$

in which $R(z)$ is a rational function of z and C is the circular path $|z| = 1$. If the sum of the residues of $R(z)$ at the poles within the circle $|z| < 1$ is denoted by Σr, the residue theorem yields $\int_C R(z)dz = 2\pi i\, \Sigma r$, so that

$$\int_0^{2\pi} F(\sin \theta, \cos \theta)\, d\theta = 2\pi i \Sigma r. \tag{22-5}$$

Example 1. As a specific illustration of this method of calculating integrals of the type (22-1), consider

$$I = \int_0^{2\pi} \frac{d\theta}{1 + \alpha \sin \theta}, \qquad 0 < \alpha < 1. \tag{22-6}$$

On making substitutions in (22-6) from (22-2) and (22-3), we get the integral

$$I = \int_C \frac{dz}{iz[1 + \alpha(z - z^{-1})/2i]}$$

$$= \frac{2}{\alpha} \int_C \frac{dz}{z^2 + (2i/\alpha)z - 1}, \tag{22-7}$$

where C is the circular path $|z| = 1$.

Since the roots of $z^2 + (2i/\alpha)z - 1 = 0$ are

$$z_1 = -\frac{i}{\alpha}(1 - \sqrt{1 - \alpha^2}), \qquad z_2 = -\frac{i}{\alpha}(1 + \sqrt{1 - \alpha^2}), \tag{22-8}$$

we can write (22-7) as

$$I = \frac{2}{\alpha} \int_C \frac{dz}{(z - z_1)(z - z_2)}. \tag{22-9}$$

But it is clear from (22-8) that for $0 < \alpha < 1$ we have $|z_1| < 1$ and $|z_2| > 1$, so that only one pole $z = z_1$ of the integrand

$$R(z) = \frac{1}{(z - z_1)(z - z_2)}$$

lies within the unit circle. The residue of $R(z)$ at $z = z_1$, by (12-6), is

$$r = \lim_{z \to z_1} R(z)(z - z_1) = \frac{1}{z_1 - z_2}$$

which, on noting (22-8), yields

$$r = \frac{\alpha}{2i\sqrt{1 - \alpha^2}}.$$

By the residue theorem, the value of (22-9), which is the same as that of the integral (22-6), is

$$I = \frac{2}{\alpha} 2\pi i r = \frac{2\pi}{\sqrt{1 - \alpha^2}}.$$

The reader can verify by the same method, or by setting $\theta = \varphi - \pi/2$, that

$$\int_0^{2\pi} \frac{d\theta}{1 + \alpha \cos \theta} = \int_0^{2\pi} \frac{d\theta}{1 + \alpha \sin \theta} = \frac{2\pi}{\sqrt{1 - \alpha^2}}, \qquad 0 < \alpha < 1. \qquad (22\text{-}10)$$

The infinite integral

$$\int_{-\infty}^{\infty} \frac{f(x)}{g(x)} \, dx, \qquad (22\text{-}11)$$

in which $f(x)$ and $g(x)$ are polynomials in x, can also be evaluated by calculating the residues. It should be noted that the integral (22-11) converges if, and only if,[1] $g(x) = 0$ has no real roots and the degree of $g(x)$ is at least two greater than that of $f(x)$.

Now, consider the complex rational function

$$R(z) = \frac{f(z)}{g(z)} \qquad (22\text{-}12)$$

which, obviously, assumes along the real axis the same values as the

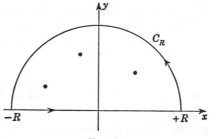

FIG. 31

integrand in (22-11). By hypothesis $g(z) = 0$ has no real roots; hence no poles of $R(z)$ lie on the real axis. We form the integral

$$\int_C R(z) \, dz = \int_C \frac{f(z)}{g(z)} \, dz$$

where the path C is the boundary of the semicircular region in the upper half of the z plane shown in Fig. 31. Since all roots of $g(z)$ lie at a finite

---

[1] This follows directly from the usual tests on convergence of improper integrals. See Chap. 2, Sec. 3.

distance from the origin, we can take the radius R of the semicircle C_R so great that all poles of $R(z) = f(z)/g(z)$, in the *upper half* of the z plane, lie within the semicircle. If the sum of the residues at these poles is Σr, the residue theorem yields

$$\int_C \frac{f(z)}{g(z)} = \int_{-R}^{R} \frac{f(x)}{g(x)}\, dx + \int_{C_R} \frac{f(z)}{g(z)}\, dz = 2\pi i \Sigma r. \qquad (22\text{-}13)$$

We show next that when the degree of $g(z)$ is at least 2 greater than that of $f(z)$, the integral $\int_{C_R} \frac{f(z)}{g(z)}\, dz \to 0$ as $R \to \infty$, so that formula (22-13) then yields

$$\int_{-\infty}^{\infty} \frac{f(x)}{g(x)}\, dx = 2\pi i \Sigma r. \qquad (22\text{-}14)$$

For proof, set $z = Re^{i\theta}$ in $R(z) = f(z)/g(z)$, and note that

$$\left| \frac{f(z)}{g(z)} \right| \leq \frac{M}{R^2}, \qquad M \text{ const,}$$

when R is sufficiently large. Hence, by (5-8)

$$\left| \int_{C_R} \frac{f(z)}{g(z)}\, dz \right| \leq \int_{C_R} \left| \frac{M}{R^2} \right| |dz| = \frac{M}{R^2} \pi R = \frac{M\pi}{R},$$

from which it follows that the integral over C_R tends to zero as $R \to \infty$. Thus under the stated restrictions on $f(z)$ and $g(z)$ ensuring the convergence of (22-11), formula (22-14) is true.

An improper integral like (22-11) should be understood in the sense

$$\lim_{\substack{R_1 \to \infty \\ R_2 \to \infty}} \int_{-R_1}^{R_2} \frac{f(x)}{g(x)}\, dx \qquad (22\text{-}15)$$

where R_1 and R_2 approach infinity in any manner. However, the method of calculation indicated in the text actually gives

$$\lim_{R \to \infty} \int_{-R}^{R} \frac{f(x)}{g(x)}\, dx \qquad (22\text{-}15a)$$

so that $R_1 = R_2$ in (22-15). The expression (22-15a) is termed the *Cauchy principal value* of (22-15). If (22-15) exists (as in the case considered in the text) then obviously (22-15a) exists and has the same value. But (22-15a) may exist when (22-15) does not; for example, take $f(x) = x$, $g(x) = 1 + x^2$.

Example 2. To illustrate the use of formula (22-14) consider an elementary integral,

$$\int_{-\infty}^{\infty} \frac{dx}{1 + x^2}.$$

Here
$$R(z) = \frac{1}{1 + z^2} \equiv \frac{1}{(z + i)(z - i)},$$

so that the only singularity of $R(z)$ in the upper half plane is the simple pole at $z = i$. Since the residue of $R(z)$ at $z = i$ is $1/2i$, formula (22-14) yields

$$\int_{-\infty}^{\infty} \frac{dx}{1 + x^2} = 2\pi i \frac{1}{2i} = \pi.$$

The essential considerations that have led us to formula (22-14) are:

1. The integral over the semicircular boundary C_R in (22-13) approaches zero as $R \to \infty$.

2. The singularities of the integrand in the upper half of the z plane are isolated and are at a finite distance from the origin.

3. There are no singular points on the real axis.

Clearly, the same procedure can be used to evaluate integrals of the form

$$\int_{-\infty}^{\infty} F(x)\, dx$$

by computing $\int_C F(z)\, dz$ as long as the integrand $F(z)$ satisfies conditions 1, 2, and 3. Occasionally, a slight modification of the procedure outlined above can be used when $|F(z)|$ is not sufficiently small in the upper half of the z plane, so that the condition 1 is not fulfilled by $F(z)$. We illustrate this in the following example.

Example 3.   Evaluate

$$\int_{-\infty}^{\infty} \frac{\cos x}{a^2 + x^2}\, dx, \qquad a > 0.$$

If we take $F(z) = (\cos z)/(a^2 + z^2)$, the method outlined above cannot be applied directly, since $|\cos z| = \frac{1}{2}|e^{iz} + e^{-iz}|$ becomes infinite when $z \to \infty$ along the y axis. However, since $\cos x$ is the real part of e^{ix}, we can write

$$\int_{-\infty}^{\infty} \frac{\cos x}{a^2 + x^2}\, dx = \text{Re} \int_{-\infty}^{\infty} \frac{e^{ix}}{a^2 + x^2}\, dx \qquad (22\text{-}16)$$

where Re stands for the "real part of."

Now, if we take

$$F(z) = \frac{e^{iz}}{a^2 + z^2}, \qquad (22\text{-}17)$$

then $|e^{iz}| = |e^{i(x+iy)}| = |e^{-y}| \leq 1$ if $y \geq 0$. Thus, $F(z)$ in (22-17) is bounded in the upper half of the z plane, and there is no difficulty in showing that $\int_{C_R} F(z)\, dz \to 0$ as $R \to \infty$. Moreover, $F(z)$ in (22-17) has only two singular points, which are poles at $z_1 = ia$ and $z_2 = -ia$. Only one of these, $z_1 = ia$, lies in the upper half plane. Accordingly,

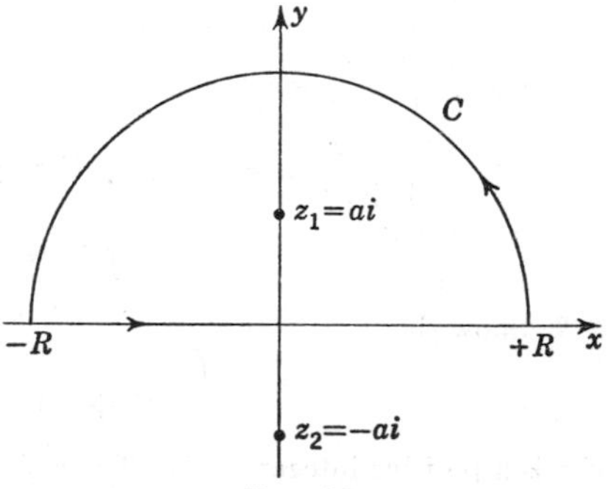

FIG. 32

$$\int_C \frac{e^{iz}}{a^2 + z^2}\, dz = 2\pi i \times \text{residue at } z_1 \qquad (22\text{-}18)$$

if C is the boundary of the semicircle (Fig. 32) and R is sufficiently large to include the point $z = z_1$.

Now the residue of (22-17) at $z = ia$ is $e^{-a}/2ai$, and since $\int_{C_R} F(z)\, dz \to 0$ as $R \to \infty$, we conclude from (22-18) that

$$\int_{-\infty}^{\infty} \frac{e^{iz}\, dz}{a^2 + z^2}\, dz = \int_{-\infty}^{\infty} \frac{e^{ix}\, dx}{a^2 + x^2} = 2\pi i \cdot \frac{e^{-a}}{2ai} = \frac{\pi e^{-a}}{a}.$$

This result is real, and hence the integral in (22-16) is

$$\int_{-\infty}^{\infty} \frac{\cos x}{a^2 + x^2}\, dx = \frac{\pi e^{-a}}{a}. \tag{22-19}$$

Inasmuch as the integrand in (22-19) is even, we conclude that

$$\int_{0}^{\infty} \frac{\cos x}{a^2 + x^2}\, dx = \frac{\pi e^{-a}}{2a}. \tag{22-20}$$

PROBLEMS

1. Use relations (22-2) and (22-3) to write the integrals $\int_{0}^{2\pi} \frac{d\theta}{\frac{5}{4} + \sin \theta}$ and $\int_{0}^{2\pi} \frac{d\theta}{5 + 3 \cos \theta}$ in the form (22-4) and evaluate the resulting integrals by the residue theorem. Check your calculations by formula (22-10).

2. Show that $\int_{0}^{2\pi} \frac{d\theta}{(1 + \alpha \cos \theta)^2} = \frac{2\pi}{(1 - \alpha^2)^{3/2}}$, $0 < \alpha < 1$.

3. Show that $\int_{-\infty}^{\infty} \frac{x^2\, dx}{(1 + x^2)^3} = \frac{\pi}{8}$.

4. Referring to Prob. 2, show that

$$\int_{0}^{\pi} \frac{d\theta}{(a + \cos \theta)^2} = \frac{\pi a}{(a^2 - 1)^{3/2}}, \qquad \text{if } a > 1.$$

5. Show that:

(a) $\int_{0}^{\infty} \frac{dx}{1 + x^4} = \frac{1}{2} \int_{-\infty}^{\infty} \frac{dx}{1 + x^4} = \frac{\pi\sqrt{2}}{4}$;

(b) $\int_{0}^{\infty} \frac{x^2\, dx}{1 + x^6} = \frac{\pi}{6}$;

(c) $\int_{0}^{\infty} \frac{\cos ax}{1 + x^2}\, dx = \frac{\pi}{2} e^{-a}$, $\qquad$ if $a \geq 0$.

6. Show that

$$\int_{0}^{\infty} \frac{\cos x\, dx}{(1 + x^2)^2} = \frac{\pi}{2} e^{-1}.$$

7. Show that

$$\int_{-\infty}^{\infty} \frac{dx}{(1 + x^2)^n} = \frac{\pi}{2^{2n-2}} \frac{(2n - 2)!}{[(n - 1)!]^2},$$

if n is a positive integer. *Hint:* The residue of $(1 + z^2)^{-n}$ at $z = i$ is

$$\frac{-n(n + 1) \ldots (2n - 2)}{(n - 1)!\, 2^{2n-1}} i.$$

One way of seeing this is to let $t = z - i$, so that $(1 + z^2)^{-n} = (it)^{-n} 2^{-n} (1 - \frac{1}{2}it)^{-n}$. The coefficient of $1/t$ is easily found by use of the binomial theorem.

CHAPTER 8

PROBABILITY

". . . la théorie des probabilités n'est que le bon sens confirmé par le calcul."—Laplace.

There is no branch of mathematics that is more intimately connected with everyday experiences than the theory of probability. Recent developments in mathematical physics, moreover, have emphasized the importance of this theory in every branch of science. A knowledge of probability is required in such diverse fields as quantum mechanics, kinetic theory, the design of experiments, and the interpretation of data. A recently developed branch of mathematics known as operations analysis applies probability methods to questions in traffic control, allocation of equipment, and the theory of strategy. Cybernetics, another field of recent origin, uses the theory to analyze problems in communication and control. In this chapter on probability the reader is introduced to some of the ideas that make the subject so useful.

FUNDAMENTALS OF PROBABILITY THEORY

1. A Definition of Probability. The idea of chance enters into everyday conversation: "It will probably rain tomorrow," "There may be a letter for me at the office," "I probably won't get double six on the next throw." It is often possible to assign a numerical measure to the notion of *probability* which these statements illustrate. Such a measure, however, must take account of the speaker's state of knowledge. For instance, in the second statement the mailman may know that a letter is there, since he put it there himself. His measure of probability and mine are therefore not the same. Probability for me is based on my knowledge, and probability for him is based on his.

From this viewpoint (which is one of several possible viewpoints) probability is a measure of ignorance. In simple cases the state of ignorance can be accounted for, and probability can be defined as follows: We agree to regard two events as *equally likely* if our ignorance is such that we have no reason to expect one rather than the other. For example a 4 or a 6 is equally likely when a true die is tossed; heads and tails are equally likely in a toss of a symmetric coin; ace of hearts and ace of spades are equally likely to be drawn from a shuffled deck.

In the latter example how shall we measure the probability that the card drawn will in fact be the ace of hearts? We say that there is "one chance out of 52" and define the probability, accordingly, to be $\frac{1}{52}$. If it is required only that the card be an ace, common sense suggests that the probability should be four times as great, for there are four aces, equally likely, and only one ace of hearts. Now, the value $\frac{4}{52}$ is, indeed, the probability that a card drawn at random is an ace. Reasoning in this way, we are led to the following definition:

DEFINITION. *Suppose there are n mutually exclusive, exhaustive, and equally likely cases. If m of these are favorable to an event A, then the probability of A is m/n.*

The term *mutually exclusive* means that two cases cannot both happen at once; the term *exhaustive* means that all possible cases are enumerated in the *n* cases. There is seldom difficulty in seeing that these conditions are satisfied, but careful analysis is sometimes needed to make sure that the cases are equally likely. For example, let two coins be tossed, and consider the probability that they both show heads. We might reason that the total number of cases is three, namely, two heads, a head and a tail, or two tails. Since only one case is favorable, the probability is $\frac{1}{3}$. Now, this reasoning is incorrect. It is true that there are three cases, but these cases are not equally likely. The case of a head and a tail is twice as likely as the others, since it can be realized with a head on the first coin or with a head on the second coin. The reader can verify that there are four equally likely cases and that the required probability is $\frac{1}{4}$.

If an event is certain to happen, then its probability is 1, since all cases are favorable. On the other hand if an event is certain not to happen its probability is zero, since no case is favorable. By means of the definition the reader may also verify the important equation

$$q = 1 - p,$$

where p is the probability that an event happens and q the probability that it fails to happen.

Since one must begin somewhere, it is impossible to define everything, and every mathematical theory contains some undefined terms. These terms should be so simple that they are easily understood and also so simple that they are not readily defined in terms of anything simpler. The notion "equally likely" is an example of such a term; it was explained and illustrated in the foregoing discussion but not defined.

Example 1. If a pair of dice is thrown what is the probability that a total of 8 shows?
The first die can fall in 6 ways, and for each of these the second can also fall in 6 ways.
The total number of ways is

$$6 + 6 + 6 + 6 + 6 + 6 = 6 \cdot 6 = 36$$

and these are equally likely in this problem. A sum of 8 can be obtained in 5 ways,
namely, as

$$2 + 6,\ 6 + 2,\ 3 + 5,\ 5 + 3,\ 4 + 4$$

and hence the desired probability is $\frac{5}{36}$.

This computation of the total number of cases illustrates an important principle of
combinatory analysis: *If one thing can be done in n different ways and another thing can
be done in m different ways, then both things can be done together or in succession in mn
different ways.*

Example 2. In a well-shuffled deck what is the probability that the top 4 cards are,
respectively, ace, two, three, and four of hearts?

To find the number of equally likely cases we consider the various possibilities for the
top 4 cards. The first card may be any one of 52; for each determination of that card
there remain 51 possibilities for the next; and so on. Repeated use of the principle
mentioned at the end of the last example gives

$$52 \cdot 51 \cdot 50 \cdot 49$$

for the total number of cases. Since only one case is favorable, the desired probability
is the reciprocal of this.

When r things are dealt into r numbered spaces from a stack of n distinct things, then
any particular arrangement of the objects is called "a permutation of n things r at a
time." If the total number of such permutations be denoted by $_nP_r$, the foregoing
reasoning yields the important formula

$$_nP_r = n(n - 1)(n - 2) \ldots (n - r + 1).$$

Example 3. If a hand of 4 cards is dealt from a shuffled deck what is the probability
that the hand consists of ace, two, three, and four of hearts?

The difference between this example and the preceding is that now the order is not
relevant. Let C denote the number of distinct 4-card hands, not counting order. Then
the number of distinct 4-card hands when the order is counted is

$$C \cdot {}_4P_4,$$

since each hand of 4 cards admits $_4P_4$ different orderings of its members. On the other
hand the number of distinct 4-card hands when order is counted is also equal to $_{52}P_4$
by Example 2. We have, therefore,

$$C \cdot {}_4P_4 = {}_{52}P_4,$$

so that

$$C = \frac{_{52}P_4}{_4P_4} = \frac{52 \cdot 51 \cdot 50 \cdot 49}{4 \cdot 3 \cdot 2 \cdot 1} = \frac{52!}{4!48!}.$$

The desired probability is the reciprocal.

When r things are taken from a stack of n things, the groups so obtained are called
"combinations of n things r at a time." If the number of such combinations is denoted
by $_nC_r$, the above reasoning gives the important formula

$$_nC_r = \frac{_nP_r}{_rP_r} = \frac{n!}{r!(n - r)!}.$$

In this formula the arrangement of members in a group is not considered. As in the case of poker hands, two groups are counted as distinct only if they have different compositions.

Example 4. What is the probability of drawing 4 white, 3 black, and 2 red balls from an urn containing 10 white, 4 black, and 3 red balls?

We suppose that the balls are not replaced. The number of ways to get 9 balls from the 17 is $_{17}C_9$. The number of ways to get 4 white from the 10 white is $_{10}C_4$. The 3 black balls can be chosen in $_4C_3$ ways, and the 2 red ones in $_3C_2$ ways. The number of favorable cases is found by multiplication (cf. Example 1), so that the desired probability is

$$\frac{_{10}C_4 \cdot _4C_3 \cdot _3C_2}{_{17}C_9} = \frac{252}{2,431}.$$

Example 5. If a number x is chosen at random on the interval $0 \leq x < 1$, what is the probability that $\frac{1}{7} \leq x < \frac{3}{7}$?

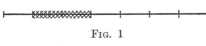

FIG. 1

We imagine the unit interval divided into 7 segments each of length $\frac{1}{7}$ (Fig. 1). Since the point may be in any one of these there are **7** cases, and the phrase "at random" ensures that these cases are equally likely. Since only **2** cases are favorable, the desired probability is $\frac{2}{7}$.

PROBLEMS

1. What is the probability that the sum of **7** appears in a single throw with two dice? What is the probability of the sum of 11? Show that **7** is the most probable throw.

2. An urn contains 20 balls: 10 white, 7 black, and 3 red. What is the probability that a ball drawn at random is red? White? Black? If 2 balls are drawn, what is the probability that both are white? If 10 balls are drawn, what is the probability that 5 are white, 2 black, and 3 red?

3. "If 3 coins are tossed, some pair is sure to come down alike. The chance that the third coin fell the same way as that pair is $\frac{1}{2}$; and hence the probability that all 3 fall alike is $\frac{1}{2}$." What (if anything) is wrong with this argument? What is the probability that 3 coins will fall alike?

4. What is the probability that a 5-card hand at poker consists of 4 kings and an odd card? 5 spades? A sequence in the same suit, such as 2, 3, 4, 5, 6 of hearts?

5. In how many ways can you seat 8 persons at a table? Arrange 8 children in a ring to dance around a Maypole? Make a bracelet of 8 different beads on a loop of string?

6. The seats in a concert hall are arranged in an m by n rectangle, the side m being parallel to the stage. What is the chance that a ticket bought at random will be for a seat in back? On the side? Somewhere on the outside rows of the rectangle?

7. Two dice are tossed. (*a*) What is the probability that the first die shows 2? (*b*) Suppose you are given the additional information that the total shown by both dice is 9. What is now the probability that the first die shows 2? (*c*) If no information is given, what is the probability that the total shown is 3? (*d*) If it is known that the first die gave 2, what is now the probability that the total is 3? (Assume that the various numbers on the second die are equally likely no matter what is known about the first die.)

2. Sample Space. The equally likely cases associated with the definition of probability represent the possible outcomes of an experiment. For instance, the 36 equally likely cases associated with a pair of dice are the 36 ways the dice may fall. Similarly if 3 coins are tossed, there are 8 equally likely cases corresponding to the 8 possible outcomes of that experiment. The set of all possible outcomes is called a *sample space;* the "points" of the sample space are events. This notion of sample space is meaningful even when the events are not equally likely and even if there are infinitely many possible outcomes. For technical reasons, however, the events composing the sample space are required to be mutually exclusive. In tossing a die the events "an even number shows" and "6 shows" are not suitable for one and the same sample space.

A finite sample space is one which has only a finite number of points. In such a space let the points (that is, events) have respective probabilities

$$p_1, p_2, \ldots, p_n$$

with $$p_1 + p_2 + \cdots + p_n = 1.$$

Suppose the first m sample points, and only those, are favorable to another event A. Then we define the probability of A to be

$$p(A) = p_1 + p_2 + \cdots + p_m \tag{2-1}$$

(and similarly if some other set of sample points is in question). Thus, the points of the sample space are weighted according to their probabilities.

The reader should observe that this definition is consistent with that of the foregoing section: If each point of the sample space has the same probability $1/n$, the result (2-1) becomes

$$p(A) = \frac{1}{n} + \frac{1}{n} + \cdots + \frac{1}{n} = \frac{m}{n}.$$

Sample spaces with constant probability are called *uniform.*

For an example of a nonuniform sample space, consider the following experiment: Four coins are tossed, and we are interested in the number of heads. An appropriate sample space is composed of the events

no heads, one head, two heads, three heads, four heads

with respective probabilities, or weights,

$$\tfrac{1}{16}, \tfrac{4}{16}, \tfrac{6}{16}, \tfrac{4}{16}, \tfrac{1}{16}.$$

These values are found by counting cases, as follows. The 4 coins can fall in 2^4, or 16, ways. They give *no heads* in only one case, namely, when they all fall tails, and hence the required probability is $\tfrac{1}{16}$. To obtain 1 head there are 4 cases: heads on the first coin or on the second coin, and so on. This gives $\tfrac{4}{16}$. For 2 heads, the 2 coins giving heads can be any 2 of the 4 coins. Since there are $_4C_2 = 6$ ways to choose 2 coins out of 4, there are 6 cases favorable to the event, *two heads*. The probability, then, is $\tfrac{6}{16}$. The other entries are found in the same way, or by symmetry.

To illustrate the use of this sample space, let us find the probability of getting at least two heads. Since the last three points of the sample space, and only those, are favorable to this event, the required probability is

$$\tfrac{6}{16} + \tfrac{4}{16} + \tfrac{1}{16} = \tfrac{11}{16}.$$

Again, the probability that there is an odd number of heads is

$$\tfrac{4}{16} + \tfrac{4}{16} = \tfrac{1}{2},$$

since that event corresponds to the second and fourth point. On the other hand, this sample space does not give the probability that the third coin will fall heads, although the underlying uniform space tells us that the probability is $\tfrac{1}{2}$.

Additional information concerning the experimental situation is apt to change the sample space. For example, if a toss of a die is known to have given an even number, the probabilities of 1, 3, and 5 are changed from $\tfrac{1}{6}$ to 0. This question is discussed in Examples 2 and 3.

When two sample spaces are constructed for a given experiment by the procedure of the text, it can be shown that they are consistent; that is, they give the same probability for any event to which they both apply. This fact is illustrated in the problems, though we do not give a formal proof.

The notion of sample space enables us to define probability even when there is no underlying set of equally likely cases. Suppose we are given n events and a corresponding set of nonnegative numbers p_i such that $p_1 + p_2 + \cdots + p_n = 1$. The events are said to form a *sample space*, the numbers p_i are called *probabilities*, and the probability of various associated events is defined by addition, as in the text. This abstract idea can be extended to sets of very general type, the role of the numbers p_i being taken by a so-called *measure* on the set. With such an approach probability theory is included in a branch of mathematics known as the theory of measure.[1] A sample space defined with the help of arbitrary numbers p_i is considered in Example 1.

Example 1. A loaded die has probabilities

$$p_1, \ p_2, \ p_3, \ p_4, \ p_5, \ p_6$$

of giving the respective values

$$1, 2, 3, 4, 5, 6.$$

What is the meaning of the condition $p_1 + p_2 + \cdots + p_6 = 1$? If this condition is satisfied, find the probability that a single toss will give either a 4 or a 6.

The condition means that one of the stated alternatives will certainly happen; for instance, the die does not land on edge. From a more abstract viewpoint, the condition means simply that the given events and probabilities form a sample space. When that is the case, the probability of getting 4 or 6 is $p_4 + p_6$ by definition.

The assumption that "the probabilities are p_i" is an example of a *statistical hypothesis*. It is an important task of statistical theory to test the validity of such hypotheses by examining the consequences.

The reader should notice that the values p_i were not given, and could hardly be given, by considering "equally likely cases." They may be estimated, however, by repeatedly tossing the die. When p_1 is the probability of the ace, it can be shown that the proportion of aces actually observed, in a large number of tosses, is likely to be close

---

[1] See Appendix C.

to p_1. If there are n tosses, and if m aces are observed, this proportion m/n is called the *relative frequency*. The connection between probability and relative frequency is discussed in Secs. 8 to 10.

Example 2. Two coins are tossed. Suppose a reliable witness tells us "at least 1 coin showed heads." What effect does this have on the uniform sample space?

The uniform sample space had the following appearance before we received the extra information:

Event.........	HH	TH	HT	TT
Probability.....	¼	¼	¼	¼

The new information assures us that the last event is ruled out but gives no indication concerning which of the other three may have occurred. Since these three events were equally likely to begin with, they are considered to be equally likely in the new situation. (That is not a theorem, but an *axiom* of probability theory.) The new sample space, therefore, is

Event.........	HH	TH	HT	TT
Probability.....	⅓	⅓	⅓	0

Example 3. The tossing of 2 coins can be described by the following sample space:

Event..........	no heads	one head	two heads
Probability.....	¼	½	¼

What happens to this sample space if we know that at least 1 coin showed heads but have no other special information?

The first event is ruled out, but we are not told which of the remaining ones occurred. It is an axiom of probability theory that the relative probabilities of the remaining events remain unchanged in a situation such as this. Since the event "1 head" is twice as likely as "2 heads" in the original space, the same is assumed in the new one. The new sample space is therefore

Event..........	no heads	one head	two heads
Probability.....	0	⅔	⅓

(remember that the probabilities must add up to 1). The reader should check that this result is consistent with that of Example 2.

If the events $E_1, E_2, \ldots, E_k$ of the sample space are the ones favorable to A and have probabilities $p_1, p_2, \ldots, p_k$, the information that A happened gives a new sample space with events $E_1, E_2, \ldots, E_k$ only. The probabilities on that new sample space are

$$cp_1, cp_2, \ldots, cp_k,$$

where c is a constant so chosen that the sum is 1:

$$c = \frac{1}{p_1 + p_2 + \cdots + p_k}.$$

This is the general assertion which is illustrated in Examples **2** and **3**.

PROBLEMS

1. A coin is tossed 3 times. Construct a uniform sample space for this experiment. (That is, make a table showing the 8 possible outcomes HHH, HHT, ... and their respective probabilities $\frac{1}{8}$, $\frac{1}{8}$, ...) According to your sample space what is the probability of at least one H? At most one H? A run of exactly two H's in succession? A run of at least two H's in succession? H appearing before T? H appearing for the first time in the second toss? The sequence THT? The sequence TTT?

2. In Prob. 1 suppose we are concerned only with the *number* of H's. Construct an appropriate sample space. (That is, make a table showing the 4 possible outcomes: no H's, one H, ... with their respective probabilities.) Decide which questions in Prob. 1 can be answered on the basis of this sample space, answer them, and verify the agreement with your answers to Prob. 1.

3. The following argument is attributed to Leibniz: "A total of 12 with 2 dice is just as likely as a total of 11. For, 12 can materialize in just one way, namely, by getting 6 on one die and 6 on the other; and 11 can also materialize in just one way, namely, by getting 6 on one die and 5 on the other." Using the notion of sample space explain what is wrong with Leibniz' conclusion. (With the uniform sample space, 11 can materialize in 2 ways. On the other hand if we choose a sample space in which the event "6 on one die and 5 on the other" is a single point, the weight of this point is different from that of the point "6 on one die and 6 on the other." The student should verify these remarks in detail.)

4. The following is due to d'Alembert: "If we want to get at least one head with 2 tosses of a coin, heads on the first toss makes the second toss unnecessary. So there are 3 cases, H, TH, and TT, of which 2 are favorable to heads. Hence the probability of heads is $\frac{2}{3}$." Discuss, with reference to the uniform sample space and also with reference to the sample space which has only the three points H, TH, TT. (Ambiguities such as this and the preceding can cause serious errors in practice if the notion of sample space is not well understood. In fact, one of the reasons for defining the sample space is to avoid this kind of difficulty.)

5. What happens to the uniform space associated with a pair of dice, if we are told that the total shown is 7?

6. Four coins are tossed. A reliable witness tells us that there are at least as many heads as tails. What is the most probable number of heads, and what is its probability? *Suggestion:* Use the sample space given in the text.

7. A coin is tossed 3 times. If we know that a sequence of 2 tails in a row did not occur, what is the probability that a sequence of 3 heads in a row did occur? *Suggestion:* Use the uniform sample space.

3. The Theorems of Total and Compound Probability.
Statements about probability are often given an abbreviated notation. If A and B are events, AB means the event "A and B"; that is, AB happens only when both A and B happen. For example, if two cards are drawn in succession without replacing, suppose A is the event "the first draw gives a king" and B is the event "the second draw gives an ace." Then AB happens if we get a king on the first draw followed by ace on the second.

It is customary to write $p(A)$ for "the probability of the event A." In the foregoing example $p(A) = \frac{4}{52}$, since there are 4 kings among the 52 cards. If nothing is known about the results of the first draw, then $p(B) = \frac{4}{52}$ also.

To see this, note that the total number of cases is $52 \cdot 51$, since there are 52 ways to get the first card and, when that card is chosen, 51 ways remain to get the second. To count the cases favorable to B, observe that the ace obtained on the second draw may be any one of the 4 aces. For each choice of this ace there remain 51 possibilities for the first card. The number of favorable cases, then, is $4 \cdot 51$, and hence

$$p(B) = \frac{4 \cdot 51}{52 \cdot 51} = \frac{4}{52}. \tag{3-1}$$

Sometimes two events A and B are so related that the information that A happened changes the probability of B. To deal with this situation it is customary to write $p_A(B)$ for "the probability of B, given A." In the example cited previously,

$$p_A(B) = \frac{4}{51} \tag{3-2}$$

(for if A happened, the first draw gave a king, and hence the 4 aces are to be found among the remaining 51 cards). On the other hand when A is the event "the first draw gives an ace" and B, as before, is the event "the second draw gives an ace," then $p_A(B) = \frac{3}{51}$ (since now only 3 aces remain when A happens). Both values for $p_A(B)$ are different from $p(B)$, the probability of ace on the second draw when nothing is said about the first draw.

In this notation *the theorem of compound probability* takes the following form:

THEOREM. *If A and B are any events, then*

$$p(AB) = p(A)p_A(B). \tag{3-3}$$

Informally, "the probability that A and B happen is the probability that A happens times the probability that B then happens." A proof is easily given by considering equally likely cases. Let n_a, n_b, and n_{ab} denote the numbers of cases favorable to A, B, and AB, respectively. Then

$$p(AB) = \frac{n_{ab}}{n} = \frac{n_a}{n}\frac{n_{ab}}{n_a}.$$

Now, n_a/n is $p(A)$ by definition. After A has happened, the only possible cases are the n_a cases favorable to A. Of these, there are n_{ab} cases favorable to B. Since the n_a cases are to be considered equally likely, the quotient n_{ab}/n_a represents the probability of B when it is known that A happened, and this gives (3-3).

To illustrate the theorem (3-3), let us find the probability of drawing 2 aces in succession from a pack of 52 cards. The probability of ace on the first trial is $\frac{4}{52}$. After the first ace has been drawn, the probability of drawing another ace from the remaining 51 cards is $\frac{3}{51}$, so that the probability of two aces is

$$\frac{4}{52} \cdot \frac{3}{51} = \frac{1}{221}.$$

This assumes that the first card is not replaced. When it is replaced, the reader will find that the desired probability is

$$\tfrac{4}{52} \cdot \tfrac{4}{52} = \tfrac{1}{169}.$$

For another illustration of the theorem (3-3), let us find the probability of drawing a white and a black ball in succession from an urn containing 30 black balls and 20 white balls. Here the probability of drawing a white ball is $\tfrac{20}{50}$. After a white ball is drawn, the probability of drawing a black ball is $\tfrac{30}{49}$. Hence the probability of drawing a white ball and a black ball in the order stated is

$$p = \tfrac{20}{50} \cdot \tfrac{30}{49} = \tfrac{12}{49}.$$

The events A and B are said to be *independent* if the information that A happened does not influence the probability of B. Hence for such events $p_A(B) = p(B)$, and the theorem of compound probability takes the form

$$p(AB) = p(A)p(B), \qquad \text{for independent events.} \qquad (3\text{-}4)$$

For instance, let a coin and a die be tossed, and let A be the event "head shows" while B is the event "4 shows." These events are independent, and hence the probability that heads and 4 both appear is

$$p(AB) = p(A)p(B) = (\tfrac{1}{2})(\tfrac{1}{6}) = \tfrac{1}{12}.$$

The result (3-4) is readily extended to any number of independent events $A, B, C, \ldots$.

Besides the theorem of compound probability, there is a second fundamental relationship, known as the *theorem of total probability*. If A and B are two events, $A + B$ is defined to be the event "A or B or both." For instance, let A be the event "a number greater than 3 shows" while B is the event "an even number shows" in a toss of

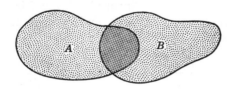

Fig. 2

a die. Then $A + B$ happens if the die gives 2, 4, 5, or 6. In this notation the theorem of total probability reads as follows:

THEOREM. *When A and B are any events, then*

$$p(A + B) = p(A) + p(B) - p(AB). \qquad (3\text{-}5)$$

We can represent the statement (3-5) diagrammatically by the intersecting point sets A and B shown in Fig. 2.

Referring to the definition of probability by equally likely cases, suppose the numbers of cases favorable to A, B, AB, and $A + B$ are denoted by

$$n_a, \ n_b, \ n_{ab}, \ n_{a+b},$$

respectively. To find the number favorable to $A + B$, it will not do simply to add n_a and n_b, for the cases favorable to both A and B are counted twice in this addition. To take account of that we must subtract n_{ab}, thus:

$$n_{a+b} = n_a + n_b - n_{ab}.$$

Dividing by n, the total number of cases, gives

$$\frac{n_{a+b}}{n} = \frac{n_a}{n} + \frac{n_b}{n} - \frac{n_{ab}}{n},$$

which is equivalent to (3-5).

To illustrate the theorem, let us find the probability that at least one die gives 4, when two dice are tossed. The probability that both give 4 is $\frac{1}{36}$. The probability that the first gives 4 is $\frac{1}{6}$, and similarly for the second. Hence the probability that at least one gives 4 is

$$p(A + B) = \tfrac{1}{6} + \tfrac{1}{6} - \tfrac{1}{36} = \tfrac{11}{36}. \qquad (3\text{-}6)$$

This is consistent with the result given by counting cases. Specifically, there are 5 cases with a 4 on the first and a number other than 4 on the second, there are 5 cases with 4 on the second and a number other than 4 on the first, and there is 1 case with 4 on both. The number of favorable cases is therefore $5 + 5 + 1 = 11$ so that (3-6) follows.

For mutually exclusive events, that is, for events A, B which cannot both happen, $p(AB) = 0$. Hence the theorem of total probability takes the form

$$p(A + B) = p(A) + p(B), \qquad \text{for mutually exclusive events.} \quad (3\text{-}7)$$

The statement (3-7) can be depicted by the nonintersecting point sets in Fig. 3.

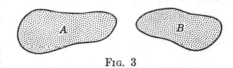

For example, in a toss of a die let A be the event "4 shows" while B is the event "5 shows." Since these

FIG. 3

events are mutually exclusive, the probability of getting either 4 or 5 is

$$p(A + B) = p(A) + p(B) = \tfrac{1}{6} + \tfrac{1}{6} = \tfrac{1}{3}.$$

A result similar to (3-7) applies to any number of mutually exclusive events A, B, C, ...

The foregoing analysis, by counting cases, establishes the theorems of total and compound probability for uniform sample spaces only. Actually the results are valid for arbitrary sample spaces, as will be indicated next.

Assuming that the sample space is finite, let the events E_i of the sample space be so numbered that
$$E_1, \ldots, E_j$$
are favorable to A alone,
$$E_{j+1}, \ldots, E_k$$
are favorable to both A and B, while
$$E_{k+1}, \ldots, E_m$$
are favorable to B alone. If the associated probabilities are p_i, then (3-5) is equivalent to the identity

$$p_1 + \cdots + p_m = (p_1 + \cdots + p_j + p_{j+1} + \cdots + p_k)$$
$$+ (p_{j+1} + \cdots + p_k + p_{k+1} + \cdots + p_m) - (p_{j+1} + \cdots + p_k).$$

The three parentheses on the right represent, respectively, $p(A)$, $p(B)$, and $p(AB)$ by definition.

To derive (3-3) for a general sample space, recall that the sample points favorable to B have the same relative weights after A happened as before. Hence, in the previous notation,

$$p(AB) = p_{j+1} + \cdots + p_k$$

$$= (p_1 + \cdots + p_k) \left(\frac{p_{j+1}}{p_1 + \cdots + p_k} + \cdots + \frac{p_k}{p_1 + \cdots + p_k} \right)$$

$$= p(A) p_A(B).$$

Example 1. The probability that Peter will solve a problem is p_1, and the probability that Paul will solve it is p_2. What is the probability that the problem will be solved if Peter and Paul work independently?

The probability that both solve it is $p_1 p_2$, by the theorem of compound probability, (3-3). Hence the probability that at least one solves it is

$$p_1 + p_2 - p_1 p_2 \qquad\qquad (3-8)$$

by the theorem of total probability, (3-5).

Example 2. Solve Example 1 by finding the probability that both fail.

Peter's probability to fail is $1 - p_1$, and Paul's probability to fail is $1 - p_2$. The probability that both fail is

$$(1 - p_1)(1 - p_2)$$

and the probability of the contrary event, that at least one succeeds, is

$$1 - (1 - p_1)(1 - p_2). \qquad\qquad (3-9)$$

The consistency of (3-8) and (3-9) is easily verified.

Example 3. A bag contains 10 white balls and 15 black balls. Two balls are drawn in succession. What is the probability that one of them is black and the other is white?

The mutually exclusive events in this problem are (a) drawing a white ball on the first trial and a black ball on the second, (b) drawing a black ball on the first trial and a white on the second. The probability of (a) is $^{10}\!\!/_{25} \cdot {}^{15}\!\!/_{24}$ and that of (b) is $^{15}\!\!/_{25} \cdot {}^{10}\!\!/_{24}$, so that the probability of either (a) or (b) is

$$^{10}\!\!/_{25} \cdot {}^{15}\!\!/_{24} + {}^{15}\!\!/_{25} \cdot {}^{10}\!\!/_{24} = \tfrac{1}{2}.$$

Example 4. How often must a pair of dice be tossed to make it more likely than not that double 6 appears at least once?

The probability that double 6 does not appear on a given toss is $^{35}\!\!/_{36}$, no matter what is known about the preceding tosses. Repeated use of the theorem of compound probability gives

$$(^{35}\!\!/_{36})^n$$

for the probability that double 6 does not appear in any of n tosses. It is desired to choose n in such a way that this probability is less than $\tfrac{1}{2}$. Thus,

$$(^{35}\!\!/_{36})^n < \tfrac{1}{2}.$$

Taking the logarithm gives

$$n \log {}^{35}\!\!/_{36} < - \log 2$$

or

$$n > \frac{\log 2}{\log {}^{36}\!\!/_{35}} = 24.6.$$

Thus 25 tosses suffice, but 24 do not.

Example 5. Peter and Paul take turns tossing a pair of dice. The first to get a throw of 7 wins. If Peter starts the game, how much better are his chances of winning than Paul's?

This problem is different from any we have considered hitherto, in that there are infinitely many possibilities. Namely, Peter may win on his first throw, or on his second throw, or on his third throw, and so forth. To apply the preceding theory, we simply consider the probability that Peter wins in n throws and take the limit as $n \to \infty$. A wide variety of questions involving infinitely many outcomes may be dealt with in a similar manner.

The probability of 7 is $\tfrac{1}{6}$, and the probability of not getting 7 is $\tfrac{5}{6}$. Hence the probability that Peter wins on his first throw is $\tfrac{1}{6}$. The probability that Peter wins on his second throw is $(\tfrac{5}{6})^2(\tfrac{1}{6})$ (since Peter's first throw and Paul's first throw must be other than 7 but Peter's second throw must be 7). Peter's probability of winning on his third throw is $(\tfrac{5}{6})^4(\tfrac{1}{6})$, and so on.

By the theorem of total probability the probability that Peter wins is

$$\tfrac{1}{6} + (\tfrac{1}{6})(\tfrac{5}{6})^2 + (\tfrac{1}{6})(\tfrac{5}{6})^4 + \cdots = (\tfrac{1}{6})(1 + r + r^2 + \cdots), \qquad \text{where } r = (\tfrac{5}{6})^2$$

$$= \frac{1}{6} \frac{1}{1-r} = \frac{1}{6} \frac{1}{1 - {}^{25}\!\!/_{36}} = \frac{6}{11}. \tag{3-10}$$

A similar procedure shows that Paul's chance of winning is $^{5}\!\!/_{11}$, or one can reason as follows: The probability that 7 does not occur in n trials is $(\tfrac{5}{6})^n$. Since the limit is zero, the probability of an eternal game is zero, and Peter or Paul is sure to win. Thus, Paul's chance is

$$1 - {}^{6}\!\!/_{11} = {}^{5}\!\!/_{11}.$$

PROBLEMS

1. What is the probability that 5 cards dealt from a pack of 52 cards are all of the same suit?

2. Five coins are tossed simultaneously. What is the probability that at least one of them shows a head? All show heads?

3. The probability that Paul will be alive 10 years hence is $\frac{5}{8}$ and that John will be alive is $\frac{3}{4}$. What is the probability that both Paul and John will be dead 10 years hence? Paul alive and John dead? John alive and Paul dead?

4. One purse contains 3 silver and 7 gold coins; another purse contains 4 silver and 8 gold coins. A purse is chosen at random, and a coin is drawn from it. What is the probability that it is a gold coin?

5. Paul and Peter are alternately throwing a pair of dice. The first man to throw a doublet is to win. If Paul throws first, what is his chance of winning on his first throw? What is the probability that Paul fails and Peter wins on his first throw?

6. How many times must a die be thrown in order that the probability that the ace appear at least once shall be greater than $\frac{1}{2}$?

7. Twenty tickets are numbered from 1 to 20, and one of them is drawn at random. What is the probability that the number is a multiple of 5 or 7? A multiple of 3 or 5?

Note that in solving the second part of this problem, it is incorrect to reason as follows: The number of tickets bearing numerals that are multiples of 3 is 6, and the number of multiples of 5 is 4. Hence the probability that the number drawn is either a multiple of 3 or of 5 is $\frac{6}{20} + \frac{4}{20} = \frac{1}{2}$. Why is this reasoning incorrect?

8. A card is chosen at random from each of 5 decks. What is the probability that all are face cards? Would the probability be larger or smaller if all 5 cards were taken from one deck, without replacing?

9. Answer the two questions in Prob. 8 if the desired hand is 1, 2, 3, 4, 5 of clubs; if the desired hand is to have at least 2 aces but is otherwise unrestricted.

10. Each of two radio tubes has probability p of burning out during the first 100 hr use. If both are put into service at the same time, what is the probability that at least one of them is still good after 100 hr? Generalize to n tubes. If $p = 0.1$, how many tubes are needed to give a probability > 0.99 that at least one is good after 100 hr?

4. Random Variables and Expectation.[1] A process is *random* if it is impossible to predict the final state from the initial state (as, for example, in a toss of a coin or a die). Associated with a random process there may be certain numerically valued variables which themselves have a random character. For instance, if X denotes the number obtained by tossing a die, then X is a variable which assumes the values

$$1, 2, 3, 4, 5, 6$$

corresponding to the six events: 1 shows, 2 shows, and so forth. The respective probabilities are

$$\tfrac{1}{6}, \tfrac{1}{6}, \tfrac{1}{6}, \tfrac{1}{6}, \tfrac{1}{6}, \tfrac{1}{6}.$$

Again if X is the number of heads obtained when 3 coins are tossed, then X is a variable which assumes the values

$$0, 1, 1, 1, 2, 2, 2, 3 \qquad (4\text{-}1)$$

---

[1] Sections 4 through 6 may be omitted on the first reading without loss of continuity, but they are essential to the developments in Sec. 13.

corresponding to the various ways the coins may fall. For instance, $X = 2$ corresponds to each of the three events: HHT, HTH, THH.

Similarly, if a gambler stakes d dollars on a game, the amount he wins assumes the values

$$d, -d$$

in correspondence with the events "he wins the game" and "he loses the game." If his probability of winning is p, the respective probabilities of $X = d$ and $X = -d$ are

$$p, 1 - p.$$

These special cases illustrate the important idea of *random variable*. A *random variable is a numerical-valued function defined on a sample space.* In symbols,

$$X(e_i) = x_i, \qquad i = 1, 2, \ldots, n, \tag{4-2}$$

where e_i are the events of the sample space and x_i are the values of the random variable X.

Let $\{e_i\}$ be a sample space of n events e_i with associated probabilities p_i. Let X be a random variable defined on $\{e_i\}$ and assuming the value x_i at the ith sample point, so that (4-2) holds. The *expectation* or *expected value* $E(X)$ is then defined by

$$E(X) = p_1 x_1 + p_2 x_2 + \cdots + p_n x_n. \tag{4-3}$$

For example, if X is the number obtained in a toss of a die, then X assumes the values 1, 2, 3, $\ldots$ with corresponding probabilities $p_i = \frac{1}{6}$. Hence

$$E(X) = \tfrac{1}{6}\cdot 1 + \tfrac{1}{6}\cdot 2 + \tfrac{1}{6}\cdot 3 + \tfrac{1}{6}\cdot 4 + \tfrac{1}{6}\cdot 5 + \tfrac{1}{6}\cdot 6 = \tfrac{7}{2}.$$

Similarly, if X is the number of heads obtained when 3 coins are tossed, then (4-1) and (4-3) give

$$E(X) = \tfrac{0}{8} + \tfrac{1}{8} + \tfrac{1}{8} + \tfrac{1}{8} + \tfrac{2}{8} + \tfrac{2}{8} + \tfrac{2}{8} + \tfrac{3}{8} = \tfrac{3}{2}$$

when we note that $p_i = \frac{1}{8}$ in this case.

By grouping terms we can write the above sum in the form

$$E(X) = \tfrac{1}{8}\cdot 0 + \tfrac{3}{8}\cdot 1 + \tfrac{3}{8}\cdot 2 + \tfrac{1}{8}\cdot 3.$$

The factors

$$0, 1, 2, 3$$

represent the *numerically distinct* values of X, and the factors

$$\tfrac{1}{8}, \tfrac{3}{8}, \tfrac{3}{8}, \tfrac{1}{8}$$

represent the probabilities corresponding to these distinct values. For example, $\frac{3}{8}$ is the probability of 2 heads when 3 coins are tossed, and hence $\frac{3}{8}$ is the probability that $X = 2$. A similar grouping of terms can be applied to the general definition (4-3) and yields the following useful theorem:

THEOREM I.   *The expectation $E(X)$ is given by*

$$E(X) = P_1x_1 + P_2x_2 + \cdots + P_rx_r$$

where x_1, x_2, ..., x_r are the numerically distinct values of X and where P_i is the probability that $X = x_i$.

Let x_i be the r distinct values of a random variable X, and let y_j be the s distinct values of another random variable Y. The *sum $X + Y$* is a random variable which is defined to be $x_i + y_j$ when $X = x_i$ and $Y = y_j$. Thus, $X + Y$ is defined on a sample space whose points consist of the rs events

$$X = x_i \qquad \text{and} \qquad Y = y_j \tag{4-4}$$

for $i = 1, 2, \ldots, r$ and $j = 1, 2, \ldots, s$. One of the most important theorems in probability theory concerns sums of variables and reads as follows:

THEOREM II.   *The expectation of the sum of two random variables is equal to the sum of the expectations, or in symbols,*

$$E(X + Y) = E(X) + E(Y). \tag{4-5}$$

To prove Eq. (4-5) let p_{ij} be the probability that simultaneously $X = x_i$ and $Y = y_j$. Thus, p_{ij} is the probability of the event (4-4). The definition of expectation yields

$$E(X + Y) = \sum p_{ij}(x_i + y_j), \tag{4-6}$$

since $x_i + y_j$ is the value of $X + Y$ which corresponds to the event (4-4). By rearrangement,

$$E(X + Y) = \sum_i x_i \left(\sum_j p_{ij} \right) + \sum_j y_j \left(\sum_i p_{ij} \right). \tag{4-7}$$

Now, $\sum_j p_{ij}$ represents the probability of

$$(X = x_i, Y = y_1) \qquad \text{or} \qquad (X = x_i, Y = y_2) \qquad \ldots \qquad \text{or}$$

$$(X = x_i, Y = y_s).$$

Hence, it represents [1] the probability P_i that $X = x_i$. Theorem I now gives

$$\sum_i x_i \left(\sum_j p_{ij} \right) = \sum_i x_i P_i = E(X)$$

and similarly,

$$\sum_j y_j \left(\sum_i p_{ij} \right) = E(Y).$$

---

[1] This shows that $\Sigma\Sigma p_{ij} = \Sigma P_i = 1$, hence that the events (4-4) actually do form a sample space.

Thus, (4-7) is equivalent to (4-5). The extension to any number of variables is immediate.

The following alternative approach to Theorem II does not require the use of Theorem I. Let X be defined on a sample space $\{a_i\}$ containing n events and Y on a space $\{b_j\}$ containing m events. Thus,

$$X(a_i) = x_i \qquad \text{and} \qquad Y(b_j) = y_j.$$

The variable $X + Y$ is defined on a sample space whose mn events e_{ij} happen when, and only when, a_i and b_j both happen. The value of $X + Y$ corresponding to the event e_{ij} is defined to be $x_i + y_j$. If p_{ij} is the probability of e_{ij}, then the definition of expectation gives (4-6), which may be written in the form (4-7) as before. Since the events of the sample space $\{b_i\}$ are mutually exclusive (Sec. 2), the sum $\sum_j p_{ij}$ represents the probability of

$$a_i \text{ and } b_1 \qquad \text{or} \qquad a_i \text{ and } b_2 \quad \ldots \quad \text{or} \qquad a_i \text{ and } b_m.$$

Hence it represents p_i, the probability of a_i. The first term in (4-7) is therefore $E(X)$ by (4-3), and similarly, the second term is $E(Y)$.

The sums

$$\sum_j p_{ij} \quad \text{and} \quad \sum_i p_{ij} \tag{4-8}$$

are called the *marginal probabilities* of a_i and b_j, respectively. In modern statistical theory it is customary to start with the larger sample space $\{e_{ij}\}$ and to define the probabilities on the smaller spaces $\{a_i\}$ and $\{b_j\}$ by means of (4-8). Theorem II is then valid, so to say, by *fiat*.

Since $\Sigma p_i = 1$, the expectation $E(X)$ in (4-3) may be interpreted as the center of mass:

$$E(X) = \frac{p_1 x_1 + p_2 x_2 + \cdots + p_n x_n}{p_1 + p_2 + \cdots + p_n}.$$

For equally likely x_i the result reduces to the arithmetic mean

$$E(X) = \frac{1}{n}(x_1 + x_2 + \cdots + x_n), \qquad \text{if each } p_i = \frac{1}{n}.$$

Thus, $E(X)$ is a measure of the location of X; it is a *typical value*. The following sections show that if sufficiently many observations of the variable X are made, the mean of those observations will almost certainly be close to $E(X)$. In this sense, $E(X)$ represents the average value attained by X in the long run.

Throughout this section random variables were denoted by capital letters to avoid confusion between the *variable* and its *values* x_i or y_j. In statistical literature the variables are usually denoted by small letters. Since the distinction has now been sufficiently emphasized, we shall often use small letters in the remainder of this chapter. Thus, depending on the context, x_i may be a set of random variables or the values of a single variable.

Example 1. Find the expected number of heads when n coins are tossed.

Let $X_i = 1$ if the ith coin shows heads and $X_i = 0$ otherwise. Then, for each i,

$$E(X_i) = \tfrac{1}{2} \cdot 1 + \tfrac{1}{2} \cdot 0 = \tfrac{1}{2}.$$

(The reader is cautioned that X_1, X_2, ... are distinct variables here, not the different values x_i of a single variable.) The number of heads m is

$$m = X_1 + X_2 + \cdots + X_n,$$

and hence

$$E(m) = E(X_1 + X_2 + \cdots + X_n)$$
$$= E(X_1) + E(X_2) + \cdots + E(X_n)$$
$$= \frac{1}{2} + \frac{1}{2} + \cdots + \frac{1}{2} = \frac{n}{2}.$$

Example 2. From an urn containing a white and b black balls, a ball is drawn at random and set aside. What is the expected number of white balls left in the urn?

Let X be the number of white balls left. If a white ball is drawn, then $X = a - 1$, whereas if a black ball is drawn, then $X = a$. Hence

$$E(X) = \frac{a}{a+b}(a-1) + \frac{b}{a+b}a = a - \frac{a}{a+b}.$$

Example 3. A deck of cards is thoroughly shuffled. We say there is a *coincidence* if a card has the same position after shuffling as it had before (e.g., if it is the fourth from the top both times). Find the expected number of coincidences.

Let $X_i = 1$ if the ith card is in the same position before and after shuffling, and let $X_i = 0$ otherwise. Then

$$E(X_i) = \tfrac{1}{52} \cdot 1 + {}^{51}\!\!\tfrac{}{52} \cdot 0 = \tfrac{1}{52}.$$

Since the number of coincidences is ΣX_i, its expectation is

$$E(X_1) + E(X_2) + \cdots + E(X_{52}) = 1.$$

PROBLEMS

1. A bent coin has probability p of giving heads and probability $q = 1 - p$ of giving tails. Let X be a random variable representing the number of heads when the coin is tossed three times; X is defined on a sample space consisting of the 8 events HHH, HHT, ... with associated probabilities p^3, p^2q, ... (a) Make a table giving the 8 values of X associated with the 8 sample points and their respective probabilities. (b) Make a second table giving the 4 distinct values of X and their probabilities. (c) Compute the expectation $E(X)$ from your table (a) and also from your table (b).

2. If X is the number of heads and Y the number of tails, find $E(XY)$ from your table in Prob. 1a and also from that in 1b. Is it true that $E(XY) = E(X)E(Y)$? *Hint:* Make a table giving the 4 values of XY in the 4 cases of Prob. 1b.

3. Peter turns up the cards one at a time from a 52-card deck, and Paul tries to guess what the cards are. Find the expected number of correct guesses (a) when Paul calls out at random, perhaps repeating himself, (b) when Paul calls off the 52 cards, naming each one just once, (c) when Paul calls out "ace of spades" each time. (Assume that Paul has no actual insight into the behavior of the cards.)

4. In Prob. 3, suppose Peter tells Paul what the card was immediately after Paul guesses. Paul has the good sense not to call any of those cards, since he knows they have been set aside. What is the expected number of correct guesses now? *Hint:* Let $X_i = 1$ if the ith guess is correct, $X_i = 0$ otherwise. $E(X_i) = ?$ The expected number of correct guesses will be found to be approximately $\log_e 52$.

5. A coin is tossed repeatedly. What is the expected number of the toss at which heads first appear? *Hint:* Let X be the number of the toss at which heads first appear. Then X has the values 1, 2, 3, ... with respective probabilities $\frac{1}{2}$, $\frac{1}{4}$, $\frac{1}{8}$, ... The reader is reminded that $\Sigma nr^n = r/(1-r)^2$ for any r such that $|r| < 1$.

5. Discrete Distributions. When the values x_i of a random variable are distinct, the associated probabilities p_i may be written in the form

$$p_i = f(x_i).$$

Since the x_i are supposed to be all the possible values of x, we must have

$$\Sigma f(x_i) = 1, \tag{5-1}$$

just as in the last section $\Sigma p_i = 1$. Also $f(x) \geq 0$, because $f(x)$ is a probability.

For example, let x be the number of heads obtained when 4 coins are tossed. If the value $x = 0, 1, 2, 3,$ or 4 is given, then the probability to assume that value is determined by the table

$x =$	0	1	2	3	4
$f(x) =$	$\frac{1}{16}$	$\frac{4}{16}$	$\frac{6}{16}$	$\frac{4}{16}$	$\frac{1}{16}$

The function $f(x)$ is called the *frequency function* for reasons which will now be explained. Suppose n observations of the variable x are made; how often should we expect $x = x_i$? To answer this question, let $X_k = 1$ if $x = x_i$ at the kth observation and $X_k = 0$ otherwise. The number of times $x = x_i$ is

$$m = X_1 + X_2 + \cdots + X_n.$$

Since the definition of expectation gives

$$E(X_k) = 1 \cdot f(x_i) + 0[1 - f(x_i)] = f(x_i),$$

we have the fundamental result

$$E(m) = nf(x_i). \tag{5-2}$$

Thus, the frequency function $f(x_i)$ is proportional to *the expected frequency of the event $x = x_i$* in a fixed number of observations.

Since the values x_i are distinct, the events $x = x_1$ and $x = x_2$ are mutually exclusive. Hence, by total probability, the probability of $x = x_1$ or $x = x_2$ is

$$f(x_1) + f(x_2).$$

In just the same way the probability of $x = x_1$, or x_2, $\ldots$, or x_k is

$$\sum_{i=1}^{k} f(x_i). \tag{5-3}$$

It is often desirable to consider the probability that x will not exceed a given value. If x_1, x_2, $\ldots$, x_k are the values of x_i which do not exceed t, then the probability that $x \leq t$ is given by the sum (5-3). That is, the event "$x \leq t$" is equivalent to the event "$x = x_1$, or $x = x_2$, $\ldots$, or $x = x_k$." It is customary to write

$$F(t) = \sum_{x_i \leq t} f(x_i) \tag{5-4}$$

for summation over the values of x_i which do not exceed t. The function $F(t)$ thus obtained is called the *distribution function;* it gives the probability that $x \leq t$. When t is so small that no x_i satisfies $x_i \leq t$, the sum (5-4) has no terms, and $F(t) = 0$ for such t. When t is so large that every x_i satisfies $x_i \leq t$, then the sum (5-4) includes every x_i. In this case (5-1) gives the value $F(t) = 1$.

For example, if x is the number of heads obtained when 4 coins are tossed, the distribution function is described by the following table:

t	$t < 0$	$0 \leq t < 1$	$1 \leq t < 2$	$2 \leq t < 3$	$3 \leq t < 4$	$4 \leq t$
$F(t)$	0	$\frac{1}{16}$	$\frac{5}{16}$	$\frac{11}{16}$	$\frac{15}{16}$	1

These entries are obtained by adding the values of $f(x)$ which were found previously. For instance, $\frac{11}{16}$ corresponds to the interval $2 \leq t < 3$ because

$$\sum_{x_i \leq t} f(x_i) = f(0) + f(1) + f(2) = \tfrac{1}{16} + \tfrac{4}{16} + \tfrac{6}{16} = \tfrac{11}{16}.$$

The value $\frac{11}{16}$ is the probability of getting at most 2 heads when 4 coins are tossed.

The variables x considered so far in this chapter are called *discrete variables* because they assume isolated values only. For instance, the number of heads obtained when several coins are tossed is an integer 0, 1, 2, 3, $\ldots$ (and cannot fill up an interval). The distribution of such a variable is called a *discrete distribution;* it is defined for all values of x, not only for the discrete set of possible values x_k. One may also think of the frequency function as being defined for all x, taking $f(x) = 0$ for values x other than the x_k. (For example, the probability of getting 3.2 heads is zero.) The fact is that we may define $f(x)$ in any *arbitrary* fashion for values other than the x_k, provided some care is taken in the interpretation of the results. This possibility is exploited in the following discussion.

Graphical representation of the functions $f(x)$ and $F(x)$ is given in Figs. 4 to 6. Figure 4 is valid as a probability for all x. The relationship of $f(x)$ and $F(x)$ is clarified, however, if $f(x)$ is modified as shown in Fig. 5. Here, the value of $f(x)$ at any integer m is used for $f(x)$ in the interval of length 1 centered about m. The resulting step function still gives the probability that $x = x_k$, provided x_k is an integer. The advantage of redefining $f(x)$ in this fashion rests upon the following

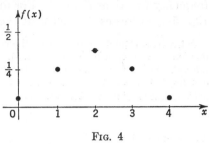

FIG. 4

property, which is easily verified: *If t is an integer, then $F(t)$ is the area under the curve of Fig. 5 up to the value $x = t + \frac{1}{2}$.* For instance, the area up to the value $x = 2\frac{1}{2}$ is found to be

$$f(0) + f(1) + f(2) = F(2)$$

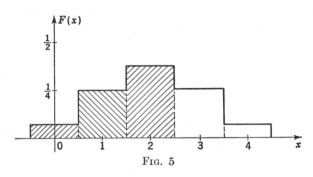

FIG. 5

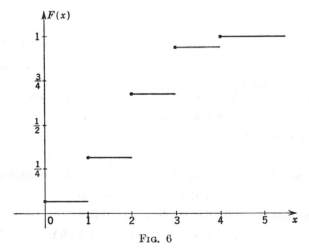

FIG. 6

by adding the areas of the shaded rectangles. When the values x_k are equally spaced, similar considerations apply to any distribution and frequency functions F and f. For unit spacing, that is, for $x_{k+1} - x_k = 1$, Eq. (5-1) expresses the fact that the area under the curve is 1.

Actually, it is possible to describe the relationship of f and F directly, without introduction of the intermediate curve (Fig. 5). The description involves the so-called *Stieltjes integral*, which is now to be defined. Let $F(t)$ be a nondecreasing function on an interval $a \leq t \leq b$, and let $\phi(t)$ be continuous. Choose a set of points $t_1, t_2, \ldots, t_n$ on the interval $[a,b]$, and choose intermediate values ξ_k,

$$t_k \leq \xi_k \leq t_{k+1}.$$

As the subdivision given by the t_ks is made finer and finer, in such a way that

$$\max |t_{k+1} - t_k| \to 0,$$

it can be shown that the expression

$$\Sigma \phi(\xi_k)[F(t_{k+1}) - F(t_k)]$$

tends to a limit (independent of the manner of subdivision and of the points ξ_k). The limit is called the *Stieltjes integral of ϕ with respect to F* and is written

$$\int_a^b \phi(t) \, dF(t).$$

When $F(t)$ is a discrete distribution corresponding to x_k and $f(x)$, the function $F(t)$ has a jump of value $f(x_k)$ at each value x_k but is constant between those values. Hence the differences

$$F(t_{k+1}) - F(t_k)$$

behave much like the function exemplified in Fig. 4. They assume the value $f(x_k)$ if the interval (t_k, t_{k+1}) contains a single point x_k, and they assume the value 0 if the interval contains no point x_k. The relationship of f and F is now described by the equation

$$F(t) = \int_{-\infty}^t dF(x)$$

where the integral is a Stieltjes integral. Although we have not defined a differential dF, we may think of $dF(x)$ as being equivalent to the frequency function $f(x)$ in the sense described above.

Example 1. In terms of the distribution function, express the probability that $a < x \leq b$, where a and b are two numbers with $a < b$.

The event "$x \leq b$" can materialize in the mutually exclusive forms

$$x \leq a \quad \text{or} \quad a < x \leq b.$$

Hence, by total probability,

$$\Pr (x \leq b) = \Pr (x \leq a) + \Pr (a < x \leq b)$$

where Pr means "the probability that." This yields the desired expression

$$\Pr (a < x \leq b) = F(b) - F(a) \tag{5-5}$$

when we recall that the distribution function $F(t)$ satisfies

$$\Pr (x \leq b) = F(b), \qquad \Pr (x \leq a) = F(a).$$

Example 2.   In terms of the frequency function $f(x)$ the expectation of any variable $y = g(x)$ is

$$E(y) = \Sigma y_k f(x_k), \qquad y_k = g(x_k). \tag{5-6}$$

We consider the variable y to be defined on a sample space whose points are the n events

$$x = x_1, \qquad x = x_2, \qquad \ldots, \qquad x = x_n.$$

The probability of the event "$x = x_k$" is $f(x_k)$; the value of y corresponding to the event "$x = x_k$" is $y_k = g(x_k)$.   Hence, (5-6) follows from the general definition of expectation.

PROBLEMS

1. Suppose a coin is tossed 5 times.   What is the probability that this experiment will yield 0, 1, 2, 3, 4, 5 heads?

2. If x is the number of heads in Prob. 1, make a table representing the frequency function $f(x)$.   Plot $f(x)$ and also the step-function modification (see Figs. 4 and 5).

3. In Prob. 1 make a table and also a graph for the distribution function $F(t)$.

4. If a coin is tossed 5 times, find the probability that the number of heads x satisfies $1 < x \leq 4$ by use of (a) the frequency function $f(x)$ computed in Prob. 2, (b) the distribution function $F(t)$ computed in Prob. 3, (c) the step-function graph obtained in Prob. 2, with reference to an appropriate area under the curve.

6. Continuous Distributions.   Since measurements are made only to a certain number of significant figures, the variables which arise as the result of an experiment are discrete.   For example, if the diameter of a shaft is measured to the nearest 0.01 in., the measurement is a variable which assumes only isolated values, such as $3.21, 3.22, 3.23, \ldots$ in.   Nevertheless it is convenient to introduce continuous variables, because they are easier [1] to handle analytically.   Such variables are now to be discussed.

Let a point be chosen at random on the interval $0 \leq x \leq 1$.   How shall we measure the probabilities associated with that event?   If the interval $(0,1)$ is divided into a number of subintervals, each of length $\Delta x = 0.1$, then the point x is equally likely to be in any of these subintervals (Fig. 7). The probability that [2] $0.5 < x < 0.8$, for example, is 0.3, since there are three favorable cases.   The probability that $0.52 < x < 0.84$ is found to

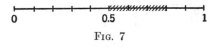

Fig. 7

be $0.84 - 0.52 = 0.32$ when we divide the interval into 100 parts, and so on.   This reasoning shows that the probability for x to be in a given subinterval of $(0,1)$ is the length of that subinterval.   If Pr stands for "the

---

[1] This remark does not justify the use of continuous variables in applied mathematics. The justification rests upon the fact that discrete variables can be approximated by continuous ones within the experimental error.

[2] In this section it will not matter whether the intervals include their end points or not.   Thus, $\Pr(a \leq x \leq b) = \Pr(a < x < b)$.

probability that," then

$$\Pr\ (a < x < b) = b - a, \qquad 0 \leq a \leq b \leq 1. \tag{6-1}$$

When (6-1) holds, the variable x is said to be *uniformly distributed* on the interval $0 \leq x \leq 1$. Since the expression (6-1) may be written

$$\Pr\ (a < x < b) = \int_a^b dx = \int_a^b 1\ dx, \tag{6-2}$$

it is customary to speak of the *probability density*, which in this case is unity.

More generally, a variable may be distributed with an arbitrary density $f(x)$. For such a variable the expression

$$f(t)\ \Delta t$$

measures, approximately, the probability that x is on the interval

$$t < x < t + \Delta t.$$

An exact expression for the probability that x is on a given interval (a,b) is [1]

$$\Pr\ (a < x < b) = \int_a^b f(x)\ dx. \tag{6-3}$$

This relation is illustrated in Fig. 8.

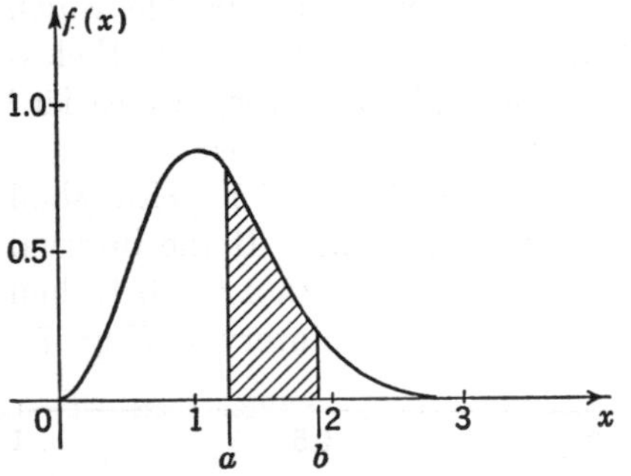

As indicated above, the function $f(x)$ is called the *probability density;* the function

$$F(t) = \int_{-\infty}^t f(x)\ dx \tag{6-4}$$

is called the *distribution function.* Evidently, $F(t)$ is the probability that x is in the interval $(-\infty, t)$; in other words,

$$F(t) = \Pr\ (x < t). \tag{6-5}$$

If $f(x)$ is continuous, then (6-4) gives

FIG. 8

$$F'(t) = f(t)$$

and one may speak of a probability differential

$$dF(t) = f(t)\ dt.$$

[1] The symbol x in (6-3) is used in two different senses. On the left x is a random variable, and on the right x is the variable of integration. The integral could have been written $\int_a^b f(\xi)\ d\xi$, for example.

To find the distribution function t associated with the uniform density $f(x)$ on the interval (0,1) we take

$$f(x) = 0, \qquad x < 0,$$

$$f(x) = 1, \qquad 0 \leq x \leq 1,$$

$$f(x) = 0, \qquad x > 1.$$

This expresses the fact that x is sure to be in the interval (0,1), and is uniformly distributed on that interval. Hence, for $0 < t < 1$,

$$F(t) = \int_{-\infty}^{t} f(x) \, dx$$

$$= \int_{-\infty}^{0} f(x) \, dx + \int_{0}^{t} f(x) \, dx$$

$$= 0 + \int_{0}^{t} 1 \, dx = t. \qquad (6\text{-}6)$$

In a similar manner one obtains

$$F(t) = 0, \qquad t < 0,$$

$$F(t) = 1, \qquad t > 1,$$

which expresses the fact that x is never <0 but is always ≤ 1.

The following density functions arise in many applications.

Poisson:

$$e^{-\mu x} \frac{(\mu x)^r}{r!}, \qquad 0 \leq x < \infty, \mu > 0, r = \text{nonnegative integer},$$

Gauss:

$$\frac{1}{\sqrt{2\pi}\,\sigma} e^{-\frac{1}{2}\left(\frac{x-\mu}{\sigma}\right)^2}, \qquad -\infty < x < \infty, \sigma > 0, -\infty < \mu < \infty,$$

Maxwell-Boltzmann:

$$4a \sqrt{\frac{a}{\pi}}\, x^2 e^{-ax^2}, \qquad 0 \leq x < \infty, a > 0.$$

The random variable is x; the parameters μ, r, a, σ are constants. For example, in the Maxwell-Boltzmann distribution x is the magnitude of the velocity of a gas molecule and $a = m/2kT$, where m is the mass, T is the temperature, and k is called the *Boltzmann constant*. A graph of the function for $a = 1$ is given in Fig. 8. The Poisson distribution is discussed in Sec. 11; the Gauss distribution in Secs. 9, 10, and 12. The latter is often called the *normal* distribution, but in this text the term *normal distribution* is applied to the case $\sigma = 1$, $\mu = 0$ only.

Densities and distribution functions are easily defined for several variables. We say that $f(x,y)$ is the probability density (or the joint probability density) for (x,y) if the probability that (x,y) is in any given region R of the xy plane is

$$\Pr[(x,y) \text{ in } R] = \iint_R f(x,y) \, dx \, dy. \tag{6-7}$$

The distribution function is

$$F(s,t) = \int_{-\infty}^{s} \int_{-\infty}^{t} f(x,y) \, dx \, dy$$

$$= \Pr[x < s \text{ and } y < t]. \tag{6-8}$$

Since probabilities are nonnegative, the density functions in (6-3) and (6-7) satisfy

$$f(x) \geq 0, \qquad f(x,y) \geq 0. \tag{6-9}$$

Since the variables always have *some* finite value, in (6-3)

$$1 = \Pr(-\infty < x < \infty) = \int_{-\infty}^{\infty} f(x) \, dx, \tag{6-10}$$

and in (6-7)

$$\int_{-\infty}^{\infty} \int_{-\infty}^{\infty} f(x,y) \, dx \, dy = 1. \tag{6-11}$$

Any integrable function $f(x)$ or $f(x,y)$ which satisfies these conditions (6-9) to (6-11) may be regarded as a probability density. The sample space is infinite; it consists of the events $x = x_0$ for every choice of x_0 or $(x,y) = (x_0,y_0)$ for every choice of (x_0,y_0).

For example, if $f(x,y) = 1/A$ in a region R of area A and $f(x,y) = 0$ elsewhere, it is easily verified that (6-11) holds. The probability that (x,y) is in a subregion R_1 contained in R is

$$\iint_{R_1} f(x,y) \, dx \, dy = \iint_{R_1} \frac{1}{A} \, dx \, dy = \frac{A_1}{A},$$

where A_1 is the area of R_1. The variable (x,y) is then said to be *uniformly distributed in R*.

The theory for finite sample spaces applies with little change to continuous distributions; for example, the expectation is defined by

$$E(x) = \int_{-\infty}^{\infty} xf(x) \, dx = \frac{\int_{-\infty}^{\infty} xf(x) \, dx}{\int_{-\infty}^{\infty} f(x) \, dx}.$$

The latter expression follows from (6-10); it shows that $E(x)$ is the x coordinate of the center of mass for the area bounded by the curve $y = f(x)$

and the x axis. More generally, the expected value of any function $y = g(x)$ is

$$\int_{-\infty}^{\infty} yf(x)\, dx, \qquad y = g(x), \tag{6-12}$$

and the sum theorem $E(x + y) = E(x) + E(y)$ is a simple consequence of the properties of integrals. Compare Sec. 5, Example 2.

Two variables x, y are said to be *independent* if the joint density $f(x,y)$ has the form

$$f(x,y) = f(x)g(y). \tag{6-13}$$

The theorem of compound probability for independent events is then valid in the form

$$\Pr\,(a < x < b, c < y < d) = \Pr\,(a < x < b)\,\Pr\,(c < y < d). \tag{6-14}$$

The theorem of total probability assumes various forms, such as

$$\Pr\,(a < x < c) = \Pr\,(a < x < b) + \Pr\,(b < x < c) \tag{6-15}$$

for $a < b < c$. Equation (6-15) is equivalent to

$$\int_a^c f(x)\, dx = \int_a^b f(x)\, dx + \int_b^c f(x)\, dx$$

which, in turn, is a known property of integrals.[1]

Example 1. A variable x is said to be uniformly distributed on (a,b) if $f(x)$ is constant on (a,b) and zero outside (a,b). Find $f(x)$ in this case.

Denoting the constant by c, we have

$$\int_{-\infty}^{\infty} f(x)\, dx = \int_a^b c\, dx = c(b - a) = 1$$

by (6-10). Solving for c yields

$$f(x) = \frac{1}{b - a}, \qquad a < x < b,$$

$$f(x) = 0, \qquad \text{elsewhere.}$$

Example 2. A stick of length a is broken at random into two pieces. Find the distribution function $F(s)$ for the length s of the shorter piece. From this find the probability density $f(l)$ for the length l of the longer piece.

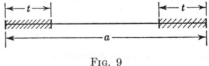

Fig. 9

Evidently $0 \leq s \leq a/2$ in every case. For any t between 0 and $a/2$ we have $s < t$ if, and only if, x is on one of the intervals $(0,t)$ or $(a - t, a)$ (see Fig. 9). The probability of that is $2t/a$, since x is uniformly distributed, and hence

$$F(s) = \frac{2s}{a}, \qquad 0 \leq s \leq \frac{a}{2},$$

$$F(s) = 0, \qquad s < 0,$$

$$F(s) = 1, \qquad s > \frac{a}{2}.$$

Since the length l of the longer piece satisfies $l = a - s$, we have $l < t$ if, and only if, $s > a - t$. By the result just obtained the probability is

$$1 - \Pr(s \leq a - t) = 1 - \frac{2(a - t)}{a}$$

for $a/2 < t < a$ and 0 or 1 otherwise. This gives the distribution function for l. By differentiation, the density is found to be

$$f(l) = \frac{2}{a}, \qquad \frac{a}{2} < l < a,$$

$$f(l) = 0, \qquad \text{elsewhere.}$$

(6-16)

The differentiation is not valid for $l = a/2$ or for $l = a$, but it does not matter how the density is defined at these isolated points.

Example 3. A stick of length a is broken at random, and the longer piece is again broken. What is the probability that the three segments can form a triangle?

Let l be the length of the longer piece. If this piece is broken at a point x, the three segments are $a - l$, x, $l - x$. The condition for a triangle is that the sum of any two segments shall exceed the third:

$$a - l + x > l - x, \qquad a - x > x, \qquad l > a - l.$$

Since $l > a/2$ automatically, these conditions reduce to

$$l - \frac{a}{2} < x < \frac{a}{2}.$$

(6-17)

It is a conceptual aid (and not incorrect) to use the theorems of total and compound probability in the following manner: The probability that l is on the interval $(l, l + dl)$ is

$$\frac{2}{a} dl$$

by (6-16). After l is chosen, the probability that x satisfies (6-17) is

$$\int_{l-a/2}^{a/2} \frac{1}{l} dx = \frac{a - l}{l},$$

since x is uniformly distributed on $(0, l)$. The probability of both these events is the product

$$\frac{a - l}{l} \frac{2}{a} dl$$

by compound probability, and total probability now gives the final answer:

$$\int_{a/2}^{a} \frac{a - l}{l} \frac{2}{a} dl = 2 \log 2 - 1.$$

Example 4. *Buffon's Needle Problem.* A needle of length a is dropped on a board which is covered with parallel lines spaced a distance $b > a$ (Fig. 10). What is the probability that the needle intersects one of the lines?

We assume that the variables x and θ of the figure are uniformly distributed, x being the distance from the center to the nearest line. There is intersection if, and only if, $|(a/2)\cos\theta| > x$. For fixed θ, the probability of this is

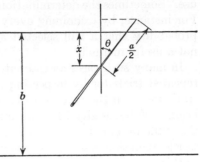

$$\frac{|(a/2)\cos\theta|}{b/2} = \frac{a|\cos\theta|}{b}$$

since x is uniformly distributed on $(0,b/2)$. Using total and compound probability as in Example 3, we obtain the final answer:

FIG. 10

$$\int_0^{2\pi} \frac{a|\cos\theta|}{b}\,\frac{d\theta}{2\pi} = \frac{a}{b}\frac{1}{2\pi}4\int_0^{\pi/2}\cos\theta\,d\theta = \frac{2a}{\pi b}.$$

PROBLEMS

1. A probability density is defined by $f(x) = 3x^2$ for $0 < x < 1$ and $f(x) = 0$ elsewhere. Find $E(x)$ and $E(x^2)$. Find the distribution function $F(x)$, and from this obtain a value m such that x is just as likely as not to exceed m. (The value m is called the *median* of x.)

2. The radius of a sphere is uniformly distributed on $(0,1)$. Find the expected value of the volume [see (6-12)]. What is the probability that the volume exceeds half its maximum value?

3. A stick of length a is broken at random into two parts. What is the expected length of the shorter part?

4. Two points are chosen at random on a line of length a. What is the probability that the three segments can form a triangle?

5. The probability density for bullets hitting a target is given by

$$f(x,y) = \frac{1}{2\pi\sigma_x\sigma_y} e^{-\frac{1}{2}\left[\left(\frac{x-m_x}{\sigma_x}\right)^2 + \left(\frac{y-m_y}{\sigma_y}\right)^2\right]}$$

where σ_x, σ_y, m_x, m_y are constant. Sketch the curves of constant density in the xy plane. What kind of curves are they?

6. We make two independent observations x_1, x_2 of a variable with distribution function $f(x)$. What is the probability that a third independent observation x_3 will fall between x_1 and x_2? Generalize to n observations. *Hint:* Use the methods of discrete probability.

PROBABILITY AND RELATIVE FREQUENCY

7. Independent Trials. It often happens that the probability of an event cannot be determined by counting cases or by other a priori considerations. Sometimes the determination is impossible in principle; for instance, one cannot compute the probabilities associated with a loaded die or the probability that a given radio tube will fail in the first hundred hours' use. Sometimes the determination is theoretically possible but impractical. For instance, by examining every nail in a 100-lb keg one could find the probability that a nail selected at random will be defective, but this is not a useful method.

In many such cases an estimate for the probability can be obtained by repeated trials (or by inspecting a suitable *sample*, in the terminology of statistics). In the case of a biased coin, for example, if 10 tosses give 7 heads, 100 tosses give 73 heads, and 1,000 tosses give 690 heads, it appears that "the probability of heads is *probably close* to 0.7." The two italicized words express a reservation which is always present in conclusions such as this.

The figures 7, 73, 690 in the above discussion represent the frequency of heads; the ratios

$$7/10, \ 73/100, \ 690/1,000$$

give the relative frequency in 10, 100, or 1,000 trials. More generally, *if an event occurs m times in n trials, the relative frequency is m/n.*

The trials in a sequence of trials are said to be *independent* if the probabilities associated with a given trial do not depend on the results of preceding trials. For example, the probability of heads on a given toss of a symmetric coin is $\frac{1}{2}$ no matter what is known about the results of previous tosses. But if we try to get an ace by drawing cards one at a time without replacing, the trials are dependent. In this case, the probability of ace in a given trial depends on the number of aces that may have been drawn previously.

When an event has constant probability p of success, the probability of m successes in n independent trials may be computed as follows. A sequence of m successes and $n - m$ failures is represented by a sequence of m letters S and $n - m$ letters F:

$$SSFFSS \ldots SF. \tag{7-1}$$

Since the trials are independent, the probability of any one such sequence is

$$ppqqpp \ldots pq = p^m q^{n-m}, \tag{7-2}$$

where $q = 1 - p$. To obtain the number of favorable sequences, observe that a sequence is determined as soon as the positions of the m letters S are fixed. The m places for these letters S can be chosen from the n places in $_nC_m$ ways, and hence the required probability is

$$p^m q^{n-m} + p^m q^{n-m} + \cdots + p^m q^{n-m} = {}_nC_m p^m q^{n-m} \tag{7-3}$$

by the theorem of total probability.

Alternatively, the reader may imagine a sample space in which each event consists of a sequence (7-1), with associated measure (7-2). Then (7-3) represents the sum of the measures of those points favorable to the event: *m successes*.

Replacing *m* by *x* gives

$$B(x) = {}_nC_x p^x q^{n-x} \equiv \frac{n!}{x!(n-x)!} p^x (1-p)^{n-x} \qquad (7\text{-}4)$$

for the probability of exactly *x* successes in *n* independent trials with constant probability *p*. The associated distribution function is

$$F(t) = {}_nC_0 q^n + {}_nC_1 pq^{n-1} + \cdots + {}_nC_t p^t q^{n-t} \qquad (7\text{-}5)$$

for integral values of *t*. This expression gives the probability of getting at most *t* successes in *n* trials.

Because of its connection with the binomial theorem (Prob. 6), the function *B(x)* is called the *binomial frequency function*, *F(t)* in (7-5) is the *binomial distribution*, and the statement that *B(x)* gives the probability of *x* successes in *n* independent trials is called the *binomial law of probability*. Since many statistical studies involve repeated trials, the binomial law has great practical importance.

To illustrate the use of the formula (7-4) let it be required to find the probability that the ace will appear exactly 4 times in the course of 10 throws of a die. Here $p = \frac{1}{6}$, $q = \frac{5}{6}$, $n = 10$, $x = 4$. Hence the probability is

$$B(4) = \frac{10!}{4!6!} \left(\frac{1}{6}\right)^4 \left(\frac{5}{6}\right)^6 = 0.05427.$$

Since the expected number of successes in one trial is *p*, the expected number in *n* trials is

$$E(x) = np \qquad (7\text{-}6)$$

[compare (5-2)]. For most distributions there is no special relation between the *expected* value and the *most probable* value, but for the binomial distribution they happen to be almost equal. Equation (7-4) yields

$$\frac{B(x+1)}{B(x)} = \frac{(n-x)p}{(x+1)q}$$

after slight simplification. Hence *B(x)* is an increasing function of the integer *x* if, and only if,

$$\frac{(n-x)p}{(x+1)q} > 1.$$

The latter inequality is the same as

$$(n-x)p > (x+1)q$$

which reduces to $np > x + q$, since $p + q = 1$. We have shown, then, that $B(x+1) > B(x)$ as long as $x < np - q$ but $B(x+1) \le B(x)$ thereafter. Since $q < 1$, this establishes that $B(x)$ is maximum for a value of x which is within 1 of the value $x = np$. Further discussion of the function $B(x)$ is given in the following sections.

Example 1. Ten tosses of a suspected die gave the result 1, 1, 1, 6, 1, 1, 3, 1, 1, 4. What is the probability of at least this many aces if the die is true?

The event "at least 7 aces" can materialize in four mutually exclusive ways: 7 aces, 8 aces, 9 aces, 10 aces. By total probability (or by use of the distribution function) the required answer is found to be

$$B(7) + B(8) + B(9) + B(10)$$

$$= {}_{10}C_7(\tfrac{1}{6})^7(\tfrac{5}{6})^3 + {}_{10}C_8(\tfrac{1}{6})^8(\tfrac{5}{6})^2 + {}_{10}C_9(\tfrac{1}{6})^9(\tfrac{5}{6}) + {}_{10}C_{10}(\tfrac{1}{6})^{10}$$

when we take $p = \tfrac{1}{6}$, $n = 10$. This reduces to 0.00027, approximately. Because the observed result has such small probability, one would reject the hypothesis "$p = \tfrac{1}{6}$" unless there is some other evidence in its favor.

Example 2. In Example 1 let p be the unknown probability of the ace in a toss of the die. (*a*) For what value of p does the expected number of aces agree with the observed number? (*b*) For what value of p is the probability of the observed result a maximum?

Since $E(x) = np$ by (7-6), the observed and expected numbers agree when $p = x/n$, that is, when $p = 0.7$. The estimate for p given by $p = x/n$ is called an *unbiased* estimate, because $E(x/n) = p$.

For part (*b*), the probability of getting 7 aces and 3 other numbers is

$$p^7q^3 \quad \text{or} \quad {}_{10}C_7 p^7 q^3, \qquad q = 1 - p,$$

depending upon whether the order is considered or not. In either case the probability is maximum when $p^7(1 - p)^3$ is maximum. This, in turn, is maximum when

$$\log p^7(1 - p)^3 = 7 \log p + 3 \log (1 - p)$$

is maximum. Differentiation gives

$$\frac{7}{p} - \frac{3}{1 - p} = 0,$$

or $p = 0.7$. An estimate for p such as this, which maximizes the probability of the observed result, is called a *maximum likelihood* estimate.

PROBLEMS

1. When 5 coins are tossed what is the probability of exactly 2 heads? At least 2 heads? What is the expected number of heads? The most probable number of heads?

2. If 5 dice are tossed simultaneously, what is the probability that (*a*) exactly 3 of them turn the ace up? (*b*) At least 3 turn the ace up?

3. If the probability that a man aged sixty will live to be seventy is 0.65, what is the probability that out of 10 men now sixty at least 7 will live to be seventy?

4. A man is promised $1 for each ace in excess of 1 that appears in 6 consecutive throws of a die. What is the value of his expectation?

5. A bag contains 20 black balls and 15 white balls. What is the chance that at least 4 in a sample of 5 balls are black?

6. (*a*) By use of the binomial theorem show that

$$(q + pt)^n = B(0) + B(1)t + B(2)t^2 + \cdots + B(n)t^n.$$

(b) Interpret the identity which arises when $t = 1$.   (c) Differentiate with respect to t, and interpret the identity which then arises for $t = 1$.   [The function $(q + pt)^n$ is called the *generating function* of the sequence $\{B(x)\}$.]

7. (a) One hundred light bulbs were tested for 500 hr, at the end of which time 57 bulbs had failed. Obtain an unbiased estimate and also a maximum-likelihood estimate for the probability of failure in 500 hr. (b) Are these two estimates of p always equal for the binomial distribution? *Hint:* In (b), compare the result of maximizing $p^m q^{n-m}$ with respect to p and the result of choosing p so that $E(x) = m$, where m is the number of observed successes.

8. In a certain agricultural experiment, the probability that a plant will have yellow flowers is $\tfrac{3}{4}$. If 10,000 plants are grown, what is the probability that the number with yellow flowers will be between 7,400 and 7,600? (To appreciate later developments observe that your answer, which should be indicated only, is difficult to compute.)

8. An Illustration.   Some interesting conclusions concerning the binomial law are suggested by an example that presents many features of the general case. Consider a purse in which are placed 2 silver and 3 gold coins, and let it be required to find the probability of drawing exactly x silver coins in n trials, the coin being replaced after each drawing. The probability of exactly x successes in n trials is given by (7-4) where p, the probability of drawing a silver coin in a single trial, is $\tfrac{2}{5}$. If the number of drawings is taken as $n = 5$, 10, or 30, the respective frequency functions $B(x)$ are

$$B(x) = {}_5C_x(\tfrac{2}{5})^x(\tfrac{3}{5})^{5-x}, \qquad n = 5,$$

$$B(x) = {}_{10}C_x(\tfrac{2}{5})^x(\tfrac{3}{5})^{10-x}, \qquad n = 10,$$

$$B(x) = {}_{30}C_x(\tfrac{2}{5})^x(\tfrac{3}{5})^{30-x}, \qquad n = 30.$$

By use of these expressions one can compute the values of $B(x)$ to any desired accuracy. The result of such a computation to four places of decimals is presented in the accompanying tables. In the third table the entry 0.0000 is made for $0 \le x \le 2$ and for $x \ge 23$ because in these cases $B(x)$ was found to be less than 0.00005. For example, the probability of drawing exactly 23 silver coins in 30 trials is

$$B(23) = {}_{30}C_{23}(\tfrac{2}{5})^{23}(\tfrac{3}{5})^7 = 0.000040128.$$

The reader can verify that the most probable values of x are exactly equal to np (and not merely within 1 of np). This behavior is always found when np is an integer.

PROBABILITY OF EXACTLY x SUCCESSES IN 5 TRIALS

x	$B(x)$	x	$B(x)$
0	0.0778	3	0.2304
1	0.2592	4	0.0768
2	0.3456	5	0.0102

PROBABILITY OF EXACTLY x SUCCESSES IN 10 TRIALS

x	$B(x)$	x	$B(x)$	x	$B(x)$
0	0.0060	4	*0.2508*	8	0.0106
1	0.0403	5	0.2007	9	0.0016
2	0.1209	6	0.1115	10	0.0001
3	0.2150	7	0.0425		

PROBABILITY OF EXACTLY x SUCCESSES IN 30 TRIALS

x	$B(x)$	x	$B(x)$	x	$B(x)$
≤ 2	0.0000	9	0.0823	16	0.0489
3	0.0003	10	0.1152	17	0.0269
4	0.0012	11	0.1396	18	0.0129
5	0.0041	12	*0.1474*	19	0.0054
6	0.0115	13	0.1360	20	0.0020
7	0.0263	14	0.1100	21	0.0006
8	0.0505	15	0.0783	22	0.0002
				≥ 23	0.0000

The values given in the tables are presented graphically in Fig. 11 after the manner described in Sec. 5. Each curve has the general shape predicted by the theory of the preceding section, but the figure shows also how the shape changes as we proceed from one curve to another. The numerical area under each curve is 1, although the curves become broader and flatter as n increases. In particular the maximum (that is, the probability of the most probable value) decreases as n increases. This is just what one would expect intuitively. (For instance, one could easily get 2 heads in 4 tosses of a coin, but one would be surprised to get exactly 500,001 heads in 1,000,002 tosses.) The fact that the curves become broader indicates that the values of x experience a wider spread when there are more trials, and this, too, one would expect. Naturally, the curves ought to get broader if the maximum is to decrease while the area remains equal to 1.

The foregoing discussion is concerned with the frequency of success in n trials. The results are very different if, instead, one considers the *relative* frequency x/n. The distribution for the variable x/n is presented graphically in Fig. 12. These curves were obtained from the preceding by the change of scale indicated on the axes, and hence, the area is still 1. Instead of becoming broader, these curves become narrower as n increases. The relative frequency x/n tends to cluster about its expected value p as n gets large. It is for this reason that relative frequency can be used to estimate an unknown probability.

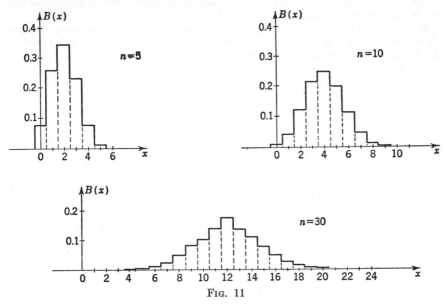

Fig. 11

The behavior suggested by this example may be summarized as follows. When the number of trials n becomes large, the absolute deviation from the expected value

$$|x - np| = |x - E(x)|$$

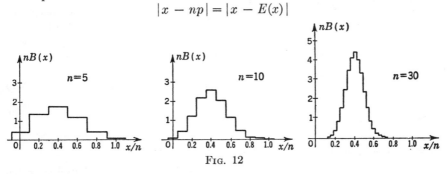

Fig. 12

is likely also to be large, but the relative deviation

$$\left|\frac{x - np}{n}\right| = \left|\frac{x}{n} - p\right| = \left|\frac{x}{n} - E\left(\frac{x}{n}\right)\right|$$

is likely to be small.[1]

---

[1] It will be seen in Sec. 9 that the first expression is usually of the order $\sqrt{n}$ and the second, of order $1/\sqrt{n}$; compare Prob. 3.

PROBLEMS

1. Plot a distribution curve like that of Fig. 11 for the probability of x successes in 4 trials when $p = \frac{2}{5}$. Shade the area corresponding to the event $1 < x \leq 3$, and find the probability of this event.

2. For $p = \frac{2}{5}$ plot the probability of the most probable number of successes versus n. (Take points at $n = 1, 2, 3, 4, 5, 10, 30$ only; cf. Prob. 1 and accompanying tables.) On the same figure plot $1/\sqrt{2\pi npq}$ versus n. (It is shown in Sec. 9 that the probability is asymptotic to $1/\sqrt{2\pi npq}$ when n is large. This expression approaches zero as $n \to \infty$, even though we are considering the *most probable* value.)

3. Using the tables and your numerical values in Prob. 2, plot $\sqrt{n}\,B(x)$ versus $(x - np)/\sqrt{n}$ for $p = \frac{2}{5}$ and for $n = 3, 4, 5, 10$. Use the same scale in each case. Formulate a conjecture concerning the behavior as $n \to \infty$, and test your conjecture by plotting five well-chosen points on the curve corresponding to $n = 30$.

9. The Laplace-de Moivre Limit Theorem.

Numerical computation of the binomial distribution is difficult when n is large. In this section an approximate formula is obtained when n and np are both large. In Sec. 11 a formula is found when n is large but np is not large. These approximations, together with the exact formula when n is moderate, cover all cases.

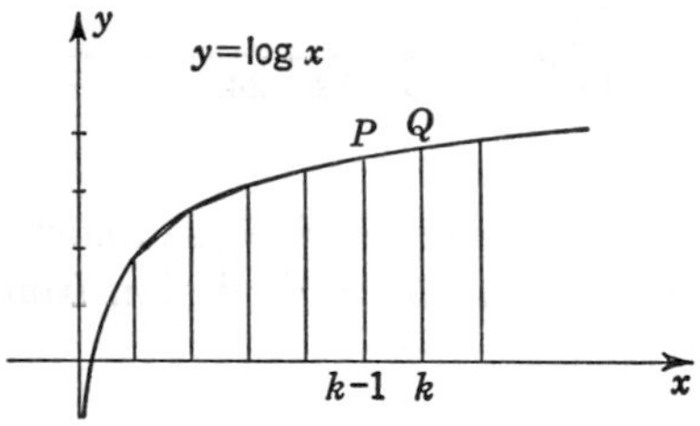

The analysis is based on the *Stirling formula*,

$$n! \sim n^n e^{-n}\sqrt{2\pi n}, \qquad (9\text{-}1)$$

which is made plausible by the following discussion. Consider the function $y = \log x$, and observe that for $k \geq 2$,

$$\int_{k-1}^{k} \log x\, dx > \tfrac{1}{2}[\log(k-1) + \log k],$$

since the right-hand member represents the trapezoidal area formed by the chord (Fig. 13) joining the points P and Q on the curve

Fig. 13

$y = \log x$. Denote the area between the chord and the curve by a_k, so that

$$\int_{k-1}^{k} \log x\, dx = \tfrac{1}{2}[\log(k-1) + \log k] + a_k. \qquad (9\text{-}2)$$

Setting $k = 2, 3, \ldots, n$ in (9-2) and adding give

$$\int_{1}^{n} \log x\, dx = \tfrac{1}{2}(\log 1 + \log 2) + \tfrac{1}{2}(\log 2 + \log 3) + \cdots$$
$$+ \tfrac{1}{2}[\log(n-1) + \log n] + (a_2 + a_3 + \cdots + a_n).$$

Integrating the left-hand member and combining the terms of the right-hand member give

$$n \log n - n + 1 = \log n! - \tfrac{1}{2}\log n + \sum_{i=2}^{n} a_i.$$

Hence,

$$\log n! = (n + \tfrac{1}{2})\log n - n + 1 - \sum_{i=2}^{n} a_i. \qquad (9\text{-}3)$$

Since each a_i is positive, it follows that

$$\log n! < (n + \tfrac{1}{2}) \log n - n + 1$$

and hence

$$n! < e\sqrt{n}\, n^n e^{-n}. \tag{9-4}$$

The expression on the right of the inequality (9-4) is, therefore, an upper bound for $n!$. To get a lower bound, solve (9-2) for a_k, perform the integration, and obtain

$$a_k = \left(k - \frac{1}{2}\right) \log \frac{k}{k-1} - 1. \tag{9-5}$$

Now, since the integrand is nonnegative,

$$\int_{k-1}^{k} \left(\frac{1}{x} - \frac{1}{k}\right)^2 dx > 0 \tag{9-6}$$

and the evaluation of (9-6) leads to the formula

$$\log \frac{k}{k-1} < \frac{2k-1}{2k(k-1)}.$$

By use of this inequality, (9-5) gives

$$a_k < \frac{1}{4k(k-1)} = \frac{1}{4}\left(\frac{1}{k-1} - \frac{1}{k}\right).$$

Hence $\displaystyle\sum_{i=2}^{n} a_i < \frac{1}{4}\left[\left(1 - \frac{1}{2}\right) + \left(\frac{1}{2} - \frac{1}{3}\right) + \cdots + \left(\frac{1}{n-1} - \frac{1}{n}\right)\right] < \frac{1}{4}.$

By means of this result and (9-3), one obtains

$$\log n! > (n + \tfrac{1}{2}) \log n - n + 1 - \tfrac{1}{4},$$

whence $n! > e^{\frac{3}{4}}\sqrt{n}\, n^n e^{-n}. \tag{9-7}$

Combining (9-4) and (9-7) furnishes the inequality [1]

$$e^{\frac{3}{4}}\sqrt{n}\, n^n e^{-n} < n! < e\sqrt{n}\, n^n e^{-n}$$

for all values of $n > 1$. Since $e = 2.718$, $e^{\frac{3}{4}} = 2.117$, and $\sqrt{2\pi} = 2.507$, we have shown that (9-1) is correct as to order of magnitude. More refined methods establish that the error is less than 10 per cent for $n \geq 1$, less than 1 per cent for $n \geq 10$, and less than 0.1 per cent for $n \geq 100$. Moreover, the percentage error approaches zero as $n \to \infty$, so that the equality is asymptotic.

In the expression

$$B(r) = \frac{n!}{r!(n-r)!}\, p^r q^{n-r} \tag{9-8}$$

for the probability of r successes in n independent trials, we assume that r, n, and $n - r$ are large enough to permit the use of Stirling's formula

---

[1] The derivation of this result is given by P. M. Hummel, *Am. Math. Monthly*, **47**:97 (1940).

(9-1). Replacing $n!$, $r!$, and $(n - r)!$ by their approximations gives, after simplification,

$$B(r) \cong \left(\frac{np}{r}\right)^r \left(\frac{nq}{n-r}\right)^{n-r} \sqrt{\frac{n}{2\pi r(n - r)}}. \qquad (9\text{-}9)$$

Let δ denote the deviation of r from the expected value np; that is,

$$\delta = r - np.$$

Then,
$$n - r = nq - \delta$$

and (9-9) becomes [1]

$$B(r) = \frac{1}{\sqrt{2\pi npq\left(1 + \dfrac{\delta}{np}\right)\left(1 - \dfrac{\delta}{nq}\right)}} \left(1 + \frac{\delta}{np}\right)^{-(np+\delta)} \left(1 - \frac{\delta}{nq}\right)^{-(nq-\delta)}$$

or
$$B(r)A = \left(1 + \frac{\delta}{np}\right)^{-(np+\delta)} \left(1 - \frac{\delta}{nq}\right)^{-(nq-\delta)}$$

where
$$A = \sqrt{2\pi npq\left(1 + \frac{\delta}{np}\right)\left(1 - \frac{\delta}{nq}\right)}.$$

Then, $\log B(r)A \cong -(np + \delta)\log\left(1 + \frac{\delta}{np}\right) - (nq - \delta)\log\left(1 - \frac{\delta}{nq}\right).$

Assuming $|\delta| < npq$, so that

$$\left|\frac{\delta}{np}\right| < 1 \qquad \text{and} \qquad \left|\frac{\delta}{nq}\right| < 1,$$

permits one to write the two convergent series

$$\log\left(1 + \frac{\delta}{np}\right) = \frac{\delta}{np} - \frac{\delta^2}{2n^2p^2} + \frac{\delta^3}{3n^3p^3} - \cdots$$

and $\quad \log\left(1 - \frac{\delta}{nq}\right) = -\frac{\delta}{nq} - \frac{\delta^2}{2n^2q^2} - \frac{\delta^3}{3n^3q^3} - \cdots.$

Hence, $\quad \log B(r)A \cong -\frac{\delta^2}{2npq} - \frac{\delta^3(p^2 - q^2)}{2\cdot 3n^2p^2q^2} - \frac{\delta^4(p^3 + q^3)}{3\cdot 4n^3p^3q^3} - \cdots.$

Now, if $|\delta|$ is so small in comparison with npq that one can neglect all terms in this expansion beyond the first and can replace A by $\sqrt{2\pi npq}$,

---

[1] Here and in similar cases which arise subsequently, we assume that $p \neq 0$ and $q \neq 0$. The cases $p = 0$ or $p = 1$ can be dealt with by inspection.

then there results the approximate formula

$$B(r) \cong \frac{1}{\sqrt{2\pi npq}} e^{-\delta^2/2npq} \tag{9-10}$$

which bears the name of *Laplace's*, or the *normal, approximation*. With $\sigma = \sqrt{npq}$, Eq. (9-10) becomes

$$B(r) \cong \frac{1}{\sqrt{2\pi}\,\sigma} e^{-\delta^2/2\sigma^2}. \tag{9-11}$$

The equality is asymptotic; that is, the ratio of the two sides tends to 1 as $n \to \infty$. A comparison of $B(r)$ with the normal approximation is given in Fig. 14.

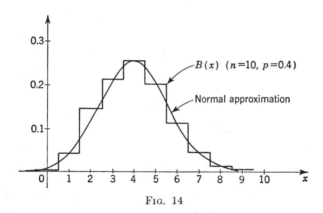

FIG. 14

The main usefulness of this result is to compute the probability

$$\sum_{r=r_1}^{r_2} B(r) \tag{9-12}$$

that the number of successes is between the given limits r_1 and r_2. Equation (9-11) shows that the sum (9-12) may be approximated by a sum

$$\sum \frac{1}{\sqrt{2\pi}\,\sigma} e^{-\delta^2/2\sigma^2} \tag{9-13}$$

over appropriate values of δ. Since $\delta = r - np$, the difference between successive values of δ is 1, and hence if we let $t = \delta/\sigma$, the difference between successive values of t is $\Delta t = 1/\sigma$. Thus (9-13) becomes a sum over t,

$$\sum \frac{1}{\sqrt{2\pi}} e^{-t^2/2}\,\Delta t. \tag{9-14}$$

As $\Delta t \to 0$, the expression (9-14) approaches an integral, which may be evaluated in terms of the function

$$\Phi(t) = \int_0^t \frac{1}{\sqrt{2\pi}} e^{-t^2/2} \, dt \tag{9-15}$$

tabulated in Appendix D. These considerations yield the following fundamental result, known as the Laplace-de Moivre limit theorem:

THEOREM. *Let x be the number of successes in n independent trials with constant probability p. Then the probability of the inequality*

$$t_1 \le \frac{x - np}{\sqrt{npq}} \le t_2 \tag{9-16}$$

approaches the limit

$$\frac{1}{\sqrt{2\pi}} \int_{t_1}^{t_2} e^{-t^2/2} \, dt = \Phi(t_2) - \Phi(t_1) \tag{9-17}$$

as $n \to \infty$.

To complete the proof one must note that the error in passing from (9-12) to (9-13) is small for large n even when the number of terms in the sum is large. A more detailed analysis, taking due account of this question, is given in William Feller, "Probability Theory and Its Applications," pp. 133–137, John Wiley & Sons, Inc., New York, 1950. It is shown that a better approximation is given by

$$\Phi\left(t_2 + \frac{1}{2\sigma}\right) - \Phi\left(t_1 - \frac{1}{2\sigma}\right), \qquad \sigma = \sqrt{npq}, \tag{9-18}$$

although the improvement is not important when n is large. An expression for the error in the approximation is derived in J. V. Uspensky, "Introduction to Mathematical Probability," p. 129, McGraw-Hill Book Company, Inc., New York, 1937.

To illustrate the use of the result (9-17), let us find the probability that the number of aces will be between 80 and 110 when a true die is tossed 600 times. Here $n = 600$, $p = \frac{1}{6}$, $q = \frac{5}{6}$, and x varies from 80 to 110. Hence

$$t_1 = \frac{80 - 100}{\sqrt{(100)(\frac{5}{6})}} = -2.19 \qquad \text{and} \qquad t_2 = \frac{110 - 100}{\sqrt{(100)(\frac{5}{6})}} = 1.09.$$

The table gives $\Phi(t_2) = \Phi(1.09) = 0.362$, and similarly

$$\Phi(-2.19) = -\Phi(2.19) = -0.486.$$

[Observe that $\Phi(-t) = -\Phi(t)$, since the curve $y = e^{-t^2/2}$ is symmetric.] Hence the required probability is, approximately,

$$0.362 - (-0.486) = 0.848.$$

Example 1. In the notation of the text, the probability $P_{\max}$ of the most probable value of r satisfies

$$P_{\max} \sim \frac{1}{\sqrt{2\pi npq}} \tag{9-19}$$

when n is large.

In Sec. 7 it was found that the most probable value is of the form

$$r = np + \theta, \qquad |\theta| < 1.$$

For this value of r we have

$$\delta = r - np = \theta$$

and hence Eq. (9-10) shows that the associated probability is asymptotic to

$$\frac{1}{\sqrt{2\pi npq}}\, e^{-\theta^2/2npq}.$$

As $n \to \infty$, the exponential tends to 1, since θ^2 is bounded, and this yields (9-19).

Example 2.   In an agricultural experiment Mendelian theory yields a probability $p = \frac{1}{4}$ that any given plant should have blue flowers. Out of 10,000 plants it was found that 2,578 had blue flowers. Does this result contradict the theory?

According to theory, there should have been 2,500 plants with blue flowers; that is, the expected number is $np = 2{,}500$. There were, in fact, 78 more than this. We have to decide if this excess is too large to be attributed to chance.

Let us find the probability that the excess will be 78 or more if the hypothesis $p = \frac{1}{4}$ is indeed correct. The inequality

$$78 \le x - np \tag{9-20}$$

becomes

$$1.801 \le \frac{x - np}{\sqrt{npq}} < \infty \tag{9-21}$$

when divided by $\sqrt{npq} = 43.3$. According to the table the probability of (9-21) is

$$\Phi(\infty) - \Phi(1.801) = 0.500 - 0.464 = 0.036.$$

Now, in a statistical test it is customary to reject the hypothesis if the hypothesis makes the probability of the observed result less than a fixed quantity α determined beforehand. The value α (which is called the *significance level* of the test) is often taken to be 0.05. Since our probability 0.036 is less than 0.05, the experimental outcome is considered too unlikely to be attributed to chance, and we reject the hypothesis "$p = \frac{1}{4}$." In this sense, the experiment contradicts Mendelian theory.

We now give another analysis which leads to the opposite conclusion. Instead of saying "the excess was 78," one could just as well say, "the discrepancy was 78," meaning

$$|x - np| = 78. \tag{9-22}$$

Both statements are equally valid descriptions of the experimental outcome. The probability of

$$|x - np| < 78$$

is found, as above, to be

$$\Phi(1.801) - \Phi(-1.801) = 0.928,$$

and hence the probability of the contrary event is

$$1 - 0.928 = 0.072.$$

Since $0.072 > 0.05$, a discrepancy of "78 or more" is sufficiently probable to be attributed to chance (if, as before, our significance level is 0.05). Hence the hypothesis is not contradicted by the experiment.[1]

[1] When the probability exceeds the significance level, as in this case, the hypothesis is not thereby *proved* but it is considered to have withstood the experimental test.

It requires statistical methods of considerable subtlety to decide between competing tests of a hypothesis such as the foregoing. These methods show that the first procedure is appropriate for testing the hypothesis "$p = \frac{1}{4}$" against the alternative "$p > \frac{1}{4}$" whereas the second is appropriate for testing the hypothesis against the alternative "$p \neq \frac{1}{4}$." A very readable account of the subject is given in P. G. Hoel, "Introduction to Mathematical Statistics," chap. 10, John Wiley & Sons, Inc., New York, 1954.

PROBLEMS

1. Two dice are tossed 1,000 times. What is, approximately, the probability of getting a sum of 4 the most probable number of times? 500 times? (Use a table of exponentials.)

2. A true coin is to be tossed 1,600 times, and it is desired to find the probability that the number of heads x will satisfy $780 \leq x \leq 830$. (a) Show that this inequality is equivalent to

$$-1 \leq \frac{x - np}{\sqrt{npq}} \leq 1.5.$$

(b) Express the probability of the latter inequality in terms of Φ by means of the normal law. (c) Using the table, evaluate the probability.

3. By means of the normal law, obtain an approximate numerical answer to Prob. 8, Sec. 7.

4. A machine has a probability $p = 0.01$ of producing a defective bottle. In one day's run, out of 10,000 bottles, 120 were defective. Find the approximate probability of at least this many defectives if the machine is running as usual.

5. A suspected die gave only 960 aces in 6,000 tosses. If the die is true, (a) what is the probability of getting at most 960 aces in 6,000 tosses? (b) What is the probability of getting a discrepancy $|x - np|$ of "40 or more"? (c) At a significance level of 0.05, does either calculation indicate that the die is loaded?

10. The Law of Large Numbers. Since $\Sigma \, B(r) = 1$ for each value of n, it is natural to expect, by the foregoing analysis, that

$$\frac{1}{\sqrt{2\pi}} \int_{-\infty}^{\infty} e^{-t^2/2} \, dt = 1. \tag{10-1}$$

For a direct proof of (10-1), define I by

$$I = \int_{-\infty}^{\infty} e^{-x^2/2} \, dx = \int_{-\infty}^{\infty} e^{-y^2/2} \, dy. \tag{10-2}$$

Then multiplication of the two expressions (10-2) yields

$$I^2 = \int_{-\infty}^{\infty} \int_{-\infty}^{\infty} e^{-(x^2+y^2)/2} \, dx \, dy \tag{10-3}$$

after changing to a double integral. In polar coordinates,

$$I^2 = \int_0^{2\pi} \int_0^{\infty} e^{-r^2/2} r \, dr \, d\theta = 2\pi \int_0^{\infty} e^{-r^2/2} \, d \, (r^2/2) = 2\pi \tag{10-4}$$

so that $I = \sqrt{2\pi}$, and (10-1) follows. The transformations leading to (10-3) and (10-4) are justified by the fact that (10-3) is an *absolutely convergent* double integral.

Equation (10-1) shows that the function

$$\frac{1}{\sqrt{2\pi}} \int_{-\infty}^{t} e^{-x^2/2}\, dx = \Phi(t) + \frac{1}{2}$$

is a distribution function; it is called the *normal distribution*. The theorem of the preceding section asserts that the variable δ/σ is approximately normally distributed when n is large. This fact will now be used to establish the following fundamental result, which is a special case of the so-called *law of large numbers*:

THEOREM. *Let x be the number of successes in n independent trials with constant probability p. If ϵ is any positive number, then the probability of the inequality*

$$\left| \frac{x}{n} - p \right| < \epsilon \tag{10-5}$$

tends to 1 as $n \to \infty$.

In other words, the *relative frequency* of the event is almost sure to be close to the *probability* of the event when the number of trials is large. For proof, write the inequality (10-5) in the form

$$-\epsilon < \frac{x - np}{n} < \epsilon$$

which becomes

$$-\epsilon \sqrt{\frac{n}{pq}} < \frac{x - np}{\sqrt{npq}} < \epsilon \sqrt{\frac{n}{pq}} \tag{10-6}$$

when multiplied by $\sqrt{n/pq}$. Given any number t_0 (no matter how large), we can choose n so that $\epsilon\sqrt{n/pq} > t_0$. In this case the probability of the inequality (10-6) is at least equal to the probability of

$$-t_0 < \frac{x - np}{\sqrt{npq}} < t_0. \tag{10-7}$$

As $n \to \infty$, the latter probability [1] tends to

$$\frac{1}{\sqrt{2\pi}} \int_{-t_0}^{t_0} e^{-t^2/2}\, dt \tag{10-8}$$

by (9-17). Since t_0 is as large as we please, Eq. (10-1) shows that the integral (10-8) is as close to 1 as we please, and this completes the proof.

[1] One must not apply (9-17) directly to (10-6), because (9-17) was obtained only for fixed t_1 and t_2 whereas the limits in (10-6) depend on n.

The theorem was established first by James Bernoulli (1654–1705) after 20 years of effort. The law of large numbers lies at the basis of all attempts to estimate a probability experimentally, and it affords a philosophical justification for such attempts. In fact, some developments of the subject *define* probability in terms of relative frequency, by the formula $p = \lim (x/n)$ as $n \to \infty$, and rely on the law of large numbers to ensure that the limit exists.

The theorem makes possible some interesting computational procedures, known as *Monte Carlo methods*. Although the method is not to be discussed at length here, we sketch an example that illustrates some of the main features. Suppose a man walks in a straight line, taking a step of length h ft every s sec (see Fig. 15). Each step is equally likely to be to the right

FIG. 15

or to the left, without regard to the preceding steps. Assuming that x is a multiple of h and t is a multiple of s, it is required to find the probability that the man is x ft from his starting point at time t.

Let $U(x,t)$ stand for the probability in question; that is, $U(x,t)$ is the probability of the man's being at point x at time t if he was at point $x = 0$ at time $t = 0$. Now, he can arrive at point x at time $t + s$ in two ways. Either he was at point $x + h$ at time t and took a step to the left, or he was at point $x - h$ at time t and took a step to the right. The probability of being at $x + h$ at time t is $U(x + h, t)$ by the definition of U, and the probability of a step to the left is $\frac{1}{2}$ by hypothesis. Hence the probability of both events is

$$\tfrac{1}{2}U(x + h, t)$$

by compound probability. In just the same way the probability of being at $x - h$ and then stepping to the right is

$$\tfrac{1}{2}U(x - h, t).$$

By total probability, the probability of getting to the point x at time $t + s$ is the sum, and we are thus led to a *difference equation* for U,

$$U(x, t + s) = \tfrac{1}{2}U(x + h, t) + \tfrac{1}{2}U(x - h, t). \qquad (10\text{-}9)$$

The boundary conditions are

$$U(x,0) = 0 \quad \text{for } x \neq 0, \qquad \sum_x U(x,t) = 1 \qquad (10\text{-}9a)$$

which express the fact that he is sure to be at the origin when $t = 0$ and sure to be at *some* point x for all t.

To apply the Monte Carlo method to this problem, we make a large number of actual random walks experimentally. The number of times we arrive at point x at time t gives an estimate for the probability $U(x,t)$ by virtue of the law of large numbers. Hence, the calculation yields an approximate solution of the problem (10-9) without any direct use of (10-9). In practice, the "random walks" are made on a computing machine by reference to a set of random numbers. Similar methods apply to difference equations of much greater complexity than (10-9).

For readers familiar with the theory of heat conduction the foregoing example yields an interesting interpretation [1] of the normal law. Subtracting $U(x,t)$ from both sides of (10-9) and dividing by s give

$$\frac{U(x, t+s) - U(x,t)}{s} = \frac{h^2}{2s}\left[\frac{U(x+h, t) - 2U(x,t) + U(x-h, t)}{h^2}\right].$$

If we set $s = h^2$ and let $h \to 0$, this becomes, formally,[2]

$$\frac{\partial U}{\partial t} = \frac{1}{2}\frac{\partial^2 U}{\partial x^2} \tag{10-10}$$

with boundary condition

$$U(x,0) = 0 \qquad \text{for } x \neq 0, \qquad \int_{-\infty}^{\infty} U(x,t)\, dx = 1. \tag{10-10a}$$

Since these are the conditions for an instantaneous source of heat at the origin, a solution is [3]

$$U(x,t) = \frac{1}{\sqrt{2\pi t}}\, e^{-x^2/2t}. \tag{10-11}$$

Now, in the random walk the probability of a steps to the right and b to the left is given approximately by the normal approximation (9-10); it turns out to be

$$\sqrt{\frac{2}{\pi(a+b)}}\, e^{-(a-b)^2/2(a+b)}. \tag{10-12}$$

If the man arrives at point x at time t, he makes t/s steps altogether and x/h more steps to the right than to the left:

$$a + b = \frac{t}{s}, \qquad a - b = \frac{x}{h}.$$

Substitution in (10-12) and setting $s = h^2$ yield

$$U(x,t) \cong \frac{1}{\sqrt{2\pi t}}\, e^{-x^2/2t}(2h) \tag{10-13}$$

for the probability. Here $2h$ is the distance between possible values of x when t is fixed, and hence the coefficient of $2h$ may be regarded as a probability density. The condition

[1] Since heat is due to random motion of the molecules, the analogy of the random-walk problem with the problem of heat flow has a physical basis as well as the mathematical basis outlined in the text.

[2] See Chap. 6, Sec. 26.

[3] See Chap. 6, Sec. 19.

"h small" means simply that the number of steps is large, so that the normal law is applicable. The analogy between (10-11) and (10-13) is evident.

The discussion shows that not only (10-9) but the problem in heat flow given by (10-10) may be attacked by making random walks. Some of the main applications of Monte Carlo methods are, in fact, to the study of partial differential equations.

Example: A true coin is tossed repeatedly. It is desired to have a probability of 0.99 that the relative frequency of heads shall be within 1 per cent of the probability of heads. How many times must the coin be tossed?

If the coin is tossed n times, the desired inequality is

$$\left|\frac{x/n - p}{p}\right| \le 0.01 \tag{10-14}$$

which is the same as

$$-0.01\sqrt{\frac{p}{q}}\,n \le \frac{x - np}{\sqrt{npq}} \le 0.01\sqrt{\frac{p}{q}}\,n. \tag{10-15}$$

Setting the probability of (10-15) equal to 0.99 and noting that $p = q$, we get

$$0.99 = \Phi(0.01\sqrt{n}) - \Phi(-0.01\sqrt{n}) = 2\Phi(0.01\sqrt{n})$$

by the normal approximation. The table gives

$$0.01\sqrt{n} = 2.58,$$

so that $n = 67{,}000$ approximately. The fact that a problem such as this will always yield a finite value for n is the essential content of the law of large numbers. Applying the law of large numbers in another fashion, we can interpret the result more or less as follows: If the whole coin-tossing experiment is repeated a great many times, in about 99 per cent of these experiments the inequality (10-14) will be verified.

PROBLEMS

1. In the Example of the text, how many times must we toss the coin to make the probability 0.95 that the relative frequency is within 5 per cent of the probability?

2. On the average a certain student is able to solve 60 per cent of the problems assigned to him. If an examination contains 8 problems and a minimum of 5 problems is required for passing, what is the student's chance of passing? *Hint:* Because of the law of large numbers, you may take the statement about the student's average performance to mean: "His probability of solving any given problem is 0.6."

3. If Paul hits a target 80 times out of 100 on the average and John hits it 90 times out of 100, what is the probability that at least one of them hits the target when they shoot simultaneously?

4. If on the average in a shipment of 10 cases of certain goods 1 case is damaged, what is the probability that out of 5 cases expected at least 4 will not be damaged?

ADDITIONAL TOPICS IN PROBABILITY

11. The Poisson Law. In the problem of repeated trials it may happen that p is too small to permit the use of the normal approximation even though n is large. A different approximation, which is called the *Poisson law* or the *law of small numbers*, is now to be obtained for this case.

Starting with the formula for the probability of r successes in n trials,

$$B(r) = \frac{n!}{r!(n-r)!} p^r (1-p)^{n-r},$$

we replace $n!$ and $(n-r)!$ by their Stirling approximations to obtain

$$B(r) \cong \frac{n^n e^{-n} \sqrt{2\pi n}}{r!(n-r)^{n-r} e^{-(n-r)} \sqrt{2\pi(n-r)}} p^r (1-p)^{n-r}$$

$$= \frac{n^r e^{-r}}{r![1 - (r/n)]^{n-r+\frac{1}{2}}} p^r (1-p)^{n-r}. \tag{11-1}$$

Since the expected value of r is np, we can assume that r is small compared with n. In this case [1]

$$\left(1 - \frac{r}{n}\right)^{n-r+\frac{1}{2}} \cong \left(1 - \frac{r}{n}\right)^n = \left[\left(1 - \frac{r}{n}\right)^{-n/r}\right]^{-r} \cong e^{-r}.$$

Similarly, since p is small,

$$(1-p)^{n-r} \cong (1-p)^n = [(1-p)^{-1/p}]^{-np} \cong e^{-np}.$$

Substituting these two expressions into (11-1) yields the desired law of small numbers:

$$B(r) \cong \frac{(np)^r}{r!} e^{-np}, \qquad n \text{ large}, np \text{ moderate}. \tag{11-2}$$

The result may be written

$$B(r) \cong \frac{\mu^r}{r!} e^{-\mu}, \tag{11-3}$$

where $\mu = np$ is the expected number of successes.

An application of this law to some specific cases may prove interesting. Suppose it is known that, on the average, in a large city 2 persons die daily of tuberculosis. What is the probability that x persons will die on any day? In this case the expected number of deaths is $\mu = 2$, so that

$$B(x) = \frac{2^x}{x!} e^{-2}.$$

---

[1] The reader is reminded that $\lim (1 + h)^{1/h} = e$ as h approaches zero through positive or negative values. See I. S. Sokolnikoff, "Advanced Calculus," pp. 28–31, McGraw-Hill Book Company, Inc., New York, 1939.

Therefore we have the following table:

x	$B(x)$	x	$B(x)$	x	$B(x)$
0	0.135	2	0.271	4	0.090
1	0.271	3	0.180	5	0.036

The Poisson law has a significance far beyond its connection with the binomial distribution, as will now be shown. Suppose points x_i are distributed at random on the x axis in such a fashion that the following assumptions are valid:

1. The probability that a given number of points is in a given interval depends only on the length of that interval (and not on any information we may have about the points in adjacent intervals).

2. If $P(\Delta x)$ is the probability of 2 or more points in an interval of length Δx, then $P(\Delta x)/\Delta x \to 0$ as $\Delta x \to 0$.

3. If $P_1(\Delta x)$ is the probability of 1 point in an interval of length Δx, then $P_1(\Delta x)/\Delta x \to k$, a constant, as $\Delta x \to 0$.

In this case the probability $P_n(x)$ of n points in an interval of length x satisfies the Poisson law

$$P_n(x) = e^{-kx} \frac{(kx)^n}{n!}. \tag{11-4}$$

To prove this result, consider an interval $(0, x + \Delta x)$ of length $x + \Delta x$. We can have n points in this interval in three mutually exclusive ways. Either there are n points in x and none in Δx, or there are $n - 1$ in x and 1 in Δx, or there are fewer than $n - 1$ in x and at least 2 in Δx. The probability of this last alternative may be written $\epsilon \, \Delta x$, where $\epsilon \to 0$ with Δx, in view of assumption 2.

Thus, by total and compound probability,

$$P_n(x + \Delta x) = P_n(x)P_0(\Delta x) + P_{n-1}(x)P_1(\Delta x) + \epsilon \, \Delta x.$$

Subtracting $P_n(x)$ from both sides and dividing by Δx give

$$\frac{P_n(x + \Delta x) - P_n(x)}{\Delta x} = P_n(x)\frac{P_0(\Delta x) - 1}{\Delta x} + P_{n-1}(x)\frac{P_1(\Delta x)}{\Delta x} + \epsilon. \tag{11-5}$$

Since there must be no point, 1 point, or more than 1 point in an interval of length Δx, we have

$$P_0(\Delta x) + P_1(\Delta x) + P(\Delta x) = 1$$

which gives

$$\frac{P_0(\Delta x) - 1}{\Delta x} = -\frac{P_1(\Delta x)}{\Delta x} - \frac{P(\Delta x)}{\Delta x}. \tag{11-6}$$

Taking the limit $\Delta x \to 0$, we obtain $-k$ in (11-6), and hence taking the limit in (11-5) gives

$$\frac{d}{dx} P_n(x) = -kP_n(x) + kP_{n-1}(x), \qquad n \geq 1. \tag{11-7}$$

For $n = 0$ the term $P_{n-1}(x)$ is to be replaced by zero, so that

$$\frac{d}{dx} P_0(x) = -kP_0(x).$$

This separable differential equation yields

$$P_0(x) = ce^{-kx} = e^{-kx}$$

where the constant $c = 1$ since $P_0(0) = 1$; that is, an interval of zero length is sure to contain no points. (This follows from assumption 2.)

Substituting $P_0(x)$ in the relation (11-7) for $n = 1$ we get

$$\frac{d}{dx} P_1(x) = -kP_1(x) + ke^{-kx}$$

which yields $P_1(x) = e^{-kx}(kx)$. Proceeding step by step or using mathematical induction, we obtain (11-4).

The following are some of the phenomena which satisfy the assumptions 1 to 3 quite accurately and which, accordingly, obey a Poisson law: the distribution of automobiles on a highway, the distribution of starting times for telephone calls, the clicks of a Geiger counter, the arrival times for customers at a theater ticket office. The first example is a spatial distribution, while the last three refer to distributions in time.

Example 1. What is the probability that the ace of spades will be drawn from a deck of cards at least once in 104 consecutive trials?

This problem can be solved with the aid of the exact law (7-4) as follows: The probability that the ace will not be drawn in the 104 trials is

$$B(0) = {}_{104}C_0(\tfrac{1}{52})^0(\tfrac{51}{52})^{104} = 0.133$$

and the probability that the ace will be drawn at least once is $1 - 0.133 = 0.867$. On the other hand, Poisson's law (11-2) gives for the probability of failure to draw the ace

$$B(0) = \frac{(104 \cdot \tfrac{1}{52})^0}{0!} e^{-104/52} = e^{-2}.$$

Hence, the probability of drawing at least one ace of spades is $1 - e^{-2} = 0.865$.

Example 2. Show that the constant k in the Poisson law (11-4) represents the expected number of points in a unit interval.

Since the probability of n points in a unit interval is

$$P_n(1) = e^{-k} \frac{k^n}{n!}$$

the expected number is

$$E(n) = \sum_{n=1}^{\infty} e^{-k} \frac{k^n}{n!} n$$

$$= e^{-k} k \sum \frac{k^{n-1}}{(n-1)!}$$

$$= e^{-k} k e^k = k.$$

PROBLEMS

1. By use of the Poisson law compute the probability of (a) just one ace in 6 tosses of a die, (b) just one double ace in 36 tosses of a pair of dice. Compare the binomial law for cases (a) and (b). Which of the two cases satisfies the assumptions of the text more exactly?

2. The probability is 0.0025 that a nail chosen at random from the output of a certain machine will be defective. What is the probability that a keg of 1,000 nails made by the machine will have at most 3 defective nails? *Hint:* The keg has "at most 3" if it has 0, 1, 2, or 3 exactly. Use the Poisson approximation.

3. In Prob. 2 it is desired to have a probability of at least 0.95 that the keg has at least 1,000 good nails. How many nails should the manufacturer put into the keg? *Hint:* If he puts in $n = 1,000 + m$ nails, he wants a probability 0.95 that the number of defective nails will be at most m. Use the Poisson law, taking $np \cong 1,000p = 2.5$.

4. On a certain one-way highway it is proposed to install a traffic signal which has a 60-sec red interval but a long green interval. The speed of the cars may be taken as 30 mph, and the expected number is 10 cars per mile of highway. Neglecting any effects of slowing down, find the probability that just n cars will be obliged to stop when the light is red. What is the probability that at most 5 cars must stop? What is the expected number that must stop? *Hint:* Assume that the cars are distributed according to the law (11-4), and see Example 2.

5. A certain circuit can transmit 3 telephone calls simultaneously. The expected number of incoming calls is 1 per minute, and each call lasts 3 min. What is the probability of getting a busy signal? *Hint:* You will find the line busy if 3 calls or more have come in during the preceding 3-min interval. Use (11-4).

12. The Theory of Errors.

In this section the methods of probability are used to analyze the effect of experimental errors in measurement. If n independent measurements give the values $m_1, m_2, \ldots, m_n$, we consider questions such as the following: What is the best estimate for the quantity being measured as determined by these measurements? What is the probability that this best estimate is within 1 per cent, say, of the true value? How much added precision is gained by increasing the number of measurements?

Proceeding to the first question, let m_1 and m_2 be two independent measurements of an unknown quantity m (such as the mass of an electron, for instance). It is desired to find a best estimate for m based on the measurements m_1 and m_2. To this end we denote the best estimate by $\theta(m_1, m_2)$ and seek to determine the function θ. Now, if both measurements are increased by a given amount α, it seems reasonable to assume that the estimate also increases by the amount α. In symbols,

$$\theta(m_1 + \alpha, \ m_2 + \alpha) = \theta(m_1, m_2) + \alpha. \tag{12-1}$$

This relation is now postulated.

Similarly, if m_1 and m_2 are multiplied by a fixed quantity β, it is reasonable to suppose that the best estimate is likewise multiplied by β. This requirement leads to

$$\theta(\beta m_1, \beta m_2) = \beta \theta(m_1, m_2) \qquad (12\text{-}2)$$

which is also postulated. [Equation (12-2) is quite obvious when we consider the effect of a change of units. For instance if grams are used instead of kilograms as the unit of mass, we expect the estimate in grams to be 1,000 times as great as the estimate in kilograms.]

Finally, since the two experiments are carried out under substantially identical conditions, it does not matter which experimental result is m_1 and which is m_2. We are thus led to postulate that θ is symmetric:

$$\theta(m_1, m_2) = \theta(m_2, m_1). \qquad (12\text{-}3)$$

It is a remarkable fact that the best estimate is wholly determined by these requirements; *if θ satisfies (12-1) to (12-3), then θ must be the arithmetic mean,*

$$\theta(m_1, m_2) = \frac{m_1 + m_2}{2}. \qquad (12\text{-}4)$$

To establish (12-4), regard m_1 and m_2 as fixed and choose $\alpha = -m_2$ in (12-1). There results

$$\theta(m_1, m_2) = m_2 + \theta(m_1 - m_2, 0). \qquad (12\text{-}5)$$

If this expression for $\theta(m_1, m_2)$ is used in the left-hand member of (12-2), one obtains

$$\beta m_2 + \theta(\beta m_1 - \beta m_2, 0) = \beta \theta(m_1, m_2). \qquad (12\text{-}6)$$

Whenever $m_1 \neq m_2$, the choice $\beta = 1/(m_1 - m_2)$ in (12-6) gives

$$m_2 + \theta(1, 0)(m_1 - m_2) = \theta(m_1, m_2) \qquad (12\text{-}7)$$

if we multiply through by $m_1 - m_2$. And now (12-3) leads to

$$m_2 + \theta(1, 0)(m_1 - m_2) = m_1 + \theta(1, 0)(m_2 - m_1)$$

which implies $\theta(1, 0) = \frac{1}{2}$. Hence (12-7) yields (12-4). The case $m_1 = m_2$ is even simpler; specifically, Eq. (12-5) gives

$$\theta(m_1, m_1) = m_1 + \theta(0, 0) \qquad (12\text{-}8)$$

and the choice $\beta = 0$ in (12-2) shows that $\theta(0, 0) = 0$.

By analogy with (12-4), one generally assumes that the best value for three or more measurements is also the arithmetic mean. Thus,

$$\theta(m_1, m_2, m_3) = \frac{m_1 + m_2 + m_3}{3}. \qquad (12\text{-}9)$$

We shall now use this assumption to determine the underlying probability distribution for the errors of measurement.

Let the true value of the quantity being measured be denoted by v. The errors, then, are

$$x_i = m_i - v. \qquad (12\text{-}10)$$

Since the experimental determinations are made under substantially identical conditions, these random variables x_i are all assumed to have the same probability density $f(x)$. And since the experiments are supposed to be independent, the joint density for two or three variables is given by the product: [1]

$$f(x_1,x_2) = f(x_1)f(x_2) \tag{12-11}$$

$$f(x_1,x_2,x_3) = f(x_1)f(x_2)f(x_3). \tag{12-11a}$$

Our task is to determine the function $f(x)$.

Now, v is the true value of the quantity being measured. It is not a random variable, and it is not at the disposal of the experimenter. Nevertheless, one can contemplate the effect of a change in v, and in particular, one can consider that value of v which would maximize the probability of the observed result. We now *postulate* that the value of v which maximizes this probability is the arithmetic mean of the measurements. In other words, *the best estimate*, (12-4) and (12-9), is assumed to be also a *maximum-likelihood estimate*. It will be found that this assumption [2] enables us to determine the form of the function f without any knowledge of the experimental process.

If the probability (12-11) is maximum when

$$v = \frac{m_1 + m_2 + m_3}{3}, \tag{12-12}$$

then the logarithm of the probability is also maximum. Thus

$$\log f(m_1 - v) + \log f(m_2 - v) + \log f(m_3 - v) \tag{12-13}$$

is maximum, as a function of v, when (12-12) holds. Setting the derivative with respect to v equal to zero in (12-13), we obtain

$$\frac{f'(m_1 - v)}{f(m_1 - v)} + \frac{f'(m_2 - v)}{f(m_2 - v)} + \frac{f'(m_3 - v)}{f(m_3 - v)} = 0.$$

If F is defined by

$$F(x) = \frac{f'(x)}{f(x)},$$

[1] If we think of the errors as being discrete variables with f the frequency function, (12-11) is simply the law of compound probability for independent events. That is, the probability of making an error x_1 in the first experiment and x_2 in the second is the product of the individual probabilities. The corresponding result for continuous variables and densities (stated in Sec. 6) is also a consequence of the theorem of compound probability. The notion of *independence* is discussed further in Sec. 13.

[2] We shall suppose also that f is positive and twice differentiable, though these requirements could be somewhat relaxed.

the foregoing result, in the notation (12-10), is

$$F(x_1) + F(x_2) + F(x_3) = 0. \qquad (12\text{-}14)$$

Equation (12-10) shows that (12-12) is equivalent to

$$x_1 + x_2 + x_3 = 0. \qquad (12\text{-}15)$$

Thus, (12-14) holds whenever (12-15) holds. The corresponding statement for two variables, obtained from (12-11), is that

$$F(x_1) + F(x_2) = 0 \qquad (12\text{-}16)$$

whenever $x_1 + x_2 = 0$, and for one variable, we have

$$F(x_1) = 0 \qquad \text{when } x_1 = 0. \qquad (12\text{-}17)$$

From (12-16) we get $-F(x_3) = F(-x_3)$ by choosing $x_1 = x_3$, $x_2 = -x_3$, and hence (12-14) gives

$$F(x_1) + F(x_2) = -F(x_3) = F(-x_3).$$

Since $-x_3 = x_1 + x_2$ by (12-15), the function F satisfies

$$F(x_1) + F(x_2) = F(x_1 + x_2).$$

Differentiating partially with respect to x_1 and x_2 leads to

$$F'(x_1) = F'(x_1 + x_2) \qquad \text{and} \qquad F'(x_2) = F'(x_1 + x_2).$$

Hence $F'(x_1) = F'(x_2)$. Holding x_2 constant, we see that $F'(x_1)$ is constant:

$$F'(x_1) = c$$

and hence $F(x_1) = cx_1$, since (12-17) gives $F(0) = 0$. The relation

$$\frac{f'(x)}{f(x)} = F(x) = cx$$

yields
$$f(x) = Ke^{\frac{1}{2}cx^2}$$

where the constant K may be found from

$$1 = \int_{-\infty}^{\infty} f(x)\, dx = K \int_{-\infty}^{\infty} e^{\frac{1}{2}cx^2}\, dx.$$

Since the integral diverges if $c \geq 0$, we set $c = -2h^2$ to obtain

$$\frac{1}{K} = \int_{-\infty}^{\infty} e^{-h^2 x^2}\, dx = \frac{1}{\sqrt{2}\,h} \int_{-\infty}^{\infty} e^{-t^2/2}\, dt = \frac{\sqrt{2\pi}}{\sqrt{2}\,h}$$

by (10-1). Hence $K = h/\sqrt{\pi}$, and

$$f(x) = \frac{h}{\sqrt{\pi}} e^{-h^2 x^2}. \qquad (12\text{-}18)$$

This result, known as the *Gaussian law of error*, states that the variable $\sqrt{2}\,hx$ is normally distributed. Specifically, the probability of

$$t_1 < \sqrt{2}\,hx < t_2 \tag{12-19}$$

is

$$\int_{t_1/(\sqrt{2}\,h)}^{t_2/(\sqrt{2}\,h)} \frac{h}{\sqrt{\pi}}\, e^{-h^2x^2}\, dx \tag{12-20}$$

by (12-18), and the change of variable $t = \sqrt{2}\,hx$ shows that (12-20) is

$$\frac{1}{\sqrt{2\pi}} \int_{t_1}^{t_2} e^{-t^2/2}\, dt = \Phi(t_2) - \Phi(t_1). \tag{12-21}$$

The most important consideration justifying the use of this analysis in practice is that systematic errors must be eliminated.

The constant h measures the accuracy of the observer and is known as the *precision constant*. That particular error which has probability $\frac{1}{2}$ to be exceeded in magnitude is called the *probable error;* it is found to be $0.4769/h$ by use of (12-19), (12-21), and Appendix D. Another interpretation of the constant h is afforded by considering the *mean-absolute error*

$$E(|x|) = \int_{-\infty}^{\infty} |x| f(x)\, dx = \frac{2h}{\sqrt{\pi}} \int_0^{\infty} xe^{-h^2x^2}\, dx = \frac{1}{h\sqrt{\pi}} = \frac{0.5642}{h} \tag{12-22}$$

and still a third interpretation is given by the *mean-square error*

$$E(x^2) = \int_{-\infty}^{\infty} x^2 f(x)\, dx = \frac{2h}{\sqrt{\pi}} \int_0^{\infty} x^2 e^{-h^2x^2}\, dx = \frac{1}{2h^2}. \tag{12-23}$$

The final question mentioned at the beginning of this section concerns the effect of increasing the number of measurements n. Since $x_i = m_i - v$, we have

$$\bar{x} = \bar{m} - v$$

where the bar denotes the arithmetic mean:

$$\bar{x} = \frac{1}{n} \Sigma x_i, \qquad \bar{m} = \frac{1}{n} \Sigma m_i.$$

Thus, the error in the mean is the mean of the errors. It is likely to be smaller than the error in a single measurement because positive and negative errors tend to cancel when we form Σx_i. For the Gaussian distribution (12-18) the situation is especially simple; namely, $\bar{x}$ has a *Gaussian distribution with precision constant* $h\sqrt{n}$, whenever the independent measurements x_i have Gaussian distributions with precision constant h. Thus, if the inequality $|x| < \alpha$ has probability p, then the inequality $|\bar{x}| < \alpha/\sqrt{n}$ has the same probability p. This result shows how much more precision is attained by increasing the number of measurements.

The proof is omitted because it involves a tedious evaluation of multiple integrals.[1] However, the essential meaning of the result is that the "scatter" or "spread" for $\bar{x}$ is $1/\sqrt{n}$ times as great as the corresponding spread for x. When interpreted in this fashion the property follows from the results established in Sec. 14.

PROBLEMS

1. (a) Show that the sum of the squares of the errors $\Sigma(m_i - v)^2$ is least if the true value v happens to be the arithmetic mean of the measurements m_i. (b) Deduce that the arithmetic mean $\bar{m}$ is a maximum-likelihood estimate for v when there are n independent measurements each satisfying (12-18). *Hint:* It is required to choose v so that

$$f(x_1, x_2, \ldots, x_n) = f(x_1)f(x_2) \ldots f(x_n) = \left(\frac{h}{\sqrt{\pi}}\right)^n e^{-h^2 \Sigma x_i^2}$$

is maximum. Use the result (a).

2. In a certain experiment which satisfies the conditions of the text, the probable error is 0.01. A measurement m_1 is about to be made. What is the probability that the interval $(m_1 - 0.02, m_1 + 0.02)$ will contain the true value v? *Hint:* First find h, then note that the stated result happens if, and only if, $|x_1| < 0.02$.

13. Variance, Covariance, and Correlation.

Two random variables x and y are said to be *independent* if the event $x = x_i$ and the event $y = y_j$ are independent events for each choice of x_i in the range of x and each y_j in the range of y. In other words, knowledge that y has a particular value must not influence the probabilities associated with x. The numbers shown on two successive tosses of a die are independent in this sense (and so were the measurements m_i considered in the last section). On the other hand, the number of heads in the first three tosses and in the first four tosses of a coin are dependent variables.

The *product* xy of two random variables is a random variable which equals $x_i y_j$ when $x = x_i$ and $y = y_j$. Although it is not usually true that the expectation of a product is the product of the expectations, this is the case when the variables are independent. In symbols,

$$E(xy) = E(x)E(y), \qquad x, y \text{ independent.} \tag{13-1}$$

The proof is simple. If p_i is the probability that $x = x_i$, and if q_j is the probability that $y = y_j$, then the assumed independence gives $p_i q_j$ for the probability that simultaneously $x = x_i$ and $y = y_j$. Hence

$$E(xy) = \Sigma\Sigma p_i q_j x_i y_j = (\Sigma p_i x_i)(\Sigma q_j y_j) = E(x)E(y).$$

[1] See J. V. Uspensky, "Introduction to Mathematical Probability," chap. 13, McGraw-Hill Book Company, Inc., 1937, for a direct verification. An indirect method based on the theory of moments is given in P. G. Hoel, "Introduction to Mathematical Statistics," sec. 6.4, John Wiley & Sons, Inc., New York, 1954. See also M. E. Munroe, "The Theory of Probability," pp. 91–96, McGraw-Hill Book Company, Inc., New York, 1951.

When a discussion involves several variables x, y, $\ldots$, it is convenient to denote expectations by the letter μ, with a subscript to indicate the variable. Thus, we write

$$E(x) = \mu_x, \qquad E(y) = \mu_y$$

and so on. For example, (13-1) in this notation takes the form

$$\mu_{xy} = \mu_x \mu_y, \qquad x,\ y \text{ independent.} \tag{13-2}$$

To measure the deviation of a variable from its expected value μ, one introduces a quantity σ defined by [1]

$$\sigma = \sqrt{E(x - \mu)^2} \qquad \text{or} \qquad \sigma^2 = E(x - \mu)^2. \tag{13-3}$$

The expression σ is called the *standard deviation*, and its square σ^2 is called the *variance*. As for μ, here, too, it is customary to use a subscript when several variables have to be distinguished. For example,

$$\sigma_x^2 = E(x - \mu_x)^2, \qquad \sigma_y^2 = E(y - \mu_y)^2.$$

To illustrate the calculation of a variance by means of the definition, let x denote the number of heads obtained when 3 coins are tossed. Since $\mu = E(x) = \frac{3}{2}$ we have the following table:

$x =$	0	1	2	3
$x - \mu =$	$-\frac{3}{2}$	$-\frac{1}{2}$	$\frac{1}{2}$	$\frac{3}{2}$
$(x - \mu)^2 =$	$\frac{9}{4}$	$\frac{1}{4}$	$\frac{1}{4}$	$\frac{9}{4}$
Probability $p_i =$	$\frac{1}{8}$	$\frac{3}{8}$	$\frac{3}{8}$	$\frac{1}{8}$

The definition of expectation now gives

$$\sigma^2 = E(x - \mu)^2 = \tfrac{1}{8} \cdot \tfrac{9}{4} + \tfrac{3}{8} \cdot \tfrac{1}{4} + \tfrac{3}{8} \cdot \tfrac{1}{4} + \tfrac{1}{8} \cdot \tfrac{9}{4} = \tfrac{3}{4}.$$

If $E(x) = \mu_x$ and $E(y) = \mu_y$, the quantity

$$\sigma_{xy}^2 = E(x - \mu_x)(y - \mu_y) \tag{13-4}$$

is called the *covariance* of x and y. The covariance is a generalization of the variance, in that the special case $y = x$ gives

$$\sigma_{xx}^2 = E(x - \mu_x)(x - \mu_x) = E(x - \mu_x)^2 = \sigma_x^2.$$

As an illustration, let us compute σ_{xy}^2 when x is the number of heads obtained on the first 2 tosses and y the number obtained altogether in 3 tosses of an unbiased coin.

[1] The intent is $E[(x - \mu)^2]$, not $[E(x - \mu)]^2$.

Here $\mu_x = 1$, $\mu_y = \frac{3}{2}$, so that we have the following table:

Event	HHH	HHT	HTH	HTT	THH	THT	TTH	TTT
$x - \mu_x$	1	1	0	0	0	0	-1	-1
$y - \mu_y$	$\frac{3}{2}$	$\frac{1}{2}$	$\frac{1}{2}$	$-\frac{1}{2}$	$\frac{1}{2}$	$-\frac{1}{2}$	$-\frac{1}{2}$	$-\frac{3}{2}$
Product	$\frac{3}{2}$	$\frac{1}{2}$	0	0	0	0	$\frac{1}{2}$	$\frac{3}{2}$

Since the associated probabilities are $\frac{1}{8}$, we take $\frac{1}{8}$ times the sum of the entries in the last row to get

$$\sigma_{xy}^2 = \frac{1}{2}. \tag{13-5}$$

We shall now obtain an expression for σ_{xy} which is often more useful than (13-4). Expanding the product in (13-4) gives

$$\sigma_{xy}^2 = E(xy - y\mu_x - x\mu_y + \mu_x\mu_y)$$
$$= E(xy) - E(y)\mu_x - E(x)\mu_y + \mu_x\mu_y.$$

Upon recalling that $E(x) = \mu_x$ and $E(y) = \mu_y$ we get

$$\sigma_{xy}^2 = E(xy) - E(x)E(y) = \mu_{xy} - \mu_x\mu_y, \tag{13-6}$$

which is the required formula.

To apply this formula to the preceding example, we construct the following table:

Event	HHH	HHT	HTH	HTT	THH	THT	TTH	TTT
x	2	2	1	1	1	1	0	0
y	3	2	2	1	2	1	1	0
xy	6	4	2	1	2	1	0	0

Taking $\frac{1}{8}$ times the sum of the last entries gives $E(xy) = 2$, and hence by (13-6)

$$\sigma_{xy}^2 = 2 - (1)(\tfrac{3}{2}) = \tfrac{1}{2}.$$

The special case $x = y$ in (13-6) gives an alternative form [1] of (13-3), namely,

$$\sigma^2 = E(x^2) - \mu^2 = E(x^2) - [E(x)]^2. \tag{13-7}$$

As an illustration the reader may apply this formula to the preceding example to obtain

$$\sigma_x^2 = \tfrac{3}{2} - (1)^2 = \tfrac{1}{2}, \qquad \sigma_y^2 = 3 - (\tfrac{3}{2})^2 = \tfrac{3}{4}. \tag{13-8}$$

[1] Note that σ^2 gives the moment of inertia of the area under the distribution curve $y = f(x)$ about the line $x = \mu$ which passes through the center of mass. From this viewpoint (13-7) is the familiar formula for moment of inertia after a change of rotational axes.

If the variables x and y are independent, (13-2) and (13-6) give $\sigma_{xy} = 0$. Hence when $\sigma_{xy} \neq 0$, the variables must be related. A quantitative measure of the strength of the relationship is given by the *correlation coefficient* ρ:

$$\rho = \frac{\sigma_{xy}^2}{\sigma_x \sigma_y}. \tag{13-9}$$

For example, in the foregoing illustration (13-5) and (13-8) yield

$$\rho = \frac{\frac{1}{2}}{\sqrt{\frac{1}{2}} \sqrt{\frac{3}{4}}} = \frac{1}{3}\sqrt{6} = 0.816. \tag{13-10}$$

Thus, if two variables x and y have a correlation coefficient $\rho = 0.8$, then they are about as strongly related as are the numbers of heads on the first two tosses and on the first three tosses of an unbiased coin.

The correlation coefficient has the value 1 if $y = x$, and, as we have already observed, $\rho = 0$ when x and y are unrelated. Moreover, ρ does not change if x and y are each multiplied by a constant factor. Thus, if the correlation coefficient indicates a certain strength of relationship for x and y, it will give the same strength of relationship for $2x$ and $3y$. Similarly, ρ is unaffected by addition of a constant; for instance, $x - 2$ and $y - 3$ have the same ρ as x and y.

In spite of having these desirable properties, ρ is not always a reliable measure of dependence, and many statistical studies have led to erroneous conclusions through an incorrect interpretation of correlation. It is quite possible to have the variables so strongly related that y is a function of x and yet $\rho = 0$. Before a correlation coefficient can be used with confidence, one must know something about the underlying probability distribution.

The variables x and y are said to have a *bivariate normal distribution* when

$$f(x,y) = e^{(ax^2 + 2bxy + cy^2 + dx + cy + f)}, \qquad a, b, \ldots \text{const.}$$

In this important case the theory of correlation has been fully developed, and it is found [1] that ρ actually does measure the strength of the relationship between x and y.

Example: A variable x is said to be "normally distributed with mean μ and variance σ^2" when its density function is

$$f(x) = \frac{1}{\sqrt{2\pi}\,\sigma} e^{-\frac{1}{2}\left(\frac{x-\mu}{\sigma}\right)^2}, \qquad \mu, \sigma \text{ const.}$$

Show that the mean is indeed μ and the variance σ^2.

By the definition of expectation,

$$E(x - \mu) = \frac{1}{\sqrt{2\pi}\,\sigma} \int_{-\infty}^{\infty} (x - \mu)e^{-\frac{1}{2}\left(\frac{x-\mu}{\sigma}\right)^2} dx = \frac{\sigma}{\sqrt{2\pi}} \int_{-\infty}^{\infty} te^{-\frac{1}{2}t^2} dt = 0$$

when we set $t = (x - \mu)/\sigma$. Hence $E(x - \mu) = 0$, which gives $E(x) = \mu$. The same change of variable leads to

$$E(x - \mu)^2 = \frac{1}{\sqrt{2\pi}} \sigma^2 \int_{-\infty}^{\infty} t^2 e^{-\frac{1}{2}t^2} dt = \sigma^2,$$

[1] See Hoel, *op. cit.*, chap. 8.

as we see upon integrating by parts and using (10-1). Since $\mu = E(x)$, the latter result $E(x - \mu)^2$ is the variance by definition.

Choosing $\mu = 0$, $\sigma = 1/(h\sqrt{2})$, we obtain (12-18), and hence the precision constant h is given by

$$h = \frac{1}{\sqrt{2}\,\sigma} \tag{13-11}$$

[cf. (12-23)]. This fact gives a method for estimating h from the data, as we shall see in the following sections.

PROBLEMS

1. Compute σ^2 if x is uniformly distributed on the interval $0 \le x \le 1$.

2. Let x be the number on top and y the number on the bottom in a toss of a true die. Compute $E(x)$, $E(y)$, $E(xy)$, and the covariance. Does your work indicate that the variables are dependent? Find the correlation coefficient.

3. Three coins are tossed. Let x be the number of heads shown by the first coin, whereas y is the number of heads shown by all the coins. Compute the correlation coefficient. Your result should be smaller than the value (13-10). Why?

14. Arithmetic Means. In many applications one does not consider a single variable, but rather one obtains the mean of a large number of variables. For instance, if x is a measure of the length of a rod, one would make several measurements $x_1, x_2, \ldots, x_n$ and use the arithmetic mean,

$$\bar{x} = \frac{x_1 + x_2 + \cdots + x_n}{n} \tag{14-1}$$

in accordance with the procedure of Sec. 12. Here the x_is are not the different values of a single variable but are n random variables describing the result of n independent measurements.

Just as one uses σ_x to indicate the standard deviation of the variable x, it is customary to let $\sigma_{\bar{x}}$ denote the standard deviation of $\bar{x}$. The following theorem enables us to compute $\sigma_{\bar{x}}$ from σ_x in many cases:

THEOREM. *If the variables x_i are independent, if they have the same expectation $E(x_i) = \mu$ and the same variance σ_x^2, then*

$$\sigma_{\bar{x}} = \frac{\sigma_x}{\sqrt{n}}. \tag{14-2}$$

For proof, observe that

$$E(x_1 + \cdots + x_n) = E(x_1) + \cdots + E(x_n) = n\mu.$$

The variance of $x_1 + \cdots + x_n$ is therefore

$$E(x_1 + \cdots + x_n - n\mu)^2,$$

which may be written

$$E[(x_1 - \mu) + (x_2 - \mu) + \cdots + (x_n - \mu)]^2.$$

Expanding the bracket we obtain

$$E\left[\sum_i (x_i - \mu)^2 + \sum_{i \neq j} (x_i - \mu)(x_j - \mu)\right]. \tag{14-3}$$

Since the variables are independent, the covariance of x_i and x_j is zero for $i \neq j$; that is,

$$E(x_i - \mu)(x_j - \mu) = 0.$$

Also the definition of σ_x gives

$$\sigma_x^2 = E(x_i - \mu)^2.$$

Hence, taking the expectation in (14-3) yields

$$E(x_1 + \cdots + x_n - n\mu)^2 = n\sigma_x^2.$$

Dividing by n^2 we have

$$E\left[\frac{x_1 + \cdots + x_n}{n} - \mu\right]^2 = \frac{\sigma_x^2}{n}$$

which gives (14-2) upon taking the square root.

The intuitive meaning of this result is approximately as follows: Suppose a single measurement varies over an interval of length l about the true value, so that l measures the scatter or spread. Then the mean of n independent measurements will have a spread of the order of $l/\sqrt{n}$ about the true value.

To illustrate the use of (14-2) let $x_i = 1$ if there is success at the ith trial in a set of independent trials with probability p, and let $x_i = 0$ otherwise. For each variable x_i we have $x_i^2 = x_i$ and hence

$$E(x_i^2) = E(x_i) = p \cdot 1 + q \cdot 0 = p.$$

By (13-7) the corresponding variance is

$$\sigma_x^2 = p - p^2 = p(1 - p) = pq$$

and (14-2) now gives

$$\sigma_{\bar{x}} = \sqrt{\frac{pq}{n}}.$$

For the variables x_i considered in the foregoing paragraph the mean $\bar{x}$ is simply the relative frequency m/n, where m is the number of successes. We have, then,

$$\left[E\left(\frac{m}{n} - p\right)^2\right]^{1/2} = \sqrt{\frac{pq}{n}} \tag{14-4}$$

which shows again that the relative frequency m/n is likely to be close to p when n is large. The corresponding result for a general variable x is based on (14-2); it leads to assertions concerning $|E(x) - \bar{x}|$ which are similar to the theorem established in Sec. 10 but of greater scope.

Multiplying (14-4) through by n we get

$$[E(m - np)^2]^{1/2} = \sqrt{npq}.$$

This gives an interpretation for the quantity $\sqrt{npq}$ that arose in connection with the normal law (Sec. 10); namely, $\sqrt{npq}$ *is the standard deviation of the number of successes m.*

15. Estimation of the Variance. If x_1, x_2, ..., x_n are n independent observations of a variable x, the *sample variance* is defined by

$$s^2 = \frac{1}{n} \Sigma(x_i - \bar{x})^2 = \overline{(x_i - \bar{x})^2}. \tag{15-1}$$

Unlike the theoretical variance σ^2, the sample variance is computed from the observations, hence is actually available. It will be seen, now, that s^2 can be used to estimate σ^2.

We have

$$E(ns^2) = \Sigma E(x_i - \bar{x})^2$$

$$= \Sigma E[(x_i - \mu) - (\bar{x} - \mu)]^2$$

$$= \Sigma[E(x_i - \mu)^2 - 2E(x_i - \mu)(\bar{x} - \mu) + E(\bar{x} - \mu)^2]. \tag{15-2}$$

Now, $E(x_i - \mu)^2 = \sigma^2$ by definition, and $E(\bar{x} - \mu)^2 = \sigma^2/n$ by (14-2). For the middle term in (15-2) we get

$$E(x_i - \mu)(\bar{x} - \mu) = \frac{1}{n} E(x_i - \mu)(x_1 + \cdots + x_i + \cdots + x_n - \mu n)$$

$$= \frac{1}{n} E(x_i - \mu)(x_i - \mu + \cdots) = \frac{1}{n} E(x_i - \mu)^2 = \frac{1}{n} \sigma^2$$

when we note that the terms not written explicitly are independent of x_i. That is, for $i \neq j$, Eq. (13-1) gives

$$E[(x_i - \mu)x_j] = E(x_i - \mu)E(x_j) = 0 \cdot \mu = 0.$$

Substituting into (15-2) yields the important formula

$$E(ns^2) = (n - 1)\sigma^2. \tag{15-3}$$

If (15-3) is divided by n, we get

$$E[\overline{(x_i - \bar{x})^2}] = \frac{n - 1}{n} \sigma^2 \tag{15-4}$$

upon recalling (15-1). On the other hand the definition of σ^2 gives

$$E[\overline{(x_i - \mu)^2}] = \sigma^2. \tag{15-5}$$

It is not surprising that (15-4) gives a smaller value than (15-5), inasmuch as the choice $\mu = \bar{x}$ is the value of μ that *minimizes* (15-5) (cf. Prob. 1, Sec. 12). The fact that (15-4) should be smaller than (15-5) is especially clear when there is only one measurement, x_1. In this case (15-4) gives zero because $x_1 = \bar{x}$.

The foregoing remarks indicate that s^2 is not a suitable estimate of σ^2; it has a tendency to be too small. But if we divide (15-3) by $n - 1$ for $n \geq 2$, we get

$$E\left(\frac{n}{n-1} s^2\right) = \sigma^2,$$

which gives the following theorem:

THEOREM. *Let $x_1, x_2, \ldots, x_n$ be n independent observations of a variable x, with $n \geq 2$. If s^2 is the sample variance, then the quantity*

$$\hat{\sigma}^2 = \frac{n}{n-1} s^2 \tag{15-6}$$

is an unbiased estimate of σ^2. That is, $E(\hat{\sigma}^2) = \sigma^2$.

To illustrate the use of the theorem, let

$$m_1 = 12, \qquad m_2 = 8, \qquad m_3 = 13$$

be three measurements of an unknown quantity whose true value is v. The errors in the measurement are $x_i = m_i - v$, but since

$$x_i - \bar{x} = m_i - v - \bar{m} + v = m_i - \bar{m} \tag{15-7}$$

we can compute s^2 *without knowing* v. By (15-1) and (15-7),

$$ns^2 = \Sigma(x_i - \bar{x})^2 = \Sigma(m_i - \bar{m})^2.$$

In this example $\bar{m} = 11$, so that

$$ns^2 = (1)^2 + (-3)^2 + (2)^2 = 14.$$

Hence an estimate for σ^2 is

$$\hat{\sigma}^2 = \frac{ns^2}{n-1} = \frac{14}{2} = 7.$$

According to (13-11) the precision constant h is estimated as $h \cong 1/(\sqrt{2}\,\hat{\sigma}) = 1/\sqrt{14}$ = 0.27. In statistics it is shown how one can determine the reliability of an estimate such as this, though we do not pursue the subject here.[1]

PROBLEMS

1. A certain experiment gave the measurements

$$m_i = 17, 21, 20, 18, 14.$$

Obtain an unbiased estimate for the variance of a single measurement, and from this, estimate the precision constant.

[1] See Hoel, *op. cit.*, chap. 10.

2. If the precision constant in Prob. 1 can be assumed exactly equal to your estimate of it, (*a*) what is the probability that the next measurement will be within 0.5 of the true value? (*b*) How many measurements must you make if you want a probability 0.95 that the mean of those measurements will be within 0.1 of the true value? *Hint:* Use the fact that the precision constant of the mean is $h\sqrt{n}$ if that of a single measurement is h.

3. In a certain measuring routine the cost of equipment and materials is negligible but the time required is proportional to the number of measurements. Give a rational method of adjusting the salaries of two observers whose working speeds are s_1 and s_2 if the precision constants of their measurements are h_1 and h_2. *Hint:* Consider the number of measurements each must make to attain equal reliability in the respective arithmetic means.

4. Discuss Prob. 3 if the cost of equipment is proportional to the length of time it is used and the cost of material is proportional to the number of measurements.

CHAPTER 9

NUMERICAL ANALYSIS

Solution of Equations

Interpolation. Empirical Formulas. Least Squares

Numerical Integration of Differential Equations

The principal concern of numerical analysis is with the construction of effective methods for the calculation of unknowns entering in the formulation of a given problem. Since every formulation of a practical problem involves assumptions and approximations, it is senseless to seek unknowns to a higher precision than is warranted by the initial data. A simple and perhaps crude technique giving the desired values within specified limits of tolerance is always to be preferred to an involved method capable of yielding an arbitrary degree of accuracy.

In recent years the growth of numerical analysis was accelerated by the demands of science and technology for numerical solutions of many pressing problems. High-speed computing machines produced for coping with such problems are certain to open new vistas in science and leave a profound imprint in all fields of human activity.

It is the object of this chapter to present the rudiments of numerical analysis essential to all concerned with the processing of numerical data. Inasmuch as the understanding of principles must precede the acquisition of computing skills, the emphasis in the following sections is placed on basic ideas and general methods rather than on special techniques useful in solving this or that problem. Among topics included here are the determination of real roots of algebraic and transcendental equations, the basic method for solving systems of linear equations, the elements of interpolation theory, and its bearing on curve fitting and numerical solution of differential equations.

SOLUTION OF EQUATIONS

1. Graphical Methods. Geometric considerations usually are a useful guide in the construction of analytic methods of solution of practical problems. This is particularly true in the problem of determination of numerical values of the roots of algebraic and transcendental equations.[1]

---

[1] A polynomial equation $x^n + a_1 x^{n-1} + \cdots + a_n = 0$ is called an *algebraic* equation. An equation $F(x) = 0$ which is not reducible to an algebraic equation is called *transcendental*. Thus, $\tan x - x = 0$ is a transcendental equation, and so is $e^x + 2 \cos x = 0$.

If $F(x)$ is a real continuous function, the equation

$$F(x) = 0 \tag{1-1}$$

may have real roots. The approximate values of such roots can be determined by graphing the function $y = F(x)$ and reading from the graph the values of x for which $y = 0$. This familiar procedure for graphical determination of real roots can frequently be simplified by rewriting (1-1) in the form

$$f(x) = g(x). \tag{1-2}$$

The abscissas of points of intersection of the curves $y = f(x)$ and $y = g(x)$ will obviously be the roots of (1-2).

Thus, an approximate value of the real root of

$$F(x) \equiv x^3 - 146.25x - 682.5 = 0$$

can be found by graphing the function

$$y = x^3 - 146.25x - 682.5.$$

It is simpler, however, to plot the cubic

$$y = x^3$$

and the straight line (Fig. 1)

$$y = 146.25x + 682.5$$

and read off from the graph the abscissa of their point of intersection P_0.

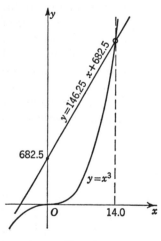

FIG. 1

An obvious disadvantage of graphical methods is that they require plotting curves on a large scale when a high degree of accuracy is desired. To avoid this, one obtains more precise values by applying one of the several methods of successive approximations discussed in Secs. 2 and 3. All these methods require that the desired root be first isolated. That is, they call for the determination of an interval which contains just the root in question and no others. If $F(x)$ is a continuous function, and if for a certain pair of real values $x = x_1$, $x = x_2$, the signs of $F(x_1)$ and $F(x_2)$ are opposite, then it is obvious that $F(x) = 0$ has at least one real root in the interval (x_1, x_2). If there are several roots in (x_1, x_2), one usually narrows down this interval by a succession of judicious trials until an interval is obtained which contains just the desired root. For efficient application of the successive-approximations methods it is desirable that this interval be as small as possible.

We note in passing that no general methods are available for the exact determination of the roots of transcendental equations. Also, there are no algebraic formulas for the solution of general algebraic equations of degree higher than 4. The so-called Cardan and Ferrari solutions of the cubic and quartic equations require the calculation of cube roots of quantities which themselves are square roots. Generally it is simpler to obtain the desired approximations by methods described in the following sections than to make use of Cardan's formulas.[1]

PROBLEMS

1. Find graphically, correct to one decimal, the real roots of:
   (a) $2^x - x^2 = 0$; (b) $x^4 - x - 1 = 0$; (c) $x^5 - x - 0.5 = 0$; (d) $e^x + x = 0$;
   (e) $\tan x - x = 0$, $\pi < x < 3\pi/2$.
Isolate the roots (that is, for each root find an interval which contains just that root and no others).

2. A sphere 2 ft in diameter is made of wood whose specific gravity is $\frac{2}{3}$. Find to one-decimal accuracy the depth h to which the sphere sinks in water. *Hint:* The volume of a spherical segment is $\pi h^2(r - h/3)$. The volume of the submerged segment is equal to the volume of displaced water, which must weigh as much as the sphere. If water weighs 62.5 lb per ft^3,

$$\pi h^2 \left(r - \frac{h}{3} \right) 62.5 = \frac{4}{3} \pi r^3 \cdot \frac{2}{3} \cdot 62.5,$$

and since $r = 1$, we have $h^3 - 3h^2 + \frac{8}{3} = 0$.

2. Simple Iterative Methods. When real roots of Eq. (1-1) have been isolated, there are many methods for computing them to any degree of accuracy. These all depend on the application of some iterative formula which furnishes values of the succeeding approximations from the preceding ones. The nature of restrictions imposed on the function $F(x)$ in the equation

$$F(x) = 0 \qquad\qquad (2\text{-}1)$$

in the two basic iterative methods discussed here is obvious from the description of the methods. The simplest of these is the method of *linear interpolation*, also known as the *method of false position*.

Let the root x_0 of (2-1) be isolated between x_1 and x_2. Then, in the

---

[1] A numerical determination of the roots of algebraic equations is frequently accomplished by some method of synthetic division (such as Horner's method) or by the root-squaring method (Graeffe's method). These special methods are discussed in many books. See, for example, F. B. Hildebrand, "Introduction to Numerical Analysis," McGraw-Hill Book Company, Inc., New York, 1956. The methods of Secs. 2 and 3 of this chapter apply to all types of equations and are generally adequate for the determination of real roots.

interval (x_1, x_2), the graph of $y = F(x)$ may have the appearance shown in Fig. 2. If the points P_1 and P_2 in Fig. 2 are joined by a straight line, it will cut the x axis at some point x_3, which usually is closer to the root x_0 than either x_1 or x_2. But from similar triangles,

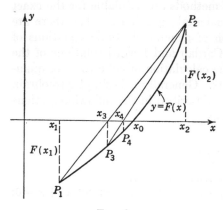

Fig. 2

$$\frac{x_3 - x_1}{-F(x_1)} = \frac{x_2 - x_3}{F(x_2)} \qquad (2\text{-}2)$$

and on solving for x_3 we get

$$x_3 = \frac{x_1 F(x_2) - x_2 F(x_1)}{F(x_2) - F(x_1)}. \qquad (2\text{-}3)$$

To obtain a closer approximation to x_0, we can determine the x intercept of the straight line joining the point P_3 in Fig. 2 with the point P_2 and thus obtain the next approximation x_4. By repeating this process we obtain a sequence of values

$$x_3, \; x_4, \; \ldots, \; x_n,$$

which generally converges to x_0. The process described here is precisely that used in interpolating tabulated values of logarithms and other functions. In effect, it replaces a small portion of the curve by a straight line.

Another useful iterative method is based on rewriting (2-1) in the form

$$f(x) = g(x). \qquad (2\text{-}4)$$

Now, if the real roots of

$$f(x) = c$$

can be determined for every real c, we can proceed as follows. Let x_1 be an approximate value of the root x_0 of (2-1). This, of course, is also an approximate root of (2-4), since (2-1) and (2-4) are equivalent equations. On setting $x = x_1$ in the right-hand member of (2-4) we get the equation

$$f(x) = g(x_1), \qquad (2\text{-}5)$$

which by hypothesis we can solve. If the solution of (2-5) is x_2, we obtain, on setting $x = x_2$ in the right-hand member of (2-4),

$$f(x) = g(x_2). \qquad (2\text{-}6)$$

The solution x_3 of (2-6) we call the third approximation, and in general, the nth approximation x_n is determined by solving

$$f(x) = g(x_{n-1}). \qquad (2\text{-}7)$$

From the geometric interpretations of this procedure, which we give next, it will be seen that the sequence $x_1, x_2, \ldots, x_n, \ldots$ converges to the root x_0 of (2-1) if, in the interval of length $2\,|\,x_1 - x_0\,|$ centered at x_0, we have

$$|f'(x)| > |g'(x)| \tag{2-8}$$

and the derivatives are bounded.

Suppose, first, that the slopes of the curves

$$y = f(x), \qquad y = g(x) \tag{2-9}$$

in the interval (x_0,x_1) (Fig. 3) have the same sign and satisfy (2-8). When $x = x_1$ is taken as the first approximation to x_0, Eq. (2-5) yields the second

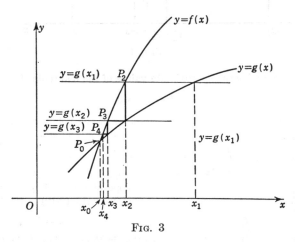

FIG. 3

approximation x_2, which corresponds to the abscissa of the point of intersection P_2 of the straight line $y = g(x_1)$ with $y = f(x)$. Equation (2-6) gives x_3, which is the abscissa of the point of intersection P_3 of the straight line $y = g(x_2)$ with $y = f(x)$, and so on. The sequence $x_1, x_2, x_3, \ldots$ obviously converges to x_0.

The situation when the slopes of the curves (2-9) satisfy (2-8) but are opposite in sign is illustrated in Fig. 4. The value x_2 determined by solving (2-5) is the abscissa of the point of intersection P_2 of $y = f(x)$ with $y = g(x_1)$. It lies on the opposite side of the root from x_1. The third approximation x_3 is the abscissa of the intersection of $y = g(x_2)$ with $y = f(x)$, and it lies on the same side as x_1 but nearer to x_0. In Fig. 3 the approach to the intersection P_0 is along a staircase path, while in Fig. 4 it is along a spiral. In either case, the rapidity of convergence [1] depends on the nature of the functions $f(x)$ and $g(x)$.

[1] Some criteria for the speed of convergence are given in Hildebrand, *op. cit.*

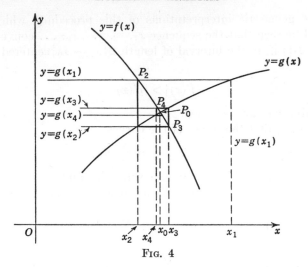

FIG. 4

Example 1. Determine the approximate values of the real roots of

$$e^x - 4x = 0. \tag{2-10}$$

The real roots of this equation are the abscissas of the points of intersection of the

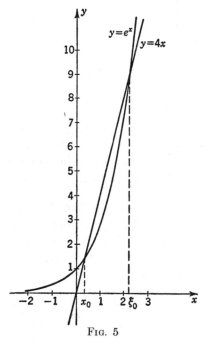

FIG. 5

curves $y = e^x$ and $y = 4x$ shown in Fig. 5. It appears that the smaller of the roots, x_0, lies in the vicinity of $x = 0.3$. The larger root, ξ_0, is close to $x = 2.1$. Since for $x = x_0$ the slope of $y = 4x$ is greater than that of $y = e^x$, we write (2-10) in the form

$$x = \tfrac{1}{4}e^x,$$

so that in the notation of Eq. (2-4)

$$f(x) = x \qquad \text{and} \qquad g(x) = \tfrac{1}{4}e^x.$$

The sequence of approximations x_n according to (2-7) is thus determined from

$$x_{n+1} = \tfrac{1}{4}e^{x_n}, \qquad n = 1, 2, \ldots . \tag{2-11}$$

If we take $x_1 = 0.3$, we get [1] from (2-11)

$$x_2 = \tfrac{1}{4}e^{0.3} = \tfrac{1}{4}(1.34986) = 0.3374$$

$$x_3 = \tfrac{1}{4}e^{x_2} = \tfrac{1}{4}(1.40130) = 0.3503$$

$$x_4 = \tfrac{1}{4}e^{x_3} = \tfrac{1}{4}(1.41949) = 0.3549$$

$$x_5 = \tfrac{1}{4}e^{x_4} = \tfrac{1}{4}(1.42603) = 0.3565$$

$$x_6 = \tfrac{1}{4}e^{x_5} = \tfrac{1}{4}(1.42832) = 0.3571$$

$$x_7 = \tfrac{1}{4}e^{x_6} = \tfrac{1}{4}(1.42917) = 0.3573.$$

[1] In performing these calculations it is convenient to use tables such as "Tables of Exponential Functions," National Bureau of Standards, Washington, D.C., 1951.

If only three-decimal-place accuracy is required, the computations can be terminated at this stage.

To obtain the second root we note that at $x = \xi_0$, the slope of $y = 4x$ is less than that of $y = e^x$. If we write (2-10) in the form

$$e^x = 4x$$

or
$$x = \log 4x,$$

so that $f(x) = x$ and $g(x) = \log 4x$, then the condition (2-8) is satisfied at $x = \xi_0$.

The desired sequence $\{x_n\}$ is now given by

$$x_{n+1} = \log 4x_n, \qquad n = 1, 2, \ldots,$$

and we can take $x_1 = 2.1$.

Using tables of natural logarithms [1] we find

$$x_2 = \log 4x_1 = \log 8.4 = 2.12823$$

$$x_3 = \log 4x_2 = \log 8.5129 = 2.14158$$

$$x_4 = \log 4x_3 = \log 8.5663 = 2.14783$$

$$x_5 = \log 4x_4 = \log 8.5913 = 2.15075$$

$$x_6 = \log 4x_5 = \log 8.6030 = 2.15211$$

$$x_7 = \log 4x_6 = \log 8.6084 = 2.15273$$

$$x_8 = \log 4x_7 = \log 8.6109 = 2.15303$$

$$x_9 = \log 4x_8 = \log 8.6121 = 2.15316.$$

The value of the root ξ_0, correct to three decimals, is 2.153. We do not give a discussion of the errors in the approximations obtained by such calculations because a rigorous analysis of errors in the iterative procedures is fairly involved.[2]

Example 2. Find an approximate value of the real root of

$$x - \tan x = 0 \tag{2-12}$$

near $x = 3\pi/2$.

From the graphs of

$$y = x \qquad \text{and} \qquad y = \tan x$$

in Fig. 6, it appears that Eq. (2-12) has just one real root in each of the intervals $(2n - 1)\pi/2 < x < (2n + 1)\pi/2$, where $n = 0, \pm 1, \pm 2, \ldots$.

It is convenient to rewrite (2-12) in the form

$$x = \tan^{-1} x,$$

so that in the notation (2-4) $f(x) = x$ and $g(x) = \tan^{-1} x$. This choice assures that the condition (2-8) is satisfied at the root x_0.

The sequence of approximations this time is given by

$$x_{n+1} = \tan^{-1} x_n, \qquad n = 1, 2, \ldots.$$

[1] For example, "Tables of Natural Logarithms," National Bureau of Standards, Washington, D.C., 1941.

[2] A brief discussion is contained in Hildebrand, *op. cit.*, chap. 10.

On taking $x_1 = 3\pi/2 = 4.7124$ radians, we find

$$x_2 = \tan^{-1} 4.7124 = 4.5033$$
$$x_3 = \tan^{-1} 4.5033 = 4.4938$$
$$x_4 = \tan^{-1} 4.4938 = 4.4935,$$

which suggest that the root x_0, correct to three decimals, is 4.493.

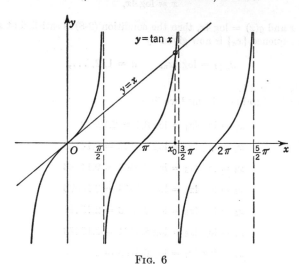

FIG. 6

These examples indicate that if it is possible to write Eq. (2-1) in the form

$$x = g(x),$$

and if $|g'(x)| \le M < 1$ in the interval of length $2|x_1 - x_0|$ centered at x_0, then the recursion formula giving the desired approximating sequence is

$$x_{n+1} = g(x_n), \qquad n = 1, 2, \ldots. \tag{2-13}$$

PROBLEMS

1. Use both methods of this section to obtain, correct to two decimals, the values of the real roots in Probs. 1 and 2 of Sec. 1.

2. Find in the manner of the examples of this section the real roots of $x^5 - x - 0.2 = 0$ correct to three decimals.

3. Newton's Method. The successive terms in the approximating sequence in the method of false position (see Fig. 2) are determined by the intersection of the secant line with the x axis. Newton proposed constructing an approximating sequence determined by the intersection with the x axis of the tangent line to the curve $y = F(x)$.

Thus let the root $x = x_0$ of

$$F(x) = 0 \tag{3-1}$$

lie in the vicinity of $x = x_1$ (see Fig. 7). The equation of the tangent line to $y = F(x)$ at $P_1(x_1, y_1)$ is

$$y - F(x_1) = F'(x_1)(x - x_1). \tag{3-2}$$

If the curve $y = F(x)$ has the appearance shown in Fig. 7, the tangent line (3-2) cuts the x axis at x_2, which is a better approximation to the root than x_1. To determine x_2 we set $y = 0$ and find

$$x_2 = x_1 - \frac{F(x_1)}{F'(x_1)}$$

if $F'(x_1) \neq 0$. Having determined x_2, we find in the same way that the tangent to $y = F(x)$ at $P_2[x_2, F(x_2)]$ intersects the axis at

$$x_3 = x_2 - \frac{F(x_2)}{F'(x_2)},$$

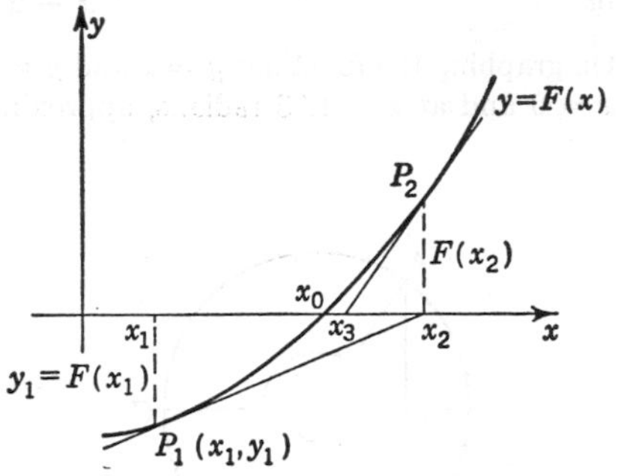

and in general,

$$x_{n+1} = x_n - \frac{F(x_n)}{F'(x_n)}, \qquad n = 1, 2, \dots. \tag{3-3}$$

FIG. 7

The geometric considerations indicate that when $y = F(x)$ is a monotone increasing or decreasing function in the interval (x_1, x_2) [so that $F'(x)$ does not change sign] and when there is no point of inflection in this interval [so that $F''(x)$ does not change sign], the sequence (3-3) converges to the root x_0.

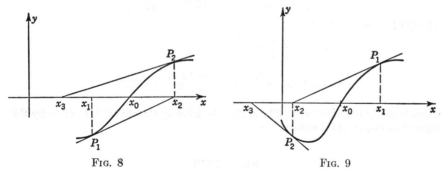

FIG. 8   FIG. 9

The situations corresponding to the cases when there is a point of inflection or a horizontal tangent to $y = F(x)$ in the vicinity of the root are illustrated in Figs. 8 and 9. It is clear from these figures that in these cases the sequence (3-3) need not converge to x_0. Thus, before applying Newton's method one should examine the behavior of $F'(x)$ and $F''(x)$ in the vicinity of the root.

Example: Find the angle subtended at the center of a circle by an arc whose length is double the length of its chord.

Let the arc BCA (Fig. 10) be of length $2BA$. If the angle subtended by this arc at the center of the circle is $2x$ radians, then the arc $BCA = 2xr$ while $BA = 2r \sin x$, r being the radius of the circle.

Our problem requires that

$$2xr = 4r \sin x,$$

or
$$x - 2 \sin x = 0. \tag{3-4}$$

On graphing the functions $y = x$ and $y = 2 \sin x$ (Fig. 11), we see that they intersect at $x = 0$ and at $x = 1.88$ radians, approximately. We reject the trivial solution $x = 0$.

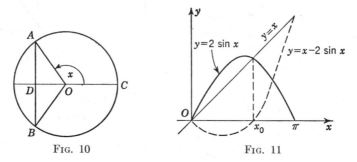

FIG. 10   FIG. 11

Since $y = x - 2 \sin x$ is obviously monotone increasing and has no point of inflection near the root x_0, we can apply formula (3-3) with $x_1 = 1.88$. We find

$$x_2 = x_1 - \frac{x_1 - 2 \sin x_1}{1 - 2 \cos x_1}$$

$$= 1.88 - \frac{1.88 - 2 \sin 1.88}{1 - 2 \cos 1.88} = 1.896.$$

The third approximation is

$$x_3 = x_2 - \frac{x_2 - 2 \sin x_2}{1 - 2 \cos x_2}$$

$$= 1.896 - \frac{1.896 - 2 \sin 1.896}{1 - 2 \cos 1.896} = 1.8955,$$

which is nearly the same as x_2. The angle subtended by the arc BCA, as given by this approximation, is 3.7910 radians.

PROBLEMS

1. Calculate by Newton's method the roots in Examples 1 and 2 of Sec. 2.

2. Solve by Newton's method Prob. 2, Sec. 1.

3. Find to three decimals by Newton's method the angle subtended at the center of a circle by a chord which cuts off a segment whose area is one-fourth that of the circle.

4. Find by Newton's method to three decimal places the real roots of the following equations: (a) $x - \cos x = 0$; (b) $x + e^x = 0$; (c) $x^4 - x - 1 = 0$; (d) $x^3 - 25 = 0$; (e) $x^5 - x - 0.2 = 0$.

4. Systems of Linear Equations.   The Gauss Reduction. No doubt the reader is familiar with Cramer's rule for solving systems of n linear equations in n unknowns by determinants.[1]   Although Cramer's rule is important in numerous theoretical considerations, it is of questionable practical value when the given system contains more than two unknowns.   Usually it is easier to obtain solutions by some process of elimination of unknowns. The simplest practical method for solving systems of linear equations, based on the idea of elimination, is the Gauss reduction method.   Its several variants form the basis for most techniques used in the solutions of large systems of equations.[2]

The idea of the method is simple.   Let it be required to solve a system of n linear equations

$$a_{11}x_1 + a_{12}x_2 + \cdots + a_{1n}x_n = c_1$$
$$a_{21}x_1 + a_{22}x_2 + \cdots + a_{2n}x_n = c_2 \tag{4-1}$$
$$\cdot \ \cdot \ \cdot \ \cdot \ \cdot \ \cdot \ \cdot \ \cdot \ \cdot \ \cdot \ \cdot \ \cdot \ \cdot \ \cdot$$
$$a_{n1}x_1 + a_{n2}x_2 + \cdots + a_{nn}x_n = c_n$$

in n unknowns x_i. We divide the first equation in (4-1) by a_{11}, solve for x_1, and use the result to eliminate x_1 in the other equations. The resulting system of $n - 1$ equations in x_2, $\ldots$, x_n is treated in the same way. That is, we divide the first of these equations by the coefficient of x_2 and use the result to eliminate x_2 from the remaining equations. After continuing the process n times [3] we obtain an equivalent system

$$x_1 + a'_{12}x_2 + a'_{13}x_3 + \cdots + a'_{1n}x_n = c'_1$$
$$x_2 + a'_{23}x_3 + \cdots + a'_{2n}x_n = c'_2$$
$$\cdot \ \cdot \ \cdot \ \cdot \ \cdot \ \cdot \ \cdot \ \cdot \ \cdot \ \cdot \ \cdot \ \cdot \ \cdot \ \cdot \ \cdot \tag{4-2}$$
$$x_{n-1} + a'_{n-1,n}x_n = c'_{n-1}$$
$$x_n = c'_n$$

provided the given system has a unique solution. The substitution $x_n = c'_n$ in the preceding equation in the set (4-2) yields the value of x_{n-1}, and by working backward we obtain in succession the values of x_{n-2}, x_{n-3}, $\ldots$, x_1.

In practice the Gauss reduction can be performed in the manner indicated in the following example.

---

[1] A summary of the properties of determinants and Cramer's rule are given in Appendix A.

[2] Among such variants are the Crout and the Gauss-Jordan reductions.   These are described in Hildebrand, *op. cit.*, and in many other books.

[3] If the coefficient of x_r in the rth equation vanishes, it is necessary to renumber the variables or equations.

Example: Solve the system

$$2.843x_1 - 1.326x_2 + 9.841x_3 = 5.643$$
$$8.673x_1 + 1.295x_2 - 3.215x_3 = 3.124 \qquad (4\text{-}3)$$
$$0.173x_1 - 7.724x_2 + 2.832x_3 = 1.694$$

by the method of Gauss' reduction.

On dividing each equation in (4-3) by the coefficients of x_1 in that equation, we get

$$x_1 - 0.46641x_2 + 3.4615x_3 = 1.9849$$
$$x_1 + 0.14931x_2 - 0.37069x_3 = 0.36020 \qquad (4\text{-}4)$$
$$x_1 - 44.647x_2 + 16.370x_3 = 9.7919.$$

The subtraction of the second equation in (4-4) from the first and the third gives

$$-0.61572x_2 + 3.8322x_3 = 1.6247$$
$$-44.796x_2 + 16.741x_3 = 9.4317$$

and, on dividing these by the coefficients of x_2, we find

$$x_2 - 6.2239x_3 = -2.6387$$
$$x_2 - 0.37372x_3 = -0.21055. \qquad (4\text{-}5)$$

Subtracting the second equation from the first in (4-5) yields

$$-5.8502x_3 = -2.4282,$$

so that
$$x_3 = 0.41506. \qquad (4\text{-}6)$$

The reduced system consists of the first equations in (4-4) and (4-5) and Eq. (4-6). It is

$$x_1 - 0.46641x_2 + 3.4615x_3 = 1.9849$$
$$x_2 - 6.2239x_3 = -2.6387 \qquad (4\text{-}7)$$
$$x_3 = 0.41506.$$

The substitution of the value of x_3 from the last into the second equation of (4-7) gives

$$x_2 = -2.6387 + 6.2239(0.41506) = -0.055408$$

and the first reduced equation finally yields

$$x_1 = 1.9849 + 0.46641(-0.055408) - 3.4615(0.41506) = 0.52232.$$

There are numerous modifications of the procedure just indicated, some of which are adapted for computations on desk calculators while others are more suitable for high-speed electronic computers.

PROBLEM

Use Cramer's rule and also apply the Gauss reduction to solve the following systems:

(a) $2x + y + 3z = 2,$
$3x - 2y - z = 1,$
$x - y + z = -1;$

(b) $2x_1 + x_2 + 3x_3 + x_4 = -2,$
$5x_1 + 3x_2 - x_3 - x_4 = 1,$
$x_1 - 2x_2 + 4x_3 + 3x_4 = 4,$
$3x_1 - x_2 + x_3 = 2;$

(c) $1.329x_1 + 1.415x_2 - 2.291x_3 = 0.532,$
$1.395x_2 - 0.531x_3 = 1.211,$
$1.001x_1 + 2.093x_3 = 0.556.$

5. An Iterative Method for Systems of Linear Equations.

Except for the round-off errors the Gauss reduction method explained in the preceding section is exact. When the determinant of the system (4-1) is different from zero, it yields the desired solution after a finite number of steps. However, successive steps leading to an equivalent triangular system (4-2) may prove laborious and ill-adapted to machine calculations. For this reason, a variety of iterative methods, which in theory require an infinite number of steps to obtain an exact solution, have been devised.

One of these methods, due [1] to L. Seidel, is based on the use of the iterative formula (2-13). The convergence of any iterative method obviously depends on the character of the system under consideration.

In many cases the system (4-1) can be rewritten so that in the ith equation the coefficient a_{ii} of the unknown x_i is numerically large compared with other coefficients. That is to say, the coefficients along the diagonal of the system (4-1) dominate the other coefficients. In this event by solving the ith equation for x_i we can rewrite such a system (4-1) in the form

$$x_1 = \frac{1}{a_{11}}(c_1 - a_{12}x_2 - a_{13}x_3 - \cdots - a_{1n}x_n),$$

$$x_2 = \frac{1}{a_{22}}(c_2 - a_{21}x_1 - a_{23}x_3 - \cdots - a_{2n}x_n), \qquad (5\text{-}1)$$

$$\cdots \cdots \cdots \cdots \cdots \cdots \cdots \cdots$$

$$x_n = \frac{1}{a_{nn}}(c_n - a_{n1}x_1 - a_{n2}x_2 - \cdots - a_{n,n-1}x_{n-1}).$$

If we set $x_1 = x_2 = \cdots = x_n = 0$ in the right-hand members of (5-1), we obtain

$$x_i^{(1)} = \frac{c_i}{a_{ii}}, \qquad i = 1, 2, \ldots, n, \qquad (5\text{-}2)$$

which is called the *first approximation* to the solution of (5-1).

The substitution of this first approximation in the right-hand members of (5-1) yields the *second approximation* $x_i^{(2)}$, and so on. The cycle is then repeated with the expectation that the values $x_i^{(k)}$ after the kth iteration are not substantially altered by further iterations.[2]

---

[1] Generally called the Gauss-Seidel method.

[2] There are several criteria for convergence of this process which generally are not easy to verify. It is known that when the coefficients in (4-1) are symmetric (so that $a_{ij} = a_{ji}$) and the matrix (a_{ij}) is positive definite, the Seidel process always converges. See Hildebrand, *op. cit.*, for a brief discussion of several criteria.

In practice the iteration process described above is usually modified by taking as the first approximation $x_1^{(1)}$ the value of x_1 obtained from the first equation in (5-1) by setting $x_2 = x_3 = \cdots = x_n = 0$. Using this value in the second equation in place of x_1 and setting $x_3 = x_4 = \cdots = x_n = 0$, one obtains the approximation $x_2^{(1)}$. To obtain $x_3^{(1)}$ one inserts for x_1 and x_2 the values $x_1^{(1)}$ and $x_2^{(1)}$ in the third equation and sets $x_4 = x_5 = \cdots = x_n = 0$. Finally, to get the value of $x_n^{(1)}$ one uses previously found values $x_1^{(1)}, \ldots, x_{n-1}^1$ in the last equation of the system (5-1). This process is repeated to obtain approximations of higher orders.

This particular choice of approximations usually improves the rapidity of convergence of the process. We illustrate it by an example.

Example: The system (4-3) can be rewritten in the form

$$8.673x_1 + 1.295x_2 - 3.215x_3 = 3.124$$
$$0.173x_1 - 7.724x_2 + 2.832x_3 = 1.694 \qquad (5\text{-}3)$$
$$2.843x_1 - 1.326x_2 + 9.841x_3 = 5.643$$

in which the diagonal coefficients dominate.

We next write (5-3) in the form (5-1) and get

$$x_1 = \frac{1}{8.673}(3.124 - 1.295x_2 + 3.215x_3)$$

$$x_2 = \frac{1}{-7.724}(1.694 - 0.173x_1 - 2.832x_3) \qquad (5\text{-}4)$$

$$x_3 = \frac{1}{9.841}(5.643 - 2.843x_1 + 1.326x_2).$$

To obtain $x_1^{(1)}$ we set $x_2 = x_3 = 0$ in the first equation in (5-4) and find

$$x_1^{(1)} = \frac{3.124}{8.673} = 0.36020.$$

Inserting this value for x_1 and setting $x_3 = 0$ in the second equation in (5-4), we get

$$x_2^{(1)} = -0.21125.$$

Finally, $x_3^{(1)} = 0.44089$ is obtained by using the values $x_1^{(1)}$ and $x_2^{(1)}$ in place of x_1 and x_2 in the third of Eqs. (5-4).

A repetition of the process yields second, third, and higher approximations. These are recorded in the table:

k	1	2	3	4	5	6	7
$x_1^{(k)}$	0.36020	0.55517	0.51780	0.52312	0.52220	0.52235	0.52233
$x_2^{(k)}$	−0.21125	−0.04523	−0.05852	−0.05501	−0.05550	−0.05543	−0.05544
$x_3^{(k)}$	0.44089	0.40694	0.41594	0.41488	0.41508	0.41505	0.41505

A comparison with the values found in Sec. 4 by the Gauss reduction method shows that in this problem six iterations were necessary to get four-decimal accuracy.

INTERPOLATION. EMPIRICAL FORMULAS. LEAST SQUARES

6. Differences.   One of the problems connected with the analysis of experimental data concerns the representation of such data by analytic formulas.   Thus, we may wish to represent, either exactly or approximately, a set of observed values (x_i, y_i) by some relationship of the form $y = f(x)$.   In such analysis the concept of *differences* is important.

We consider a set of pairs of values (x_i, y_i), where $i = 0, 1, \ldots, n$, which can be represented by points in the xy plane.   The differences between successive pairs of ordinates y_{i+1} and y_i we call the *first forward differences* of the ys and we denote them by Δy_i.   Thus,

$$\Delta y_i = y_{i+1} - y_i, \qquad i = 0, 1, 2, \ldots, n. \tag{6-1}$$

The *second forward differences* are defined by

$$\Delta^2 y_i = \Delta y_{i+1} - \Delta y_i$$

and, in general, the *kth forward differences are*

$$\Delta^k y_i = \Delta^{k-1} y_{i+1} - \Delta^{k-1} y_i. \tag{6-2}$$

These differences are usually represented in a tabular form:

TABLE 1

x	y	Δy	$\Delta^2 y$	$\Delta^3 y$	$\Delta^4 y$
x_0	y_0				
		Δy_0			
x_1	y_1		$\Delta^2 y_0$		
		Δy_1		$\Delta^3 y_0$	
x_2	y_2		$\Delta^2 y_1$		$\Delta^4 y_0$
		Δy_2		$\Delta^3 y_1$	
x_3	y_3		$\Delta^2 y_2$		
		Δy_3			
x_4	y_4				
x_{n-1}	y_{n-1}				
		Δy_{n-1}			
x_n	y_n				

in which the quantities in each column represent the differences between the quantities in the preceding column. These are usually placed midway between the quantities being subtracted, so that the forward differences with like subscripts lie along the diagonals indicated in the table by arrows.

We note that if the rth differences $\Delta^r y_i$ are constant, then all differences of order higher than r are zero.[1]

Now, it follows from (6-1) and (6-2) that

$$y_1 = y_0 + \Delta y_0$$

$$y_2 = y_1 + \Delta y_1 = (y_0 + \Delta y_0) + (\Delta^2 y_0 + \Delta y_0) = y_0 + 2\Delta y_0 + \Delta^2 y_0$$

$$y_3 = y_2 + \Delta y_2 = (y_0 + 2\Delta y_0 + \Delta^2 y_0) + (\Delta^2 y_1 + \Delta y_1)$$

$$= (y_0 + 2\Delta y_0 + \Delta^2 y_0) + (\Delta^3 y_0 + \Delta^2 y_0 + \Delta^2 y_0 + \Delta y_0)$$

$$= y_0 + 3\Delta y_0 + 3\Delta^2 y_0 + \Delta^3 y_0.$$

These results can be written symbolically as

$$y_1 = (1 + \Delta)y_0, \qquad y_2 = (1 + \Delta)^2 y_0, \qquad y_3 = (1 + \Delta)^3 y_0$$

in which $(1 + \Delta)^k$ is an operator on y_0 with the exponent on the Δ indicating the order of the difference. The difference operator Δ is analogous to the differential operator D introduced in Chap. 1.

We easily establish by induction that

$$y_k = (1 + \Delta)^k y_0, \qquad k = 1, 2, \ldots, \tag{6-3}$$

or, in the expanded form,

$$y_k = y_0 + k\,\Delta y_0 + \frac{k(k-1)}{2!}\,\Delta^2 y_0 + \frac{k(k-1)(k-2)}{3!}\,\Delta^3 y_0 + \cdots. \tag{6-4}$$

Formula (6-4) enables us to represent every value y_k in terms of y_0 and the forward differences $\Delta y_0, \Delta^2 y_0, \ldots$.

We can derive a similar formula by starting with the values of the ys at the end of Table 1 and forming the *backward* differences defined as follows: The first backward differences ∇y_i are

$$\nabla y_i = y_i - y_{i-1}. \tag{6-5}$$

The second backward differences $\nabla^2 y_i$ are defined by

$$\nabla^2 y_i = \nabla y_i - \nabla y_{i-1}, \tag{6-6}$$

and in general, the kth backward differences $\nabla^k y_i$ are

$$\nabla^k y_i = \nabla^{k-1} y_i - \nabla^{k-1} y_{i-1}. \tag{6-7}$$

---

[1] A differences table in a specific numerical example appears in the Example of the next section.

A table of backward differences is indicated in Table 2, where the differences $\nabla^k y_i$ with a fixed subscript i lie along the diagonals slanting up, as shown by arrows.

TABLE 2

x	y	∇y	$\nabla^2 y$	$\nabla^3 y$	$\nabla^4 y$
x_0	y_0				
.					
.	.				.
.	.	.		.	
x_{n-4}	y_{n-4}				
x_{n-3}	y_{n-3}	∇y_{n-3}	$\nabla^2 y_{n-2}$		
x_{n-2}	y_{n-2}	∇y_{n-2}	$\nabla^2 y_{n-1}$	$\nabla^3 y_{n-1}$	$\nabla^4 y_n$
x_{n-1}	y_{n-1}	∇y_{n-1}	$\nabla^2 y_n$	$\nabla^3 y_n$	
x_n	y_n	∇y_n			

Now, from (6-5) to (6-7) we deduce that

$$\nabla^2 y_n = \nabla y_n - \nabla y_{n-1} = y_n - 2y_{n-1} + y_{n-2}$$

$$\nabla^3 y_n = \nabla^2 y_n - \nabla^2 y_{n-1} = y_n - 3y_{n-1} + 3y_{n-2} - y_{n-3}$$

and in general

$$\nabla^k y_n = \nabla^{k-1} y_n - \nabla^{k-1} y_{n-1} = \sum_{r=0}^{k} (-1)^r \binom{k}{r} y_{n-r}, \qquad (6\text{-}8)$$

where

$$\binom{k}{r} = \frac{k(k-1)(k-2) \dots (k-r+1)}{r!} \qquad (6\text{-}9)$$

is the binomial coefficient of x^r in the expansion of $(1 + x)^k$.

By using (6-8) successively in the definitions of backward differences we find

$$y_{n-1} = y_n - \nabla y_n \equiv (1 - \nabla)y_n,$$

$$y_{n-2} = y_n - 2\nabla y_n + \nabla^2 y_n \equiv (1 - \nabla)^2 y_n,$$

and, in general,

$$y_{n-k} = (1 - \nabla)^k y_n, \qquad (6\text{-}10)$$

where ∇ is the backward-difference operator. The formula (6-10) when expanded reads

$$y_{n-k} = y_n - k\nabla y_n + \frac{k(k-1)}{2!}\nabla^2 y_n - \frac{k(k-1)(k-2)}{3!}\nabla^3 y_n + \cdots.$$

$$(6\text{-}11)$$

It shows that any value of y in Table 2 can be expressed in terms of y_n and backward differences $\nabla^k y_n$.

We shall use formulas (6-4) and (6-11) to derive certain interpolation formulas and to deduce some formulas for numerical integration.

PROBLEMS

1. Compute the forward and backward differences for the following set of data:

x	1	2	3	4	5	6	7	8
y	2.105	2.808	3.614	4.604	5.857	7.451	9.467	11.985

2. Write expressions for the y_k, $k = 1, 2, \ldots$, in Prob. 1 by using (6-4) and (6-11).

7. Polynomial Representation of Data. Unless a statement to the contrary is made, we shall suppose henceforth that the values x_i in a given set of data (x_i, y_i), where $i = 0, 1, 2, \ldots, n$, are equally spaced. If the spacing interval is h, then

$$x_1 = x_0 + h, \qquad x_2 = x_0 + 2h, \ldots, x_n = x_0 + nh.$$

We pose the problem of representing the data by some formula $y = f(x)$, which for $x = x_0 + kh$ yields $y_k = f(x_0 + kh)$. We shall frequently write f_k for y_k.

We observed in the preceding section that whenever the rth differences of the ys are constant, then all differences of order higher than r vanish. In this event formula (6-4) yields

$$y_k = y_0 + \binom{k}{1}\Delta y_0 + \binom{k}{2}\Delta^2 y_0 + \cdots + \binom{k}{r}\Delta^r y_0, \qquad (7\text{-}1)$$

where the binomial coefficients $\binom{k}{r}$ are defined by

$$\binom{k}{r} = \frac{k(k-1)(k-2) \ldots (k-r+1)}{r!}. \qquad (7\text{-}2)$$

Since the x_i are spaced h units apart,

$$x_k = x_0 + kh, \qquad k = 1, 2, \ldots, n,$$

so that

$$k = \frac{x_k - x_0}{h}. \qquad (7\text{-}3)$$

Now the expression (7-2) is a polynomial of degree r in k. Therefore, on substituting in (7-1) for k from (7-3) we obtain a polynomial of degree r in x_k. When like powers of x_k are collected, (7-1) takes the form

$$y_k = a_0 + a_1 x_k + a_2 x_k^2 + \cdots + a_r x_k^r. \qquad (7\text{-}4)$$

Accordingly, the polynomial in x,

$$y(x) = a_0 + a_1 x + a_2 x^2 + \cdots + a_r x^r, \qquad (7\text{-}5)$$

assumes the values y_k when we set $x = x_k$. Thus, when the rth differences of the y_k are constant and the x_k are equally spaced, the polynomial (7-5) represents these data exactly.

It is easy to prove a converse to the effect that the rth differences of the polynomial (7-5) are constant. It would suffice to show that the first difference $\Delta y(x) = y(x + h) - y(x)$ formed with the aid of (7-5) is a polynomial of degree $r - 1$, for if differencing a polynomial once reduces its degree by 1, r successive differencings would yield a polynomial of degree 0, that is, a constant.[1]

When rth differences in a given set of data are not constant but differ from one another by negligible amounts, the polynomial (7-5) represents the data approximately.

Example: The set of data and the forward differences tabulated below suggest that these data can be represented by a cubic polynomial $y = a_0 + a_1 x + a_2 x^2 + a_3 x^3$ if two-decimal accuracy is sufficient.

x	y	Δy	$\Delta^2 y$	$\Delta^3 y$	$\Delta^4 y$
1	2.105				
		0.703			
2	2.808		0.103		
		0.806		0.081	
3	3.614		0.184		-0.002
		0.990		0.079	
4	4.604		0.263		-0.001
		1.253		0.078	
5	5.857		0.341		$+0.003$
		1.594		0.081	
6	7.451		0.422		-0.001
		2.016		0.080	
7	9.467		0.502		
		2.518			
8	11.985				

[1] We leave it to the reader to show that $\Delta y(x)$ is, indeed, a polynomial of degree $r - 1$. The result is analogous to the theorem that the derivative of a polynomial of degree r is a polynomial of degree $r - 1$. The expression $\Delta y = y(x + h) - y(x)$ save for the factor $1/h$ is the difference quotient used in defining the derivative.

The coefficients a_i in this polynomial can be determined with the aid of formula (7-4) by using (7-1) with $r = 3$ and by taking

$$y_0 = 2.105, \qquad \Delta y_0 = 0.703, \qquad \Delta^2 y_0 = 0.103, \qquad \Delta^3 y_0 = 0.081.$$

Since such calculations present no interest, we do not give them here. It is more sensible to determine the a_i by the method of least squares of Sec. 11.

PROBLEMS

1. Given the table:

x	19	20	21	22	23	24	25
y	81.00	90.25	100.00	110.25	121.00	132.25	144.00

Compute second forward differences, and represent the data by $y = a_0 + a_1 x + a_2 x^2$. Determine a_0, a_1, a_2 so that the polynomial passes through (a) the first three points, (b) the last three points.

2. Discuss the calculation of the y_k in Prob. 1 from (6-4) and (6-11).

8. Newton's Interpolation Formulas. When the data (x_i, y_i), where $i = 0, 1, 2, \ldots, n$, are presented in tabular form, an infinite number of analytic relations $y = f(x)$ can be devised such that $y_i = f(x_i)$ either exactly or approximately. Once a suitable form of $f(x)$ is determined, the formula $y = f(x)$ can be used to calculate the ordinates y for xs not appearing in the table. That is, the formula can be used for interpolation or extrapolation.

The simplest of such formulas is a linear relationship based on the assumption that the values of y in the interval (x_i, x_{i+1}) can be represented by

$$y = y_i + \frac{y_{i+1} - y_i}{x_{i+1} - x_i}(x - x_i). \tag{8-1}$$

Formula (8-1) is precisely that used in estimating the values of such tabulated functions as logarithms by the process of "interpolation by proportional parts."

More accurate interpolation formulas are based on the assumption that the desired value of y can be computed from a polynomial

$$y = a_0 + a_1 x + a_2 x^2 + \cdots + a_m x^m \tag{8-2}$$

in which $m + 1$ coefficients a_i are so chosen that $m + 1$ pairs of tabulated values (x_i, y_i) satisfy (8-2) exactly.[1]

In the preceding section we saw that when the data are represented by a

---

[1] These $m + 1$ pairs may include the entire set of given values (x_i, y_i), or they may be a subset so chosen that $|x - x_i|$ is as small as possible.

polynomial of degree m, then all forward differences of order higher than m vanish. Accordingly, formula (6-4) yields

$$y_k = y_0 + k\,\Delta y_0 + \frac{k(k-1)}{2!}\Delta^2 y_0 + \cdots + \frac{k(k-1)\,\ldots\,(k-m+1)}{m!}\Delta^m y_0$$
$$(8\text{-}3)$$

and, since the x_i are equally spaced, $x_k = x_0 + kh$, so that

$$k = \frac{x_k - x_0}{h}.$$

On inserting this value of k in (8-3) we get

$$y_k = y_0 + \frac{x_k - x_0}{h}\,\Delta y_0 + \frac{(x_k - x_0)(x_k - x_0 - h)}{2!h^2}\Delta^2 y_0 + \cdots$$

$$+ \frac{(x_k - x_0)(x_k - x_0 - h)\,\ldots\,(x_k - x_0 - mh + h)}{m!h^m}\Delta^m y_0. \quad (8\text{-}4)$$

This relation is satisfied by $m + 1$ pairs of the tabulated values. If we assume that the value of y corresponding to an arbitrary x can be obtained from (8-4) by replacing x_k by x, we get the formula

$$y(x) = y_0 + \frac{x - x_0}{h}\,\Delta y_0 + \frac{(x - x_0)(x - x_0 - h)}{2!h^2}\Delta^2 y_0 + \cdots$$

$$+ \frac{(x - x_0)(x - x_0 - h)\,\ldots\,(x - x_0 - mh + h)}{m!h^m}\Delta^m y_0 \quad (8\text{-}5)$$

known as *Newton's forward-difference interpolation formula*. This formula can, of course, be used for either interpolation or extrapolation.

By replacing $(x - x_0)/h$ by a dimensionless variable X which represents the distance of x from x_0 in units of h, we get from (8-5)

$$y_X = y_0 + X\,\Delta y_0 + \frac{X(X-1)}{2!}\Delta^2 y_0 + \cdots$$

$$+ \frac{X(X-1)\,\ldots\,(X-m+1)}{m!}\Delta^m y_0, \quad (8\text{-}6)$$

where $X = (x - x_0)/h$ and $y_X = y(x_0 + hX) = y(x)$.

A similar calculation based on the use of (6-11) yields *Newton's backward-difference interpolation formula*

$$y_{n+X} = y_n + X\,\nabla y_n + \frac{X(X+1)}{2!}\nabla^2 y_n + \cdots$$

$$+ \frac{X(X+1)\,\ldots\,(X+m-1)}{m!}\nabla^m y_n \quad (8\text{-}7)$$

where $$X = \frac{x - x_n}{h}, \qquad \text{so that } x = x_n + hX,$$

and $$y_{n+X} = y(x_n + hX) = y(x).$$

When the data cannot be represented by a polynomial, the right-hand members of (8-6) and (8-7) are infinite series involving differences of all orders.

Formulas (8-6) and (8-7) can be used to compute derivatives of tabulated functions. Thus, on differentiating successively (8-5) with respect to x and setting $x = x_0$ in the result, we get

$$y'(x_0) = \frac{1}{h}\left(\Delta y_0 - \frac{1}{2}\Delta^2 y_0 + \frac{1}{3}\Delta^3 y_0 - \frac{1}{4}\Delta^4 y_0 + \frac{1}{5}\Delta^5 y_0 - \cdots\right)$$

$$y''(x_0) = \frac{1}{h^2}\left(\Delta^2 y_0 - \Delta^3 y_0 + \frac{11}{12}\Delta^4 y_0 - \frac{5}{6}\Delta^5 y_0 + \cdots\right)$$

$$\qquad\qquad (8\text{-}8)$$

$$y'''(x_0) = \frac{1}{h^3}\left(\Delta^3 y_0 - \frac{3}{2}\Delta^4 y_0 + \frac{7}{4}\Delta^5 y_0 - \cdots\right)$$

$$y^{\mathrm{iv}}(x_0) = \frac{1}{h^4}\left(\Delta^4 y_0 - 2\Delta^5 y_0 + \cdots\right).$$

Formulas (8-8) should be used with caution because even when $y = f(x)$ is well represented by the polynomial $P(x)$, the derivatives of $f(x)$ may differ significantly from those of $P(x)$.

Example: Using the data given in the Example in Sec. **7**, determine an approximate value for the y corresponding to $x = 2.2$.

First, let y be determined by using only the two neighboring observed values (hence, $m = 1$). Then, $x_0 = 2$, $y_0 = 2.808$, $\Delta y_0 = 0.806$, and $X = (2.2 - 2)/1 = 0.2$. Hence,

$$y = 2.808 + 0.2(0.806) = 2.969,$$

which has been reduced to three decimal places because the observed data are not given more accurately. This is simply a straight-line interpolation by proportional parts.

If the three nearest values are chosen, $m = 2$, $x_0 = 1$, $y_0 = 2.105$, $\Delta y_0 = 0.703$, $\Delta^2 y_0 = 0.103$, and $X = 2.2 - 1 = 1.2$. Then,

$$y = 2.105 + 1.2(0.703) + \frac{(1.2)(0.2)}{2!}(0.103) = 2.961,$$

correct to three decimal places.

If the four nearest values are chosen, $m = 3$, $x_0 = 1$, $y_0 = 2.105$, $\Delta y_0 = 0.703$, $\Delta^2 y_0 = 0.103$, $\Delta^3 y_0 = 0.081$, and $X = 1.2$. Therefore,

$$y = 2.105 + 1.2(0.703) + \frac{(1.2)(0.2)}{2}(0.103) + \frac{(1.2)(0.2)(-0.8)}{6}(0.081) = 2.958,$$

correct to three decimal places.

PROBLEMS

1. Compute with the aid of formulas (8-6) and (8-7) the approximate values of y corresponding to $x = 5.5$ from the data of the Example in Sec. 7. Use two and three neighboring values.

2. Extrapolate the value of y for $x = 8.2$ from the data in the Example of Sec. 7 with the aid of (a) formula (8-6), (b) formula (8-7). Use $m = 2$.

3. Compute $y'(1)$ and $y''(1)$ from the data of the Example of Sec. 7 with the aid of (8-8).

9. Lagrange's Interpolation Formula. The interpolation formulas developed in the preceding section apply only when the given set of x_i is an arithmetic progression. If this is not the case, some other type of formula must be applied.

As in Sec. 8, select the $m + 1$ pairs of observed values for which $|x - x_i|$ is as small as possible, and denote them by (x_i, y_i) where $i = 0, 1, 2, \ldots, m$. Let the mth-degree polynomials $P_k(x)$, where $k = 0, 1, 2, \ldots, m$, be defined by

$$P_k(x) = \frac{(x - x_0)(x - x_1) \ldots (x - x_m)}{x - x_k} \equiv \prod_{\substack{i=0 \\ i \neq k}}^{m} (x - x_i). \qquad (9\text{-}1)$$

Then, the coefficients A_k of the equation

$$y = \sum_{k=0}^{m} A_k P_k(x)$$

can be determined so that this equation is satisfied by each of the $m + 1$ pairs of observed values (x_i, y_i). For if $x = x_k$, then

$$A_k = \frac{y_k}{P_k(x_k)},$$

since $P_k(x_i) = 0$ if $i \neq k$. Therefore,

$$y = \sum_{k=0}^{m} \frac{y_k P_k(x)}{P_k(x_k)} \qquad (9\text{-}2)$$

is the equation of the mth-degree polynomial which passes through the $m + 1$ points whose coordinates are (x_i, y_i). If x is chosen as any value in the range of the x_i, (9-2) determines an approximate value for the corresponding y.

Equation (9-2) is known as *Lagrange's interpolation formula*. Obviously, it can be applied when the x_i are in arithmetic progression but (8-5) is preferable in that it requires less tedious calculation. Since only one mth-degree polynomial can be passed through $m + 1$ distinct points, it follows that (8-5), or its equivalent (8-6), and (9-2) are merely different forms of the same equation and will furnish the same value for y.

Example: Using the data

v	10	15	22.5	33.75	50.625	75.937
p	0.300	0.675	1.519	3.417	7.689	17.300

apply Lagrange's formula to find the value of p corresponding to $v = 21$.

If the two neighboring pairs of observed values are chosen so that $m = 1$,

$$p = 0.675\frac{21 - 22.5}{15 - 22.5} + 1.519\frac{21 - 15}{22.5 - 15} = 1.350,$$

correct to three decimal places.

If the three nearest values are chosen so that $m = 2$,

$$p = 0.3\frac{(21 - 15)(21 - 22.5)}{(10 - 15)(10 - 22.5)} + 0.675\frac{(21 - 10)(21 - 22.5)}{(15 - 10)(15 - 22.5)}$$

$$+ 1.519\frac{(21 - 10)(21 - 15)}{(22.5 - 10)(22.5 - 15)} = 1.323,$$

correct to three decimal places.

PROBLEMS

1. Using the data of the Example in Sec. 9, find an approximate value for p when $v = 30$. Use $m = 1$ and $m = 2$.

2. Use $m = 1$, 2, and 3 in formula (8-6) to find an approximate value of θ when $t = 2.3$, given

t	0	1	2	3	4	5	6	7	8
θ	60.00	51.66	44.46	38.28	32.94	28.32	24.42	21.06	18.06

3. Given the data

x	0.16	0.4	1.0	2.5	6.25	15.625
y	2	2.210	2.421	2.661	2.929	3.222

find an approximate value of y corresponding to $x = 2$. Use formula (9-2) with $m = 1$ and $m = 2$.

4. Given the data

C	19	20	21	22	23	24	25
H	81.00	90.25	100.00	110.25	121.00	132.25	144.00

find an approximate value of H when $C = 21.6$. Use formulas (8-6) and (8-7) with $m = 1$, 2, and 3.

10. Empirical Formulas. A given set of discrete data can be represented analytically in infinitely many ways. Such analytic representations are called *empirical formulas*, and the choice of the functional form for an empirical formula ordinarily depends on the use to be made of the formula. Thus, if a given set of data is to be represented by a function $f(x)$ which enters in the differential equation

$$L(u) = f(x),$$

the form of $f(x)$ may well depend on the ease with which this equation can be solved. For some types of differential operators L it may be wise to take $f(x)$ as an algebraic polynomial, in others as an exponential, and so on. Because of the commonness of algebraic and trigonometric polynomials in applications, we confine our discussion of empirical formulas primarily to these two types.

The first step usually taken by an experimenter in appraising a set of observed values (x_i, y_i) is to plot them on some coordinate paper and draw a curve through the plotted points. If the points (x_i, y_i), when plotted on a rectangular coordinate paper, lie approximately on a straight line, he assumes that the equation $y = mx + b$ represents the relationship. To determine the constants m and b, the slope and the y intercept may be read off the graph or they may be calculated by solving two linear equations for m and b got by substituting the coordinates of two judiciously chosen points on $y = mx + b$.

If the plot of points on a logarithmic coordinate paper indicates that they lie on a straight line, the desired relationship has the form

$$y = ax^m,$$

for on taking logarithms, we get

$$\log y = \log a + m \log x,$$

and if coordinate axes X, Y are marked so that $\log y = Y$ and $\log x = X$, we get a linear equation

$$Y = \log a + mX.$$

Again the constants a and m can be either read off the graph or computed by solving a pair of linear equations for m and $\log a$.

Similarly, the data can be represented by an exponential function

$$y = a10^{mx}$$

if the values (x_i, y_i) when plotted on a semilogarithmic paper fall on a straight line, for on taking logarithms to the base 10, we get

$$\log y = \log a + mx,$$

which is linear in $\log y$ and x.

When none of these simple functional relationships fits the data, one may determine, with the aid of Sec. 7, if the data can be fitted by a polynomial. It should be stressed, however, that ordinarily the choice of an empirical formula is governed by whatever uses are to be made of it. Once a formula is chosen, the parameters entering in it (such as the coefficients in the polynomial representation) can be determined by imposing some criterion for the goodness of fit of the data by the chosen function. The method of least squares, presented in the next section, provides one of the most commonly used of such criteria.

PROBLEMS

1. Plot the following data on a rectangular, logarithmic, or semilogarithmic paper to determine the approximate functional relationships between y and x.

(a)

x	3	4	5	6	7	8	9	10	11	12
y	5	5.6	6	6.4	7	7.5	8.2	8.6	9	9.5

(b)

x	1	2	3	4	5	6	7	8	9
y	2.5	3.5	4.3	5	5.6	6.2	6.6	7.1	7.5

(c)

x	1	2	3	4	5	6	7	8
y	0.5	0.8	1.2	1.9	3	4.8	7.5	11.9

2. Verify that the data in Probs. 2, 3, and 4 in Sec. 9 may be approximated by the following types of functions: $\theta = a10^{mt}$, $y = ax^m$, $H = a_0 + a_1C + a_2C^2$, respectively. Determine the parameters graphically or analytically.

11. The Method of Least Squares. We saw in Sec. 7 that the $m + 1$ coefficients in the polynomial

$$y = a_0 + a_1x + \cdots + a_mx^m \qquad (11\text{-}1)$$

can always be determined so that a given set of $m + 1$ points (x_i, y_i), where the xs are unequal, lies on the curve (11-1). When the x_i are equally spaced, the desired polynomial is determined by the formula (8-5) and, in the more general case, by (9-2).

When the number of points is large, the degree m of the polynomial (11-1) is high, and an attempt to represent the data exactly by (11-1) not only is laborious but may be foolish, for the experimental data invariably contain observational errors and it may be more sensible to represent the data approximately by some function $y = f(x)$ which contains a few unknown parameters. These parameters can then be determined so that the curve $y = f(x)$ fits the data in "the best possible way." The criteria as to what constitutes "the best possible way" are, of course, arbitrary.

For example, we may attempt to fit the set of plotted points in Fig. 12 by the straight line

$$y = a_1 + a_2 x$$

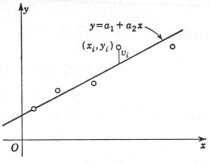

and choose the parameters a_1 and a_2 so that the sum of the squares of the vertical deviations of the plotted points from this line is as small as possible.

Fig. 12

More generally, if we choose to represent a set of data (x_i, y_i), where $i = 1, 2, \ldots, n$, by some relationship $y = f(x)$, containing r unknown parameters $a_1, a_2, \ldots, a_r$, and form the deviations (or the *residuals*, as they are also called)

$$v_i = f(x_i) - y_i, \tag{11-2}$$

the sum of the squares of the deviations

$$S \equiv \sum_{i=1}^{n} v_i^2 = \sum_{i=1}^{n} [f(x_i) - y_i]^2 \tag{11-3}$$

is clearly a function of $a_1, a_2, \ldots, a_r$. We can then determine the as so that S is a minimum.

Now, if $S(a_1, a_2, \ldots, a_r)$ is a minimum, then at the point in question

$$\frac{\partial S}{\partial a_1} = 0, \qquad \frac{\partial S}{\partial a_2} = 0, \qquad \ldots, \qquad \frac{\partial S}{\partial a_r} = 0. \tag{11-4}$$

The set of r equations (11-4), called *normal equations*, serves to determine the r unknown as in $y = f(x)$. This particular criterion of the "best fit" of data is known as the *principle of least squares*, and the method of determining the unknown parameters with its aid is called the *method of least squares*. It was introduced and fully developed by Gauss [1] when he was a youth of seventeen!

We indicate the construction of the normal equations first by supposing that $y = f(x)$ is a linear function

$$y = a_1 + a_2 x. \tag{11-5}$$

---

[1] The criterion of least squares plays a fundamental role in the approximation of a suitably restricted function $f(x)$ by a linear combination of orthogonal functions. As is shown in Chap. 2, Sec. 23, the partial sums of Fourier series give the best fit in the sense of least squares. It should be noted, however, that the polynomials giving the best fit to $f(x)$ in the sense of least squares, in general, are *not* the partial sums of Maclaurin's or Taylor's series for $f(x)$.

The residuals (11-2) for (11-5) are

$$v_i = (a_1 + a_2 x_i) - y_i,$$

so that
$$S = \sum_{i=1}^{n} v_i^2$$

$$= (a_1 + a_2 x_1 - y_1)^2 + (a_1 + a_2 x_2 - y_2)^2$$
$$+ \cdots + (a_1 + a_2 x_n - y_n)^2.$$

On differentiating S with respect to a_1 and a_2, we deduce two equations:

$$\frac{\partial S}{\partial a_1} = 2(a_1 + a_2 x_1 - y_1) + 2(a_1 + a_2 x_2 - y_2)$$
$$+ \cdots + 2(a_1 + a_2 x_n - y_n) = 0,$$

$$\frac{\partial S}{\partial a_2} = 2x_1(a_1 + a_2 x_1 - y_1) + 2x_2(a_1 + a_2 x_2 - y_2)$$
$$+ \cdots + 2x_n(a_1 + a_2 x_n - y_n) = 0.$$

If we divide out the factor 2 and collect the coefficients of a_1 and a_2, we get

$$na_1 + \left(\sum_{i=1}^{n} x_i\right) a_2 = \sum_{i=1}^{n} y_i,$$

$$\left(\sum_{i=1}^{n} x_i\right) a_1 + \left(\sum_{i=1}^{n} x_i^2\right) a_2 = \sum_{i=1}^{n} x_i y_i. \tag{11-6}$$

These equations can be easily solved for a_1 and a_2.

Example 1. We illustrate the use of Eqs. (11-6) by calculating the coefficients in $y = a_1 + a_2 x$ to fit the following data:

x	1	2	3	4
y	1.7	1.8	2.3	3.2

In this case $n = 4$, and since

$$\sum_{i=1}^{4} x_i = 1 + 2 + 3 + 4 = 10,$$

$$\sum_{i=1}^{4} y_i = 1.7 + 1.8 + 2.3 + 3.2 = 9,$$

$$\sum_{i=1}^{4} x_i^2 = 1 + 4 + 9 + 16 = 30,$$

$$\sum_{i=1}^{4} x_i y_i = 1.7 + 2(1.8) + 3(2.3) + 4(3.2) = 25,$$

the system (11-6) reads

$$4a_1 + 10a_2 = 9,$$

$$10a_1 + 30a_2 = 25.$$

Solving for a_1 and a_2, we get $a_1 = 1$, $a_2 = \frac{1}{2}$, so that the desired straight line fitting the data in the sense of least squares is $y = 1 + \frac{1}{2}x$.

We suppose next that $y = f(x)$ is a polynomial

$$y = a_1 + a_2x + a_3x^2 + \cdots + a_rx^{r-1}$$

$$= \sum_{j=1}^{r} a_jx^{j-1}. \tag{11-7}$$

The residuals v_i this time are

$$v_i = \sum_{j=1}^{r} a_jx_i^{j-1} - y_i. \tag{11-8}$$

Since

$$S = \sum_{i=1}^{n} v_i^2,$$

Eqs. (11-4) can be written as

$$\frac{\partial S}{\partial a_k} = 2 \sum_{i=1}^{n} v_i \frac{\partial v_i}{\partial a_k} = 0, \qquad k = 1, 2, \ldots, r. \tag{11-9}$$

From (11-8),

$$\frac{\partial v_i}{\partial a_k} = x_i^{k-1},$$

so that, on dividing out the factor 2, we can write the normal equations (11-9) as

$$\sum_{i=1}^{n} v_ix_i^{k-1} = 0. \tag{11-10}$$

The substitution from (11-8) in (11-10) yields

$$\sum_{i=1}^{n} \left(\sum_{j=1}^{r} a_jx_i^{j-1} - y_i \right) x_i^{k-1} = 0,$$

and on collecting the coefficients of the a_j, we get a set of r linear equations

$$\sum_{j=1}^{r} \left(\sum_{i=1}^{n} x_i^{j+k-2} \right) a_j = \sum_{i=1}^{n} x_i^{k-1}y_i, \qquad k = 1, 2, \ldots, r, \tag{11-11}$$

for $a_1, a_2, \ldots, a_r$.

We illustrate the use of these equations by two examples.

Example 2. Let the data in Example 1 be fitted by $y = a_1 + a_2 x + a_3 x^2$. Then

$$v_i = a_1 + a_2 x_i + a_3 x_i^2 - y_i$$

and

$$\frac{\partial v_i}{\partial a_1} = 1, \qquad \frac{\partial v_i}{\partial a_2} = x_i, \qquad \frac{\partial v_i}{\partial a_3} = x_i^2.$$

The normal equations

$$\sum_{i=1}^{4} v_i \frac{\partial v_i}{\partial a_k} = 0, \qquad k = 1, 2, 3,$$

are

$$\sum_{i=1}^{4} (a_1 + a_2 x_i + a_3 x_i^2 - y_i) \cdot 1 = 0,$$

$$\sum_{i=1}^{4} (a_1 + a_2 x_i + a_3 x_i^2 - y_i) x_i = 0,$$

$$\sum_{i=1}^{4} (a_1 + a_2 x_i + a_3 x_i^2 - y_i) x_i^2 = 0.$$

If the coefficients of the a_j are collected and the normal equations put in the form (11-11), one obtains the three equations

$$4a_1 + \left(\sum_{i=1}^{4} x_i \right) a_2 + \left(\sum_{i=1}^{4} x_i^2 \right) a_3 = \sum_{i=1}^{4} y_i,$$

$$\left(\sum_{i=1}^{4} x_i \right) a_1 + \left(\sum_{i=1}^{4} x_i^2 \right) a_2 + \left(\sum_{i=1}^{4} x_i^3 \right) a_3 = \sum_{i=1}^{4} x_i y_i,$$

$$\left(\sum_{i=1}^{4} x_i^2 \right) a_1 + \left(\sum_{i=1}^{4} x_i^3 \right) a_2 + \left(\sum_{i=1}^{4} x_i^4 \right) a_3 = \sum_{i=1}^{4} x_i^2 y_i.$$

Now,

$$\sum_{i=1}^{4} x_i = 1 + 2 + 3 + 4 = 10, \qquad \sum_{i=1}^{4} x_i^2 = 1 + 4 + 9 + 16 = 30,$$

$$\sum_{i=1}^{4} x_i y_i = 1.7 + 3.6 + 6.9 + 12.8 = 25, \text{ etc.}$$

The equations become

$$4a_1 + 10a_2 + 30a_3 = 9,$$

$$10a_1 + 30a_2 + 100a_3 = 25,$$

$$30a_1 + 100a_2 + 354a_3 = 80.8;$$

and the solutions are $a_1 = 2$, $a_2 = -0.5$, $a_3 = 0.2$.

Example 3. Let us apply the method of least squares to fit the data

x	1	2	3	4	5	6	7	8
y	2.105	2.808	3.614	4.604	5.857	7.451	9.467	11.985

by the polynomial $y = a_1 + a_2 x + a_3 x^2 + a_4 x^3$.

In this case $n = 8$ and Eqs. (11-11) yield four normal equations obtained by setting $k = 1, 2, 3, 4$.   They are

$$8a_1 + \left(\sum_{i=1}^{8} x_i\right) a_2 + \left(\sum_{i=1}^{8} x_i^2\right) a_3 + \left(\sum_{i=1}^{8} x_i^3\right) a_4 = \sum_{i=1}^{8} y_i,$$

$$\left(\sum_{i=1}^{8} x_i\right) a_1 + \left(\sum_{i=1}^{8} x_i^2\right) a_2 + \left(\sum_{i=1}^{8} x_i^3\right) a_3 + \left(\sum_{i=1}^{8} x_i^4\right) a_4 = \sum_{i=1}^{8} x_i y_i,$$

$$\left(\sum_{i=1}^{8} x_i^2\right) a_1 + \left(\sum_{i=1}^{8} x_i^3\right) a_2 + \left(\sum_{i=1}^{8} x_i^4\right) a_3 + \left(\sum_{i=1}^{8} x_i^5\right) a_4 = \sum_{i=1}^{8} x_i^2 y_i,$$

$$\left(\sum_{i=1}^{8} x_i^3\right) a_1 + \left(\sum_{i=1}^{8} x_i^4\right) a_2 + \left(\sum_{i=1}^{8} x_i^5\right) a_3 + \left(\sum_{i=1}^{8} x_i^6\right) a_4 = \sum_{i=1}^{8} x_i^3 y_i.$$

From the form of the coefficients of the a_k, it is seen that it is convenient to make a table of the powers of the x_i and to form the sums Σx_i^j and $\Sigma x_i^j y_i$ before attempting to write down the equations in explicit form.

x_i	x_i^2	x_i^3	x_i^4	x_i^5	x_i^6
1	1	1	1	1	1
2	4	8	16	32	64
3	9	27	81	243	729
4	16	64	256	1,024	4,096
5	25	125	625	3,125	15,625
6	36	216	1,296	7,776	46,656
7	49	343	2,401	16,807	117,649
8	64	512	4,096	32,768	262,144
Σx_i^j 36	204	1,296	8,772	61,776	446,964

x_i	y_i	$x_i y_i$	$x_i^2 y_i$	$x_i^3 y_i$
1	2.105	2.105	2.105	2.105
2	2.808	5.616	11.232	22.464
3	3.614	10.842	32.526	97.578
4	4.604	18.416	73.664	294.656
5	5.857	29.285	146.425	732.125
6	7.451	44.706	268.236	1,609.416
7	9.467	66.269	463.883	3,247.181
8	11.985	95.880	767.040	6,136.320
$\Sigma x_i^j y_i$	47.891	273.119	1,765.111	12,141.845

When the values given in the tables are inserted, the normal equations become

$$8a_1 + 36a_2 + 204a_3 + 1{,}296a_4 = 47.891,$$
$$36a_1 + 204a_2 + 1{,}296a_3 + 8{,}772a_4 = 273.119,$$
$$204a_1 + 1{,}296a_2 + 8{,}772a_3 + 61{,}776a_4 = 1{,}765.111,$$
$$1{,}296a_1 + 8{,}772a_2 + 61{,}776a_3 + 446{,}964a_4 = 12{,}141.845.$$

The solutions are

$$a_1 = 1.426, \qquad a_2 = 0.693, \qquad a_3 = -0.028, \qquad a_4 = 0.013.$$

Therefore, the equation, as determined by the method of least squares, is

$$y = 1.426 + 0.693x - 0.028x^2 + 0.013x^3.$$

The normal equations (11-11), corresponding to the polynomial representation of data, are linear in the coefficients a_i. They need not be linear in the unknown parameters if the function $y = f(x)$ is not a polynomial in x. In this event the solution of the system (11-4) may prove difficult, and one may be obliged to seek an approximate solution by replacing the exact residuals (11-2) by approximate residuals which are linear in the unknowns. This is accomplished by expanding $y = f(x)$, treated as a function of $a_1, a_2, \ldots, a_r$, in Taylor's series in terms of $a_i - \bar{a}_i \equiv \Delta a_i$, where the $\bar{a}_i$ are approximate values of the a_i. The values of $\bar{a}_i$ may be obtained by graphical means or by solving any r of the equations $y_i = f(x_i)$. The expansion gives

$$y = f(x, a_1, \ldots, a_r) \equiv f(x, \bar{a}_1 + \Delta a_1, \ldots, \bar{a}_r + \Delta a_r)$$

$$= f(x, \bar{a}_1, \ldots, \bar{a}_r) + \sum_{k=1}^{r} \frac{\partial f}{\partial \bar{a}_k} \Delta a_k$$

$$+ \frac{1}{2!} \sum_{j,k=1}^{r} \frac{\partial^2 f}{\partial \bar{a}_j \, \partial \bar{a}_k} \Delta a_j \, \Delta a_k + \cdots, \qquad (11\text{-}12)$$

where

$$\frac{\partial f}{\partial \bar{a}_k} \equiv \frac{\partial f}{\partial a_k} \bigg|_{a_k = \bar{a}_k}, \qquad \frac{\partial^2 f}{\partial \bar{a}_j \, \partial \bar{a}_k} \equiv \frac{\partial^2 f}{\partial a_j \, \partial a_k} \bigg|_{\substack{a_j = \bar{a}_j \\ a_k = \bar{a}_k}}, \text{ etc.}$$

Assuming that the $\bar{a}_i$ are chosen so that the Δa_i are small, the terms of degree higher than the first can be neglected and (11-12) becomes

$$y = f(x, \bar{a}_1, \ldots, \bar{a}_r) + \sum_{k=1}^{r} \frac{\partial f}{\partial \bar{a}_k} \Delta a_k.$$

The n observation equations are then replaced by the n approximate equations

$$\bar{y}_i = f(x_i, \bar{a}_i, \ldots, \bar{a}_r) + \sum_{k=1}^{r} \frac{\partial f}{\partial \bar{a}_k} \Delta a_k. \qquad (11\text{-}13)$$

If (11-13) is used, the residuals v_i will be linear in the Δa_k, and hence the resulting conditions, which become

$$\frac{\partial S}{\partial(\Delta a_k)} = 0, \qquad k = 1, 2, \ldots, r, \qquad (11\text{-}14)$$

also will be linear in the Δa_k. Equations (11-14) are called the normal equations in this case.

We illustrate the use of Eqs. (11-14) in Example 4.

Example 4. We seek to determine the constants k and a in the formula $\theta = ka^t$ chosen to represent the following data:

t	1	2	3	4
θ	51.66	44.46	38.28	32.94

The determination of k and a in this problem can be reduced to the solution of two linear equations, for if we write $\theta = ka^t$ in the form

$$\theta = k10^{bt}$$

then on taking logarithms to the base 10, we get

$$\log \theta = \log k + bt.$$

Setting $\log \theta = y$ and $\log k = K$, we get

$$y = K + bt \qquad (11\text{-}15)$$

which is linear in K and b. These constants can be determined by the procedure described above, which leads to the solution of a pair of linear equations.[1]

To illustrate the use of formulas (11-12) to (11-14), we follow a more laborious route which gives an approximation to the original equation.

When the values recorded in the table are plotted on semilogarithmic paper, it is found that $k = 60$ and $a = 10^{-0.065} = 0.86$, approximately. This suggests using $k_0 = 60$ and $a_0 = 0.9$ as the first approximations. The first two terms of the expansion in Taylor's series in terms of $\Delta k = k - 60$ and $\Delta a = a - 0.9$ are

$$\theta = 60(0.9)^t + \left(\frac{\partial\theta}{\partial k}\right)_{\substack{k=60\\a=0.9}} \Delta k + \left(\frac{\partial\theta}{\partial a}\right)_{\substack{k=60\\a=0.9}} \Delta a$$

$$= 60(0.9)^t + (0.9)^t \Delta k + 60t(0.9)^{t-1} \Delta a.$$

If the values (t_i, θ_i) are substituted in this equation, four equations result, namely,

$$\theta_i = 60(0.9)^{t_i} + (0.9)^{t_i} \Delta k + 60t_i(0.9)^{t_i-1} \Delta a, \qquad i = 1, 2, 3, 4.$$

The problem of obtaining from these four equations the values of Δk and Δa, which furnish the desired values of θ_i, is precisely the same as in the case in which the original equation is linear in its constants. The residual equations are

$$v_i = (0.9)^{t_i} \Delta k + 60t_i(0.9)^{t_i-1} \Delta a + 60(0.9)^{t_i} - \theta_i, \qquad i = 1, 2, 3, 4.$$

[1] However, the approximation obtained by this means does not give an approximation to the *original* equation in the sense of least squares.

Therefore

$$S \equiv \sum_{i=1}^{4} v_i^2 = \sum_{i=1}^{4} [(0.9)^{t_i} \Delta k + 60 t_i (0.9)^{t_i - 1} \Delta a + 60(0.9)^{t_i} - \theta_i]^2,$$

and the normal equations

$$\frac{\partial S}{\partial (\Delta k)} = 0 \quad \text{and} \quad \frac{\partial S}{\partial (\Delta a)} = 0$$

become

$$2 \sum_{i=1}^{4} [0.9^{t_i} \Delta k + 60 t_i (0.9)^{t_i - 1} \Delta a + 60(0.9)^{t_i} - \theta_i] 0.9^{t_i} = 0$$

and

$$2 \sum_{i=1}^{4} [0.9^{t_i} \Delta k + 60 t_i (0.9)^{t_i - 1} \Delta a + 60(0.9)^{t_i} - \theta_i] 60 t_i (0.9)^{t_i - 1} = 0.$$

When these equations are written in the form

$$p \, \Delta k + q \, \Delta a = r,$$

with all common factors divided out, they are

$$\sum_{i=1}^{4} (0.9)^{2t_i} \Delta k + 60 \sum_{i=1}^{4} t_i (0.9)^{2t_i - 1} \Delta a = \sum_{i=1}^{4} \theta_i (0.9)^{t_i} - 60 \sum_{i=1}^{4} (0.9)^{2t_i}$$

and

$$\sum_{i=1}^{4} t_i (0.9)^{2t_i - 1} \Delta k + 60 \sum_{i=1}^{4} t_i^2 (0.9)^{2t_i - 2} \Delta a = \sum_{i=1}^{4} \theta_i t_i (0.9)^{t_i - 1} - 60 \sum_{i=1}^{4} t_i (0.9)^{2t_i - 1}.$$

As in Example 3, the coefficients are computed most conveniently by the use of a table.

t_i	1	2	3	4	Totals
$(0.9)^{t_i}$	0.9	0.81	0.729	0.6561	
$(0.9)^{2t_i}$	0.81	0.6561	0.531441	0.43046721	2.42800821
$t_i(0.9)^{2t_i - 1}$	0.9	1.458	1.77147	1.9131876	6.0426576
$t_i^2(0.9)^{2t_i - 2}$	1	3.24	5.9049	8.503056	18.647956
$(\theta_i)(0.9)^{t_i}$	46.494	36.0126	27.90612	21.611934	132.024654
$(\theta_i t_i)(0.9)^{t_i - 1}$	51.66	80.028	93.0204	96.05304	320.76144

Substituting the values of the sums from the table gives

$$2.42800821 \, \Delta k + 362.559456 \, \Delta a = 132.024654 - 145.6804926$$

and

$$6.0426576 \, \Delta k + 1{,}118.87736 \, \Delta a = 320.76144 - 362.559456.$$

Reducing all the numbers to four decimal places gives the following equations to solve for Δk and Δa:

$$2.4280\ \Delta k + 362.5595\ \Delta a = -13.6558,$$

$$6.0427\ \Delta k + 1{,}118.8774\ \Delta a = -41.7980.$$

The solutions are

$$\Delta k = -0.238 \quad \text{and} \quad \Delta a = -0.036.$$

Hence, the required equation is

$$\theta = 59.762(0.864)^t.$$

PROBLEMS

1. Apply the method of least squares to find the constants in $y = a_1 + a_2x + a_3x^2$ to fit the data

x	1	2	3	4	5	6
y	3.13	3.76	6.94	12.62	20.86	31.53

2. Determine by the method of least squares the constants a and n in $p = av^n$ to fit the following data by writing the equation in the form

$$\log p = n \log v + \log a.$$

v	10	15	22.5	33.7	50.6	75.9
p	0.300	0.675	1.519	3.417	7.689	17.300

Hint: Set $\log p = y$, $\log v = x$, and determine the constants in the resulting linear equation.

3. Compare the result of Example 4 with the calculation of the constants in (11-15).

12. Harmonic Analysis.   The problem of representing a suitable periodic function in a trigonometric series was considered in some detail in Chap. 2.   In this section we give a brief discussion of the problem of fitting a finite trigonometric sum to a set of observed values (x_i,y_i).   Let the set of observed values

$$(x_0,y_0),\ (x_1,y_1),\ \ldots,\ (x_{2n-1},y_{2n-1}),\ (x_{2n},y_{2n}),\ \ldots$$

be such that the values of y start repeating with y_{2n} (that is, $y_{2n} = y_0$, $y_{2n+1} = y_1$, etc.).   It will be assumed that the x_i are equally spaced, that $x_0 = 0$, and that $x_{2n} = 2\pi$.   [If $x_0 \neq 0$ and the period is c instead of 2π, the variable can be changed by setting

$$\theta_i = \frac{2\pi}{c}(x_i - x_0).$$

The discussion would then be carried through for θ_i and y_i in place of the

x_i and y_i used below.] Under these assumptions

$$x_i = i\frac{2\pi}{2n} = \frac{i\pi}{n}.$$

The trigonometric polynomial

$$y = A_0 + \sum_{k=1}^{n} A_k \cos kx + \sum_{k=1}^{n-1} B_k \sin kx \qquad (12\text{-}1)$$

contains the $2n$ unknown constants

$$A_0, A_1, A_2, \ldots, A_n, B_1, B_2, \ldots, B_{n-1},$$

which can be determined so that (12-1) will pass through the $2n$ given points (x_i, y_i) by solving the $2n$ simultaneous equations

$$y_i = A_0 + \sum_{k=1}^{n} A_k \cos kx_i + \sum_{k=1}^{n-1} B_k \sin kx_i, \qquad i = 0, 1, 2, \ldots, 2n - 1.$$

Since $x_i = i\pi/n$, these equations become

$$y_i = A_0 + \sum_{k=1}^{n} A_k \cos\frac{ik\pi}{n} + \sum_{k=1}^{n-1} B_k \sin\frac{ik\pi}{n},$$

$$i = 0, 1, 2, \ldots, 2n - 1. \qquad (12\text{-}2)$$

The solution of Eqs. (12-2) is much simplified by means of a scheme somewhat similar to that used in determining the Fourier coefficients. Multiplying both sides of each equation by the coefficient of A_0 (that is, by unity) and adding the results give

$$\sum_{i=0}^{2n-1} y_i = 2nA_0 + \sum_{k=1}^{n}\left(\sum_{i=0}^{2n-1}\cos\frac{ik\pi}{n}\right)A_k + \sum_{k=1}^{n-1}\left(\sum_{i=0}^{2n-1}\sin\frac{ik\pi}{n}\right)B_k.$$

It can be established that (cf. Example 1, Sec. 17, Chap. 2)

$$\sum_{i=0}^{2n-1}\cos\frac{ik\pi}{n} = 0, \qquad k = 1, 2, \ldots, n$$

and

$$\sum_{i=0}^{2n-1}\sin\frac{ik\pi}{n} = 0, \qquad k = 1, 2, \ldots, n - 1.$$

Therefore,

$$2nA_0 = \sum_{i=0}^{2n-1} y_i. \qquad (12\text{-}3)$$

Multiplying both sides of each equation in (12-2) by the coefficient of A_j

in it, and adding the results, gives

$$\sum_{i=0}^{2n-1} y_i \cos \frac{ij\pi}{n} = \sum_{k=1}^{n} \left(\sum_{i=0}^{2n-1} \cos \frac{ik\pi}{n} \cos \frac{ij\pi}{n} \right) A_k$$

$$+ \sum_{k=1}^{n-1} \left(\sum_{i=0}^{2n-1} \sin \frac{ik\pi}{n} \cos \frac{ij\pi}{n} \right) B_k$$

for $j = 1, 2, \ldots, n - 1$. But

$$\sum_{i=0}^{2n-1} \cos \frac{ik\pi}{n} \cos \frac{ij\pi}{n} = 0, \qquad \text{if } k \neq j,$$

$$= n, \qquad \text{if } k = j,$$

and
$$\sum_{i=0}^{2n-1} \sin \frac{ik\pi}{n} \cos \frac{ij\pi}{n} = 0$$

for all values of k. Therefore,

$$nA_j = \sum_{i=0}^{2n-1} y_i \cos \frac{ij\pi}{n}, \qquad j = 1, 2, \ldots, n - 1. \tag{12-4}$$

To determine the coefficient of A_n the procedure is precisely the same, but

$$\sum_{i=0}^{2n-1} \cos \frac{ik\pi}{n} \cos i\pi = 0, \qquad \text{if } k \neq n,$$

$$= 2n, \qquad \text{if } k = n.$$

Hence,
$$2nA_n = \sum_{i=0}^{2n-1} y_i \cos i\pi. \tag{12-5}$$

Similarly, on multiplying both sides of each equation of (12-2) by the coefficient of B_k in it and adding, one finds that

$$nB_j = \sum_{i=0}^{2n-1} y_i \sin \frac{ij\pi}{n}, \qquad j = 1, 2, \ldots, n - 1. \tag{12-6}$$

Equations (12-3) to (12-6) give the constants in (12-1). A compact schematic arrangement is often used to simplify the labor of evaluating these constants. It will be illustrated in the so-called "6-ordinate" case, that is, when $2n = 6$. The method is based on the equations that determine the constants, together with relations such as

$$\sin \frac{\pi}{n} = \sin \frac{(n-1)\pi}{n} = -\sin \frac{(n+1)\pi}{n} = -\sin \frac{(2n-1)\pi}{n},$$

$$\cos \frac{\pi}{n} = -\cos \frac{(n-1)\pi}{n} = -\cos \frac{(n+1)\pi}{n} = \cos \frac{(2n-1)\pi}{n}.$$

Six-ordinate Scheme. Here, $2n = 6$; the given points are (x_i, y_i), where $x_i = i\pi/3$ $(i = 0, 1, 2, 3, 4, 5)$; and Eq. (12-1) becomes

$$y = A_0 + A_1 \cos x + A_2 \cos 2x + A_3 \cos 3x + B_1 \sin x + B_2 \sin 2x.$$

Make the following table of definitions:

	$y_0\ y_1\ y_2$	$v_0\ v_1$	$w_0\ w_1$
	$y_3\ y_4\ y_5$	v_2	w_2
Sum.....	$v_0\ v_1\ v_2$	$p_0\ p_1$	$r_0\ r_1$
Difference	$w_0\ w_1\ w_2$	q_1	s_1

It can be checked easily that Eqs. (12-3) to (12-6), with $n = 3$, become

$$6A_0 = p_0 + p_1, \qquad 3A_1 = r_0 + \tfrac{1}{2}s_1, \qquad 3A_2 = p_0 - \tfrac{1}{2}p_1,$$

$$6A_3 = r_0 - s_1, \qquad 3B_1 = \frac{\sqrt{3}}{2}\,r_1, \qquad 3B_2 = \frac{\sqrt{3}}{2}\,q_1.$$

Example: In particular, suppose that the given points are

x	0	$\dfrac{\pi}{3}$	$\dfrac{2\pi}{3}$	π	$\dfrac{4\pi}{3}$	$\dfrac{5\pi}{3}$	2π
y	1.0	1.4	1.9	1.7	1.5	1.2	1.0

Upon using these values of y in the table of definitions above,

$$
\begin{array}{ccc}
1.0 & 1.4 & 1.9 \\
1.7 & 1.5 & 1.2
\end{array}
$$

$$
\begin{array}{lll}
v_0 = 2.7 & v_1 = 2.9 & v_2 = 3.1 \\
w_0 = -0.7 & w_1 = -0.1 & w_2 = 0.7
\end{array}
$$

$$
\begin{array}{cccc}
2.7 & 2.9 & -0.7 & -0.1 \\
    & 3.1 &   & 0.7
\end{array}
$$

$$
\begin{array}{llll}
p_0 = 2.7 & p_1 = 6.0 & r_0 = -0.7 & r_1 = 0.6 \\
          & q_1 = -0.2 &   & s_1 = -0.8
\end{array}
$$

Therefore, the equations determining the values of the constants are

$$
\begin{array}{lll}
6A_0 = 2.7 + 6.0 = 8.7 & \text{and} & A_0 = 1.45, \\
3A_1 = -0.7 - 0.4 = -1.1 & \text{and} & A_1 = -0.37, \\
3A_2 = 2.7 - 3.0 = -0.3 & \text{and} & A_2 = -0.10, \\
6A_3 = -0.7 + 0.8 = 0.1 & \text{and} & A_3 = 0.02,
\end{array}
$$

$$3B_1 = \frac{\sqrt{3}}{2}(0.6) = 0.3\sqrt{3} \qquad \text{and} \qquad B_1 = 0.17,$$

$$3B_2 = \frac{\sqrt{3}}{2}(-0.2) = -0.1\sqrt{3} \qquad \text{and} \qquad B_2 = -0.06.$$

Hence, the curve of type (12-1) that fits the given data is

$$y = 1.45 - 0.37 \cos x - 0.10 \cos 2x + 0.02 \cos 3x + 0.17 \sin x - 0.06 \sin 2x.$$

A convenient check upon the computations is furnished by the relations

$$A_0 + A_1 + A_2 + A_3 = y_0 \quad \text{and} \quad B_1 + B_2 = \frac{\sqrt{3}}{3}(y_1 - y_5).$$

Substituting the values found above in the left-hand members gives

$$1.45 - 0.37 - 0.10 + 0.02 = 1.0 \quad \text{and} \quad 0.17 - 0.06 = 0.11,$$

which check with the values of the right-hand members.

Similar tables can be constructed for 8-ordinates, 12-ordinates, etc.

NUMERICAL INTEGRATION OF DIFFERENTIAL EQUATIONS

13. Numerical Integration. The reader is familiar with the interpretation of the definite integral $\int_a^b f(x)\, dx$ as the area under the curve $y = f(x)$ between the ordinates $x = a$ and $x = b$. This interpretation underlies the construction of formulas for numerical integration contained in this section.

It will be recalled that if the function $f(x)$ is such that its indefinite integral can be obtained, then the fundamental theorem of integral calculus provides an easy means for evaluating the definite integral.[1] However when $f(x)$ does not have an indefinite integral expressible in terms of known functions, or when the values of $f(x)$ are given in tabular form, formulas for numerical integration are generally used to obtain an approximate value of the integral.

Formulas for numerical integration, or *mechanical quadrature*, are obtained by replacing the function $f(x)$ specified at a given number of points in the interval (a,b) by a polynomial (8-5) or (9-2), depending on whether the values of x are equally or unequally spaced.

If the values of $y = f(x)$ are known at $m + 1$ points x_i, where $i = 0, 1, 2, \ldots, m$, which are spaced h units apart, an approximate value of the integral $\int_{x_0}^{x_m} f(x)\, dx$ can be computed by substituting in the integrand an approximate polynomial representation of $y = f(x)$ given by (8-5) or, equivalently, (8-6). We thus get for equally spaced values x_i

$$\int_0^m y\, dX = \int_0^m \left[y_0 + X\, \Delta y_0 + \frac{X(X-1)}{2!} \Delta^2 y_0 \right.$$
$$\left. + \cdots + \frac{X(X-1) \ldots (X-m+1)}{m!} \Delta^m y_0 \right] dX, \quad (13\text{-}1)$$

[1] See Chap. 3, Sec. 13. The evaluation of difficult integrals by power series is discussed in Chap. 2, Sec. 10.

where X is the dimensionless variable defined by

$$X = \frac{x - x_0}{h},$$ (13-2)

and $X = m$ for

$$x_m = x_0 + mh.$$ (13-3)

If $m = 1$, formula (13-1) yields

$$\int_0^1 y \, dX = \int_0^1 (y_0 + X \, \Delta y_0) \, dX = y_0 + \frac{\Delta y_0}{2} = y_0 + \frac{y_1 - y_0}{2} = \frac{1}{2}(y_0 + y_1).$$

But from (13-2) $dX = dx/h$, and on recalling (13-3), we see that this formula can be written as

$$\int_{x_0}^{x_1} y \, dx = \frac{h}{2}(y_0 + y_1).$$ (13-4)

Since y_0 is the ordinate of $y = f(x)$ at $x = x_0$ and y_1 is the ordinate at $x = x_1$, the right-hand member in (13-4) represents the area of the first trapezoid shown in Fig. 13.   The choice of $m = 1$ in the calculations

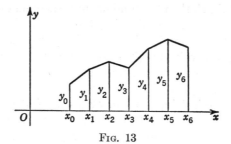

Fig. 13

leading to (13-4) corresponds to replacing $y = f(x)$ in the interval (x_0, x_1) by the straight line through (x_0, y_0) and (x_1, y_1).

The successive application of (13-4) to intervals (x_1, x_2), (x_2, x_3), $\ldots$, (x_{n-1}, x_n) yields

$$\int_{x_0}^{x_n} y \, dx = \int_{x_0}^{x_1} y \, dx + \int_{x_1}^{x_2} y \, dx + \cdots + \int_{x_{n-1}}^{x_n} y \, dx$$

$$= \frac{h}{2}(y_0 + y_1) + \frac{h}{2}(y_1 + y_2) + \cdots + \frac{h}{2}(y_{n-1} + y_n)$$

$$= \frac{h}{2}(y_0 + 2y_1 + 2y_2 + \cdots + 2y_{n-1} + y_n).$$ (13-5)

Formula (13-5) is known as the *trapezoidal rule*, for it gives the value of the sum of the areas of the n trapezoids whose bases are the ordinates $y_0, y_1, y_2, \ldots, y_n$. Figure 13 shows the six trapezoids in the case of $n = 6$. If $m = 2$, (13-1) becomes

$$\int_0^2 y \, dX = \int_0^2 \left[y_0 + X \, \Delta y_0 + \frac{(X^2 - X)}{2} \Delta^2 y_0 \right] dX$$

$$= 2y_0 + 2 \, \Delta y_0 + \frac{1}{2} \left(\frac{8}{3} - 2 \right) \Delta^2 y_0$$

$$= 2y_0 + 2(y_1 - y_0) + \frac{1}{3} (y_2 - 2y_1 + y_0)$$

$$= \frac{1}{3} y_0 + \frac{4}{3} y_1 + \frac{1}{3} y_2,$$

or

$$\int_{x_0}^{x_2} y \, dx = \frac{h}{3} (y_0 + 4y_1 + y_2). \tag{13-6}$$

Suppose that there are $n + 1$ pairs of given values, where n is even. If these $n + 1$ pairs are divided into the groups of three pairs with abscissas $x_{2i}, x_{2i+1}, x_{2i+2}$, where $i = 0, 1, \ldots, (n - 2)/2$, then (13-6) can be applied to each group. Hence,

$$\int_{x_0}^{x_n} y \, dx = \int_{x_0}^{x_2} y \, dx + \int_{x_2}^{x_4} y \, dx + \cdots + \int_{x_{n-2}}^{x_n} y \, dx$$

$$= \frac{h}{3} (y_0 + 4y_1 + y_2) + \frac{h}{3} (y_2 + 4y_3 + y_4)$$

$$+ \cdots + \frac{h}{3} (y_{n-2} + 4y_{n-1} + y_n)$$

$$= \frac{h}{3} [y_0 + y_n + 4(y_1 + y_3 + \cdots + y_{n-1})$$

$$+ 2(y_2 + y_4 + \cdots + y_{n-2})]. \tag{13-7}$$

Formula (13-7) is known as *Simpson's rule* with $m = 2$. Interpreted geometrically, it gives the value of the sum of the areas under the second-degree parabolas that have been passed through the points (x_{2i}, y_{2i}), (x_{2i+1}, y_{2i+1}), and (x_{2i+2}, y_{2i+2}), where $i = 0, 1, 2, \ldots, (n - 2)/2$.

If $m = 3$, (13-1) states that

$$\int_0^3 y\, dX = \int_0^3 \left(y_0 + X\, \Delta y_0 + \frac{X^2 - X}{2} \Delta^2 y_0 + \frac{X^3 - 3X^2 + 2X}{6} \Delta^3 y_0 \right) dX$$

$$= 3y_0 + \frac{9}{2} \Delta y_0 + \left(\frac{9}{2} - \frac{9}{4} \right) \Delta^2 y_0 + \left(\frac{27}{8} - \frac{9}{2} + \frac{3}{2} \right) \Delta^3 y_0$$

$$= 3y_0 + \frac{9}{2} (y_1 - y_0) + \frac{9}{4} (y_2 - 2y_1 + y_0)$$

$$+ \frac{3}{8} (y_3 - 3y_2 + 3y_1 - y_0)$$

$$= \frac{3}{8} (y_0 + 3y_1 + 3y_2 + y_3),$$

or

$$\int_{x_0}^{x_3} y\, dx = \frac{3h}{8} (y_0 + 3y_1 + 3y_2 + y_3). \tag{13-8}$$

If $n + 1$ pairs of values are given, and if n is a multiple of 3, then (13-8) can be applied successively to groups of four pairs of values to give

$$\int_{x_0}^{x_n} y\, dx = \frac{3h}{8} [y_0 + y_n + 3(y_1 + y_2 + y_4 + y_5 + \cdots + y_{n-2} + y_{n-1})$$

$$+ 2(y_3 + y_6 + \cdots + y_{n-3})]. \tag{13-9}$$

Formula (13-9) is called Simpson's rule with $m = 3$. It is not encountered so frequently as (13-5) or (13-7). Other formulas for numerical integration can be derived by setting $m = 4, 5, \ldots$ in (13-1), but the three given here are sufficient for ordinary purposes. In most cases, better results are obtained by securing a large number of observed or computed values, so that h will be small, and using (13-5) or (13-7).

Example 1. Using the data given in the Example of Sec. 7, find an approximate value for $\int_1^7 y\, dx$.

Using the trapezoidal rule (13-5) gives

$$\int_1^7 y\, dx = \tfrac{1}{2}(2.105 + 5.616 + 7.228 + 9.208 + 11.714 + 14.902 + 9.467) = 30.120.$$

Using (13-7) gives

$$\int_1^7 y\, dx = \tfrac{1}{3}[2.105 + 9.467 + 4(2.808 + 4.604 + 7.451) + 2(3.614 + 5.857)] = 29.989.$$

Using (13-9) gives

$$\int_1^7 y\, dx = \tfrac{3}{8}[2.105 + 9.467 + 3(2.808 + 3.614 + 5.857 + 7.451) + 2(4.604)] = 29.989.$$

If numerical integration is to be used in a problem in which the form of $f(x)$ is known, the set of values (x_i,y_i) can usually be chosen so that the x_i form an arithmetic progression and one of the formulas deduced above can be applied. Even if it is expedient to choose values closer together for some parts of the range than for other parts, these formulas can be applied successively, with appropriate values of h, to those sets of values for which the x_i form an arithmetic progression. However, if the set of given values was obtained by observation, it is frequently convenient to use a formula that does not require that the x_i form an arithmetic progression.

Suppose that a set of pairs of observed values (x_i,y_i), where $i = 0, 1, 2, \ldots, m$, is given. The points (x_i,y_i) all lie on the curve whose equation is given by (9-2). The area under this curve between $x = x_0$ and $x = x_m$ is an approximation to the value of $\int_{x_0}^{x_m} y\, dx$. The area under the curve (9-2) is

$$\int_{x_0}^{x_m} y\, dx = \sum_{k=0}^{m} \frac{y_k}{P_k(x_k)} \int_{x_0}^{x_m} P_k(x)\, dx, \tag{13-10}$$

in which the expressions for the $P_k(x)$ are given by (9-1).

If $m = 1$, (9-1) and (13-10) give

$$\int_{x_0}^{x_1} y\, dx = \frac{y_0}{x_0 - x_1} \int_{x_0}^{x_1} (x - x_1)\, dx + \frac{y_1}{x_1 - x_0} \int_{x_0}^{x_1} (x - x_0)\, dx$$

$$= \frac{x_1 - x_0}{2} (y_0 + y_1). \tag{13-11}$$

Formula (13-11) is identical with (13-4), as would be expected, but the formula corresponding to (13-5) is

$$\int_{x_0}^{x_n} y\, dx = \tfrac{1}{2}[(x_1 - x_0)(y_0 + y_1) + (x_2 - x_1)(y_1 + y_2)$$

$$+ \cdots + (x_n - x_{n-1})(y_{n-1} + y_n)]. \tag{13-12}$$

If $m = 2$, (13-10) becomes

$$\int_{x_0}^{x_2} y\, dx = \frac{y_0}{P_0(x_0)} \int_{x_0}^{x_2} (x - x_1)(x - x_2)\, dx$$

$$+ \frac{y_1}{P_1(x_1)} \int_{x_0}^{x_2} (x - x_0)(x - x_2)\, dx$$

$$+ \frac{y_2}{P_2(x_2)} \int_{x_0}^{x_2} (x - x_0)(x - x_1)\, dx$$

$$= \frac{y_0}{P_0(x_0)} \left[\frac{x_2^3 - x_0^3}{3} - \frac{(x_1 + x_2)(x_2^2 - x_0^2)}{2} + x_1 x_2 (x_2 - x_0) \right]$$

$$+ \frac{y_1}{P_1(x_1)} \left[\frac{x_2^3 - x_0^3}{3} - \frac{(x_0 + x_2)(x_2^2 - x_0^2)}{2} + x_0 x_2 (x_2 - x_0) \right]$$

$$+ \frac{y_2}{P_2(x_2)} \left[\frac{x_2^3 - x_0^3}{3} - \frac{(x_0 + x_1)(x_2^2 - x_0^2)}{2} + x_0 x_1 (x_2 - x_0) \right]$$

$$= \frac{(x_2 - x_0)^2}{6} \left[\frac{y_0}{P_0(x_0)} (3x_1 - 2x_0 - x_2) + \frac{y_1}{P_1(x_1)} (x_0 - x_2) \right.$$

$$\left. + \frac{y_2}{P_2(x_2)} (2x_2 + x_0 - 3x_1) \right]. \quad (13\text{-}13)$$

Formula (13-13) reduces to (13-6) when $x_1 - x_0 = x_2 - x_1 = h$. The formula that corresponds to (13-7) is too long and complicated to be of practical importance, and hence it is omitted here. It is simpler to apply (13-13) successively to groups of three values and then add the results.

Example 2. Using the data given in Prob. 3, Sec. 9, find an approximate value of $\int_{0.16}^{6.25} y \, dx$.

Using (13-12) determines

$$\int_{0.16}^{6.25} y \, dx = \frac{1}{2}[0.24(4.210) + 0.6(4.631) + 1.5(5.082) + 3.75(5.590)] = 16.187.$$

Applying (13-13) successively to the first three values and to the last three values gives

$$\int_{0.16}^{6.25} y \, dx = \frac{(0.84)^2}{6} \left[\frac{2(1.2 - 0.32 - 1)}{(-0.24)(-0.84)} + \frac{2.210(-0.84)}{(0.24)(-0.6)} + \frac{2.421(2 + 0.16 - 1.2)}{(0.84)(0.6)} \right]$$

$$+ \frac{(5.25)^2}{6} \left[\frac{2.421(7.5 - 2 - 6.25)}{(-1.5)(-5.25)} + \frac{2.661(-5.25)}{(1.5)(-3.75)} \right.$$

$$\left. + \frac{2.929(12.5 + 1 - 7.5)}{(5.25)(3.75)} \right] = 17.194.$$

PROBLEMS

1. Determine the values of $\int_1^7 y \, dx$ by applying (13-5) and (13-7) to the following data:

x	1	2	3	4	5	6	7
y	2.157	3.519	4.198	4.539	4.708	4.792	4.835

2. Apply formula (13-12) to compute $\int_{10}^{50.625} p \, dv$ from the data of the Example in Sec. 9.

3. Work the preceding problem by applying (13-13).

4. Apply formulas (13-5) and (13-7) to compute $\int_{19}^{25} H \, dC$ from the data of Prob. 4, Sec. 9.

5. Find approximate values of $\int_{0}^{6} \sqrt{4 + x^3} \, dx$ by applying formulas (13-5) and (13-7) with $x_m = m$, $m = 0, 1, 2, \ldots, 6$.

14. Euler's Polygonal Curves. The methods available for the exact solution of differential equations, as we noted in Chap. 1, apply only to a few, principally linear, types of differential equations. Many equations arising in applications are not solvable by such methods, and one is obliged to devise techniques for the determination of approximate solutions.

We begin with the consideration of the first-order equation

$$y' = f(x,y) \tag{14-1}$$

and seek its solution $y = y(x)$ taking on a prescribed value $y_0 = y(x_0)$ at $x = x_0$.

At each point of the region where $f(x,y)$ is continuous Eq. (14-1) determines the slope of the integral curve passing through that point. The equation of the tangent line at the point (x_0,y_0) to the integral curve $y = y(x)$ is

$$y - y_0 = f(x_0,y_0)(x - x_0). \tag{14-2}$$

If we advance along this line a short distance to a point (x_1,y_1), we can compute from (14-1) the value $y'(x_1) = f(x_1,y_1)$ which, in general, will not be equal to the slope of $y = y(x)$ at $x = x_1$, because the point (x_1,y_1) ordinarily will not lie on the integral curve $y = y(x)$. But if (x_1,y_1) is close to (x_0,y_0), the slope of the integral curve at $x = x_1$ will not differ much from $f(x_1,y_1)$. To put it differently, the linear function (14-2) approximates the solution of (14-1) in the neighborhood of the point (x_0,y_0). (See Fig. 1 in Chap. 1, Sec. 1.)

We consider next the straight line through (x_1,y_1) with the slope $f(x_1,y_1)$ and proceed along it a small distance to a point (x_2,y_2). At (x_2,y_2) we draw another straight line with the slope $f(x_2,y_2)$ and advance along it to a point (x_3,y_3). By continuing this construction we obtain a polygon consisting of short straight-line segments joining the points (x_0,y_0), (x_1,y_1), (x_2,y_2), $\ldots$, (x_n,y_n). The polygonal curve so obtained is called *Euler's polygon*. This polygonal curve can be expected to approximate the integral curve reasonably well when the points (x_i,y_i) are not too far apart and the end point (x_n,y_n) is not too far away from (x_0,y_0).

The end points of the segments forming Euler's polygon clearly satisfy [cf. (14-2)]

$$y_1 - y_0 = f(x_0, y_0)(x_1 - x_0)$$

$$y_2 - y_1 = f(x_1, y_1)(x_2 - x_1) \qquad (14\text{-}3)$$

$$\cdots \cdots \cdots \cdots \cdots \cdots \cdots \cdots$$

$$y_n - y_{n-1} = f(x_{n-1}, y_{n-1})(x_n - x_{n-1})$$

and if each interval $x_i - x_{i-1}$ is of length h, we can write (14-3) as

$$y_{m+1} = y_m + f(x_m, y_m)h, \qquad m = 0, 1, 2, \ldots, n - 1. \qquad (14\text{-}4)$$

The recursion formula (14-4) enables us to compute successively the approximate values of the ordinates of the integral curve $y = y(x)$ at $x_k = x_0 + kh$, where $k = 1, 2, \ldots, n$. It may suffice for rough calculations if the spacing interval h is small and m not too large.

A more accurate formula can be obtained by constructing, instead of the chain of rectilinear segments, a chain made up of parabolic segments. Thus, we can draw through (x_1, y_1) a parabola

$$y = a_0 + a_1(x - x_1) + a_2(x - x_1)^2 \qquad (14\text{-}5)$$

which at $x = x_0$ has the slope $f(x_0, y_0)$ and at $x = x_1$ the slope $f(x_1, y_1)$. A simple calculation of the constants in (14-5) yields

$$y_2 = y_1 + \{y'(x_1) + \tfrac{1}{2}[y'(x_1) - y'(x_0)]\}h. \qquad (14\text{-}6)$$

This formula serves to determine y_2 if $y_1 = y(x_1)$, $y'(x_1)$, and the difference $\nabla y_1' \equiv y'(x_1) - y'(x_0)$ are known. Now, if we suppose that the solution $y(x)$ can be represented by Taylor's formula

$$y(x) = y_0 + y'(x_0)(x - x_0) + \tfrac{1}{2}y''(x_0)(x - x_0)^2 + \cdots + R_n, \qquad (14\text{-}7)$$

we can calculate the needed quantities in the right-hand member of (14-6).

The coefficients in (14-7) can be calculated from (14-1) whenever $f(x, y)$ has a sufficient number of partial derivatives, for on setting (x_0, y_0) in (14-1), we get $y'(x_0) = f(x_0, y_0)$. Differentiating (14-1) with respect to x yields [1]

$$y''(x) = f_x(x, y) + f_y(x, y)y'(x), \qquad (14\text{-}8)$$

and substituting $x = x_0$, $y = y_0$ in (14-8) gives

$$y''(x_0) = f_x(x_0, y_0) + f_y(x_0, y_0)y'(x_0).$$

By differentiating (14-8), we obtain $y'''(x)$, and so on. The value of R_n in (14-7) in general cannot be computed, but by neglecting it we get an approximate value of $y(x)$.

Once the coefficients in (14-7) are determined, we use (14-7) to compute

[1] We use the subscript notation for partial derivatives introduced in Sec. 2, Chap. 3.

$y(x_1) = y_1$. The value of $y'(x_1)$ is then determined by (14-1), since $y'(x_1) = f(x_1, y_1)$. The substitution in (14-6) then yields y_2.

Having computed y_2, we can advance another step and compute y_3 from [cf. (14-6)]

$$y_3 = y_2 + \{y'(x_2) + \tfrac{1}{2}[y'(x_2) - y'(x_1)]\}h.$$

This requires calculating $y'(x_2)$ from (14-1).

The general recursion formula, based on the parabolic approximation, is

$$y_{m+1} = y_m + [y'(x_m) + \tfrac{1}{2}\,\nabla y'(x_m)]h, \qquad (14\text{-}9)$$

where $\nabla y'(x_m) = y'(x_m) - y'(x_{m-1})$.

More elaborate recursion formulas can be constructed by using polynomials of higher degree instead of (14-5). Such formulas lie at the basis of the Adams method of integration of differential equations discussed in the next section.

PROBLEMS

1. Construct a polygonal approximation, in the interval $(-1,1)$, to the solution of $y' = \tfrac{1}{2}xy$ which is such that $y(0) = 1$. Take the spacing interval $h = 0.2$. Also obtain the exact solution, and plot it on the same sheet of paper.

2. Determine the coefficients in (14-5), and thus deduce (14-6).

3. Use the equation in Prob. 1 to illustrate the calculation of y_2 from formula (14-6). Also obtain y_3. Take $x_0 = 0$, $y_0 = 1$, $x_1 = 0.2$, $x_2 = 0.4$.

15. The Adams Method. We extend the considerations of the preceding section by developing a step-by-step procedure for computing an approximate solution of

$$y' = f(x,y) \qquad (15\text{-}1)$$

taking on a prescribed value y_0 at $x = x_0$. The ordinates y_m, approximating the ordinates of the integral curve $y = y(x)$ at $x = x_m$, will be determined for equally spaced values of x, so that $x_m = x_0 + hm$, where $m = 0, 1, 2, \ldots$. Thus our approximate solution will appear in a tabulated form for a discrete set of values of x.

By the Fundamental Theorem of Integral Calculus,

$$\int_{x_m}^{x_{m+1}} y'(x)\,dx \equiv \int_{x_m}^{x_{m+1}} \left(\frac{dy}{dx}\right) dx = y(x_m + h) - y(x_m)$$

so that

$$y_{m+1} = y_m + \int_{x_m}^{x_m+h} y'(x)\,dx, \qquad (15\text{-}2)$$

where $y_{m+1} \equiv y(x_m + h)$ and $y_m \equiv y(x_m)$.

Now, if the variable x in the integral of (15-2) is replaced by

$$x = x_m + hX \qquad (15\text{-}3)$$

where X is a new dimensionless variable, (15-2) becomes [1]

$$y_{m+1} = y_m + h \int_0^1 y'(x_m + hX) \, dX. \tag{15-4}$$

But we saw in Sec. 8 that when a function $y'(x)$ is approximated by a polynomial of degree n taking on the values $y'_m, y'_{m-1}, \ldots, y'_{m-n}$ at $x = x_m$, $x_{m-1}, \ldots, x_{m-n}$, then [cf. (8-7)]

$$y'(x_m + hX) = y'_m + X \, \nabla y'_m + \frac{X(X+1)}{2!} \, \nabla^2 y'_m + \cdots$$

$$+ \frac{X(X+1) \ldots (X+n-1)}{n!} \, \nabla^n y'_m. \tag{15-5}$$

If we insert (15-5) in (15-4) and carry out simple integrations, we find that

$$y_{m+1} = y_m + h(y'_m + \tfrac{1}{2} \, \nabla y'_m + \tfrac{5}{12} \, \nabla^2 y'_m + \tfrac{3}{8} \, \nabla^3 y'_m + {}^{251}\!/_{720} \, \nabla^4 y'_m$$

$$+ \cdots + a_n \, \nabla^n y'_m), \tag{15-6}$$

where

$$a_n = \int_0^1 \frac{X(X+1) \ldots (X+n-1)}{n!} \, dX. \tag{15-7}$$

Formula (15-6) enables us to compute the ordinate y_{m+1} if we know y_m, y'_m, and the backward differences $\nabla^k y'_m$. When the $\nabla y'_m$ vanish, (15-6) reduces to (14-4), and when the $\nabla^2 y'_m$ vanish, we get (14-9). As was the case with (14-9), the values of y_m, y'_m and the $\nabla^k y'_m$ in (15-6) are not available to us at the start. They must be computed by some means before (15-6) can be used to evaluate y_{m+1}. The number of the $\nabla^k y_m$ depends on the degree n of the polynomial chosen to approximate $y'(x)$. Once we agree on the value of n, we can compute y_m, y'_m and the requisite number of the $\nabla^k y'_m$ with the aid of Taylor's representation of the solution $y = y(x)$, as was done in Sec. 14.

We illustrate the procedure in detail in the following example.

Example: Use Adams' method to obtain, in the interval $(0,1)$, an approximate solution of

$$y' = y + x, \tag{15-8}$$

taking on the value $y_0 = 1$ at $x = 0$.

Let us subdivide the interval $(0,1)$ into subintervals of length $h = 0.1$, so that

$$x_k = x_0 + kh = 0.1k, \qquad k = 0, 1, 2, \ldots, 10.$$

Furthermore, let us agree to retain in (15-6) the differences of y'_m up to and including those of order 3. This corresponds to approximating $y'(x)$ in (15-2) by a polynomial of degree 3.

---

[1] By (15-3) $dx = h \, dX$, and at the limits $x = x_m$ and $x = x_m + h$, the values of X are $X = 0$ and $X = 1$.

To compute y_{m+1} from (15-6) we need y_m, y'_m, $\nabla y'_m$, $\nabla^2 y'_m$, and $\nabla^3 y'_m$. The calculation of the third differences $\nabla^3 y'_m$ requires at least four values y'_m, y'_{m-1}, y'_{m-2}, y'_{m-3}, as is obvious from the following table.

$$
\begin{array}{ccccc}
\vdots & \vdots & \vdots & & \vdots \\
\vdots & \vdots & \vdots & & \vdots \\
y'_{m-3} & & & & \\
 & \nabla y'_{m-2} & & & \\
y'_{m-2} & & \nabla^2 y'_{m-1} & & \\
 & \nabla y'_{m-1} & & \nabla^3 y'_m & \\
y'_{m-1} & & \nabla^2 y'_m & & \\
 & \nabla y'_m & & & \\
y'_m & & & &
\end{array}
$$

If we determine y'_0, y'_1, y'_2, y'_3, we shall be in a position to fill in the values in this table with $m = 3$ and then proceed to determine y_4 from (15-6).

Since $y_0 = 1$ for $x_0 = 0$, Eq. (15-8) yields

$$y'_0 = 1. \tag{15-9}$$

To compute y_1, y_2, and y_3 we use Taylor's series

$$y(x) = y_0 + y'_0(x - x_0) + \frac{y''_0}{2!}(x - x_0)^2 + \frac{y'''_0}{3!}(x - x_0)^3 + \cdots \tag{15-10}$$

with $y_0 = 1$ and $x_0 = 0$. The coefficients in (15-10) can be calculated from (15-8). Differentiating (15-8), we get

$$y''(x) = y'(x) + 1, \tag{15-11}$$

and on setting $x = 0$ and recalling that $y'(0) = y'_0 = 1$, we get $y''(0) = 2$. Successive differentiations of (15-11) give

$$y'''(x) = y''(x), \qquad y^{IV}(x) = y'''(x), \qquad \ldots, \qquad y^{(n)}(x) = y^{(n-1)}(x), \tag{15-12}$$

and since $y''(0) = 2$, we get from (15-12)

$$y'''(0) = 2, \qquad y^{IV}(0) = 2, \qquad \ldots, \qquad y^{(n)}(0) = 2.$$

Accordingly, (15-10) becomes

$$y(x) = 1 + x + x^2 + \frac{x^3}{3} + \frac{x^4}{3 \cdot 4} + \frac{x^5}{3 \cdot 4 \cdot 5} + \cdots.$$

Setting $x = 0.1$, we get

$$y_1 = 1 + 0.1 + (0.1)^2 + \frac{(0.1)^3}{3} + \frac{(0.1)^4}{3 \cdot 4} + \frac{(0.1)^5}{3 \cdot 4 \cdot 5} + \cdots = 1.1103.$$

In the same way using $x = 0.2$ and $x = 0.3$, we obtain

$$y_2 = 1.2428, \qquad y_3 = 1.3997.$$

The desired values of y_1', y_2', and y_3' can now be computed from (15-8). We find that

$$y_1' = y_1 + x_1 = 1.1103 + 0.1 = 1.2103$$

$$y_2' = y_2 + x_2 = 1.2428 + 0.2 = 1.4428$$

$$y_3' = y_3 + x_3 = 1.3997 + 0.3 = 1.6997.$$

We can now proceed to construct the table of differences shown below.

x	y	y'	$\nabla y'$	$\nabla^2 y'$	$\nabla^3 y'$
0	1.0000	1.0000			
			0.2103		
0.1	1.1103	1.2103		0.0222	
			0.2325		0.0022
0.2	1.2428	1.4428		0.0244	
			0.2569		0.0026
0.3	1.3997	1.6997		0.0270	
			0.2839		
0.4	1.5836	1.9836			
0.5	1.7974				

The substitution from this table in (15-6), with $m = 3$ and $n = 3$, yields

$$y_4 = 1.3997 + 0.1[1.6997 + \tfrac{1}{2}(0.2569) + \tfrac{5}{12}(0.0244) + \tfrac{3}{8}(0.0022)]$$

$$= 1.5836.$$

This value is recorded in the table for $x = 0.4$.

To compute y_5 we must extend the table, since formula (15-6) requires the knowledge of y_4' and assorted differences of y_4'. By (15-8)

$$y_4' = y_4 + x_4 = 1.5836 + 0.4 = 1.9836.$$

The calculated values (recorded below the heavy line in the table) can now be used in (15-6), with $m = 4$, $n = 3$, to compute y_5. We have

$$y_5 = 1.5836 + 0.1[1.9836 + \tfrac{1}{2}(0.2839) + \tfrac{5}{12}(0.0270) + \tfrac{3}{8}(0.0026)]$$

$$= 1.7974.$$

This value is recorded in the table for $x = 0.5$.

We leave it to the reader to make further extensions in the table required for the calculation of y_6, y_7, ..., y_{10}.

PROBLEMS

1. Complete the table in the Example of Sec. 15 by computing y_6, y_7, ..., y_{10}.

2. Since (15-8) is a linear equation, its solution satisfying the condition $y(0) = 1$

is easily found to be $y = 2e^x - x - 1$. Compare the exact and the approximate values $y_1, y_2, \ldots, y_{10}$.

3. Apply the Adams method to obtain an approximate solution of $y' = y$ with $y(0) = 1$. Use $h = 0.1$, and compute $y(0.3)$, $y(0.4)$, $y(0.5)$, and $y(0.6)$ from (15-6) with $n = 2$. Compare with the exact solution.

4. Use $h = 0.1$ and (15-6) with $n = 3$ to find an approximate value of $y(-0.6)$ for the integral curve of $y' = x^2 + y^2$ through $(-1,0)$.

16. Equations of Higher Order. Systems of Equations.

The methods of Secs. 14 and 15 can be extended to obtain numerical solutions of equations of higher order. Thus, the second-order equation

$$y'' = f(x,y,y') \tag{16-1}$$

with initial conditions

$$y(x_0) = y_0, \qquad y'(x_0) = y_0' \tag{16-2}$$

can be written as a system of two equations of first order by setting

$$y' = z. \tag{16-3}$$

The substitution in (16-1) from (16-3) then yields the second equation

$$z' = f(x,y,z). \tag{16-4}$$

In indicating the extension we shall consider, instead of the system (16-3) and (16-4), a more general system

$$\begin{aligned} y' &= f_1(x,y,z), \\ z' &= f_2(x,y,z), \end{aligned} \tag{16-5}$$

with initial conditions

$$y(x_0) = y_0, \qquad z(x_0) = z_0. \tag{16-6}$$

When solutions of the system (16-5) can be expanded in Taylor's series

$$\begin{aligned} y(x) &= y(x_0) + y'(x_0)(x - x_0) + \frac{y''(x_0)}{2!}(x - x_0)^2 + \cdots, \\[2mm] z(x) &= z(x_0) + z'(x_0)(x - x_0) + \frac{z''(x_0)}{2!}(x - x_0)^2 + \cdots, \end{aligned} \tag{16-7}$$

the coefficients in (16-7) can be computed by differentiating Eqs. (16-5) successively as was done [1] in Secs. 14 and 15.

The construction of Euler's polygonal approximation also follows the pattern of Sec. 14. Thus, the equation of the straight line through (x_0,y_0,z_0) tangent to the integral curve of the system (16-5) is [2]

$$\begin{aligned} y - y_0 &= f_1(x_0,y_0,z_0)(x - x_0), \\ z - z_0 &= f_2(x_0,y_0,z_0)(x - x_0). \end{aligned} \tag{16-8}$$

---

[1] See in this connection Sec. 6, Chap. 3.

[2] The integral curve of the system (16-5) is, in general, a space curve, so that the tangent line to it is determined by the intersection of the planes (16-8).

When abscissas are spaced uniformly h units apart,

$$x_1 = x_0 + h, \qquad x_2 = x_0 + 2h, \ldots, x_k = x_0 + kh,$$

and from (16-8) it follows that the approximate solutions at $x_1, x_2, \ldots$ are

$$y_1 = y_0 + f_1(x_0, y_0, z_0)h,$$
$$z_1 = z_0 + f_2(x_0, y_0, z_0)h,$$
$$y_2 = y_1 + f_1(x_1, y_1, z_1)h,$$
$$z_2 = z_1 + f_2(x_1, y_1, z_1)h,$$

$$. \quad . \quad . \quad . \quad . \quad . \quad . \quad . \quad . \quad . \quad .$$
$$. \quad . \quad . \quad . \quad . \quad . \quad . \quad . \quad . \quad . \quad .$$

$$y_{k+1} = y_k + f_1(x_k, y_k, z_k)h,$$
$$z_{k+1} = z_k + f_2(x_k, y_k, z_k)h.$$

If, instead of approximating the solution in each interval by a linear function, we make use of the polynomial approximations in the manner of Sec. 15, we obtain

$$y_{m+1} = y_m + h[y'_m + \tfrac{1}{2}\nabla y'_m + \tfrac{5}{12}\nabla^2 y'_m + \cdots + a_n \nabla^n y'_m]$$
$$z_{m+1} = z_m + h[z'_m + \tfrac{1}{2}\nabla z'_m + \tfrac{5}{12}\nabla^2 z'_m + \cdots + a_n \nabla^n y'_m] \tag{16-9}$$

with a_n determined by (15-7).

In computing y_{m+1} and z_{m+1} from (16-9), we must first obtain the values of y_m, z_m, y'_m, z'_m and the required differences, as was done in Sec. 15.

Example: Obtain the solution of the system

$$y' = x + z$$
$$z' = 1 + y \tag{16-10}$$

in the form (16-7), which is such that

$$y(0) = -1, \qquad z(0) = 1. \tag{16-11}$$

On setting $x_0 = 0$ in (16-7) we get

$$y(x) = y(0) + y'(0)x + \frac{1}{2!}y''(0)x^2 + \cdots$$
$$z(x) = z(0) + z'(0)x + \frac{1}{2!}z''(0)x^2 + \cdots, \tag{16-12}$$

the coefficients in which can be computed by differentiating (16-10) and noting (16-11). We obtain from (16-10)

$$y''(x) = 1 + z'(x), \qquad z''(x) = y'(x)$$
$$y'''(x) = z''(x), \qquad z'''(x) = y''(x)$$
$$. \quad . \quad . \quad . \quad . \quad . \quad . \qquad . \quad . \quad . \quad . \quad . \quad . \tag{16-13}$$
$$y^{(n)}(x) = z^{(n-1)}(x), \qquad z^{(n)}(x) = y^{(n-1)}(x).$$

The substitution from (16-11) in (16-10) yields $y'(0) = 1$, $z'(0) = 1 - 1 = 0$, and making use of these values in (16-13) we find

$$y''(0) = 1 + 0 = 1, \qquad z''(0) = y'(0) = 1,$$

$$y'''(0) = z''(0) = 1, \qquad z'''(0) = y''(0) = 1,$$

$$\cdots\cdots\cdots\cdots \qquad \cdots\cdots\cdots\cdots$$

$$y^{(n)}(0) = 1, \qquad z^{(n)}(0) = 1.$$

Accordingly, (16-12) yields

$$y(x) = -1 + x + \frac{x^2}{2!} + \frac{x^3}{3!} + \cdots$$

$$(16\text{-}14)$$

$$z(x) = 1 + 0x + \frac{x^2}{2!} + \frac{x^3}{3!} + \cdots.$$

By eliminating z from the system (16-10) we see that it is equivalent to the second-order equation

$$y'' - y = 2$$

with $y(0) = -1$, $y'(0) = 1$. Its solution is readily found to be

$$y = e^x - 2,$$

$$(16\text{-}15)$$

and from the first of Eqs. (16-10) we conclude that

$$z = e^x - x.$$

$$(16\text{-}16)$$

The Maclaurin expansions of these solutions are precisely (16-14).

It may be instructive to compute the polygonal approximations to the solution of (16-10) at $x = 0.2$ and $x = 0.4$.

On setting the differences in (16-9) equal to zero, we get

$$y_{m+1} = y_m + h y'_m, \qquad z_{m+1} = z_m + h z'_m.$$

$$(16\text{-}17)$$

Now, if we take $x_1 = 0.2$, so that $h = 0.2$, we obtain from (16-17)

$$y_1 = y(0.2) = -1 + (0.2)1 = -0.8,$$

$$z_1 = z(0.2) = 1 + (0.2)0 = 1,$$

since $y'_0 = 1$ and $z'_0 = 0$.

The exact solution (16-15) and (16-16) yields

$$y(0.2) = e^{0.2} - 2 = -0.7786,$$

$$z(0.2) = e^{0.2} - 0.2 = 1.0214.$$

Using $y_1 = -0.8$, $z_1 = 1$ in (16-17), we obtain

$$y_2 = y(0.4) = y_1 + 0.2 y'_1,$$

$$z_2 = z(0.4) = z_1 + 0.2 z'_1.$$

$$(16\text{-}18)$$

The values of y'_1 and z'_1 can be calculated from (16-10) by setting $x = 0.2$, $z = 1$, and $y = -0.8$. We find that

$$y'_1 = 0.2 + 1 = 1.2, \qquad z'_1 = 1 + y_1 = 1 - 0.8 = 0.2,$$

and then (16-18) yields

$$y_2 = -0.8 + (0.2)(1.2) = -0.56,$$

$$z_2 = 1 + (0.2)(0.2) = 1.04,$$

while the corresponding exact values are

$$y(0.4) = e^{0.4} - 2 = -0.5082,$$

$$z(0.4) = e^{0.4} - 0.4 = 1.0918.$$

The reader is advised to obtain more accurate polygonal approximations by taking the interval $h = 0.1$ and to compare the polygonal approximations with the values given by (16-9) in which the differences of order higher than 1 are set equal to zero.

PROBLEMS

1. Obtain from (16-7) a fourth-degree polynomial approximation to the solution of

$$y' = e^x + z, \qquad z' = e^{-x} + y$$

with $y(0) = 0$ and $z(0) = 0$.

2. Use a polygonal approximation to compute y_1, y_2, y_3, y_4 for the system in Prob. 1 by taking $x_1 = 0.1$, $x_2 = 0.2$, $x_3 = 0.3$, $x_4 = 0.4$.

3. Use a polygonal approximation to compute y_1, y_2, y_3, corresponding to $x_1 = 0.1$, $x_2 = 0.2$, $x_3 = 0.3$ for $y'' - y^2 = x$, with initial conditions $y(0) = 1$, $y'(0) = 0$. *Hint:* Set $y' = z$, and consider the system $y' = z$, $z' = x + y^2$ with $y(0) = 1$ and $z(0) = 0$.

4. Obtain the solution for Prob. 3 in Maclaurin's series.

5. Solve the system in Prob. 3 by the Adams method. Retain only the second differences in (16-9), and use the result of Prob. 4 to start the iteration.

17. Boundary-value Problems.

In many physical problems solutions of the second- and higher-order differential equations are required which satisfy preassigned conditions at more than one point of the interval. A simple example of this occurs in the study of deflections of a beam supported at several points. Problems of this sort are termed *boundary-value problems* to distinguish them from *initial-value problems* in which the conditions on solutions are imposed only at one point.

An important feature of the boundary-value problems is that their solutions (if they exist at all) need not be unique.[1] When the general solution of the differential equation can be obtained, the conditions imposed on solutions of the boundary-value problem can usually be met by determining the values of arbitrary constants in the general solution [2] so that the specified conditions are satisfied. However, general solutions of differential equations can rarely be written down, and one is obliged to seek solutions of boundary-value problems by numerical methods. The

---

[1] See, for example, our discussion of two interesting two-point boundary-value problems in Sec. 34, Chap. 1.

[2] This was the procedure followed in solving the boundary-value problems in Sec. 34, Chap. 1.

methods available for numerical solution of initial-value problems require that the integral curve be uniquely determined at the starting point and thus do not apply to problems in which solutions must satisfy specified conditions at more than one point.   To solve a boundary-value problem numerically one must employ laborious trial-and-error procedures utilizing the solutions of suitable initial-value problems.

We outline briefly the procedure commonly followed in solving a two-point boundary-value problem for the second-order differential equation.[1]

Let it be required to determine a solution of

$$y'' = f(x,y,y') \qquad (17\text{-}1)$$

which assumes at the end points of the interval $a \leq x \leq b$ the values

$$y(a) = A, \qquad y(b) = B. \qquad (17\text{-}2)$$

Now, if in addition to the value $y(a) = A$ we specify the slope $y'(a)$ at $x = a$, the solution of (17-1) is uniquely determined,[2] but this solution will satisfy the condition $y(b) = B$ only for some value of the slope $y'(a)$ which is not known.[3]   Physical or geometric considerations may suggest an approximate value of the slope, say $y'(a) = C$, which is such that the integral curve of (17-1) satisfying the conditions

$$y(a) = A, \qquad y'(a) = C \qquad (17\text{-}3)$$

also satisfies the condition $y(b) = B$.

The procedure used in solving the boundary-value problem consists in actually constructing the solution $y = y(x)$ satisfying the conditions (17-3) and computing the value of $y(x)$ at $x = b$.   If it is tolerably near B, we have the desired approximate solution of the boundary-value problem. If not, we choose another value of the slope $y'(a)$ and try again.   The procedure is clearly laborious and far from being elegant.

18. Characteristic-value Problems.   Closely associated with boundary-value problems are *characteristic-value problems*.   These are generally concerned with solutions of the two-point boundary-value problems for differential equations containing parameters.

A simple instance of the characteristic-value problem occurs in the study of small vibrations of an elastic string of finite length.[4]   When initial shape and initial velocity of the string are specified, its subsequent displacement

---

[1] For a more detailed discussion of such problems see W. E. Milne, "Numerical Solutions of Differential Equations," chap. 7, John Wiley & Sons, Inc., New York, 1952.

[2] We suppose that $f(x,y,y')$ is such that the initial-value problem has a unique solution.

[3] We assume that the boundary-value problem in (17-1) and (17-2) indeed has a solution.

[4] See Chap. 6.

$u(x,t)$ is determined by solving the equation

$$\frac{\partial^2 u}{\partial t^2} = a^2 \frac{\partial^2 u}{\partial x^2}, \tag{18-1}$$

where a is a physical constant. If the string is of length l and its ends are fixed at $x = 0$ and $x = l$, the solution of (18-1) must satisfy the end conditions

$$u(0,t) = 0, \qquad u(l,t) = 0. \tag{18-2}$$

When we attempt to obtain solutions of (18-1) by the method of separation of variables,[1] that is, by assuming that $u(x,t)$ is expressible in the form

$$u(x,t) = y(x)T(t), \tag{18-3}$$

where $y(x)$ is a function of x alone and $T(t)$ is a function of t alone, we are led to a pair of ordinary differential equations

$$\frac{d^2 y}{dx^2} + \lambda^2 y = 0, \tag{18-4}$$

$$\frac{d^2 T}{dt^2} + a^2 \lambda^2 T = 0,$$

where λ is a constant. This constant must be chosen so that the end conditions (18-2) are satisfied.

From the assumed form of solution (18-3) and from (18-2) it follows that the solutions of (18-4) must be such that

$$y(0) = 0, \qquad y(l) = 0. \tag{18-5}$$

We thus have a two-point boundary-value problem for Eq. (18-4) with the end conditions (18-5).

The determination of suitable solutions this time is very simple because the general solution of (18-4) is

$$y = c_1 \cos \lambda x + c_2 \sin \lambda x. \tag{18-6}$$

If we impose the conditions (18-5) on (18-6) and reject the trivial solution $y \equiv 0$, we find infinitely many solutions

$$y = c_2 \sin \lambda x, \tag{18-7}$$

where
$$\lambda = \frac{k\pi}{l}, \qquad k = 1, 2, \ldots. \tag{18-8}$$

The values of λ in (18-8) are called the *characteristic values* of the boundary-value problem of (18-4) and (18-5), and the solutions (18-7) with appropriate λs are *characteristic functions* of this problem.[2]

[1] See Sec. 10, Chap. 6.

[2] The terms *eigenvalue* and *eigenfunction* are used by some writers to mean "characteristic value" and "characteristic function," respectively. These stem from German words *Eigenwert* and *Eigenfunktion*. We eschew the hybrids, since this book is written in English.

The simplicity of the characteristic-value problem defined by (18-4) and (18-5) masks some important features of the general problem. These features become clearer if we consider the determination of small vibrations of an elastic rod of variable cross section. In this case the separation of variables in the appropriate partial differential equation leads to the equation

$$\frac{d^2}{dx^2} \left[p(x) \frac{d^2y}{dx^2} \right] - \lambda q(x)y = 0, \tag{18-9}$$

in which $p(x)$ and $q(x)$ are known functions and λ an unknown constant. If the rod is of length l, with the end points at $x = 0$ and $x = l$, the solutions of (18-9) must satisfy suitable conditions determined by the mode of fixing the ends. If the end $x = 0$ is clamped, then $y(0) = y'(0) = 0$; if it is simply supported, then $y(0) = y''(0) = 0$; if it is free, then $y''(0) = y'''(0) = 0$. Similar conditions are imposed at the end $x = l$.

For definiteness, we suppose that the ends of the rod are free (a ship floating at sea). We then seek a solution of (18-9) such that

$$y''(0) = y'''(0) = 0, \qquad y''(l) = y'''(l) = 0. \tag{18-10}$$

Since (18-9) is a linear equation, its general solution is the sum of four linearly independent solutions

$$y(x,\lambda) = c_1 y_1(x,\lambda) + c_2 y_2(x,\lambda) + c_3 y_3(x,\lambda) + c_4 y_4(x,\lambda) \tag{18-11}$$

where λ is the parameter appearing in (18-9) and the c_i are arbitrary constants. On imposing the end conditions (18-10) on (18-11) we get a system of four equations:

$$c_1 y_1''(0,\lambda) + c_2 y_2''(0,\lambda) + c_3 y_3''(0,\lambda) + c_4 y_4''(0,\lambda) = 0,$$
$$c_1 y_1'''(0,\lambda) + c_2 y_2'''(0,\lambda) + c_3 y_3'''(0,\lambda) + c_4 y_4'''(0,\lambda) = 0,$$
$$c_1 y_1''(l,\lambda) + c_2 y_2''(l,\lambda) + c_3 y_3''(l,\lambda) + c_4 y_4''(l,\lambda) = 0,$$
$$c_1 y_1'''(l,\lambda) + c_2 y_2'''(l,\lambda) + c_3 y_3'''(l,\lambda) + c_4 y_4'''(l,\lambda) = 0.$$

This system of four linear equations in the unknowns c_i will have a nontrivial solution if, and only if, the determinant $D(\lambda)$ of the coefficients of the cs is zero.[1] The equation

$$D(\lambda) = 0 \tag{18-12}$$

is the *characteristic equation,* and its solutions are the *characteristic values* of the problem. In general (18-12) is a transcendental equation, and its solution poses many vexing problems.[2] Usually it is solved by numerical

---

[1] See Appendix A.

[2] An instance of a simple transcendental characteristic equation appears in Sec. 10, Chap. 6, Eq. (10-16), in which the parameter is denoted by β. See also Sec. 36, Chap. 1, Eq. (36-4), where $D(\lambda) = 0$ is an algebraic equation.

methods. Because of the importance of characteristic equations in analyzing the behavior of dynamical systems, they have been studied extensively and there is a vast literature on the subject of numerical determination of characteristic values.[1]

19. Method of Finite Differences. We conclude this chapter with a brief description of the most commonly used method for solving boundary-value problems in partial differential equations, known as the *method of finite differences*. In this method the differential equation is replaced by an approximating difference equation, and the continuous region in which the solution is desired by a set of discrete points. This permits one to reduce the problem to the solution of a system of algebraic equations, which may involve hundreds of unknowns. Ordinarily, some iterative technique has to be devised to solve such systems, and high-speed electronic computers have been developed largely because of the need for coping with problems of this sort.

The main disadvantage of all numerical techniques is that they give numerical values for unknown functions at a set of discrete points instead of the analytic expressions defined over the initial region R. Of course, when the boundary-value data are determined by measurements at a finite set of points of R, the difference-equations methods may be the best mode of attack on the problem. Any analytic technique would require fitting curves to the discontinuous data.

We proceed to the outline of the general procedure followed in reducing the given analytic boundary-value problem to a problem in difference equations. For definiteness let the region R be bounded by a simple closed curve C. We seek to determine the function $u(x,y)$ satisfying a given differential equation in R. From the definition of partial derivatives it follows that [2]

$$\frac{\partial u}{\partial x} = \lim_{h \to 0} \frac{u(x + h,\, y) - u(x,y)}{h}.$$

Also, if the second partial derivatives are continuous one can show that

$$\frac{\partial^2 u}{\partial x^2} = \lim_{h \to 0} \frac{u(x + h,\, y) - 2u(x,y) + u(x - h,\, y)}{h^2},$$

$$\frac{\partial^2 u}{\partial x\, \partial y} = \lim_{\substack{h \to 0 \\ k \to 0}} \frac{u(x + h,\, y + k) - u(x + h,\, y) - u(x,\, y + k) + u(x,y)}{hk},$$

and so on.

For small values of h and k the partial derivatives are nearly equal to

[1] For bibliography see Milne, *op. cit.*, and F. B. Hildebrand, "Introduction to Numerical Analysis," McGraw-Hill Book Company, Inc., New York, 1956.

[2] See Chap. 3, and Chap. 6, Sec. 21.

the difference quotients appearing in the right-hand members of these formulas. If one replaces derivatives in the given differential equation by difference quotients, there results a difference equation which is a good approximation to the given equation when h and k are small.

Thus, to Laplace's equation

$$\nabla^2 u \equiv \frac{\partial^2 u}{\partial x^2} + \frac{\partial^2 u}{\partial y^2} = 0,$$

there corresponds the difference equation

$$\Delta_{xx} u + \Delta_{yy} u = 0,$$

where

$$\Delta_{xx} u \equiv \frac{1}{h^2} [u(x + h, y) - 2u(x,y) + u(x - h, y)],$$

$$\Delta_{yy} u \equiv \frac{1}{h^2} [u(x, y + h) - 2u(x,y) + u(x, y - h)].$$

In a difference equation the values of $u(x,y)$ are related at a set of discrete points determined by the choices of h and k. Ordinarily these points are chosen so that they form a square net [1] with specified mesh size h.

The usual procedure is to cover the region R by a net consisting of two sets of mutually orthogonal lines a distance h apart (Fig. 14) and mark off a polygonal contour C' so that it approximates sufficiently closely the boundary C. The domain R' in which the solution of the difference equation is sought is formed by the lattice points of the net contained within C'. The assigned boundary values on C are then transferred in some manner to the lattice points on C'. When the lattice points on C' do not coincide with points on C, the desired values can be got by interpolation.[2]

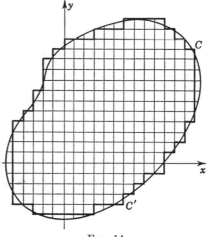

FIG. 14

----

[1] Rectangular, polygonal, and curvilinear nets are also used. See, for example, D. Y. Panov, "Handbook on Numerical Solution of Partial Differential Equations," Moscow, 1951, which contains a good account of the difference-equations techniques. See also Appendix to S. Timoshenko and J. N. Goodier's "Theory of Elasticity," 1951.

[2] See, for example, Milne, *op. cit.*, or L. M. Milne-Thomson, "Calculus of Finite Differences," 1933.

One then seeks a solution of the difference equation which satisfies the boundary conditions imposed at the lattice points on C'. Usually, this leads to a consideration of a system of a large number of algebraic equations in many unknowns.[1]

---

[1] Further discussion of difference equations is given in Chap. 6, Secs. 26 and **27**, and in Chap. 8, Sec. 10. See also chap. 10 by T. J. Higgins in L. E. Grinter (ed.), "Numerical Methods of Analysis in Engineering," 1949.

The literature on finite-difference methods is extensive. An illustration of the use of the method of finite differences in solving a boundary-value problem in Laplace's equation is included in I. S. Sokolnikoff, "Mathematical Theory of Elasticity," sec. 124, McGraw-Hill Book Company, Inc., New York, 1956, which contains further references.

APPENDIX

Appendix D.   Table of $\Phi(x) = \dfrac{1}{\sqrt{2\pi}} \displaystyle\int_0^x e^{-t^2/2}\, dt.$

DETERMINANTS

1. The Definition and Properties of Determinants. A determinant of the first order consists of a single element a and has the value a. A determinant of the second order contains four elements in a 2-by-2 square array and has the value

$$\begin{vmatrix} a_1 & a_2 \\ b_1 & b_2 \end{vmatrix} = a_1 b_2 - a_2 b_1. \tag{1-1}$$

A determinant of third order is similarly defined, in terms of second-order determinants:

$$\begin{vmatrix} a_1 & a_2 & a_3 \\ b_1 & b_2 & b_3 \\ c_1 & c_2 & c_3 \end{vmatrix} = a_1 \begin{vmatrix} b_2 & b_3 \\ c_2 & c_3 \end{vmatrix} - a_2 \begin{vmatrix} b_1 & b_3 \\ c_1 & c_3 \end{vmatrix} + a_3 \begin{vmatrix} b_1 & b_2 \\ c_1 & c_2 \end{vmatrix}. \tag{1-2}$$

By analogy, a determinant of order n consists of a square n-by-n array of elements a_{ij}:

$$\begin{vmatrix} a_{11} & a_{12} & \cdots & a_{1n} \\ a_{21} & a_{22} & \cdots & a_{2n} \\ \cdot & \cdot & \cdots & \cdot \\ a_{n1} & a_{n2} & \cdots & a_{nn} \end{vmatrix}$$

to which a numerical value is assigned as follows: Denoting the determinant by D, let the elements in the first row be a_{1i}, and let M_{1i} be the determinant of order $n - 1$ formed when the first row and ith column of D are deleted. Then, by definition,

$$D = a_{11}M_{11} - a_{12}M_{12} + \cdots + (-1)^{1+n}a_{1n}M_{1n}. \tag{1-3}$$

The definition is inductive; a determinant of order n is defined in terms of those having order $n - 1$.

The expansion (1-3) is termed a *Laplace development* of the determinant on elements of the first row. The determinant M_{1i} is called the *minor* of the element a_{1i}; the signed determinant $(-1)^{1+i}M_{1i}$ is the *cofactor* of a_{1i}. More generally, the determinant M_{ij} formed when the ith row and

jth column are deleted is the *minor* of the element a_{ij} in this row and column. The signed determinant

$$A_{ij} = (-1)^{i+j}M_{ij} \qquad (1\text{-}4)$$

is the *cofactor* of a_{ij}. It is a fundamental theorem that *a determinant may be evaluated by a Laplace development on any row or column;* in other words,

$$\begin{vmatrix} a_{11} & a_{12} \cdots a_{1n} \\ a_{21} & a_{22} \cdots a_{2n} \\ \cdot & \cdot \cdot \cdot \cdot \cdot \cdot \cdot \\ \cdot & \cdot \cdot \cdot \cdot \cdot \cdot \cdot \\ a_{n1} & a_{n2} \cdots a_{nn} \end{vmatrix} = \sum_{i=1}^{n} a_{ij}A_{ij} = \sum_{j=1}^{n} a_{ij}A_{ij}. \qquad (1\text{-}5)$$

The proof may be given by induction directly or may be based on the following considerations, which are also established by induction. The expansion of an nth-order determinant is a sum of the $n!$ terms $(-1)^k a_{k_1 1} a_{k_2 2} \ldots a_{k_n n}$, where $k_1, k_2, \ldots, k_n$ are the numbers $1, 2, \ldots, n$ in some order. The integer k is defined as the number of *inversions of order* of the subscripts $k_1, k_2, \ldots, k_n$ from the normal order $1, 2, \ldots, n$ where a particular arrangement is said to have k inversions of order if it is necessary to make k successive interchanges of adjacent elements in order to make the arrangement assume the normal order. There are $n!$ terms, since there are $n!$ permutations of the n first subscripts, and each term contains as a factor one, and only one, element from each row and one, and only one, element from each column.

For example, consider the third-order determinant

$$D = \begin{vmatrix} a_{11} & a_{12} & a_{13} \\ a_{21} & a_{22} & a_{23} \\ a_{31} & a_{32} & a_{33} \end{vmatrix}.$$

The six terms of the expansion are, apart from sign,

$$a_{11}a_{22}a_{33}, \ a_{11}a_{32}a_{23}, \ a_{21}a_{12}a_{33}, \ a_{21}a_{32}a_{13}, \ a_{31}a_{12}a_{23}, \ a_{31}a_{22}a_{13}.$$

The first term, in which the first subscripts have the normal order, is called the diagonal term, and its sign is positive. In the second term the arrangement 132 requires the interchange of 2 and 3 to make it assume the normal order; therefore $k = 1$, and the term has a negative sign. Similarly, the third term has a negative sign. The fourth term has a positive sign, for the arrangement 231 requires the interchange of 3 and 1 followed by the interchange of 2 and 1 to assume the normal order. Similarly, the fifth term has a positive sign. In the sixth term, it is necessary to make three interchanges (3 and 2, 3 and 1, and 2 and 1) in order to arrive at the normal order; hence, this term will have a negative sign. It follows that

$$D = a_{11}a_{22}a_{33} - a_{11}a_{32}a_{23} - a_{21}a_{12}a_{33} + a_{21}a_{32}a_{13} + a_{31}a_{12}a_{23} - a_{31}a_{22}a_{13}.$$

The main result of this discussion is that a determinant is the sum of all the $n!$ products which can be formed by taking *exactly one element from each row and each column* and multiplying by 1 or -1 according to a definite rule.

Example 1. By a development on the second column, evaluate

$$D = \begin{vmatrix} 1 & 0 & -1 & 2 \\ 6 & 0 & 4 & 3 \\ 4 & 7 & 0 & 2 \\ 2 & 0 & 2 & 3 \end{vmatrix}.$$

The $(-1)^{i+j}$ rule for determining sign means that the sign of the minors alternates as we proceed from one element to an adjacent one in the same row or column, and the sign starts with $+$ in the upper left-hand corner. Thus,

$$D = 0(-M_{12}) + 0(M_{22}) + 7(-M_{32}) + 0(M_{42}).$$

Crossing out the row and column containing 7 gives the determinant M_{32}, whence

$$D = -7M_{32} = (-7)\begin{vmatrix} 1 & -1 & 2 \\ 6 & 4 & 3 \\ 2 & 2 & 3 \end{vmatrix} = (-7)\left[(1)\begin{vmatrix} 4 & 3 \\ 2 & 3 \end{vmatrix} - (-1)\begin{vmatrix} 6 & 3 \\ 2 & 3 \end{vmatrix} + (2)\begin{vmatrix} 6 & 4 \\ 2 & 2 \end{vmatrix} \right]$$

$$= (-7)[(1)(6) - (-1)(12) + 2(4)] = -182.$$

Example 2. The following determinant is said to be in *diagonal form*. Show that its value is *abcd* no matter what elements are put in place of the *s:

$$D = \begin{vmatrix} a & * & * & * \\ 0 & b & * & * \\ 0 & 0 & c & * \\ 0 & 0 & 0 & d \end{vmatrix}.$$

Successive Laplace developments on first columns give

$$D = a\begin{vmatrix} b & * & * \\ 0 & c & * \\ 0 & 0 & d \end{vmatrix} = ab\begin{vmatrix} c & * \\ 0 & d \end{vmatrix} = abcd.$$

Evidently, a similar result is true in general.

Example 3. If the elements are differentiable functions of t, show that the derivative of the determinant (1-2) is

$$\begin{vmatrix} a_1' & a_2' & a_3' \\ b_1 & b_2 & b_3 \\ c_1 & c_2 & c_3 \end{vmatrix} + \begin{vmatrix} a_1 & a_2 & a_3 \\ b_1' & b_2' & b_3' \\ c_1 & c_2 & c_3 \end{vmatrix} + \begin{vmatrix} a_1 & a_2 & a_3 \\ b_1 & b_2 & b_3 \\ c_1' & c_2' & c_3' \end{vmatrix}.$$

A typical term in the expansion is $\pm a_i b_j c_k$. Differentiating gives

$$\pm (a_i b_j c_k)' = \pm a_i' b_j c_k \pm a_i b_j' c_k \pm a_i b_j c_k',$$

and the sum on i, j, k of these three types of terms yields the expanded form of the three determinants. A corresponding result for determinants of order n is proved in the same way.

The fundamental theorem (1-5) leads to some important properties of determinants that are now enumerated.

1. *If each element in a row or column of a determinant is zero, the determinant is zero.*

2. *If each element in a row or column is multiplied by m, the determinant is multiplied by m.*

3. *If each element of a row or column is a sum of two terms, the determinant equals the sum of the two corresponding determinants; for example,*

$$\begin{vmatrix} a_1 & b_1 & c_1 \\ a+\alpha & b+\beta & c+\gamma \\ a_2 & b_2 & c_2 \end{vmatrix} = \begin{vmatrix} a_1 & b_1 & c_1 \\ a & b & c \\ a_2 & b_2 & c_2 \end{vmatrix} + \begin{vmatrix} a_1 & b_1 & c_1 \\ \alpha & \beta & \gamma \\ a_2 & b_2 & c_2 \end{vmatrix}. \quad (1\text{-}6)$$

These three results become obvious when we make a Laplace development on the row or column in question. In (1-6), for example, let A, B, C be the cofactors of the elements in the second row. The determinant is

$$(a + \alpha)A + (b + \beta)B + (c + \gamma)C,$$

which equals $(aA + bB + cC) + (\alpha A + \beta B + \gamma C)$. This, in turn, is the sum of the expansions of the two determinants on the right of (1-6). The proof for n-by-n determinants is very similar and should be supplied by the reader.

4. *If two rows or two columns are proportional, the determinant is zero.*

5. *If two rows or two columns are interchanged, the determinant changes sign.*

6. *If rows and columns are interchanged, the determinant is unaltered.*

The properties 4, 5, and 6 are easily verified for 2-by-2 determinants, then proved in general by mathematical induction. To obtain item 6, for example, expand the original determinant on elements of the first row and the new one on elements of the first column. The theorem for order n then follows from the theorem for order $n - 1$. As an illustration we have

$$\begin{vmatrix} a_1 & b_1 & c_1 \\ a_2 & b_2 & c_2 \\ a_3 & b_3 & c_3 \end{vmatrix} = a_1 \begin{vmatrix} b_2 & c_2 \\ b_3 & c_3 \end{vmatrix} - a_2 \begin{vmatrix} b_1 & c_1 \\ b_3 & c_3 \end{vmatrix} + a_3 \begin{vmatrix} b_1 & c_1 \\ b_2 & c_2 \end{vmatrix}, \quad (1\text{-}7)$$

which coincides with the expansion (1-2) when we interchange rows and columns of the second-order determinants on the right-hand side of (1-7).

7. *The value of a determinant is unaltered if a multiple of one row (or column) is added to another.*

8. *If the cofactors for one row (or column) are combined with the elements of another, as in (1-8), the resulting sum is zero:*

$$\sum_{i=1}^{n} a_{ij}A_{ik} = 0, \qquad \sum_{i=1}^{n} a_{ji}A_{ki} = 0, \qquad k \neq j. \qquad (1\text{-}8)$$

These results follow from those already established. To illustrate the proof of item 7, we have

$$
\begin{vmatrix} a_1 & b_1 + mc_1 & c_1 \\ a_2 & b_2 + mc_2 & c_2 \\ a_3 & b_3 + mc_3 & c_3 \end{vmatrix} = \begin{vmatrix} a_1 & b_1 & c_1 \\ a_2 & b_2 & c_2 \\ a_3 & b_3 & c_3 \end{vmatrix} + \begin{vmatrix} a_1 & mc_1 & c_1 \\ a_2 & mc_2 & c_2 \\ a_3 & mc_3 & c_3 \end{vmatrix} \tag{1-9}
$$

by 3; and the second determinant on the right of (1-9) is zero by 4. The reader should extend the proof to n-by-n determinants.

The result 8 follows from 4. Thus, the first expression (1-8) is the expansion of the determinant which arises when the row

$$
a_{1k}, a_{2k}, \ldots, a_{nk}
$$

is replaced by $a_{1j}, a_{2j}, \ldots, a_{nk}$, and hence it is the expansion of a determinant with two equal rows.

9. *If two determinants A and B of order n are given and a new determinant C is formed, the element in the ith row and jth column of which is obtained by multiplying each element in the ith row of A by the corresponding element in the jth row of B and adding the products thus formed, then $C = AB$.*

Thus, if the elements of A and B are denoted by a_{ij} and b_{ij}, respectively, then the element c_{ij} in the ith row and jth column of the product determinant C is

$$
c_{ij} = a_{i1}b_{j1} + a_{i2}b_{j2} + \cdots + a_{in}b_{jn}. \tag{1-10}
$$

The validity of rule 9 for determinants of order n follows from considerations entirely similar to those we give next for the case when $n = 2$.

If the determinants A and B are of second order, formula (1-10) states that their product C is

$$
C = \begin{vmatrix} a_{11}b_{11} + a_{12}b_{12} & a_{11}b_{21} + a_{12}b_{22} \\ a_{21}b_{11} + a_{22}b_{12} & a_{21}b_{21} + a_{22}b_{22} \end{vmatrix}. \tag{1-11}
$$

Since the elements in (1-11) are binomials, we can write C by using property 3 as the sum of four determinants:

$$
C = \begin{vmatrix} a_{11}b_{11} & a_{11}b_{21} \\ a_{21}b_{11} & a_{21}b_{21} \end{vmatrix} + \begin{vmatrix} a_{11}b_{11} & a_{12}b_{22} \\ a_{21}b_{11} & a_{22}b_{22} \end{vmatrix}
$$

$$
+ \begin{vmatrix} a_{12}b_{12} & a_{11}b_{21} \\ a_{22}b_{12} & a_{21}b_{21} \end{vmatrix} + \begin{vmatrix} a_{12}b_{12} & a_{12}b_{22} \\ a_{22}b_{12} & a_{22}b_{22} \end{vmatrix}.
$$

On factoring out the elements a_{11} and a_{21} in the first determinant, we obtain a determinant with two like columns, and hence its value is zero. Similar remarks apply to the fourth determinant. The second determinant, on factoring out b_{11} and b_{22}, yields $b_{11}b_{22}A$, while the third has the value $-b_{12}b_{21}A$. Thus

$$C = A(b_{11}b_{22} - b_{12}b_{21})$$
$$= AB.$$

Similar, but much more laborious, calculations can be carried out for determinants of higher order to establish the validity of rule 9.

Since the value of a determinant is unchanged when its rows and columns are interchanged, there are four ways in which the determinant C may be written. Thus, if we interchange the rows and columns of B, the elements c_{ij} in C will be given by (1-10) in which the subscripts on the bs are interchanged.[1]

Example 4. Without expanding show that

$$\begin{vmatrix} 1 & x_1 & x_1^2 \\ 1 & x_2 & x_2^2 \\ 1 & x_3 & x_3^2 \end{vmatrix} = (x_1 - x_2)(x_3 - x_2)(x_1 - x_3).$$

The determinant is a polynomial in x_1, and it vanishes when $x_1 = x_2$, since the first two rows are then proportional. Hence it is divisible by $x_1 - x_2$. Similarly, it is divisible by $x_3 - x_2$ and $x_1 - x_3$. It therefore equals

$$E(x_1 - x_2)(x_3 - x_2)(x_1 - x_3)$$

for some polynomial E. Since the determinant is of degree 3 in x_1, x_2, x_3, we must have $E = $ const, and comparing coefficients of $x_2 x_3^2$ shows that $E = 1$.

Example 5. Write the product of the determinants

$$A = \begin{vmatrix} 1 & 2 & 1 \\ 3 & 0 & 1 \\ 0 & 2 & 1 \end{vmatrix} \quad \text{and} \quad B = \begin{vmatrix} -1 & 4 & 2 \\ 2 & -1 & 3 \\ 0 & 2 & -1 \end{vmatrix}$$

as a single determinant of third order.

Using rule 9 we find

$$AB = \begin{vmatrix} -1+8+2 & 2-2+3 & 0+4-1 \\ -3+0+2 & 6-0+3 & 0+0-1 \\ 0+8+2 & 0-2+3 & 0+4-1 \end{vmatrix}$$
$$= \begin{vmatrix} 9 & 3 & 3 \\ -1 & 9 & -1 \\ 10 & 1 & 3 \end{vmatrix}.$$

To check the result, we find on expanding the determinants A, B, and AB that $A = -2$, $B = 21$, and $AB = -42$.

Example 6. Show that a trigonometric polynomial

$$y = a_1 \sin x + a_2 \sin 2x + a_3 \sin 3x \qquad (1\text{-}12)$$

[1] Cf. Eq. (15-3), Chap. 4.

passing through three assigned points (x_i, y_i) is given, in general, by

$$
\begin{vmatrix}
y & \sin x & \sin 2x & \sin 3x \\
y_1 & \sin x_1 & \sin 2x_1 & \sin 3x_1 \\
y_2 & \sin x_2 & \sin 2x_2 & \sin 3x_2 \\
y_3 & \sin x_3 & \sin 2x_3 & \sin 3x_3
\end{vmatrix} = 0.
$$

Expanding on the first row gives

$$c_1 y + c_2 \sin x + c_3 \sin 2x + c_4 \sin 3x = 0$$

where c_i are the appropriate cofactors. Hence y has the form (1-12), if $c_1 \neq 0$. Moreover, when $x = x_i$ and $y = y_i$ the equation is true, since two rows of the determinant are then equal.

PROBLEMS

1. By a Laplace development on the first row, evaluate

$$
\begin{vmatrix} 1 & 2 & 3 \\ 3 & 1 & 2 \\ 2 & 3 & 1 \end{vmatrix}, \quad
\begin{vmatrix} -1 & 2 & 2 \\ -3 & 6 & 6 \\ 5 & 7 & 9 \end{vmatrix}, \quad
\begin{vmatrix} 1 & 0 & 0 \\ 0 & 0 & 1 \\ 0 & 1 & 0 \end{vmatrix}, \quad
\begin{vmatrix} 1 & 2 & 3 \\ 4 & 5 & 6 \\ 7 & 8 & 9 \end{vmatrix}.
$$

2. Evaluate the determinants in Prob. 1 by a Laplace development on (a) the first column, (b) the second row.

3. Evaluate this determinant by development on

(a) The first column
(b) The second row
(c) The first row
(d) The third column

$$
\begin{vmatrix}
1 & -1 & 1 & -1 \\
0 & 1 & -1 & 1 \\
0 & 0 & 1 & -1 \\
1 & 0 & 0 & 1
\end{vmatrix}.
$$

4. Show that

$$
\begin{vmatrix} x_1 & 1 \\ x_2 & 1 \end{vmatrix}, \quad \frac{1}{2} \begin{vmatrix} x_1 & y_1 & 1 \\ x_2 & y_2 & 1 \\ x_3 & y_3 & 1 \end{vmatrix},
$$

represent, respectively, the (signed) length of the segment (x_1, x_2) and the area of the triangle with vertices (x_i, y_i).

5. Evaluate, using some of the properties 1 to 7:

$$
\begin{vmatrix} x & 1 & 1 \\ 1 & x & 1 \\ 1 & 1 & x \end{vmatrix}, \quad
\begin{vmatrix} y+z & x & x \\ y & x+z & y \\ z & z & x+y \end{vmatrix}, \quad
\begin{vmatrix} 0 & -a & -b \\ a & 0 & -c \\ b & c & 0 \end{vmatrix}.
$$

Hint: In the last determinant, interchange rows and columns.

6. Write out as determinants of third order the product of the first determinant in Prob. 1 by the second and third determinants.

7. Using determinants, find a, b, c if $y = a + b \cos x + c \cos 2x$ passes through $(0,0)$, $(\pi/2, 1)$, $(\pi, -2)$.

8. (a) Find a cubic containing the points $(0,1)$, $(1,-1)$, $(3,4)$, $(4,0)$. *Hint:* Consider a determinant with top row y, 1, x, x^2, x^3. (b) Write the equation of a polynomial of degree n whose graph contains $n + 1$ assigned points (x_i, y_i).

2. Cramer's Rule. Consider the set of simultaneous equations

$$a_1 x + b_1 y + c_1 z = d_1,$$

$$a_2 x + b_2 y + c_2 z = d_2, \tag{2-1}$$

$$a_3 x + b_3 y + c_3 z = d_3.$$

Now, by 2 and 7 of the preceding section,

$$x \begin{vmatrix} a_1 & b_1 & c_1 \\ a_2 & b_2 & c_2 \\ a_3 & b_3 & c_3 \end{vmatrix} = \begin{vmatrix} a_1 x & b_1 & c_1 \\ a_2 x & b_2 & c_2 \\ a_3 x & b_3 & c_3 \end{vmatrix} = \begin{vmatrix} a_1 x + b_1 y + c_1 z & b_1 & c_1 \\ a_2 x + b_2 y + c_2 z & b_2 & c_2 \\ a_3 x + b_3 y + c_3 z & b_3 & c_3 \end{vmatrix}.$$

Hence if x satisfies (2-1), it is necessary that

$$x \begin{vmatrix} a_1 & b_1 & c_1 \\ a_2 & b_2 & c_2 \\ a_3 & b_3 & c_3 \end{vmatrix} = \begin{vmatrix} d_1 & b_1 & c_1 \\ d_2 & b_2 & c_2 \\ d_3 & b_3 & c_3 \end{vmatrix}. \tag{2-2}$$

The determinant on the left of (2-2) is termed the *coefficient determinant* of the system (2-1); we denote it by D. Equation (2-2) and the corresponding relations for y and z may then be written

$$xD = \begin{vmatrix} d_1 & b_1 & c_1 \\ d_2 & b_2 & c_2 \\ d_3 & b_3 & c_3 \end{vmatrix}, \quad yD = \begin{vmatrix} a_1 & d_1 & c_1 \\ a_2 & d_2 & c_2 \\ a_3 & d_3 & c_3 \end{vmatrix}, \quad zD = \begin{vmatrix} a_1 & b_1 & d_1 \\ a_2 & b_2 & d_2 \\ a_3 & b_3 & d_3 \end{vmatrix}. \tag{2-3}$$

If $D \neq 0$, we may divide by D to express x, y, and z as quotients of two determinants.

To show that these values of x, y, and z actually satisfy the system (2-1), substitute into (2-1) and multiply through by D. The equations become

$$a_k \begin{vmatrix} d_1 & b_1 & c_1 \\ d_2 & b_2 & c_2 \\ d_3 & b_3 & c_3 \end{vmatrix} + b_k \begin{vmatrix} a_1 & d_1 & c_1 \\ a_2 & d_2 & c_2 \\ a_3 & d_3 & c_3 \end{vmatrix} + c_k \begin{vmatrix} a_1 & b_1 & d_1 \\ a_2 & b_2 & d_2 \\ a_3 & b_3 & d_3 \end{vmatrix} = d_k \begin{vmatrix} a_1 & b_1 & c_1 \\ a_2 & b_2 & c_2 \\ a_3 & b_3 & c_3 \end{vmatrix}$$

with $k = 1$, 2, or 3 respectively. Now, the determinant

$$\begin{vmatrix} a_k & b_k & c_k & d_k \\ a_1 & b_1 & c_1 & d_1 \\ a_2 & b_2 & c_2 & d_2 \\ a_3 & b_3 & c_3 & d_3 \end{vmatrix}$$

is zero because two rows are equal, and it yields the desired relation when expanded on elements of the first row (use Theorem 5 of the preceding section).

The foregoing method applies to n equations in n unknowns, and yields CRAMER'S RULE: *Let* [1]

$$a_{11}x_1 + a_{12}x_1 + \cdots + a_{1n}x_n = k_1,$$

$$a_{21}x_1 + a_{22}x_2 + \cdots + a_{2n}x_n = k_2,$$

$$\cdot \; \cdot \; \cdot \; \cdot \; \cdot \; \cdot \; \cdot \; \cdot \; \cdot \; \cdot \; \cdot \; \cdot \; \cdot \; \cdot \; \cdot \; \cdot$$

$$a_{n1}x_1 + a_{n2}x_2 + \cdots + a_{nn}x_n = k_n \tag{2-4}$$

be a system of n equations in the n unknowns x_i such that the coefficient determinant D is not zero. The system (2-4) has a unique solution $x_i = D_i/D$, where D_i is the determinant formed by replacing the elements $a_{1i}, a_{2i}, \ldots, a_{ni}$ of the ith column of D by $k_1, k_2, \ldots, k_n$ respectively.

Consider the *homogeneous system* which arises from (2-4) when the right-hand members are replaced by zero. This system obviously has a solution $x_1 = x_2 = \cdots = x_n = 0$, the *trivial solution*. If the coefficient determinant is not zero, the solution is unique by Cramer's rule. Hence *a homogeneous system can have a nontrivial solution only if the coefficient determinant is zero.* One can prove, conversely, that there is always a nontrivial solution of the homogeneous equations if the determinant is zero.

The rectangular array

$$\begin{pmatrix} a_1 & b_1 & c_1 & d_1 \\ a_2 & b_2 & c_2 & d_2 \\ a_3 & b_3 & c_3 & d_3 \end{pmatrix} \tag{2-5}$$

is termed the *augmented matrix* of the system (2-1). By striking out one or another column of the matrix (2-5), we are led to the square arrays

$$\begin{pmatrix} b_1 & c_1 & d_1 \\ b_2 & c_2 & d_2 \\ b_3 & c_3 & d_3 \end{pmatrix}, \quad \begin{pmatrix} a_1 & c_1 & d_1 \\ a_2 & c_2 & d_2 \\ a_3 & c_3 & d_3 \end{pmatrix}, \quad \begin{pmatrix} a_1 & b_1 & d_1 \\ a_2 & b_2 & d_2 \\ a_3 & b_3 & d_3 \end{pmatrix}, \quad \begin{pmatrix} a_1 & b_1 & c_1 \\ a_2 & b_2 & c_2 \\ a_3 & b_3 & c_3 \end{pmatrix}.$$

Since these arrays are square, they have corresponding determinants. Now (2-3) shows that all these determinants must be zero if $D = 0$ and if the system (2-1) actually has a solution. In other words, if $D = 0$ but a third-order determinant formed from (2-5) is not zero, then the system (2-1) is inconsistent.

The foregoing results are included in a general theory of linear systems, which is now discussed. An m-by-n *matrix* is a system of mn quantities a_{ij}, called *elements*, arranged in m rows and n columns. The array is cus-

[1] A compact derivation of this rule is given in Sec. 15, Chap. 4.

tomarily enclosed in parentheses, thus:

$$A \equiv \begin{pmatrix} a_{11} & a_{12} & \cdots & a_{1n} \\ a_{21} & a_{22} & \cdots & a_{2n} \\ \cdot & \cdot & \cdots & \cdot \\ a_{m1} & a_{m2} & \cdots & a_{mn} \end{pmatrix}.$$

If $m = n$, then A is the *coefficient matrix* of the system (2-4); the *augmented matrix* is obtained by adjoining a column with elements (in order) k_1, k_2, ..., k_n. If the matrix is square, one can form *the determinant of the matrix*, a determinant whose elements have the same arrangement as those of the matrix. From any matrix, smaller matrices can be formed by striking out some of the rows and columns. Certain of these smaller matrices are square, and their determinants are called *determinants of the matrix*. A matrix A is said to be of *rank r* if there is at least one r-rowed determinant of A that is not zero, whereas all determinants of A of order higher than r are zero or nonexistent. (The latter alternative arises if r equals the smaller of the two numbers m and n.) The rank is zero if all elements are zero. With these preliminaries we can state the following FUNDAMENTAL THEOREM: *Suppose we are given a set of m linear equations in n unknowns. Let the rank of the coefficient matrix be r, and let the rank of the augmented matrix be r'. If r' > r, the equations have no solution. If r' = r = n, there is one, and only one, solution. If r' = r < n, we may give arbitrary values to n − r of the unknowns and express the others in terms of these.*

The proof is too long for inclusion here. Important special cases were established, however, by the proof of Cramer's rule and by the discussion of (2-5). Further discussion of matrices is given in Chap. 4.

The r unknowns which are expressed in terms of the others must be associated with some nonvanishing determinant of order r.

Example 1. By Cramer's rule, find x and y, given

$$3x + y + 2z = 3,$$
$$2x - 3y - z = -3, \tag{2-6}$$
$$x + 2y + z = 4.$$

The coefficient determinant D is found to be 8, so that

$$8x = \begin{vmatrix} 3 & 1 & 2 \\ -3 & -3 & -1 \\ 4 & 2 & 1 \end{vmatrix} = 8, \qquad 8y = \begin{vmatrix} 3 & 3 & 2 \\ 2 & -3 & -1 \\ 1 & 4 & 1 \end{vmatrix} = 16.$$

Thus, $x = 1$, $y = 2$. If z is desired, one can find it from the third equation (2-6):

$$z = 4 - x - 2y = 4 - 1 - 4 = -1.$$

Example 2. For what values of λ do the equations

$$ax + by = \lambda x,$$

$$cx + dy = \lambda y \qquad (2\text{-}7)$$

have a solution other than $x = y = 0$?

Transposing to the left gives the homogeneous system

$$(a - \lambda)x + by = 0,$$

$$cx + (d - \lambda)y = 0.$$

For a nontrivial solution, the coefficient determinant must vanish:

$$\begin{vmatrix} a - \lambda & b \\ c & d - \lambda \end{vmatrix} \equiv \lambda^2 - (a + d)\lambda + (ad - bc) = 0. \qquad (2\text{-}8)$$

Thus, (2-7) has a nontrivial solution if, and only if, λ satisfies the quadratic (2-8).

Example 3. If the equations

$$ax^2 + bx + c = 0,$$

$$\alpha x^2 + \beta x + \gamma = 0 \qquad (2\text{-}9)$$

have a common root, show that

$$\begin{vmatrix} a & b & c & 0 \\ 0 & a & b & c \\ \alpha & \beta & \gamma & 0 \\ 0 & \alpha & \beta & \gamma \end{vmatrix} = 0. \qquad (2\text{-}10)$$

If x is the common root, (2-9) gives

$$ax^3 + bx^2 + cx \qquad\;\; = 0,$$

$$ax^2 + bx + c = 0,$$

$$\alpha x^3 + \beta x^2 + \gamma x \qquad\;\; = 0, \qquad (2\text{-}11)$$

$$\alpha x^2 + \beta x + \gamma = 0.$$

The system (2-11) is a homogeneous linear system in the "unknowns" x^3, x^2, x, 1, of which one (namely, 1) is not zero. Hence the coefficient determinant vanishes, and (2-10) follows.

Example 4. Give a necessary condition that these three lines be concurrent:

$$ax + by + c = 0,$$

$$a_1 x + b_1 y + c_1 = 0, \qquad (2\text{-}12)$$

$$a_2 x + b_2 y + c_2 = 0.$$

Let (x,y) be the point at which the three lines meet. With this particular choice of x and y, the three equations (2-12) are satisfied simultaneously. Now, these equations may be regarded as simultaneous equations in three unknowns x, y, and 1, one of which (namely, 1) is not zero. Hence the coefficient determinant vanishes:

$$\begin{vmatrix} a & b & c \\ a_1 & b_1 & c_1 \\ a_2 & b_2 & c_2 \end{vmatrix} = 0.$$

(The condition is also sufficient if no two of the three lines are parallel. The reader should observe the duality between points and lines which is illustrated by this and the following example.)

Example 5. Find a necessary and sufficient condition that the three points (x,y), (x_1,y_1), (x_2,y_2) lie on a line.

If the equation of the line is

$$ax + by + c = 0 \qquad\qquad (2\text{-}13)$$

we have, besides (2-13),

$$ax_1 + by_1 + c = 0,$$

$$ax_2 + by_2 + c = 0.$$

These equations may be regarded as a system in the unknowns a, b, c, which cannot all vanish if (2-13) represents a line. Hence the coefficient determinant must vanish:

$$\begin{vmatrix} x & y & 1 \\ x_1 & y_1 & 1 \\ x_2 & y_2 & 1 \end{vmatrix} = 0. \qquad\qquad (2\text{-}14)$$

Conversely, (2-14) ensures that the system has a nontrivial solution a, b, c. Compare Prob. 4, Sec. 1.

Example 6. Show that the following equations are consistent if, and only if, $k = 9$:

$$2x + 3y = 1,$$

$$x - 2y = 4, \qquad\qquad (2\text{-}15)$$

$$4x - y = k.$$

The coefficient matrix has rank 2, and hence the equations are consistent if, and only if, the augmented matrix also has rank 2. This entails

$$\begin{vmatrix} 2 & 3 & 1 \\ 1 & -2 & 4 \\ 4 & -1 & k \end{vmatrix} = 0,$$

which yields $1(7) - 4(-14) + k(-7) = 0$ or $k = 9$. The same result is found if we regard (2-15) as a system in the three unknowns x, y, k and solve by Cramer's rule. The reader should obtain the result of Examples 3 and 4 by considering the augmented matrix, as in the present example.

PROBLEMS

1. Solve, by Cramer's rule, the systems:

(a) $x + 2y + 3z = 3,$
  $2x - y + z = 6,$
  $3x + y - z = 4;$

(b) $2x + y + 3z = 2,$
  $3x - 2y - 2z = 1,$
  $x - y + z = -1;$

(c) $x + 2y = 1,$
  $2x - y - 2z = 3,$
  $-x + y + 3z = 2;$

(d) $2x + y + 3z + w = -2,$
  $5x + 3y - z - w = 1,$
  $x - 2y + 4z + 3w = 4,$
  $3x - y + z = 2.$

2. Obtain nonzero solutions when they exist.

(a) $x + 3y - 2z = 0,$
$\quad 2x - y + z = 0;$

(b) $x - 2y = 0,$
$\quad 3x + y = 0,$
$\quad 2x - y = 0;$

(c) $3x - 2y + z = 0,$
$\quad x + 2y - 2z = 0,$
$\quad 2x - y + 2z = 0;$

(d) $2x - 4y + 3z = 0,$
$\quad x + 2y - 2z = 0,$
$\quad 3x - 2y + z = 0;$

(e) $4x - 2y + z = 0,$
$\quad 2x - y + 3z = 0,$
$\quad 2x - y - 2z = 0,$
$\quad 6x - 3y + 4z = 0;$

(f) $x + 2y + 2z = 0,$
$\quad 3x - y + z = 0,$
$\quad 2x + 3y + 2z = 0,$
$\quad x + 4y - 2z = 0.$

3. Investigate the following systems and find solutions whenever the systems are consistent:

(a) $x - 2y = 3,$
$\quad 2x + y = 1,$
$\quad 3x - y = 4;$

(b) $2x + y - z = 1,$
$\quad x - 2y + z = 3,$
$\quad 4x - 3y + z = 5;$

(c) $3x + 2y = 4,$
$\quad x - 3y = 1,$
$\quad 2x + 5y = -1;$

(d) $2x - y + 3z = 4,$
$\quad x + y - 3z = -1,$
$\quad 5x - y + 3z = 7.$

4. (a) Give a necessary and sufficient condition that four points in space be coplanar. (b) Give a necessary and sufficient condition that four planes be concurrent.

5. As in Example 5, find a necessary and sufficient condition that four points lie on a circle.

6. Give a relation which the coefficients must satisfy if

$$ax^3 + bx^2 + cx + d = 0,$$

$$\alpha x^2 + \beta x + \gamma = 0$$

have a common root.

7. Give a condition on the coefficients of a general cubic $f(x)$ if it has a double root. *Hint*: $f(x)$ and $f'(x)$ have a root in common.

8. The system $ax + by = c$, $\alpha x + \beta y = \gamma$ represents two lines which may intersect at one point, may be parallel, or may coincide. Discuss the system geometrically, and thus obtain all the relevant results involving rank. *Hint*: Begin by showing that the lines are parallel if, and only if, the coefficient determinant is zero.

9. An equation $ax + by + cz = d$ represents a plane, and two planes are parallel if, and only if, corresponding coefficients a, b, c are proportional:

$$a = ka_1, \qquad b = kb_1, \qquad c = kc_1.$$

(You may assume these geometric facts.) As in Prob. 8, give a complete geometric discussion of the behavior of two equations in three unknowns.

10. As in Prob. 9, discuss the general system of three equations in three unknowns.

APPENDIX B

THE LAPLACE TRANSFORM

The use of Laplace tranforms for solving ordinary differential equations has its origin in a symbolic method developed by the English engineer Oliver Heaviside. It enables one to solve many problems without going to the trouble of finding the general solution and then evaluating the arbitrary constants. The procedure can be extended to systems of equations, to partial differential equations, and to integral equations, and it often yields results more readily than other techniques.

1. Definition of the Laplace Transform. The function $F(p)$ given by

$$F(p) = \int_0^\infty f(x)e^{-px}\,dx = \mathbf{L}(f) \tag{1-1}$$

is called the *Laplace transform* of $f(x)$, and the operator $\mathbf{L}$ that transforms f into F is called the *Laplace transform operator*. The operator $\mathbf{L}$ is *linear;* that is,

$$\mathbf{L}(f + g) = \mathbf{L}(f) + \mathbf{L}(g), \tag{1-2}$$

$$\mathbf{L}(cf) = c\mathbf{L}(f), \tag{1-3}$$

where c is any constant. Indeed, the definition of $\mathbf{L}$ shows that (1-2) is equivalent to

$$\int_0^\infty [f(x) + g(x)]e^{-px}\,dx = \int_0^\infty f(x)e^{-px}\,dx + \int_0^\infty g(x)e^{-px}\,dx$$

and this is a familiar property of integrals. The proof of (1-3) is similar.

To illustrate the calculation of a Laplace transform let $f(x) = e^{ax}$, where a is constant. The transform is

$$\int_0^\infty e^{ax}e^{-px}\,dx = \int_0^\infty e^{-(p-a)x}\,dx = \frac{e^{-(p-a)x}}{-(p-a)}\Big|_0^\infty = \frac{1}{p-a} \tag{1-4}$$

provided $p > a$. When $p \le a$, the integral diverges.

This example enables us to investigate the convergence of (1-1) for a general function $f(x)$, provided

$f(x)$ is piecewise continuous [1] on every finite interval

and   (1-5)

$|f(x)| \le Me^{ax}$ for some choice of the constants M and a.

Under these conditions the integral converges for $p > a$, just as in the foregoing example. In fact,

$$\int_0^l |f(x)|e^{-px}\, dx \le \int_0^l Me^{ax}e^{-px}\, dx \le M \int_0^\infty e^{-(p-a)x}\, dx.$$

Since the latter integral has the finite value (1-4), the integral on the left remains bounded as $l \to \infty$. This establishes not only the convergence but the *absolute* convergence of the integral defining $\mathbf{L}(f)$. The convergence is uniform if $p \ge a_0 > a$, where a_0 is fixed, and hence the operations we shall carry out later are justified.

The integral on the right of the foregoing inequality tends to zero as $p \to \infty$. This shows that

$$\lim_{p \to \infty} F(p) = 0 \qquad\qquad\qquad (1\text{-}6)$$

for all functions $F = \mathbf{L}(f)$ such that f satisfies (1-5). It is found, more generally, that $F(p) \to 0$ if $\mathbf{L}(f)$ converges for any finite value $p = p_0$, even when (1-5) does not hold. Hence, if $\lim F(p) \ne 0$ as $p \to \infty$, then $F(p)$ cannot be the Laplace transform of any function $f(x)$.

Example 1. Let $f(x) = x^b$. The change of variable $t = px$ yields

$$\int_0^\infty x^b e^{-px}\, dx = \int_0^\infty \left(\frac{t}{p}\right)^b e^{-t} \frac{dt}{p} = \frac{1}{p^{b+1}} \int_0^\infty t^b e^{-t}\, dt.$$

According to Chap. 2, Sec. 14, the latter integral is convergent for $b > -1$ and represents the generalized factorial $b!$. Hence

$$\mathbf{L}(x^b) = b!\, p^{-(b+1)} \qquad \text{for } b > -1. \qquad\qquad (1\text{-}7)$$

When b is negative, x^b is infinite at $x = 0$ and (1-5) does not hold.

By comparing the integral for $\mathbf{L}(f)$ with that for $\mathbf{L}(Mx^b)$ near the origin, one finds that (1-5) is really needed only for $x \ge 1$, provided $f(x)$ is piecewise continuous for $x > 0$ and satisfies the additional condition

$$|f(x)| \le Mx^b \text{ on } 0 < x < 1 \qquad \text{for some constant } b > -1.$$

Whenever we take a Laplace transform $\mathbf{L}(f)$ in the sequel, it is understood that $p > a$ and that f satisfies (1-5) or the more refined condition just described. On the other hand it is not required that $f(x)$ be real. For example, (1-4) holds when a is complex provided

$$p > \mathrm{Re}\,(a).$$

---

[1] See Chap. 2, Sec. 25. The following discussion uses a comparison test for integrals, which can be verified in the same way as the corresponding test for series. Cf. Chap. 2, Sec. 4, Theorem I, and Chap. 2, Sec. 6, Theorem I.

Example 2. The choice $a = ib$ in (1-4) yields

$$\mathbf{L}(e^{ibx}) = \mathbf{L}(\cos bx + i \sin bx) = \frac{1}{p - ib}.$$

Upon equating real and imaginary parts with due regard to (1-2) we get

$$\mathbf{L}(\cos bx) = \frac{p}{p^2 + b^2}, \qquad \mathbf{L}(\sin bx) = \frac{b}{p^2 + b^2} \tag{1-8}$$

for all real b. Differentiation with respect to b gives

$$\mathbf{L}(x \cos bx) = \frac{p^2 - b^2}{(p^2 + b^2)^2}, \qquad \mathbf{L}(x \sin bx) = \frac{2bp}{(p^2 + b^2)^2}. \tag{1-9}$$

Proceeding in this fashion one can construct a table of transforms, such as Table 2 given at the end of this appendix. Indeed, we have already derived entries 1a, 2a, 2b, 3b, and 4a of Table 2; and entry 3a can be obtained from (1-8) and (1-9), since $\mathbf{L}$ is linear.

2. Some Uses of the Laplace Transform.

If $\mathbf{L}[f(x)] = F(p)$, integration by parts leads to

$$\mathbf{L}[f'(x)] = pF(p) - f(0) \tag{2-1}$$

provided the hypothesis (1-5) applies to $f'(x)$ as well as to $f(x)$. That is,

$$\int_0^\infty e^{-px} f'(x)\, dx = e^{-px} f(x)\Big|_0^\infty + \int_0^\infty pe^{-px} f(x)\, dx. \tag{2-2}$$

For sufficiently large p Eq. (1-5) shows that $e^{-px}f(x) \to 0$ as $x \to \infty$, and the desired result follows.

The choice $f(x) = y$ in (2-1) gives

$$\mathbf{L}(y') = p\mathbf{L}(y) - y(0) \tag{2-3}$$

and the choice $f(x) = y'$ gives

$$\mathbf{L}(y'') = p\mathbf{L}(y') - y'(0) = p[p\mathbf{L}(y) - y(0)] - y'(0)$$

in view of (2-3). Hence

$$\mathbf{L}(y'') = p^2\mathbf{L}(y) - py(0) - y'(0). \tag{2-4}$$

The transform of the higher derivatives can be obtained similarly. For instance,

$$\mathbf{L}(y''') = p^3\mathbf{L}(y) - p^2 y(0) - py'(0) - y''(0). \tag{2-5}$$

These relations enable us to solve differential equations with constant coefficients.

As an illustration consider the problem

$$y'' + y = f(t), \qquad y(0) = y'(0) = 0, \tag{2-6}$$

which describes the response of a resonant circuit to an input $f(t)$. To make the problem definite let $f(t) = 0$ for $t < 0$, but $f(t) = 1$ for $t \geq 0$. (A switch

to a constant-voltage source is closed at time $t = 0$ and remains closed thereafter.)   The transform of (2-6) gives

$$p^2 \mathbf{L}(y) + \mathbf{L}(y) = \mathbf{L}(f) = p^{-1}$$

when we use (2-4) and the entry 1a of Table 2 with $a = 0$. Solving for
$\mathbf{L}(y)$,

$$\mathbf{L}(y) = \frac{1}{p(p^2 + 1)}.$$

It can be shown that a continuous function y is determined on $(0,\infty)$
as soon as its transform $\mathbf{L}(y)$ is known.   Hence, the foregoing equation
contains the solution implicitly.   To find the solution explicitly we use
partial fractions; thus

$$\mathbf{L}(y) = \frac{1}{p} - \frac{p}{p^2 + 1}.$$

The entries 1a and 2b of Table 2 give the desired answer

$$y = 1 - \cos t \quad \text{for } t \geq 0, \qquad y = 0 \quad \text{for } t \leq 0. \tag{2-7}$$

It is an especial merit of the Laplace transform that the initial conditions
are satisfied automatically.   In the foregoing illustration we did not find
the general solution and then determine the constants so that $y(0) = y'(0)$
$= 0$.   Nevertheless, the expression (2-7) satisfies these conditions, as the
reader can verify.

To illustrate further the introduction of initial conditions we shall solve

$$y''' - y' = \sin x \tag{2-8}$$

subject to

$$y(0) = 2, \qquad y'(0) = 0, \qquad y''(0) = 1. \tag{2-9}$$

The Laplace transform of (2-8) yields

$$p^3 \mathbf{L}(y) - 2p^2 - 1 - [p\mathbf{L}(y) - 2] = \mathbf{L}(\sin x) = (p^2 + 1)^{-1}$$

when we use (2-5), (2-3), and entry 2a of Table 2. Solving for $\mathbf{L}(y)$,

$$\mathbf{L}(y) = \frac{2p^2 - 1}{p^3 - p} + \frac{1}{(p^2 + 1)(p^3 - p)}.$$

By partial fractions

$$\mathbf{L}(y) = \frac{3}{4(p + 1)} + \frac{3}{4(p - 1)} + \frac{p}{2(p^2 + 1)}$$

and entries 1a and 2b of Table 2 give

$$y = \tfrac{3}{4}e^{-x} + \tfrac{3}{4}e^{x} + \tfrac{1}{2}\cos x.$$

The Laplace transform can also be used to solve systems of differential equations. As an illustration, let it be required to find y if

$$y' + 2z' + y - z = 25,$$
$$2y' + z = 25e^x, \tag{2-10}$$

with the initial conditions

$$y(0) = 0, \qquad z(0) = 25. \tag{2-11}$$

The transform of (2-10) leads to

$$p\mathbf{L}(y) + 2[p\mathbf{L}(z) - 25] + \mathbf{L}(y) - \mathbf{L}(z) = \frac{25}{p},$$

$$2p\mathbf{L}(y) + \mathbf{L}(z) = \frac{25}{p-1},$$

which simplifies to

$$(p+1)\mathbf{L}(y) + (2p-1)\mathbf{L}(z) = \frac{25(2p+1)}{p},$$

$$2p\mathbf{L}(y) + \mathbf{L}(z) = 25(p-1)^{-1}.$$

Solving for $\mathbf{L}(y)$, we get

$$\mathbf{L}(y) = \frac{25}{4p(p-1)^2(p+\frac{1}{4})}$$

$$= \frac{25}{p} - \frac{9}{p-1} + \frac{5}{(p-1)^2} - \frac{16}{p+\frac{1}{4}}.$$

by Partial Fractions

According to entries 1a and 1b of Table 2,

$$y = 25 - 9e^x + 5xe^x - 16e^{-x/4}.$$

It should be noted that this method enables us to find y without finding z. Also no extraneous roots are introduced, and the initial conditions are satisfied automatically.

PROBLEMS

1. If y satisfies $y'' - 3y' + 2y = 4$, $y(0) = 2$, $y'(0) = 3$, show that

$$\mathbf{L}(y) = \frac{2p^2 - 3p + 4}{p(p-1)(p-2)}.$$

Deduce that $y = 2 - 3e^x + 3e^{2x}$.

2. Solve by means of the Laplace transform

$$y'' + 4y = \sin x, \qquad y(0) = 1, \qquad y'(0) = 0.$$

3. Find $\mathbf{L}(y)$, and solve

$$y''' + y'' = e^x + x + 1, \qquad y(0) = y'(0) = y''(0) = 0.$$

4. Find $L(z)$ in Eqs. (2-10) and (2-11) of the text, and deduce that

$$z = 33e^x - 10xe^x - 8e^{-x/4}.$$

5. Solve by means of the Laplace transform and check by substituting into the given system:

$$y' + 3y + z' + 2z = e^{-2x}, \qquad y(0) = 0,$$
$$2y' + 2y + z' + z = 1, \qquad z(0) = 0.$$

6. Find y, given that

$$y' + z' = z' + w' = w' + y' = y, \qquad y(0) = z(0) = w(0) = 1.$$

7. If $f'(x)$ satisfies (1-5), show that $f(x)$ satisfies a condition of the same type, though

perhaps with a different value of a.   *Hint:* $f(x) = \int_0^x f'(t)\,dt + f(0).$

3. Discontinuities.   The Dirac Distribution.   Closing a switch in an electrical circuit introduces a discontinuity in the corresponding input function [cf. the discussion of (2-6)].   A discontinuity may also be produced by a sudden impulse in a mechanical system.   The Laplace transform is a most effective means of dealing with such situations, because the transform of many discontinuous functions is just as simple as $L(e^x)$ or $L(\sin x)$.

In this section we shall consider the response of a system to an impulse function which acts over a very short time interval but produces a large effect.   The physical situation is typified by a lightning stroke on a transmission line or by a hammer blow on a mechanical system.

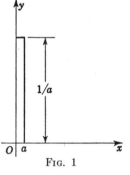

FIG. 1

To formulate the idea of an impulse, let a be a small positive constant and let $\delta_a(x)$ be the function illustrated in Fig. 1.   That is,

$$\delta_a(x) = a^{-1} \qquad \text{for } 0 < x < a$$

and $\delta_a(x) = 0$ elsewhere.   The Laplace transform is

$$L[\delta_a(x)] = \int_0^a a^{-1}e^{-px}\,dx = (pa)^{-1}(1 - e^{-pa}).$$

By the Taylor series for e^{-pa}

$$L[\delta_a(x)] = 1 - \tfrac{1}{2}(pa) + \cdots \to 1$$

as $a \to 0$.   It is customary to introduce an expression $\delta(x)$ which is thought to be the limit of $\delta_a(x)$ as $a \to 0$ and to say that

$$L[\delta(x)] = 1. \tag{3-1}$$

We call $\delta(x)$ the *Dirac distribution* or the *unit impulse,* and we take (3-1) as the basic defining property.   The legitimacy of this procedure requires further discussion, which will be given presently. First, however, the use of $\delta(x)$ will be illustrated by an example.

The displacement y of a weight suspended by a spring with stiffness 1 is determined by the system

$$y'' + y = f(t), \qquad y(0) = y'(0) = 0,$$

where $f(t)$ = force function
$\qquad t$ = time
$\qquad ' = d/dt.$

To determine the response to a unit impulse at $t = 0$ we replace $f(t)$ by $\delta(t)$; thus

$$y'' + y = \delta(t).$$

The Laplace transform yields

$$p^2\mathbf{L}(y) + \mathbf{L}(y) = \mathbf{L}[\delta(t)] = 1$$

when we use (3-1). Hence $\mathbf{L}(y) = 1/(1 + p^2)$, or

$$y = \sin t, \qquad t > 0.$$

The initial conditions require $y = 0$ for $t \leq 0$, and the graph has the appearance illustrated in the accompanying Fig. 2.

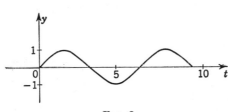

FIG. 2

The function y is continuous, but it is not differentiable at $t = 0$. Thus, the initial condition $y'(0) = 0$ is *not* satisfied. Indeed, $y'(t) \to 0$ as $t \to 0$ through negative values, but $y'(t) = \cos t \to 1$ as $t \to 0$ through positive values. The unit impulse produces a jump, of magnitude 1, in $y'(t)$.

To investigate the meaning of the foregoing result, we solve

$$y'' + y = \delta_a(t), \qquad y(0) = y'(0) = 0$$

and then let $a \to 0$. The general solution is

$$y = c_0 \sin t + c_1 \cos t, \qquad t < 0,$$

$$y = c_2 \sin t + c_3 \cos t + a^{-1}, \qquad 0 < t < a,$$

$$y = c_4 \sin t + c_5 \cos t, \qquad t > a.$$

By the initial conditions,

$$c_0 = c_1 = c_2 = 0, \qquad c_3 = \frac{-1}{a}.$$

To determine c_4 and c_5 we require that y and y' be continuous at $t = a$. This gives

$$-a^{-1}\cos a + a^{-1} = c_4 \sin a + c_5 \cos a,$$

$$a^{-1}\sin a = c_4 \cos a - c_5 \sin a.$$

Hence $c_4 = a^{-1} \sin a$, $c_5 = a^{-1}(\cos a - 1)$, and our solution is

$$y = 0, \quad t < 0,$$

$$y = a^{-1}(1 - \cos t), \quad 0 < t < a,$$

$$y = a^{-1} \sin a \sin t - a^{-1}(1 - \cos a) \cos t, \quad a < t.$$

Since $a^{-1}(1 - \cos t) \leq a^{-1}(1 - \cos a) \to 0$ as $a \to 0$, and since $a^{-1} \sin a \to 1$ as $a \to 0$, we see that letting $a \to 0$ gives the solution which was obtained previously by the method of Laplace transforms.

Although $\delta(x)$ is often called the "Dirac delta function," it is not a function. Indeed, we have already observed that $\mathbf{L}(f) \to 0$ as $p \to \infty$ for every function f, and δ does not have this property, because $\mathbf{L}(\delta) = 1$. It is possible to generalize the concept of function and to generalize, correspondingly, the definition of $\mathbf{L}$. The process leads to a branch of mathematics known as the *theory of distributions*.[1] In this theory manipulations with $\delta(x)$ of the type carried out in the foregoing discussion are fully justified.

Although a brief and correct definition of the *unit impulse* $\delta(x)$ is not easily given, it is easy to define what is meant by the *response of a system to the unit impulse*. Namely, find the response to the function $\delta_a(x)$, as in the foregoing example, and then let $a \to 0$. The Laplace transform gives the result of such a calculation directly, without introduction of $\delta_a(x)$.

PROBLEMS

1. The voltage V of a certain circuit satisfies

$$V'' + 4V' + 3V = E(t)$$

where E is the applied voltage. Find the response of the system to a unit impulse at $t = 0$ if $V = 0$ for $t < 0$.

2. (*a*) Solve the equations

$$y' = \delta(x), \qquad y'' = \delta(x), \qquad y''' = \delta(x)$$

assuming that $y = 0$ for $x < 0$ and that y and as many derivatives as possible are continuous. (*b*) Show that y, y', and y'' have a jump of value 1 at $x = 0$ in the three cases, respectively.

3. A certain function $U(x)$ satisfies

$$\alpha^2 U'' - \beta^2 U = -\tfrac{1}{2}\delta(x), \qquad x > 0$$

where α and β are positive constants. It is known further that $U(-x) = U(x)$, U is continuous, and $U \to 0$ as $x \to \infty$. Obtain the solution

$$U = (2\alpha\beta)^{-1} e^{-(\beta/\alpha)|x|}.$$

Hint: In forming $\mathbf{L}(U'')$, take $U(0) = c$, $U'(0) = 0$ where c is a suitably chosen constant.

---

[1] L. Schwartz, "La théorie de distribution," Hermann & Cie, Paris, 1950. See also B. Friedman, "Principles and Techniques of Applied Mathematics," chap. 3, John Wiley & Sons, Inc., New York, 1956.

4. The singular solution $u(x,t)$ for heat conduction satisfies

$$u_t = \alpha^2 u_{xx}, \qquad u(x,0) = \tfrac{1}{2}\delta(x).$$

(a) If $U(x,p) = \mathbf{L}(u)$, where the transform is with respect to t, show that $\alpha^2 U_{xx} - pU = -\tfrac{1}{2}\delta(x)$. (b) Using the result of Prob. 3 followed by Table 2, deduce that

$$u(x,t) = \frac{1}{2\alpha(\pi t)^{\frac{1}{2}}} e^{-x^2/(4\alpha^2 t)}.$$

Hint: The role taken by x in the table is taken by t in this problem.

4. Additional Properties of the Transform. The usefulness of the Laplace transform is greatly increased by the properties tabulated in Table 1. Entries $1a$, $1b$, and $4a$ were derived in the foregoing discussion, and the others will be derived now. To deduce the relation $2a$ we have

$$\int_0^\infty f(x - c)e^{-px}\, dx = \int_{-c}^\infty f(t)e^{-p(t+c)}\, dt = e^{-pc} \int_{-c}^\infty f(t)e^{-pt}\, dt$$

upon setting $t = x - c$. The limits $(-c,\infty)$ can be changed to $(0,\infty)$ if $f(t) = 0$ on the interval $(-c,0)$, and $2a$ follows. In particular, $2a$ holds if $c \geq 0$ and $f(t) = 0$ for $t < 0$. The relation $2b$ is simply the identity

$$\int_0^\infty e^{-(p-c)x}f(x)\, dx = \int_0^\infty e^{-px}e^{cx}f(x)\, dx.$$

This is valid without restriction on c, provided p is large enough.

For $3a$ we let $t = cx$ to obtain

$$\int_0^\infty f(cx)e^{-px}\, dx = \int_0^\infty f(t)e^{-(p/c)t}d\left(\frac{t}{c}\right) = \frac{1}{c} F\left(\frac{p}{c}\right)$$

as desired, provided $c > 0$. Writing $1/c$ instead of c in $3a$ gives $3b$, again for $c > 0$.

The result $4b$ follows by differentiating (1-1). For $5a$ we apply $4a$ to the function

$$f_1(x) = \int_0^x f(t)\, dt,$$

noting that $f_1(0) = 0$ and that $f_1'(x) = f(x)$ at points of continuity. The result $5b$ follows from integration of (1-1).

The *convolution theorem*, item 6 in Table 1, can be established by the following device: Since the Laplace transform involves $f(x)$ only on the range $(0,\infty)$, we can agree to take $f(x) = 0$ for all negative x. With a similar convention for $g(x)$, the respective Laplace transforms may be written in the form [1]

---

[1] Transforms of the type (4-1) are called *bilateral*, in contrast to the *unilateral* transform (1-1). An account of the bilateral Laplace transform may be found in B. Van der Pol and H. Bremmer, "Operational Calculus," Cambridge University Press, London, 1950.

$$L(f) = \int_{-\infty}^{\infty} e^{-px} f(x)\, dx, \qquad L(g) = \int_{-\infty}^{\infty} e^{-px} g(x)\, dx, \qquad (4\text{-}1)$$

and the function $h(x)$ of Table 1, entry 6, is equal to

$$h(x) = \int_{-\infty}^{\infty} f(\xi) g(x - \xi)\, d\xi. \qquad (4\text{-}2)$$

Indeed, the lower limit $-\infty$ in (4-2) may be replaced by zero because $f(\xi) = 0$ when ξ is negative, and the upper limit may be replaced by x because $g(x - \xi) = 0$ when $x - \xi$ is negative. Given (4-1) and (4-2), the convolution theorem $L(h) = L(f)L(g)$ can be proved by a discussion which is practically identical with a discussion given previously, and hence we do not repeat the argument here.[1]

Example: Periodic Functions. Let $P_0(x)$ be the function illustrated in Fig. 3, so that

$$P_0(x) = 1 \qquad \text{for } 0 < x < a, \qquad P_0(x) = 0 \qquad \text{elsewhere.}$$

Direct computation gives the transform

$$L[P_0(x)] = \int_0^a e^{-px}\, dx = p^{-1}(1 - e^{-ap}).$$

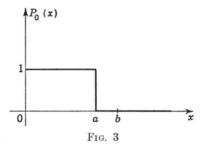

If the function is translated c units to the right, as shown in Fig. 4, the result is

$$L[P_0(x - c)] = p^{-1}(1 - e^{-ap}) e^{-pc} \qquad (4\text{-}3)$$

by Table 1, entry 2a. Upon choosing $c = 0$, $c = b$, $c = 2b$, $c = 3b$, ... and adding, we get a *square wave*[2] $y = P(x)$. According to (4-3) the Laplace transform is

Fig. 3

$$L[P(x)] = p^{-1}(1 - e^{-ap})(1 + e^{-pb} + e^{-2pb} + e^{-3pb} + \cdots) = p^{-1}\frac{1 - e^{-ap}}{1 - e^{-bp}}$$

when we recall the formula $1/(1 - r)$ for sum of a geometric series (Chap. 2, Sec. 1).

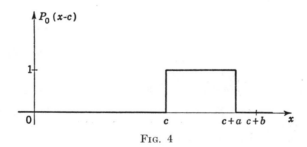

Fig. 4

---

[1] See Chap. 6, Sec. 18. In the present case the integrals are absolutely convergent, the change in order of integration is justified, and the process actually gives a valid proof.

[2] See Fig. 5. It is left for the reader to sketch the graph when $b = a$ and when $b < a$.

The procedure just described can be applied to any periodic function $P(x)$ and yields the formula

$$\mathbf{L}[P(x)] = (1 - e^{-bp})^{-1}\, \mathbf{L}[P_0(x)]$$

where b is the period and where $P_0(x) = P(x)$ on $0 < x < b$ but $P_0(x) = 0$ elsewhere.

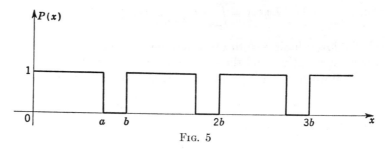

FIG. 5

For example, the reader can verify that the transform of the *sawtooth wave* shown in Fig. 6 is

$$(1 - e^{-bp})^{-1}ab^{-1}p^{-2}[1 - e^{-bp}(1 + bp)]. \tag{4-4}$$

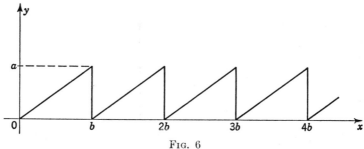

FIG. 6

PROBLEMS

1. Find a function $f(x)$ whose transform is

$$\frac{2p - 5}{3p^2 + 12p + 8}.$$

Hint: By completing the square the expression can be written in the form

$$\frac{2p - 5}{3(p + 2)^2 - 4} = \frac{2(p + 2) - 9}{3(p + 2)^2 - 4} = \frac{2}{3}\frac{p + 2}{(p + 2)^2 - \frac{4}{3}} - \frac{3}{(p + 2)^2 - \frac{4}{3}}.$$

Use Table 2, entries 2a and 2b, with $a = 2i/\sqrt{3}$ (see also Table 2, entry 7). Then use Table 1, entry 2b, with $c = -2$.

2. As in Prob. 1 find a function whose transform is

(a) $\dfrac{p + 1}{p^2 + 2p + 2}$, (b) $\dfrac{2p + 3}{2p^2 + 4p}$, (c) $\dfrac{p}{p^2 + 3p + 1}$.

3. Derive Table 2, entry 1b, from Table 2, entry 4a.

4. Derive Table 2, 5a, from Table 2, 5b, and Table 1, 4b.

5. Derive Table 2, 4b, from Table 2, 2a, and Table 1, 5b.

6. If $f(x) = x^{a-1}$ and $g(x) = x^{b-1}$, show that

$$f * g = x^{a+b-1} \int_0^1 t^{a-1}(1 - t)^{b-1} \, dt.$$

Hint: Let $\xi = tx$ in the definition of $f * g$ (Table 1, entry 6).

7. From Prob. 6 deduce the *Euler formula for the beta function*

$$B(a,b) = \int_0^1 t^{a-1}(1 - t)^{b-1} \, dt = \frac{(a - 1)!(b - 1)!}{(a + b - 1)!}.$$

Hint: By the convolution theorem applied to the result of Prob. 6,

$$\mathbf{L}[B(a,b)x^{a+b-1}] = \mathbf{L}(x^{a-1})\mathbf{L}(x^{b-1}).$$

5. Steady-state Solutions.   The Laplace transform will now be used to solve the general linear equation with constant coefficients,

$$y^{(n)} + a_{n-1}y^{(n-1)} + \cdots + a_1 y' + a_0 y = f(x), \tag{5-1}$$

subject to the initial conditions

$$y(0) = 0, \qquad y'(0) = 0, \qquad \ldots, \qquad y^{(n-1)}(0) = 0. \tag{5-2}$$

The solution satisfying (5-2) is called the *steady-state* solution of (5-1), because in many physical problems the effect of the initial conditions decays exponentially as x increases.

By repeated use of Table 1, entry 4a,

$$\mathbf{L}[y^{(k)}] = p^k \mathbf{L}(y), \tag{5-3}$$

for $k = 0, 1, 2, \ldots, n$, provided (5-2) holds. Hence the transform of (5-1) yields $G(p)\mathbf{L}(y) = \mathbf{L}(f)$, or

$$\mathbf{L}(y) = \frac{1}{G(p)} \mathbf{L}(f), \tag{5-4}$$

where $\qquad G(p) = p^n + a_{n-1}p^{n-1} + \cdots + a_1 p + a_0.$

Determination of y from (5-4) is especially easy when $G(p)$ has only simple roots $p_k \neq 0$. Indeed, expanding $1/G(p)$ in partial fractions leads to

$$\mathbf{L}(y) = \mathbf{L}(f)\Sigma \frac{A_k}{p - p_k} \tag{5-5}$$

where the A_ks are constant.[1] Since Table 2, entry 1a, gives

$$\Sigma \frac{A_k}{p - p_k} = \Sigma A_k \mathbf{L}(e^{p_k x}) = \mathbf{L}(\Sigma A_k e^{p_k x}),$$

Eq. (5-5) may be written

$$\mathbf{L}(y) = \mathbf{L}(f)\mathbf{L}(\Sigma A_k e^{p_k x}).$$

---

[1] If we multiply through by $p - p_k$ and let $p \to p_k$, it is found that $1/A_k = G'(p_k)$.

Comparing with Table 1, entry 6, gives *Heaviside's expansion theorem*

$$y = \sum_{k=1}^{n} A_k \int_0^x f(\xi) e^{p_k(x-\xi)} \, d\xi. \tag{5-6}$$

The essence of the method is that (5-4) leads to

$$\mathbf{L}(y) = \mathbf{L}(f)\mathbf{L}(g)$$

provided g is a function such that $1/G(p) = \mathbf{L}(g)$. By the convolution theorem,

$$y = f * g = \int_0^x f(\xi) g(x - \xi) \, d\xi.$$

This formula is valid even when $G(p)$ has multiple roots, though the determination of g may then be more difficult.

The function g can be thought to be the steady-state solution of

$$g^{(n)} + a_{n-1} g^{(n-1)} + \cdots + a_1 g' + a_0 g = \delta(x) \tag{5-7}$$

because the transform of (5-7) yields $G(p)\mathbf{L}(g) = 1$. However, since we have not developed the theory of distributions, it is better to avoid the use of $\delta(x)$. This question will be discussed next.

Let $h(x)$ be the steady-state solution of

$$h^{(n)} + a_{n-1} h^{(n-1)} + \cdots + a_1 h' + a_0 h = I(x) \tag{5-8}$$

where $I(x)$ denotes the *Heaviside unit function:*

$$I(x) = 0 \quad \text{for } x < 0, \quad I(x) = 1 \quad \text{for } x > 0.$$

The Laplace transform of (5-8) yields $G(p)\mathbf{L}(h) = 1/p$, so that

$$\mathbf{L}(h) = \frac{1}{pG(p)}.$$

Writing (5-4) in the form

$$\mathbf{L}(y) = p\mathbf{L}(f) \frac{1}{pG(p)} = p\mathbf{L}(f)\mathbf{L}(h)$$

we obtain

$$\mathbf{L}(y) = [\mathbf{L}(f') + f(0)]\mathbf{L}(h) = \mathbf{L}(f')\mathbf{L}(h) + f(0)\mathbf{L}(h)$$

by Table 1, entry 4a. The convolution theorem now yields

$$y = \int_0^x f'(\xi) h(x - \xi) \, d\xi + f(0) h(x). \tag{5-9}$$

Thus, *the steady-state solution of* (5-1) *can be obtained from the steady-state solution of* (5-8) *by means of the formula* (5-9). This important fact is known as the *superposition principle.*

As in the derivation of (2-4) one can show that

$$\mathbf{L}(y^{(k)}) = p^k \mathbf{L}(y) - p^{k-1}y(0) - p^{k-2}y'(0) - \cdots - y^{(k-1)}(0).$$

By means of this formula the Laplace transform can be used to solve (5-1) subject to the general initial conditions

$$y(0) = y_0, \qquad y'(0) = y_1, \qquad \ldots, \qquad y^{(n-1)}(0) = y_{n-1}.$$

It should be emphasized, however, that the superposition principle applies to steady-state solutions only.

PROBLEMS

1. Find the steady-state solution of

$$y'' + 3y' + 2y = f(x)$$

by use of Heaviside's expansion theorem.

2. Evaluate the result of Prob. 1 explicitly when

(a) $f(x) = I(x)$, (b) $f(x) = e^{3x}$, (c) $f(x) = x$.

3. By means of the superposition principle obtain the solutions (b) and (c) in Prob. 2 from the solution (a).

6. Integral Equations. An equation of the type

$$g(x) = \lambda f(x) + \int_0^x f(\xi)k(x - \xi)\,d\xi \tag{6-1}$$

where λ is constant is called an *integral equation*. It is supposed that g and k are known and that f is to be found. Because of its close relation to the convolution theorem, this equation lends itself to analysis by means of the Laplace transform. Indeed, taking the transform of (6-1) yields

$$\mathbf{L}(g) = \lambda \mathbf{L}(f) + \mathbf{L}(f)\mathbf{L}(k)$$

when we use the convolution theorem. Hence

$$\mathbf{L}(f) = \frac{\mathbf{L}(g)}{\lambda + \mathbf{L}(k)}$$

and from this, f can often be found. The process will now be illustrated by an example.

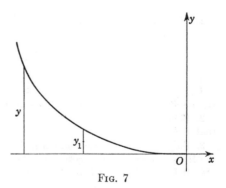

FIG. 7

Starting from rest, a particle slides down a frictionless curve under gravity (see Fig. 7). It is required to determine the shape of the curve so that the time of descent will be independent of the starting point. A curve of this sort is called a *tautochrone*. As we shall see presently, the only tautochrones are cycloids.[1]

---

[1] For another interesting property of the cycloid see Chap. 3, Sec. 14, Prob. 3.

If the particle starts at a height y, its velocity v when the height is $y_1 = \eta$ can be found by equating potential and kinetic energies. The result is

$$\tfrac{1}{2}mv^2 = mg(y - \eta) \qquad \text{or} \qquad v = (2g)^{\frac{1}{2}}(y - \eta)^{\frac{1}{2}} \tag{6-2}$$

where g is the acceleration of gravity. Denoting the arc along the curve by s, we see that the time for descent is

$$\int \frac{ds}{v} = \int \frac{1}{v}\frac{ds}{d\eta} \, d\eta = \int \frac{1}{v} f(\eta) \, d\eta$$

where $f(\eta)$ stands for ds/dy at $y = \eta$. Since the time is constant and since v is given by (6-2), the problem reduces to

$$\int_0^y f(\eta)(y - \eta)^{-\frac{1}{2}} \, d\eta = c_0$$

where c_0 is constant. This is an integral equation for f.

Taking the Laplace transform gives $\mathbf{L}(f)\mathbf{L}(y^{-\frac{1}{2}}) = \mathbf{L}(c_0)$, or

$$\mathbf{L}(f)(-\tfrac{1}{2})! p^{-\frac{1}{2}} = c_0 p^{-1}.$$

This gives $\mathbf{L}(f) = c_1 p^{-\frac{1}{2}}$, where c_1 is constant, and hence $f(y) = c y^{-\frac{1}{2}}$, where c is constant. Thus we are led to the differential equation

$$f(y) = \frac{ds}{dy} = \left[1 + \left(\frac{dx}{dy}\right)^2\right]^{\frac{1}{2}} = c y^{-\frac{1}{2}}.$$

If we set $y = c^2 \sin^2 \tfrac{1}{2}\phi$, a short calculation yields

$$x = \tfrac{1}{2}c^2(\phi + \sin \phi), \qquad y = \tfrac{1}{2}c^2(1 - \cos \phi)$$

which are the parametric equations of a cycloid.

REVIEW PROBLEMS

1. The current I in an RL circuit satisfies

$$L\frac{dI}{dt} + RI = V$$

where $V = V(t)$ is the applied voltage. At time $t = 0$ a switch is closed, so that V suddenly assumes the value $V_0 + A \sin \omega t$. (Here L, R, V_0, A, and ω are constants.) By use of the Laplace transform find I for $t > 0$.

2. Find the response of the circuit in Prob. 1 to a unit impulse at time $t = 0$, assuming that $V = 0$ for $t < 0$.

3. Find the steady-state solution in Prob. 1 when V is an arbitrary function by (a) the Heaviside expansion theorem, (b) the superposition principle.

4. If $\mathbf{L}(y) = F(p)$ use Table 1, entry 4b, to obtain

$$\mathbf{L}(xy) = -F', \qquad \mathbf{L}(xy') = -(pF)', \qquad \mathbf{L}(xy'') = -(p^2 F)' + y(0).$$

5. A function y satisfies $xy'' + y' + xy = 0$ and has a Laplace transform $\mathbf{L}(y) = F(p)$. By use of Prob. 4 show that

$$F'(1 + p^2) = -pF,$$

and thus deduce that $y = c J_0(x)$ where c is constant.

6. An insulated rod extending along the positive x axis is initially at temperature 0, and the end $x = 0$ has the temperature $f(t)$ at time t. The temperature $u(x,t)$ satisfies

$$u_t = \alpha^2 u_{xx}, \qquad u(x,0) = 0, \qquad u(0,t) = f(t).$$

(a) If $U(x,p)$ is the transform of u with respect to t, show that

$$U = \mathbf{L}(f)e^{-\sqrt{p}\,x/\alpha}.$$

[Assume that $U \to 0$ as $x \to \infty$, and note that $U(0,p) = \mathbf{L}(f)$.]

(b) By writing $U = \mathbf{L}(f)\mathbf{L}(g)$, where g is found from Table 2, deduce that

$$u(x,t) = \frac{x}{2\alpha\sqrt{\pi}} \int_0^t \frac{e^{-x^2/[4\alpha^2(t-\tau)]}}{(t-\tau)^{3/2}} f(\tau)\,d\tau.$$

7. Use the Laplace transform to solve some of the text examples and problems in Chap. 1, Secs. 21 to 26.

TABLE 1.   PROPERTIES OF $\mathbf{L}[f(x)] = F(p)$

	a	b
1	$\mathbf{L}(f + g) = \mathbf{L}(f) + \mathbf{L}(g)$	$\mathbf{L}(cf) = c\mathbf{L}(f)$
2	$\mathbf{L}[f(x - c)] = e^{-pc}F(p)$	$F(p - c) = \mathbf{L}[e^{cx}f(x)]$
3	$\mathbf{L}[f(cx)] = \dfrac{1}{c} F\left(\dfrac{p}{c}\right)$	$F(cp) = \mathbf{L}\left[\dfrac{1}{c}f\left(\dfrac{x}{c}\right)\right]$
4	$\mathbf{L}[f'(x)] = pF(p) - f(0)$	$F'(p) = \mathbf{L}[-xf(x)]$
5	$\mathbf{L}\left[\displaystyle\int_0^x f(t)\,dt\right] = \dfrac{F(p)}{p}$	$\displaystyle\int_\rho^\infty F(p)\,dp = \mathbf{L}\left[\dfrac{f(x)}{x}\right]$
6	$\mathbf{L}(f)\mathbf{L}(g) = \mathbf{L}(h)$	where $h(x) = \displaystyle\int_0^x f(\xi)g(x - \xi)\,d\xi$

TABLE 2. PAIRS OF TRANSFORMS $f(x)$ AND $F(p)$

	a		b	
1	e^{ax}	$\dfrac{1}{p-a}$	$\dfrac{1}{(p-a)^b}$	$\dfrac{e^{ax}x^{b-1}}{(b-1)!}$
2	$\dfrac{\sin ax}{a}$	$\dfrac{1}{p^2+a^2}$	$\dfrac{p}{p^2+a^2}$	$\cos ax$
3	$\dfrac{\sin ax - ax\cos ax}{2a^3}$	$\dfrac{1}{(p^2+a^2)^2}$	$\dfrac{p}{(p^2+a^2)^2}$	$\dfrac{x\sin ax}{2a}$
4	x^a	$\dfrac{a!}{p^{a+1}}$	$\tan^{-1}\dfrac{a}{p}$	$\dfrac{\sin ax}{x}$
5	$\dfrac{e^{-a^2/(4x)}}{x^{1/2}}$	$\left(\dfrac{\pi}{p}\right)^{1/2}e^{-a\sqrt{p}}$	$\dfrac{2\sqrt{\pi}}{a}e^{-a\cdot\sqrt{p}}$	$\dfrac{e^{-a^2/(4x)}}{x^{3/2}}$
6	$J_0(ax)$	$\dfrac{1}{(p^2+a^2)^{1/2}}$	$\dfrac{a}{(p^2+a^2)^{3/2}}$	$xJ_1(ax)$
7	$\cos iax = \cosh ax$		$\sin iax = i\sinh ax$	

COMPARISON OF THE RIEMANN AND
LEBESGUE INTEGRALS

1. The Riemann Integral. Let a function $f(x)$ be given on the interval $a \leq x \leq b$ (Fig. 1). To define the *Riemann integral*

$$\int_a^b f(x) \, dx \tag{1-1}$$

we divide the interval $[a,b]$ into smaller intervals by points x_k,

$$a = x_0 < x_1 < x_2 \cdots < x_n = b.$$

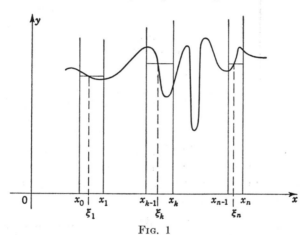

Fig. 1

It will be desirable to consider a sequence of subdivisions which are made finer and finer by choosing more and more points x_k. The precise requirement is

$$n \to \infty \quad \text{and} \quad \max_k |x_k - x_{k-1}| \to 0.$$

To describe this situation we say, in brief, that the subdivision becomes *arbitrarily fine*.

Let ξ_k be an arbitrary point on the interval $[x_{k-1}, x_k]$. With $y_k = f(\xi_k)$ as shown in Fig. 1, the sum

$$s = y_1(x_1 - x_0) + y_2(x_2 - x_1) + \cdots + y_n(x_n - x_{n-1}) \tag{1-2}$$

represents a certain area that presumably approximates the area under the curve $y = f(x)$. The geometric interpretation suggests that s has a unique limit s_0, independent of the manner of subdivision, provided the subdivision becomes arbitrarily fine. When s actually does have this behavior, $f(x)$ is said to be *Riemann integrable*, and the limit s_0 is called the *Riemann integral*.

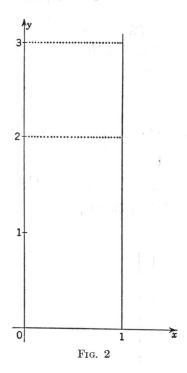

FIG. 2

The Riemann integral does not exist if $f(x)$ oscillates too violently. For example, let $a = 0$, $b = 1$ and define

$$f(x) = 2 \qquad \text{for } x \text{ rational,}[1]$$
$$f(x) = 3 \qquad \text{for } x \text{ irrational.} \tag{1-3}$$

It is easily shown that every interval (no matter how small) contains both rational and irrational numbers, so that the graph of $f(x)$ has the appearance suggested by Fig. 2. If we choose ξ_k rational, then $f(\xi_k) = 2$ and

$$s = 2(x_1 - x_0) + 2(x_2 - x_1) + \cdots$$
$$+ 2(x_n - x_{n-1}) = 2(x_n - x_0) = 2$$

no matter how fine the subdivision may be. On the other hand, if the ξ_ks are all irrational, then $s = 3$. This shows that the limit of s depends on the manner of subdivision and, hence, that the Riemann integral does not exist. As we shall see presently, the Lebesgue integral for this function does exist and can be evaluated explicitly.

2. Measure. The decisive idea in the Lebesgue integral is the notion of *measure*, which will now be described. The measure of an open [2] interval $a < x < b$ is simply the length $b - a$. If a set consists of a finite collection of such intervals (Fig. 3), the measure is the sum of the lengths. The

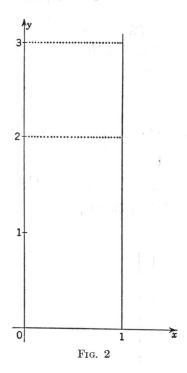

FIG. 3

same definition applies when there are infinitely many intervals. The sum of the lengths is now an infinite series, but since the terms are positive, *the sum does not depend on the order of the terms* (Chap. 2, Sec. 6, Theorem III). Thus, the measure is well defined in this case also.

[1] A *rational* number is a fraction p/q where p and q are integers. Thus $\frac{1}{3}$ and $-1\frac{7}{8}$ are rational, but $\sqrt{2}$ is not.

[2] An interval is *open* if the end points do not belong to the interval and *closed* if they do. Thus $a \leq x \leq b$ is a closed interval.

The notion of measure can be extended to still more general sets E as follows. Let I be a collection of open intervals which contains [1] E, and let $m(I)$ denote the measure of I. We approximate E better and better by these sets I, so that $m(I)$ becomes smaller and smaller. The smallest value for $m(I)$ which is given by this process is called the *outer measure* of E and is denoted by $m_0(E)$.

Strictly speaking, the "smallest value" need not be attained, and the precise definition of outer measure is as follows: The outer measure is the largest number c such that $m(I) \geq c$ for all sets I of the above-described type. The number c is called the *greatest lower bound* of the numbers $m(I)$; its existence can be established by the fundamental principle quoted in Chap. 2, Sec. 1.

A collection of open intervals, such as I in the foregoing discussion, is called an *open set*. As we have seen, outer measure is defined by considering the open sets containing E. The points of $[a,b]$ not belonging to a given open set form a *closed set*. By considering closed sets contained in E one can define the inner measure $m_i(E)$. If $m_i(E) = m_0(E)$, the set E is said to be *measurable* and the common value is called the *measure* of E.

To illustrate the calculation of a measure, let the set E consist of the rational points x on $0 \leq x \leq 1$, that is, the points whose coordinate x is a rational number. By taking first the rational numbers p/q with denominator $q = 1$, then those with $q = 2$, and so on, we see that the rational numbers can be arranged in a sequence

$$r_1, r_2, r_3, \ldots, r_n, \ldots. \tag{2-1}$$

Given $\epsilon > 0$, construct an open interval of length $\epsilon/2$ centered at r_1, an interval of length $\epsilon/2^2$ centered at r_2, and so on. The nth interval is of length $\epsilon/2^n$ and is centered at r_n. If I denotes the set consisting of all these open intervals, then

$$m(I) \leq \frac{\epsilon}{2} + \frac{\epsilon}{2^2} + \cdots + \frac{\epsilon}{2^n} + \cdots = \epsilon. \tag{2-2}$$

[We have inequality rather than equality in (2-2) because some of the intervals may overlap.]

The foregoing construction shows that the outer measure of E is $\leq \epsilon$. Since ϵ is arbitrary, the outer measure must be zero. Because $m_i(E) \leq m_0(E)$, it follows that the inner measure is also zero and, hence, $m(E) = 0$.

As a second illustration we shall find $m(E')$, where E' is the set of all irrational numbers on $[0,1]$. One of the most important properties of measure is that it is *additive;* if E and E' are two measurable sets with no point in common, then

$$m(E + E') = m(E) + m(E').$$

(We use $E + E'$ as an abbreviation for the set of all the points belonging either to E or to E'.) In the present case E is the set of rational points on $[0,1]$, and E' the set of irrational points on $[0,1]$. Evidently $E + E'$ is the set of all points on $[0,1]$, so that $m(E + E') = 1$. The above equation then gives

$$m(E') = 1 - m(E) = 1 - 0 = 1.$$

[1] That is, every point of E is interior to one of the intervals belonging to the set I.

3. The Lebesgue Integral. A function $y = f(x)$ is said to be *measurable* if the set of points x at which $f(x) < c$ is measurable for any and all choices of the constant c. It can be shown that the set e_k at which $y_{k-1} \leq f(x) < y_k$ is then measurable for all choices of y_{k-1} and y_k. To define the Lebesgue integral of $f(x)$, let the y axis be subdivided by points y_k as shown in Fig. 4, and form the sum

$$\sigma = y_1 m(e_1) + y_2 m(e_2) + \cdots + y_n m(e_n).$$

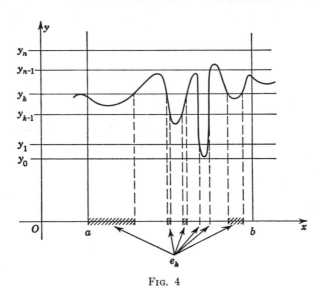

FIG. 4

When $f(x)$ is measurable and bounded, the sum σ has a unique limit σ_0, independent of the manner of subdivision, provided the subdivision becomes arbitrarily fine. This limit σ_0 is called the *Lebesgue integral* of $f(x)$ and is written in the form (1-1).

The most obvious difference between Riemann's definition and Lebesgue's is that in the former the x axis and in the latter the y axis is subdivided. This distinction, however, is superficial. The important fact is that Riemann's definition is based on the notion *length of an interval* whereas Lebesgue's is based on the more general notion, *measure of a set*. The intervals $x_k - x_{k-1}$ in Riemann's definition play the same role as the sets e_k in Lebesgue's.

Riemann's definition breaks down if $f(x)$ does not remain close to y_k throughout most of the intervals $[x_{k-1},x_k]$. Lebesgue's definition cannot break down in this way, because $f(x)$ is automatically close to y_k throughout the set e_k. That is why (in contrast to the former definition) the latter carries with it an assertion that the integral actually exists.

To illustrate the calculation of a Lebesgue integral we shall integrate the function (1-3) illustrated in Fig. 2. If the intervals (y_{p-1},y_p) and (y_{q-1},y_q) contain 2 and 3, respectively (Fig. 5), then the sets e_p and e_q are the only ones that are not empty. Thus $m(e_k) = 0$ for $k \neq p$ or q, and the sum reduces to

$$\sigma = y_p m(e_p) + y_q m(e_q).$$

Since e_p is the set of rational points and e_q the set of irrational points, these sets have the measures 0 and 1, respectively. Hence $\sigma = y_q$. As the subdivision becomes arbitrarily fine, $y_q \to 3$ and the Lebesgue integral is found to be

$$\int_0^1 f(x)\,dx = 3. \qquad (3\text{-}1)$$

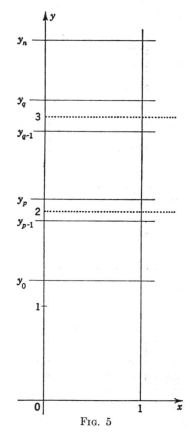

It can be shown that if the Riemann integral exists, then the Lebesgue integral exists also and the two have the same value. On the other hand, the latter may exist when the former does not, as we have just seen. Because of its greater generality the Lebesgue integral has many desirable properties, of which we mention the following:

LEBESGUE THEOREM ON BOUNDED CONVERGENCE. *Suppose* $|f_n(x)| \leq M$ *where* M *is constant, suppose* $f_n(x)$ *are Lebesgue integrable, and suppose* $\lim f_n(x) = f(x)$ *on an interval* $[a,b]$. *Then* $f(x)$ *is Lebesgue integrable, and*

$$\lim \int_a^b f_n(x)\,dx = \int_a^b f(x)\,dx.$$

To see why the theorem fails for Riemann integrals, let $f_n(x) = 2$ at the first n rational points r_k in the sequence (2-1) and $f_n(x) = 3$ elsewhere. Then $|f_n(x)| \leq 3$, and as a Riemann or Lebesgue integral,

$$\int_0^1 f_n(x)\,dx = 3. \qquad (3\text{-}2)$$

FIG. 5

Evidently, $\lim f_n(x) = f(x)$, where $f(x)$ is the function (1-3). Taking the limit of the expression (3-2) as $n \to \infty$, we get

$$\lim \int_0^1 f_n(x)\,dx = 3 = \int_0^1 f(x)\,dx \qquad (3\text{-}3)$$

provided the latter integral is the Lebesgue integral (3-1). Equation (3-3) does not hold for Riemann integration because, as we have seen, $f(x)$ is not Riemann integrable.

$$\textbf{TABLE OF } \Phi(x) = \frac{1}{\sqrt{2\pi}} \int_0^x e^{-t^2/2}\, dt \text{ *}$$

x	0.00	0.01	0.02	0.03	0.04	0.05	0.06	0.07	0.08	0.09
0.0	0.0000	0.0040	0.0080	0.0120	0.0160	0.0199	0.0239	0.0279	0.0319	0.0359
0.1	0.0398	0.0438	0.0478	0.0517	0.0557	0.0596	0.0636	0.0675	0.0714	0.0753
0.2	0.0793	0.0832	0.0871	0.0910	0.0948	0.0987	0.1026	0.1064	0.1103	0.1141
0.3	0.1179	0.1217	0.1255	0.1293	0.1331	0.1368	0.1406	0.1443	0.1480	0.1517
0.4	0.1554	0.1591	0.1628	0.1664	0.1700	0.1736	0.1772	0.1808	0.1844	0.1879
0.5	0.1915	0.1950	0.1985	0.2019	0.2054	0.2088	0.2123	0.2157	0.2190	0.2224
0.6	0.2257	0.2291	0.2324	0.2357	0.2389	0.2422	0.2454	0.2486	0.2517	0.2549
0.7	0.2580	0.2611	0.2642	0.2673	0.2704	0.2734	0.2764	0.2794	0.2823	0.2852
0.8	0.2881	0.2910	0.2939	0.2967	0.2995	0.3023	0.3051	0.3078	0.3106	0.3133
0.9	0.3159	0.3186	0.3212	0.3238	0.3264	0.3289	0.3315	0.3340	0.3365	0.3389
1.0	0.3413	0.3438	0.3461	0.3485	0.3508	0.3531	0.3554	0.3577	0.3599	0.3621
1.1	0.3643	0.3665	0.3686	0.3708	0.3729	0.3749	0.3770	0.3790	0.3810	0.3830
1.2	0.3849	0.3869	0.3888	0.3907	0.3925	0.3944	0.3962	0.3980	0.3997	0.4015
1.3	0.4032	0.4049	0.4066	0.4082	0.4099	0.4115	0.4131	0.4147	0.4162	0.4177
1.4	0.4192	0.4207	0.4222	0.4236	0.4251	0.4265	0.4279	0.4292	0.4306	0.4319
1.5	0.4332	0.4345	0.4357	0.4370	0.4382	0.4394	0.4406	0.4418	0.4429	0.4441
1.6	0.4452	0.4463	0.4474	0.4484	0.4495	0.4505	0.4515	0.4525	0.4535	0.4545
1.7	0.4554	0.4564	0.4573	0.4582	0.4591	0.4599	0.4608	0.4616	0.4625	0.4633
1.8	0.4641	0.4649	0.4656	0.4664	0.4671	0.4678	0.4686	0.4693	0.4699	0.4706
1.9	0.4713	0.4719	0.4726	0.4732	0.4738	0.4744	0.4750	0.4756	0.4761	0.4767
2.0	0.4772	0.4778	0.4783	0.4788	0.4793	0.4798	0.4803	0.4808	0.4812	0.4817
2.1	0.4821	0.4826	0.4830	0.4834	0.4838	0.4842	0.4846	0.4850	0.4854	0.4857
2.2	0.4861	0.4864	0.4868	0.4871	0.4875	0.4878	0.4881	0.4884	0.4887	0.4890
2.3	0.4893	0.4896	0.4898	0.4901	0.4904	0.4906	0.4909	0.4911	0.4913	0.4916
2.4	0.4918	0.4920	0.4922	0.4925	0.4927	0.4929	0.4931	0.4932	0.4934	0.4936
2.5	0.4938	0.4940	0.4941	0.4943	0.4945	0.4946	0.4948	0.4949	0.4951	0.4952
2.6	0.4953	0.4955	0.4956	0.4957	0.4959	0.4960	0.4961	0.4962	0.4963	0.4964
2.7	0.4965	0.4966	0.4967	0.4968	0.4969	0.4970	0.4971	0.4972	0.4973	0.4974
2.8	0.4974	0.4975	0.4976	0.4977	0.4977	0.4978	0.4979	0.4979	0.4980	0.4981
2.9	0.4981	0.4982	0.4982	0.4983	0.4984	0.4984	0.4985	0.4985	0.4986	0.4986
3.0	0.4987	0.4987	0.4987	0.4988	0.4988	0.4989	0.4989	0.4989	0.4990	0.4990

x	0.0	0.2	0.4	0.6	0.8
1.0	0.3413447	0.3849303	0.4192433	0.4452007	0.4640697
2.0	0.4772499	0.4860966	0.4918025	0.4953388	0.4974449
3.0	0.4986501	0.4993129	0.4996631	0.4998409	0.4999277
4.0	0.4999683	0.4999867	0.4999946	0.4999979	0.4999992

ANSWERS

CHAPTER 1

Section 1, Pages 10–11

  1. Ordinary, fourth order. **2.** Partial, fourth order. **3.** Ordinary, first order.
  4. Ordinary, first order. **5.** Ordinary, second order. **6.** Partial, second order.
  7. Ordinary, second order. **8.** Ordinary, third order.
  14. $y = x^2$; $y = x^2$; $y = x^2 + 1$; $y = x^2 - 2$.
  15. $y = \dfrac{x^3}{3} + x$; $y = \dfrac{x^3}{3} + c_1 x + c_2$.

Section 3, Pages 13–14

  1. $3\sqrt[3]{3}$.

  2. $\dfrac{dC}{dt} = -k_2 C - \dfrac{dB}{dt}$.

  3. $p = -k$; $a = kc/(k_1 - k)$.

  4. $(\log 2)/2$.

  5. $v = 30e^{-kt}$; $s = \dfrac{30}{k}(1 - e^{-kt})$.

  6. 2.32 hr; ∞.

  7. 2 in.

Section 4, Page 15

  2. The rate q would be thought of as $f(t)q$ instead, where $f(t) = 0$ for $0 \le t < t_0$ and $f(t) = 1$ for $t \ge t_0$. Equation (4-5) would be written $dx/dt = wr + f(t)q - rx/g$.
  3. $dx/dt = wr + kA_0 e^{-kt} - rx/g$. **5.** $(A - x)/(B - x) = (A/B)e^{kt(A-B)}$.
  6. Let x represent amount of substance dissolved after time t, A the amount of substance present when $x = 0$, $t = 0$, and c the proportionality constant. If v is the volume of solvent and S the saturate concentration, then $dx/dt = c(A - x) \times (S - x/v)$ if the dissolving substance does not change the volume v of the solvent.

Section 6, Page 18

  1. $\sin^{-1} x - \sin^{-1} y = c$.

  2. $(y - 1)/(y + 1) = ce^{x^2}$.

  3. $2 \cos y - \sin x \cos x + x = c$.

  4. $(\sec x - \tan y)\Big|_{(0,1)}^{(x,y)} = 0$.

  5. $(\tan^{-1} y - 2\sqrt{1 + x})\Big|_{(0,1)}^{(x,y)} = 0$.

  6. $(y + 1)/(x + 1) = 2$.

Section 7, Page 20

  1. $\left[\dfrac{y}{x}\left(3 + \dfrac{y^2}{x^2}\right)\right]^{1/6} = \dfrac{c}{x}$.

  2. $\sin^{-1} \dfrac{y}{x} - \log x = c$.

  3. $\sin \dfrac{y}{x} + \log x = c$.

  4. $x^2 - 2xy - y^2 = -2$.

5. $\log y + \dfrac{x^3}{3y^3} = \dfrac{1}{3}.$ 　　　　　**6.** $y - x + y \log x = 0.$

7. $2 \tan^{-1}(e^y) + \log \tanh \dfrac{x}{2} = c.$ 　　　　**8.** $y = ce^{-2\sqrt{x/y}}.$

9. $x = ce^{2\sqrt{y/x}}.$ 　　　　**10.** $\dfrac{1}{x} - \dfrac{1}{y} - \log y = c.$

11. $\log x + e^{-y/x} = c.$ 　　　　**12.** $y(2 - \log y) = \frac{1}{2}\tan^2 x + c.$

Section 8, Page 22

1. $e^x + x + y = c.$ 　　**2.** Not exact. 　　**3.** $x^3 y - xy^3 = c.$
4. $xy = c.$ 　　**5.** $\sin(y/x) = c.$ 　　**6.** $x^2 + y^2 = c.$
7. Not exact. 　　**8.** $x^2 + \sin xy = c.$ 　　**9.** $x^2 y + xy^2 + x = c.$
10. Not exact.

Section 9, Page 23

7. $y/x + x = c.$ 　　**8.** $x = cye^{1/xy}.$ 　　**9.** $yx^3 = ce^y.$
10. $y - 2\tan^{-1}(x/y) = c.$ 　**11.** $(x/y)e^y = c.$ 　　**12.** $y + x^2/y = c.$

Section 10, Page 25

1. $1 + \sqrt{x^2 + 1} = cxe^{-y\sqrt{x^2+1}}.$ 　　　　**2.** $y = \dfrac{x^3 + c}{3(x^2 + 1)}.$

3. $y = e^{-x^2}(x - 1).$ 　　　　**4.** $y = 1 - 2e^{-x^2/2}.$

5. $y = \cos^2 x + 2(\sin x - 1).$ 　　**6.** $y = 2\sin x - x\cos x + \dfrac{2}{x}\cos x + \dfrac{c}{x}.$

8. $y = \sin x + ce^x.$ 　　　　**9.** $x = ce^{(1/x)\sqrt{x^2-y^2}}.$
10. $x = 1 + ce^{-y^2/2}.$ 　　　　**11.** $x(1 + 4y^2)^{3/8} = c.$
12. $y = ce^{-(1-x)^2/2}.$

13. $x\sin^{-1}x + \sqrt{1 - x^2} + y^2/2 - e^y(y - 1) = c.$

Section 11, Page 27

1. $y = c_1 e^{3x}; \; y = c_2 e^{-x}.$ 　　　　**2.** $y = x + c_1; \; y = x + c_2.$

3. $y = \dfrac{p^4 - 2}{p^2}; \; x = 2p - \dfrac{4}{3p^3} + c.$

4. $y = \log(p^3 + 2p); \; x = -\dfrac{1}{p} + \dfrac{2}{\sqrt{2}}\tan^{-1}\dfrac{p}{\sqrt{2}} + c.$

5. $y = \dfrac{c^2 x + 1}{c}; \; y = 2\sqrt{x}.$ 　　　　**6.** $\sin^{-1}y \pm x = c.$

7. $y = ce^x; \; y = c - x^2.$ 　　　　**8.** $y = e^x + c; \; y = c - x^2/2.$

Section 12, Pages 28–29

1. $y^4 = (48x^{-2} - 96x^{-4} - 4)\cos x + (16x^{-1} - 96x^{-3})\sin x + cx^{-4}.$
2. $y^{-2} = x + \frac{1}{2} + ce^{2x}.$ 　　　　**3.** $y^{-5} = \frac{5}{2}x^3 + cx^5.$
4. $x = y\log cx.$ 　　　　**5.** $y^{-1} = 1 + \log x + cx.$

6. $y^{-2} = 1 + x^2 + ce^{x^2}.$ 　　**7.** $\dfrac{dv}{du} = \dfrac{u + v}{2u + v}; \; x = u - 3, \; y = v + 4.$

8. $\dfrac{du}{dx} - 3 = \dfrac{u - 1}{u}; \; u = 3x + y + 7.$

9. $\dfrac{dv}{du} = \sin\dfrac{u - v}{u + v}; \; x = u - \dfrac{5}{2}, \; y = v - \dfrac{1}{2}.$

10. $\dfrac{du}{dx} - 1 = \cos u; \ u = x + y.$ **11.** $x^{-2} = y + \frac{1}{2} + ce^{2y}.$

12. $2x = y^3 + cy.$ **13.** $y = \log(xy - c).$

14. $x \sec y = \log|\sec y + \tan y| + c.$ **15.** $y \tan^{-1} x = c.$

16. $\tan^{-1} y - \tan^{-1} x = c.$ **17.** $4xy + y^4 = c.$ **18.** $x \sin 2y = c.$

19. $e^{x-y} = c - x.$ **20.** $x^{-2} = y + \frac{1}{2} + ce^{2y}.$ **21.** $4x = 2y - 1 + ce^{-2y}.$

23. $y = e^{3x} + ce^{2x}.$ **24.** $y^2 = 2x^2 e^y + cx^2.$

Section 14, Page 33

1. $y = cx.$ **2.** $x^2 - y^2 = c.$

3. $x^2 + ny^2 = c.$ **5.** $\theta = c.$

9. Self-orthogonal family.

10. $x^2 - 2ax + y^2 = 0; \ 2xyy' + x^2 - y^2 = 0;$ a family of orthogonal curves is $x^2 - 2ay + y^2 = 0.$

Section 15, Page 34

1. $(a)\ y = cx;\ (b)\ x^2 + y^2 = c^2.$

2. $(a)\ c \pm x = \sqrt{1 - y^2} - \log[(1 + \sqrt{1 - y^2})/y];\ (b)\ y = ce^x.$

3. $(a)\ y = e^x;\ (b)\ y = \cosh x.$

4. $y^{v+v_0} = c(x + \sqrt{x^2 + y^2})^v.$ **5.** $t = |x_0|b/(b^2 - a^2);\ \frac{1}{2}|x_0| - \epsilon.$

Section 19, Page 46

1. $t = 100/g$ sec.

6. $\tan \theta = \tan \theta_0 + 2eE/(\omega m_0 c).$

Section 20, Pages 49–50

2. $v = \sqrt{2gh}, \ s = \frac{1}{2}gt^2 \sin \theta.$

4. $v = v_1(1 - e^{-gt/v_1}); \ (v/v_1)^2 = 1 - e^{2ksg/w}.$

5. $y = -\dfrac{g}{2v_0^2 \cos^2 \alpha} x^2 + x \tan \alpha.$

Section 21, Page 54

2. $y = -e^x + e^{2x}; \ y = 0.$ **4.** $y = -2x^2 + 4x.$ **5.** $y = e^{2x} + 2xe^{2x}; \ y = 0.$

Section 22, Page 56

1. $y = c_1 e^{-9x} + c_2 e^{6x}.$ **2.** $y = c_1 e^{3x} + c_2 e^{2x}.$ **3.** $y = c_1 e^x + c_2 x e^x.$

4. $y = c_1 e^{2x} + c_2 e^{-2x}.$ **5.** $y = c_1 \cos 2x + c_2 \sin 2x.$

6. $y = c_1 e^{2x} + c_2 x e^{2x}.$ **7.** $y = c_1 e^{2x} \cos x + c_2 e^{2x} \sin x.$

Section 23, Page 58

1. $y = c_1 e^{-x} + c_2 e^{x/2}.$ **2.** $y = c_1 e^x + c_2 e^{-x}.$ **3.** $y = c_1 e^{2x} + c_2 e^{-x}.$

4. $y = c_1 e^{3x} + c_2 x e^{3x}.$ **5.** $y = c_1 e^{-x} + c_2 x e^{-x}.$

Section 24, Page 63

1. $y = c_1 e^{3x} + c_2 e^{2x} + \frac{1}{2} e^{4x}.$ **2.** $y = (c_1 + c_2 x)e^{-x} + x - 2.$

3. $y = c_1 e^{-3x} + c_2 e^{-2x} + \frac{1}{12} e^x.$ **4.** $y = (c_1 + c_2 x)e^x + x + 2.$

5. $y = c_1 e^x + c_2 e^{-x} - 5x + 2.$ **6.** $y = c_1 e^x + c_2 e^{-x} + e^{2x}(x/3 - \frac{7}{9}).$

7. $y = (c_1 + c_2 x)e^x + x^3 e^x/6.$ **8.** $y = c_1 e^{3x} + c_2 x e^{3x} + x^2 e^{3x}/2.$

9. $y = c_1 + c_2 e^{-9x} + x/3.$

10. $y = c_1 \sin 3x + c_2 \cos 3x + \dfrac{9x^2 - 18x + 7}{81}.$

11. $y = c_1 e^x + c_2 e^{-x} + xe^x/2.$ **12.** $y = c_1 \sin x + c_2 \cos x + x^3 - 5x.$

13. $y = c_1 e^{3x} + c_2 e^{2x} + e^{2x}\left(\dfrac{-x^4}{4} - x^3 - 3x^2 - 6x\right).$

14. $y = c_1 e^x + c_2 x e^x + e^x\left(\dfrac{x^3}{6} - \dfrac{x^2}{2}\right).$ **15.** $y = c_1 e^{2x} + c_2 e^{3x} + \dfrac{2x^2 + 6x + 3}{4}.$

16. $y = c_1 + c_2 e^{5x} - \dfrac{x^3}{5} - \dfrac{13x^2}{25} + \dfrac{24x}{125}.$ **17.** $y = -4e^{-x} + 2e^{-4x} + 2e^x.$

18. $y = 1 - e^{-x} + x^2 - x.$ **19.** $y = 0.$

20. $y = (3x - 4)/9.$ **21.** $y = 0.$

22. $y = 2e^{-x} - 5e^{-3x}/9 + x/3 - \frac{4}{9}.$

Section 25, Page 66

1. $y = c_1 e^x + c_2 e^{2x} - (3 \sin 2x + \cos 2x)/20.$

2. $y = c_1 \sin 2x + c_2 \cos 2x - (\cos 3x)/5.$

3. $y = c_1 e^x + c_2 e^{-x/2} + 2 \sin x.$

4. $y = c_1 e^{-2x} + c_2 e^{-3x} + 3x e^{-2x} + e^{3x}/30.$

5. $y = e^{-x}(c_1 \sin 2x + c_2 \cos 2x) + e^x(\frac{1}{20} \sin 2x - \frac{1}{10} \cos 2x).$

6. $y = c_1 e^{3x} + c_2 e^{-2x} - \frac{1}{6} e^{3x} \cos 3x.$

7. $y = c_1 e^{-5x} + c_2 e^{-5x} + x e^{5x}/10 - x^2/25 + 4x/25 - \frac{2}{625}.$

8. $y = c_1 \sin x + c_2 \cos x + \frac{9}{8} \cos 3x - \sin 2x.$

9. $y = -e^x/4 + e^{-x}/4 - \frac{1}{2} \sin x.$

10. $y = 0.$

11. $y = -\frac{1}{4} + \frac{3}{20} e^{2x} + e^{-x}(\frac{1}{10} \cos x - \frac{1}{5} \sin x).$

12. $y = -\cos x + (x/2) \sin x + 1.$

Section 26, Page 70

1. $y = c_1 + c_2 e^{-3x/2} + c_3 e^{5x}.$

2. $y = c_1 \sin x + c_2 \cos x + e^{-x}(c_3 \cos 2x + c_4 \sin 2x).$

3. $y = c_1 e^{-x} + c_2 x e^{-x} + c_3 x^2 e^{-x}.$

4. $y = c_1 e^{-2x} + c_2 e^x \sin(\sqrt{3}\,x) + c_3 e^x \cos(\sqrt{3}\,x).$

5. $y = (c_1 + c_2 x)e^x + c_3.$

6. $y = (c_1 + c_2 x + c_3 x^2)e^{-x} + c_4.$

7. $y = c_1 \cos kx + c_2 \sin kx + c_3 \cosh kx + c_4 \sinh kx.$

9. $y = c_1 + e^{x/2}\left(c_2 \cos \dfrac{\sqrt{15}}{2}x + c_3 \sin \dfrac{\sqrt{15}}{2}x\right) + \dfrac{x^2}{2} + \dfrac{x}{4} + \dfrac{e^x}{4}.$

10. $y = e^{x/\sqrt{2}}\left(c_1 \sin \dfrac{\sqrt{2}}{2}x + c_2 \cos \dfrac{\sqrt{2}}{2}x\right) + e^{-x/\sqrt{2}}\left(c_3 \sin \dfrac{\sqrt{2}}{2}x + c_4 \cos \dfrac{\sqrt{2}}{2}x\right)$
$+ 2 \cos x.$

11. $y = c_1 e^x + c_2 e^{2x} + c_3 x e^{2x} - x^2/4 - x - 1\frac{1}{8}.$

12. $y = c_1 e^{-x} + c_2 e^x + c_3 e^{2x} + \frac{1}{2} + x e^x/2.$

13. $y = e^{-2x}/3 + 17e^x/12 + 7e^{-x}/2 - e^{-3x}/4 - 2x^2 + 2x - 5.$

Section 27, Page 72

1. Dependent.   **2.** Independent.   **3.** Independent.

4. Dependent.   **5.** Independent.   **6.** Dependent.

7. Independent.

Section 28, Pages 75–76

1. (a) $y = (x^3 - x^2)/3 - 2x/9 - \frac{2}{27}$; (b) $y = e^x/12$; (c) $y = x + 2$; (d) $y = \sin x$.

3. $y = -(x^2 \log x)/9$.   **4.** $y = c_1 e^x + c_2 x + x^2 + 1$.

Section 29, Page 77

3. $v' = c/[x^2(1 - x^2)]$.

Section 30, Page 79

1. $y = c_1 x^{-2} + c_2 x^{-1} + \frac{1}{2} \log x - \frac{3}{4}$.

2. $y = c_1 x^2 + c_2 x^{(5+\sqrt{21})/2} + c_3 x^{(5-\sqrt{21})/2} - \frac{1}{2}$.

3. $y = c_1 x^{(1+\sqrt{3i})/2} + c_2 x^{(1-\sqrt{3i})/2} + x^2/3$.

4. $y = c_1 x^2 + c_2 x - x[(\log x)^2/2 + \log x]$.

5. $y = c_1 x^2 + c_2 x^3$.   **6.** $y = c_1 x^n + c_2 x^{-n-1}$.

Section 32, Pages 85–86

1. $y = 2 \cos \sqrt{10}\, t, \dfrac{\sqrt{10}}{2\pi}$; $y = 2 \cos \sqrt{10}\, t + \sqrt{10} \sin \sqrt{10}\, t$.

3. $y = 10 \cos \sqrt{245}\, t$.

4. $y = 10 e^{-5t}(\cos \sqrt{220}\, t + \dfrac{5}{\sqrt{220}} \sin \sqrt{220}\, t)$; $R = 400\sqrt{245}$ dynes.

5. $V = 100\sqrt{2}\, e^{-500t} \cos \left(500t - \dfrac{\pi}{4} \right)$; $V = 100 e^{-500\sqrt{2}t}(1 + 500\sqrt{2}\, t)$.

6. $V = 20\sqrt{5}\, e^{-50,000t}(5 \sinh 10,000\sqrt{5}\, t + \sqrt{5} \cosh 10,000\sqrt{5}\, t)$.

10. $10 \dfrac{d^2y}{dt^2} + 10gy = 0$; max $y = \sqrt{3}$, total drop $2 + \sqrt{3}$.

Section 35, Pages 99–100

1. $y = c_1 \cos t + c_2 \sin t$; $x = c_1 \sin t - c_2 \cos t$.

2. $y = c_1 e^t + c_2 e^{-t}$; $x = c_1 e^t - c_2 e^{-t}$.

3. $y = e^t(c_1 + c_2 t)$; $x = e^t(c_1 + c_2/2 + c_2 t)$.

4. $y = c_1 e^t + c_2 e^{-t} + c_3 \cos t + c_4 \sin t$; $x = c_1 e^t + c_2 e^{-t} - c_3 \cos t - c_4 \sin t$.

5. $y = c_1(1 + \sqrt{2})e^{\sqrt{2}t} + c_2(1 - \sqrt{2})e^{-\sqrt{2}t}$; $x = c_1 e^{\sqrt{2}t} + c_2 e^{-\sqrt{2}t}$.

6. $y = c_1 e^{\frac{1}{2}(3+\sqrt{17})t} + c_2 e^{\frac{1}{2}(3-\sqrt{17})t} + \frac{1}{2}$;

$x = c_1 \left(\dfrac{3 + \sqrt{17}}{2} \right) e^{\frac{1}{2}(3+\sqrt{17})t} + c_2 \left(\dfrac{3 - \sqrt{17}}{2} \right) e^{\frac{1}{2}(3-\sqrt{17})t} + \dfrac{e^t}{2} - \dfrac{1}{2}$.

9. Cycloid of radius $mE/(eH^2)$.

Section 36, Page 106

1. $y_1 = c_1 e^{-x} + c_2 e^{3x}$; $y_2 = 2(c_2 e^{3x} - c_1 e^{-x})$.

CHAPTER 2

Section 2, Page 118

3. $1(c)$, $1(e)$ for $x = 0, \pm\pi, \pm 2\pi, \ldots$; none in Prob. 2.

4. $1(b)$, $1(e)$ for $x \neq 0, \pm\pi, \pm 2\pi, \ldots$; $2(a)$, $2(d)$.

5. $1(a)$, $1(d)$; $2(b)$, $2(c)$, $2(f)$.   **7.** (a) Yes; (b) no.

Section 3, Pages 121–122

1. div, $e^{-1}, \dfrac{1}{3}, \dfrac{1}{\log 2}$, div.   **2.** Con, con, div, con, div.

3. (a) $c < 0$; (b) con for $c < 0$.   **4.** $e^{999} < n < e^{1000}$.

5. $\frac{1}{3} < s < \frac{4}{3}$, $1.08190 < s < 1.08267$.   One term; eight terms.

Section 4, Page 124

1. Div, con, con, div.   **2.** Div, con, div, con, con.   **3.** Con, div, con, con.

4. (b) No. For example, $a_n = n$, $b_n = n$, $c_n = 1 - n$, $d_n = 2 - n$.

5. $N \geq -\dfrac{\log(9\epsilon)}{\log 10}$.

Section 5, Page 127

1. Con, div, con, con for $|x| < \sqrt{2}$, con.   **2.** Con, con for $c > 1$ only, div.

3. Con, con, con, div.

Section 6, Page 132

1. Cond con: div, abs con, abs con, abs con.

2. Abs con: $|x| < 1$, all x, $|x| < 1$, $|x| > 1$, $-\frac{4}{3} < x < 4$, $x = 0$, $|x - 2| < 1$, all x. Cond con: $x = 1$, never, never, $x = -1$, $x = -\frac{4}{3}$, never, $x = -3$.

3. 0.95.

Section 7, Pages 137–138

3. Unif con for (a) $-\infty < x < \infty$; (b) $|x| \leq c < 0.1$; (c) $|(2/\pi)x - n| \geq c > 0$, where n is the odd integer nearest to $(2/\pi)x$; (d) $1 < c \leq |x| < \infty$.

4. Unif con for (a) $-\infty < x < \infty$; (b) $|x| \leq c < 0.1$; (c) $2x/\pi =$ odd integer or $|(2/\pi)x - n| \geq c > 0$, where n is the odd integer nearest to $(2/\pi)x$; (d) $|x| \geq c > 1$ or $|x| \leq c < 1$.

5. Yes, no, no, yes.   **6.** No.

Section 8, Pages 142–143

1. Con for $-1 < x < 1$, $-\sqrt{2} < x < \sqrt{2}$, all x, $-3 < x < 3$, $-\sqrt[4]{3} < x < \sqrt[4]{3}$.

3. (b) $\tan^{-1} x = \sum \dfrac{(-1)^n}{2n + 1} x^{2n+1}$.   **4.** (d) $2.72, 0.368$.

5. $\Sigma(-1)^n \dfrac{x^{4n+1}}{4n + 1}$, $\displaystyle\sum_0^\infty (-1)^{n-1} \dfrac{x^{5n+6}}{(n + 1)(5n + 6)}$, $\sum \dfrac{n + 1}{3n + 6} x^{3n+7}$.

Section 9, Pages 146–147

1. (a) $\sum \dfrac{2^n x^n}{n!} = e^2 \sum \dfrac{2^n (x - 1)^n}{n!}$;

(b) $\Sigma(-1)^n \dfrac{\pi^{2n+1}}{(2n + 1)!} x^{2n+1} = \Sigma(-1)^{n-1} \dfrac{\pi^{2n+1}(x - 1)^{2n+1}}{(2n + 1)!}$;

(c) $\cos 1 \, \Sigma(-1)^n \dfrac{x^{2n}}{(2n)!} + \sin 1 \, \Sigma(-1)^n \dfrac{x^{2n+1}}{(2n + 1)!} = \Sigma(-1)^n \dfrac{(x - 1)^{2n}}{(2n)!}$

(d) $2 + x^2 = 3 + 2(x - 1) + (x - 1)^2$;

(e) $\sum \dfrac{(-1)^n}{2^{n+1}} x^n = \sum \dfrac{(-1)^n}{3^{n+1}} (x - 1)^n$.

2. (a) $e^a \sum \dfrac{(x - a)^n}{n!}$; (b) $\Sigma(-1)^n \dfrac{(x - 1)^{n+1}}{n + 1}$.

3. (a) $\Sigma(-1)^n(x-1)^n$; (b) $-\dfrac{1}{4}\Sigma\left(1+\dfrac{(-1)^n}{3^{n+1}}\right)(x-1)^n$;

   (c) $-\dfrac{1}{8}\Sigma\left(1+2(-1)^n-\dfrac{(-1)^n}{3^{n+1}}\right)(x-1)^n$.

4. $\dfrac{1}{2}\Sigma(-1)^n\dfrac{1}{(2n)!}\left(x-\dfrac{\pi}{6}\right)^{2n}+\dfrac{1}{2}\sqrt{3}\,\Sigma(-1)^n\dfrac{1}{(2n+1)!}\left(x-\dfrac{\pi}{6}\right)^{2n+1}$.

6. $\Sigma(-1)^n\dfrac{x^{2n}}{n!}$, $\Sigma(-1)^n\dfrac{x^{4n+2}}{(2n+1)!}$, $2\sum\dfrac{x^{2n}}{(2n)!}$, $\sum\dfrac{x^{2n+1}}{(2n+1)!}$, $\Sigma(-1)^n\dfrac{x^{4n+4}}{n+1}$.

Section 10, Page 149

1. (a) $\Sigma(-1)^n\dfrac{x^{2n+1}}{(2n+1)n!}$; (b) $2\sum\dfrac{x^{2n+1}}{(2n+1)(2n+1)!}$;

   (c) $\Sigma(-1)^n\dfrac{x^{4n+3}}{(4n+3)(2n+1)!}$; (d) $\Sigma(-1)^n\dfrac{x^{2n+1}}{(2n+1)(2n+1)!}$.

3. $\Sigma(-1)^n\dfrac{x^{p+n}}{n!(p+n)}$ for $p>0$ and all x.

4. $\dfrac{1}{p}+\displaystyle\sum_1^\infty\dfrac{(q-1)(q-2)\cdots(q-n)}{n!(p+n)(-1)^n},q>0,\,p\neq0,-1,-2,\cdots$.

Section 11, Pages 152–153

2. (a) $x+\frac{1}{3}x^3+\frac{2}{15}x^5+\cdots$; (b) $1+x+\frac{1}{2}x^2+\cdots$;

   (c) $1+\frac{1}{2}x^2+\frac{5}{24}x^4+\cdots$; (d) $\frac{1}{2}+\frac{1}{4}x-\frac{1}{48}x^3+\cdots$;

   (e) $1-\frac{1}{2}x-\frac{1}{12}x^2+\cdots$; (f) $1-\frac{1}{4}x^2-\frac{1}{96}x^4+\cdots$.

3. (a) 0.00133.　　　　　　　　　　**4.** $1\frac{0}{3}+\frac{4}{3}x^2+\cdots$.

5. 3.004, 0.985, 0.839, 2.036.　　　**6.** 0.310, 0.020, -1.025, 0.94.

7. $|\alpha|\le0.24$ radian $=14°$.　　　**9.** $\frac{1}{3}x^3-\frac{1}{42}x^7$.

Section 12, Page 155

1. $\Sigma\dfrac{2^n}{n!}x^n$, $1+x+2\displaystyle\sum_{n=2}^\infty\dfrac{x^n}{n!}$, 1.　　　**2.** $y=1+x^2+\frac{1}{2}x^4$; $k=2$.

3. $\sin^{-1}x=\sum\dfrac{1\cdot3\cdots(2n-1)}{2\cdot4\cdots2n}\dfrac{1}{2n+1}x^{2n+1}$.

Section 13, Page 159

1. (a) $a_0\Sigma(-1)^n\dfrac{x^{2n}}{(2n)!}+a_1\Sigma(-1)^n\dfrac{x^{2n+1}}{(2n+1)!}$;

   (b) $1+a_0\cos x+a_1\sin x$;

   (c) $a_0\left(1+\dfrac{x^3}{3!}+\dfrac{1\cdot4x^6}{6!}+\dfrac{1\cdot4\cdot7x^9}{9!}+\cdots\right)+\left(a_1\dfrac{x}{1!}+\dfrac{2x^4}{4!}+\dfrac{2\cdot5x^7}{7!}+\dfrac{2\cdot5\cdot8^1x}{10!}\right.$

$$+\cdots\Big)+\left(\dfrac{x^2}{2!}+\dfrac{3x^5}{5!}+\dfrac{3\cdot6x^8}{8!}+\dfrac{3\cdot6\cdot9x^{11}}{11!}+\cdots\right).$$

2. (a) e^x; (b) $x-1$.　　　　　　**3.** $c_1\Sigma(-1)^n\dfrac{x^n}{n!}+c_2\Sigma x^n$.

Section 14, Pages 165–166

5. $a_n=-\dfrac{1}{(n+p)n}a_{n-2}$.　　　**7.** (b) $\sqrt{\dfrac{2}{\pi x}}\,(c_1\cos x+c_2\sin x)$.

Section 17, Page 171

2. $\dfrac{\sin (n+1)x/2 \sin (nx/2)}{\sin (x/2)}$, $x \neq 0, \pm 2\pi, \pm 4\pi, \ldots$.

4. 12π.

Section 18, Pages 182–183

2. $\dfrac{3}{8}\pi + \sum_1^\infty \dfrac{(-1)^{n-1}}{2(2n-1)} \cos (2n-1)x + \sum_1^\infty \dfrac{(-1)^n}{4n} \sin 2nx + \sum_1^\infty (-1)^{n-1} \dfrac{1}{2n} \sin nx.$

Section 19, Page 187

1. $e, e, o, e, o,$ neither, e.

Section 20, Pages 191–192

2. $\dfrac{4}{\pi} \sum_0^\infty \dfrac{\sin (2n+1)(\pi/2)x}{2n+1}.$

3. $\dfrac{1}{2} - \sum_1^\infty \dfrac{4}{\pi^2(2n-1)^2} \cos (2n-1)\pi x.$

4. $\cos \pi x$.

Section 23, Page 204

2. $a_1 = \dfrac{4}{\pi}$; $a_2 = 0$; $a_3 = \dfrac{4}{3\pi}.$

CHAPTER 3

Section 1, Page 219

(a) Entire xy plane; (b) entire xy plane; (c) $y^2 \leq 5$;
(d) $x^2 + y^2 \neq 0$; (e) $x \neq 0$; (f) $(x-1)^2 + y^2 \leq 1$.

Section 2, Page 222

1. (a) $\dfrac{-y}{x^2}, \dfrac{1}{x}$; (b) $3x^2y - \dfrac{y}{x^2+y^2}, x^3 + \dfrac{x}{x^2+y^2}$;

(c) $y \cos xy + 1$, $x \cos xy$; (d) $e^x \log y$, e^x/y;

(e) $2xy + \dfrac{1}{\sqrt{1-x^2}}, x^2.$

2. (a) $2xy - z^2, x^2 + z, y - 2xz$; (b) $yz + \dfrac{1}{x}, xz + \dfrac{1}{y}, xy$;

(c) $\dfrac{z}{\sqrt{y^2-x^2}}, \dfrac{-zx}{y\sqrt{y^2-x^2}}, \sin^{-1}\dfrac{x}{y}$;

(d) $\dfrac{x}{\sqrt{x^2+y^2+z^2}}, \dfrac{y}{\sqrt{x^2+y^2+z^2}}, \dfrac{z}{\sqrt{x^2+y^2+z^2}}$;

(e) $\dfrac{-x}{(x^2+y^2+z^2)^{3/2}}, \dfrac{-y}{(x^2+y^2+z^2)^{3/2}}, \dfrac{-z}{(x^2+y^2+z^2)^{3/2}}.$

Section 3, Pages 227–228

1. $\pi/6$ ft^3.
2. 11.7 ft.
3. 0.139 ft.
4. 2,250.
5. 10.85
6. $8.64.
7. 0.112; 0.054.
8. 53.78; 0.93.
9. 0.003π; 0.3 per cent.
10. 1.6π; π.

Section 4, Page 230

1. $xx_0/a^2 + yy_0/b^2 = 1.$ **2.** $x(x_0^2 - ay_0) + y(y_0^2 - ax_0) = ax_0y_0.$

4. $ay + bx = \sqrt{2}\,ab.$

5. (a) $e^{t^2}\left(2t\sin\dfrac{t-1}{t} + \dfrac{1}{t^2}\cos\dfrac{t-1}{t}\right);$

(b) $2r(1 - 3\tan^2\theta),\ -6r^2\tan\theta\sec^2\theta.$

6. (a) $2x,\ 2(x + \tan x\sec^2 x);$

(b) $\cos\theta\dfrac{\partial V}{\partial x} + \sin\theta\dfrac{\partial V}{\partial y},\ r\left(\cos\theta\dfrac{\partial V}{\partial y} - \sin\theta\dfrac{\partial V}{\partial x}\right),\ \dfrac{\partial V}{\partial z}.$

Section 5, Page 235

1. (a) $y' = -\dfrac{\sec y + 3x^2y^2}{x\sec y\tan y + 2x^3y}\,;$

(b) $z_x = \dfrac{3x^2y}{\cos z - 3z^2}\,;\ (c)\ z_y = \dfrac{3x^2y}{\cos z - 3z^2}.$

2. $\dfrac{1}{x^2 + y^2}\left(x\sqrt{x^2 + y^2}\,\dfrac{\partial f}{\partial u} - y\,\dfrac{\partial f}{\partial v}\right);\ \dfrac{1}{x^2 + y^2}\left(y\sqrt{x^2 + y^2}\,\dfrac{\partial f}{\partial u} + x\,\dfrac{\partial f}{\partial v}\right);$

$(x^2 + y^2)^{-\frac{1}{2}}\sqrt{(x^2 + y^2)\left(\dfrac{\partial f}{\partial u}\right)^2 + \left(\dfrac{\partial f}{\partial v}\right)^2}.$

5. $du = 2x\,dx + 2y\,dy = 2r\,dr.$

6. $f_u = \dfrac{e^{xy}}{u^2 + v^2}(uy + vx);\ f_v = \dfrac{e^{xy}}{u^2 + v^2}(vy - ux).$

Section 8, Page 246

1. $(\pi + 1)/\sqrt{2}$

3. $\frac{1}{2}[3\sqrt{3} + 1 + e(1 + \sqrt{3})] \doteq 6.811.$

Section 9, Page 249

1. $a/3,\ a/3,\ a/3.$ **2.** $8abc/3\sqrt{3}.$ **3.** $a/3,\ b/3,\ c/3.$

4. $\sqrt{3}\,P/(2\sqrt{3} + 3),\ (\sqrt{3} + 1)P/2(2\sqrt{3} + 3),\ P/(2\sqrt{3} + 3).$

5. $l = h = \dfrac{1}{5\pi}\sqrt[3]{60\pi^2 V},\ d = \sqrt{5}\,l.$

Section 10, Page 254

3. (a) $105°45',\ 90°;$ (b) $164°15',\ 90.°$ **5.** $d/\sqrt{a^2 + b^2 + c^2}.$

Section 12, Pages 260–261

1. $\dfrac{\pi^2}{4} + \left(\dfrac{\pi^2}{4} - \dfrac{\pi}{2}\right)h + (\pi - 1)k + (\pi - 1)hk + k^2$

$+ \dfrac{\pi^3}{48}h^3 + \dfrac{\pi^2}{8}h^2k + \left(1 + \dfrac{\pi}{4}\right)hk^2 + \dfrac{1}{6}k^3 + \cdots$

where $h = x - 1,\ k = y - \dfrac{\pi}{2}$

2. $e\left\{1 + (h + k) + \dfrac{1}{2!}[h^2 + 4hk + k^2] + \cdots\right\},\ h = x - 1,\ k = y - 1$

3. $1 + x + \dfrac{1}{2!}(x^2 - y^2) + \dfrac{1}{3!}(x^3 - 3xy^2) + \dfrac{1}{4!}(x^4 - 6x^2y^2 + y^4) + \cdots$

Section 13, Pages 263–264

1. $\dfrac{\pi\sin(\pi\alpha/2)}{2\alpha} + \dfrac{\cos(\pi\alpha/2) - 1}{\alpha^2}.$ **2.** $\alpha\pi.$

3. $\alpha\left(\dfrac{\pi}{2} - \log 2\right).$

4. $-\tan\alpha.$

5. $2x^2.$

7. $\alpha\pi(\alpha^2 - 1)^{-\frac{3}{2}}.$

Section 14, Page 269

5. $\dfrac{d}{dx}(py') - qy - f = 0.$

Section 16, Pages 276–277

1. $\frac{1}{2}\pi a^4/h.$

2. $u\,du\,dv.$

3. $u^2v\,du\,dv\,dw.$

5. $32a^3/9.$

6. $\pi(1 - e^{-a^2}).$

Section 17, Page 281

1. $\pi a^2/2.$

2. $4a^2(\pi/2 - 1).$

3. $\frac{4}{3}a^3(\pi/2 - \frac{2}{3}).$

4. $8a^2.$

5. $\bar{x} = a\cos^2(\alpha/2).$

CHAPTER 4

Section 2, Page 291

2. $\mathbf{A} + \mathbf{B} + \mathbf{C} = 0.$

3. $\mathbf{A} = \frac{1}{2}(\mathbf{S} + \mathbf{D}),\ \mathbf{B} = \frac{1}{2}(\mathbf{S} - \mathbf{D}).$

5. $(a)\ \dfrac{\mathbf{A}}{|\mathbf{A}|}\ ;\ (b)\ \dfrac{k}{2}\left(\dfrac{\mathbf{A}}{|\mathbf{A}|} + \dfrac{\mathbf{B}}{|\mathbf{B}|}\right).$

Section 3, Page 293

1. $(a)\ 5\mathbf{j},\ -5\mathbf{j};\ (b)\ \mathbf{A} + \mathbf{B} = 2\mathbf{i} + 3\mathbf{j} + 4\mathbf{k};\ (\mathbf{A} + \mathbf{B}) + \mathbf{C} = 3\mathbf{i} + 3\mathbf{j} + 3\mathbf{k};$
$\mathbf{B} + \mathbf{C} = 2\mathbf{i} + \mathbf{j};$ associative law;
$(c)\ 5\mathbf{i} + 10\mathbf{j} \times 15\mathbf{k},\ -2\mathbf{i} - 4\mathbf{j} - 6\mathbf{k},\ 3\mathbf{i} + 6\mathbf{j} + 9\mathbf{k},\ 3\mathbf{i} + 6\mathbf{j} + 9\mathbf{k};$
$(d)\ 3\mathbf{i} + 6\mathbf{j} + 9\mathbf{k},\ 3\mathbf{i} + 3\mathbf{j} + 3\mathbf{k},\ 6\mathbf{i} + 9\mathbf{j} + 12\mathbf{k};$
$(e)\ -4.$

Section 4, Page 294

1. $(a)\ 10,\ 2,\ 8;\ (b)\ 6,\ 4,\ \mathbf{i} + 3\mathbf{j} + \mathbf{k},\ 10;\ (c)\ 12;$
$(d)\ \cos^{-1}3/\sqrt{21};\ (e)\ 4/\sqrt{5};\ (f)\ s = 4;\ (g)\ -\mathbf{i} - \mathbf{j} + \mathbf{k}.$

2. $(b)\ x = -20;\ y = 8;\ z = 1.$

Section 5, Pages 296–297

1. $(a)\ -2\mathbf{i} + 3\mathbf{j} - 4\mathbf{k},\ 5\mathbf{i} - 4\mathbf{j} + 3\mathbf{k},\ 3\mathbf{i} - \mathbf{j} - \mathbf{k},\ 2\mathbf{i} + 3\mathbf{j} + 3\mathbf{k},\ 3\mathbf{i} - \mathbf{j} - \mathbf{k};$
$(c)\ 13\mathbf{i} + 2\mathbf{j} + 2\mathbf{k};\ (d)\ \sqrt{177}/2.$

Section 6, Pages 298–299

2. $(a)\ 0;\ (b)\ x = \frac{8}{5};\ (d)\ 0,0.$

Section 7, Pages 301–302

1. $(a)\ \mathbf{R}'(t) = 2\mathbf{i} + 6t\mathbf{j} + 3t^2\mathbf{k};\ (b)\ \mathbf{R}'(1) = 2\mathbf{i} + 6\mathbf{j} + 3\mathbf{k};$
$(c)\ \mathbf{v} = 2\mathbf{i} + 6\mathbf{j} + 3\mathbf{k},\ |\mathbf{v}| = 7.$

2. $(a)\ \mathbf{v} = \mathbf{R}'(t) = \mathbf{i} + \mathbf{j}\cos t - \mathbf{k}\sin t;\ |\mathbf{R}'(t)| = \sqrt{2};$
$(b)\ s = 2\sqrt{2}.$

Section 8, Pages 305–306

1. $(a)\ W = 0;\ (b)\ W = -2;\ (c)\ W = 4.$

2. $(a)\ \mathbf{T} = -\mathbf{i} + 2\mathbf{j} - 3\mathbf{k};\ (b)\ \mathbf{T} = 2\mathbf{i} + 4\mathbf{j} + 4\mathbf{k}.$

3. (a) $\mathbf{v} = k\mathbf{A} \times \mathbf{B}$; (b) $\mathbf{v} = k\mathbf{C} \times (\mathbf{A} - \mathbf{B})$.
6. (a) $\mathbf{R} = \tfrac{1}{3}(2\mathbf{i} + 5\mathbf{j})$; (b) $\mathbf{R}(1,2) = \tfrac{1}{3}(4\mathbf{i} + \mathbf{j})$.

Section 9, Page 308

1. (a) $\mathbf{n} = \mathbf{i} + 2\mathbf{j} + 3\mathbf{k}$; (b) $\cos^{-1} 6/\sqrt{42}$; (c) $9/\sqrt{14}$.
2. (a) $\mathbf{i} + 2\mathbf{j} + 3\mathbf{k}$; (b) $x = 1 + t$; $y = 2t$; $z = 1 + 3t$; (c) $\sqrt{9/7}$;
   (e) $\tfrac{3}{2}\mathbf{i} + \mathbf{j} + \tfrac{5}{2}\mathbf{k}$; (f) $\tfrac{8}{9}\mathbf{i} - \tfrac{2}{9}\mathbf{j} + \tfrac{2}{3}\mathbf{k}$.
3. (a) $\mathbf{R} = 5\mathbf{i} - 2\mathbf{j} + (-4\mathbf{i} + 4\mathbf{j} - \mathbf{k})t$; (b) $-4\mathbf{i} + 4\mathbf{j} - \mathbf{k}$;
   (d) $-4x + 4y - z + c = 0$; (e) $\mathbf{R} = -3\mathbf{i} + \mathbf{k} + (-4\mathbf{i} + 4\mathbf{j} - \mathbf{k})t$.
4. (a) $D^2 = 3t^2 + 8$; (b) $t = 0$; $D = 2\sqrt{2}$.
5. $\mathbf{R} = (\mathbf{i} + \mathbf{j} + 3\mathbf{k})t$, $(-\tfrac{1}{8}, -\tfrac{1}{8}, -\tfrac{3}{8})$.

Section 10, Page 311

1. $\mathbf{n} = a\mathbf{i} + b\mathbf{j} + c\mathbf{k}$.
2. (a) $-\mathbf{i} + 6\mathbf{j} + 2\mathbf{k}$; (c) $2\mathbf{i} + \mathbf{j} + 3\mathbf{k} + (-\mathbf{i} + 6\mathbf{j} + 2\mathbf{k})t = R$.
4. $\theta = \cos^{-1} 9/\sqrt{102}$.
5. $-16\mathbf{i} + 8\mathbf{j} + 4\mathbf{k}$.

Section 11, Pages 315–316

1. (a) $(-\mathbf{i} + \mathbf{j} - \mathbf{k})/\sqrt{3}$; (b) $-x + (y + 2) - (z - 2) = 0$;
   (c) $\sqrt{3} + \log(1 + \sqrt{3/2})$.
2. (a) $\mathbf{v} = 2t\mathbf{i} + 2\mathbf{j} + 2t\mathbf{k}$; $\mathbf{A} = 2\mathbf{i} + 2\mathbf{k}$; (b) $v = 2\sqrt{2t^2 + 1}$;
   (c) $\kappa = \dfrac{\sqrt{4t^2 + 2}}{2(2t^2 + 1)^2}$; $N = \dfrac{\mathbf{i} - 2t\mathbf{j} + \mathbf{k}}{\sqrt{4t^2 + 2}}$.
3. Let $\mathbf{R}(t) = (a_2t^2 + a_1t + a_0)\mathbf{i} + (b_2t^2 + b_1t + b_0)\mathbf{j} + (c_2t^2 + c_1t + c_0)\mathbf{k}$; then an equation of the plane through the plane curve is
   $(b_1c_2 - b_2c_1)(x - a_0) + (a_2c_1 - a_1c_2)(y - b_0) + (b_2a_1 - b_1a_2)(z - c_0) = 0$.
5. (a) $\mathbf{T} = (\mathbf{i} + 2\mathbf{j})/\sqrt{5}$; $\mathbf{N} = (\mathbf{j} - 2\mathbf{i})/\sqrt{5}$;
   (b) $\mathbf{V} = \mathbf{i} + 2\mathbf{j}$; $\mathbf{A} = 2\mathbf{j}$; (c) $V_t = \sqrt{5}$; $A_t = 4/\sqrt{5}$;
   (d) $s' = \sqrt{1 + 4t^2}$; $s'' = 4t/\sqrt{1 + 4t^2}$.
6. (a) $A_n = 2/\sqrt{5}$; (b) $\kappa = 2/(5\sqrt{5})$.

CHAPTER 5

Section 2, Pages 366–367

2. $g_{11} = 1$, $g_{22} = \rho^2$, $g_{33} = \rho^2 \sin^2\theta$, $g_{12} = g_{23} = g_{13} = 0$, where $\rho = x_1$; $\theta = x_2$; $\phi = x_3$.

Section 3, Page 372

1. At $(1,2,3)$, $\nabla u = 2\mathbf{i} + 4\mathbf{j} + 6\mathbf{k}$; $du/dn = 2\sqrt{14}$;
   At $(0,1,2)$, $\nabla u = 2\mathbf{j} + 4\mathbf{k}$; $du/dn = 2\sqrt{5}$.
2. (a) $-(\mathbf{i}x + \mathbf{j}y + \mathbf{k}z)(x^2 + y^2 + z^2)^{-3/2}$;
   (b) $2(\mathbf{i}x + \mathbf{j}y + \mathbf{k}z)(x^2 + y^2 + z^2)^{-1}$.
3. $du/ds = -3/\sqrt{6}$.   4. $du/ds = -7/\sqrt{5}$.
5. $\mathbf{n} = \tfrac{1}{3}(\mathbf{i} - 2\mathbf{j} + 2\mathbf{k})$.   6. $\tfrac{1}{3}(2\mathbf{i} - 2\mathbf{j} - \mathbf{k})$, $\tfrac{1}{3}(-2\mathbf{i} + 2\mathbf{j} + \mathbf{k})$.
8. $du/ds = -3$.   9. $dv/ds = 6/\sqrt{5}$.

Section 4, Pages 377–378

1. 0.   2. $\dfrac{\pi^2 + 4}{8}$.   3. (a) $\tfrac{5}{6}$; (b) $-\tfrac{1}{2}$; (c) $\tfrac{5}{3}$.

4. Helical path, $\pi^2/8 - 1$; rectilinear path, $\pi^2/8 - 1$.
5. (a) $W = -g$; (b) $W = -g$.

Section 5, Page 382

1. $\frac{3}{2}$.
2. $u(x,y) = xy + \frac{1}{3}y^3 - \frac{1}{3}x^3$.
4. (a) $u = xyz$; (b) xyz.
5. 0; $u = \log r$.
6. 0.
8. $(x^2 + y^2 + z^2)^{-\frac{1}{2}} - (x_0^2 + y_0^2 + z_0^2)^{-\frac{1}{2}}$.

Section 7, Page 388

1. (a) 3; (b) $2/r$; (c) 0.
2. 0, $2/r$.
5. $5u$, 0.

Section 8, Pages 390–391

2. $\pi a^2 b$.
3. $4\pi abc$.
4. $4\pi a^5$.

Section 9, Pages 395–396

1. (a) $1\frac{3}{8}$; (b) $\frac{1}{2}$; (c) $\dfrac{\pi}{2}$; (d) $-\sqrt{3}/4$; (e) $1\frac{7}{2}$.

2. (a) $\mathbf{v} = \mathbf{i}(x^2 + y^2) + \mathbf{j}2xy$; $u = x^3/3 + xy^2$;

  (b) $\mathbf{v} = \dfrac{1 - y^2}{(1 + x)^3}\mathbf{i} + \dfrac{y}{(1 + x)^2}\,j$; $u = \dfrac{1}{2}\dfrac{y^2 - 1}{(1 + x)^2}$;

  (c) $\mathbf{v} = \mathbf{i}y\cos x + \mathbf{j}\sin x$; $u = y\sin x$;

  (d) $\mathbf{v} = \mathbf{i}xy(1 - x^2)^{-\frac{1}{2}} - \mathbf{j}(1 - x^2)^{\frac{1}{2}}$; $u = -y(1 - x^2)^{\frac{1}{2}}$;

  (e) $\mathbf{v} = \mathbf{i}(x + 1) + \mathbf{j}(y + 1)$; $u = \frac{1}{2}[(x + 1)^2 + (y + 1)^2]$.

3. (a) 2π; (b) 2π.
4. 6π.
5. 6π.

Section 10, Page 399

2. (a) 0; (b) 0; (c) 0.

Section 11, Page 402

2. $-\pi$.
3. 0.
4. 0.

Section 12, Page 405

2. $\mathbf{w} = \mathbf{j}(xy - \frac{1}{2}x^2) + \mathbf{k}[z(x + y) - \frac{1}{2}(x^2 + y^2)]$.
3. $u = xy^2 + x^2z^2 - x$.
4. $\mathbf{w} = \mathbf{j}(xyz^2 - \frac{1}{2}x^2z) + \mathbf{k}(-\frac{1}{2}x^2y + x^3yz)$.
5. No.

Section 13, Page 408

1. $\nabla u = \mathbf{r}_1 \dfrac{\partial u}{\partial r} + \dfrac{\boldsymbol{\theta}_1}{r}\dfrac{\partial u}{\partial \theta} + \mathbf{k}\dfrac{\partial u}{\partial z}$.

2. $\nabla^2 = \dfrac{1}{(u^2 + v^2)u}\dfrac{\partial}{\partial u} + \dfrac{1}{(u^2 + v^2)v}\dfrac{\partial}{\partial v} + \dfrac{1}{u^2 + v^2}\dfrac{\partial^2}{\partial u^2} + \dfrac{1}{u^2 + v^2}\dfrac{\partial^2}{\partial v^2} + \dfrac{1}{u^2 v^2}\dfrac{\partial^2}{\partial \phi^2}$.

3. $\operatorname{div}\mathbf{F} = -3p\cos\theta/r^4$, $\operatorname{curl}\mathbf{F} = 0$.

Section 15, Page 414

2. Irrotational.
4. $\Phi = x^2 - y^2$, hyperbolas.
8. Irrotational and solenoidal.
10. $\Phi = y^3 - 3x^2y$; $\Phi = x(x^2 + y^2)^{-1}$.

ANSWERS

CHAPTER 6

Section 1, Pages 429–431

2. (a) $[1 + (x - at)^2]^{-1}$, $-2(x - at)[1 + (x - at)^2]^{-2}$;
   (b) $2(1 + a^2t^2)^{-1}$, $2(1 + x^2)^{-1}$, $(l^2 - 2l + 2)^{-1} + (l^2 + 2l + 2)^{-1}$.

3. $u_{xy}u - u_x u_y = 0$.

7. (a) $f_1(y + m_1 x)$, $f_2(y + m_2 x)$.

9. (a) $F_1(y - ax) + F_2(y + ax)$; (b) $F_1(y - 2x) + F_2(y + x)$;
   (c) $F_1(x + iy) + F_2(x - iy)$; (d) $F_1(y + x) + xF_2(y + x)$.

10. (d) $F_1(y - 5x) + F_2(y + x) - y^4/60 + x^3/6$.

11. (a) $\dfrac{x^2}{4} + F_1(2y + x) + F_2(y - x)$; (b) $\dfrac{x^4}{12} + F_1(y - ax) + F_2(y + ax)$;
    (c) $\tfrac{1}{6}x^3 + \tfrac{1}{12}y^3 + F_1(y - 2x) + F_2(y - x)$.

Section 4, Page 440

2. $u(0,\pi) = \dfrac{1}{2a}\sin 2a\pi$; $u_t(0,\pi) = \tfrac{1}{2}\cos 2a\pi$.

3. $a = \pm\dfrac{\pi}{15} + \dfrac{2n\pi}{5}$, $n = 0, \pm1, \pm2, \ldots$.

4. $\mathrm{Const} + (2a)^{-1}e^{-x^2}$.   5. $ae^{-x^2}(2x^2 - 1)$.

Section 5, Pages 445–446

1. $-l, \pm2l, \pm3l, \ldots$.

Section 6, Page 449

2. (b) $b/2$.

3. (a) $\dfrac{8b}{\pi^2}\displaystyle\sum_{n=0}^{\infty}(-1)^n\dfrac{1}{(2n+1)^2}\sin\dfrac{(2n+1)\pi x}{l}$.

Section 8, Pages 454–455

1. 0.45 oscillation per sec.

Section 9, Pages 458–459

1. 2.07×10^6 cal/(m²)(day).

4. (c) $\dfrac{2kc_n l}{\pi n\alpha^2}[1 - e^{-(\alpha n\pi/l)^2 t}]$.

Section 10, Pages 462–463

4. (b) $u(x,t) = \Sigma c_n e^{-[\alpha(2n-1)/2l]^2 t}\sin\dfrac{\pi}{l}(2n - 1)x$;

   $c_n = \dfrac{2}{l}\displaystyle\int_0^l f(x)\sin\dfrac{\pi}{l}(2n - 1)x\,dx$.

7. $\Sigma a_n\cos\dfrac{n\pi at}{l}\sin\dfrac{n\pi x}{l}$; $a_n = \dfrac{2}{l}\displaystyle\int_0^l f(x)\sin\dfrac{n\pi x}{l}\,dx$.

8. $\Sigma b_n\sin\dfrac{n\pi at}{l}\sin\dfrac{n\pi x}{l}$; $b_n = \dfrac{2}{n\pi a}\displaystyle\int_0^l g(x)\sin\dfrac{n\pi x}{l}\,dx$.

Section 11, Pages 466–467

3. $0.44883, 0.14922, 0.00004$.

5. $u(x,y) = \dfrac{400}{\pi}\displaystyle\sum\dfrac{1}{2n - 1}e^{-(2n-1)\pi y/10}\sin(2n - 1)\dfrac{\pi x}{10}$.

6. $u(x,t) = \dfrac{400}{\pi} \sum \dfrac{1}{2n-1} e^{-[\alpha(2n-1)\pi/10]^2 t} \sin (2n-1)\dfrac{\pi x}{10}.$

7. 35.5, 41.9.

Section 12, Page 471

5. $U(r,\theta) = \dfrac{1}{2\pi} \displaystyle\int_0^\pi \left[\dfrac{R^2 - r^2}{R^2 - 2Rr\cos(\theta-\phi)+r^2} - \dfrac{R^2-r^2}{R^2 - 2Rr\cos(\theta+\phi)+r^2} \right] f(\phi)\,d\phi.$

6. $U(r,\theta) = \dfrac{1}{2\pi} \displaystyle\int_0^{2\pi} \dfrac{r^2 - R^2}{r^2 - 2rR\cos(\theta-\phi)+R^2} f(\phi)\,d\phi.$

Section 13, Page 474

1. $U = 50 + \dfrac{200}{\pi} \sum \dfrac{1}{(2n-1)a^{2n-1}} r^{2n-1}\sin(2n-1)\theta.$

2. $U = \dfrac{50}{\pi} \displaystyle\int_0^\pi \dfrac{a^2 - r^2}{a^2 - 2ar\cos(\theta-\phi)+r^2}\,d\phi.$

3. $U = \dfrac{400}{\pi} \sum \dfrac{1}{(2n-1)a^{2n-1}} r^{2n-1}\sin(2n-1)\theta.$

4. $u(x,y) = \Sigma a_n \sin \pi nx \sinh \pi ny;\ a_n = \dfrac{2}{\sinh \pi n} \displaystyle\int_0^1 f(x)\sin \pi nx\,dx.$

Section 14, Page 479

1. $(a)\ \dfrac{\gamma}{2}\left(\dfrac{1}{a^2}+\dfrac{1}{b^2}\right)^{\frac12};\ (b)\ \dfrac{\pi}{10}\gamma\left(\dfrac{1}{a^2}+\dfrac{1}{b^2}\right)^{\frac12}$

Section 15, Page 482

1. $\displaystyle\sum_{m\,n} J_0(k_n r)\cos m\dfrac{\pi}{b} z(A_{mn}\cos\omega_{mn}t + B_{mn}\sin\omega_{mn}t);\ \omega_{mn}^2 = \gamma^2\left(k_n^2 + \dfrac{\pi^2 m^2}{b^2}\right).$

2. $\Sigma A_n e^{-\alpha^2 k_n^2 t} J_0(k_n r),$ where $1 = \Sigma A_n J_0(k_n r).$

Section 18, Page 490

2. $(\pi\alpha^2 t)^{-\frac12} \displaystyle\int_0^\infty f(\xi)e^{-(x^2+\xi^2)/(4\alpha^2 t)}\cosh\dfrac{x\xi}{2\alpha^2 t}\,d\xi.$

3. $(\pi\alpha^2 t)^{-\frac12} \displaystyle\int_0^\infty f(\xi)e^{-(x^2+\xi^2)/(4\alpha^2 t)}\sinh\dfrac{x\xi}{2\alpha^2 t}\,d\xi.$

4. $(4\pi\alpha^2 t)^{-\frac12} \displaystyle\int_0^l f(s)\left\{\sum_{n=-\infty}^\infty [e^{-(x-2nl-s)^2/(4\alpha^2 t)} \pm e^{-(x-2nl+s)^2/(4\alpha^2 t)}]\right\}ds.$

Section 19, Page 493

3. $u(x,y,t) = (4\pi^2\alpha t)^{-1} \displaystyle\int_{-\infty}^{+\infty}\int_{-\infty}^{+\infty} e^{-[(x-x_1)^2+(y-y_1)^2]/(4\alpha^2 t)}f(x_1,y_1)\,dx_1\,dy_1.$

4. $u(x,y,z,t) = \displaystyle\int_0^t\int_{-\infty}^{+\infty}\int_{-\infty}^{+\infty} \dfrac{f(y_1,z_1,t_1)}{[4\pi\alpha^2(t-t_1)]^{\frac32}} e^{-[x^2+(y-y_1)^2+(z-z_1)^2]/[4\alpha^2(t-t_1)]}\,dy_1\,dz_1\,dt_1.$

5. $u(x,y,t) = \displaystyle\int_0^t\int_{-\infty}^{+\infty} \dfrac{f(y_1,t_1)}{4\pi\alpha^2(t-t_1)} e^{-[x^2+(y-y_1)^2]/4\alpha^2(t-t_1)}\,dy_1\,dt_1.$

$u(x,t) = \displaystyle\int_0^t \dfrac{f(t_1)}{[4\pi\alpha^2(t-t_1)]^{\frac12}} e^{-x^2/4\alpha^2(t-t_1)}\,dt_1.$

Section 24, Page 507

1. $|k| < 2, = 2, > 2.$
2. Respectively m, in or outside the unit circle $x^2 + y^2 = 1.$
5. (a) $[ce^y + (1 - c)e^{-y}] \sin x.$

Section 26, Page 512

2. At the lattice points in the region $y \geq x,\ x > 0;\ y \geq h - x,\ x \leq 0.$
3. $\frac{2}{7}.$

Section 27, Page 514

1. 19.   2. 2.   3. 2.

Section 28, Page 517

1. $I(x,t) = \dfrac{12}{Rl} - \displaystyle\sum_{n=1}^{\infty} \left(\dfrac{2}{l} \int_0^l \dfrac{6}{l}\, \xi \sin \dfrac{n\pi\xi}{l}\, d\xi \right) e^{-(1/RC)(n\pi/l)^2 t} \dfrac{n\pi}{Rl} \cos \dfrac{n\pi x}{l}.$

2. $V = \dfrac{3x}{50} + \dfrac{4}{\pi} \displaystyle\sum_{n=1}^{\infty} \dfrac{1}{n} \sin \dfrac{n\pi x}{100}\, e^{-2n^2\pi t/0.0024}.$

3. $I = 0.6 + 1.1 \displaystyle\sum_{n=1}^{\infty} (-1)^n \cos \dfrac{n\pi x}{1,000}\, e^{-2n^2\pi t/0.6}.$

Section 29, Page 519

3. $U_{rs} = 0;\ U_{rr} = 0;\ U_{rr} + U_{ss} = 0.$

CHAPTER 7

Section 1, Page 533

1. (a) $2,\ \pi/3$; (b) $2\sqrt{2},\ \pi/4$; (c) $2,\ \pi$; (d) $1,\ 3\pi/2$;
   (e) $\sqrt{2}/2,\ 7\pi/4$; (f) $1,\ \pi/2$; (g) $\frac{3}{4},\ \pi/3$; (h) $4,\ \pi.$
2. (a) -8; (b) $-1 + i$; (c) $(2 - \sqrt{3})/2 - /(2 + \sqrt{3})/2.$
3. (a) 1; (b) 1; (c) 1.
4. $\cos(\pi/6) + i \sin(\pi/6),\ \cos(\pi/6 + 2\pi/3) + i \sin(\pi/6 + 2\pi/3),$
   $\cos(\pi/6 + 4\pi/3) + i \sin(\pi/6 + 4\pi/3).$
7. (a) $1,\ \frac{1}{2}(-1 + i\sqrt{3}),\ \frac{1}{2}(-1 - i\sqrt{3})$; (b) $1,\ i,\ -i,\ -1.$
16. (a) Circle $x^2 + y^2 = 1$; (b) circular region $x^2 + y^2 < 1$;
    (c) region exterior to the circle $x^2 + y^2 = 1$ including the boundary.
18. (a) Circle radius 2, center at $(1,0)$; (b) circle radius $1/\sqrt{\text{const}}$, center at $(0,0)$.

Section 2, Page 535

1. (a) $(x^2 - y^2 - x + 1) + i(2xy - y)$; (b) $x/(x^2 + y^2) - iy/(x^2 + y^2)$;
   (d) $(x^2 + y^2 - 1)/[x^2 + (y + 1)^2] - i2x/[x^2 + (y + 1)^2]$;
   (f) $x + i2y$; (g) $(x^2 + y^2)^{-1}.$
2. (a) Open region $x < 3,\ -\infty < y < \infty$;
   (b) The region $y \geq 1,\ -\infty < x < \infty$;
   (c) The region exterior to the circle of radius 1 with center at the origin and in-cluding circular boundary;
   (d) Circular ring centered at the origin with interior radius 1, exterior radius 2, including the boundary of the inner circle;
   (e) Open circular region with center at $(1,0)$ of radius 1;

(f) Closed circular region of radius 1 with center at $z_0 = x_0 + iy_0$;

(g) Open region exterior to the circle of radius 2 with center at $(0, -1)$.

Section 3, Pages 539–540

3. (a) $\frac{1}{2}(e^{-1} + e) \cos 2 + \frac{1}{2}i(e^{-1} - e) \sin 2$; ($c$) $e^{i \log \sqrt{2} - (\pi/4 + 2k\pi)}$; ($e$) $e^{\pi/2 + 2k\pi}$.

4. (c) $\frac{1}{2}(e + e^{-1}) \sin 1 + \frac{1}{2}i(e - e^{-1}) \cos 1$;

(d) $e^{x^2 - y^2}(\cos 2xy + i \sin 2xy)$;

(e) $e^{x/(x^2 + y^2)}\{\cos [y/(x^2 + y^2)] - i \sin [y/(x^2 + y^2)]\}$.

5. (a) $\log 4 + \pi i$; (b) $\log 5 + i\pi/2$; (e) $e^{-\pi/2}$; (f) $e(\cos 1 + i \sin 1)$;

(g) $\frac{1}{2}i(e^2 - e^{-2})$.

6. (a) $(\pi + 2\pi k)i$; (b) $\pi/2 + 2\pi k - i \log (2 \pm \sqrt{3})$; ($d$) $2\pi k, k = 0, \pm 1, \pm 2, \pm \cdots$.

Section 4, Page 545

3. (b) $z = -1$; (c) $z = 0$; (d) $z = \pi/2 + k\pi, k = 0, \pm 1, \pm 2, \ldots$; ($e$) $z = 1, z = -1$;

(f), (g), (h) at all points; (i) $z = 0$, (k) $z = \pm i$.

Section 5, Page 548

1. $\frac{1}{3}(2 + 11i)$.

2. 1 along rectilinear, $1 + i/3$ along parabolic.

5. 0.   **6.** 0.   **7.** (-2).

Section 7, Page 555

2. $2\pi i$.   **3.** 2, upper half; -2, lower half.

5. 0.   **10.** (a) 0; (b) 0; (c) $-\pi i$; (d) πi.

Section 8, Page 559

1. $2\pi i(8 - 13i)$.   **3.** (a) 0; (b) $2\pi i$; (d) 0; (e) $2\pi i$.

6. $-2\pi i$.

Section 9, Page 561

1. $u \cong x^3 - 3xy^2$.

2. (a) $x + iy$; (b) $\cosh y \cos x - i \sinh y \sin x$; ($d$) $e^x(\cos y + i \sin y)$.

Section 10, Pages 564–565

2. $\displaystyle\sum_{n=1}^{\infty} (-1)^{n-1} \frac{(z - 1)^n}{n}$, $R = 1$.

3. (a) $\displaystyle\sum_{n=0}^{\infty} \frac{z^n}{n!}$, $R = \infty$; (b) $\displaystyle\sum_{n=1}^{\infty} \frac{(-1)^{n-1}z^{2n-1}}{(2n - 1)!}$, $R = \infty$;

(d) $\displaystyle\sum_{n=1}^{\infty} (-1)^{n-1}\frac{z^n}{n}$, $R = 1$.

Section 11, Page 569

1. (a) $\dfrac{1}{z} + 2 + 3z + 4z^2 + \cdots$;

(b) $\dfrac{1}{(1 - z)^2} + \dfrac{1}{1 - z} + 1 + (1 - z) + (1 - z)^2 + (1 - z)^3 + \cdots$.

2. $1 - \dfrac{1}{z^2} + \dfrac{1}{2!z^4} - \dfrac{1}{3!z^6} + \dfrac{1}{4!z^8} - \cdots$.

3. Functions *are* expressed in Laurent's series.

4. (a) $-\dfrac{1}{z-1} - 1 - (z-1) - (z-1)^2 - \cdots;$

(b) $\dfrac{2}{z} + \dfrac{3}{z^2} + \dfrac{1+2^2}{z^3} + \dfrac{1+2^3}{z^4} + \cdots;$

(c) $-\dfrac{1}{2} - \dfrac{z}{2^2} - \dfrac{z^2}{2^3} - \dfrac{z^3}{2^4} - \cdots + \dfrac{1}{z} + \dfrac{1}{z^2} + \dfrac{1}{z^3} + \cdots.$

Section 12, Pages 572–573

1. (a) $+\dfrac{1}{z^3} - \dfrac{1}{2!}\dfrac{1}{z} + \dfrac{1}{4!}z - \dfrac{1}{6!}z^3 + \cdots$, residue $(-\frac{1}{2})$;

(b) $1 - \dfrac{1}{z^2} + \dfrac{1}{2!}\dfrac{1}{z^4} - \dfrac{1}{3!}\dfrac{1}{z^6} + \cdots$, residue (0);

(e) $\dfrac{1}{z^2} - \dfrac{1}{z} + \dfrac{1}{2!} - \dfrac{z}{3!} + \dfrac{z^2}{4!} - \cdots$, residue (-1);

(f) $z^2 + z + \dfrac{1}{2!} + \dfrac{1}{3!z} + \dfrac{1}{4!z^2} + \cdots$, residue $(\frac{1}{3}!)$;

(g) $-\dfrac{2}{z^3} - \dfrac{4}{2!z^2} - \dfrac{8}{3!z} - \dfrac{16}{4!} - \dfrac{32z}{5!} - \cdots$, residue $(-\frac{8}{3}!)$:

(i) Residue $-\frac{1}{2}$ at $z = 1$, residue $\frac{1}{2}$ at $z = -1$.

6. No.

Section 13, Page 574

1. (a) $-\pi i$; (c) $2\pi i/3!$; (d) $-8\pi i/3$; (f) $0°$.

2. $2\pi i$. **4.** (a) 0; (b) $2\pi i$.

Section 18, Page 586

1. (a) $\cos x \cosh y$, $\sin x \sinh y$; (b) $e^x \cos y$, $e^x \sin y$;

(d) $\log (x^2 + y^2)^{\frac{1}{2}}$, $\tan^{-1}(y/x)$; (e) $x/(x^2 + y^2)$, $-y/(x^2 + y^2)$.

2. (c) $v = e^x \sin y - x$; (d) $\sinh x \sin y$.

CHAPTER 8

Section 1, Page 612

1. $\frac{1}{6}$, $\frac{1}{18}$.

3. $\frac{1}{4}$.

5. $8!$, $7!$, $7!/2$.

7. (a) $\frac{1}{6}$; (b) 0; (c) $\frac{1}{18}$; (d) $\frac{1}{6}$.

2. $\frac{3}{20}$, $\frac{1}{2}$, $\frac{7}{20}$, $\frac{9}{38}$, $1{,}323/46{,}189$.

4. $\dfrac{48!5!}{52!}$, $\dfrac{13!47!}{8!52!}$, $36\dfrac{47!5!}{52!}$.

6. $\dfrac{1}{n}$, $\dfrac{2}{m}$, $\dfrac{2m+2n-4}{mn}$.

Section 2, Page 616

1. $\frac{7}{8}$, $\frac{1}{2}$, $\frac{1}{4}$, $\frac{3}{8}$, $\frac{1}{2}$, $\frac{1}{4}$, $\frac{1}{8}$, $\frac{1}{8}$.

6. $\frac{6}{11}$.

2. Questions 1, 2, 8 can be answered.

7. $\frac{1}{5}$.

Section 3, Pages 621–622

1. $33/16{,}660$.

3. $\frac{3}{32}$, $\frac{5}{32}$, $\frac{9}{32}$.

2. $\frac{31}{32}$, $\frac{1}{32}$.

4. $\frac{41}{60}$.

5. $\frac{1}{6}$, $\frac{5}{36}$.

6. $n > (\log 2)/(\log 6 - \log 5)$.

7. $\frac{3}{10}$, $\frac{9}{20}$.

8. $\left(\dfrac{3}{13}\right)^5 > \dfrac{12 \cdot 11 \ldots 8}{52 \cdot 51 \ldots 48}$.

9. $\dfrac{5!}{52^5} < \dfrac{5!}{52 \ldots 48}$, $\dfrac{18{,}781}{13^5} > \dfrac{270{,}840}{52 \cdot 51 \cdot 50 \cdot 49}$.

10. $1 - p^n$, $n = 3$.

Section 4, Pages 626–627

1. $3p$.

2. $E(XY) = 6pq$.

3. (a) 1; (b) 1; (c) 1.

4. $\frac{1}{52} + \frac{1}{51} + \frac{1}{50} + \cdots + \frac{1}{1} = 6.83$.

5. 2.

Section 5, Page 631

1. $\frac{1}{32}$, $\frac{5}{32}$, $\frac{10}{32}$, $\frac{10}{32}$, $\frac{5}{32}$, $\frac{1}{32}$.

4. $\frac{25}{32}$.

Section 6, Page 637

1. 0.75, 0.60, $F(x) = x^3$ for $0 < x < 1$, $m = 0.794$.

2. $\frac{1}{3}\pi$, 0.206.

3. $\frac{1}{4}a$.

4. $\frac{1}{4}$.

6. $\frac{1}{3}$.

Section 7, Pages 640–641

1. $\frac{5}{16}$, $\frac{3}{16}$, $\frac{5}{2}$, 2 and 3.

2. (a) 125/3,888, (b) $\frac{23}{648}$.

3. $(0.65)^{10} + 10(0.65)^9(0.35) + 45(0.65)^8(0.35)^2 + 120(0.65)^7(0.35)^3$.

4. $5(\frac{1}{6})^6 + 4(\frac{1}{6})^5(\frac{5}{6}) + 45(\frac{1}{6})^4(\frac{5}{6})^2 + 40(\frac{1}{6})^3(\frac{5}{6})^3 + 15(\frac{1}{6})^2(\frac{5}{6})^4$.

5. 741/2,728.

7. 0.57, 0.57, $\dfrac{m}{n} = \dfrac{m}{n}$.

Section 8, Page 644

1. 0.499.

Section 9, Page 650

1. 0.039.

2. $\phi(1.5) - \phi(-1.0) = 0.806$.

3. 0.979.

4. 0.0222.

5. 0.083, 0.166, no.

Section 10, Page 654

1. 1,540.

2. 46,413/78,125.

3. $\frac{49}{50}$.

4. 0.91854.

Section 11, Page 658

1. (a) 0.368, 0.402; (b) 0.368, 0.373.

2. 0.758.

3. 1,005.

4. Expected number = 5.

5. 0.577.

Section 12, Page 663

2. 0.82.

Section 13, Page 667

1. $\frac{1}{12}$.

2. $\frac{7}{2}$, $\frac{7}{2}$, $\frac{28}{3}$, yes, $\rho = -1$.

3. $\frac{1}{3}\sqrt{3} = 0.577$.

Section 15, Pages 670–671

  1. 7.5, 0.26.   **2.** 0.145, 54.

CHAPTER 9

Section 1, Page 679

  1. (a) $-0.8 < x_1 < -0.7$, $x_2 = 2$, $x_3 = 4$;
     (b) $-0.8 < x_1 < -0.7$, $1.2 < x_2 < 1.3$;
     (c) $-0.8 < x_1 < -0.7$, $-0.6 < x_2 < -0.5$, $1.0 < x_3 < 1.1$;
     (d) $-0.6 < x_1 < 0.5$; (e) $4.4 < x_1 < 4.5$.
  2. $h = 1.23$.

Section 2, Page 684

  1. Prob. 1: (a) -0.75; (b) -0.73, 1.22; (c) -0.77, -0.55, 1.08; (d) -0.57; (e) 4.49;
     Prob. 2: 1.226.
  2. -0.942, -0.200, 1.045.

Section 3, Page 686

  3. 2.310 radians.
  4. (a) 0.739; (b) 0.567; (c) -0.725, 1.221; (d) 2.924; (e) 1.045, -0.942, -0.200.

Section 4, Pages 688–689

  (a) $x = {}^{15}\!/_{13}$; $y = {}^{20}\!/_{13}$; $z = -{}^{8}\!/_{13}$;
  (b) $x_1 = 1$; $x_2 = -1$; $x_3 = -2$; $x_4 = 3$;
  (c) $x_1 = -0.107$; $x_2 = 0.988$; $x_3 = 0.317$.

Section 7, Pages 694–696

  1. $y = 0.25x^2 - 0.50x + 0.25$.

Section 8, Page 696

  2. 9.466, 12.549.

Section 9, Page 700

  1. 2.784, 2.700.   **2.** If $\theta_0 = 60$, $\theta = 40.82$, 42.52, 42.50.
  3. 2.581, 2.627.   **4.** 106.09.

Section 10, Page 702

  1. (a) $y = \frac{1}{2}x + \frac{7}{2}$; (b) $y = 2.5x^{0.5}$; (c) $0.3(10^{0.2x})$.

Section 11, Page 711

  1. $y = 4.98 - 3.13x + 1.26x^2$.
  3. $K = 1.778$; $b = \bar{1}.9349$; $\theta = 60.02(0.861)^t$.

Section 12, Page 715

  1. $y = 0.75 + 0.10 \cos x - 0.05 \cos 3x - 0.29 \sin x$.
  2. $y = 0.85 - 0.25 \cos 2x - 0.05 \cos 4x + 0.05 \cos 6x + 0.26 \sin 2x - 0.03 \sin 4x$.

Section 13, Pages 720–721

  1. 25.252, 25.068.   **2.** 132.137.
  3. 128.6.   **4.** 666.25, 666.00.
  5. 39.30, 38.98.

Section 14, Page 723

1. $y(\pm 0.2) = 1$; $y(\pm 0.4) = 1.02$; $y(\pm 0.6) = 1.061$; $y(\pm 0.8) = 1.124$; $y(\pm 1.0)$ $= 1.214$. The corresponding exact values are 1.010, 1.041, 1.094, 1.174, 1.284.

2. $y = y_1 + y'(x_1)(x - x_1) + \dfrac{1}{2h}[y'(x_1) - y'(x_0)](x - x_1)^2$.

3. $y_1 = 1.0100$; $y_2 = 1.0403$; $y_3 = 1.0927$.

Section 15, Pages 726–727

1. $y_6 = 2.0442$; $y_7 = 2.3274$; $y_8 = 2.6509$; $y_9 = 3.0190$; $y_{10} = 3.4363$.

3. $y(0.3) = 1.3498$; $y(0.4) = 1.4917$; $y(0.5) = 1.6485$; $y(0.6) = 1.8218$.

4. 0.2740.

Section 16, Page 730

1. $y = x + x^2 + \frac{1}{6}x^3 + \frac{1}{6}x^4 + R_4$; $z = x + \frac{1}{2}x^3 + \bar{R}_4$.

2. 0.1, 0.2205, 0.3627, 0.5281.

3. 1.01, 1.031, 1.063.

4. $y = 1 + \frac{1}{2}x^2 + \frac{1}{6}x^3 + \frac{1}{12}x^4 + \frac{1}{60}x^5 + \cdots$;
$z = x + \frac{1}{2}x^2 + \frac{1}{3}x^3 + \frac{1}{12}x^4 + \cdots$.

5. 1.0052, 1.0215, 1.0502.

APPENDIX A

Section 1, Page 747

1. $(18, 0, -1, 0)$.   **2.** $(18, 0, -1, 0)$.   **3.** 1.

Section 2, Pages 752–753

1. (a) $(2, -1, 1)$; (b) $(1, \frac{3}{2}, -\frac{1}{2})$; (c) $(3, -1, 2)$; (d) $(1, -1, -2, 3)$.

2. (a) $(-k/7, 5k/7, k)$; (b) $(0, 0)$; (c) $(0, 0, 0)$; (d) $(k/4, 7k/8, k)$; (e) $(k, 2k, 0)$;
(f) $(0, 0, 0)$.

3. (a) $(1, -1)$; (b) inconsistent; (c) inconsistent; (d) $(1, 3k -2, k)$.

APPENDIX B

Section 2, Pages 758–759

2. $y = \cos 2x + \frac{1}{3}\sin x - \frac{1}{6}\sin 2x$.   **3.** $y = \frac{1}{2}e^x - \frac{1}{2}e^{-x} + \frac{1}{6}x^3 - x$.

5. $y = 2 + e^{-2x} - xe^{-x} - 3e^{-x}$.   **6.** $y = e^{\frac{1}{2}x}$.

Section 3, Pages 761–762

1. $V = \frac{1}{2}e^{-t} - \frac{1}{2}e^{-3t}$.   **2.** $y = 1$, $y = x$, $y = \frac{1}{2}x^2$ for $x > 0$.

Section 4, Pages 764–765

1. $\dfrac{2}{3} e^{-2x} \cosh \dfrac{2}{\sqrt{3}} x - \dfrac{3}{2} \sqrt{3}\, e^{-2x} \sinh \dfrac{2}{\sqrt{3}} x$.

2. (a) $e^{-x}\cos x$; (b) $e^{-x}\cosh x + \frac{1}{2}e^{-x}\sinh x = \frac{3}{4} + \frac{1}{4}e^{-2x}$;
(c) $e^{-\frac{1}{2}x}(\cosh \frac{1}{2}\sqrt{5}\, x - \frac{3}{5}\sqrt{5} \sinh \frac{1}{2}\sqrt{5}\, x)$.

Section 5, Page 767

1. $y = \displaystyle\int_0^x f(\xi)e^{-x+\xi}\, d\xi - \int_0^x f(\xi)e^{-2x+2\xi}\, d\xi$.

2. (a) $\frac{1}{2} - e^{-x} + \frac{1}{2}e^{-2x}$; (b) $\frac{1}{20}e^{3x} - \frac{1}{4}e^{-x} + \frac{1}{5}e^{-2x}$;

(c) $\frac{1}{2}x - \frac{3}{4} + e^{-x} - \frac{1}{4}e^{-2x}$.

Section 6, Pages 768–769

1. $\dfrac{V_0}{R} + \left(c\omega L - \dfrac{V_0}{R}\right)e^{-(R/L)t} - c\omega L \cos \omega t + cR \sin \omega t$ with $c = \dfrac{A}{R^2 + \omega^2 L^2}$.

2. $L^{-1}e^{-(R/L)t}$.

3. $L^{-1}\displaystyle\int_0^t V(\tau)e^{-(R/L)(t-\tau)}\,d\tau = R^{-1}\displaystyle\int_0^t V'(\tau)[1 - e^{-(R/L)(t-\tau)}]\,d\tau$

$$+ \frac{V(0)}{R}[1 - e^{-(R/L)t}].$$

INDEX

The letter *p*. after a page number refers to a problem, the letter *n*. to a footnote.